# HANDLOADER'S DIGEST



## 17th EDITION

Edited by
Bob Bell

DBI BOOKS
*a division of Krause Publications, Inc.*

## About Our Covers

Hornady's Lock-N-Load AP (Automatic Progressive) reloading press combines innovative design with high-tech manufacturing techniques to give the reloader a machine that will turn out large quantities of either rifle or handgun ammunition.

This press features Hornady's new Lock-N-Load die bushing system that allows you to switch dies in a matter of seconds without any readjustments. Standard-thread dies screw into the bushings and are loaded and unloaded from the press with a simple twist. The locking action holds the dies in a solid, perfectly aligned position. The five-station die platform allows the flexibility to add individual seating and crimping dies, or a taper-crimp die to the progressive process.

The Lock-N-Load AP press comes with Hornady's Deluxe powder measure with micrometer dial for precise charge settings. The measure automatically dispenses a charge with every pull of the press handle when a shell is present in the station. It's easily adjusted and mounts just like the dies.

Priming is handled by an all-new primer slide that automatically picks up primers while the shellplate is held secure and level by the shellplate retainer.

Because the press opening is offset, there's easy access to the shellplate. Changeover is easy and adjustment-free since the shellplate bolt and lock nut are independant of the rest of the press.

The Lock-N-Load press automatically advances in half-clicks at the top and bottom of each stroke, giving very smooth rotation. Hornady's Power-Pac cast linkage arms rotate on steel pins that run completely through the one-piece frame, giving strength and precision. There's enough leverage to handle tough resizing chores, and the handle is offset to provide a clear view of your work.

Shown with the AP press is Hornady's Magnetic Scale that weighs bullet or powder to within $^{1}/_{10}$-grain accuracy over a 510-grain range. Its over/under feature gives quick readouts without changing scale settings.

Hornady's Custom-Grade New Dimension reloading dies are guaranteed to never scratch a cartridge case. The pistol dies at left feature a no-lube titanium-coated sizing ring that eliminates the need for lubing cases and makes expensive carbide dies unnecessaary.

For those just getting into the reloading hobby, Hornady offers their *Introduction to Metallic Reloading* video tape that gives step-by-step instructions on how to safely and efficiently reload ammunition.

At top right is the *Hornady Handbook of Cartridge Reloading*, Fourth Edition, with over 1200 pages of instructions, ballistics charts and valuable loading data for most popular accepted loads, as well as the newest calibers, bullets and powders.

The new Lock-N-Load AP reloading press represents precision engineering and quality in an affordable tool that will last a lifetime. If you're in the market for a high-volume progressive press with all the good features, take a hard look at the Lock-N-Load—it's one of the best.

Photo by John Hanusin.


## HANDLOADER'S DIGEST STAFF

**EDITOR-IN-CHIEF**
*Bob Bell*

**SENIOR STAFF EDITORS**
*Harold A. Murtz*
*Ray Ordorica*

**ASSOCIATE EDITOR**
*Robert S.L. Anderson*

**PRODUCTION MANAGER**
*John L. Duoba*

**EDITORIAL/PRODUCTION ASSOCIATE**
*Karen Rasmussen*

**ASSISTANT TO THE EDITOR**
*Lilo Anderson*

**TECHNICAL EDITOR**
*M.L. McPherson*

**ELECTRONIC PUBLISHING MANAGER**
*Nancy J. Mellem*

**ELECTRONIC PUBLISHING ASSOCIATE**
*Laura M. Mielzynski*

**GRAPHIC DESIGN**
*John L. Duoba*
*Bill Limbaugh*

**MANAGING EDITOR**
*Pamela J. Johnson*

**PUBLISHER**
*Charles T. Hartigan*





**ISBN 0-87349-192-0**

**Library of Congress Catalog #62-15069**

# VIEWS FROM THE BENCH

I THINK ABOUT handloading from time to time, and sometimes wonder about things. For instance, as long as I can remember, a common statement has been, "Rimfire cartridges can't be handloaded." I wonder if that's true.

Obviously, no one having a reasonable amount of common sense and being of only average ability, and limited resources, both mechanical and economical, would want to venture into this area. But there are people who don't have these limitations. Some of these are top-quality gunsmiths, advanced handloaders, open-minded theorists. Yet no one, to my knowledge (rumors don't count), has done any work here.

Why should they want to, you ask. Current top grades of 22 Long Rifle target ammunition are extremely accurate when mated to the rifle. Nevertheless, it seems to me, the term "extremely accurate" reflects only a comparison to run-of-the-mill ammo. Doubtless, the best match stuff is far more accurate and consistent than plinking ammo picked up in a local hardware store, but is it "extremely accurate" when compared with a 224 or 6mm Benchrest cartridge? Will it shoot groups that are measured in thousandths of an inch, or even large fractions of an inch, at 100 yards—assuming that the best rifles are used and the best riflemen, of whom we have many, do the shooting?

There are lots of reasons such results are difficult—impossible—at the moment. But in the end, difficulties are simply something to be overcome, as shooters have been doing since the invention of gunpowder. What kind of scores would Olympic riflemen like Lones Wigger or Gary Anderson have turned in if they'd had near-perfect ammo? It's at the Olympic level, of course, that such accuracy would be most appreciated, and few of us are Olympians. So maybe the factories figure that current accuracy is more than sufficient for a low-velocity—and therefore short-range— cartridge to be used by tens of millions of plinkers. But what do those few Olympic shooters think? Would they be willing to handload their ammo, if allowed? I don't know whether current rules cover such a possibility, but rules, too, are open to change. And the guys now into rimfire-benchrest shooting ought to be considered.

Suppose that handloading were allowed. Primed empty cases could probably be had from the factories, and an obvious observation is that they could be made in considerably shorter length than is now used for the 22 LR; this would eliminate the excess airspace that centerfire benchresters long ago found to be a problem, due to the random positioning and therefore ignition of powder.

This alone might be a big step forward. It might be simply a matter of using the Short case with a LR bullet in a custom chamber, perhaps a Hart rimfire barrel. Even better bullets would help, too. And everyone knows we have many outstanding bullet makers in the country to call on, if necessary. I doubt if it would be, though. Probably the R&D divisions of the big ammunition companies already know all that's required, if anyone should get around to asking.

Anyway, with five or six million handloaders in the country, it seems likely that a few have already been working in this area. Perhaps as private experimenters they've even used jacketed bullets of various shapes and diameters in their custom barrels. If you happen to be one of them, or know someone who is, let me hear from you, OK? There should be a good article in it—one we'd all be interested in.

Now just turn the page for a listing of this year's articles. Don Henry is back with an account of his friend Norman Tonn's work with a couple of impressive 9.3s, which proves that some Germans are as fervid as many Americans about *wildkatz*. And Dick VanDenburg continues his coverage of handloading pioneers with a look at J.R. Mattern, a Pennsylvanian who did much work and writing in this field, so deserves our interest and respect. Then Richard Lee, who started a big handloading tool company with his little Lee Loader so many years ago, gives a firsthand account of the trials and tribulations often involved in such an endeavor. Incidentally, Dick's new manual, *Modern Reloading*, in preparation as this article was written, is now available. It's excellent, and we highly recommend it.

There are a lot of other articles, of course, and we could go on writing about others' writings for hours, but space is always limited here, so you'll have to read them for yourself. That's better anyway.

*—Bob Bell*

# CONTENTS

## FEATURES

# CONTENTS

## FEATURES



## CATALOG

# Wildcatting the 9.3

**This hunter, alone in a snowy wonderland, took a 5x5 bull elk with a rifle he built for a cartridge he created—using his own handloads.**

The 9.3 U.S.A. loaded with (from left) 230 Hawk, 250 Barnes X, 270 Speer and 300-grain Hawk bullets.

The 9.3R North American cartridge (from left): the 270-grain Speer bullet in a case not yet fire-formed; the same after fire-forming; the 247-grain RWS bullet loaded in reformed case.

by DON L. HENRY

IF ONE REMEMBERS that money is among the poorest measures of wealth, Norman Tonn is a rich man—for reasons that will become obvious. Tonn built his first two 9.3s for the 9.3x62 Mauser cartridge. Not only were they test beds for ballistics that enlightened his wildcat cartridge developments, but building them also revealed desirable dimensions such as barrel contour, length and twist rate. And suppliers of 9.3 barrels and gunsmithing were discovered. Both are accurate and effective big game rifles.

German reloading manuals warn against making brass from other cases because the 9.3x62 is extra thick and strong in the head to withstand the pressures generated by that high-intensity cartridge. Because 9.3x62 and 9.3x64 brass is relatively expensive, Tonn, the consummate shooter, wanted a 9.3 he could afford to enjoy. Often.

One 9.3x62 was built on a surplus 98-pattern FN Model 1950 Mauser action. It was fitted with a 1:12-inch-twist barrel from Siskiyou Gun Works. Gunsmith Jim Wasmundt chambered the 22-inch barrel. After stocking and glass-bedding by Tonn, the finished rifle weighed 9 pounds. Although he prefers a stiff barrel, this one is .720-inch at the muzzle. He didn't think it would weigh this much. It delivered .85- to 1-inch 100-yard and 1.5-inch 200-yard groups. Velocity was 2375 fps with his favorite load. Norma factory ammo delivered 2310 fps.

The second 9.3x62 was gotten up on a surplus M98 Vz24 action made by Ceskoslovenska Zbrojovka, Brno. Barrel and gunsmithing were from same sources, twist 1:12 inches, but this one was 20 inches long and .735-inch at the muzzle. It weighed 8 pounds. With peep sight, this one delivered 1.4-inch 100-yard groups. With the same handload used in the FN 50, the shorter barrel delivered 2265 fps, but the Norma load gave 2320 fps—10 fps faster than the 2-inch longer barrel. Figure that.

Tonn's third 9.3 was a 9.3x64 Brenneke on a Mark X action. He discussed throating for this cartridge with gunsmith C.P. Donnelly of Siskiyou Gun Works, who barreled and chambered this rifle. The European throat is more like a Weatherby freebore and very long. While it contributes to velocity, it is often detrimental to accuracy. Norm chose a shorter throat like those used with most American cartridges because to him accuracy outshines velocity except in advertising. This rifle has a 25-inch barrel, .675 at the muzzle.

Armed with his own handloads for a cartridge he developed, in a rifle he designed, Norman Tonn took his first whole elk, a 5x5, with a well-placed shot at 129 paces. Imagine the satisfaction.

Norman wrote, "I share Dieter Sturm's enthusiasm for the 9.3 Brenneke, but I find his data with the 270-grain Speer bullet to be quite optimistic in my rifle. I would guess that his rifle has 'freebore.' *Lyman Reloading Handbook No. 45* states that one should reduce the charge by 5 percent in rifles without freebore. That matches exactly with my test results." Later, Norm's wife bought a 9.3 Brenneke for him from Herr Sturm, and it did indeed have freebore, which accounts for velocities that he was not able to achieve safely with his more closely throated and conservatively loaded accurate rifles.

## Hooked on 9.3s

Norman Tonn shoots more 9.3s and knows as much about rifles of this caliber as anyone I have heard of or read about. He is the son of a gunsmith, a German language scholar who has lived, taught and studied arms in Europe. He is a teacher, a lifelong hunter and a collector of 9.3-caliber arms, including a 9.3x62 M1924 Mannlicher-Schoenauer and a M1972 Mannlicher-Schoenauer 9.3x64 Brenneke. His shooting collection includes 9.3 single shots and Continental combination guns, and currently he has on order a pistol barrel for his 9.3R North American wildcat T/C Contender. As builder of his own match-grade rifles and creator of 9.3 wildcat cartridges, he is a practical ballistician.

Norm blames your narrator:

"Years ago when I was a typical American gun fancier who needed only fifty-four more kinds of firearms in sixty-two different calibers, I met my high-school friend, Don Henry, at a class reunion. Until then, I had forgotten his lack of decorum and his seditious behavior in American Problems class that got him expelled so he could go hunting for three days while I had to sit in school, thereby solving his notion of a practical American problem.

"He started talking about 9.3x57, 9.3x62, 9.3x64, 9.3x74 and other math problems. I remembered that he had taken an advanced math class because of a smart and pretty freshman girl named Sharon. Having memorized multiplication tables only to twelve times twelve, I was still figuring the sum of 9.3x57 when I realized that he was talking guns.

"I bought a copy of *Cartridges of the World* and studied it more assiduously than I did for a college class called Linguistics and Philology. I discovered metrics.

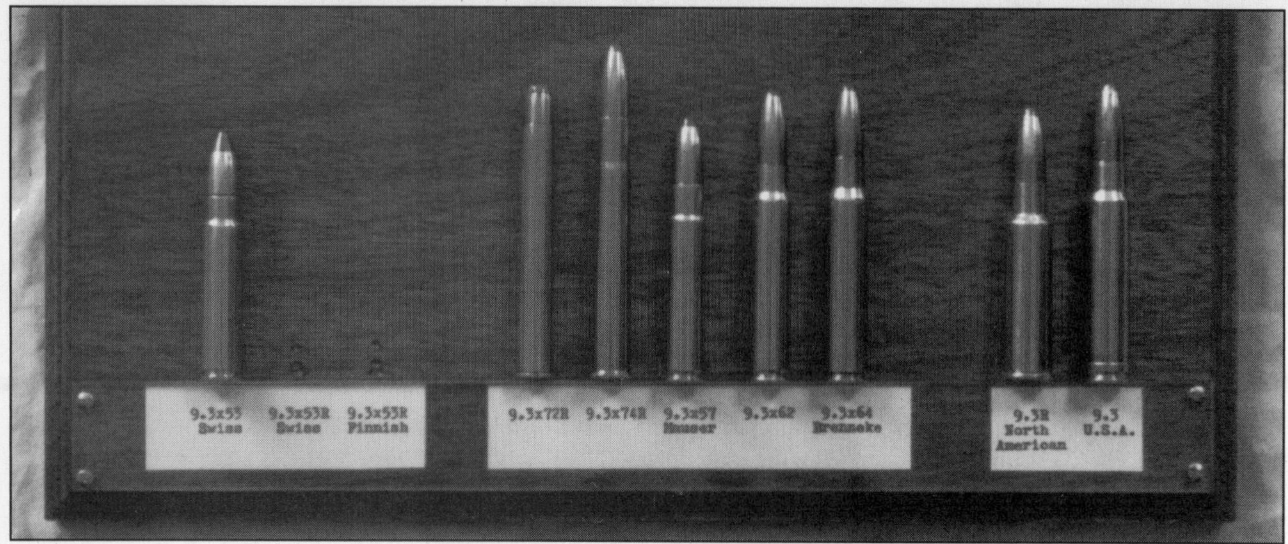


The world's 9.3-caliber cartridges were all created for hunting. The 9.3x53 Swiss also comes in a rimmed version, which differs from the 9.3x53R Finnish. Currently loaded 9.3s (center set) include the 9.3x72R (.364-inch bullet), 9.3x74R, 9.3x57, 9.3x62 Mauser and 9.3x64 Brenneke. Tonn's wildcats, the 9.3R North American and the 9.3 U.S.A., are on the right.

"The M98 Mausers I had planned to rebarrel to 35 Whelen and 338-06 suddenly became 9.3x62s. My wife understood that the insidious arguments of Don Henry made me do it and that it was his fault I couldn't replace the coat I bought from an East German refugee for her Christmas in 1967.

"Now, years later, she will speak to Mr. Henry when he calls because I've made so many good investments in metric collectibles on his astute advice—which is, invariably, 'If you don't buy it, I will.'

"By the way, the sum of 9.3x74 is 688.2—unless you add the rim which makes it 697.5."

### Strictly Sporting

According to Barnes' *Cartridges of the World*, there never was a strictly military 9.3 cartridge. The *Catalogue of DWM Cartridge Case Pattern Numbers*, published in HANDLOADER'S DIGEST, 13th edition, shows #294B, 9.3x65R; #294V, 9.3x60R; #474F, 9.3x86R; #569, 9.3x70; and #601, 9.3x70R, in addition to those listed in the chart with this article. All are sporting rounds.

Early this century, the British had a quartet of sporting 36-calibers, using from .360- to .367-inch bullets, but all have disappeared.

In America, the .366-bore (groove diameter) was popular in muzzleloading squirrel rifle days. Colt made 36-caliber revolvers around the mid-19th century. Since the advent of smokeless powder, the 36-bore hasn't been popular here.

In Europe, however, its popularity never waned. The Sauer-made Luftwaffe survival drilling was chambered for the 9.3x74R sporting round, the only 9.3 cartridge known to have been military issue.

The 9.3 is not unpopular in North America for lack of bullets. Available grain weights and types here are 193 TMF RWS, 200 Hawk, 235 Hawk, 247 RWS, 250 Speer, 250 Swift, 250 Barnes X, 270 Speer, 285 TMR RWS, 285 Hawk, 286 Norma Alaskan, 286 A-Square SP Lion Load, 286 A-Square SP Dead Tough, 286 A-Square Monolithic Solid, 286 Barnes X, 286 Norma SPRN, 286 Barnes FMJ, 300 Swift, 300 Hawk, 320 Hawk, 215 cast NEI, 250 cast Rapine, and 250 cast Lyman. Others are available from Woodleigh and Thunderbird Cartridge Co.

### Design Objectives

Penetrating power was one of Tonn's prime objectives. "I read so often in magazines about how the best bullet and load will expend all of its energy inside the animal," Norm said. "Every animal I have harvested where the bullet went completely through seemed to drop quickly."

To obtain this goal, he wanted case capacity equal to or greater than the 9.3x64 Brenneke, which would presumably give similar performance—all things being equal, which, of course, they never are. Table B shows how well his wildcats approach the objective with conservative loads. Table A shows why.

Theoretically, then, Tonn's two wildcats should give performance equal to or better than the 9.3x64 at identical pressures.

### Actions and Pressures

For reasons of cost and weight, Tonn determined that his wildcats would fit standard-length military surplus actions. This decision necessarily limited safe working pressures to those for which the actions were originally intended.

The 9.3 North American was designed for the Siamese Mauser action. Thailand converted some of these rifles for the U.S. 30-06 in 1952.

**TABLE A: CASE CAPACITIES**

| Cartridge | Brass | —Bullet— Wgt. Grs. | Type | O.A.L. (ins.) | Grains Water |
|---|---|---|---|---|---|
| ***No bullet seated*** | | | | | |
| 9.3x64 | RWS | — | — | 86.3 | |
| 9.3R North American | reformed WW 348 | — | — | 87.2 | |
| 9.3 U.S.A. | reformed Fed. 338 | — | — | 87.8 | |
| ***With bullet seated*** | | | | | |
| 9.3x64 | RWS | 270 | Speer | 3.363 | 79.0 |
| 9.3R North American | reformed WW 348 | 270 | Speer | 3.080 | 82.5 |
| 9.3 U.S.A. | reformed Fed. 338 | 250 | Barnes X | 3.360 | 81.2 |

The 9.3 North American cartridge and the Siamese Mauser-based sporting rifle built for it, both by Norman Tonn. They are shown on his gunsmith father's machinist's chest with the H-380 powder and Speer 270-grain bullets used in load development.

The 9.3R North American wildcat cartridge with a few of the American-made 9.3 bullets suitable for it.

Since the 30-06 is loaded to a bit over 50,000 psi, it appears that the action can take it. In *Bolt Action Rifles*, revised edition, pp. 245-248, Frank de Haas writes, "[T]o be on the safe side the Siamese Mauser action should be limited to cartridges that do not develop much over 45,000 psi breech pressure." The loads which Tonn developed for his 9.3 N.A. are, therefore, conservatively tailored for the Siamese action and do not reflect the capability of the cartridge in a stronger rifle.

Tonn's 9.3 U.S.A. was built on a commercial Mark X action. It is adequate for higher pressure loads than the surplus Siamese.

### Standard Established

Tonn set 9.3x62 and 9.3x64 performance as a goal because they are the most powerful 9.3 commercial cartridges. He wrote:

"I put together a 9.3 Brenneke on a Mark X action. The Europeans use a fair amount of freebore in their rifles for this cartridge, which means they are able to boost velocity, but with a sacrifice. I chose a shorter throat for accuracy. My fastest load with the Speer 270-grain bullet is with 71.8 grains of IMR-4350 for 2630 fps instrumental velocity 12 feet from the muzzle. The rifle is extremely accurate, but my maximum loads were not even up to starting loads that I have seen published for this cartridge.

"My chance to compare loads came when I got a Mannlicher-Schoenauer M72 chambered 9.3x64. The 25.6-inch barrel has a 1:14.2 twist. The 'Schusstest' target certificate accompanying it shows a 1.4-inch three-shot group at 100 meters. I hoped for better and would gladly give up some velocity to get it.

"Dieter Sturm's loads for this rifle in *Handloader* No. 147 showed a 270-grain Speer semi-spitzer over a starting load of 76.0 grains of IMR-4350 and a maximum of 78.0 grains, both using a CCI 200 primer, giving 2875 fps. Mr. Sturm shows 77.0 grains as maximum for the 286-grain bullet. Bill Caldwell, in *Handloader*, Nov.-Dec. 1972, gives 76.0 grains of the same powder as maximum.

"My loads used RWS brass, the 270-grain Speer bullet, and Federal 215 primers. Overall cartridge length

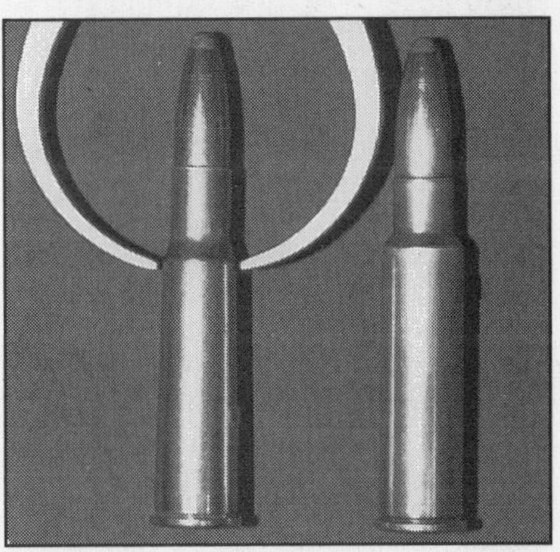

The 9.3R North American, built on 348 Winchester brass, before and after fire-forming. The caliper indicates a difference between the reformed and unfired shoulder.

The 9.3 U.S.A. wildcat is a 338 Winchester case necked up to 366-caliber with no other changes. On a commercial Mark X action Acraglass bedded in a fiberglass stock, it is a "rain rifle" adequate for any game found in the U.S.A. Shown with it are 250-grain Barnes X bullets, which are loaded over IMR-4350 powder. This rifle and this cartridge dropped a bull elk with a single shot each season it has been afield.

The 9.3 U.S.A. with just a few of the U.S.-made 9.3-caliber bullets suitable for it.

with this bullet loaded for the Mannlicher-Schoenauer M72 is 3.36 inches. A starting load of 69.8 grains of IMR-4350 produced groups over 3.5 inches; 74 grains, at 2831 fps, shot consistent 1.25-inch groups. Accuracy fell off drastically with 75.0 grains, and brass showed slight signs of stress.

"The RWS 285-grain TMR bullet factory load, at 2745 fps, went into 2.75 inches. This rifle liked the RWS 293-grain TUG bullet round, at 2539 fps, which shot 1.25-inch groups. Advertised velocity for these two rounds is 2690 fps for the 285-grain TMR and 2570 fps for the 293-grain TUG."

In teenage years I was a hot-rod handloader, having chronographed advertised Weatherby velocities from a standard 270 Winchester that too soon developed excessive headspace. Norm never was that intrepid. A conservative fellow, he prefers to err on the side of caution and accuracy.

Tonn's M72 M-S rifle weighs 9 pounds, unloaded. Neither the rifle nor the ammo for it are financial or physical lightweights. Besides, like his 9.3x62 Model 1924 original Mannlicher-Schoenauer, he considers it too fine to risk using beyond a formal target range.

The major objectives for building his wildcats, besides the considerable fun of it, were to obtain the advantages of the bigger 9.3's powerful performance in a personally sporterized rifle, shooting efficient cartridges based on inexpensive brass that fit commonly available standard-length surplus actions. In short, cheap power!

### 9.3R North American

This cartridge is the 348 Ackley Improved necked up to .366-inch. Cases are formed by running the 348 case through the resizer die. Brass is then loaded and fire-formed. Created for the Siamese Mauser action that takes a rimmed cartridge, pressures must be kept below the safe operating limit of that gun. When building a rifle for any cartridge, and especially a wildcat with little or no reliable pressure information available, any action should be checked for suitability by an experienced gunsmith, of course.

### 9.3 U.S.A.

This 9.3 is the 338 Winchester Magnum necked up to .366-inch with no other dimensional changes. Tonn finds this round's recoil in his 8-pound rifle approximately equal to shooting a 30-06 in a 7-pound piece. He describes recoil as "tolerable."

"The 9.3 U.S.A. was able to better the velocity just a bit over the 9.3x64 Brenneke fired in my Mannlicher-Schoenauer M71 rifle. The advantage over the Brenneke is that cartridge cases are much less expensive. Brenneke 9.3s are loaded only by RWS in Germany."

## Big Game Performance

### Half an Elk

Tonn's two 9.3s are wildcats of lion caliber capable of killing the largest

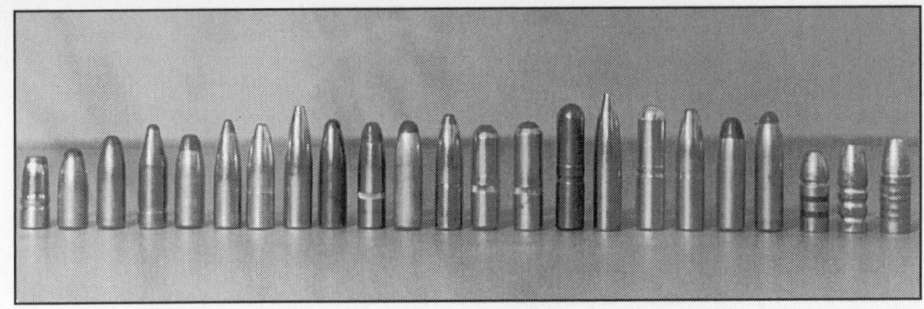

Bullets available for the 9.3 include (from left): 193 TMF RWS, 200 Hawk, 235 Hawk, 247 RWS, 250 Speer (discontinued), 250 Swift, 250 Barnes X, 270 Speer, 285 TMR RWS, 285 Hawk, 286 Norma Alaskan, 286 A-Square SP Lion Load, 286 A-Square SP Dead Tough, 286 A-Square Monolithic Solid, 286 Barnes X, 286 Norma SPRN, 286 Barnes FMJ, 300 Swift, 300 Hawk, 320 Hawk, 215 cast NEI, 250 cast Rapine and 250 cast Lyman.

game. Because he calls them "American" and "U.S.A.," think of them as cougars.

Proficient hunter and award-winning expert marksman that he is, Norm's nemesis remained the elk. He passed up uncertain long shots as unsportsmanlike. He pushed elk to others on drive hunts. Bulls were killed by his partners on either side of him. He wanted a trophy of his own.

In the season of '93, his partner hit a bull elk with a 30-06. It would have likely gone down in a few hundred yards. In this country, that could also mean a couple of thousand feet down into a canyon. Norm immediately anchored the animal with a shot through the shoulder with the 9.3 U.S.A. "It wasn't my bull," Norm said. "We shared it. So far, I've shot half an elk."

**Killer Cat**

"I found a mile-wide mostly open basin into which elk coming down from high country gravitated. Earlier, I had passed up a shot at a spike. On this day, I had elk in twos, threes and fours, moving all directions. Over fifty head, cows and calves. As they wandered out of the basin, I could see more coming in over the saddle a mile away. Up the ridge, a single trotted my direction. When he broke through trees 200 yards away, I saw antlers—antlers worth having.

"Up came the 9.3 U.S.A. The crosshairs settled on his oncoming chest. At the 'ker-whoom' the bull flinched, staggered and fell beside a small pine 129 long paces from the muzzle. I sat beside him for the hunter's meditation after giving the beautiful wapiti his 'last bite,' saying *Waidmannsdank!*—hunter's thanks. Looking into the sky, I said it again. Then, since no one else was there to do it, I said *Waidmannsheil!* (which means well-done, salute and honor to the hunter when spoken after the kill; and good and successful hunting when given in greeting at any time).

"I like the 9.3 U.S.A. The recoil is not worth mentioning; anyone who can handle a 30-06 can handle the 9.3 U.S.A. The 250-grain Barnes X-Bullet, chronographed at over 2700 fps, had plowed through the muscle and bone of the shoulder with very little meat damage. It continued back through lungs, liver and kidneys and exited near the anus. I agree with the Europeans who are just about apologetic for those bullets that they advertise 'We cannot guarantee an exit wound.' I want complete penetration. My experience on deer has shown quicker drops with complete penetration, as compared to those where the bullet expended all of its energy inside the animal.

"Later that day, two members of our party hit a spike bull a total of four times with a 30-06 and a 280 Remington before bringing it down. They are both excellent elk hunters and marksmen. When they skinned and quartered it, they found a 243 bullet in the elk's flank that had shed its core and penetrated only a little.

"My partner, Fred Wendt, got a 338 and I went to the 9.3 because we wanted complete penetration, not only to reach the vitals, but also to break the bull down with one shot.

"I took some razzing about the 'last bite' even though I explained that it was a ritual of respect. Curiously, another bull taken by our group the next day was given the honor by the successful hunter. *Waidmannsdank! und Waidmannsheil!*"

Imagine the satisfaction of this day: The man, alone in a snowy wonderland, ended his forty-year hunt with a 5x5 bull elk taken with one well-placed shot using his own handloads from a rifle he built for a cartridge he created.

*Waidmannsheil*, indeed!

**TABLE B: COMPARISON OF 9.3 CARTRIDGES**

| Cartridge | Bullet Wgt. Grs. | Velocity (fps) | Energy (fpe) | Source |
|---|---|---|---|---|
| 9.3x53 Swiss | 200 | 2000 | 1780 | Barnes |
| 9.3x53R Swiss | 200 | 2054 | 1960 | Barnes |
| 9.3x57 Mauser | 232 | 2330 | 2785 | Barnes |
| 9.3x57 Mauser | 286 | 2065 | 2714 | Barnes |
| 9.3x62 Mauser | 232 | 2640 | 3550 | Norma |
| 9.3x62 Mauser | 270 | 2583 | 4000 | Speer |
| 9.3x62 Mauser | 286 | 2360 | 3544 | Factory |
| 9.3x64 Brenneke | 262 | 2768 | 4465 | Barnes |
| 9.3x65R Brenneke | 286 | 2650 | 4490 | Barnes |
| 9.3x65R Brenneke | 293 | 2660 | 4640 | DWN/RWS |
| 9.3x72R (.364 bullet)* | 193 | 2020 | 1750 | Barnes |
| 9.3x74R | 232 | 2630 | 3535 | Norma |
| 9.3x74R | 270 | 2328 | 3250 | Speer |
| 9.3x74R | 286 | 2360 | 3530 | Norma |
| 9.3 North American** | 247 | 2432 | 3243 | Tonn |
| 9.3 North American** | 250 | 2340 | 3040 | Tonn |
| 9.3 North American** | 270 | 2566 | 3945 | Tonn |
| 9.3 U.S.A. | 250 X | 2695 | 4033 | Tonn |
| 9.3 U.S.A. | 270 | 2589 | 4018 | Tonn |
| 9.3 U.S.A. | 300 | 2443 | 3975 | Tonn |

*From the straight-cased sporting cartridge family of 9.3x48R, 9.3x57R, 9.3x70R, 9.3x72R, 9.3x80R and 9.3x82R, of which the 9.3x72R survives.

**Because wildcat cartridges are not standardized, we are, regrettably, unwilling to publish loading data. Tonn's loads were developed with only one powder for each of his wildcats. His conservative velocities from the 9.3 N.A. were achieved with H-380 powder. Powder used for the 9.3 U.S.A. was IMR-4350. Load development for these cartridges with additional powders continues in anticipation of higher velocities.

For hiking, camping or hunting, the 41 Special is an outstanding choice—moderate power and fun to shoot.

# SHOOT A 41 SPECIAL

by
DAVID WARD

I'M TIRED OF magnums. Admit it: Magnums aren't really fun to shoot and are limited in application. Touch one off, and it belches fire and smoke. Recoil can be downright punishing. Certainly, the first few shots are exciting. But fun? No way. Keep your eye on that macho dude in the cammie pants shooting his 44 Magnum at the range, and you'll probably see him slink around the corner and massage his hand after only a few cylinders, even if he uses a glove for padding!

Don't get me wrong. Full-power magnums are great for big game or varmint hunting with a handgun. But full-power handgun hunting makes up only a small percentage of all the shooting that we generally do. If you like to shoot, chances are that the loads you shoot least often are magnum loads.

These days more and more people are discovering that the most useful, and sometimes the most effective and certainly the most fun, loads are those that fit into the medium-power level. No doubt the vast majority of big-bore slugs sent downrange, or after small game and the like, are medium loads. There's simply not much of Br'er Rabbit left to eat after he's been vaporized with 200 grains of lead streaking along in the neighborhood of 1400 fps. Remember how those gallon jugs exploded when hit by a magnum?

In the non-sporting arena, the hot

(Above) Here is the author's modified RCBS 41 Magnum expander-decapper die. A small amount of the threaded portion that secures the decapping pin had to be removed, and the case mouth had to be flared with the pin removed. RCBS' 41 AE dies could be used without modification, as could new 41 Magnum dies.

The 41 Magnum softpoint is compared to the 41 Special. The shorter case of the Special provides more efficient burning of light and medium charges of powder.

The expander-decapper die showing a longer portion of pin protruding after die modification. The strength of the pin allows perfect functioning.

These 41 Specials were loaded with cast bullets (from left): 177-grain NEI HP, 195-grain NEI, 215-grain RCBS SWC and 200-grain Lee SWC.

ticket these days is not the 10mm designed originally as the primo law enforcement round. The 10mm is essentially a 41 Magnum for a semi-auto pistol, and it is too potent to shoot all of the time. It's hard on the pistol and on the shooter. So, Smith & Wesson and Olin Manufacturing teamed up and brought out what *is* the hot ticket these days, and that is the 40 S&W. Easily loaded to the 450 fpe range, the 40 S&W nicely fills a niche for a powerful, but not too powerful, law enforcement or defense cartridge. Ditto the 41 Action Express, although it is somewhat limited in availability.

It would seem, then, that the auto-pistol folks have it all figured out for the moment. Something in 40- to 41-caliber moving a 155- to 200-grain bullet along at 950 to 1100 fps is a darned good load. Well, what about us revolver people? The same load should work just as well for us, be it defending the castle or putting meat in the pot. What have we got in the medium-power 40-caliber niche?

Nothing, really. We can load down the 41 Magnum, but that leaves a considerable amount of wasted space in the long magnum case. It works, but it is not too efficient. That is one of the reasons that Olin and S&W went to a shorter case. The only other option is to switch calibers and make use of the shorter-length 44 Special or the 45 Auto Rim. Both are excellent cartridges, and with a modest amount of work at the loading bench, all three will send an appropriate projectile on its way within the parameters set out above.

The two shorter cartridges offer a couple of advantages over reduced loads in the full-length magnum brass. The smaller volume of the Special and the Auto Rim mean a more consistent ignition of powder, especially with light charges of the fast-

Which is the low-power load? Two 41 Magnums loaded with the same bullet make identification difficult.

**LOADING DATA: 41 SPECIAL**

| Powder Wgt. Grs./Type | MV (fps) | Comments |
|---|---|---|
| **177-grain NEI HP** | | |
| 4.7/Bullseye | 854 | |
| 5.5/Bullseye | 975 | |
| 6.0/Bullseye | 1079 | |
| 7.2/Unique | 1090 | |
| 5.5/AA No.5 | 769 | |
| 7.6/AA No.5 | 1063 | |
| 9.6/Blue Dot | 1115 | full case |
| 6.2/Green Dot | 1084 | |
| **195-grain NEI** | | |
| 4.5/Bullseye | 807 | |
| 5.6/Bullseye | 993 | accurate |
| 6.5/Unique | 911 | |
| 7.1/Unique | 1096 | max |
| 6.0/AA No.5 | 751 | |
| 7.3/AA No.5 | 1007 | |
| 9.0/Blue Dot | 1039 | |
| 6.0/Green Dot | 973 | |
| 6.4/Green Dot | 1024 | |
| 5.5/AA No.2 | 962 | |

| Powder Wgt. Grs./Type | MV (fps) | Comments |
|---|---|---|
| **200-grain Speer HP** | | |
| 6.9/Unique | 1057 | good load |
| 9.0/Blue Dot | 1063 | |
| 6.5/Green Dot | 1014 | |
| **200-grain Lee** | | |
| 5.5/Bullseye | 985 | |
| 7.1/AA No.5 | 969 | 4 shots in 7/8" |
| 6.3/Green Dot | 1001 | accurate |
| 5.5/AA No.2 | 978 | |
| **215-grain RCBS** | | |
| 5.0/Bullseye | 884 | |
| 6.0/Bullseye | 998 | near max |
| 6.6/Unique | 984 | |
| 7.7/AA No.5 | 1098 | max, 573 fpe |
| 5.0/AA No.2 | 843 | |
| 6.0/AA No.2 | 1021 | |
| 8.9/Blue Dot | 1047 | |
| 9.2/Blue Dot | 1108 | 583 fpe |
| 6.0/Green Dot | 962 | |

Winchester cases, CCI 300 primers. Velocities are an average of ten shots measured on a ProTach Competiton Chronograph 7 feet from muzzle. Temp: 58 degrees F.

burners like Bullseye and AA No. 2. They are more efficient. Also the shorter cases make for immediate identification of moderate loads, assuming that you don't try to load them to magnum velocities. With that in mind, the 44 Special and the 45 Auto Rim make fine choices for home defense, hunting or target work.

However, I shoot the 41 Magnum. And I like 41-caliber. Wouldn't it be nice to have a less powerful, easily distinguishable cartridge in 41-caliber that would chamber in your 41 Magnum revolver? I thought so, but unfortunately there were none around. So I made one. It's easy to do, and it works quite nicely.

Before the "How To," though, let me explain the "Why" in choosing certain dimensional parameters. It all ties back to the development of the 44 Special from the 44 Russian. Considered the top target and field cartridge of its day (the late 1800s), the Russian's case length of .970-inch was not quite large enough in capacity to efficiently handle full charges of the new smokeless powders available at the time. So the case was lengthened some 0.20-inch with all other dimensions remaining the same. Presto! Enter the 44 Special. It, too, is well known for excellent accuracy; it was in the past, and is again today, a popular and useful cartridge.

Obviously, the extra case length of the Special allowed for very efficient use of modern smokeless powders. Experimenters like the late Elmer Keith and others cranked velocities

These bullets were used for the 41 Special (from left): 177-grain NEI HP, 195-grain NEI, 200-grain Lee SWC, 215-grain RCBS SWC and 200-grain Speer HP.

The short Special case ejects easily from the long 41 Magnum cylinder.

(Above) A 2x Leupold EER scope was mounted on an S&W Model 57 for accuracy tests. Targets shot from the rest at 25 yards show the potential of the 41 Special.

into what are now magnum ranges and were directly responsible for the creation of the 44 Magnum, itself a lengthened 44 Special.

You might call my work in the development of a 41 Special a case of reverse cartridge evolution. No pun intended. A short 41 that could be magnumized would be redundant; the magnum version is already here. So, I did not want a cartridge that could be turned into a short 41 Magnum. I wanted sort of a 41 Russian. A rimmed version of the 40 S&W or 41 AE.

Hence the decision for a case length of exactly 1.000 inch. It gave enough room to easily obtain velocities up to about 1100 fps, but not much more. Ah ha! you say. That's the same as the old lead bullet police loading originally offered in the full-length magnum case. True, I say back, but the short case has an advantage, especially for police work. Since it cannot be easily overloaded, the 41 Special would make a dandy load for a five-shot, medium-framed service revolver that magnum loads might unduly stress. Perfect for those in law enforcement who are revolver fans and want to pack a bigger bore than 357 Magnum, but want some-

(Below) This target was shot at 25 yards with 215-grain RCBS SWC and 6.0 grains of Bullseye.

thing weighing less than a pants-drooping 48 or so ounces. The resurgence of interest in the 44 Special is because of this very concept. Charter Arms was first to chamber it in the five-shot Bulldog. Since then, Taurus and Rossi have offered medium-frame five-shot snubbie-type revolvers in 44 Special. Both come with warnings that the 44 Special is not to be magnumized and used in the guns. Stay at 950 to 1000 fps, please. Either of the two revolvers could easily be rechambered and rebarreled for the 41 Special. The resulting five-shooter would make an outstanding trail gun. Otherwise, check it out in your full-sized 41 Magnum.

Enough of that. Here's how to do it. Take fifty standard 41 Magnum cases, put each into the case trimmer, and cut to 1.000-inch. Chamfer the case mouth and you're ready to load. I used an RCBS power trimmer attachment that allows the use of a regular power drill, and it took maybe twenty minutes total. Not bad for a "wildcat."

For the actual loading process, it's just like loading the full-length case except for one thing, and that may not affect everyone. My 41 Magnum dies from RCBS are of 1976 vintage with the addition of a tungsten carbide die in the middle 1980s. With those dies, decapping is done at the same time as case mouth flaring. The new Special case is just short enough that the case cannot be flared without removing the threaded protrusion onto which the decapping pin holder is threaded. With the protrusion shortened, and the pin and holder removed, I can flare the case mouth. It adds a step to the loading process. New RCBS dies decap in the sizer die, so the problem is solved. Or you could get a set of 41 AE dies from RCBS and not worry about anything, since the dimensions are the same except for the case length and rebated rim.

This case is made to order for cast bullet loading, because the moderate velocities generated do not encourage leading, even from soft, swaged bullets. Casting straight wheelweights, I used four styles from three makers: a 200-grain SWC from Lee, a 215-grain SWC from RCBS, and a 195-grain FP from NEI that could also be cast as a 177-grain HP using the same mould with a HP nose pin. Along with those, I used a Speer 200-grain jacketed HP because it has so much lead exposed. None of the Sierra or Hornady softpoints or hollowpoints were tested because it was felt that they were designed for magnum velocities. Although I did not crimp any of the bullets and did not notice any bullet movement, the taper crimp seater die in the RCBS 41 AE die set would provide a nice tight fit.

Best powders for the small 41 Special case are the medium- and fast-

(Above) A flyer spoiled this otherwise nice 25-yard group using Green Dot and a 195-grain NEI bullet.

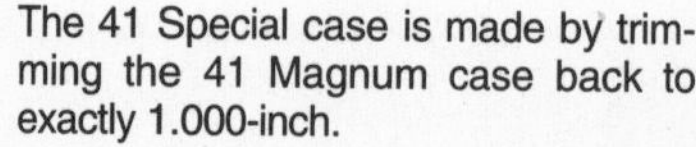

The 41 Special case is made by trimming the 41 Magnum case back to exactly 1.000-inch.

Making cases is a simple task on any case trimmer. Use of a power trimming attachment is even easier.

burners. I happened to have Bullseye, Unique, Green Dot, Blue Dot, AA No.2, and AA No.5 on hand, so they were used in this project. All are capable of producing excellent accuracy with any of the bullets used. Blue Dot is a bit slow and begins to take the Special over 1100 fps, as can Green Dot and AA No.5. All work well in the 1000 fps range, though.

If you are looking for more versatility in loading data than I have developed here, you can always use published data for the 41 Action Express. Since the Special case is slightly larger in volume than the 41 AE case, theoretically you can't get into trouble using those loads.

Just remember you're not making a magnum here. We've already got magnum loads. I had to remind myself of that several times during load development, as the velocities crept over the 1100 fps limits I'd set. Also remember that fast powders like Bullseye and AA No.2 can still build dangerously high pressures very quickly in a small case, so be careful. These loads were safe in my test pistol; they may not be in yours. Reduce starting loads by 10 percent and work up gradually.

All load development, testing and accuracy work was performed in my 6-inch Model 57 Smith & Wesson, an absolute delight to shoot with the Special. During accuracy tests, I mounted a Leupold M8 2x EER scope to help eliminate one accuracy variable and shot over a sandbagged rest at 25 yards to eliminate another. The better groups averaged $1^1/_2$-$2^1/_2$ inches at that distance. The accompanying chart shows various loads developed, chronographed velocities and comments.

Now that we've got it, what do we do with it? There are plenty of applications for the 41 Special. First, like the 44 Special and the 45 Auto Rim, it makes a fine general-purpose revolver cartridge. It is easily distinguishable from those special-purpose, full-house 41 Magnum loads. As a trail load, it will handle anything you're likely to encounter in the Lower 48 with two or four legs, except grizzly bear. And let's face it, the chances of meeting *Ursus horribilus* these days anywhere beyond the zoo or a few areas in the Northern Rockies are very slim. Other than those specialized situations (where you would pack the full magnum loads anyway), the up to 580 fpe available in the 41 Special should be more than adequate to see you through.

For home defense, you won't find another revolver cartridge that's any better. Many feel that 41-caliber is an ideal compromise of bullet weight, velocity, energy and penetration. Complete penetration of your house and your neighbor's with a hot magnum load is hardly ideal. The Special, along with a number of other cartridges, offers a more moderate and yet still effective load.

For target work or casual shooting, the Special should provide the same service and versatility as its 38-, 44- and 45-caliber cousins, offering moderate recoil coupled with fine accuracy. Ditto for small game hunting, if that's your choice for your big-bore handgunning. A big slug at low to moderate speed puts game in the pot without ruining much meat in the process. And the shorter case of the Special is identifiable at a glance. You won't stuff a 1400 fps magnum load into the revolver by accident.

The 38 Special and the 44 Special offer certain advantages over their long-cased magnum brothers. They must, or they would not have survived after the introduction of high-velocity cartridges. So it is with the 41 Special. It is useful, easy to load and fun to shoot. If you like the 41 Magnum, shoot a 41 Special, too. •

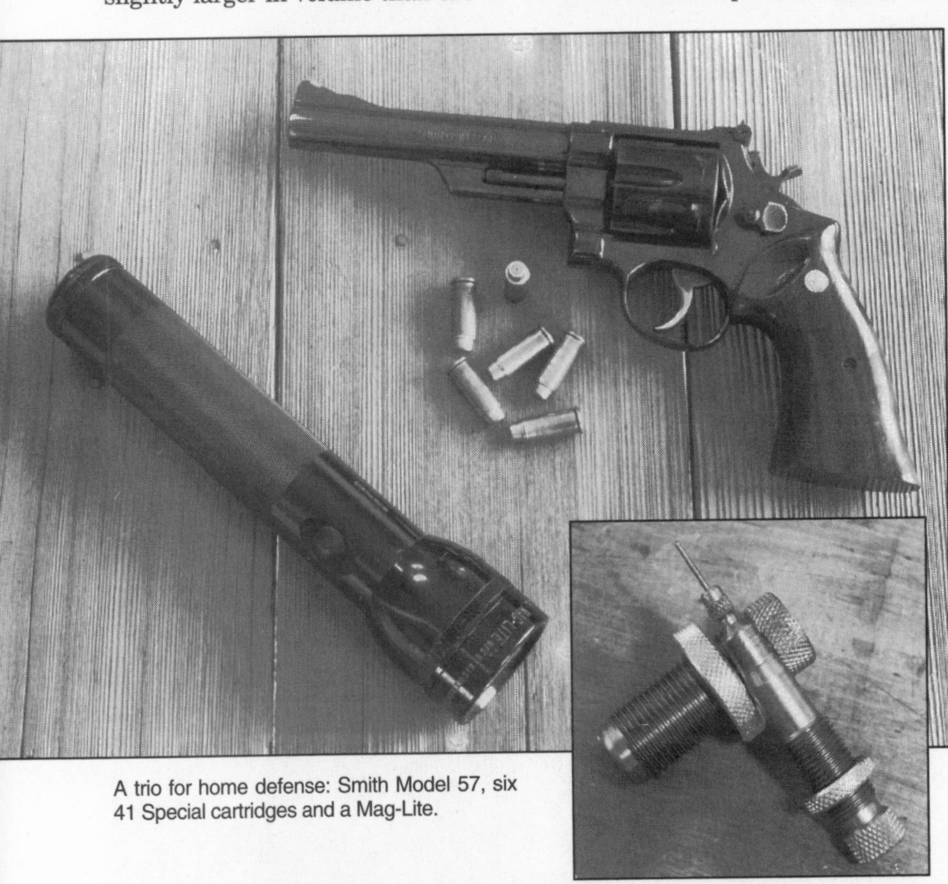

A trio for home defense: Smith Model 57, six 41 Special cartridges and a Mag-Lite.

(Above) Shortening the threaded protrusion that holds the decapping pin on the author's older 41 Magnum die is necessary to flare the case mouth on the shorter Special case.

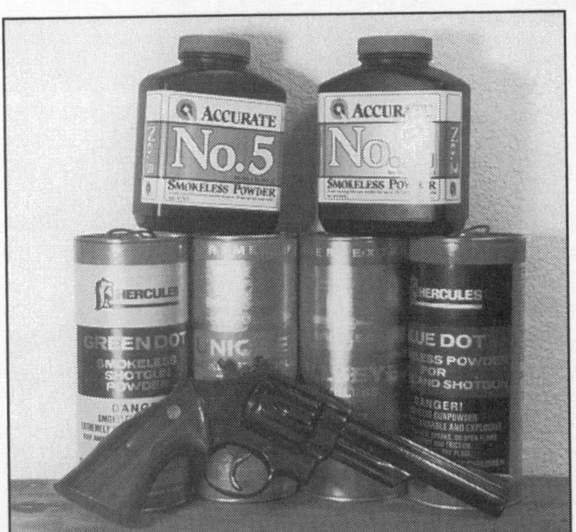


Medium- and fast-burning powders were used in load development for the 41 Special: (top) AA No.5 and AA No.2; (bottom) Green Dot, Unique, Bullseye and Blue Dot.

The need for an average-weight, scopesighted rifle to handle deer and elk in the woods led me to a little wildcat...

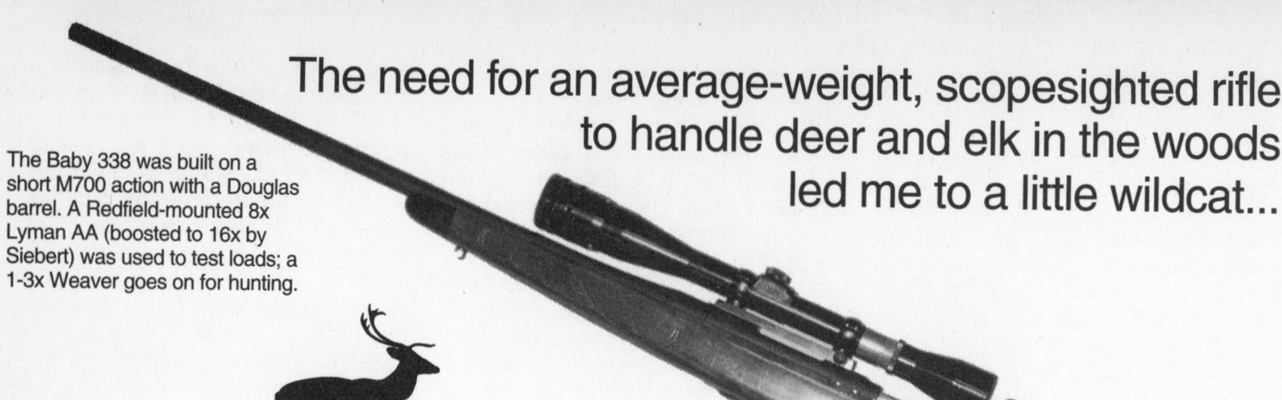

The Baby 338 was built on a short M700 action with a Douglas barrel. A Redfield-mounted 8x Lyman AA (boosted to 16x by Siebert) was used to test loads; a 1-3x Weaver goes on for hunting.

# THE BABY 338

by BOB BELL

RIGHT AT THE beginning, I want it understood that this cartridge is not original with me. A number of guys throughout the country are using it. I had no trouble getting dies from RCBS, and I expect other makers can supply them too. Not even the name is original. Back in the late '40s, batting the breeze with Idaho gunsmith Charley Evans, he mentioned a locally popular wildcat he'd come up with by necking down the 300 Savage case to hold a .277 bullet so lever-action fans could be happy with their M99s. I'm not sure if the result was in any way superior to the 300, but some guys just had to have a 270-caliber, even one not equal to the regular Winchester cartridge. I guess it was the O'Connor influence. Charley called his wildcat the "Baby 270," thus the "Baby 338." Might be more accurate to call it the 33-08, 'cause it's simply the 308 Winchester case necked up to take a 338 bullet, with no other changes.

(Below) The Baby 338 accounted for this seven-point on almost the last day of the season for Bell. The 175-grain X-Bullet angled completely through the body almost lengthwise for and instant kill.

Why fool around with a little wildcat like this? Well, I'm not sure that anyone needs justification for such an action, but the truth is I really did have a reason. Some years back, I had some physical problems, and the docs said no more shooting heavy-recoil cartridges. I thought at first they were referring to stuff like the 505 Gibbs, 600 Nitro Express, etc., but they said no, they meant my little ol' 338 Magnum, which has been my favorite North American big game whomper since 1960, when I had my first one built.

So I gave things some thought. I wanted something dependable on elk-size game in the woods. I thought of going back to my Model 71 348, which had taken a truckload of deer and elk many years ago. But it weighed 8½ pounds, ready to go, and had only iron sights. I still had the old Stith Streamline mount that

(Below) Bob (Ol' Baldy) Wise gets ready to touch off a shot during a preliminary sight-in, to make sure we wouldn't put a bullet through the screens.

(Above) Bell reloaded 338-08 cases during the chronographing session. Having two tools set up simultaneously and pre-weighed powder charges made it possible to decap and neck-size on one tool and seat bullets on other without switching dies.

(Right) Here is a downrange view during a chronographing session at the Carlisle (PA) Rod & Gun Club.

allowed me to fit a 2½x Texan, but it added another pound and wasn't entirely satisfactory, the scope necessarily being offset quite a bit. And 9½ pounds, though not especially noticeable to a kid in his early 20s, is a bit much for a guy my age.

So I looked through the gun rack some more and spotted a short Model 700 that had been barreled for the 7mm-08 before Remington commercialized the cartridge. By this time, I had a 788 and a Model Seven for that load, and obviously didn't need three of them. If I replaced the barrel with one based on the 308 case, I could have a scopesighted rig that weighed only about 7½ pounds. This would be significantly lighter than the M71, without being too light, and still have the advantage of good optics.

It would have been simple and maybe logical to go with the 358 Winchester. It would be easy to get cases, and factory ammo would be available, if needed. But I wanted to load Nosler Partitions, and at the time they didn't make them in 35-caliber. Years before, Bob Hagel had told me the 210-grain Partition 338 was his favorite elk bullet, and I doubt that anyone knows more about elk hunting than Hagel, so I was set on using Partitions. Then, it was the only "premium." Now there are many.

Gunsmith Jim Peightal fitted and chambered a light 24-inch Douglas barrel. While he was doing that, I neck-expanded sixty new Winchester 308 cases and loaded them with a moderate charge of IMR-4895 and 200-grain bullets, seated out far enough that they'd contact the rifling lands and thus shove the case back against the bolt face, resulting in minimum headspace after firing. For testfiring, I also replaced the low-power hunting scope with a Lyman All-American that Wally Siebert had boosted to 16x many years ago.

I had several boxes of 200-grain Hornady flatpoints on hand, so I used those for the original firing. They grouped OK for unselected loads—fifteen three-shot groups averaged 1.72 inches at 100 yards—and the fired cases showed Peightal had done a fine, smooth chambering job. I then switched to 200-grain spitzers from Hornady and Speer, with the results shown in Table I. Velocities and standard deviations were taken on an Oehler 35P chronograph.

I don't know if the top loads in the table are maximum or not. I stopped increasing powder charges when velocity reached about 2500 fps. That's all I was looking for. It matched the factory velocity of the 200-grain 348 load that had proved itself many times in seasons long past, so I knew the Baby 338 would take care of my needs.

Then I selected five deer loads that gave the 200-grain bullets the velocity I wanted—48.0/IMR-4895, 51.0/W-748, 48.0/IMR-4320, 45.0/AA2520, and 44.0/IMR-3031—and charged ten cases with each load. I didn't seat a bullet at that time, but put them in an MTM box with a thick cardboard layer over the mouths held firmly in place by the lid so they couldn't spill. Then I took them, plus 200-grain bullets, a box of Winchester 120 primers, and reloading tools to the range. I also checked the 175-grain Barnes and 210-grain Nosler for velocity and accuracy (looking forward to my next elk hunt), but didn't have enough on hand at the time to check case durability.

(Left) All the stuff needed just to clock some bullet speeds. Tools are a new RCBS Partner and an ancient Super Pacific—still one of my favorites because it works on the upstroke.

(Incidentally, I think "standard" bullets are preferable to so-called premiums for deer. Over the years, it has seemed to me that the premiums don't expand as quickly as I want on deer- and caribou-size game, which obviously are a lot smaller and "softer" than elk and moose. I'm glad we have a fine selection of premium bullets nowadays, and on certain critters they're advisable, but let's not forget that for generations standard bullets accounted for millions of animals, and there's no doubt they can go on doing so just fine.)

Anyway, using a single case with each of the five powders listed above, I loaded and fired it ten times with 200-grain bullets. I figured that if a case showed no unusual pressure signs with a given load for this many shots, it should be OK. I don't know if this is a reasonable "pressure test," but it seems practical.

The fired cases still look like new—no neck splits, no enlarged primer pockets, and not one shot gave a sticky bolt lift. As always, of course, anyone trying this cartridge in a different gun should start low and work up gradually, always keeping close watch for signs of excessive pressure.

For various reasons, I've been unable to get to elk country yet with this rig. I have killed a few whitetails with it using the 200-grain flatpoint Hornady, spitzer Speer and, recently, out of curiosity, the 175-grain Barnes X. All shots were at woods ranges, and all kills were instantaneous from body shots. All bullets went through, so could not be recovered for examination. As it happened, the X bullet went in the left flank just ahead of the near hindquarter, angled through the body of a seven-point and exited through the right shoulder. For all I know, it's still going.

So this Baby 338 seems to meet the requirements I set for it. Accuracy with the better loads averages well under 2 MOA, which is plenty good for my targets. It's better than I can shoot offhand (and maybe better than you under hunting conditions). Perhaps I'll get to use it on elk next October in Idaho. I'm confident it will do the job. ●

**TABLE 1: BABY 338 LOADS**

| —Bullet— Wgt. Grs. | Type | Load (Grs./Powder) | MV (fps) | SD (fps) | Group (ins.) |
|---|---|---|---|---|---|
| 175 | Barnes X | 42.0/H-322 | 2467 | 37 | 1.70 |
| 200 | Hornady | 44.0/W-748 | 2212 | — | — |
| 200 | Hornady | 46.0/W-748 | 2317 | — | — |
| 200 | Hornady | 48.0/W-748 | 2390 | — | — |
| 200 | Hornady | 49.0/W-748 | 2463 | 27 | 1.37 |
| 200 | Hornady | 50.0/W-748 | 2468 | 41 | 1.80 |
| 200 | Hornady | 51.0/W-748 | 2501 | 39 | 2.12 |
| 200 | Hornady | 42.0/IMR-4895 | 2296 | — | — |
| 200 | Hornady | 44.0/IMR-4895 | 2401 | — | — |
| 200 | Hornady | 46.0/IMR-4895 | 2494 | 15 | 0.93 |
| 200 | Hornady | 48.0/IMR-4895 | 2554 | 07 | 1.56 |
| 200 | Hornady | 49.0/IMR-4895 | 2589 | 05 | 0.81 |
| 200 | Hornady | 40.0/IMR-3031 | 2231 | — | — |
| 200 | Hornady | 42.0/IMR-3031 | 2365 | — | — |
| 200 | Hornady | 43.0/IMR-3031 | 2423 | 13 | 1.37 |
| 200 | Hornady | 44.0/IMR-3031 | 2490 | 07 | 0.81 |
| 200 | Hornady | 45.0/IMR-3031 | 2494 | 03 | 1.43 |
| 200 | Hornady | 42.0/IMR-4320 | 2254 | — | — |
| 200 | Hornady | 44.0/IMR-4320 | 2339 | — | — |
| 200 | Hornady | 46.0/IMR-4320 | 2446 | — | — |
| 200 | Hornady | 47.0/IMR-4320 | 2460 | 10 | 1.18 |
| 200 | Hornady | 48.0/IMR-4320 | 2507 | 02 | 2.06 |
| 200 | Hornady | 49.0/IMR-4320 | 2556 | 10 | 2.93 |
| 200 | Hornady | 43.0/AA2520 | 2362 | 17 | 1.37 |
| 200 | Hornady | 44.0/AA2520 | 2420 | 10 | 2.06 |
| 200 | Hornady | 45.0/AA2520 | 2473 | 15 | 2.50 |
| 210 | Nosler | 43.0/AA2015 | 2493 | 23 | 1.68 |

Winchester cases and 120 primers used for all shots.
Groups were three shots at 100 yards from a shaky bench on a windy day.
All shots went into a group of 5.31 inches (5 inches high x 4.06 wide).
One five-shot group (1 each: 45/2520, 45/3031, 49/4895, 49/4320, 51/748) went 3.25 inches; without 748 load, 2 inches.
Oehler 35P chronograph; instumental velocities taken at 15 feet; no correction made for muzzle velocity.

THREE DECADES AGO in *The Graduate*, a single word of career wisdom was whispered into Dustin Hoffman's ear: "plastics." The intention of this noteworthy advice was for Hoffman to seek out a career in this revolutionary new product. It turned out that was very good advice. Today, we find our lives surrounded by plastic in every shape and form imaginable, and the shooting industry is no exception. Possibly the most important use for the shooter is shotshell wadding.

No one will argue that plastic wads haven't revolutionized shotgunning performance. The protective ability of these wads allows the shot to travel through the bore with a tremendous degree of protection. As a result, pellets leave the barrel in almost the same perfect spherical form they had when the shot was loaded into the hull. But while the advantages of the plastic shotcup and wad are nothing short of remarkable, the use of these on a regular basis can result in a problem.

With old-style wadding, usually cardboard and/or felt, virtually no shot protection was present. In the transitional period between felt and plastic, there was a time when a flimsy wrap was used to surround the shot charge. This was an attempt to provide a protective barrier between the shot and the bore's surface. But this method was not too successful, and much of the shot was still flattened and disfigured when it left the muzzle. A few manufacturers still cling to this type of construction in some of their "over the counter" shells. No doubt this is done to keep manufacturing costs down. The result is less dense patterns, often with holes large enough for a bird to escape through. To me, the savings in cost simply isn't worth the disadvantage of poor patterns.

Felt-style wadding is pretty much a thing of the past. While some upland hunters, looking for more open patterns, may still play around with felt, most would agree that plastic is far superior. Plastic wads are much easier to load and more readily available, and provide more consistent results. If more open patterns are desirable, most reloaders find that spreader-

**Today's shotcup/wads are doubtless far superior to the old felt and cardboard versions, but they can cause...**

# PLASTIC PROBLEMS

by THOMAS C. TABOR

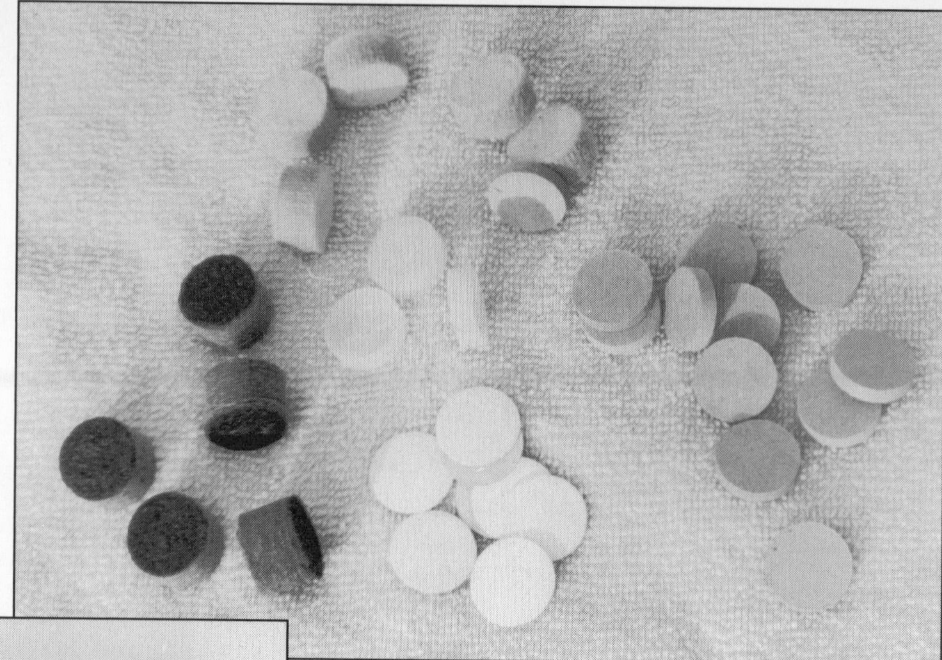

Older wad columns were made up of a mixture of cardboard and felt wadding. A combination of several wadding thicknesses was needed to adjust for differences in powder and shot volume.

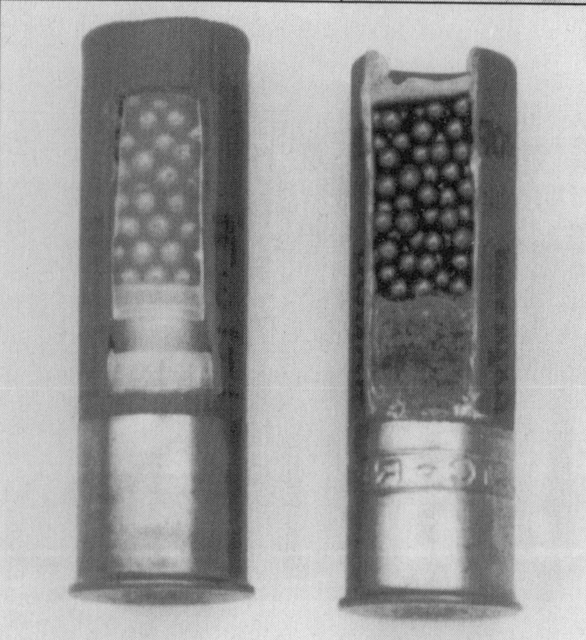

Cutaway shotshells show the differences in their construction. The one on the left has today's shotcup wad, while that on the right has the old-style wad column of felt and cardboard.

type wadding is a better way to go. Most are constructed with a post moulded into the center of the shotcup. This helps to open the pattern and is believed to provide a more uniform spread of shot.

Usually, the old-style wad column was one or two thick compressed felt wads on top of a thin nitro card. The nitro card was seated firmly on top of the powder to provide a gas seal to help build up pressure. When we compare the sealing ability of nitro cards to that of plastic wads, we find that, again, plastic is tremendously superior. With its better seal, the plastic wad produces more uniform performance shot-to-shot and higher velocity and energy. A few manufac-

These fired wads clearly show the effects of intense heat. As wads travel down the bore, their surfaces are softened, and the result is scorched-in plastic residue.

turers produce a plastic base wad without incorporating a shotcup. These provide a better gas seal than the cardboard nitro wad does, but they do nothing to protect the shot from deformation.

### There's One Drawback

But with all of the advantages that the plastic shotcup-style wads have, there is a downside. Just like the ol' cliché goes, "there's no free lunch," a shooter doesn't get something for nothing here either. While plastic is superior in almost every way, it does create a significant problem inside the shotgun bore. The high temperatures generated by burning a spoonfull of smokeless powder is enough to turn most plastics into a gooey mass. The only thing that keeps the wad from total meltdown is the short exposure time. It takes only an instant for the wad and shot charge to clear the barrel.

If we look at a used wad, we will see evidence of this intense heat. The surface is often pitted, charred and discolored. This means that, at least, the outer surface of the plastic has become pliable and soft during the ignition process. And after the first shot, the bore is hot as well. Combine this with a charge traveling $1^1/_2$ times the speed of a transcontinental airliner and what you have is a lot of stubborn, scorched-in plastic bore residue to deal with. And just like that breakfast egg you scorched the other morning, this mess doesn't scour off very easily.

Plastic buildup inside the bore may not pose as much threat to safety as pits and rust do; nevertheless, any restriction or resistance inside the bore should be avoided at all costs. If this contamination gets too heavy, common sense would suggest that it could result in increased pressure and possibly have an effect on patterns.

It seems, too, that society sometimes adds to its own problems. In our desire to do everything as quick and easily as possible, we produce things that sometimes encourage or exacerbate problems. The "new age" shotgun cleaning rods now being marketed are an example. These make quick work of wiping clean the burned powder residue with a single swipe of the bore. These rods look like a normal shotgun cleaning rod whose entire length has been wrapped with a soft, wool-like fleece material. Used properly for a quick bore wipe after a hunt, these are great. The problem comes when the shooter feels that this is an adequate cleaning job. A lot of my friends feel that it is. They look down the bore and it's shiny, so they think it must be clean. In reality, a thorough cleaning is necessary.

This fleece-style rod is great for a quick cleaning job in the field. It will remove powder residue just fine, but it will not remove the stubborn scorched-in plastic. For this, a more thorough cleaning will be necessary. Because of the protective design of this rod, it can be used from the muzzle without fear of damage.

Even conventional methods of cleaning will not usually touch this stubborn plastic buildup. You simply have to get in there with the heavy-duty stuff to ensure that all plastic residue is knocked loose. I recommend the occasional shooter use the following cleaning method at least once every year. For those who shoot more frequently—like trap and Skeet shooters or hunters who take every opportunity to pursue gamebirds—two to four times per year may be necessary.

### What To Do

Assemble several new shotgun cleaning brushes of the proper gauge. These brushes are made of various materials by about a dozen different manufacturers. I like to start with a new stainless steel brush. After I've made some real progress cutting through the stubborn stuff, I switch to a bronze brush. The stainless bristles in all likelihood will be harder than the metal of your barrel *and excessive use could cause scoring*. So use stainless brushes moderately and check often to make sure the bore isn't being scratched, especially if it's older and you know it's not chrome-plated. When using the stainless, you

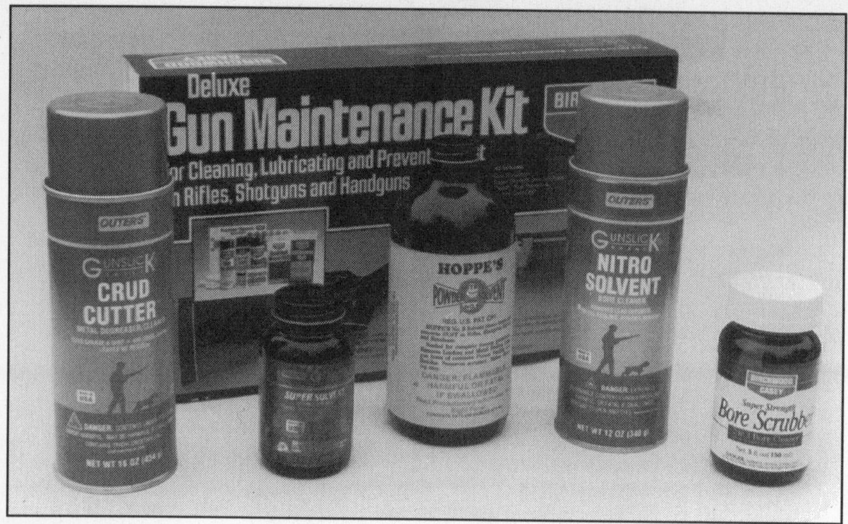


A wide range of cleaning solvents and products is available today. All I've used are great. Some, however, are better than others for removing tough plastic residue. Follow the manufacturers' recommendations when making your selection.

should make sure plenty of solvent is present to act as a lubricant. While most people don't think of solvent as a lubricant, in this case it does provide a degree of friction reduction and at the same time gives you the penetration ability needed to get the job done.

Keep the bore saturated and check it frequently for any signs of scratching. In a pinch, a bronze brush can be used for the entire operation. It is best to avoid nylon totally. Nylon is great for removing powder residue after the bore has been scoured clean, but it will not be effective at getting under the tough plastic.

Cleaning brushes are not indestructible. They become less effective with use and should be replaced fairly frequently. You are repeatedly forcing a brush through a bore that has a smaller diameter than the brush itself. This is necessary to get the desired cleaning results. Nevertheless, over time the brush bristles will become bent, angled and twisted. When this happens, the effectiveness of the brush is reduced and should be replaced.

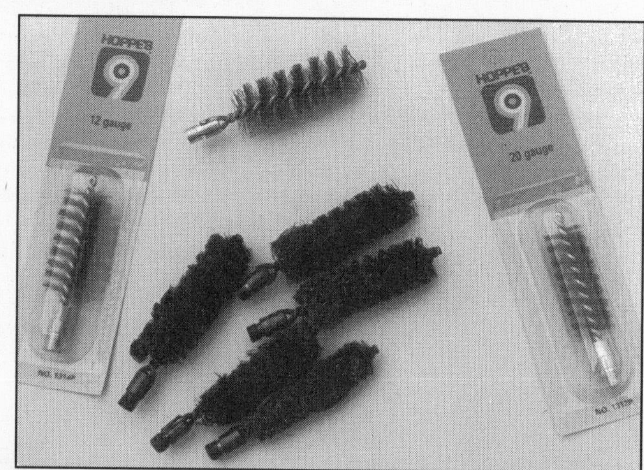


Cleaning brushes take a lot of abuse and should be replaced frequently. Shown are a few of the old ones that the author should have thrown away a long time ago and some newly purchased replacements.

It may be necessary for you to get a cleaning rod that you can devote to this type of cleaning. The handle must be removable. A few models allow you to do this. If you can find one, it will add to the convenience of the rod as you will be able to use it for other cleaning processes as well. But many models require that you cut off the handle with a hacksaw.

Once the handle has been removed,

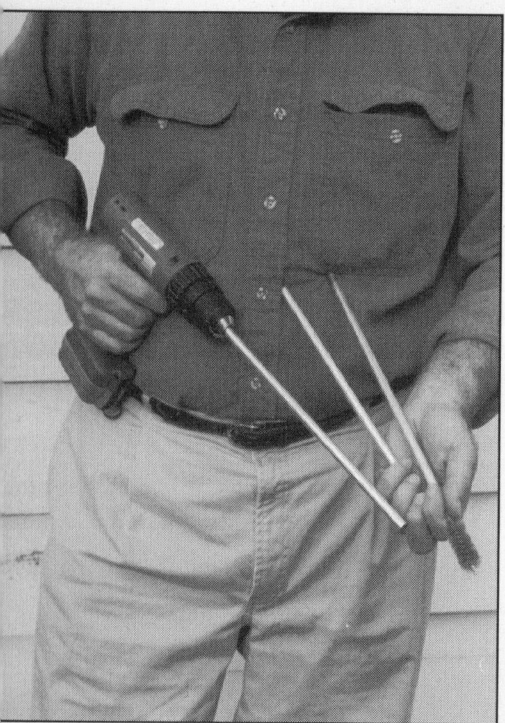

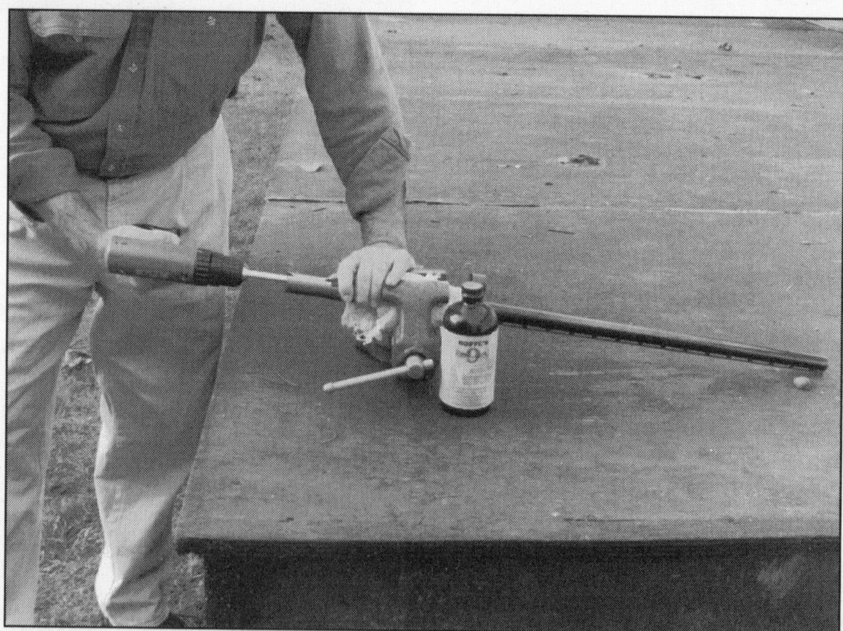

(Left) Once its handle has been removed, the cleaning rod can be mounted in a drill.

(Above) A vise can hold the barrel during the cleaning process, but make sure its jaws are well padded to protect the barrel.

The most vulnerable point for damage from solvents and oils is where the wood joins the metal. Penetration can eventually cause wood damage, possibly resulting in stock replacement.

place the cleaning rod in a variable-speed electric drill. In some cases, a drill press can be used, but I find a hand-held drill works best. If you can, remove the barrel(s). Starting from the chamber end whenever possible, insert the cleaning rod with the brush and drill attached. While a shotgun barrel's crown might not be as crucial as a rifle barrel's, it is important to protect it nevertheless. Entering from the chamber end helps to prevent damage.

Once the rod has been chucked securely in the drill and the brush started into the bore, pour a tablespoon of good-quality bore solvent into the chamber and over the brush. Next, at a very slow rate of speed, start the drill. Be careful to center the rod and not allow it to strike the inside of the barrel or chamber. You may opt to use a bore guide, but I usually get by without one by using my fingers as a guide.

The use of a variable-speed drill is very important. One of the new cordless drills is an excellent choice. Keep the speed fairly slow until you get the feel of the exercise.

If you don't have a good vise to mount your barrel in, the cleaning process may become a two-person operation, one holding the barrel with the other operating the drill. If you do use a vise, make sure the jaws are well padded to prevent damage to the barrel.

Most of the plastic buildup will occur just prior to and inside the actual choke area. The choke in most shotgun barrels occurs in the last 2 to 3 inches, so most of your effort should be devoted to that location. Nevertheless, some buildup will generally be present throughout the bore.

At a slow rate of revolutions, move up and down the barrel. If your drill is reversible, occasionally switch to the other direction. Barrels that have years of buildup may require overnight soaking with solvent. It takes a lot of solvent to fill a 12-gauge barrel after plugging. A cheaper method involves running a well-soaked solvent rag down the bore repeatedly. Try to saturate the bore, then let it sit for a hour or so and repeat the process. Doing this several times over the period of a day will achieve the same results as soaking it overnight, and you won't have to use nearly as much solvent.

Periodically check your progress by running a clean rag down it. Once you feel that the stubborn stuff has been removed, shift to a bronze brush for the final scrubbing.

### Keep in Mind

A word of caution.... Do not leave solvent in the bore after the cleaning is accomplished. Solvent can cause rust to form. Once the scouring job is complete, it is extremely important that you take extra care to remove any residual solvent. I learned this the hard way as a youth. I knew better, but must have gotten sidetracked for I forgot to clean out the solvent from a fine Churchill 30-06. Weeks later, I was shocked when I looked down the barrel to find the bore totally covered in rust and deep pits already formed. I finally sold my shame, but I still remember that incident, and it hasn't happened again.

A dry rag run through the bore will remove most of the solvent, but you should follow with a well-saturated oil patch. It's never a good idea to let a lot of oil sit in the bore, so a dry patch should always follow the oiling process. This should be passed through several times as a final step.

It's easy to forget about outside gun surfaces when cleaning the bore, but remember that solvent has more than likely covered it as well. A thorough wiping with a lightly oiled rag will suffice for removing the solvent and any fingerprints that you have left behind.

All cleaning-product manufacturers have their own brand of oil products, and they all work great. WD-40 also works well if you don't use too much. A sticky film will develop if you allow WD-40 to air dry on a firearm's surface.

Another thing to watch for is getting solvent or oil on the stock. In most cases, it will not damage the finish, but if allowed to soak into unfinished wood areas, it can cause you real headaches and sometimes very expensive ones. Some oils have great penetrating ability, which works great for freeing rusty screws and parts. They can, however, penetrate into unfinished wood areas such as those where the wood joins the metal, and this can be disastrous. Oil-soaked wood will cause deterioration and rot very quickly. I've seen stocks that looked perfect on the outside, but when the action was removed, the internal wood was literally disintegrated. This usually means an expensive stock replacement.

One more related piece of advice is worthy of sharing. Scattergunners who reload plastic hulls should frequently check the gun's chamber for rust. Plastic hulls seem to stimulate rust in the chamber more so than paper hulls. I'm not sure why that is, though possibly some nasty gas is generated in the firing process. Whatever causes it, chamber rust can be a problem, so it is a good idea to pay careful attention to this area and frequently clean it.

I would never want to go back to the old style of shotgun wad; there simply are too many advantages to plastic. Nevertheless, a shotgunner must be alert to the problems that can result from years of hot plastic traveling down the bore and take precautions to remove any buildup. Think of it like your kitchen pans. Isn't it a good idea to scour them once in awhile to remove that scorched on tough stuff? ●

HANDLOADING PIONEER

# J.R. MATTERN

WAGON ROADS CONNECTED the small towns of the central Pennsylvania valley in the latter part of the 19th century. Farms populated the area; the surrounding mountains and forests teemed with wildlife. Bald Eagle Creek started in the Appalachians to the west, coursing down to the valley floor before turning northeast and beginning its journey to join the Susquehanna. On its way, it passed the little community of Julian, which the inhabitants pronounced "Julie-Ann."

It was in this vicinity that Henry Kryder Mattern and Mina Clark Mattern were to live and raise a family. The family farm was called "Mudlick" after a natural geological formation on the property. Henry and his father constructed the large house in which the family lived.

As farmers, the Matterns were very successful. Henry's fields consistently produced high crop yields. Mina, not to be outdone, developed her own enterprise which she called "Locust Hill Farm." She raised chickens, hundreds of them, and daily shipped eggs all over the region.

On October 5, 1886, the couple's first child, John Randall Mattern, was born. Another son, Gilbert, and a daughter, Marion, were to follow. John Randall was to become famous as a true pioneer in the field of handloading.

### The Early Years

In such a time and place, guns would have held a position of prominence in every home and on every farm. Hunting; the slaughter of cows, pigs and sheep for food; predator control; defense; and sport all called for the gun. Young John Randall was introduced to hunting and shooting at an early age, as was every boy. The time had passed for the muzzle-loader, although no doubt there were plenty of them around. Even the newer breech-loading guns with self-contained cartridges were in for a change. A new gunpowder—called smokeless—was set to replace the time-honored black.

As any frugal man would have realized, the cartridge case was unharmed by the firing of a shot. With the advent of outside-priming, the reloading of these cases with fresh primer, powder and bullet became an eminently practical thing to do. The young Mattern realized this; indeed, it was something that would fascinate him the rest of his life. He started reloading blackpowder cartridges, particularly the 45-70, but as he was to write later, by the time he was thirteen or fourteen he was loading cartridges with the new smokeless.

While his shooting and outdoor education was progressing nicely, his formal education was not being neglected. Mattern's parents, both intelligent and successful, clearly saw the value of education, and when the time came, they enrolled their son in nearby Bellefonte Academy, a prep school of the day. Mattern possessed a brilliant mind and a photographic memory. After graduation, he decided to teach rather than continue as a student and for awhile taught in a one-room schoolhouse in the area.

Mattern married Mary Sharer, and in time a son, Henry, and daughter, Zella, were born. He developed an interest in horticulture to the point that he left teaching and took employment with the Horace McFarland Co., a Maryland nursery. While with the nursery, Mattern wrote

The Mattern homestead at Mudlick farm.

extensively for the company and had several articles on horticulture published in the *Saturday Evening Post* and *Country Gentleman*. A book, *Horticulture*, was also published.

With the beginning of conflict in Europe, yet before America's entry into what would be World War I, Mattern joined the U.S. Army's ballistic test facility, the Aberdeen Proving Grounds, in Aberdeen, Maryland, as a civilian ballistics expert.

He started reloading before smokeless came along—and wrote about it in articles and in a book still worth reading.

John Randall Mattern in his fifties.

### A Career in Firearms Writing

Mattern began writing about guns and reloading in his twenties. Interestingly, when he wrote or signed his name he used J.R. Mattern or J. Randall Mattern. However, his spoken name was always Randall. To family, friends and acquaintances, he was simply Randall Mattern. His shooting-oriented efforts were widely published in *Field & Stream, Outdoor Life, Outers Book, Rod and Gun of Canada* and others. He also established a mail-order company specializing in reloading equipment and components, which he operated for many years. In the April 1913 issue of *Field & Stream*, he made his case for high-velocity cartridges and their attendant higher revolutions per minute of bullet spin, which he felt increased killing power materially. He was referring to what we would today call the temporary wound cavity and how it affects flesh and organs not directly impacted by the bullet.

In the same article, he also gave some indication of his firearms battery and love of hunting: "I own and use a .22HP, a .30-06, a .30-30, a .45-70 for high and low velocity cartridges, and a .280 Ross besides smaller fry. I got thirty-five shots at big game last fall, and brought in my share of the bacon."

In the October 1914 issue of the *Outers Book*, Mattern began a two-part article, "Knowing Your Smokeless Rifle Powders." Written with marvelous clarity, he explained the relationship between the various powders and the range of pressure under which they must operate. Although dated in its reference to specific now-obsolete powders, few handloaders today could read the series without improving their understanding of the subject.

As did most such students of the shooting game, Mattern corresponded with the acknowledged experts of the day: Paul Curtis, shooting editor of *Field & Stream*; Chauncey Thomas of *Outdoor Life*; Townsend Whelen; Julian Hatcher; and F.C. Ness, among others. He also corresponded with men for whom the gun was a constant companion and workaday tool, and who, in turn, helped shape Mattern's thinking on calibers, bullet weight and construction. Bud Dalrymple, a government hunter who sought wolves and other predators across the Northwest, was one.

Dalrymple became famous for rebarreling handguns, primarily

by R.H. VANDENBURG, JR.

Colt revolvers, with a smoothbore barrel for efficient shot load use. F.H. "Bert" Riggall, an Alberta, Canada, rancher and big game guide, was another. Riggall guided Martin Bovey to a world-record Rocky Mountain bighorn sheep in 1924 and gained some notoriety for pulling 190-grain Winchester Silvertip bullets from 303 Savage cartridges and seating them in 30-30 cases over large helpings of IMR-3031 powder. They were used quite successfully on big Alberta elk.

Another correspondent and close friend of Mattern's was C.S. Landis, gun writer and author of several books on varmint rifles. Landis was shooting editor of *Rod and Gun of Canada* for over forty years. Landis and Mattern were friends as young men, but apparently at one point they had a falling out and the friendship was never repaired. Bob Bell, editor of HANDLOADERS' DIGEST, was a friend of Landis's, and ironically it was Landis who encouraged Bell, while he was at Penn State University, to visit Mattern. Bell recalls traveling over to the Mattern family farm to meet the great man. "It was a big house, partially closed off. We sat in the kitchen and talked about guns and reloading. Mattern had a blanket around his shoulders for warmth. All the time we talked, he toyed with a straight-line bullet seater he had in his hand." The time would have been the 1950s, and Mattern, then in his seventies, clearly retained his lifelong interest in handloading.

Mattern's loading bench in the 1920s.

After WWI, Mattern left the Aberdeen Proving Grounds and joined the Atlas Powder Co. in Wilmington, Delaware. Atlas was one of the spin-off companies created in 1912 when the Dupont Powder Co. was broken up.

All the time Mattern was in Maryland at the nursery, or at Aberdeen, and even while he was at Atlas, his family remained at home. Mary was a renowned gardener. She and the children simply stayed at Mudlick, and Mattern commuted back and forth by train.

In what was to be a most fortunate event for Mattern, and for shooters and handloaders everywhere, in 1922, Thomas G. Samworth, a director of the National Rifle Association, agreed to become an editor of the organization's journal, *Arms and the Man*. Samworth contacted many of the leading arms authorities and encouraged them to become regular contributors to the magazine. One of the first was J.R. Mattern, who began a series of articles entitled "Handloading Ammunition." Samworth was also instrumental in changing the magazine's name. When the first issue with its new title, *The American Rifleman*, was published on June 1, 1923, it included Chapter 17 of Mattern's series. Samworth also felt the NRA should publish hardcover books on arms-related topics. The first was a series of six articles by Townsend Whelen bound together and titled *Amateur Gunsmithing*. The book was profitable, but Samworth's superior, Col. A.J. Macnab, disapproved of the idea. Samworth responded in typical Samworth fashion: He resigned and started his own publishing company.

Having already made contact with many of the leading arms writers, Samworth simply contacted them again and let it be known he would publish their work. Again one of the first was J.R. Mattern. Mattern expanded on the serialized version of the subject and in December 1926 *Handloading Ammunition* by J.R. Mattern became the first book published by Samworth's new Small Arms Technical Publishing Co.

It was the first hardcover book published on handloading and was an immediate success. It was also a testament to Mattern's deeply held beliefs regarding handloading and shooting. Students in the field associate Mattern with three fundamental ideas. First was that to maintain competency with the rifle called for a minimum of 1000 shots fired offhand—every year. Second was the concept of versatility. On page 15 is perhaps the most eloquent picture on the subject of handloading ever published. It simply depicts eleven 30-06 cartridges arranged in a row. Each round has a different bullet, intended for a different purpose and loaded to a different velocity. Included are bullets weighing from 220 down to 90 grains and a 50-grain round ball load. (A .310-inch round ball weighs about 45 grains. Mattern recommended that round balls be at least .005-inch over groove diameter.) The picture speaks volumes about what one can

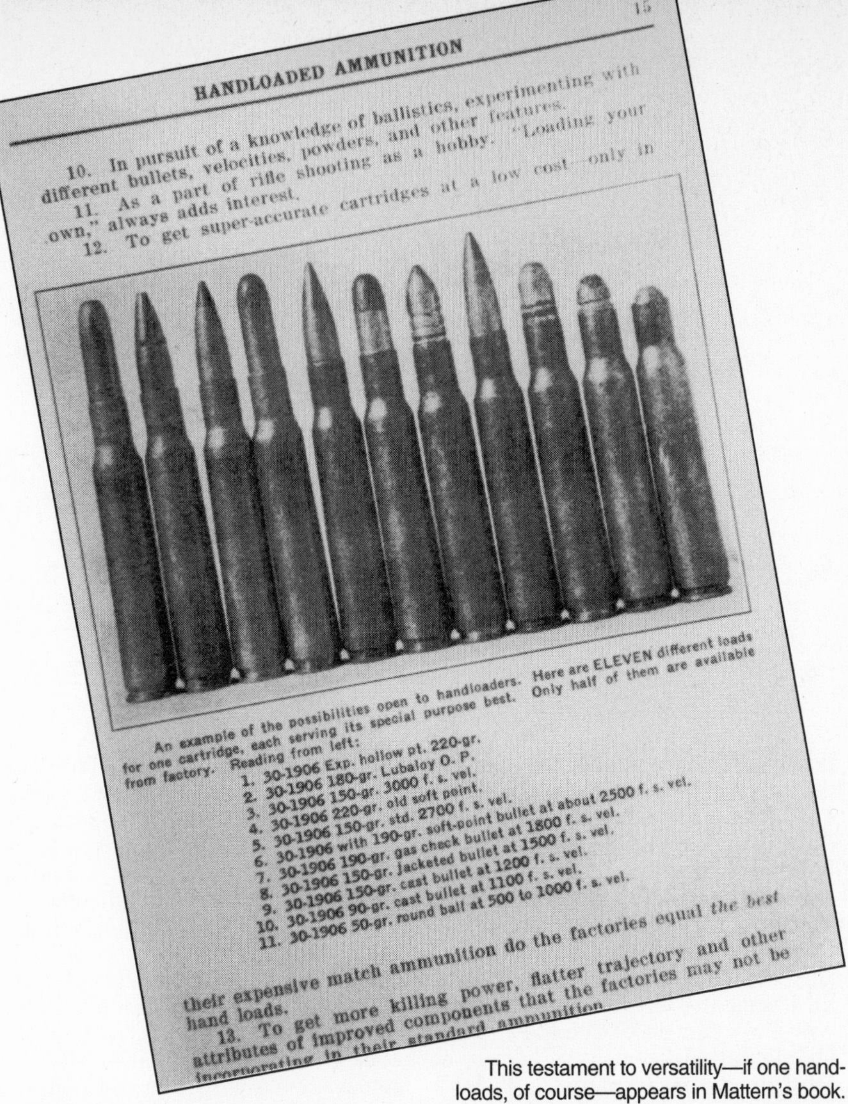

15

HANDLOADED AMMUNITION

10. In pursuit of a knowledge of ballistics, experimenting with different bullets, velocities, powders, and other features.

11. As a part of rifle shooting as a hobby. "Loading your own," always adds interest.

12. To get super-accurate cartridges at a low cost—only in

An example of the possibilities open to handloaders. Here are ELEVEN different loads for one cartridge, each serving its special purpose best. Only half of them are available from factory. Reading from left:

1. 30-1906 Exp. hollow pt. 220-gr.
2. 30-1906 180-gr. Lubaloy O. P.
3. 30-1906 150-gr. 3000 f. s. vel.
4. 30-1906 220-gr. old soft point.
5. 30-1906 150-gr. std. 2700 f. s. vel.
6. 30-1906 with 190-gr. soft-point bullet at about 2500 f. s. vel.
7. 30-1906 190-gr. gas check bullet at 1800 f. s. vel.
8. 30-1906 150-gr. jacketed bullet at 1500 f. s. vel.
9. 30-1906 150-gr. cast bullet at 1200 f. s. vel.
10. 30-1906 90-gr. cast bullet at 1100 f. s. vel.
11. 30-1906 50-gr. round ball at 500 to 1000 f. s. vel.

their expensive match ammunition do the factories equal *the best* hand loads.

13. To get more killing power, flatter trajectory and other attributes of improved components that the factories may not be incorporating in their standard ammunition.

This testament to versatility—if one handloads, of course—appears in Mattern's book.

accomplish with a single gun and cartridge, if one handloads, of course. Third was Mattern's five classes of reduced loads:

1. Velocity 600 fps. Cellar loads, extremely light; accurate range 50 feet.
2. Velocity 800 fps. Gallery loads, only slightly heavier; range 25 yards.
3. Velocity 1000 fps. Short outdoor loads; accurate range 50 to 100 yards.
4. Velocity 1400 fps. Standard outdoor reduced loads; accurate range 200 yards.
5. Velocity 1800 fps. Mid-range loads; accurate to 600 yards in 30-caliber rifle.

Not all classes are needed by everyone, but one might be surprised at the usefulness of one or more. This writer is a great fan of the round ball load referred to in the previously mentioned picture. It would be an example of the first or second class, depending on the amount of powder used. When hunting big game in the Western mountains, a pocket will always hold a few of these loads in the event blue grouse are happened upon. An example of the third class, a lightweight cast bullet at about 1000 fps serves a similar purpose while extending the range, but is noisier and reserved for after the big game hunting is done. This writer's offhand rifle practice load, a 154-grain cast 30-caliber bullet at a measured 1568 fps, closely approximates Mattern's fourth class and sees extensive use throughout the year.

### Ahead of His Time

Today's students of handloading history will enjoy Chapter 2 of *Handloading Ammunition*, "Tools for Handloading." For example, most handloaders are familiar with the Lyman No. 55 powder measure. Some may remember its predecessor, the No. 5. Few, however, will remember the No. 6. It was made during the time of the No. 5 but had two reservoirs, one large and one small, which emptied into a common drop tube and operated by a single stroke of the handle. The small reservoir deposited a "priming charge" of blackpowder to assist the ignition of the main charge, from the larger reservoir, of smokeless or larger-grained black. Improvements in primers eventually made the product obsolete. Interesting also is Mattern's operating procedure for the Bond and Ideal powder measures:

> The knack in operating Bond and Ideal powder-measuring machines lies in fastening them securely to a firm table, then working the handle and revolving the cylinder with the least possible disturbance. The lever should not strike against its back-stop as you raise it, nor against the frame as you bring it down to discharge the portion of the powder cut off from the reservoir.

Modern handloaders are generally encouraged to smack the handle smartly against its stop, both at the top and bottom of the stroke, as consistently as possible. In fact, the Lyman No. 55 measure has a striker, to be operated as desired at either, or both, the top and bottom of the stroke. The newer Lee Auto-Disk powder measures, however, are at their best when operated using a technique such as Mattern prescribes.

In support of his belief in versatility, Mattern strongly recommended reduced loads. In Chapter 17, "Reduced Loads," he wrote:

> The first "high power" rifle owned by the writer was a .303 Savage. Each year it was the custom to buy 200 factory full-charge cartridges, but this ammunition was perhaps only a tenth of the total used. The rest was made up of a cast bullet and various charges of powder. One charge much used was a 32 Long rim-fire case full of King's smokeless shotgun powder, and I well remember with what fears this charge was tried when raised from the 32 Short case full of that powder. Probably the greatest amount was eight or nine grains weight. Anyhow, it was so light that the report was insignificant. One day a farmer refused to use it for shooting his hogs on the ground that the bullet might glance from the skull.
>
> It actually would drive the bullet through the head in any position. When the bullets were well made and the loading was done with care, it was a famous sparrow load, capable of picking off those small marks up to fifty yards. Good loading was a problem, however, as we had not progressed in those days to a point where we saw the necessity of investing real

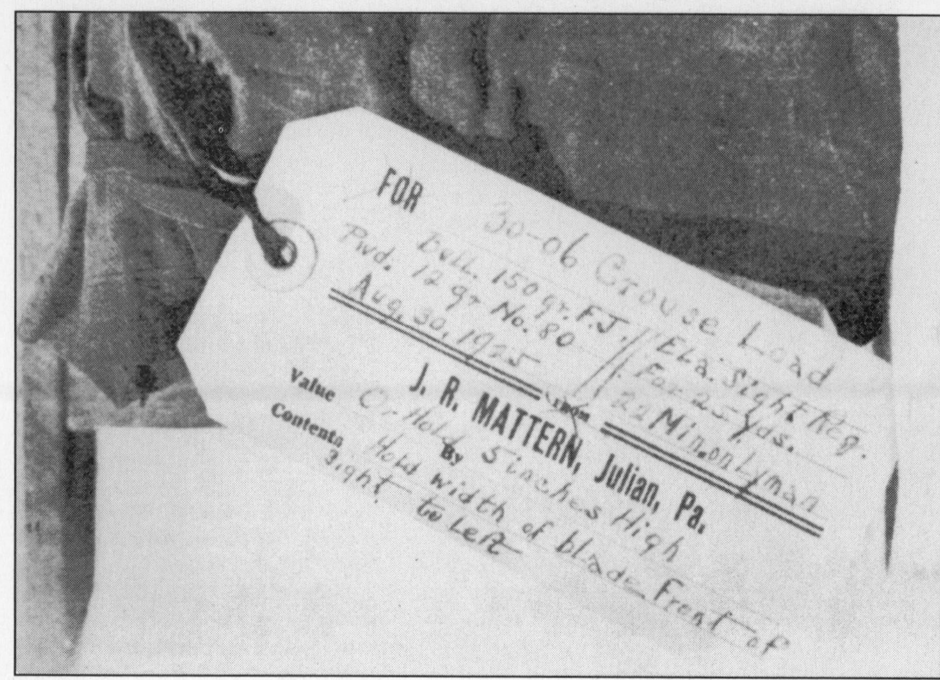


Proper labeling is important. The tag was used by Mattern in his mail-order reloading business.

money in dies for resizing the expanded cases. My old .303 Savage load accounted for uncounted dozens of game animals and birds. Its stock was notched for items from deer and bear down to rabbits, or maybe squirrels. Anyhow, when the boy thought he had outgrown a mere .303 Savage and attempted to sell it, he had to buy a new stock. The purchaser objected to the old one because of notches along its top and bottom edges. Only reduced charges could make the old .303 such an all-around useful gun.

Mattern also wrote of reduced loads for the 45-70, 30-40, 30-06 and many others. He strongly recommended that only cases that had been fired with a full charge in a given gun be used for reduced loads in that gun. Such cases produced more accurate ammunition and a better case-to-chamber fit.

It is always fascinating to find that products or procedures thought to be relatively new are, in fact, quite old. Several such revelations are found in *Handloading Ammunition*. For example, Mattern wrote of using fillers to hold powder charges down against the primer when the charge was insufficient to fill, or nearly fill, the case. He didn't have Dacron or other modern synthetics; he resorted to ground sawdust, cork or cornmeal. Mattern also wrote of making cast bullets with a soft lead nose and an alloyed body. The lead nose was cast first in one mould and then placed in a full-sized one. The alloyed lead was poured in to fill the cavity, the hot alloy bonding with the softer nose to create a single bullet. Both Lyman and Belding & Mull made such moulds. Today's handloader would associate "whisper" loads with a series of new proprietary cartridges developed by J. D. Jones of SSK Industries fame. Jones' Whisper is a small case and very heavy bullet at subsonic velocity in suppressed arms for military and police use. The 300 Whisper cartridge is also gaining fame with lighter bullets and higher velocity as a handgun hunting and silhouette round. Three-quarters of a century before, Mattern wrote of "whisper" loads to describe quiet and inexpensive handloads, regardless of bullet weight.

Chapter 26 is entitled "Suggestions on Popular Cartridges" and would be insightful reading even today. Mattern covered rifle and handgun cartridges, both modern and the earlier blackpowder. Versatility was the theme, and with each cartridge he showed the reader how to expand its usefulness through handloading a variety of bullets of differing weights and velocities.

Chapter 27, "Ballistic Tabulations and Data," in a section entitled "Loads for Popular Cartridges" is perhaps the book's high water mark. Mattern reviews each cartridge from the 22 Savage High Powder to the 50-110 Winchester and lists a variety of loads. Pressure is included where appropriate, and the remarks column is at once informative and delightful. For the 30-06 Springfield, he lists three pages (104 entries) of Full Power Loads and two pages (77 entries) of Mid Range and Short Range Loads. Some examples are listed in a chart nearby.

Obviously, most of the powder references are obsolete, but a careful review of bullet weight and type, velocity and the remarks column will turn up a variety of still useful loads. The rest of the book covered the various reloading components, tools and accessories, and record keeping. Oth-

**MATTERN'S 30-06 SPRINGFIELD LOADS**

| —Bullet— Wgt. Grs | Type | MV (fps) | Load (Grs./Powder) | Pressure | Remarks |
|---|---|---|---|---|---|
| 220 | jacketed | 2385 | 50.0/No. 15, Lot 2 | 52,000 | "Best moose load" said Whelen in 1920 |
| 170 | jacketed, RT | 2667 | 45.5/Hi Vel | 47,000 | One of the best target loads |
| 190 | jacketed | 2000 | 31.0/Hi Vel | — | Duplicates 30-30 or 303 Savage in power |
| 150-154 | solid | 1275 | 13.5/No. 80 | — | Fine 100- and 200-yard practice load |
| 150 | jacketed | 1508 | 18.0/No. 80 | 17,620 | Whelen's small game load—famous for accuracy |

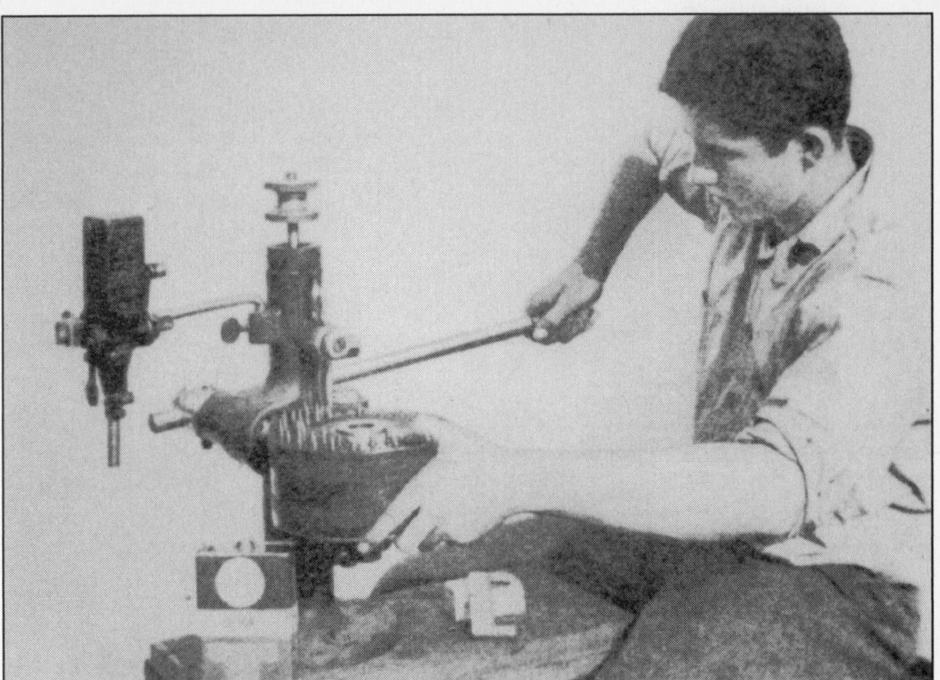

A young Mattern operating a Frasier reloading press. The Frasier was designed for high-volume efforts.

er chapters were devoted to "Obtaining Maximum Accuracy," "Handloading for Various Purposes," "Quantity Handloading" and loading foreign, obsolete and blackpowder cartridges.

The photographs in the book were all taken by Mattern, who also did the developing and printing. They were quite good and were a source of some pride. An interesting aside: When Thomas Samworth published his last book in 1953, it was also about handloading—*Principles and Practice of Loading Ammunition* by Earl Naramore. In the forward, Naramore acknowledged that several of the photographs in his book first appeared in Mattern's *Handloading Ammunition*.

After the book was published, Mattern continued to write about guns and handloading throughout the 1920s. The August 1930 issue of *Field & Stream* contains the last Mattern article this writer has been able to uncover. Entitled "Digging into the New Game Bullets," it was an exceptional treatise on the subject of bullet construction. He gave his readers some understanding of bullet makeup, including jacket construction, thickness, penetration and mushrooming, and how each, along with velocity, affects terminal performance.

In 1930, Mattern returned home for good and went to work for the Pennsylvania Game Commission as a land title examiner. He earned the position by teaching himself the craft of surveying. Sadly, however, in 1932, his wife Mary died of cancer. Mattern stayed with the Game Commission until 1940. By then, having become a registered professional engineer, he devoted the rest of his working life to surveying and engineering efforts, primarily developing water systems for such regional projects as the Milesburg Water Authority, the Bald Eagle Area High School, and others in Stormstown and Port Matilda, all near his beloved Mudlick Farm. In 1940, Mattern married Hallie Kirk, a divorcee with two sons, Norman and Vernon.

### Memories of the Man

Nancy Beyer Bachman is Mattern's granddaughter—the daughter of Zella and the current owner of Mudlick Farm. She spent a good deal of time as a young girl with her grandfather. "He was never a fashion plate," she says. "He preferred brown suits and a brown and white shirt. But he was always clean and neat, and carried himself with great bearing and dignity. He was meticulous in everything he did. He was a very friendly person, always waving at people he knew. Everyone liked him. He was a great listener and treated everyone, regardless of their station in life, with respect. He could listen to someone make a case that he knew wasn't so and simply say, 'That's an interesting point of view.'"

One of Mattern's close friends was Thornton W. Burgess, the famous writer. Burgess may be best remembered for his Mother Westwind stories for children.

Mattern was also proud of his Swiss heritage. A favorite story was: "Question: What happens when 2000 Swiss meet 4000 Germans? Answer: I guess the Swiss will have to shoot twice." While the story would no doubt fail the critique of political correctness today, for those who lived through World Wars I and II, it was just fine.

Bachman also remembered her grandfather's remarkable memory. "He could quote the muzzle velocity of every bullet weight in every caliber you ever heard of. He also knew the penetration of each bullet into wood, and the kind of wood and what velocity produced what penetration."

Mattern was a great believer that children should be taught to handle firearms. For children and grandchildren, boys and girls, instruction began at the age of six. Safety, how to shoot, and the importance of the first shot were drummed into them. Nancy Bachman recalled one year as a young girl when deer season rolled around: "I was to use a Parker 16-gauge. Grandfather handed me one shell (she called it a 'punkin ball') and said, 'That's all you need'...I shot my deer in the head." One must wonder who was more proud, grandfather or granddaughter?

Mattern could shoot, too. In a letter to this writer, his granddaughter wrote, "He could shoot straighter than anyone I ever knew. Once he shot a wild dog in mid-air that was about to kill my sister's horse. He got the dog in the head with one shot as it was jumping for the horse's nose."

Perhaps the most telling tales of Randall Mattern the man also came from his granddaughter.

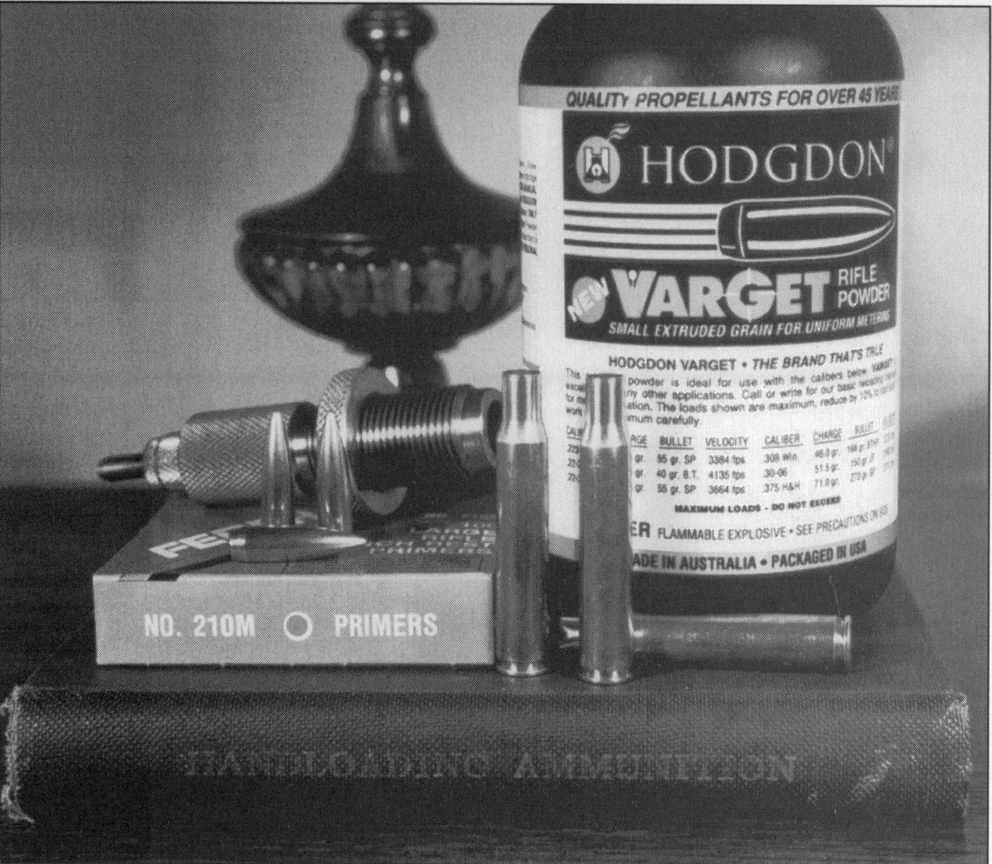


Mattern's book, although written in the 1920s, is still a useful tool for the modern handloader.

Once when I was a young girl, my grandfather had to attend a Water Authority meeting and he asked me to go with him. I didn't particularly want to; I had no knowledge of or interest in the subject. My mother said, "Your grandfather wants you to go with him. Go." We went to the meeting and took our seats. Immediately the meeting turned into a shouting match between two factions. I didn't know what was going on or what to make of all this. The chairman of the meeting had lost all control. People were just shouting at each other.

Finally my grandfather stood up. Immediately, the room became completely silent. The chairman, obviously with great relief, said "Mr. Mattern, would you care to speak." My grandfather briefly restated the problem and spoke on behalf of each side, stating each's advantages. He then pointed out the shortcomings of each and said, "But I think we have a solution." Members of each side left the meeting feeling good and knowing that they had contributed to that solution. That was Randall Mattern.

And another:

My grandfather was often called to Harrisburg to testify as an expert witness in court cases involving ballistics or surveying. He was rarely questioned severely. The consensus seemed to be if Randall Mattern said it, it was so. High praise, and not easily earned!

On September 5, 1970, John Randall Mattern died, one month to the day before his eighty-fourth birthday. "Both the viewing and the ceremony were packed," said his granddaughter, "All churches were represented. There were judges, lawyers, engineers, friends and acquaintances from all walks of life. My grandfather had great dignity and treated everyone with respect. He was a natural leader and a wonderful man."

He was also an extraordinary man, by all accounts. In a lifetime that spanned from the days of the horse-drawn carriage to a man on the moon, he was a teacher, horticulturist, writer, ballistics expert, surveyor and engineer. He also had the respect of his peers and the love of his family.

It is difficult today to overstate what Mattern meant to the generations of handloaders who eagerly read his writings. Without his guidance and that of a few who followed, handloading might be much different today. Certainly any trail followed by any aspiring handloader of the present was first blazed many years ago by J.R. Mattern. If we could speak to him about the present state of handloading, one can't help but believe he'd be pleased by the advancements in the accuracy of factory guns and ammunition, amazed by the variety of tools and accessories available, and astonished by the number of powders and other components on the market. Asked to comment on the level of sophistication employed by many handloaders today in the preparation of their ammunition, he'd no doubt smile and say "I knew all that—seventy-five years ago." He was, indeed, a pioneer. ●

**Acknowledgements**

The author wishes to express his sincere thanks to Jim Foral, fellow writer and author of *Gunwriters of Yesteryear* for his assistance in locating early Mattern articles. Also to Nancy Beyer Bachman for her support and help in piecing together so many personal aspects of her grandfather's life, and for providing photographs and other memorabilia for study and publication.

Excess case capacity allows powder position to shift, which affects ballistics. Here's an easy solution...

# DEEP-SEAT REVOLVER BULLETS

## To Improve Accuracy and Consistency

I HAVE BEEN loading revolver cartridges for decades. Since I am something of a perfectionist, it seems odd it took me all this time to figure out that it might be beneficial to seat typical cast bullets deeper and crimp the case mouth over the bullet's ogive, rather than into the crimping groove. Typically, this approach shortens the loaded cartridge about 0.1-inch, and to maintain the same pressure, one has to reduce the powder charge accordingly.

Several things got me started down this road. Primarily, it was a study I did with the 38-40 Winchester where I demonstrated that no combination of primer and powder I could come up with would eliminate sensitivity to powder position. (I tested a dozen likely powders, six types of primers, and fired 3000 rounds over the chronograph.) As an extension of that study, I later showed that any powder charge that leaves *any* unused space in the case will exhibit some level of sensitivity to powder position, in revolver and pistol loads. Since the powder charge in most standard revolver loads does not fill the available space, all such loads will exhibit some variability as a result of the vagaries of powder position.

(For non-believers out there, consider a recent study done by Oehler Research where a case 70 percent full of Unique in a 38 Special load generated 74 percent more pressure when the powder was against the primer than when it was against the bullet—this during level firing.)

At about that time, I was also looking for a superior 44 Special load using a 180-grain truncated-cone cast bullet from Colorado Cast Bullets. Compared to typical (heavier) cast bullets, these are a big improvement for practice loads in my Charter Arms Bulldog. The main benefit is a vast recoil reduction. Since it is shorter than typical 215- to 240-grain bullets, it will stabilize at lower velocity. Since it is lighter, it also produces less recoil, even at the same muzzle velocity.

With typical 240-grain SWC bullets, the minimum velocity that produces consistent accuracy from the Bulldog is about 750 fps. With this 180-grain TC, 650 fps is adequate. Recoil energy of the latter load is less than half of the former—and when

by M.L. McPHERSON

fired from a 20-ounce gun such a vast difference matters! However, with the 180-grain bullet, the standard deviation of my best loads, using W-231, went from the 25 fps I was getting with 215- or 240-grain bullets to about 33 fps, an increase of one-third. This seemed excessive. I hoped a more consistent load might deliver better accuracy. As things turned out, it did.

With that goal in mind, I loaded up some cases using Hodgdon Clays powder, which is bulkier than W-231 and, therefore, uses up more of the available powder space in a normal load. With my 38-40 testing fresh in mind, I decided to try seating the bullets deeper and crimping over the ogive. In this instance, the loaded rounds were .085-inch shorter (1.460 to 1.375), and I made a minor downward adjustment in powder charge (about 0.3-grain) to compensate.

Hodgdon's Powder Co. verified this to be a safe low-pressure plinking load. With an OAL of 1.375 inches and using Federal's 150 primer, the correct charge of Clays is 4.5 grains.

The results were startling. The standard-length load generated just over 20 fps standard deviation. The deep-seated load, with the charge reduced to deliver the same velocity, produced only 4 fps standard deviation! That was the first low-pressure revolver cartridge load I had ever concocted that consistently produced less than 20 fps standard deviation. I had learned something.

Recently, I was setting up to load several hundred 44 Magnum cartridges using Bullet Meister's superb 240-grain cast SWC bullet for a plinking load at about 1000 fps. It occurred to me that this mild 44 Magnum load might also benefit from deep bullet seating. I wanted to test a load with Accurate's N-100, which, like Clays, is a low-density double-base powder, among the best for such loads.

The best currently available powders for these applications are probably 700-X, N-100 and Clays, which have densities of about 0.45 grams per cubic centimeter. (Many pistol powders are nearer 0.6, and typical rifle powders are between 0.85 and 1.0.) It would certainly be wonderful for us revolver and blackpowder rifle cartridge shooters if someone could introduce an even bulkier smokeless powder series. If it were possible to offer a series of powders with a density near 0.3 and with the proper burning rates, one could fill the case in many of these cartridges and, thereby, eliminate powder-position effects. Alas, such low densities may simply be impossible to achieve.

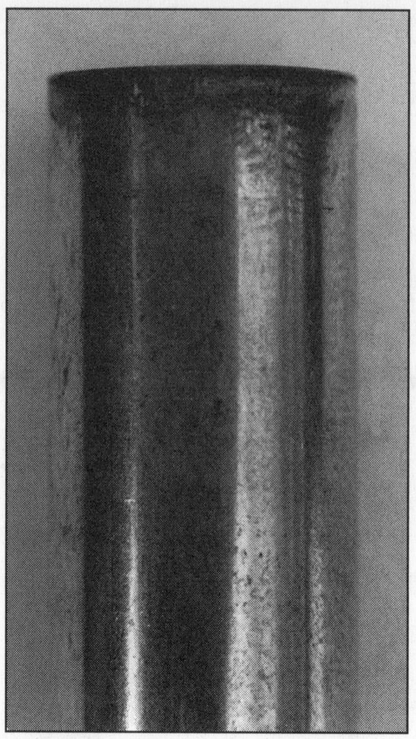

This 44 Magnum case fired a normally seated load (1.61 inches OAL). Note the *slight* amount of smoky residue on the case exterior near the mouth. Only the top side of these cases had any external residue.

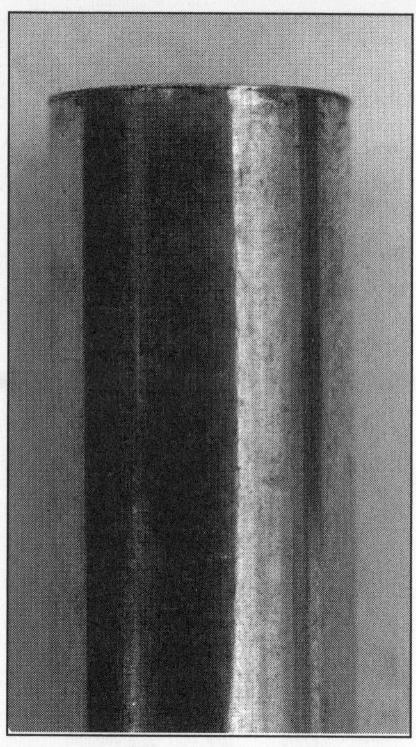

This 44 Magnum case fired a deep-seated load (1.52 inches OAL). Note the almost total lack of smoky residue on the case exterior. Extraordinary!

I estimated that I should use about 7.3 grains of N-100 with the bullet seated normally. Since 44 Magnum N-100 loads were not yet published at the time of my testing, I called Accurate and verified this load. I also got loading data for a 240-grain cast bullet seated deep in the 44 Magnum. Compared to the standard loading, the necessary reduction turned out to be *about* 0.4-grain to maintain the same velocity with similar pressure. Therefore, I began loading a batch of cartridges using 6.9 grains.

(I should note that I also eventually tested deep-seated loads at 7.1 and 6.8 grains, just to be thorough. The 6.8-grain load was not quite as consistent, and the 7.1-grain load was too hot for the bullet used. I also tested standard-length loads at 7.1 and 7.5 grains. Ultimately, the 7.3-grain load was the most consistent.)

About 200 rounds into the initial loading process, it occurred to me that it would be interesting to make a serious comparison of standard-length versus deep-seated loads. At that point, I stopped loading and prepared forty once-fired cases of uniform weight (108.0 ± 0.3 grains) with the following modifications, all intended to minimize shot-to-shot variations:

1) Flash-hole deburring and uniforming with K&M tool;
2) Cutting primer pockets to a uniform depth and squaring bottom with K&M tool;
3) Trimming cases to uniform length, deburring inside and out with RCBS's TrimPro;
4) Seating primers to a uniform pellet preload with a hand priming tool. (I had sized and decapped all these cases using Redding's Titanium Carbide die.)

I finished loading these rounds on my Dillon 550B, beginning at the powder-charging station. The Dillon powder measure dispenses very uniform charges of N-100. Redding's seating die, adjusted to not apply any crimp, seated the bullets. The final stage held Redding's Profile Crimp die, adjusted to give a light roll crimp. After loading twenty deep-seated rounds, I readjusted the bullet seating stem and the powder measure, and loaded twenty standard-length rounds.

It is important to note that I kept all other load parameters and loading practices as consistent as possible. The only differences between the deep-seated and standard-length

These two groups were shot using 44 Magnum deep-seated (1.52 OAL) 240-grain SWC test loads. This load (7.1 grains N-100 with Federal 150 primer) is clearly too hot for this bullet. Note on the right target that at least three of the five bullets were partly tipped as they hit the target. (The final, 6.9-grain load did not exhibit this tendency.)

These two groups were shot using 44 Magnum standard-length (1.61 OAL) 240-grain SWC loads. This load (7.3 grains N-100 with Federal 150 primer) was particularly position-sensitive (from left): typical target with powder against the primer and typical target with powder against the bullet.

loads were seating depth and powder charge. In neither instance did the crimping stage impinge the case's mouth against the bullet with excessive force; it turned the case mouth just enough to touch the bullet. The die applied the same degree of crimp with both loads.

During shooting, I took equal precautions to minimize variables. I fired all test shots from the same chamber of a Hawes revolver. I accuracy-tested these cartridges (and other similar loads that lacked the extra case preparation steps) at 25 yards: five five-shot groups for each. Table 1 lists the test results. The wind, with gusts reaching 20 mph, was against me, and the open sights on that revolver are not the best in the world. No doubt, the limitations of my shooting skills corrupted this accuracy data, but I did the shooting in alternating sets (one target with each type of load in each set). With so many targets fired, the results should be reasonably representative of the accuracy of any one class of loads. I trust these results enough to do future loading for short-range plinking-style loads using the deep-seating technique.

My intention was to test several things relating to deep seating versus standard seating. First, what was the difference in velocity consistency? Second, what was the difference in powder-position effect? Third, what was the difference in accuracy?

On two counts, I was not disappointed. The deep-seated loads showed considerably better accuracy and much less velocity variation as a result of powder position. However, surprisingly, the 1.61-inch load showed significantly better ballistic uniformity, compared to the 1.52-inch load. I do not have an explanation for this. However, as a class, both of these loads, regardless of testing protocol, were among the most consistent revolver loads I have ever tested; for any normal revolver shooting, velocity variations in this range should be of little consequence.

It is also worth noting that all these loads were *exceptionally* clean. However, the 1.52-inch loads were notably cleaner; both the gun and the fired case had slightly less residue. Moreover, the gun stayed sufficiently clean during the entire testing process (over 200 rounds) that it simply did not matter. Believe me this is not typical of low-pressure 44 Magnum loads.

Note that Table 1 also lists data with powder either "forward" or

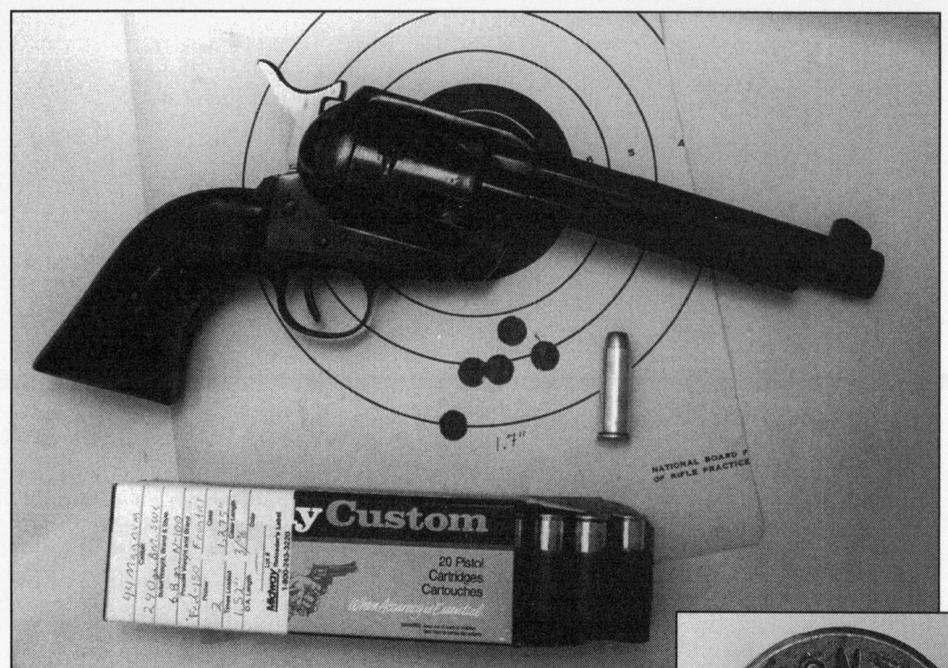


The Hawes 44 Magnum test revolver shown with deep-seated test load (1.52 inches OAL) and typical 25-yard target.

These fully prepped 44 Magnum cases used in the experimental loads show the healthy firing pin indent produced by the Hawes revolver. Perhaps this contributes to the consistent velocities.

"back" in the case. To accomplish this, I cocked the hammer to bring the round into battery and pointed the gun either up or down, as required. Then, with my thumb interposing the hammer and the firing pin, I slapped the side of the gun several times before carefully leveling it to fire. This is not good safety practice (and it does little to help one's concentration in shooting targets), but it is the only method of settling the powder as near the primer, or bullet, as possible. Should you have occasion to do similar powder-position-effect tests, use every precaution to avoid an unpleasant, inadvertent discharge....

For low-pressure target loads using fast-burning powders (typically powders similar in burning rate to Bullseye), one can calculate a proper charge reduction to maintain *approximately* the same pressure and velocity with *minor* alterations in cartridge overall length. **Caution:** Never seat any full wadcutter bullet deeper than the overall length recommended in the appropriate data. Because these bullets leave so little usable powder space, minor seating depth variations can radically alter pressures. For example, in the 38 Special, seating a 148-grain WC .1-inch deeper can *double* chamber pressure!

Table 2 shows *approximate* powder reductions to maintain *similar* velocity and pressure when deep-seating SWC, TC or RN bullets in the following cartridges (only for powders similar in burning rate to Bullseye).

This table is only approximate and for low-pressure loads at or near the starting charge in listed data. *If your intention is to load at or near the maximum listed load, do not deep-seat bullets.* The resulting reduction in usable powder space makes it impossible to achieve the velocity of standard-length loads without loading to higher pressures. The sole purpose of this technique is to allow one to assemble mid-range target loads of superior accuracy. ●

**TABLE 1: 44 MAGNUM BALLISTICS AND ACCURACY RESULTS**

| Powder Position | Velocity (fps) | SD (fps) | 5-Shot Group (ins.) |
|---|---|---|---|
| **44 Magnum OAL 1.61 inches** | | | |
| Level | 992 | 7 | 2.5 |
| Forward | 995 | 5 | 3.0 |
| Back | 1032 | 3 | 1.4 |
| **44 Magnum OAL 1.52 inches** | | | |
| Level | 994 | 10 | 2.1 |
| Forward | 985 | 13 | 2.1 |
| Back | 994 | 9 | 1.9 |

Load data: Match prepped Frontier cases of 107.7-108.3 grains. Federal 150 primers seated to uniform pellet preload. N-100 dumped via Dillon powder measure at 6.9 grains (1.52") or 7.3 grains (1.61"). Bullet Meister 240-grain SWC bullet.

**TABLE 2: CALCULATING POWDER CHANGE FOR SEEP SEATING**

| Change In OAL (ins.) | Powder Reduction (Grs. Wt.) 32 LC 32 H&R | 38 Spl. 357 Mag. | 41 Mag. | 44 Spl. 44 Mag. | 45 S&W 45 Colt 454 Casull |
|---|---|---|---|---|---|
| -0.050 | 0.05 | 0.07 | 0.09 | 0.10 | 0.11 |
| -0.075 | 0.11 | 0.14 | 0.18 | 0.20 | 0.22 |
| -0.100 | 0.16 | 0.21 | 0.27 | 0.30 | 0.33 |
| -0.125 | 0.22 | 0.28 | 0.36 | 0.40 | 0.44 |
| -0.150 | 0.27 | 0.35 | 0.45 | 0.50 | 0.55 |

by DON LEWIS

The author holds his Belding & Mull Model 28 Straightline Reloading Press, which, along with a 1950 handbook, saw lots of use in his early days of reloading. Note the shellholding cradle slides on a heavy round rod and is held in a straight line with the bullet seating die.

# THE VINTAGE BELDING & MULL MODEL 28 PRESS

This half-century-old tool still turns out ammo that will make ragged-hole groups.

Photos by HELEN LEWIS

I HAD JUST finished cranking out 100 rounds of 22-250 ammo on a progressive reloading press without making even a minor mistake. I did not run an actual time check, but the job couldn't have taken fifteen minutes, and I wasn't trying to hurry.

I scrutinized the primers for dents and seating heights in the MTM shell box for a few seconds, then placed the box on another reloading bench. It might have been a coincidence, but the box of reloads rested against my old Belding & Mull Model 28 Straightline press. For a few seconds, I stared at the old press. Small, compact and easy to operate, the 4-pound Model 28 represents simplicity at its best. Although the old press had been idle for several decades, I thought of the thousands of rounds I had cranked out for my early M722 and, later, my Remington 40XB-BR bench rig. I had to smile when I thought about the time difference required for loading a hundred rounds on the progressive and laboriously doing the same number on the B&M Model 28. A lot more time would have been consumed using the old 28, but for handloaders in the early 1950s, the Model 28 Straightline was literally a work of art.

In the 1950 *Belding & Mull Handbook,* it says, "Belding & Mull Reloading Equipment has been manufactured and sold worldwide for more than 26 years and has the approval of experienced shooters everywhere." Two decades earlier, about 1930, B&M had offered their Model 24 Straightline Reloading Tool. I assume the Model 24 was followed by the Model 26 and then the Model 28 Improved.

"Straightline" simply means that all forces applied are in a straight line—true to the axis of the case. Plier/pincer-type reloading tools apply forces at an angle to the axis. This off-center application of forces tends to squeeze the cartridge case to one side and somewhat reduce the accuracy of the assembled ammunition. With the Straightline, there is no tendency for the case to cant or wobble.

Operating the Model 28 starts with decapping a fired case. The decapping rod is installed in the hinged bar. A fired case is then slipped over the end of the decapping rod, and both are dropped into the sliding cradle where they are held centered. As the sliding cradle is pushed forward, the decapping pin enters the bottom of the flash hole and the primer is easily pushed out. The cradle slides on a heavy round rod. The hinged bar is also on the rod, which has four holes drilled through it to adapt to different-length cases. A tapered pin pushed through the side of the hinged bar holds the rod firmly in place.

To replace the fired primer, the lever handle is drawn back until the decapping pin is withdrawn from the primer recess. A new primer is dropped into a slot behind the case head, and the backward stroke of the handle is completed. The primer seating punch is adjustable to obtain correct seating depth.

Although dies were available for full-length resizing, I stuck with neck sizing since I used separate brass for the 722 and 40XB-BR. To neck size, the decapping pin was removed, and the neck die and expander were attached. The expander plug was attached to the hinged bar, which must be locked in place with the tapered pin. The head of the case is placed in the sliding cradle, and the operating handle is moved forward. This movement forces the case neck into the die and reduces its diameter. As the handle is moved backward, the case neck is pulled over the expanding plug, which enlarges it to a uniform inside diameter correct to hold the bullet.

Bullet seating is not exactly a snap with the Model 28. The tool is best placed on an incline or even in an upright position to keep powder from spilling out of the case. Normally, I belled the case mouth slightly and started the bullet by hand. The charged case and bullet are inserted into the seating die, and the base of the case is pushed down into the sliding cradle. The Model 28 has no provision for crimping.

Over the decades, I've accumulated a good many metallic-case reloading presses, from single-stage types such as RCBS's Rockchucker and Hornady's 007 to advanced progressive presses such as Lee's Load-Master and Dillon's XL650 complete with case feeder. Why do I allow the old Model 28 Straightline to take up much-needed bench space? The answer for me is simple. The Model 28 played a major role when home reloading was in its infancy. Without the advent of B&M's Straightline, thousands of today's gray-haired shooters (myself included) might not have had the satisfaction of knowing that handloaded ammo could be more accurate in our rifles than factory fodder.

My B&M Straightline might never crank out another round, but it will always remain a permanent fixture in my reloading shop. Maybe I'm sentimental, but that seems proper for such an important piece of Americana. ●

The author begins the bullet seating process by hand-seating a bullet before inserting the cartridge into the seating die.

(Left) Once the cartridge is inside the bullet seating die, the author holds down the hinge bar with his left hand and levers the press handle with his right hand. Note the press is on an incline to keep powder from spilling out of the case.

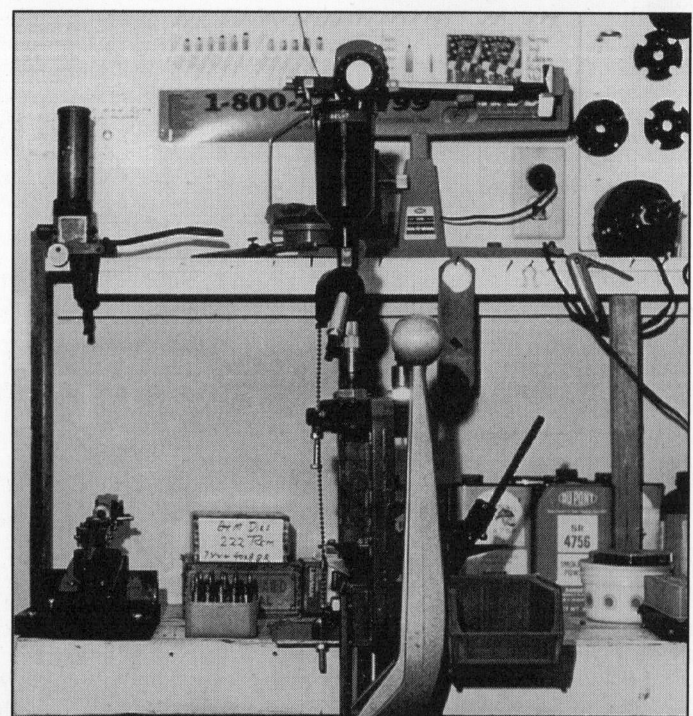


The B&M Model 28, with powder measure, rests beside a Lee Load-Master progressive press.

These five-shot 100-yard groups were fired from a Remington 40XB-BR using ammo loaded on the B&M M28 press.

# Middle Magnums

The three cartridges have similar ballistics when (left to right) the 264 is loaded with a 140-grain bullet, the 7mm with a 160-grain and the 300 with a 180-grain.

## Seeking to maximize power for North American game while still keeping recoil at manageable levels? Take a look at these numbers.

by John Haviland

BIG GAME HUNTERS who favor magnum rifles are inclined to look in the middle of the cartridge roster for hunting in North America. They want a cartridge that has enough bullet weight and energy for a bull elk silhouetted in the early morning distance, yet with a recoil mild enough that it won't short circuit the central nervous system. Three of these favored middle magnums are the 264 Winchester, 7mm Remington and 300 Winchester. This is how they compare.

### The 264 Winchester Magnum

While I was recording the velocities of a variety of 264 loads at the shooting range, a retired gentleman strolled over to visit. "I remember when the 264 came out in the late '50s," he said. "It was pretty popular there for a few years. Then the word got around that the 26-inch barrels on the old Model 70 Winchesters were a pain to carry, but if you cut the length of the barrels down, the 264 wasn't any better than a 270."

The man watched me shoot a few groups then happily went on his way.

The 264 I was shooting did have a 26-inch barrel. However, it was not a Winchester Model 70. The barrel was made by Bill Hobaugh and was fitted to a 1944 German Model 98 Mauser action with a new bolt handle and Buehler safety. Buehler bases and rings held a 2-7x Leupold scope.

The first thing I noticed when shooting the rifle was how fast the barrel heated up. After only three shots, the heat waves rising from the barrel made the target seem to waver in the mirage seen through the scope. I rolled a tube from a paper target and put it over the objective lens of the scope; that helped cut the mirage. However, after as few as six shots spread over five minutes, the barrel was so hot I couldn't touch it. That is to be expected when you're blowing so much powder through such a small bore.

With a small bore, large case and long bullets, I limited my loads to relatively slow burning powders, with W-760 and IMR-4350 having the fastest burning rates. All of the powders listed in the table except W-760 produced uniform velocities. Standard deviations from average velocities were from 20 to 4 fps. W-760 had SDs of 40 and 45 fps respectively with 120- and 140-grain bullets. Yet the two loads grouped into .75-inch at 100 yards. The large air pocket left in the case when the cartridge was loaded with W-760 no doubt allowed the powder to settle any which way and produced the large velocity swings.

Two rather new powders suitable for the 264 are Hodgdon's 1000 and

Winchester Magnum Rifle. H-1000 performed extremely well with the 140-grain bullet. Winchester did not have any data available for the 264 using their Magnum Rifle powder, so I carefully developed my own loads. Winchester's David Price said WMR was similar to their discontinued W-785, so I started on the light side with W-785 data. I worked up to 61 grains of WMR for the 140-grain bullet and 65 grains for the 120-grain bullet. Perhaps I could have shot heavier charges of WMR, but I prefer to let Winchester's technicians push the outer limits of pressure. Although the velocity I recorded with WMR was only average, accuracy was excellent.

Reloading manuals show a wide variation in loads for the 264. Several manuals I checked for maximum loads with 140-grain bullets varied 5 or 6 grains for the same powder. Old and new manuals published by the same company differed. The Speer Manual No. 8 from 1970 listed 1 to 6 grains more with some powders for the 264 than their current 12th edition—a common phenomenon in recommendations, of course.

To stay on the safe side, I used current data. With current maximum loads, I never experienced the erratic pressures the 264 has been noted for in the past. Besides, I would much rather reload my cases a few more times than squeeze the last drop of velocity out a cartridge.

A number of bullet weights are readily available for the 264, from an 85-grain hollowpoint up to a 160-grain round-nose. I have never seen a 264 Magnum used on small game except an occasional coyote that sauntered past. I see the 264 exclusively as a big game cartridge, which excludes the 85- and 100-grain bullets for it. One exception is the Barnes 100-grain X-Bullet. This hollowpoint should stay in one piece on big game, even launched at 3500 fps from a 264. The

### 264 WINCHESTER LOADS

| —Load— | | MV |
|---|---|---|
| Powder | Wgt. Grs. | Avg. (fps) |
| **Remington factory 140-gr.** | | |
| — | — | 2993 |
| **Speer 140-gr. Spitzer** | | |
| H-1000 | 68.0 | 3168 |
| H-870 | 73.0 | 3082 |
| H-4831 | 61.0 | 3024 |
| IMR-4350 | 52.0 | 2942 |
| WMR | 61.0 | 2906 |
| WMR | 60.0 | 2886 |
| W-760 | 56.0 | 2855 |
| IMR-4831 | 54.0 | 2853 |
| WMR | 59.0 | 2848 |
| H-4350 | 53.0 | 2705 |
| **Speer 120-gr. Spitzer** | | |
| H-4831 | 65.0 | 3217 |
| H-1000 | 72.0 | 3180 |
| WMR | 65.0 | 3160 |
| H-870 | 76.0 | 3152 |
| WMR | 64.0 | 3143 |
| W-760 | 59.0 | 3101 |
| IMR-4350 | 56.0 | 3078 |
| IMR-4831 | 57.5 | 3073 |
| H-4350 | 57.0 | 3052 |

Firearm: Model 98 action; 26″ Hobaugh barrel; Remington cases; Winchester large rifle magnum primers; overall loaded cartridge length = 3.3″.

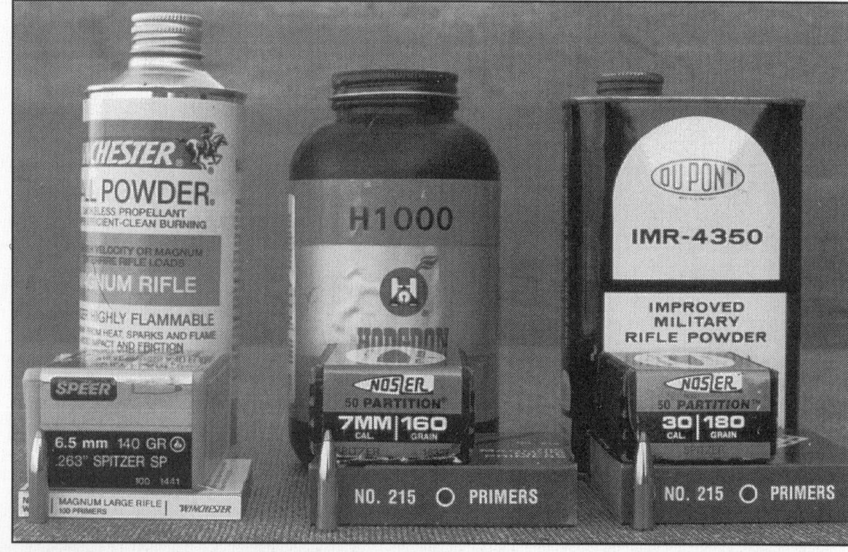


(Above) A good load for each of the middle magnums (left to right). For the 264 Winchester Magnum, a 140-grain Speer bullet, Winchester Magnum Large Rifle primers and WMR powder. For the 7mm Remington Magnum, Federal 215 primers, 160-grain Nosler bullet and H-1000 powder. For the 300 Winchester Magnum, Federal 215 primers, 180-grain Nosler bullet and IMR-4350 powder.

(Left) The 264 produced very good accuracy with 120-grain Speer bullets and Winchester Magnum Rifle powder.

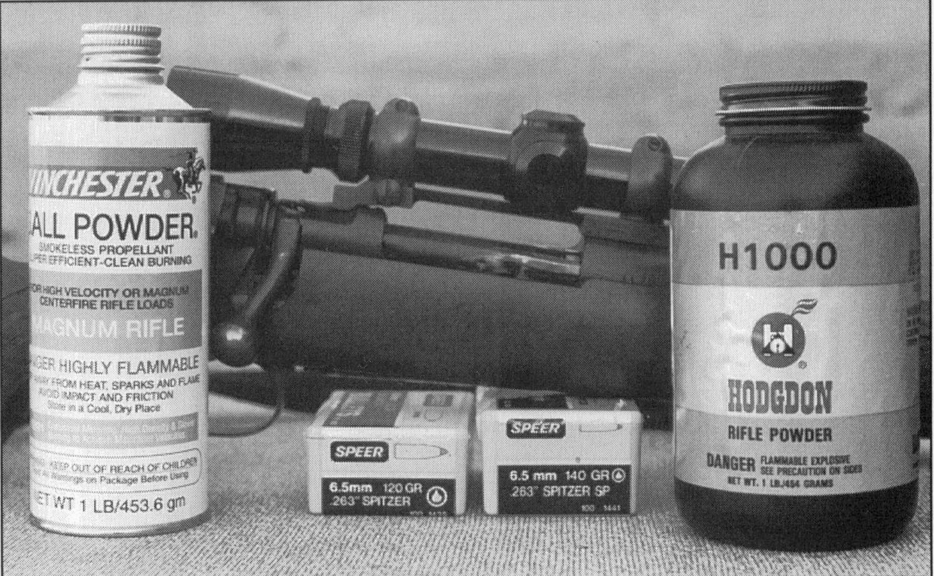


Two relatively new powders, H-1000 and WMR, produced good bullet velocity and accuracy in the 264 Winchester.

W-760 powder had standard deviations of 40 and 45 fps respectively with 120- and 140-grain bullets in the 264 Winchester. Yet the two loads grouped into .75-inch at 100 yards.

Reloading manuals show a wide variation in loads for the 264. Several manuals I checked for maximum loads with 140-grain bullets varied 6 to 8 grains for the same powder. Even old and new manuals published by the same company differed. The Speer Manual No. 8 listed 4 or so grains more powder for the 264 than their current 12th edition.

| 7MM REMINGTON MAGNUM LOADS | | | | | |
|---|---|---|---|---|---|
| Bullet | | | Load | | MV |
| Manuf. | Wgt. Grs. | Type | Powder | Wgt. Grs. | Avg. (fps) |
| Winchester | 150 | Power Point | —Factory— | | 2977 |
| Remington | 160 | Swift | —Factory— | | 2855 |
| Speer | 115 | HP | IMR-4831 | 70.0 | 3461 |
| Hornady | 120 | HP | H-4831 | 71.0 | 3259 |
| Hornady | 120 | HP | H-870 | 80.0 | 3087 |
| Hornady | 120 | HP | H-870 | 79.0 | 3021 |
| Speer | 130 | BT | W-760 | 56.5 | 3151 |
| Speer | 145 | Spitzer | H-870 | 79.0 | 2989 |
| Speer | 145 | Spitzer | WMR | 67.0 | 2981 |
| Speer | 145 | Spitzer | WMR | 66.0 | 2970 |
| Speer | 160 | Mag-Tip | H-1000 | 71.0 | 2977 |
| Speer | 160 | Mag-Tip | WMR | 66.0 | 2875 |
| Speer | 160 | Mag-Tip | WMR | 65.0 | 2838 |
| Speer | 160 | BT | H-870 | 79.0 | 3025 |
| Speer | 160 | BT | IMR-4831 | 62.0 | 2923 |
| Speer | 160 | BT | IMR-7828 | 66.0 | 2838 |
| Speer | 160 | BT | IMR-4350 | 58.0 | 2769 |
| Nosler | 162 | SB | H-1000 | 72.5 | 3160 |
| Nosler | 162 | SB | IMR-4831 | 62.0 | 2924 |
| Nosler | 162 | SB | W-760 | 53.9 | 2870 |
| Speer | 175 | Mag-Tip | H-1000 | 72.0 | 3088 |
| Speer | 175 | Mag-Tip | H-870 | 77.0 | 2850 |
| Speer | 175 | Mag-Tip | IMR-4831 | 60.0 | 2732 |
| Woodland | 190 | — | H-870 | 72.0 | 2663 |
| Woodland | 190 | — | IMR-7828 | 63.0 | 2645 |

Firearm: Remington Model 700 Classic; 24″ barrel; Federal or Winchester cases; Federal 215 primers; cartridge overall loaded length = 3.24″.

6.5mm 160-grain bullets all have a blunt point which hurts them for long range shooting—which is the whole point of the 264 Magnum.

Everyone I know who hunts with a 264 shoots 140-grain bullets. My brother-in-law, Neil, and his circle of friends are stalwart 264 shooters. Their favorite quarry is elk. They have never had any problem killing bulls either up close in the timber or across a wide park of grass with 140-grain bullets. The last elk Neil shot with his 264 was a six-point walking along in the open at what Neil estimated was nearly 400 yards. The bull took one hit through the lungs. Neil found him dead a couple of steps inside the trees.

The 264 works for him, and if he's happy, so am I.

### 7mm Remington Magnum

The 7mm Remington Magnum is so popular in the valley where I live the local plywood mill hands out boxes of 7 Mag shells instead of turkeys for Christmas. When I worked there, I knew at least ten guys who traded off their old 30-06s for new 7mm Magnums.

Not to be left out, I bought a 7mm Magnum in a Remington 700 Classic with a 24-inch barrel. I mounted a 2-

The wide variety of bullet weights from 115 to 175 grains for the 7mm Remington Magnum will take care of most hunting situations.

7x Leupold and worked up a load that included a 160-grain Speer bullet and IMR-4350 powder. I guessed its velocity was at least 3000 fps. The recoil with the load was about like my old 30-06 shooting 180-grain bullets. After all, the 7mm used only a few grains more of the same powder. Yet the best the rifle shot was 1.5-inch groups at 100 yards. But that was OK because I had heard magnums didn't group quite as well as smaller cartridges.

The rifle worked fine that first season. My antelope and deer each stood about 150 yards away, and each was ready for the freezer after one shot.

In late November, I climbed the side of a mountain for an hour in the dark to reach a park of grass. My reward was seeing a string of elk running toward me. I lay in the snow with the rifle ready, waiting for the elk to come closer. First was a big cow, then a bull, several more cows and another bull bringing up the rear. When they came within about 150 yards I shot the first bull. It fell and never moved. Examination showed the bullet had entered the front of its chest, angled through the lungs and exited behind the short ribs. I was pleased.

Then for my birthday the following year my wife bought me an Oehler Model 33 Chronotach. The velocities the machine diplayed made me think this magnum stuff was all in my head. The 160s from my 7mm showed 2769 fps, which was a good 200 fps less than I had guessed. My old 30-06 loaded with 180-grain bullets at 2776 fps was right up there with the 7 Mag.

Desperately I tried other, slower burning powders with the 160-grain bullet. With IMR-4831, -7828 and H-870, the maximum speed the rifle safely produced was 2925 fps. That was somewhat better, but still not worth the price of a stamp to write the folks back home.

I asked a few fellows at work what loads they used in their 7mms. Their choices were similar to mine. When I asked why they thought the 7 Mag was so much better than the 30-06, they reacted like I had insulted their wives. "It's a magnum!" they replied. "It's just got a lot more punch."

During the evenings one winter, I paired a variety of bullet weights and powders for the Big 7, thinking I could come up with that fictional all-around cartridge good for hunting everything from gophers to grizzlies.

Speer 115-grain hollowpoints and a top weight of IMR-4831 produced groups under 1/2-inch and a speed of 3461 fps. That combination shoots as flat over 400 yards as the 220 Swift, which many consider the fastest and finest cartridge to ever set its crosshairs on a coyote. However, the magnum has two problems as a long-range small game rifle. I usually shoot from the prone position to take advantage of its accuracy at long range. I can take the whack from the 7 Mag for a few shots from this position, but the repeated recoil really adds up. The second problem is that the short bullets going so fast completely destroy a target. With coyotes and fox, the whole idea is to retrieve a usable hide.

One morning, my mother-in-law was affectionately looking out the window at a whitetail doe and its fawn when a coyote boldly ran out of the brush and started circling the deer. Lorraine yelled for me to bring my rifle. Obeying her command, I sneaked out the back door of the house with my 7mm and into the corral behind the barn. The coyote was still busy with the deer and failed to notice the rifle barrel poke out between the poles of the corral. When the coyote stood clear, I touched off a shot. After the corral dust settled I saw the deer looking at a dead coyote.

Coyotes hides brought about $40 then. But when I picked up that one it was obvious Singer himself couldn't have sewn back together what the 115-grain bullet had torn apart.

You'd think 130-, 140- and 145-grain bullets from the 7mm Magnum would make sort of a super 270 Winchester. It would if the magnum launched those weight bullets appreciably faster than the standard 270. All I could safely squeeze out of the magnum was 3150 fps, although some reloading manuals list faster speeds.

Only with its heaviest bullets does the 7mm Magnum show a noticeable improvement over smaller cartridges like the 270 and 280, and then only with the right powder.

A few years ago, a I stumbled across a comparatively new Hodgdon powder that gives these heavy bullets in the 7mm Magnum a big boost in power and accuracy. Hodgdon's 1000 is an extruded powder that is slower burning than H-4831 but faster than H-870 ball powder. Ron Reiber, of Hodgdon, said H-1000 is an excellent powder for the 7mm Magnum shooting the 160- and 175-grain bullets. "With an overbore cartridge, like the 7mm Magnum, you need a powder that rises slowly to peak pressure to give the bullet time to start moving and give it a sustained push," Reiber said.

The large powder capacity of the 7mm Magnum case also requires a powder to fill it full for the best accuracy. "When you're looking for a powder for the 7mm Magnum," Reiber said, "you want it to fill the case or even be lightly compressed when the bullet is seated. That keeps the powder tight and in place."

A powder charge that only partially fills the case sloshes around and leaves air pockets in the case. "The flame from the primer jumps these air gaps and has lost a lot of its steam before it starts to ignite the powder," Reiber said. "But with a tight column of powder, the primer flame starts burning it right away when the primer is still at full power." This creates a uniform burn from shot to shot and results in better accuracy.

This was apparent after comparing my old loads with H-1000. Shot-

**300 WINCHESTER MAGNUM LOADS**

| —Bullet— | | | —Load— | | MV | Source |
|---|---|---|---|---|---|---|
| Manuf. | Wgt. Grs. | Type | Powder | Wgt. Grs. | Avg. (fps) | |
| Winchester | 190 | Silvertip Supreme | —Factory— | | 2876 | — |
| Speer | 150 | SP | H-4350 | 76.0 | 3219 | From Speer #12 |
| Hornady | 165 | SP | IMR-4350 | 69.7 | 2900 | From Hornady 4th Ed. |
| Hornady | 180 | BT | WMR | 74.0 | 3005 | — |
| Hornady | 180 | BT | IMR-4350 | 69.1 | 2900 | — |
| Nosler | 200 | Par. | IMR-4350 | 66.0 | 2863 | — |
| Nosler | 200 | Par. | IMR-4350 | 68.0 | 2992 | — |
| — | 180 | SP | WMR | 74.0 | 2960 | From Winchester |
| — | 190 | SPBT | WMR | 74.0 | 2920 | From Winchester |
| — | 200 | SP | WMR | 69.0 | 2750 | From Winchester |
| — | 220 | SP | WMR | 68.2 | 2665 | From Winchester |

Firearm: Post-'64 Model 70 Winchester action; 24″ Lilja stainless steel barrel; Winchester cases; Federal 215 primers

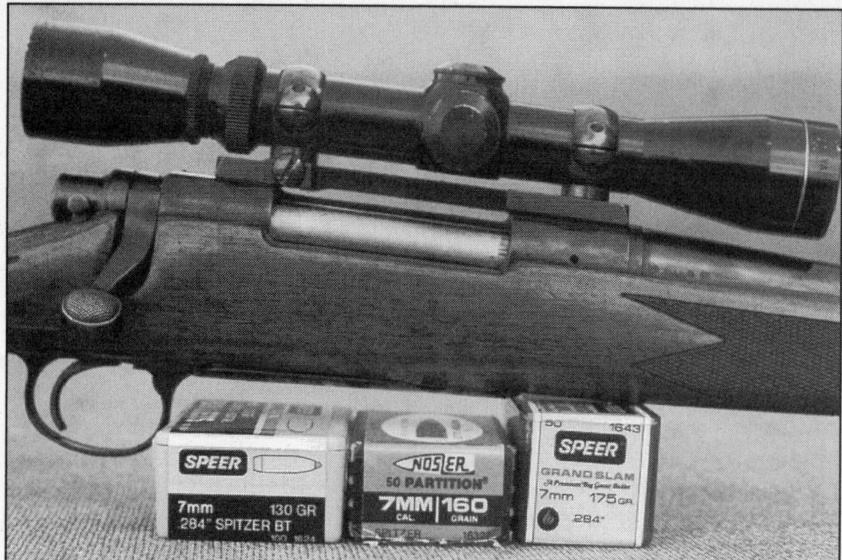


(Left) Bullets from 130 (left) to 175 grains (right) are suitable for hunting big game with the 7mm Remington Magnum. The 160-grain bullet (middle) might be the best weight for the 7mm Magnum.

(Below) H-1000 powder finally makes the 7mm Remington worthy of its magnum name.

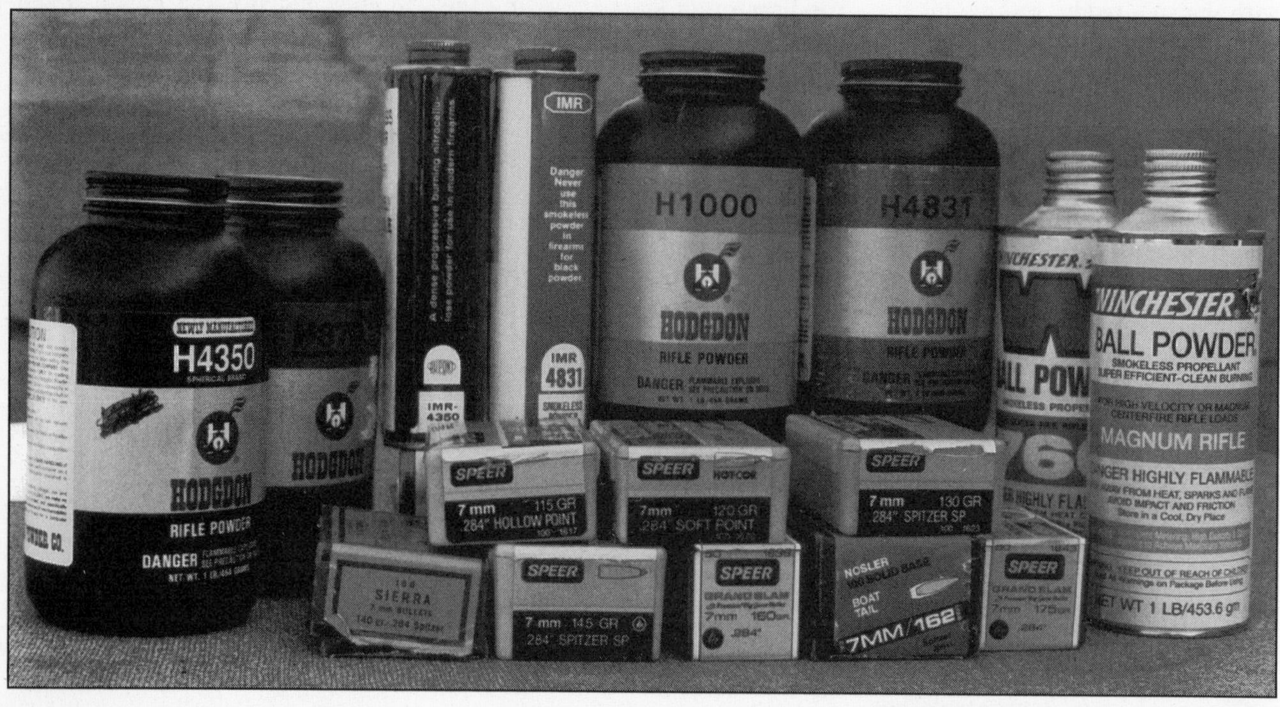


to-shot velocities with IMR-4350 and -4831 varied 75 to 85 fps shooting 160-grain bullets. With nearly a full case of H-1000, velocity spread dropped to 50 fps. Speed jumped from 2925 fps to 3160 fps with the 162-grain Nosler Solid Base bullet. The 175-grain Speer Mag-Tip bullets loaded with H-1000 had a spread of only 21 fps and a speed of 3088 fps.

Accuracy also improved. The original loads averaged 1.5 inches for three shots at 100 yards. With H-1000, the 162-grain Nosler Solid Base and Speer 175-grain Grand Slam bullets often land in .75-inch. The Speer 175-grain shot as tight as .5—always less than 1 inch.

I finally got the 7mm Remington to live up to its magnum name.

## 300 Winchester Magnum

The 300 Winchester exudes the characteristics of a magnum. Its large cartridge case of powder, heavy bullets and resulting recoil say this is a rifle for big boys.

With all that power, I guess it's kind of odd that the only big game I have shot with a 300 are mule deer and pronghorns. I can report, though, they always fell over dead—immediately—when the bullets sailed through their ribs and out the other side.

All that surplus energy is better spent on bigger big game like elk, moose and grizzlies. Most of the fanatical elk hunters I know carry 300 Winchesters. Every one of them shoots either 180- or 200-grain bullets. They quite rightly reason these heavy bullets flying around 3000 fps or more hold onto their energy to bore a big deep hole at long range. These hunters know that while 150- or 165-grain bullets leave the barrel of a 300 a couple hundred feet per second faster, these lighter bullets shed their speed and energy more quickly. In the bat of an eye that it takes the bullets to reach 100 yards, a 180-grain bullet has retained about 100 foot-pounds more energy than the faster-starting 150-grain bullet. The heavy bullet amplifies its advantage as the yardage increases.

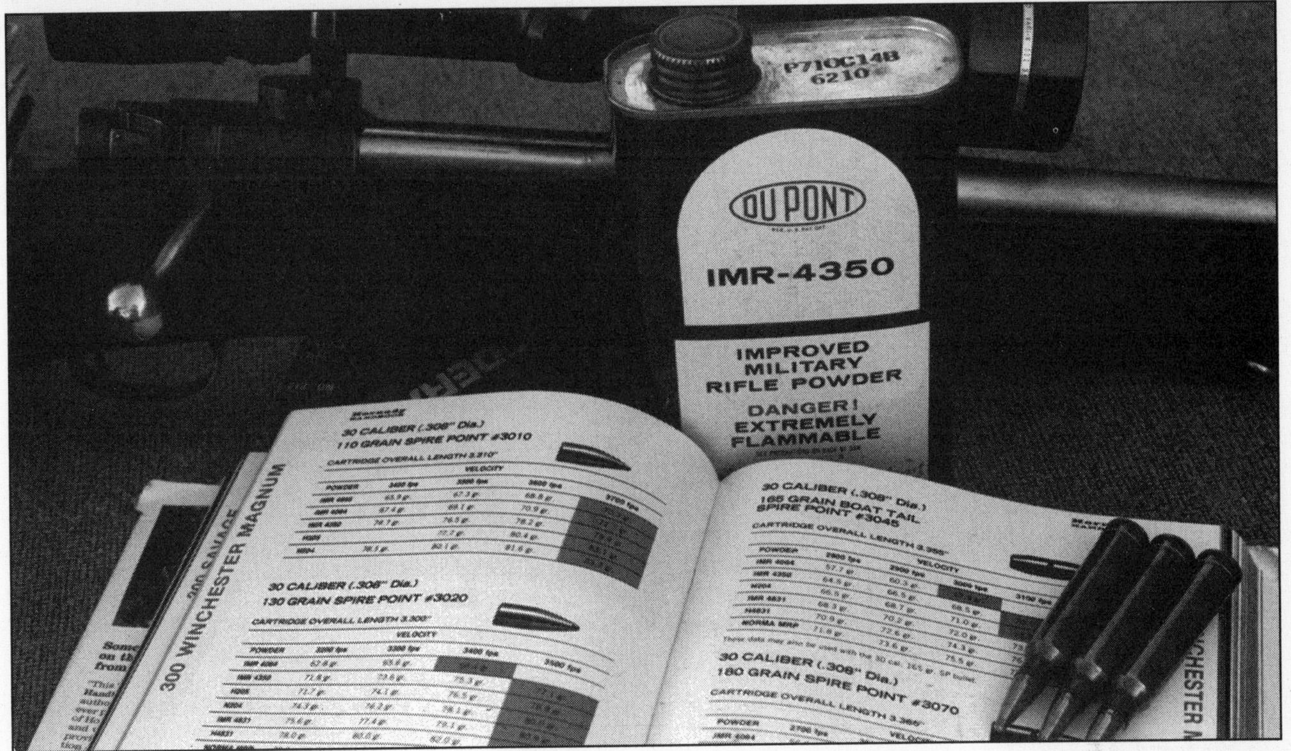


The Hornady reloading manual suggested a number of useful loads for the 300 Winchester Magnum. IMR-4350 proved to be a good performer.

The 300 Winchester seems to reach its top speeds with faster burning powders than do the 264 or 7mm Magnums. Neither Hodgdon, IMR-4831 nor IMR-7828 produced more velocity for me with a 180-grain Hornady bullet than did lighter charges of IMR-4350 from the 24-inch barrel of my test 300. The same thing occurred with 200-grain Nosler Partition bullets.

The 200-grain Nosler Partition is the only bullet my friend Dave Roberts shoots in his 300 anymore for big game. Last October, I watched him shoot an antelope buck so far across the prairie I had to look through my binoculars to see its horns. Dave has hunted down the spine of the Rockies with his 300, taking every species of big game except sheep.

Armed with a properly loaded 300 Winchester Magnum, a hunter is ready for big and bigger game.

### Comparisons

A recap of all of this shows the three cartridges have similar ballistics when the 264 is loaded with a 140-grain bullet, the 7mm with a 160-grain and the 300 with a 180-grain. A glance at various reloading manuals determines these three bullets weights, with similar shapes, have comparable sectional densities and ballistic coefficients. The three cartridges shoot their respective bullets at about 3100 fps, and therefore, their trajectories and bullet speeds remain fairly even.

As far as energy coming out the barrel, the top spot goes to the 300, the 7mm second and then the 264. That's because of the heavier bullets. The difference between the 264 and 300 is roughly 400 foot-pounds of energy at 400 yards, with the 7mm just about halfway between them. There's really not that much difference between the three. A properly hit elk would never know the difference.

All three cartridges deliver fine accuracy.

Reloading for each was easy. I made sure the cases were kept trimmed to the correct length, as I have found cases that are even a smidgen too long are the cause of inaccuracy and wild pressures. I ignored the belts on the cases. I set the sizing die so the cases headspace in the chambers on their shoulders, not the belts.

A constant criticism of the 264, 7mm and 300 Magnums is their short necks. Somewhere it must be chiseled in stone that it's a crime for a bullet to reach below the case neck into the powder space. The penalty for breaking this law is said to be inaccuracy and reduced powder capacity. Call me a criminal, then, because I seat bullets deeply in all three cartridges. I've never suffered any noticeable inaccuracy or lack of room for powder due to seating bullets deeply in magnum cases.

One of the pluses of these middle magnums is they fit in standard-length actions. A slight disadvantage to this is the bullets may not be seated out enough to reach just short of the rifling. With some rifles, I have noticed that seating the bullet just short of the rifling helps accuracy a tiny bit. I've failed to notice it in magnum hunting rifles.

The problem with the 264 is that it's moribund. Winchester chambers their Model 70 in 264 and a couple of small shops make 264s, but that's about it. Cases are still fairly easy to find. Its only advantage is that it produces noticeably less recoil than the 7mm and 300. Still, if you're not into the herd mentality of shooting what everyone else does, the 264 is a good choice.

The 7mm and 300 are very popular. I see an even split between the two among hunters. The 7mm has the advantage of less recoil, but for those who can handle the kick, the 300 has the edge with its heavier bullets.

If I were in the market for a middle magnum I would pass on the 264 unless the rifle was a bargain, and take one each of the 7mm and 300 Magnums. •

# What's New ON THE LOADING BENCH

by R.H. VANDENBURG, JR.

THE PAST YEAR has seen continued growth in the shooting sports. New ammunition, perhaps, has dominated the scene, but close by has been the handloading market, especially in the area of components. However, the world of new tools and accessories has hardly lagged behind with the release of several new manuals, the introduction of a spate of new presses and the development of a number of items destined to make the handloader's life more interesting.

**Accurate Arms'** *The Accurate Solution For Reloading 1997* is the company's latest guide. It is small—and free for the asking—and serves to keep its customers informed between editions of its larger reloading manual. This year's release is really quite a pamphlet in its own right. Larger than before, it includes a section on Cowboy Action Shooting, and a separate section on XMP-5744 divided into handgun data and rifle data, as well as the usual sections on handguns, rifles and shotguns. The booklet also sets out the list of Accurate powders using their current names. Several have undergone a name change recently. For example: MR-223 is now 2230; 2015 BR, XMR 2015; 2495 BR, XMR 2495; 4350, XMR 4350; and 3100, XMR 3100.

An insert covers Accurate's latest powder: Data Powder 2200. Best suited for the 223 Remington and 7.62x39 cartridges, it fits between 1680 and 2230 on Accurate's burning rate chart. There are now twenty-one powders in the Accurate line.

**Ballistic Products, Inc.**, those purveyors of just about everything related to shotshell reloading, has revised a few more of its manuals. *G/BP High Performance Sporting Loads* is now in its fourth revision, and *Status of Steel* is in its eighth. The former addresses reloading for Sporting Clays and live bird shooting using BPI's imported shotshell wads; the latter deals with steel shot loading for hunting.

**Barnes Bullets** is constantly increasing its product line, including X-Bullets for handgun cartridges. Of interest here is their latest ballistics software, "Barnes Ballistics for Windows." Specific load and gun data can be entered and displayed along with trajectory data on the same page in both graph and table form. Wind deflection and striking velocities can be calculated, as can the effect of external forces such as temperature, altitude, shooting angle and other factors.

As this is written, Barnes is also ready to release its second loading manual, which includes much information on the latest Barnes bullets. There is a lot of tested data on the X-Bullets. Bullet lengths and bearing surfaces differ from other makes of similar weight, and those differences must be taken into consideration when reloading.

**Blount, Inc.**, parent company of RCBS, CCI, Weaver, Outers, Speer, Ram-Line and Simmons, has been busy as usual. While each subsidiary has one or more new products of interest, RCBS draws the handloader's attention with its new Powder-

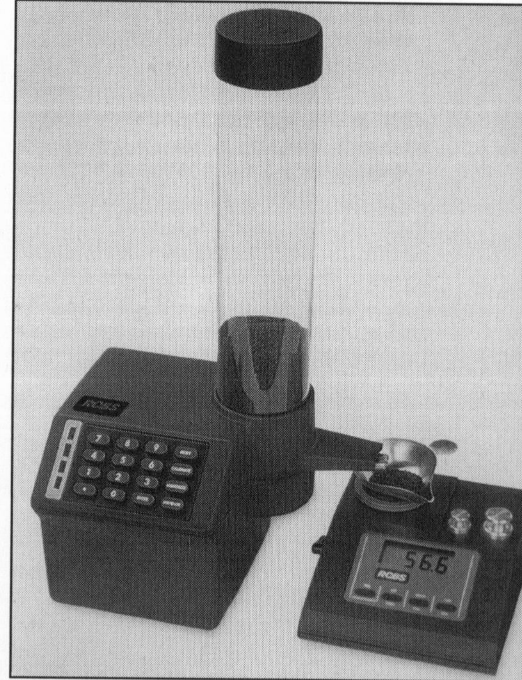

Blount/RCBS' PowderMaster Electronic Trickler and PowderPro Digital Scale.

Blount/RCBS' Die Wrench Lock Tool.

Master Electronic Powder Dispenser. It works in conjunction with an electronic scale, and the unit is quite impressive. It has a hopper to hold the powder and a keyboard for operator control. The unit cable connects to the PowderPro Digital Scale, and the two units operate in concert. The user begins by filling the hopper with powder and calibrating the unit. Calibration "teaches" the PowderMaster the flow rate, which allows the powder to be dispensed as rapidly as possible without overthrowing the charge. Then the operator enters the desired charge and depresses the "dispense" button. The unit quickly drops a precisely weighed charge in the pan that sits upon the attached scale.

The handloader dumps the powder into a waiting case, replaces the pan and depresses the "dispense" button again. While the pan is being filled, the handloader seats a bullet, picks up another case and repeats the process. It's quicker than weighing charges mechanically and more accurate than throwing charges with a measure—much more accurate with some powders.

Two new electronic scales also have been announced. The Rangemaster Digital Scale replaces the RCBS Model 90. Capacity is increased to 1500 grains, and the price is reduced considerably. The scale operates on AC current or one 9-volt battery. Accuracy within .1-grain is assured. The scale cover is designed to allow placing a powder trickler near the pan platform for dribbling in the last few kernels of powder. The second new scale is the Partner Digital. Powered by one 9-volt battery, it can easily be used away from the bench. Accuracy is within .1-grain up to 300 grains and within .2-grains up to its capacity of 750 grains.

Also new this year is a Die Lock Ring Wrench. Designed for $^7/_8$x14 hex nuts used with many reloading dies, the wrench makes quick work of tightening or removing loading dies from a press. I got to review the powder dispenser and scales at the most recent SHOT Show in Las Vegas, and was impressed with their quality and general usefulness. The wrench I did not get to see until I got home, and RCBS sent me one in lieu of a picture. I was surprised by the lack of outside dimensions of standardization in the $^7/_8$x14 nuts so widely used within the industry. Nevertheless, the wrench worked with all I tried, although some fits were much better than others.

Cast bullet shooters weren't forgotten either as RCBS has added a new 40-caliber, 400-grain bullet for Black Powder Silhouette shooting. Almost spitzer-shaped with a very small meplat, the bullet is flat-based with four grease grooves. Identified as the 40-400-BPS (for Black Powder Silhouette), it differs from the older 40-400-CSA (for C. Sharps Arms) in ogive, meplat size and number of grease grooves. The new bullet will more likely see use in rifles chambered for Winchester or other 40 calibers rather than the Sharps proprietary cartridges.

**Borra Performance** is the manufacturer of a new and nifty reloading bench. Company literature calls it the Ultimate Reloading Table, and it has more of a furniture look than just a bench. Built of oak and oak-veneer plywood, the table provides quite a bit of lockable storage space, as well as a recessed press mounting area and an eye-level location for a powder scale. Height, 61 inches; width, 32 inches; depth, 25 inches.

Borra Performance's Reloading Table.

**Brownells** recently became the exclusive licensee of J-B cleaning compound. They will assume all responsibility for marketing and manufacture. J-B has become the darling of the benchrest crowd (as well as other knowledgeable shooters) for removing powder and metal fouling. Used in conjunction with Kroil or a Kroil/Shooter's Choice mix, it is a favorite of top competitors. Interestingly, when I received a sample jar from Brownells announcing their new arrangement, I realized I had containers of J-B from the '70s, '80s and '90s. Each is different in color, consistency and, it seems to me, smell. It takes a good product to stay around that long, and Brownells deserves a pat on the back for ensuring that it will continue to be available.

Brownells' JB Bore Cleaning Compound.

Dave Corbin of **Corbin Manufacturing & Supply, Inc.**, hasn't been sitting still either. First, he introduced a new book, *The Corbin Handbook of Bullet Swaging, No. 8.* An update of the previous versions, it covers bullet swaging, bullet construction and design, shotgun slugs, and much more, in detail. At 220 pages and $9.50, it's a steal!

Corbin has also announced a 50-caliber jacketed pistol-bullet-making kit. Included are a swaging press, dies, lead wire and core cutter. The press can also be used for traditional reloading.

Finally, Corbin has just upgraded their Series II swaging press. The

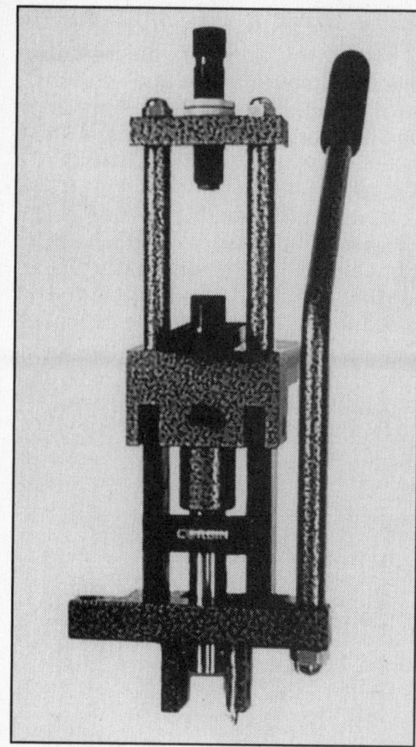

Corbin's Series II Swaging Press.

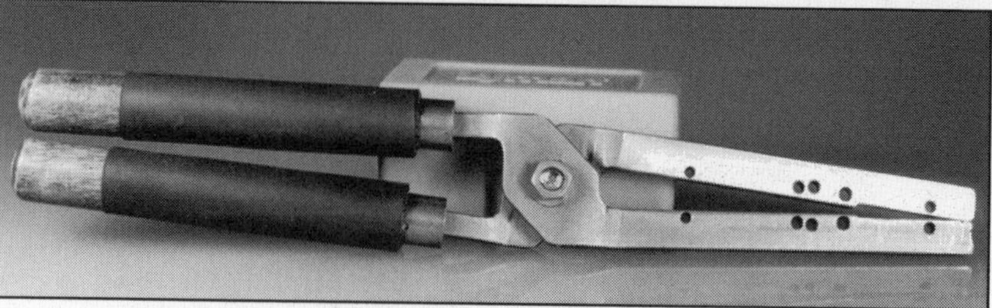

Graf & Sons Universal Mould Handles.

press is a dual-stroke model (2-inch for swaging, 4-inch for reloading). A ram extender accepts standard shellholders and guides spent primers into a removable tray. An improved link lock-up eliminates uneven torque being applied to the ram, and roller bearings are used in the linkage assembly. The press is machined steel rather than cast, and stroke length is easily changed via a "grenade pin" release. The press head has a standard 7/8x14 threaded hole, but can be replaced with one having a custom thread for experimental work. This top-of-the-line single-stage press will handle all reloading and swaging needs, and is equally suitable for left- or right-hand users.

**Dillon Precision** has added two new presses to its already outstanding lineup. The AT 500 is a turret-style loader built on Dillon's popular progressive RL 500 B frame. Designed for those whose reloading output doesn't require a progressive loader, the AT 500 can be upgraded to a 550 B should conditions warrant. The press uses interchangeable toolheads that hold up to four dies and an indexable, universal shellplate that positions the cases.

The SL 900 is Dillon's first entry into the shotshell reloading game. Built on a chopped and channeled, as it were, 650 frame, the press is offered in 2¾-inch 12-gauge only at this time and is factory-adjusted for the Winchester AA shell. All features are automatic except wad insertion. The operator fills the powder, shot, primer and shell containers; inserts a wad in the tilt-out guide; and pulls the handle. The powder dispensing system uses an adjustable measure—as do Dillon's metallic loaders—that does not require bushings. The shot hopper takes a full 25 pounds of shot, and the case feeder holds 80 cases. Conversion to other gauges involves simply swapping toolheads and does not require die adjustments. I had an opportunity to view the shotshell reloader in operation at the 1997 SHOT Show. Two thoughts remain: One, it is a large machine with the automatic feeders in place; and two, this thing is as slick as an eel in grease. You'll like it.

**Efficient Machinery Co.** has come out with a reloading bench that combines sturdiness and adjustability to a degree rarely seen. The bench is available in two top widths (61 and 49 inches) and three heights (33, 36.5 or 41 inches). It comes in kit form, and all pieces are held together with PVC fasteners (threaded pipes and nuts). Load capacity is 1000 pounds. A backboard kit with adjustable shelves for manuals or a powder scale is an option. All in all, very nice.

**Federal Cartridge Co.** has updated their *Shotshell Reloading Data* booklet. New powders included this time are American Select from Alliant and AA Plus from Winchester. As you may know, Federal is back in the brass business, thank goodness. Both match-grade and field-grade cases are being offered in select calibers.

**Graf & Sons** is a mail-order firm specializing in reloading components, guns and accessories. However, Willy Coffer, a Graf employee, has developed something special: a cast bullet mould handle that will work with

Dillion Precision's AT 500 Turret Press.

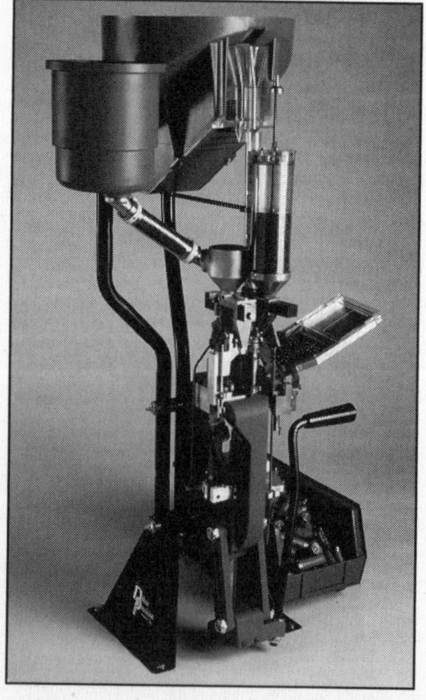

Dillion Precision's SL 900 Shotshell Loader.

almost anyone's mould blocks. Coffer sent me a prototype, and I have used it with both one- and two-cavity blocks from Lyman as well as two-cavity blocks from RCBS. The one-cavity Lyman blocks were the old, smaller style that called for Lyman "small" handles. The original idea was that multiple blocks could be used at the same time. My prototype needs a little polishing on one set of holes, but I believe I can use it with two of the Lyman small blocks. Frankly, I do not want to use it with two two-cavity moulds at the same time. My casting technique is to use two moulds alternately—one is "setting up," while the other is being emptied and refilled. But I would welcome the chance to use two small single-cavity moulds in conjunction with one two-cavity.

**Hodgdon Powder Co.** has several new items. First is its *Shotshell Data Manual*. The book is beautifully bound, with slick paper and many color photographs. Authored by Don Zutz and edited by Hodgdon's Ron Reiber, with additional articles by Nick Sisley and Tom Roster, the book is impressive. A complete reference section includes both chamber and cartridge drawings of all popular gauges and case lengths. There are sections of load data for lead shot, lead buckshot, lead slugs, steel shot and bismuth shot. Interestingly, the steel shot section includes only data for the 12-gauge, 2¾-inch shell with ⅞- and 1-ounce *target* loads. No hunting loads are included. According to Reiber, the testing of many popular steel shot loads revealed numerous instances in which pressures exceeded prudent loading practices. The problem is with the available wads. Wads for lead shot and steel target loads have a collapsible section that provides some pressure relief as the powder burns. Steel hunting wads do not, and pressure spikes due to changes in powder or powder lots, wads, primers, shells or crimps can all have a dangerous effect with possible damage to the gun and injury to the shooter. Think about that awhile!

The book's load data uses only Hodgdon powders, of course, but it references most popular shells, primers and wads. Primers include the CCI 209SC, which was developed for use primarily with Hodgdon's Clays powders and the recently discontinued Winchester AATP. The text is chock full of articles that should benefit any shotgunner.

Hodgdon's B.L.A.S.T. ballistics program.

The only fault I can find with the book is a very small one. In referencing the various shot and their relative sizes, it is implied that shot of a given size is the same diameter whether lead, steel or bismuth. This is not true. Bismuth shot is larger, usually by about .005-inch. The reason is to make each bismuth pellet weigh approximately the same as lead. It works, but as a result a given weight and size of bismuth shot will occupy more space than a corresponding amount of lead shot. There is also, in a discussion on shot, a reference to bismuth fragmenting under setback that seems to be overstated. Recent lots of bismuth, with 3 percent tin, that I've tested have shown little or no evidence of this. Still, it's a very good book and should be a welcome addition to any shotshell reloader's library.

Hodgdon has also issued its annual *Basic Reloader's Manual*, which includes data for handgun, rifle and shotgun reloading. There is a new powder—H50 BMG—for the 50 BMG and some new bullet weights. Dropped from the '97 printing were the 224, 240 and 257 Weatherby cartridges; the 7-30 Waters; and the 284 Winchester. In the pistol section, the 6mm TCU and the 41 AE are gone as well. There are numerous changes in the shotshell section, including new charge weights, primers and wads. Only lead shot loads are listed. The booklet is free from your dealer or from Hodgdon.

Hoppe's Semi-Auto Solvent.

The company has also introduced its first computer program. Called "B.L.A.S.T." (Ballistic Loading And Software Tables), the program includes the Barnes external ballistics program, Hodgdon's reloading data from its manuals, a special Cowboy Action section, lead bullet loads for

Hoppe's synthetic gun care products.

rifles and a handgun silhouette section. Load, trajectory and other data can appear on the screen together and be printed.

**Hoppe's**, the gun care and accessory folks, has introduced a new bore cleaner called Semi-Auto Solvent. What makes it unique is the absence of residue after use that might impede the action of some tight-fitting competition autos. I have been using the cleaner for the last couple of months on revolvers and autoloading pistols, but not of competition grade. Nevertheless, I have been impressed with the cleaner and its ability to remove lead, metal and powder fouling. It's good stuff. Hoppe's has also joined forces with Castrol to develop a series of new gun-care products using all-synthetic formulas. So far, the lineup includes Gunlube, Rustprotector, Field Cleaner and Gunstripper. Each is available in 4-ounce spray cans.

**Hornady** wins this year's "most innovative" prize with their new Lock-N-Load die mounting system. The system begins with two new presses. The first, the Lock-N-Load Classic Loader, is a single-stage press. In the top of the press, where the reloading die would ordinarily go, is a 1¼x12 UNF threaded hole. Into the hole is threaded a bushing. Onto the standard ⅞x14 die is threaded another bushing. The two bushings join together by inserting the die bushing into the press bushing and giving a slight twist. Once the die is properly adjusted, it can be removed and replaced without losing adjustment. Bushings are sold separately so that any ⅞x14 die can be used. The Lock-N-Load system can be used on any other single-stage press that has a 1¼x12 hole with a removable die sleeve such as the RCBS Rockchucker and some earlier Lyman and Redding presses.

The single-stage press will be sold in two configurations. The Lock-N-Load Classic Reloading Package includes the press, automatic primer feed and three die bushings. The Lock-N-Load Classic Kit includes the press, a powder measure, scale, manual, primer flipper, primer pocket cleaners, case neck brushes and handles, powder funnel, deburring tool, wrench, loading block and case lube. The previous Hornady single-stage press, the 00-7, has been discontinued.

The second press, the Lock-N-Load Automatic Progressive, is similar to the old Projector progressive press, but utilizes the Lock-N-Load system. The press has a solid top with stations for five dies and the same rotating shellplate that was used on the Projector press. Other new features include a powder drop system that operates only when a case is present, improved access for case insertion, improved automatic indexing with manual override, automatic case ejection and an in-line automatic priming system with manual on-off switch. Tubes can be removed without spilling the primers.

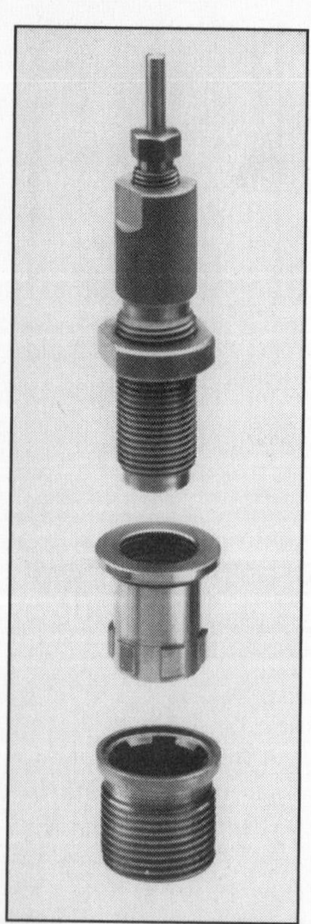

Hornady's Lock-N-Load Die System.

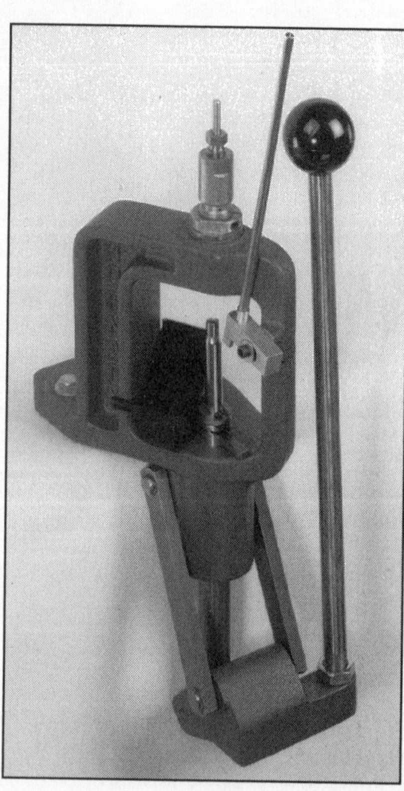

Hornady's Lock-N-Load Classic Reloading Press.

Hornady's Lock-N-Load Automatic Progressive Press.

The Lock-N-Load Automatic Progressive Press comes with a powder measure, the Auto Powder Drop feature, one shellplate, five bushing sets and cartridge catcher. The earlier Projector progressive press has also been discontinued.

I can not help but mention **Huntington**. After the Huntington family sold the business, RCBS, to Blount, Inc., Huntington was established as a distributor of many standard and hard-to-find reloading products. This is the place to find all RCBS products, as well as those of many other manufacturers. What impresses me most, I think, is the clarity with which the products are described. Also of great importance are the lists of special-order and case forming dies. Not only is this a great source for products, it is also an invaluable reference book.

**Iosso Products** has announced a new paste bore cleaner. This idea (bore cleaner in paste form) seems to be coming into its own. Safer to transport than liquids, they do not spill or run onto wood stocks, and little, if any, is wasted. On top of that, many users claim they are more effective than liquid cleaners. I'm still undecided about that, but make no mistake about it, they do work.

Iosso Products' Paste Bore Cleaner.

**Lee Precision**, after several years of heavy development, is taking a breather this year. However, Richard Lee, the company's founder and father of president John Lee, has written the company's first significant reloading manual. *Modern Reloading* is divided into two parts, text and load data. The text is part reminiscence, part Lee company history, written in typical, sometimes blunt, Lee style.

Errors are few, and only one seems worthy of comment. In a section on shotshell reloading (Chapter 11), the statement "chilled shot is hard shot" is made. This hasn't been true for years. In fact, because dropped shot, the softest type, is generally not available, chilled shot may be the softest shot most reloaders ever see. High antimony, or magnum, shot is considerably harder than chilled shot, generally having an antimony content of from 2 to 6 percent, depending on shot size, as compared to the chilled shot range of 1/2 to 2 percent.

The load data section of the manual is a collection of information for metallic cartridges from most of the powder manufacturers. There are also some listings for Nobel powders, which most handloaders will not be familiar with. The data is arranged by bullet weight for each caliber. Barnes X-Bullets are given their own category. Lee uses a formula of highest velocity, safe pressures, amount of powder and loading density to "rate" the load data, and has arranged it in a best-to-worst order. He is careful to explain that even the lowest listed data is still good, but suggests that the best loads for a given caliber and bullet weight will be found in the upper half of each list. This is a very interesting approach and should get most handloaders off on the right foot. For reduced loads, Lee suggests selecting loads from the center of each list that produce moderate velocities with reasonably high pressures. To calculate a reduced load of a specific velocity, Lee has developed a formula to aid the handloader in selecting the right powder and charge. All in all, well worth reading.

**Lyman Products** always gets my attention; I started, back when the earth was flat, with Lyman tools. Most are still on my bench earning their keep. This year, the company has added a few more items for consideration. First is the new Crusher II, an upgraded version of the old Orange Crush single-stage press. This was always a good press; now it's better. A new base design is machined flat to better attach to your bench, and the new "Silver Hammertone" color is really quite attractive. This follows on the heels of last year's upgrade of Lyman's turret press, the T-Mag II. The Crusher II press will be packaged alone or in two kits. A Crusher Pro Kit will include the press, a scale, lube kit, loading block and reloading manual. The Crusher Expert Kit will

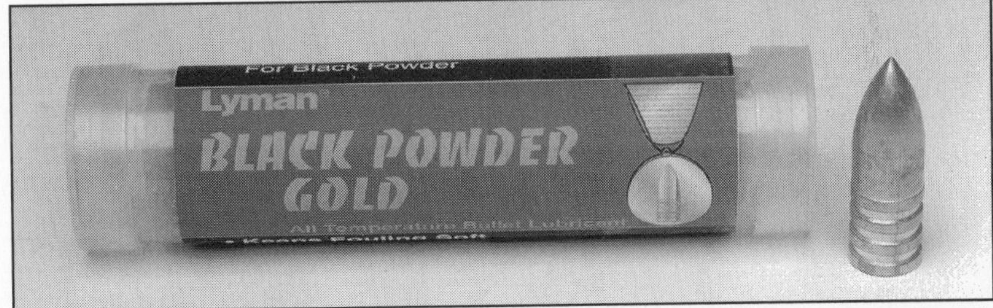


Lyman Product's Black Powder Gold Lube.

Lyman Product's Cowboy Action cast bullet moulds: 38 Special/357 Magnum, 44-40, 44 Special/Magnum and 45 Colt.

include the press and all the accessories one needs for reloading, including powder measure, scale, case trimmer, primer tray, manual, etc.

New dies on this year's Lyman list include the 9x23 Winchester and the 7mm STW. Bullet casters have not been forgotten either as Lyman has added two new lubes and six moulds. One lube is Black Powder Gold, targeted at Black Powder Rifle Silhouette shooters. The second, Super Moly, is a standard rifle and handgun bullet lube with molybdenum (one assumes molybdenum disulfide) in the formula. Two of the new moulds are also for the blackpowder gang. A 40-caliber Snover weighs 400 grains and has a nominal diameter of .410-inch. A 45-caliber Postell is a hefty 535 grains and is actually enjoying a return engagement, as Lyman had once before offered this mould but dropped it. This time it's back by popular demand.

The popular Cowboy Action Shooting game has prompted the development of four more moulds. Offered in 38/357, 44-40, 44 Special/44 Magnum and 45 Colt, the moulds are all essentially the same design: a flattened round-nose similar to the old "standard" bullet for the 45 Colt. These old designs usually had two lube grooves and were crimped over the ogive. Many of us have used the top lube groove as a crimp groove, but often, depending on cylinder length, this wasn't possible. Even Lyman recommended against it. Bullets crimped over the ogive and then used in tubular-magazine lever actions were sometimes set back by recoil, raising pressures. The new bullets all have one somewhat larger lube groove and a legitimate crimp groove. The meplat on the new design is much wider than on the older style, making a more satisfactory hunting bullet as well. My first reaction to seeing the 45 Colt bullet was to order the mould. Lyman also offers the bullets from all six moulds, cast, lubed and ready to shoot.

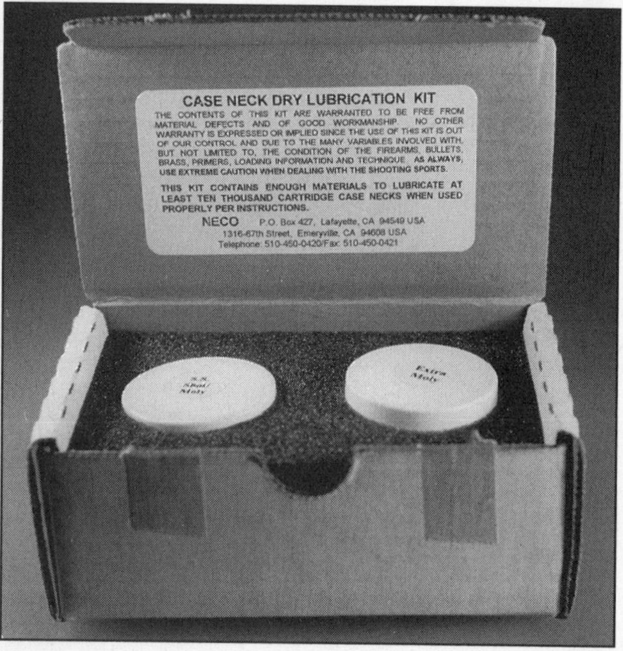


NECO's Neck Luber Kit.

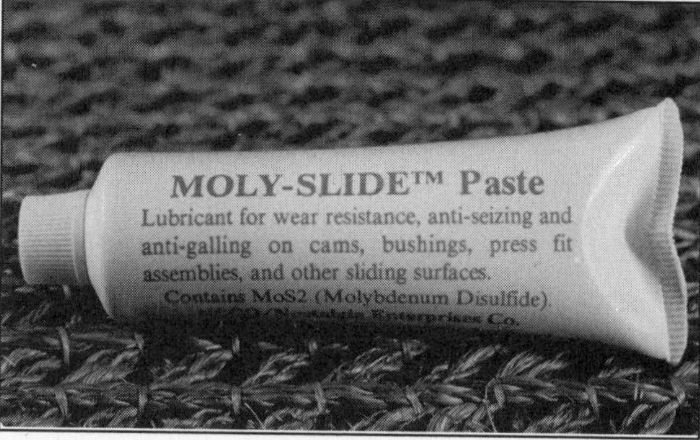


NECO's Moly-Slide Paste.

Roger Johnston of **NECO (Nostalgia Enterprises Co.)** has several new products. For the shooter, Moly-Slide is a molybdenum disulfide paste designed to reduce friction in close-fitting metal parts such as pistol slides, bolts and other moving parts. The paste is 60 percent moly with no graphite.

For the handloader, NECO has developed the NECO Neck Luber. A container holds molybdenum disulfide and steel balls. The handloader simply dips a cartridge case in the mixture, mouth first, up to the shoulder. A fine coat of "moly" will be distributed on the case neck, inside and out, for easy sizing. A deluxe version uses stainless steel balls and has an extra supply of moly. An economy version uses carbon steel balls and has no extra moly. Either should last the handloader a very long time. I have been using the neck lube kit for some time now and am quite impressed. It sure beats inside neck lubing with a brush. Just remember to lightly tap the case as it is removed to prevent bridging of the shot.

Walt Melanger of **NEI Handtools**, makers of first-rate bullet moulds, continues to add to his designs. At least twenty-two moulds have been added since last year. His catalog is a must for cast bullet shooters and very easy to understand. There are well over 500 moulds from which to choose.

**Nosler Bullets** is out with its newest reloading manual, the *Nosler Reloading Guide, Number Four*. It is bigger and better than its predecessor. There is a very instructive article by Rick Jamison on when to choose the Ballistic Tip or Partition bullets. Articles by John Barsness, J. Wayne Fears, Mitch Maxberry and others complement a first-rate effort. Load data is presented numerically and graphically. The most accurate load for each powder and the most accurate powder is given for each caliber, along with load density and velocity for each load. This is an excellent reloading manual—a requirement for users of Nosler bullets—and that includes everyone, doesn't it?

**Rapine Bullet Moulds** continues to grow. There are new shotgun slugs, in 12- and 20-gauge, to be used in regular shot wads. Both are hollow-base; the 12-gauge offering weighs 500 grains, the 20-gauge 380. Also new this year are moulds geared toward Cowboy Action shooters, including a 45 Colt mould that drops a 155-grain bullet. When first told the weight, I said, "You mean 255 grains." Assured that 155 is correct, I just sighed. Softer recoil and quicker recovery are the reasons, of course. I had naively hoped that Cowboy Action Shooting might be the one place spared the influences of "gamesmanship." Not to

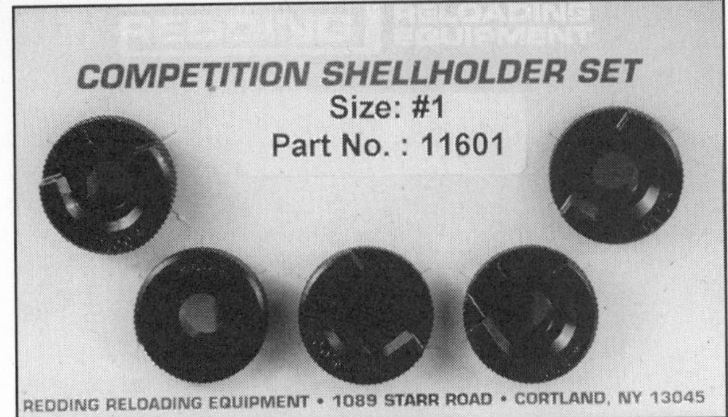


Redding-Saeco's Competition Shellholder Set.

Nosler Bullet's *Reloading Guide, Number Four.*

Reloading Specialties' All Seal Primer and Crimp Sealant.

be. Nevertheless, the mould should be a good one.

**Redding-Saeco** had a very busy year last year, so I didn't expect too much this time around. Instead of a lot of new things, we get something even better—a really good idea. Redding's new Competition Shellholders consist of a five-piece set of shellholders for a given case head size that are machined .002, .004, .006, .008 and .010 over the standard shellholder thickness of .125-inch. The purpose is to allow the sizer die to mate flush with the shellholder, assuring proper alignment without setting the case shoulder back. I ordered the .473-inch (for the 243, 308, 30-06, etc.) set and began to experiment. For years, I have used my own special technique to ensure proper die alignment within the press, but this is much better. Perhaps of more importance is that, with the proper measuring tools, the handloader can learn a great deal about his chamber, his die setup and what works best—just by using these shellholders. For example, in my 243 Winchester, I found, using a Stoney Point datum line-to-case-head headspace tool, that full-length sizing with the .010-inch shellholder actually increased case head-to-datum line measurement by .010-inch, making chambering a round difficult. Experimenting, I found the .006-inch shellholder provided a perfect case-to-chamber fit. This is for this one chamber and die set, of course. The point is that there is much to be learned here, and this tool can help.

**Reloading Specialties**, the shotshell and steel shot reloading specialists company is out with its fourth edition of *Steel Shotshell Reloading Handbook*. It's chock-full of recipes and tips on safely reloading steel shot. Anyone contemplating reloading steel shot will find this manual invaluable.

The company also has introduced a new weatherproofing sealer for primer and case mouths. Called the All Seal primer and crimp sealer, it comes in a half-ounce bottle with applicator and should be sufficient for hundreds of shells.

**Shooting Chrony** has announced a couple of interesting changes. First, the company has brought back its Chrony F-1, a very affordable chronograph. The F-1 is not fancy, it simply registers bullet speed and displays it on an LCD readout. The speed continues to be displayed until the next shot is fired. The F-1 can also be upgraded to other Shooting Chrony models.

Second, all of the Shooting Chrony line (F-1, Delta, Alpha, Beta and Gamma models) can be upgraded to a new Master version. This contains a remote 1/2-inch LCD readout that rests on the shooter's bench. All other models have the readout unit as part of the downrange screen setup.

**Sinclair International** manufactures quite a few things under their own name and carries a number of items for the accuracy buff

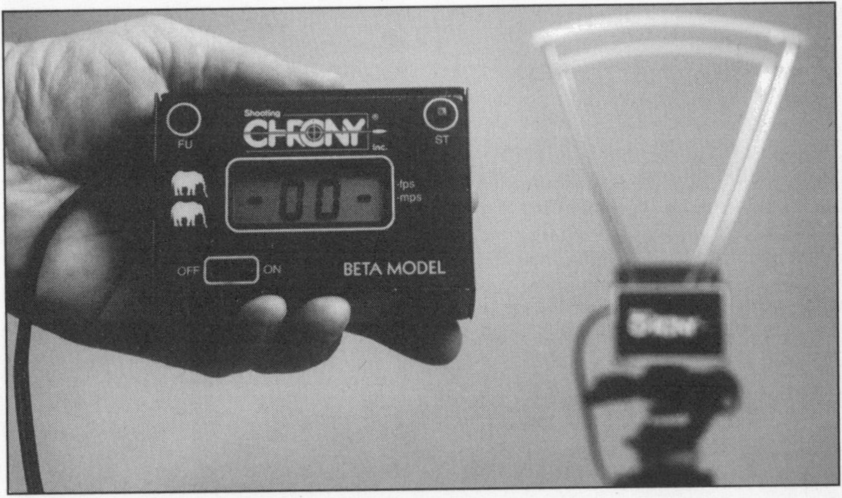


Shooting Chrony's Master Remote Display.

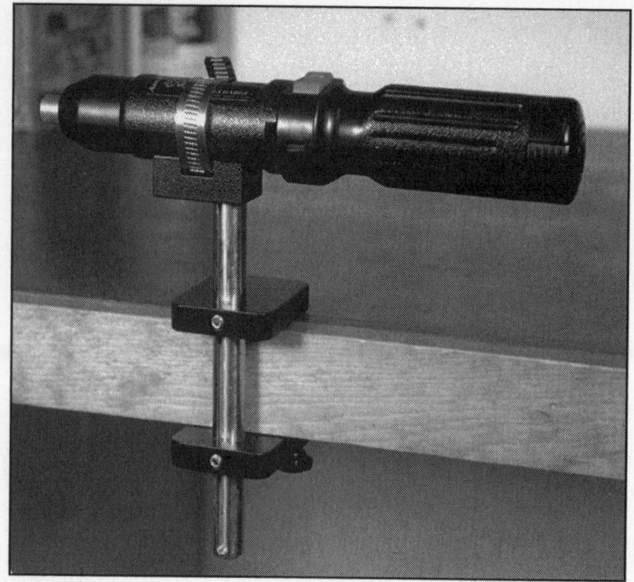

Sinclair International's Case Prep Center with electric screwdriver.

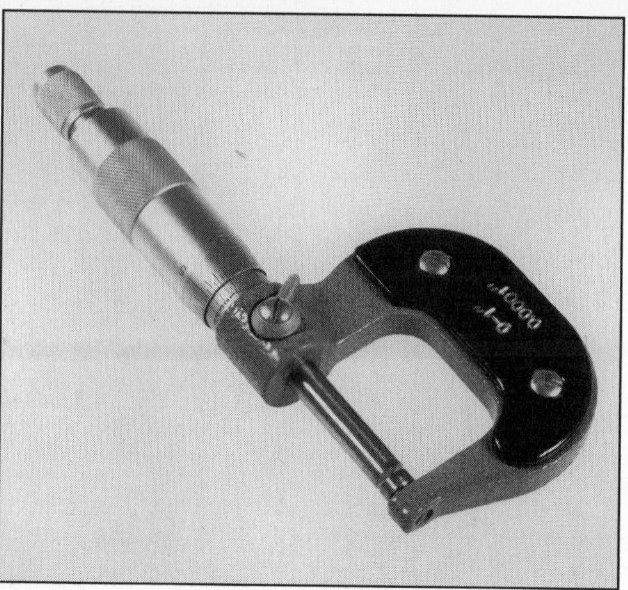

Sinclair International's Micrometer.

made by others. New this year is the Sinclair Powder Measure Stand, a truly interesting product. It holds a powder measure, is adjustable horizontally and vertically, and can be clamped to most loading benches. It is ideal for use at the range and can be easily packed away when not in use. I have been using one for several months now and am constantly finding more ways to take advantage of its versatility. Good product! Also new is a Case Prep Center built around the adjustable measure stand and a holder for many power tools. A Case Trimmer Bracket that attaches to the stand works with Wilson trimmers or neck turners. A Case Holder for spinning cases is similar to a shellholder with a hex shaft attached. It works with power screwdrivers or drill motors, and is available in several head sizes. A Deburring Tool Holder also has a hex shaft and works with power tools. Most deburring tools can be inserted in the holder.

Other new products include a neck turning lube, a reasonably priced micrometer, and a Speedy Die, which sets the shoulder back and neck sizes without sizing the body. It uses Wilson or Redding bushings to size the neck. A decapping stem is part of the die. In use, a headspace measuring tool is recommended.

Sinclair also manufactures cleaning rod cases. They are designed for Dewey cleaning rods and come singly or in pairs with a connecting bracket. I have been using a pair at home, wall mounted using a couple of simple "L" brackets to hold a variety of rods. It is really the best system I have seen for storing and protecting one-piece rods.

**Tombstone Smoke-n-Deals** has added several new products, including a nice leather-bound carrying case aimed at Cowboy Action shooters. The company also manufactures reloading dies for the 400 Cor-Bon. These include a carbide sizer and a profile crimp. The sizer also serves as a case forming die. Cases are formed from 45 ACP brass and can even be formed at the first-step, sizing-and-decapping station on progressive loaders.

**VihtaVouri Oy** has updated its booklet *Reloading Guide for Rifles and Handguns 1-97*. It offers loading data for most popular calibers and is available free from Kaltron-Pettibone, the importer.

**Winchester's** *Reloading Components Catalog, 15th Edition*, should be out by the time you read this. The new booklet will include data on Fail-Safe bullets, the new 9x23 Winchester and 454 Casull calibers, and Cowboy Action load data. Interestingly, it will include some powders not of Winchester manufacture. Shotshell data will include light recoil target loads and loads using the new AA Plus powder. •

Tombstone Smoke-n-Deals' 400 Cor-Bon carbide reloading dies.

VihtaVouri Oy's *Reloading Guide for Rifles and Handguns 1-97.*

When a progressive press is stripped down to only a couple operations, it becomes a partial. This versatility still saves time, while also allowing flexibility for the handloader.

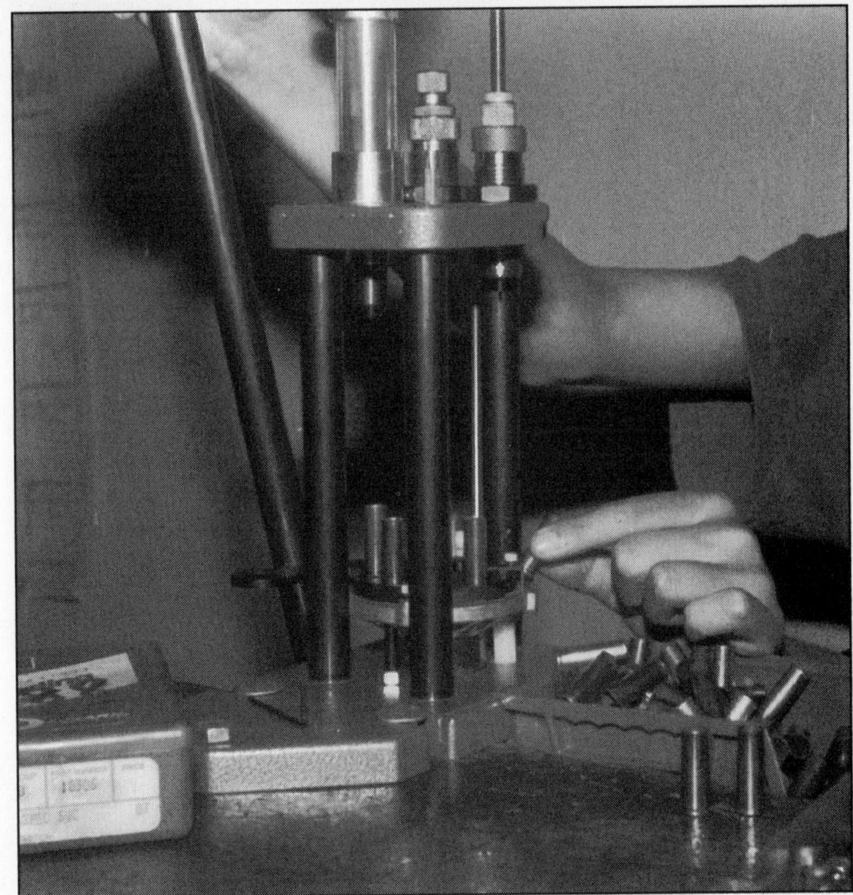

We've all used single-stage presses, and some prefer progressives, but this Montana shooter settled on a...

# PARTIAL PROGRESSIVE

by JOHN HAVILAND

WITH THE FIRST stroke of the handle on my progressive reloading press, I knew it would save countless hours loading big batches of handgun cartridges, compared to my old single-stage press. But I later found the progressive press is a versatile machine that can also perform from one to several reloading steps.

My progressive press is an RCBS Ammomaster. Progressive presses made by Dillon, Hornady and others operate in a similar manner as my Ammomaster. A fired case is inserted into the shellplate at the first station. You pull the press handle, which raises the case into the sizing die on the head of the press. When the handle is lowered, the shell rotates around to the next station where, if it's a straight-wall case, the mouth is flared and a new primer is seated. At this second station, a carrier slides out to pick up a primer from the primer tube reservoir. The primer is seated when the case is lowered all the way. Another pull of the handle rotates the case to the third station and trips the powder measure to charge the case with powder. The next pull of the handle runs the charged case, with a bullet set in the case mouth, into the seating die and seats the bullet in the case. A final pull of the handle kicks out the loaded round. All the while, more shells are rotating through the loading process.

With straight-wall handgun cartridges, I operate the press the way it is intended—as a progressive press. I just feed an empty case into the press at each stroke of the handle. I religiously watch each station as a primer is seated, powder is dropped, and a bullet is seated. I smile when a loaded shell drops into the ammo catcher bin. My grandmother must have had the same feeling of accomplishment when she used her new automatic washing machine after decades of washing clothes by hand.

However, a progressive press is versatile. It can pump out a loaded cartridge with every stroke of the handle or, converted to a partial progressive press, perform only one or a couple of loading steps at a time, and much more quickly than a single-stage press. This is an advantage when the cases need extra preparation to produce quality loaded cartridges.

For example, after a few firings, the grime on handgun cases and the residue in primer pockets need to be attended to. So I disconnect the primer and powder dispensing systems and screw out the bullet seating die. I feed the cases into the press, sizing them, knocking out the primers and expanding the case mouths. This takes about a fifth of the time it would on a single-stage press because I have to feed the cases through the press only once, instead of twice as with a single stage press, and the cases eject automatically. All the sized cases go into my tumbler for a bath.

With the cases bright and shiny, I remove the sizing and depriming dies from the press. Then I screw in the bullet seating die and reattach the primer and powder systems. The clean cases are fed into the press for final loading. Out come loaded cartridges, clean as a new penny.

With rifle cases, I like to remove the lubrication and residue from the primer pockets each time they are resized. I screw the rifle sizing die into the first station on the press. If the cases will be loaded with cast bullets, I also add a neck expanding die to the station after the one holding the powder measure. The primer and powder systems are disconnected.

I feed all the rifle cases through the press. After the cases are clean, I trim them to the proper length, if they need it. Nit-picky reloaders may also want to seat the primers by hand for that extra touch of consistency. I don't bother because my RCBS Ammomaster seats primers just fine for my needs.

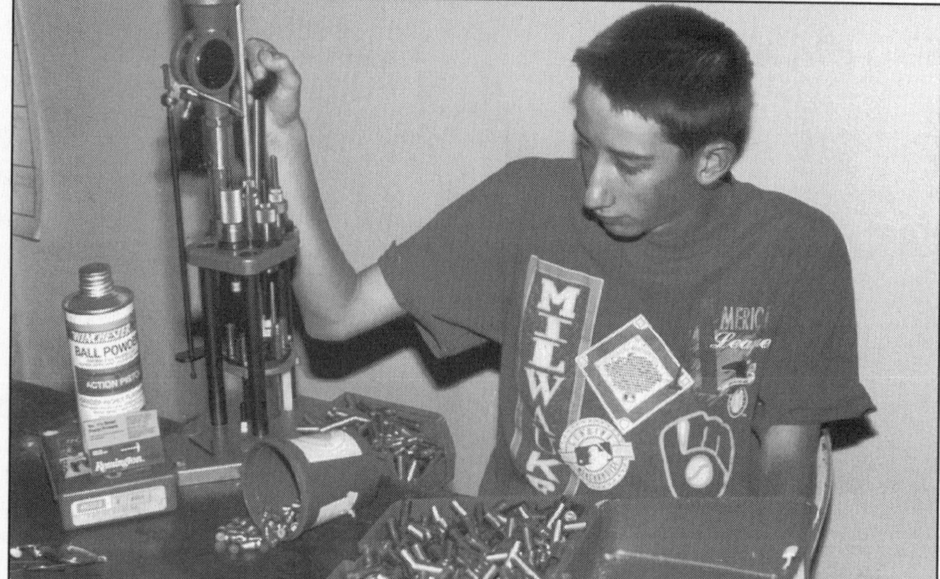


Loading lots of cartridges fast is what a progressive press is designed to do. Sometimes a reloader wants to do only a step or two at a time.

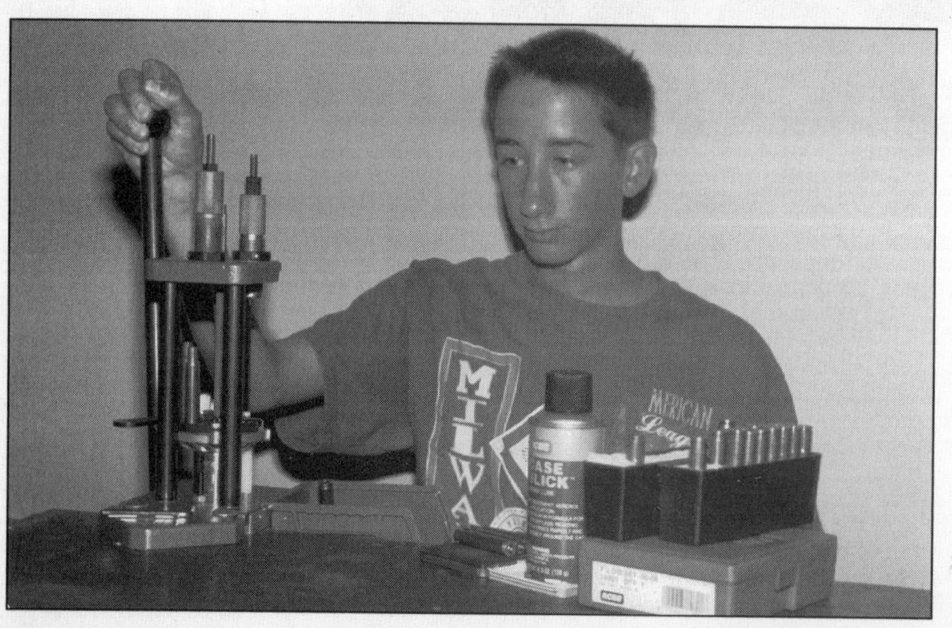


I like to clean the lubrication and primer pocket residue from rifle cases each time they are resized. I screw the sizing die into the press and a neck-expanding die in the station after the powder measure if the cases will be loaded with cast bullets.

When loading rifle cartridges with cast bullets and a flake-type powder, like Unique, I feed the cleaned and trimmed cases into the press and use the powder measure to charge them.

Loading tubular powders in a measure on a progressive press can be a problem because powder weights can vary. I remove the measure and pour in a correctly weighed charge.

With rifle cases ready to load, I remove the sizing and neck expanding dies from the press. I screw in the bullet seating die and reconnect the primer and powder measure systems. Shells are fed through the press for priming, powder charging and bullet seating. Cleaned, trimmed and loaded shells kick out ready to shoot.

Final loading is quick with flake or spherical powders. Charges of these are uniform from a volumetric powder measure because the grains pack closely. Charges that I've checked of flake-shaped Unique or ball-shaped W-760 vary, at most, only a couple tenths of a grain when dumped from a good powder measure.

However, the weight of many tubular-shaped powders can vary quite a bit when dumped from a measure on a progressive press. I have detected variations of up to 2 grains with some powders such as Hodgdon 4350 and 1000. This is a concern for the hunter shooting maximum loads or the long-range target shooter who wants the most consistent velocities.

So I remove the powder measure from my Ammomaster when I load rifle cartridges, like my 7mm Magnum, with a maximum charge of tubular powder. I mount the measure on my bench at the side of the press, dispense a slightly low charge from it, then weigh it on a scale, dribbling in the last few grains with a powder trickler. With the press ram up, I pour the powder through a funnel into the case.

Removing the automatic step of powder dispensing can result in another problem—forgetfulness. Cartridges work poorly without powder. An easy way to guard against this is to add an RCBS powder checker die in the station after the powder measure. The plunger in the die is adjusted on a case with the correct amount of powder. As each case enters the die, the plunger rises to a mark, providing visual proof that the correct amount of powder is in the case.

This system of full progressive, partial, or single-step reloading makes a progressive press a versatile machine, indeed. The only use I can think of for my slow old single-stage press is to prop open the front door during the heat of summer. ●

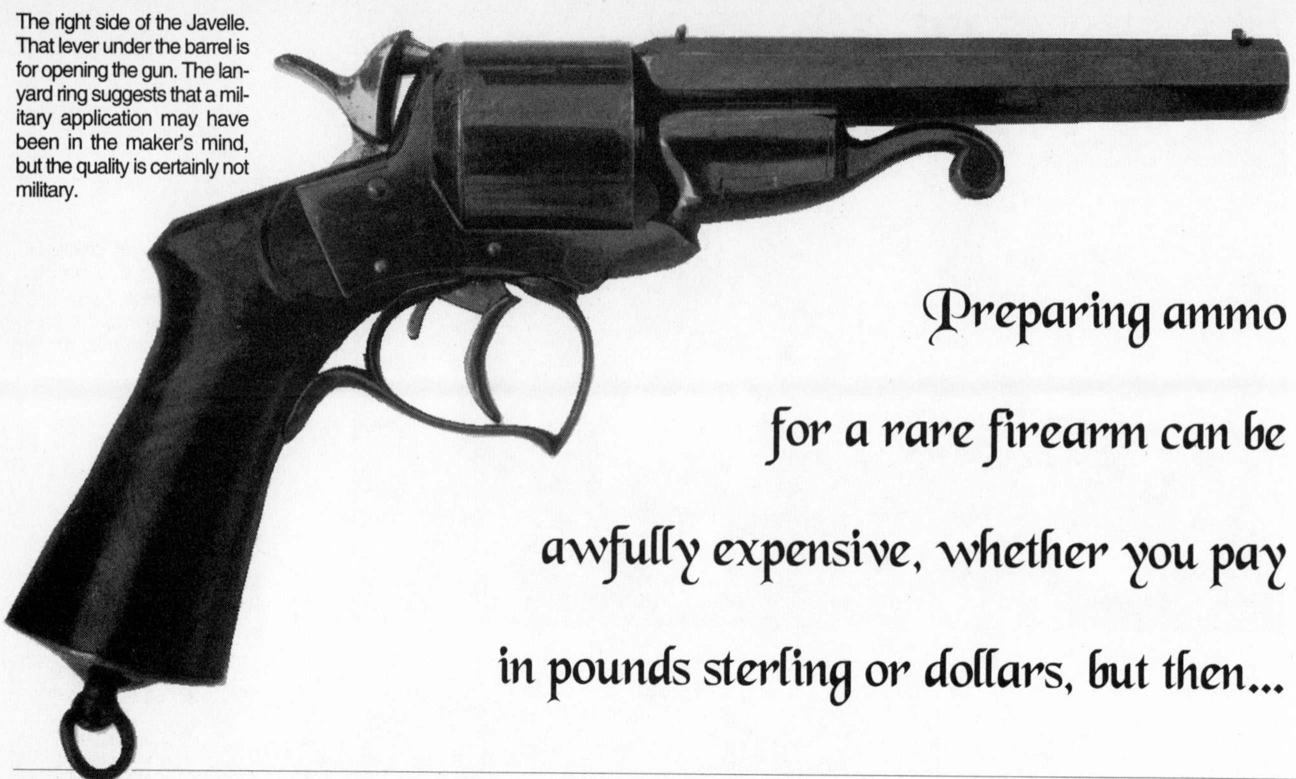
The right side of the Javelle. That lever under the barrel is for opening the gun. The lanyard ring suggests that a military application may have been in the maker's mind, but the quality is certainly not military.

# Preparing ammo for a rare firearm can be awfully expensive, whether you pay in pounds sterling or dollars, but then...

SETTING UP TO reload for rare or obsolete firearms can be an expensive business. Dies and bullet moulds or swaging dies must all be made or bought, and if the cartridge is unique, setup costs for making a relatively small number of cases can work out at several dollars per case. A few makers in various parts of the world will produce any sort of cartridge case from turned brass. In England we have North Devon Firearms Services, but no matter who is the maker, a low price depends on making them in quantity.

Recent years have seen an enormous growth of interest in Britain in what are called generically *classic* weapons. Muzzleloaders fall into that general field, but they have been catered for over a long period. The term *classic* is generally taken to refer to early breechloaders, and they are categorized by specific datelines and into classes such as military, target, pocket pistol, vest pocket pistol and so on, so that like may compete with like in matches. Revolvers and semi-autos are usually separated, and there are classes, for example, for shoulder-stocked pistols.

Matches for these firearms are held at local, regional and national levels, sometimes as part of larger events such as the national pistol meeting or the Imperial target rifle championships at Bisley. Sometimes the classics stand alone, attracting large numbers of competitors. The largest such shoot is the Trafalgar Meeting at Bisley each fall. The spirit of these meetings is quite remarkable because the guns are what matter. At one such, I recently chatted on the firing point with a competitor getting ready to shoot his Remington rolling block in a military rifle class. We were discussing a rolling block rook and rabbit rifle with some peculiar features and comparing it with the competitor's rifle. The range officer was listening intently as were many of the competitors. Suddenly, the range officer looked at his watch and apologetically pointed out that the detail was fifteen minutes overdue and he had better break up the discussion.

Such events have raised the general level of interest in early breechloading firearms, with the general classification running right up to the end of World War II. In some matches, the British 303, either the Lee-Enfield or the P14, and the U.S. P17 compete against the Mauser K98 or the Russian Mosin-Nagant. In a country where an owner must show that he has a "good reason" for possessing any handgun, it creates a justification for owning almost as many of these older weapons as a man can lay his hands on. Prices, of course, have kept pace with the level of interest.

The matches have also meant that guns kept only as collectibles, and shot rarely if at all, are being brought out of the attic and into competitive shooting, even if only occasionally. Along with the mainstream guns, like the various Lee-Enfield, Krag, Springfield and Mauser rifles or the Luger, Colt, Webley, Smith & Wesson and Mauser pistols, have come the rare and the unusual. One such came from my own collection in the form of a Javelle, an exquisite if unusual handgun acquired many years before from a small gunshop in the North of England. There was no indication of how it came to be in that shop.

Michel Javelle of 54 Rue Beaubrun, St. Etienne, France, patented his articulated-frame breech-loading revolver in France on July 5, 1859. One year later, he took out a further patent, this time for a central-fire cartridge which may be unique. The mid-1800s were a period of enormous change in the firearms of the world.

by COLIN GREENWOOD

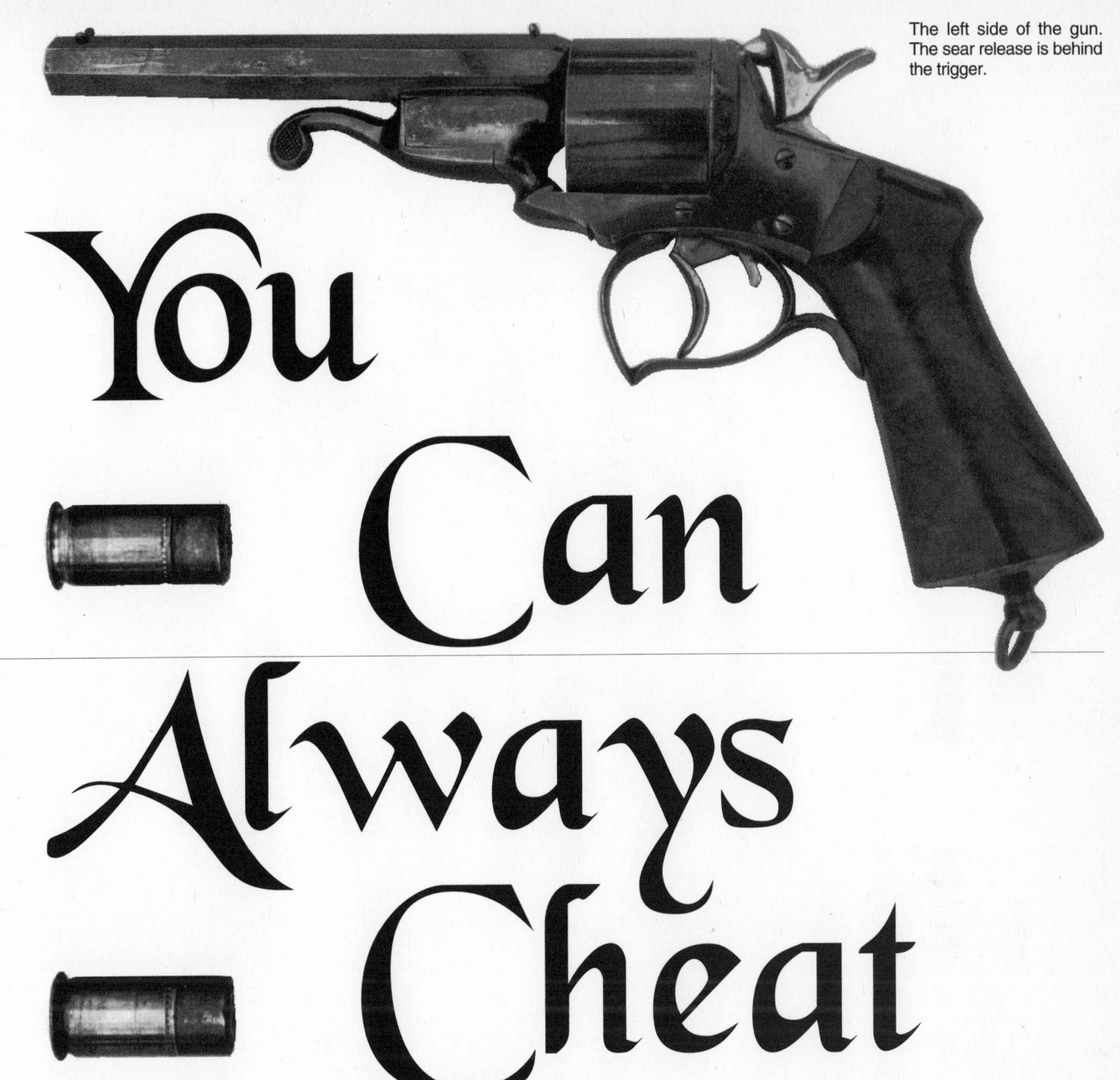

The left side of the gun. The sear release is behind the trigger.

# You Can Always Cheat

The vast majority of arms were still percussion, but the large-caliber rimfire case was making headway in the U.S. whilst the Lefaucheux pinfire was popular in Europe. A variety of central-fire cartridges were being developed, but an efficient system was not yet on hand.

Javelle's revolver was originally made in 11.5mm (12mm) pinfire, using the already well-established Lefaucheux system. The change to central fire took place very shortly after the revolver was patented, and few pinfire versions would have been made. The gun is 11 inches long, with a 5½-inch barrel. The six-shot cylinder is 1⅝ inches in diameter and 1⅜ inches long. The frame is articulated. Rotating the lever beneath the barrel toward the right unlocks the frame, which is hinged at the front of the large lug under the barrel. This hinge operates a clam-like closure which locks onto the cylinder axis. This closure has four deep grooves in its circumference. This is not a thread, though it looks like one at first glance. With that hinge open, the gun then hinges again partway along the bottom strap, under the cylinder, allowing the barrel and front frame to drop to an angle of 90 degrees from the body. The cylinder is then slid forward, off its axis.

Several other designs of the time utilized a removable cylinder, and it is sometimes suggested that the system involved keeping spare cylinders loaded so that they could be slid on for rapid reloading. I think not. The cartridges could not be kept in the spare cylinder without some form of additional closure. In any event, there is no sign of these spare cylinders with the guns that come to light. When the system of reloading is compared to the muzzleloader or even the gate-loaded single-action cartridge revolver, it has few drawbacks. Fired cartridges could be pushed out by means of the cylinder axis if necessary.

(Left) The lever is moved through almost 90 degrees, and the barrel drops to reveal the clam-like hold on the grooves at the front of the cylinder axis.

(Below) With the first movement complete, the frame hinges in front of the trigger guard to give full clearance for the cylinder.

(Below) The cylinder slides off its axis, which can be used to remove fired cases.

Javelle's revolver is double or single action. Immediately behind the trigger is a lug which actually operates the hammer release. In double action, the trigger itself pulls back the hammer until it touches the lug, when the hammer falls. In single action, the trigger comes back almost into contact with the lug as the gun is cocked. The hammer does not rebound after firing and a half-cock keeps it clear of the cylinder, but does not lock the action. The double action will operate freely from the half-cock position. The sights consist of a round-topped semi-barleycorn foresight with a deep but narrow rear sight notch, the upper part of which is V-shaped while the bottom part is straight. The one-piece grip on this gun is made from root rosewood and is by far the nicest piece of wood I have ever seen on a handgun. Workmanship and finish are superb throughout, and the gun remains in very good condition with just two small areas where the finish has suffered.

Javelle's central-fire cartridge of 1860 was intended to allow the gun owner to make his own cases and to

A closeup of the action area shows the quality of workmanship. Note the very blunt hammer nose.

keep the gun shooting when far from supplies. Muzzleloaders still predominated, and finding a shop that stocked cartridges would not be easy. Javelle devised a cast lead/tin cartridge case which he later replaced with one made of iron. The original cartridge case was cast of a lead alloy having a tin content approaching 50 percent. Casting was done by dipping the mould into the pot rather than by pouring. One auctioneer described some surviving cases as having a rim at each end, but, in fact, the top rim was made to fold by hand into the crimping groove of the bullet. The bullet had a primer pocket cast into its base and an internal pin ran from the center of the case head (what would be the primer pocket on a modern cartridge) to the base of the bullet. In the tin cases, the bullet was hand seated and the tin was crimped into place, possibly using what looks like the sprue cutter on the mould found with one of these guns. In the iron cartridge, the case mouth had a coarse thread and the bullet was screwed down until the internal rod was in contact with the primer in the base of the bullet. When the gun was fired, the hammer nose hit the base of the internal pin which transferred the blow to the primer in the base of the bullet and ignited the blackpowder charge. Cartridges are extremely rare and often incorrectly identified.

To get this quite rare gun shooting again could well have been a costly business. Cases could have been turned from brass or soft iron, using the dimensions of the chambers and incorporating a coarse thread into which the bullet could be screwed. A bullet mould would have to be shaped to make an outside-lubricated 'heeled' bullet. It would then be necessary to make internal rods to stretch from the base of the seated bullet to the center of the case head with a collar to stop them falling through. Making a thousand or so of these would reduce unit costs, but making even a couple of dozen cases with the necessary mould, internal rods, etc., would produce a very high unit cost for a gun that it was intended to shoot only very occasionally.

One of the attractions of handloading is that you can always cheat. There is more than one way of skinning a cat. It was decided that this gun would be made to shoot using only the equipment and accessories actually to hand. Some of these have been collected over many years of

This Javelle was sold by Christies in London in 1986. Note the cartridge cases with their internal transfer pin and what the catalogue described as a "rim" at each end of some cases. These were the cast tin cases ready to be crimped into the bullet when it was loaded. The cases without the top "rim" are of iron. (Photo courtesy Christies Auction House.)

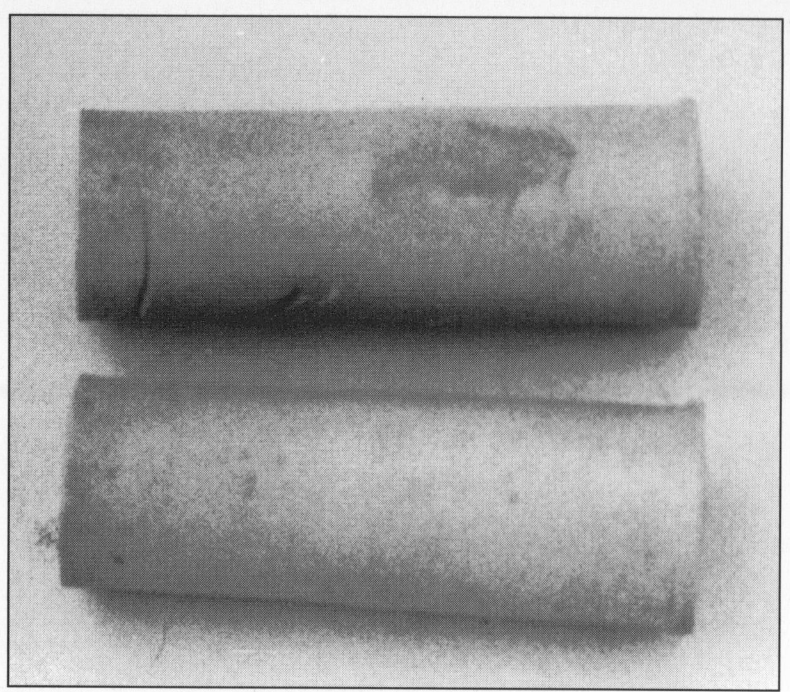

Chamber casts were taken with non-shrinking auto body filler.

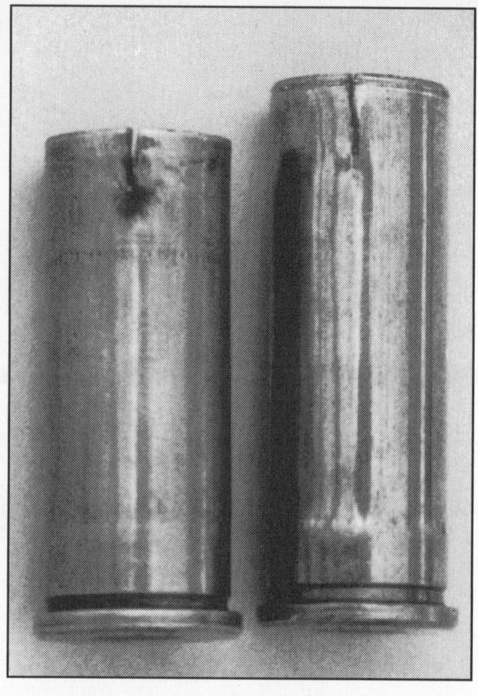

Cases were made from 44 Magnum and 44 Special cases that had developed neck splits.

handloading, but nothing was bought for the job.

Step number one was to establish dimensions. Chamber casts were taken using an auto body filler with an almost zero shrinkage during setting. Chambers must be thinly but very carefully oiled so that the filler does not stick. The finished chamber casts slipped out easily and showed all the necessary features. In the past, it has been suggested that more sophisticated materials should be used, including those used by dental technicians to take impressions. Non-shrinking auto body filler has proved more than adequate in the many guns in which I have used it. Before we get too excited about .001-inch of shrinkage, we should note that neither firearms nor ammunition are made to such close tolerances.

Next, the barrel was slugged to get the internal measurements; all relevant measurements were tabulated in inches: overall cylinder length 1.40; case length 0.78; rim diameter 0.485; case head 0.470; case mouth 0.463; chamber throat diameter 0.450; bore slug 0.456.

This was going to be a very low-pressure cartridge. The large bullet in a small case was common to many revolvers of the period, and it really wasn't necessary to be too concerned about the odd thousandth of an inch. We tried a lot of different cartridge cases to find one that would work and finally settled for 44 Special or Magnum cases cut down. Here was anoth-

(Above) To trim the cases, they were first marked off in a cannelure tool.

(Left) The marked case was then easy to cut accurately with a small pipe cutter.

The cut-down cases had to have the rim thickness reduced. A spinner was used in a drill chuck. The case was held against the spinner with a hardwood block and the file applied to the underside of the rim.

Bullets were made from commerical 455 Manstopper bullets intended for the Webley revolver. They were swaged down in a 44 Magnum bullet swaging die to give a necked, outside-lubricated, hollow-base wadcutter. The swaging die from North Devon Firearms Services works in any stable reloading press. This one is by Simplex of Australia.

er economy as many handloaders will have a small stock of 44 Magnum cases in which the case mouth has developed a tiny split. These were salvaged and cut down to the correct length.

You cannot trim just under 1/2-inch off the length of a 44 Magnum case on a conventional case trimmer. We used a cannelure tool to mark the cases around their body at the right point. This device was actually designed for putting crimping grooves into bullets. Two vertical pillars have collars against which the bullet or case rotates. Beneath them is a screw to adjust the position of the crimp along the case. An arm swings round to press the case against the pillars and the crimping wheel is located on that arm with a handle to rotate it. This particular machine was handmade in England, but an identical device is offered by CH Tool & Die as their CH4D Cannelure Tool. After rolling in a good deep cannelure, a pipe cutter easily follows the groove to cut the cases off accurately. Case mouths can then be deburred inside and out with a hand deburring tool.

The rim on the 44 Magnum case is much too thick and a little too wide. Rims must be thinned on the front face using a power drill in a stand and a case spinner. The case spinner is no more than a slightly tapered mandrel which is fitted into the drill chuck. I use several of them of different sizes and make or alter them as required by the simple expedient of applying a file to mild steel rod as it is turned in the drill chuck. I stole the idea from Dean Grennell after reading his *ABCs of Handloading* (DBI Books) in the 1980s. The case is held against the tapered mandrel with a block of hardwood; a small file, with a blank face to the case body, is applied to the inside of the rim. Measurement was by way of trying the case in the chamber, not by micrometer.

The original 220-grain hollow-base Manstopper before and after conversion to an outside-lubricated, necked bullet.

Now we had cases that chambered snugly, and snapping a few caps confirmed that all was well. Cases could be resized in standard 44 Special dies, but the neck expander plug would not reach down to them. Neck expansion was achieved by using the spinner in the case mouth, giving it a light tap with a wooden mallet. The sized and neck-expanded cases were then capped.

Bullets were going to be a problem.

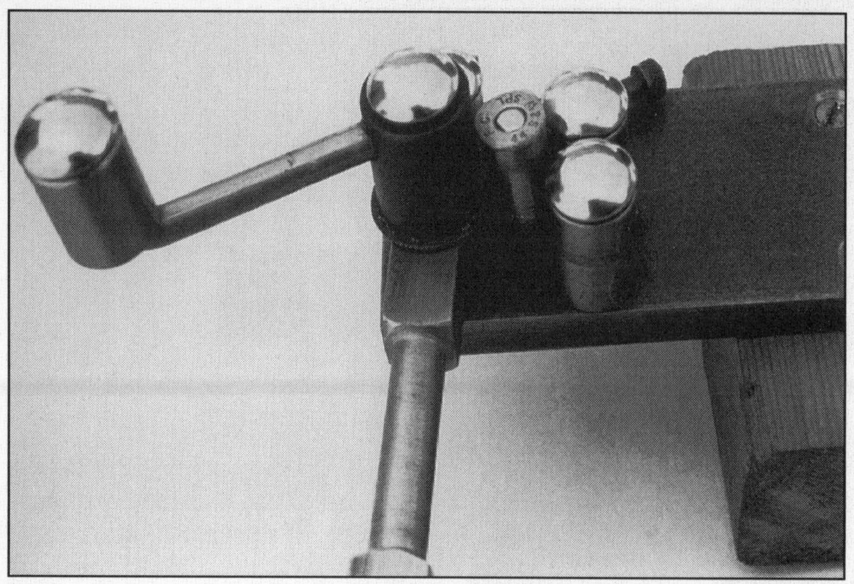

(Above) An original 44 Special case with some finished Javelle cartridges. Note the much thinned rim of the Javelle cases.

(Left) Most of the reloading was possible by making adjustments to 44 Special dies, but the case could not be crimped. The cannelure tool was brought into action again to crimp the case onto the bullet close to the mouth.

They had to have a bore diameter of about 0.456-inch, but had to be seated inside a 44 Magnum case. That created a requirement for an outside-lubricated heeled bullet, and whilst we had swaging dies to create such bullets in both 380 and 320, we had nothing for this gun. More trial and error followed until we settled on a stock of hollow-based Manstopper bullets designed for the Webley 455 revolver. These miked out at 0.4559-inch, near enough for anyone. The bullets are 0.56-inch long and have a deep hollow base. The only problem was that they would not fit into the cartridge case. The solution was relatively simple. We entered the base of the bullet into a 44 bullet swaging die which was already to hand, producing a heeled wadcutter bullet. Lubrication was by Alox dip.

We had no intention of pushing things with this gun, so we started with a load of just 5 grains of FFFg behind our 220-grain bullet. While we could seat a bullet by lowering the bullet punch of a 44 Special die as far as it would go, there was no way that our existing dies would crimp the case after the bullet was seated. Back, then, to our cannelure tool. Because of our method of expanding the case necks, we needed to keep the crimp as near the mouth as possible. After a couple of experiments, we got it right. The resulting cartridge looks right for the job, the bullet being perfectly in line with the outside of the case and a quite pretty looking cannelure holding the two together.

That was a very light load, but all the cartridges worked. However, there was no need of a chronograph to see that both velocity and energy were very low. The bullets almost all bounced off a thick softwood block, only making an indentation on the surface.

Blackpowder cases were designed to be filled with powder, allowing for the bullet to be seated onto the powder, often compressing the charge. Not until smokeless powder came to be used in cartridges designed for black did internal air space create a new dimension.

With the first load using only 5 grains of FFFg, the bullets bounced off thick softwood posts. The front section of the bullet had taken the rifling well, but the hollow base had not expanded. Moving up to 10.5 grains produced satisfactory loads.

Bearing in mind that the original cartridge would have had to accommodate the transfer pin within the powder space, a highly compressed charge was not likely. By measurement and trial, it was found that 10.5 grains of FFFg filled the case without compression, and a batch of cases was loaded up. Over the chronograph, this load gave good results. For ten rounds, we got an average velocity of 532 fps. One odd round gave 673 fps, which could neither be explained nor repeated in later tests. With that exception the velocity spread was acceptable.

The target used in matches with classic handguns is usually that which was used by the British National Rifle Association pre-1914. It has a 3-inch aiming mark with a 2-inch bull within it and is normally shot at 10 and 20 yards range. Starting at 10 yards, it was found that the Javelle was shooting significantly high even with a six-o-clock hold. It suddenly became clear why the sights had been designed as they were. When a fine sight was taken, with the tip of the foresight at the bottom of the shoulders on the rearsight notch, it shot only a little above point of aim. At 20 yards, a full sight picture was used with the foresight almost to the top of the notch to get the same result. For those used to the modern sight picture of Patridge sights, this takes a bit of getting used to, but the logic of it is undeniable. No need for screwdrivers to adjust the sights between our ranges or for little screws in adjustable sights that might go wrong. But it seems that either our forebears had good eyesight or they wore spectacles all the time. Those sights are just not that easy to see unless the light is very good.

A 220-grain bullet at 532 fps might seem very low powered, but it falls right in with comparable cartridges of its day such as the 44 Bulldog. In any case, it is going to be used against nothing tougher than paper, and it is going to be used relatively rarely, just to give it some exercise from time to time. For those purposes, the load will do very nicely. ●

# An Inside Look at Lee Precision

by Richard Lee

The Lee complex today is a far cry from the early days, when the entire business was operated from Dick Lee's basement.

Number-one son, John, now in the driver's seat at Lee Precision, literally grew up in the tool and die shop, and has been instrumental in many innovations.

**Trying to determine a reloading tool company's origins is usually handicapped by the dust of decades. Here is an account straight from the guy who started one...**

THE LEE RELOADING business began in the late '50s, about the time some of the pioneers in the industry were beginning to blossom. These were people like Ray Speer of the Speer Bullet Co.; Fred Huntington, founder of RCBS; Joyce Hornady of Hornady bullets; and George Puth, inventor of the Acme shotshell reloader. MEC, C&H Tool, Hollywood, Herter's, and a host of others were making reloading tools. Many others, unnamed, are no longer in the business.

Reloading was having a grand revival after a long dormant period. I was introduced to reloading through the loan of a book from Jerry Golner, a fellow tool and die maker. The *Lyman Ideal Handbook No. 40* explained the process clearly, but we could not justify a week's wages to buy a reloading tool. Being toolmakers, we did what toolmakers do best—we built our own tool. I designed it and Jerry made it at home on his lathe. With some redesign and testing, the Lee Loader for shotshells was born, along with a new company called Lee Custom Engineering.

With the easy part behind us, I took to the road with a trunk full of tools and sold them to sporting-goods stores. One of the trips was cut short. When I called home from Oregon one evening, my wife Molly said, "You

(Left) The old Knickerbocker building in downtown Hartford, Wisconsin, had more space than Lee Precision needed early on, but now there are three buildings on a 19-acre site.

better get home if you want to be here to greet your first son!" I don't know how she knew it would be a son, but it was, and we named him John. We already had Linda and Mary, and were yet to have Susan and Robert.

Friendly folks from all over the country helped me learn about the distribution system for all products, especially sporting goods. We sold 1500 tools the first year and twice that many the second year. With that kind of growth, I thought we would have a rosy time ahead, but Jerry didn't care to take the risk, so we split the partnership. Molly and I went on alone. She kept the books then and continues to do so. The business didn't double every year, of course, but eventually developed into a profitable venture.

Customers wanted a Lee Loader for metallic cartridges so I invented one for rifle cartridges and then one for pistol cartridges. We operated the business from my basement and later expanded into the garage. Continued growth finally allowed us to build a home in the country with a bigger basement from which to work. The new home included a 50-foot indoor range and a 100-yard outdoor rifle range. There was nothing fancy. The indoor range was lined with workbenches for assembling Lee Loaders, and assembly is all we did. All the parts were made by subcontractors and were assembled and packaged at home.

Our letterhead boldly proclaimed us, "The World's Largest Producer of Reloading Kits," never mentioning that we were also the *only* producer of reloading kits. You see, until we did it no one had considered the kit approach. Reloading then was only for the anointed few who learned how to reload from friends, books, or from a few progressive gun stores. Reloading was so limited that we would include a list of almost every gun shop in the country that carried primers, gun-

(Above) Technician Dave Shono, here surrounded by stacks of die blanks, is the guy many callers ask to speak to, even when the phone is answered by company founder Richard Lee.

One of numerous female operators checks a bullet seating die for dimensional correctness.

An employee processes a sizing die on CNC turning center. Most handloaders don't realize how die tolerances have improved since WWII, but they benefit, nevertheless.

powder, wads, shot and bullets. The list was not very long.

Lee changed the situation quickly. Consider the options available at the time: Buy a press, powder measure, powder scale and a book on how to reload, all for over $100; or the Lee Loader option, which had everything you needed including complete instruction and load data for $9.98. Sales were great. Every reloading tool manufacturer loved Lee, because folks got started with a Lee Loader and then progressed upward to more expensive tools and equipment. I was prospering, but could see trouble on the horizon. Back then, there was a 93-percent top income-tax rate at $220,000. While I was still a long way from the top tax bracket, my taxes were becoming very punitive, and incentive for growth was stifled.

A tax attorney came to my rescue. I sold controlling interest in the company and licensed the patents to the company. Royalties were taxed at only 50 percent of the ordinary income rate. Even if I made it to the top rate, my taxes would be only 48 percent on the royalty portion. That solved my tax problems but created an even larger problem, as I was now a minority shareholder.

Business rapidly outgrew my basement workshop. The local postmaster, Bob Riley, suggested the corporation should buy the old Knickerbocker building located in downtown Hartford, Wisconsin. It was an old knitting mill located on the millpond, and it even had the mill race in the basement. Two stories with about 14,000 square feet of production space was far more than we needed, but we bought it. With all that space, we began machining our own products and added several employees. These were very exciting times for us. New inventions and products quickly filled the building with machinery and coworkers. The first affordable hand priming tool, case trimmer, chamfer tool, and the Lee Target Model Reloader are some of the products of the 1960s. We also produced the first powder dipper kit with thirteen dippers, and this became an immediate success. Lee Loader customers became comfortable using powder dippers designed for smokeless powders. No doubt Dean Grennell, a gifted new gun writer, had an impact on their acceptance with his reloading articles. He was one of the few writers who realized that dippers are safe and practical. Dean encouraged readers to use dippers with his special technique that produces excellent uniformity—push the dipper base first into the powder and let the powder flow over the top, then strike it level with a card.

The good times suddenly came to a screeching halt when I was fired. That was possible because I was a minority shareholder at Lee Custom Engineering. My patent royalties and salary stopped. Along came lawsuits and countersuits. Big bucks went out for lawyers. Fortunately, I had foreseen problems and started Lee Precision, Inc.

Our first products were aluminum bullet moulds and electric melters. These involved three new inventions, which allowed us to manufacture better moulds and melters at significantly less cost. Many happy entrants into the world of bullet casting allowed us to eventually become the world's largest manufacturer of bullet casting equipment. This is a meaningful title, as other companies had been making bullet casting equipment for decades.

The income from the new Lee Precision company enabled me to take one of my biggest gambles. I designed a shotshell loader that could be made very economically. It had more features than those currently being offered. Pricing it at only $29.98 with a complete set of shot and powder bushings made it a bargain. The unknown quantity was: Would anyone buy a reloader with dies made of nylon? The gamble was the huge investment for tooling needed to produce the Lee Load-All. If I was wrong and it did not live up to expectations, there would be hard times.

The Lee Load-All for shotgun shells was an immediate success. The concept of selling the tool complete with load data and a complete set of shot and powder bushings, at about half the price of that offered by the competition, made it a winner. Selecting the proper material and manufacturing process was the key to success. A complete set of dies was moulded integrally with the carrier. Nylon dies work better because they are slipperier than the highest polished steel. They never wear out and cannot rust; size control is easy; there's no assembly; and they cost much less than conventionally produced tools. This item gained us the dubious reputation of the company that makes plastic tools. Not enviable but highly successful, and many users will attest to their durability. I have never seen a worn-out Lee Load-All. To overcome the objection to the use of an appropriate if not traditional material, we have consistently offered the most liberal guarantees in the industry.

Within a short time, Lee Precision started competing with Lee Custom Engineering. This was possible because they had stopped paying royalties on my patents. The rights to manufacture the Lee Loader reverted to me. Unfortunately, the resulting confusion to our customers was distressing. I knew the most important asset of any business is its customers. Our faithful customers became confused because there were two companies with the Lee name, and I was powerless to do anything about the situation.

This experience taught me another important lesson. While I was head honcho at Lee Custom Engineering, I felt completely comfortable offering a lifetime guarantee with our products. When I was fired, it became impossible for me to honor the lifetime guarantee. It struck me that "lifetime guarantee" really means life of the company, not life of the user. I would never again offer an open-ended guarantee because it lacks sincerity and is a gimmick to trap the unsuspecting or unthinking customer. That's the reason Lee Precision today offers a two-year guarantee. The customer is assured of a reasonable and realistic backing to the product. The vast majority of our customers, 99.9 percent or more, do not abuse the guarantee. Reloaders truly are a very special group. This lifelong experience of dealing with the salt of the earth helped us make another bold decision. Lee products now also carry a satisfaction guarantee or your money back. Such a guarantee would never have entered my mind in my younger days. My son, John, current president, and I discussed the feasibility of such a bold offer some years back and agreed our experience with our customers was so positive that it was the proper thing to do. The results have been extremely favorable. You sleep well knowing every customer is a happy customer.

Possibly because of our aggressive competition, Lee Custom Engineering soon ran out of customers and money. This hurried a settlement with my old company. They could no longer use my name and soon went bankrupt. The major creditor was a large law firm.

The episode taught me I could overcome almost any adversity and be better for it. New opportunities arose. I continued to invent new and successful products. One of the nicest features about being able to start over is that you get a second chance to improve the product. I redesigned the old priming tool, which had screw-in shellholders, to accept a simple snap-in shellholder. It cost less and worked better. A tray to feed the primers was added and the Lee Auto-Prime became the most popular priming system ever produced. Other products received a similar transformation. For instance, the Dipper Kit, which is now systematically incremented, was increased to fifteen sizes. We always try to make every product a little better because we know customers are very intelligent and can recognize value.

The reloading industry is unlike any other. People who buy a $20,000 automobile hope they get a good one because they don't expect much satisfaction from the car maker if the new car has problems. Yet, a person who buys a reloading tool can call the company and talk to the president about problems, desires, and his last hunt. We receive thousands of calls and letters that keep us aware of the needs and wants of the users. I will always treasure the memories of phone conversations and letters from our customers. Thank you very much for sharing your reloading experiences and giving us a chance to help with your problems. In later years, we hired technicians to handle these calls, and an interesting transformation occurred. After John took the reins, I maintained a back office and would sometimes take a call if the technicians were busy. It made me feel

The Lee Loader for shotshells started it all.

quite useless when I'd answer the call with, "Hello, this is Dick Lee, can I help you?" and the reply would be, "I was hoping to talk to Dave."

After a string of successes, we entered the reloading press and die business. John had been working with me in the shop during his vacations and in his free time since he was fourteen. At that early age, he was a better machinist than some of the people I had worked with in the trade. He went off to an abbreviated higher education and then went to work for Milwaukee Electric Tool for a couple of years to see how the real world functioned. He finally came back to Lee Precision to form the best father-son team that ever existed. The enthusiasm of youth allowed him to have the enviable attitude of "I can do anything." No challenge was too big. It got him in over his head a few times, but nothing so bad that hard work couldn't overcome.

This was the start of an era where the other reloading companies ceased to welcome us. We no longer simply got people started in the reloading hobby. Reloaders could progress with Lee equipment. One of my favorite recollections is of the Lee Carbide 7/8-14 dies for pistol calibers. I had long enjoyed competitive pistol league shooting. This requires much practice and reloading. As far as I was concerned, any die we would make for handguns would be carbide.

Richard Lee is now retired, so he has a bit more time to shoot his favorite rifle, a Weaver-scoped Model 700 in 222 Remington Magnum. But he still comes into his office to work on the loading manual and answer technical phone calls.

(Below) The Lee Loader kit was also made for rifle and handgun cartridges. It got countless guys started in handloading because it turned out good ammo and sold for less than ten bucks. The old HD editor has a stack of 'em.

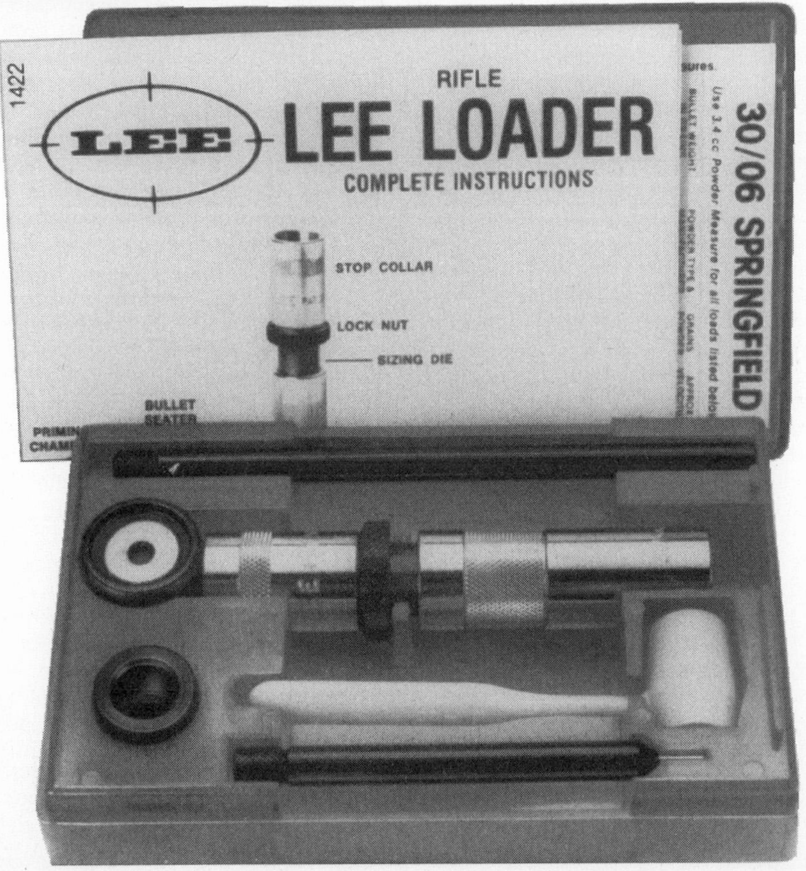


Our first carbide dies were not the best, and we didn't make much profit on them. The redeeming features were the design and price. They were about half the price of those offered by the competition. We sold a lot, but the high cost of the carbide inserts sapped all the profit. John told me he could grind them at significantly less cost and they'd be just as good as those being supplied. After a monumental effort, which included building a new grinding machine, he fulfilled his promise. John didn't stop there. He went on to make another machine that ground the dies to a special contour that eliminated the belt left on the case where the die stops. I designed a machine to polish them automatically and our costs came under control.

What really pushed our carbide-die sales into the number-one position was the invention of the Auto-Disk powder measure. For the first time, the cartridge case could be charged while expanding the mouth, all automatically.

Our experience gained in the early years helped Lee dies become popular. Customers want and need the kit approach. We have always included the proper shellholder, a powder dipper, and appropriate loads for use with the dipper. The data supplied today includes virtually every load published by the powder suppliers. We believe they are the best source because they have the equipment and motive to publish the best data for their powders. The data includes not only the "never exceed" or maximum loads, but also starting loads, the best dipper to use, the setting for the Perfect Powder Measure, and the cavity for the Auto-Disk Powder measure. The nicest thing about this data is that it is sorted by bullet weight and velocity. The best loads are near the top of the list. This type of presentation is bringing some changes in how the powder manufacturers offer their data. The trend of ever lighter and product-liability-resistant loads is beginning to give way to realistic charges. Being at the top of the list helps sell gunpowder.

Kit sales have been the secret to success for Lee Precision. The Lee Loader and Load-All were highly successful kits in terms of units. Our most successful product, in terms of dollars, has to be the Lee Pro 1000. I consider the Pro 1000 a kit because it includes everything needed to start reloading. Dies, powder measure, shellplate, case feeder, load data, and complete instructions make it practical for your first reloads to be loaded progressively. I don't recommend it for your first reloading experience, but thousands have started with the Pro 1000.

Because of my personal shooting, I have made several progressive handgun reloading presses. Many years ago, I converted a Lyman All American press to load progressively and even sent the drawings to Lyman in hopes they would produce a similar yet better machine. I would have been their first eager customer. They rejected the idea with their thanks and the comment that the market was not big enough. Through the years, I have built many progressive presses for my personal use and prototypes for a marketable version. I've even made one from an old Herter's press for 45 ACP, special dies and all. I also made a couple of motor-driven models and some H-frame versions.

Not everything I have designed made it to the market. Right now I'm working on my fifth bullet lubricator/sizer. I spent time explaining about the progressive press because it has occupied more of my development time than any other product. It's a difficult design project. Look at how many unsuccessful progressive presses have come and gone. There must be at least a dozen that did not make it. Again, this emphasizes just how astute the consumer is. Customers recognize value. The Lee Pro 1000 is the number-one progressive press of all time because of the value it represents and because it is a kit. No other progressive press supplies everything you need (except components) to begin reloading right out of the box. I am not worried about giving any secrets away. Other manufacturers apparently cannot or will not go through the extra expense and effort to package a complete kit.

For some years, Lee rifle dies sold well, but we did not dominate the field. We needed what Bill Gates in his book, *The Road Ahead,* referred to as the "killer application," that certain something that gives you an unsurpassed advantage over everything else on the market. I designed a collet crimper similar to the Lee Collet die. It squeezes only the very end of the case into the bullet for a perfect factory-type crimp. Factories crimp the bullet in place for improved accuracy and better utility. For the first time, anyone could load ammunition that was as good as factory ammunition. The timing was perfect. It was during a period when many gun writers were writing negatively about reloading and how good factory ammunition was. It's a dirty secret that more ammunition is ruined during the crimping process than any other operation. The Lee factory-type crimp also solved that problem. The collet crimpers sold like hotcakes, and we began including them in our new PaceSetter dies.

Shooting, of course, is the reason for handloading. It's fun in itself and also proves the dependability and efficiency of Lee dies.

That was too much for one of our competitors. They had been burned by the success of our carbide dies and didn't want the "killer application" to do the same with the rifle dies. They spent more money on negative ads about the factory-type crimp dies than we did advertising them. Consumers are not stupid. Sales skyrocketed us into the number-one position in both pistol and rifle die sales.

The question most asked of Lee Precision is, What's new? I'm always flattered because reloaders have learned to expect new and innovative products from us. Always, at least one and often multiple new products are being developed. Unfortunately, we can rarely disclose new inventions before introduction. The reason is security and patent rights. We release the information in our annual catalog. If it will be available at a future date, we include the estimated date. We normally charge a dollar for the catalog, but here's how to get one free. Write to us at Lee Precision, Inc., and say, "Dick Lee told me in HANDLOADER'S DIGEST to ask for a free catalog."

Although I am retired, I'm working on a reloading manual unlike any you have ever seen. It will have the latest load data printed in a very organized and easy-to-use format. There will be information never before published. It will give a different outlook on reloading which may be a little controversial, but always interesting. Anyone who has devoted a lifetime to an avocation that is also his vocation has something of interest to tell.

The story of Lee is a success story. I derive a special satisfaction of accomplishment from Lee customers twice breaking the world record for 1000-yard shooting. Broken first by Rick Taylor using a Lee Loader, that record lasted for seven years. Recently, Robert Frey broke the record again using Lee Collet dies.

The current phase of the Lee story has been underway for several years. The company is under the competent direction of John Lee and has grown significantly since he has taken the helm. He has ably expanded production equipment, plant size and the number of workers. Three buildings on a 19-acre site have been constructed and then expanded under his direction. John is an accomplished handgunner, trapshooter, and an occasional rifleman. He casts his bullets and reloads his ammunition, so he understands the customer's needs and desires. As a team, we became the largest manufacturer in almost every type of reloading equipment. Only because of his presence, enthusiasm, and talent did Lee Precision begin making presses and dies for metallic cartridges. Without his youthful ambition and enthusiasm, I would have been content to coast to retirement. John will maintain Lee Precision, currently the only family-owned full-line reloading company, as the undisputed innovative leader.

Your suggestions are always appreciated and help us to be responsive to your needs. Thanks very much for all that you have done for us. I sincerely hope you enjoy your Lee equipment as much as we delight in serving you. ●

# A Useful Set of Dies

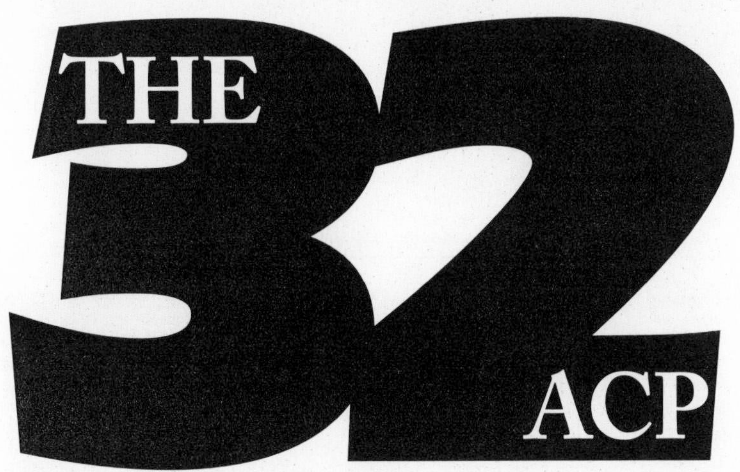


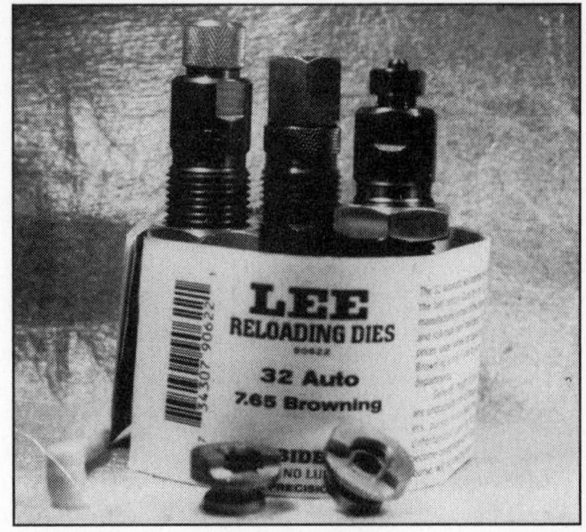


A set of Lee Precision reloading dies for the 32 ACP and shellholders for the 32 ACP and 32 S&W.

# Why Buy Four When One Will Do?

RECENTLY, I PURCHASED a delightful S&W Model 631 in 32 H&R Magnum and needed reloading dies. However, to gain more versatility, instead of 32 Magnum dies, I got a set of Lee dies for the semi-rimmed 32 ACP and an extra shellholder for the rimmed 32 S&W.

Even non-shooters know that 22 Shorts and Longs will shoot interchangeably in a 22 Long Rifle chamber. However, this is simply one example of a common principle: When straight-cased cartridges share a common case diameter, compatible operating pressures and compatible rim configuration, shorter cartridges may be used in chambers designed for longer cartridges.

The principle extends to reloading; a set of dies for a short cartridge may be used to reload a longer one. Common examples include the 38 Special/357 Magnum and the 44 Special/44 Magnum, but there are many other combinations. A set of 32 ACP dies can reload four current 32 cartridges. In order of case length, they are the 32 S&W (.61), the 32 ACP (.68), the 32 S&W Long (.95) and the 32 H&R Magnum (1.08). All are rimmed except the 32 ACP, which is semi-rimmed. My new revolver provided an opportunity to explore the versatility of the 32 ACP dies.

The interchangeability of these cartridges goes from shortest to longest. The 32 S&W will fit in the chambers of both the 32 S&W Long and the 32 Magnum. The 32 Long also fits in the 32 Magnum. Since the 32 ACP is semi-rimmed, it can be used in 32 S&W Long or 32 H&R Magnum chambers, but it is slightly too long for the 32 S&W chamber. Normally, the rim of the 32 S&W should prevent its chambering in a 32 ACP.

All four of these cartridges can be reloaded with a set of 32 ACP dies and two shellholders (from left): 32 ACP (7.65 Browning), 32 S&W, 32 S&W Long and 32 H&R Magnum.

by MARSHALL R. WILLIAMS

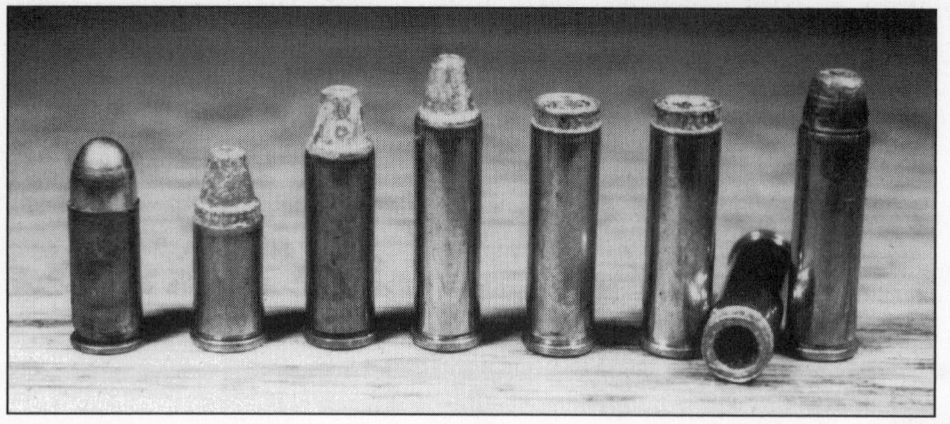

Handloads assembled with 32 ACP dies (from left): 32 ACP with 71-grain FMJ; 32 S&W, 32 S&W Long, and 32 Magnum with Hornady 90-grain SWC; 32 Magnum with 90-grain HBWC; 32 Magnum with hollowpoint wadcutter; and a 32 Magnum with old-style Hornady 85-grain JHP.

(Below) Hornady offers a selection of suitable bullets for different 32s.

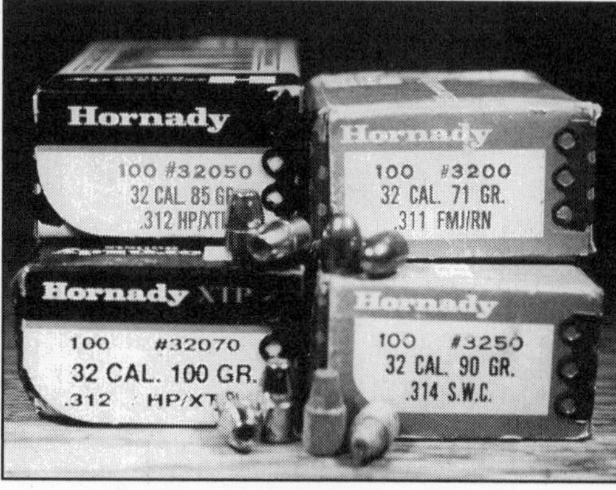


### Bullet Selection

Bullet selection and bore dimensions merit some discussion. The generally accepted bullet diameter for the 32 S&W, 32 S&W Long and 32 H&R Magnum is .312-inch for jacketed and .314 for swaged lead bullets. I slugged the barrel of my S&W Model 631, and groove diameter appears to be about .314. Hornady's revolver bullets include JHPs of .312, and swaged 90-grain HBWCs and SWCs of .314-inch. All proved accurate in my revolver.

My first reloading effort with the new dies was the 32 S&W. Once this was America's most popular revolver cartridge for self-defense, and millions of little inexpensive revolvers were chambered for it.

With correct adjustments, the 32 ACP dies worked perfectly for that cartridge, the 32 S&W Long and the 32 H&R Magnum. However, the crimping shoulder of the 32 ACP bullet seating die cannot be adjusted low enough to crimp the short case of the 32 S&W. The original 32 S&W design did not include a bullet crimp, and the negligible recoil is hardly likely to pull the bullets. Nevertheless, I think that crimping promotes consistent ballistics. Apparently, so do the manufacturers; all 32 S&W cartridges that I have examined show the bullet crimped in place. If I were seriously concerned about this shortcoming, I would take a big bastard cut mill file and shorten the bullet seating die about $1/16$-inch.

To obtain 32 S&W cases to load, I fired some aged factory cartridges in my 4-inch Model 631. The first six averaged 635 fps for 79 foot-pounds of energy (fpe). The consistency of the five rounds was good, but one cartridge delivered only 569 fps. Without that round, the average velocity jumped to 652 fps for 83 fpe. Even my aging, presbyopic and astigmatic eyes could clearly see these bullets in flight as they ambled toward the target. Nevertheless, as piddling as this performance sounds, the bullets will penetrate a grown man front to back.

The most impressive thing about this load was its near-total lack of recoil. It gave the gentlest of shoves to the small revolver and felt rather like a standard-velocity 22 LR in my 22-32 Kit Gun. I had no 85- or 88-grain bullets to reload the 32 S&W, but the 90-grain Hornady SWC was close enough. Alliant Unique, while possibly not the best choice for the low pressure 32 S&W, is a most versatile and useful powder, giving good performance at modest pressures in a wide range of calibers. I tried 2 grains in the 32 S&W and got 648 fps and 84 fpe.

This equaled factory performance. Accuracy was good; five shots went into 2 inches at 25 yards. While it is difficult to accurately judge pressures from the appearance of fired primers, clearly these pressures were modest.

### Bullet/Bore Diameters

Next, I tried the 32 ACP, probably the world's most popular semi-auto pistol cartridge. Its accepted bullet diameter is .311-inch, but some authorities contend that the correct diameter is smaller, at .308-.309. Pistols in this caliber have been made in virtually every country that had any arms industry, and even in some that had none. Thus, it would be surprising if there were no variation in bore and groove diameters. I have just slugged the barrels on three 32 autos: a Colt, an Ortgies and a WWII-vintage Walther PP. All had groove diameters larger than .311-inch. The Colt and Ortgies slugged .312, and the Walther .314-inch. American factory ammo worked very well in all three, as did reloads with .311 jacketed bullets. Somewhat surprisingly, Hornady 100-grain 30-caliber Plinkers, .308 diameter, gave satisfactory accuracy in the Walther, the largest bore of the lot.

For a 32 ACP factory load, I tried Federal's 71-grain RNJ ammo. Five shots in an old Colt 32 ACP averaged almost exactly the factory advertised 905 fps and 129 fpe. Gun and ammunition proved accurate, grouping into just $2^1/_2$ inches at 25 yards. My 32 ACP reload consisted of 3.1 grains of Unique and Hornady's 71-grain FMJ round-nose bullet of .311-inch diameter. *This is a maximum load and should be approached with caution.* It should be used only in well-designed pistols in good condition. If you have any doubt about the strength or condition of your pistol, do not use this load. Even then, I suggest starting with 2.5 grains and working up as pressure signs permit. In the vintage Colt, this load averaged a hot 1015 fps for 162 fpe, and five shots plopped neatly into 3 inches at 25 yards. Notwithstanding its performance, pressures appeared normal.

Because the 32 ACP is a semi-rimmed cartridge, in a pinch it will work in either the 32 S&W Long or the 32 Magnum chamber. Out of curiosity, I tried the Federal factory load in my Model 631. Velocity averaged only 670 fps for 71 fpe. Accuracy was so-so, about 4 inches at 25 yards. I also tried six of my handloads in the M631. Velocity was low, 778 fps for 95 fpe, and accuracy was disappointing. Five shots spread into

A factory 32 ACP (left) and a 32 ACP handload featuring the Hornady 71-grain FMJ.

A 32 S&W factory load (left) and a handload with the Hornady 90-grain SWC.

A factory 32 S&W Long (left) and a handloaded Hornady 90-grain SWC.

Federal factory 32 Magnum with 85-grain Hi-Shok bullet; reloads with 85-grain Hornady JHP, 90-grain Hornady HPWC, 90-grain Hornady SWC and 90-grain HBWC.

7 inches at 25 yards. No doubt there is considerable gas blow-by when shooting a 32 ACP in a 32 Magnum. Clearly the 32 ACP load would only be an expedient in a 32 revolver, so it is hardly a problem.

I had no factory 32 S&W Long ammunition on hand, but I had empty cases, so I tried two reloads. First was a Hornady 90-grain swaged semi-wadcutter and Winchester's recommended load of 2.8 grains of 231. This produced an average of 766 fps and 117 fpe. Consistency and accuracy were very good with this load. And second, since I had used Unique in the 32 S&W and 32 ACP, I decided to try it in all of the 32s. In the 32 S&W Long, 2.5 grains pushed the 90-grain SWC up to 706 fps and 100 fpe. Again, accuracy was quite good with five shots plopping into about 2½ inches.

For a factory 32 Magnum load, I fired the Federal 85-grain Hi-Shok. It was very accurate and certainly pleasant to shoot, but averaged only 927 fps and 162 fpe, well below the advertised 1100 fps and 230 fpe. Nevertheless, this still exceeds the factory ballistics of other 32-caliber cartridges. My first handload in the 32 Magnum case consisted of an old-style 85-grain .312 Hornady JHP bullet with an Alliant-recommended load of 6.6 grains of Blue Dot. This load produced a very satisfying 1047 fps for 206 fpe, and accuracy was excellent. Such a load equals the energy of the best of the 380 hollowpoint loads, and I cannot imagine that the 32 Magnum would be less effective for self-defense or small game shooting. Nevertheless, recoil in the revolver remains quite pleasant, something I cannot say about hot loads in many blowback 380 designs.

I also tried 3/Unique with the 90-grain Hornady SWC. It averaged 786 fps for 123 fpe. Accuracy was like the other loads with this bullet, about 2½ to 3 inches.

### Lead Bullet Loads

As a concession to my interest in bullseye shooting, I tried some lead bullet reloads that I thought would likely give best accuracy. In my experience, Unique is most accurate at higher pressures than I thought I was getting. So, I was determined to try W-231, a faster burning powder that has given me excellent target accuracy in a variety of arms.

My first target load in the 32 Magnum was 3.1/231 with the Hornady 90-grain HBWC. The bullet seater in the 32 ACP die is not long enough to seat this bullet flush with the case mouth. As I prefer to load hollow-base wadcutters out about ⅛-inch, this did not concern me. The load averaged 833 fps and gave excellent accuracy. I shot this load one-handed, NRA Bullseye style, and at 25 yards, I was easily able to keep my shots in the black. I feel confident I could equal my best offhand results using this load.

Whenever hollow-base wadcutters are used, someone always wants to load them backward as *hollowpoints* to improve stopping power. I loaded a small number this way using the same 3.1 grains of W-231. Accuracy remained good. Shooting offhand, NRA-style, I could not tell how much accuracy fell off, if any. Velocity was a little slower, averaging 818 fps. This is somewhat surprising when one considers that loading density increases when the bullets are seated open end forward.

Finally, for a possible 50-yard outdoor target load, I tried 3.4/231 and the Hornady 90-grain SWC. This load perked along at 866 fps and also gave good accuracy. In general, I feel I could do about as well with this gun and these loads as I did with my old 38 target revolver.

The foregoing amply demonstrates the versatility of a set of 32 ACP/S&W dies (and of the 32 Magnum revolver), but 32 dies offer other possibilities. In addition to these current cartridges, one can reload several obsolete pistol rounds, including the French 7.65 MAS, a.k.a. the 32 French Long; the 30 Pederson; the 7.63 Mannlicher; and the tiny 7.65 Roth-Sauer. Moreover, if you are satisfied with neck-sizing only, the dies can also load the 32-20 and practically all 30-caliber rifle cartridges. Thus, a set of dies for the 32 ACP or 32 S&W is really quite useful around a reloading bench. ●

# HYPERVELOCITY RIFLES

## Many experimenters still have the need for speed

by KONRAD F. SCHREIER, JR.

EVER SINCE THE introduction of nitrocellulose "smokeless" powder in the 1890s, rifle muzzle velocities have been increasing.

Military and civilian rifles achieving muzzle velocities approaching 3000 feet per second (fps) were developed before World War I. At that time, most authorities believed that building a practical gun having a muzzle velocity over 3000 fps was not possible.

In 1917, the legendary German firm of Frederick Krupp, A.G., developed the incredible Paris Gun. On 23 March 1918, the first of these monster cannon began lobbing 8.3-inch, 264-pound shells into the French capital of Paris from very long range.

It wasn't until after the end of World War I that Lt. Col. Henry W. Miller of the U.S. Army Ordnance Department investigated and published a description of the Paris Gun: It fired its projectiles from distances up to 70 miles at muzzle velocities from 4900 to 5300 fps. Col. Miller's paper boosted interest in hypervelocity guns—those with muzzle velocities over 3500 fps.

The German's World War I Paris Gun was a monster, having a barrel over 120 feet long. It weighed some 160 tons. It was no more of a tactical military weapon than Germany's WWII V1 buzz-bomb and V2 ballistic rocket, but it did prove that hypervelocity guns could be built.

Ever since the early 1920s, ordnance engineers have been experimenting with hypervelocity guns, including shoulder-fired rifles. During World War II, the U.S. armed forces Office of Scientific Research and Development (OSRD) studied and published a great deal about hypervelocity guns and ammunition. Since OSRD was a collection of the best scientists and engineers in their fields, it isn't at all surprising that they came up with many fundamental conclusions relating to hypervelocity guns that still apply. Figure 1 shows four ways they reported for building hypervelocity shoulder rifles; they suggest what can and can't be done.

The most common way of attaining hypervelocities is by firing a lightweight projectile in a regular gun with standard rifling (Figure 1A). One typical example of this is a 30-06 rifle firing 120- to 125-grain bullets instead of the 150- to 220-grain bullets usually used. It is thus possible to attain velocities well over 3000 fps with correct powder charges in a suitable rifle. Similarly, it is possible to attain velocities approaching 4000 fps by firing bullets weighing only 100-110 grains.

Unfortunately, these light 30-06 bullets are usually fired in barrels having a 1:10-inch rifling twist, a rate intended to stabilize longer, heavier bullets. Therefore, a serious loss of accuracy results with the short, light bullets. Accuracy is further affected because short, light bullets at hypervelocities are much more affected by air resistance than are long, heavy bullets at conventional velocities.

### Bronze Bullets

Another way to achieve hypervelocity is to use a bullet of similar profile to heavier ones, but made of a lighter material. Years ago, the writer had a friend at Aberdeen Proving Grounds who was fascinated with this hypervelocity-rifle approach and did extensive experimenting with it. He lathe-turned 30-caliber bronze bullets that weighed about 20-percent less than regular jacketed bullets having the same profile. His bronze bullet with the profile of the very accurate 172-grain boattail weighed about 137 grains. Another bullet with the profile of a 152-grain flat-base weighed about 120 grains.

These bronze bullets did achieve hypervelocity muzzle velocities, but they lacked both the range and accuracy of conventional jacketed bullets because they were not nearly as well stabilized by the rifled barrel. He considered his experiments pretty much a failure, but it was really fun to watch those bullets being fired in the early evening gloom, since they literally glowed in the dark, as all hypervelocity bullets do. Partly, this is because they get so hot in firing that they shed glowing metal particles in flight.

Another way of getting hypervelocity from a conventional rifle is to fire a lightweight bullet in a sabot, which strips away and falls as the bullet leaves the muzzle (Figure 1B). Ballisticians have been experimenting with this system since the 1920s. In the late '30s, ordnance engineer-gunsmith-experimenter Ed Howe tried it and got 30-06 velocities upwards of 4500 fps, but he could not get the sabot to strip away uniformly enough to get the accuracy he wanted, so he dropped the idea.

However, after more than a decade of experimenting, Remington introduced in 1977 their 30-06/224 Accelerator cartridge with a discarding-sabot lightweight bullet (Figure 2). This Accelerator load fires a conventional jacketed bullet encased in a fingered plastic sabot at a muzzle velocity of about 4080 fps, making it one of the fastest factory loads ever offered. It has adequate accuracy to about 400 yards, but its velocity falls off to about half (2800 fps) at that range.

As far as the writer knows, Remington has never made their Accelerator sabot bullets available as components to handloading experimenters, but I suspect if they did the factory velocities would be improved upon. The U.S. armed forces have found this system to be very effective in their 50-caliber Saboted Lightweight Armor Penetrator (SLAP) hypervelocity ammunition for Browning machineguns used as special-purpose sniper rifles.

Another way of making a hypervelocity rifle is to use a very strong action with a long and heavy barrel relative to the caliber of bullet it fires (Figure 1C). All shooters are familiar with this system, which is used in 22 centerfire rifles such as the 220 Swift. Factory loads in the Swift have fired 45-grain bullets faster than 4100 fps muzzle velocity. Such small calibers are considered best for experimenters who want to shoot at hypervelocities.

### Increased Bullet Weight

The 223 Remington cartridge, also known as the U.S. Army 5.56mm, is in this family. The early standard military load, designated the M193, fires a 55-grain bullet at 3250 fps. The 5.56mm/223 Remington has been around since the late 1950s, and there has always been serious experimenting to get better accuracy with it at ranges beyond 300 yards. To accomplish this, the U.S. and other armies have gone from the 55-grain to the 62-grain bullet. This really helps; however, muzzle velocity is barely over 3000 fps.

Handloading experimenters find 22-caliber hypervelocity rifles the easiest to experiment with because not only are bullets from under 50 to over 70 grains available, so also are barrels with different rifling twists. With modern powders and good bullets, velocities up to 5000 fps are possible.

Velocities beyond 5000 fps are not easily achieved by any but the most sophisticated and best-equipped experimenters. Conventional jacketed bullets tend to disintegrate as they leave the bore. However, advanced experimenters have attained velocities in the 7000 to 8000 fps range using special powders, guns and bullets. That is the present practical upper limit. These are usually attained with cartridges such as the 22-06, which have large powder capacities relative to the bore and bullet size, and great care is essential since the relatively huge powder charges used can do unexpected things—like melt brass cartridge cases, and even detonate and blow up the rifle.

The interior ballistics involved in reaching hypervelocities (Figure 4) are often expressed as *pressure-travel* curves (Figure 5). These curves show the pressure in a rifle's bore as the bullet travels down it, and they are important tools for gun and ammunition designers. Engineers draw them based on complex mathematical calculations, and then test them using complex test-firing instrumentation with equipment seldom available to

## Figure 1

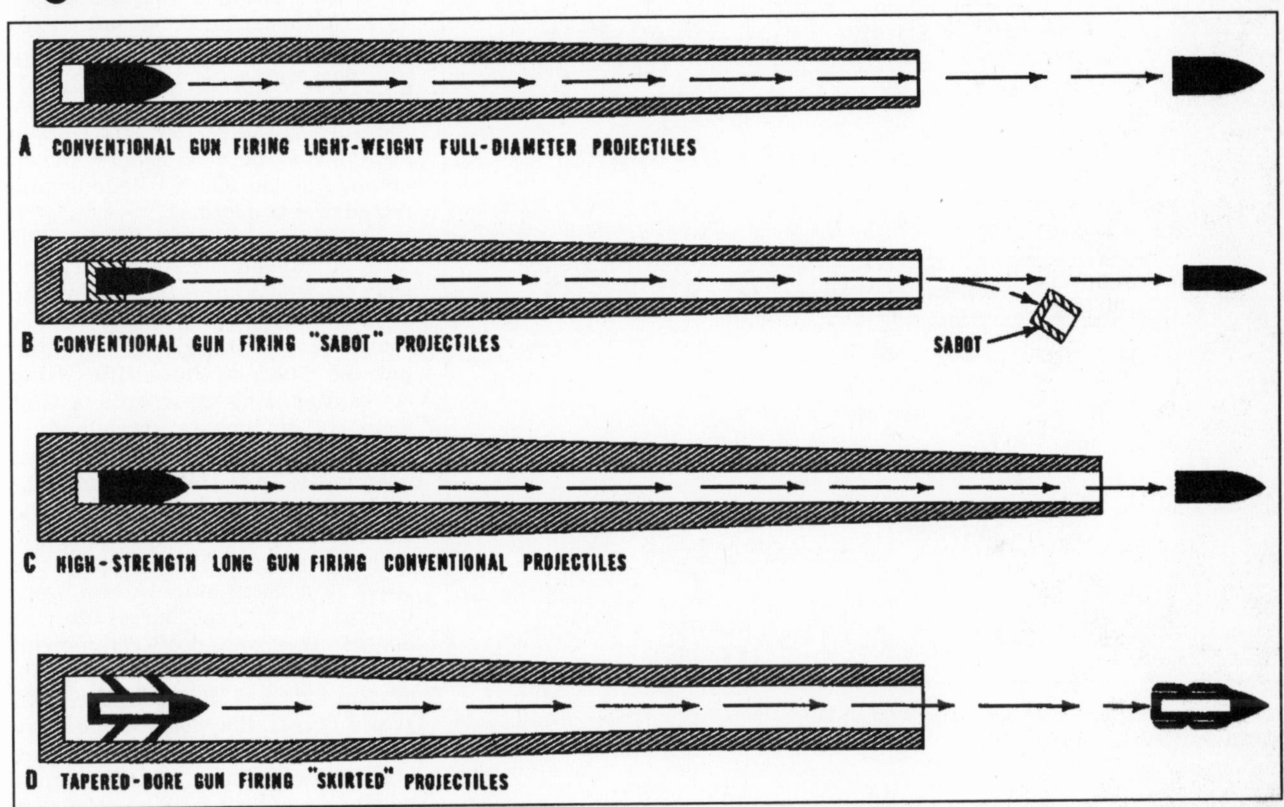


Schematics of the four systems used in successfully building hypervelocity rifles. (U.S. Navy)

## Figure 2

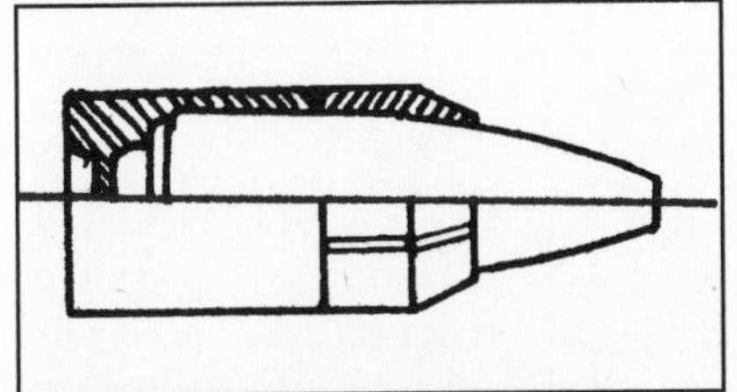

A drawing of the discarding-sabot bullet fired in Remington's 30-06/224 Accelerator hypervelocity rifle cartridge. The durable plastic discarding sabot (crosshatched) falls off the 55-grain jacketed bullet as it leaves the rifle's muzzle.

## Figure 3

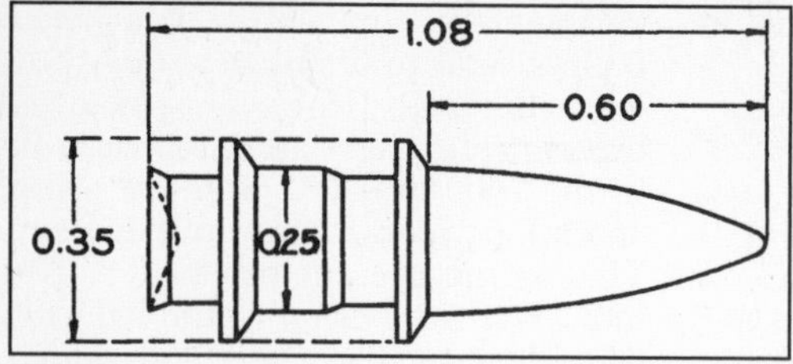


A sketch of the Gerlich 35-25-caliber collapsible-skirt deformable rifle bullet tested by the U.S. Army Frankford Arsenal in a taper-bore rifled barrel in about 1933. It was fired in a modified U.S. Army 30-caliber rifle cartridge case, and velocities in excess of 4000 fps were attained. (U.S. Army)

## Figure 4

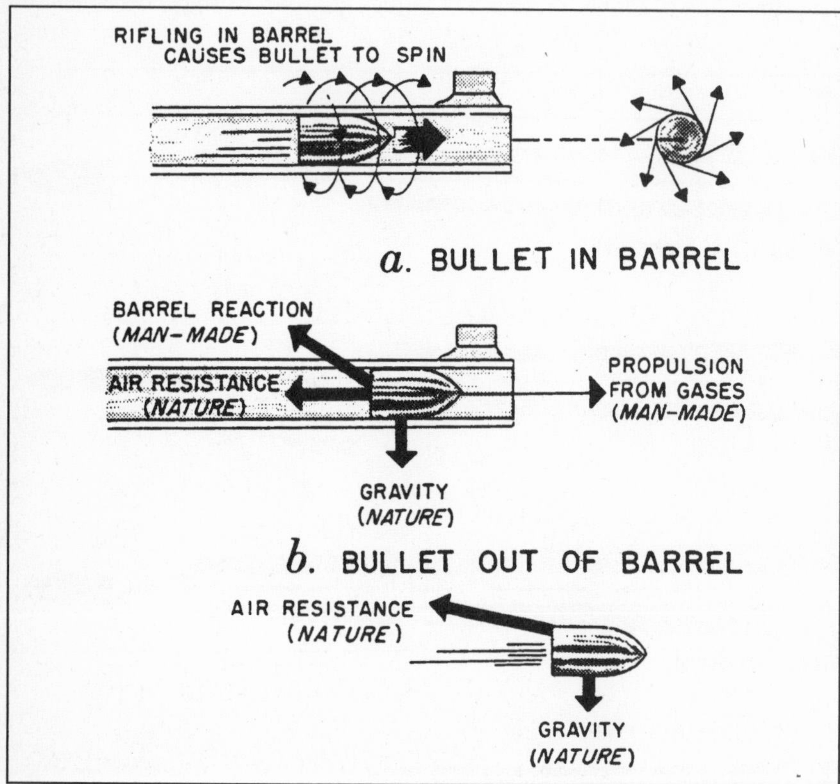


A sketch of what affects any bullet. Those in (a) are interior ballistic factors; those in (b) are exterior factors. (U.S. Army)

## Figure 5

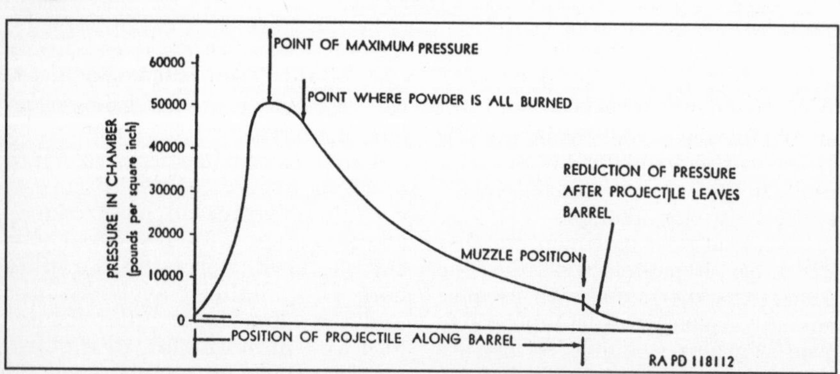


The pressure-travel curve for the standard U.S. Army 30-caliber Ball cartridge M2 (30-06 rifle) firing a 152-grain jacketed bullet at an average muzzle velocity of 2800 fps in a 24-inch barrel, using about 50 grains of improved military rifle powder and developing a chamber pressure of about 50,000 pounds per square inch. This is a typical modern conventional military rifle cartridge. (U.S. Army)

experimenters outside a ballistics research labratory.

Everything about the cartridge and rifle affects the pressure-travel curve: powder, primer, bullet, bore and rifling. Handloaders experimenting with hypervelocities can study pressure-travel curves to help them understand what they are doing and what happens in the rifle.

### Taper Bore

The three means already mentioned of attaining hypervelocity in a rifle are generally within the capabilities of handloading experimenters, but a fourth is not: the taper-bore deformable bullet system (Figure 1D). While this idea goes back before 1900, it wasn't until the late 1920s that Herman Gerlich, an American gun designer working in Germany, developed and promoted it for sporting rifles. By about 1930, the Gerlich system had become widely known among riflemen. Gerlich actually promoted it in two forms.

The first Gerlich "Ultra" rifles built in the late 1920s had rifling that tapered from full depth at the breech end to a small smoothbore section at the muzzle. Using large powder charges, these rifles fired conventional jacketed bullets that were soft enough to accommodate the tapered rifling. This system was used in the 7mm Halger Ultra Magnum rifles sold in the 1930s. The claimed muzzle velocity was in the 4000 fps range. Unfortunately, the rifles and their ammunition were very expensive, and barrel life was poor, so they were not a commercial success. When the OSRD tested this system for the U.S. armed forces in World War II, they could not achieve the velocity Gerlich claimed; they stated the velocity measurement equipment Gerlich used was perhaps a bit optimistic.

Gerlich's other taper-bore/deformable bullet hypervelocity system did work. It used a tapered rifled bore and a special skirted deformable bullet (Figure 3). In the 1930s, the U.S. Army Ordnance Department experimented with a 30-24 caliber taper-bore rifle on this Gerlich system, firing the load in a special test rifle. They dropped it after they found its accuracy was erratic because the bullet skirts did not collapse uniformly. Winchester also developed a 36-28 taper-bore on this Gerlich system in the mid-1930s, but abandoned it because of poor accuracy and the fact that its overall cost was much higher than anybody would be willing to pay. However, both the U.S. Army and Winchester Gerlichs did attain velocities well over 4000 fps.

In World War II, the German army built and used Gerlich taper-bore skirted deformable-projectile antitank guns in several calibers, including 2.8-2.0cm, 42-28mm and 75-55mm. They ceased work on them by 1943 because they were so difficult to make and were no more effective than regular-bore antitank guns of equivalent caliber firing subcaliber projectiles, similar to the U.S. Army's Armor Piercing Discarding Sabot (APDS) projectiles developed in World War II and still in use. This APDS system is, of course, the same system used by Remington in their hypervelocity Accelerator rifle cartridges.

### Flight Factors

Once the hypervelocity bullet leaves the barrel, exterior ballistics (Figure 4) take over. The factors that affect the bullet most in flight are velocity, the spin imparted by the rifling and aerodynamic drag. These all affect the stability of the bullet. This can be observed by firing through a linear series of paper targets spaced about 5 feet apart. The holes will usually show how badly the projectile is wobbling, if it is. If a good ballistic chronograph is available, the velocity can be measured. Further measurements are usually beyond the capabilities of anything but a ballistics research laboratory.

An experimenter wishing to look into the mathematics of external ballistics will find the late Maj. Gen. Julian Hatcher's *Hatcher's Notebook* a good place to start. Chapter 13, "Notes on Gunpowder," introduces interior ballistics and other important subjects, and Chapter 23 is on exterior ballistics.

Hypervelocity riflemen usually shoot from a benchrest to get the best possible performance from their rifles. They usually use a 22 centerfire because rifles, components and even barrels with different rifling twists are available at reasonable costs. Some hypervelocity riflemen experiment with different loadings they assemble right at the range.

While some truly remarkable performance has been achieved by firing light bullets, they are more affected by several factors than heavier bullets fired at conventional velocities. Wind, from any quarter, has a greater effect on a light bullet's flight at any velocity. Any kind of obstruction, even light rain, grass or snowflakes, can deflect a light bullet and sometimes cause it to disintegrate. The centrifugal force caused by the very high rotational rate can cause bullets to disintegrate as they leave the muzzle. The rapid velocity loss of light high-speed bullets due to their low ballistic coefficients can be very frustrating.

There is one basic safety measure recommended to people who experiment with hypervelocity loads or any heavy load, for that matter. The first few shots should be fired as if they were proof loads, with everybody including the rifleman well clear of the rifle. This can be done by lashing the rifle to a heavy truck tire and pulling its trigger with a cord 20 or so feet long. However, if you have to resort to this tactic very often, you're probably doing something wrong. ●

This pressure-travel curve shows what happens with the same powder as in Figure 5 in different grain configurations and burning rates. (A) is fast-burning, (B) is medium-burning, and (C) is slow-burning, all loaded to obtain about the same muzzle velocity. (U.S. Army)

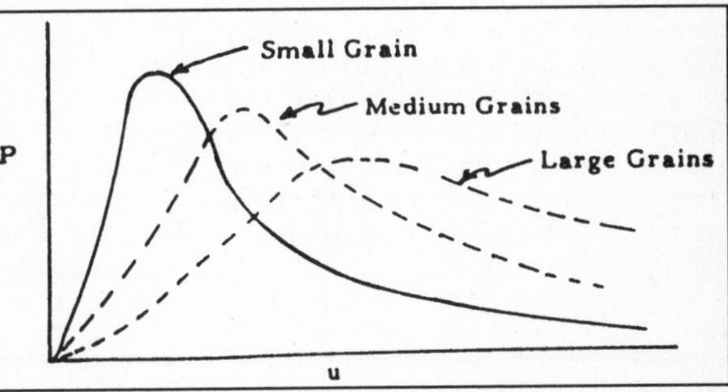


This pressure-travel curve shows what happens when powder of the same chemical composition is prepared in small, medium and large grains. This is the sort of thing ballistic laboratories can do, but most experimenters should *never* try. Altering powder in any way, or mixing powders, can be *very* dangerous. (U.S. Army)

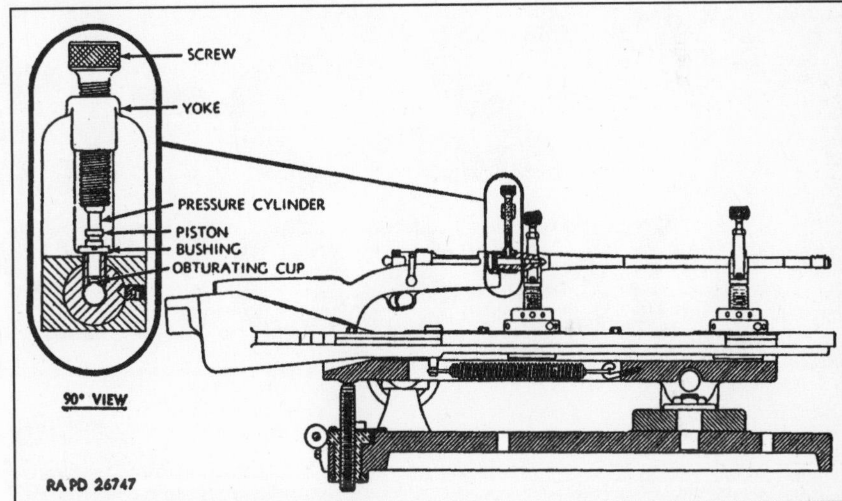


This typical pressure-test rifle fixture is the type ballistics research laboratories use to test-fire experimental rifle ammunition. This equipment is seldom available to amateur experimenters, and only those with advanced engineering and mechanical skills should attempt to build one. (U.S. Army)

### Author's Note

The information in this article was drawn from U.S. armed forces manuals, documents and similar publications. The writer has observed hypervelocity experiments being carried out at fully equipped ballistics research laboratories.

IT STARTED WITH a failure. I couldn't find a nice bolt-action 250 Savage. In fact, I couldn't find *any* kind of bolt-action 250. You might not think that's so unusual, but I work in a gun store and see many hundreds of rifles every year. So I resorted to the gun enthusiast's credo: If you can't find one, build one.

When I'd decided to build a rifle, I already knew that I'd use a Remington Model 788 action. This clunky-looking long-discontinued rifle action is my favorite simply because I've never seen one that wasn't supremely accurate. I don't know whether it's the 788's extremely fast lock time, the heavy-walled round receiver that's so easy to bed, or some mystery factor that makes 788s shoot such tiny groups. And I don't care. They shoot, and I love them for it.

The natural choice would have been to simply rebarrel a 788 originally chambered for the 22-250. But spare magazines for 788s in that caliber are the most difficult to come by, as are after-market synthetic stocks. So I agonized for a few days until the little light bulb over my head flashed on. Instead of building just a rifle, why not build a cartridge/rifle combo? I'd combine a 788 rifle and my desire for a quarter-inch bore with my all-time favorite cartridge—the 308 Winchester—and build a 25-308. At the time, it seemed like a good idea. Since then, it has seemed downright brilliant.

At this point, I'd like to claim that the idea of necking down the 308 Winchester to 25-caliber was all mine. But that would be a lie. The 308 has been the subject of intense wildcatting efforts since the moment it was released to the civilian world in 1952. Gun greats like Fred Huntington, Warren Page and others took 308 Winchester brass still smoking from Winchester's introduction and went straight to their reloading benches. In no time at all, 308-based wildcats from 224 to 358 calibers were proliferating. Commercial cartridge companies have since legitimatized such outstanding performers as the 243, the 7mm-08 and the 358. Other wildcat calibers on the 308 case, such as the 22, 6.5mm, 270, 338—and 25—have remained almost unknown.

### But Why Call It Souper?

The 25-308 was originally developed by P.F. Lambert of Washington, D.C., according to Speer's *Reloading Manual for Wildcat Cartridges* (Number 4), published in 1960. (Incidentally, this rarely

# THE 25-308 IS SOUPER

A Remington Model 788 rifle chambered in 25-308 with a Burris 4-12x scope makes an ideal varmint/medium game rig, says the author. An Oehler 35P chronograph was used during all load development.

encountered little book is the only manual solely for wildcat cartridges ever published, so far as I know.) In all my readings about reloading over the past thirty-five years, I cannot recall ever reading another reference to Lambert. But if the only contribution he ever made to reloading was the 25 Souper, as he named it, he deserves accolades. Why "Souper" instead of "Super"? Beats me, unless you've seen what one does to a varmint.

Lambert's work also led to another most fortunate circumstance, as I was soon to learn. My first call to Huntington Die Specialties revealed that they stock RCBS dies for the 25-308 on the shelf. No extremely expensive custom dies would be needed for my project! With this delightful bit of news, I completely committed myself.

To construct the rifle, I turned to Mike Bellm, the gunsmith who took over P.O. Ackley's world-famous rifle works in Salt Lake City after Ackley's retirement. These days, Mike pretty much concentrates on the Thompson/Center Contender and does little work on rifles. But because we'd become fairly close while collaborating on Contender projects, he agreed to craft a barrel for my new rifle. And craft it he did.

While Mike was doing his magic, I researched loading data and also did as much case preparation as possible. For brass, I obtained 100 new 7mm-08 cases by Remington.

Why not use more plentiful 243 or 308 brass? Because I thought 308 necks would thicken when necked down and might require turning. And I avoided 243 brass because 25-308 rounds look a lot like 243s and might even chamber in a 243 rifle. If anyone accidentally fired a .257-inch diameter bullet down a .243-inch bore, there's no telling what might occur. On the other hand, if someone relied on the headstamp alone and unknowingly fired a 25-308 in a 7mm-08, no excess pressure would develop.

First, I sized the cases just enough to leave a barely perceptible bump at the junction of neck and shoulder. Then I trimmed the cases to 2.00 inches, chamfered the necks and deburred the flash holes. That done, I seated spent primers in ten randomly chosen cases, weighed each one and averaged the results. Then I filled each case to the brim with water, weighed them again and averaged those totals. Average water capacity was found to be within a tenth or so of 53.0 grains.

*Never widely popular, but always dependable, this nearly half-century-old wildcat just won't go away*

by ROCKY RAAB

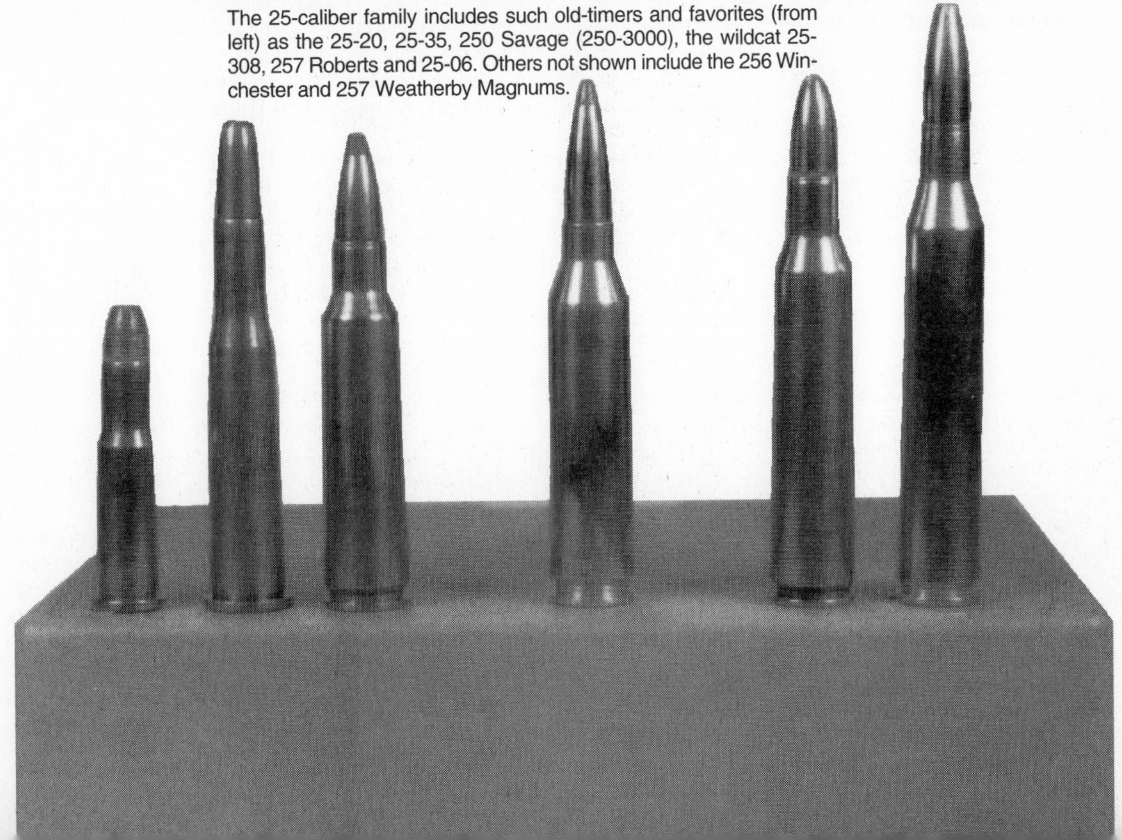

The 25-caliber family includes such old-timers and favorites (from left) as the 25-20, 25-35, 250 Savage (250-3000), the wildcat 25-308, 257 Roberts and 25-06. Others not shown include the 256 Winchester and 257 Weatherby Magnums.

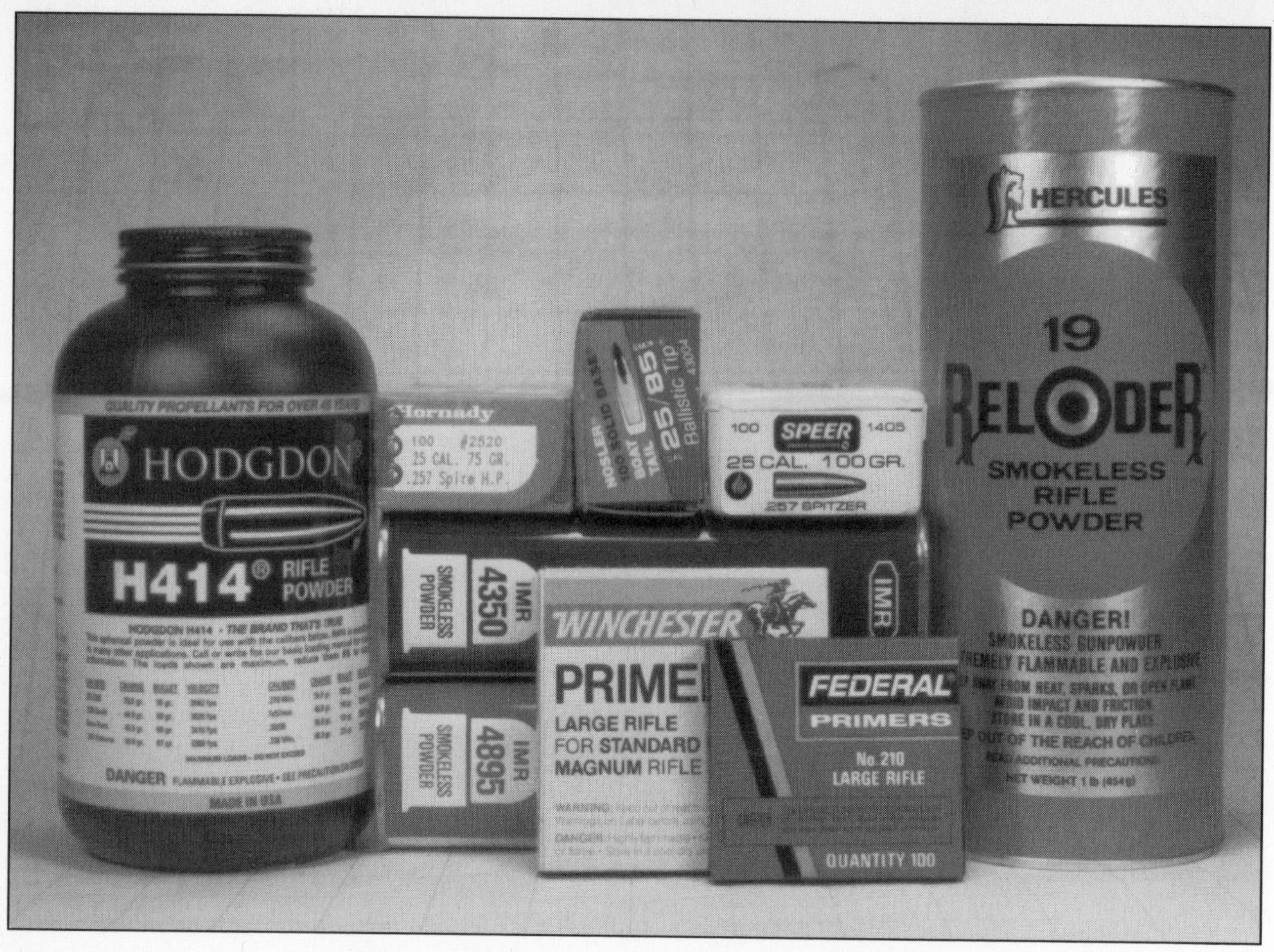


The author developed accurate loads with three bullets and an assortment of other components. The 25-308 proved to be predictable and not at all finicky about component selection.

Firing up my computer and Wayne Blackwell's indispensable Load From A Disk (LFD) program revealed that other 25-caliber cartridges have these approximate water capacities: 250 Savage, 46.0 grains; 257 Roberts, 55.0 grains; 25-06, 66.0 grains; 257 Weatherby, 84.0 grains. These are gross capacities, based on water filled to the brim of the neck. They do *not* represent powder loading capacities under any circumstances. But they do reflect maximum case volume, and this factor is one of the keys in developing load data with the LFD program.

While I was in LFD, I calculated several suggested loads using bullets of 75, 87, 100 and 120 grains. I compared the predicted results with the data in the Speer wildcat manual and was comforted to find that the manual's charges and velocities compared nicely to Blackwell's LFD. So far so good. Next, I compared loading tables for the 243 Winchester to the 25-308. Because the two have virtually identical case measurements and only a slight difference in bullet diameter, I reasoned that 243 data wouldn't be too far off from the 25-308.

Then, because one cannot be too careful when working up data for a new cartridge, I also studied load tables for the 257 Roberts. The Roberts generally has only about 2 grains greater gross water capacity than the 25-308 and uses identical bullets, so the comparison seems valid. Here again, things seemed to be very close. Coming at the problem from two directions (identical case with similar bullets versus similar case with identical bullets) gave me a great deal of confidence in establishing the starting loads for all four bullet weights.

Finally, I researched back issues of several shooting magazines for articles on 25-caliber wildcats in general and the 25 Souper in particular. I found passing mention of the cartridge in two old articles and even some load data in a piece by veteran cartridge developer Layne Simpson. But surprisingly, I found no reference in either *Cartridges of the World* or *Wildcat Cartridges*, both of which I keep on my sagging reference shelf.

Just as I was about to go twitchy with anticipation, the rifle arrived. As fast as possible, I fitted a stock to the barreled action, mounted a scope and proceeded to final case preparation. By alternately turning down the sizing die and trying a case in the rifle, I reached the point where the bolt would just freely close, thus optimizing case sizing for that rifle's exact headspace. I set up bullet seating depth by barely seating a bullet in an empty sized case, then alternately trying the round and screwing down the seater stem until the bolt barely closed again. Then I gave the seater adjustment exactly one turn down and locked it. Finally, it was time to load live ammo.

I rechecked my load calculations and dispensed a moderate charge of old faithful IMR-4895 under Hornady 75-grain hollowpoints. I hoped that this load would be stout enough to properly fireform cases and yet mild enough to gently break in the new barrel. The first loaded round looked great, fed slickly from the rifle's magazine and locked smoothly into the chamber. Damn, this was exciting! Soon I had 100 rounds loaded, and it was finally time to shoot.

A few days later I set up at the range, gently closed the bolt and—with only a bit of trepidation—squeezed off my very first round of 25-308. There was a moderate report, mild recoil and no resistance on opening the bolt. The chronograph display showed 3300, just a little lower than expected. My micrometer showed no undue expansion of the case, and I proceeded with my planned schedule of barrel break-in. I cleaned the barrel after every shot for the first twenty, every other shot for the next forty, then every fifth shot through one hundred. The barrel was allowed to cool between cleaning and shooting every time. After firing the first sixty rounds, I set up a target.

OK already, enough of the "First I did this and then I did that" stuff. How does the darn thing shoot? I'd already boresighted the scope and wasn't too surprised to see a hole on the target when I started my first five-shot series. I was a bit surprised to see the second bullet land only an inch or so from the first. But I was absolutely astounded to watch the next three land squarely atop the second hole, enlarging it only a little. My range calipers slid down until, when the jaws touched the extreme outside edges of the four-shot hole, the dial read 0.57. Center to center, the group was 0.313-inch. Unbelievable.

It's probable that my uncontrolled chuckling interfered with my shooting, but the first eight groups still averaged about 1 inch. I knew then that the fun was just beginning.

## Load Development

The simplest way to develop loads is to begin with the heaviest bullet weight you plan to use and slowly work up powder charges. Then, when you peak, you can simply substitute the next lighter bullet over the same charge of the same powder and be reasonably assured of a safe starting load in that weight. So despite the fun I'd had with the fireforming loads and the 75-grain hollowpoint, I began my serious load work with 100-grain bullets. If I had any plans to shoot game larger than mule deer with my 25, I would have started with 120-grain bullets. But I have better cartridges for elk and such, so 100-grain pills are enough for me.

(Left to right) The 308 Winchester relates to the 30-06 in the same way the 25-308 relates to the 25-06. The smaller cartridge delivers nearly the same performance as the larger with lighter bullet weights.

Full-length sets of 25 Souper (also called 25-308) dies are available off the shelf from RCBS at reasonable prices. Not exactly a top-ten seller, according to RCBS, but still a standard stock item.

Case forming is simple using the regular sizing die. Slowly run in regular 308 or 7mm-08 cases until the rifle's bolt just closes on the reformed case (center). A fully fireformed case is at the right. Use extreme caution not to mix 25-308 rounds with 243 rounds. For this reason, the author recommends never using 243 brass to form 25 Souper cases.

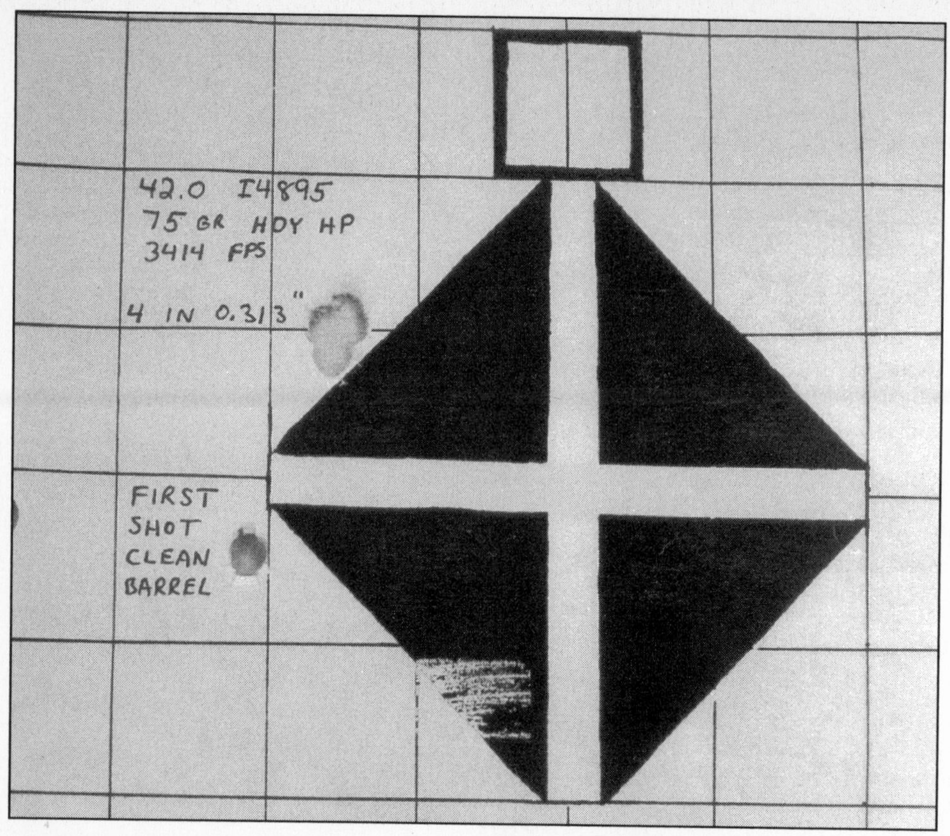


The first group recorded from the 25-308 put four shots through one ragged hole measuring 0.313-inch. The first shot from a clean barrel went just over an inch low.

According to my load notes, I range-tested more than twenty-three combinations using Speer and Nosler bullets and seven different powders. Only two combinations exceeded 2-inch groups. One was a very light starting load using Hodgdon 4831 that immediately tightened up with a heavier charge, and the other was a too-long load that pushed the bullet into the rifling. It, too, tightened up when I seated the bullet a tad deeper. Velocities with the 100-grain bullets ran from 2960 to 3100 fps at maximum pressures. Best consistency with this bullet weight came with Hodgdon 414 and IMR-4350 powders. I got great results with the wicked but discontinued Nosler Solid Base bullets, but I have so few of these left that I almost wept with each trigger pull. I did prove to my satisfaction that powders slower than 4350 or faster than 4895 are less than ideal.

Dropping to 85-grain bullets, I stuck with H-414 and IMR-4350, and added IMR-4895. The only bullet tried has been the Nosler Ballistic Tip. I don't see much use for this in-between bullet weight, but I plan to use this unbelievably devastating bullet on coyotes. I only tried a few combinations of each powder in this weight, but soon found that IMR-4350 is a winner. Sub-inch groups all day long at 3275 fps isn't a bad place to stop load development.

My general-purpose varmint load would be built around the Hornady 75-grain hollowpoint. And naturally, I went back to IMR-4895 because of the excellent results of my fireforming groups. I tried several other powders as well, but my first choice turned out to be the best of all. I stopped charge increases a comfortable margin under maximum case expansion with this bullet because much of my varmint shooting is done in the heat of summer, which boosts pressures. Still, velocities of 3450 fps are more than enough. And groups run too small to put in print, lest I risk the last shreds of my credibility.

By the way, I think it wise not to print exact charge weights here. Because my rifle is essentially handmade in a wildcat chambering, its specifications are unique. My loads therefore may be safe only in this gun. If you wish to build a 25-308 for yourself, follow standard practices for safe load development. The 25-308 is tractable and predictable, not prone to sudden pressure buildups with small charge increases, at least with the powders I've used.

After several years of great shooting, I'd like to report on its effectiveness on game of all types. So far, however, the deer haven't cooperated while I've carried the 25, so I can't comment on 100-grain bullet performance on medium game. But on prairie dogs, foxes and rockchucks, the Hornady 75-grain hollowpoint is definitely a red-mist performer. Even way out past 400 steps, prairie dogs are either launched many feet upward or blown into pieces. Closer in, the results are more devastating. If you've noted the increase in performance on varmints of the 22-250 over the 223, you may take my word that the 25-308 beats the 22-250 by a similar margin.

Beyond its performance in the field, the rifle is a joy to shoot. Recoil is mild enough that, with 75-grain loads, a snug hold on the forearm keeps the target in view through 12x magnification. Loads of 100 grains come back a bit firmer, but even the smallest of shooters would not find it uncomfortable to shoot. It's just about identical to the 243.

Which brings me to one of the most common questions I get: "Why not just use a 243?" To which I could begin a discourse on improved case-to-bore expansion ratios, improved bullet rotational radius and other esoterica. The real reason, of course, is obvious to the most casual of Handloader's Digest readers. I built it because the quarter-inch bore has always fascinated me. I built it because it *isn't* a plain-vanilla 243. Because it's a challenge. Just because. ●

Sometimes everyone's shotgunning is pathetic.
Did you ever wonder...

# Is Cold Weather Killing Your Shotgun Performance?

by THOMAS C. TABOR

MY HEAVY JACKET and thick wool sweater seemed non-existent as the arctic-like temperature drove deep into my bones. But my shooting performance was foremost in my mind. And on that particular day, it could only be described as "embarrassing." Nevertheless, I had my mind made up that I would finish out my limit of chukars no matter how long it took, or how far the mercury plunged. It wasn't that I hadn't had sufficient opportunity to fill my not so liberal limit several times over. In fact, the hunting was great—it was only my performance that was bordering on pathetic. Even though I often registered what I felt were solid hits, those birds seemed to be wearing suits of armor.

That particular outing has stood out in my mind for years. The ice- and snow-covered landscape of the Horse Heaven Hills of Washington state had never provided such a challenge to my game-getting ability, and this puzzled me deeply. The temperature was well below freezing, somewhere around 10 or 15 degrees, and I was shooting the same handloads that I always used, but they were not doing their usual job. Feathers flew, but wings kept on flapping as the coveys disappeared over the closest outcropping. Disgust was even showing on my faithful vizsla pointer's face, and I'm sure her thoughts contained a lot of profanity, too—most of which was directed at me personally. After all, she was doing her part; what was my problem?

The two shotguns used during the testing were a Browning A5 semi-auto 12-gauge and a Winchester Model 12 pump in 20-gauge.

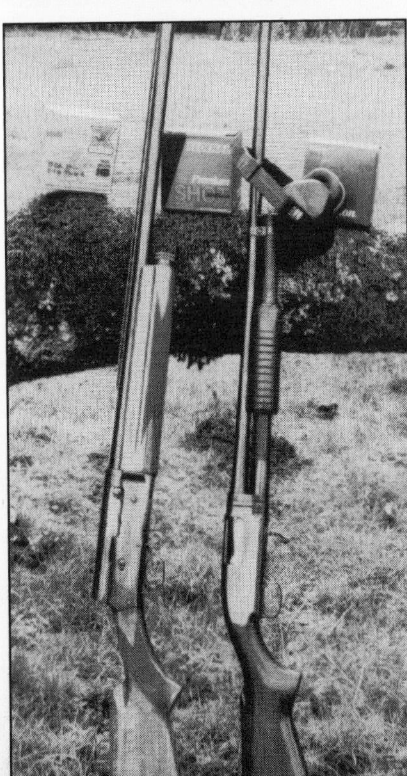

At the time, I blamed my poor showing on the fact that I was wearing too many clothes to be able to mount my shotgun properly; or I thought maybe I was sluggish from the cold and not swinging through the bird; or the clear air made the birds appear closer than they really were; or it was the late season and the chukars had their heaviest layer of feathers; or...? Yet, the more I thought about my thirty-plus years of bird hunting, the more times I could recall cold conditions and poor performance seeming to go hand in hand.

### A New Theory Develops

But while I made excuses at the time for my dismal performance, the Horse Heaven Hills incident in particular continued to puzzle me. Finally, I came to believe that something else may have contributed to this problem other than my earlier justifications. I had heard or read somewhere that temperature could affect the burning rate of powder and therefore change a shell's performance. We'd actually kicked this theory around at the trap club on a couple of occasions while huddled around the stove, but all we had to go on was speculation. Could temperature have enough effect on velocity to alter a shooter's performance? I vowed to find out.

Quite honestly, going into the performance tests that follow, I did not know what I was going to find. Even if I proved that temperature could affect velocity, that wouldn't necessarily put the issue of the Horse Heaven Hills to rest. Nevertheless, I decided that it would certainly help me to better understand what happens in the field, hopefully providing information on how to better my performance in such situations.

If my tests were going to accomplish what I set out to do, I felt I should have a representative sampling of shotshells from the three major manufacturers: Federal, Remington and Winchester. I chose three commonly used rounds from each, consisting of two in 12-gauge and one in 20. Essentially, I wanted common 12-gauge field and target rounds, plus a moderate load in 20-gauge. All were 2¾-inch shells. This would provide a good base from which to draw assumptions and conclusions for both hunters and claybird shooters.

I believe it is important to state that my purpose was to determine, in general, whether temperature fluctuations could affect performance. It was not my intention to compare one particular shell type, manufacturer, or style with another. Because of the diverse number of commercially loaded shotshells on the market today, plus the unending combinations open to today's handloader, trying to rate and compare individual shells with one another would be unproductive, in my opinion. To further support this objective, there is no guarantee that commercially manufactured shotshells will stay the same from year to year or even lot to lot. Manufacturers of these products continually strive to improve them, and sometimes this involves changes that could affect performance at different temperatures. While some load-specific data is interesting and certainly stimulates thought, in this writer's mind it is much better to view the results on a more holistic basis. Overall conclusions are more important than detailed specifics on individual loads.

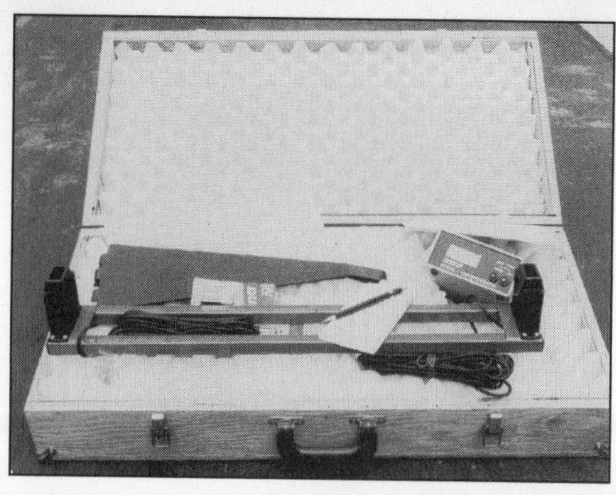

A PACT 1 chronograph provided a reliable tool for monitoring the velocities of the subject shotshells.

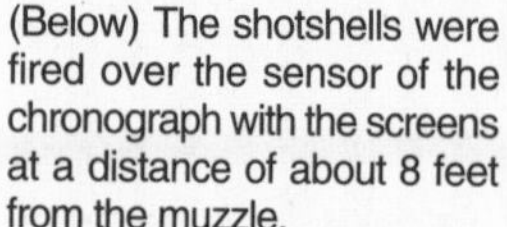

(Below) The shotshells were fired over the sensor of the chronograph with the screens at a distance of about 8 feet from the muzzle.

### Testing the Theory

I chose three temperatures for shell testing: a low of 0 degrees, freezing or 32 degrees, and 100 degrees (Fahrenheit). Shooters are commonly exposed to each of these temperature levels, whether they are trap or Skeet shooters or hunters that get afield during the entire season. Some readers may doubt that their shells will ever see 100 degrees F., but it should be kept in mind that most of us tend to think in terms of temperatures *in the shade*, rather than in direct sunlight. Yet, we seldom restrict our bird hunting to shady areas. Temperatures as low as the 60s or 70s in the shade may still subject our shotshells to 100 degrees in actual hunting conditions.

After conditioning ten rounds of each shotshell type at the three temperature ranges, they were fired over a PACT 1 chronograph 8 feet from the muzzle. This distance was based on the chronograph manufacturer's recommendation. It eliminates the chance of muzzle blast affecting the readings.

The major challenge I faced in this simulation was maintaining consistent temperatures. Once the temperature of choice was reached, it would have to be maintained long enough to ensure that the shells were completely and uniformly warmed or cooled throughout. Warming or cooling only on the surface would not simulate conditions adequately.

It is logical to assume that in actual hunting conditions the ambient air and firearm temperature would be approximately the same as the shells. Yet it would be difficult to thoroughly simulate these conditions in my tests. I do not believe, however, that air temperature and the temperature of the shotgun have much influence on generated velocity. Nevertheless, I fired the rounds as quickly as possible in the 100-degree tests. By doing so the barrel was warmed substantially after the first couple of rounds were shot. In the 0- and 32-degree

For his tests, the author purchased a small used warmer-style oven from Goodwill Industries. In order to keep the temperature as low as 100 degrees, holes were cut in the top for ventilation.

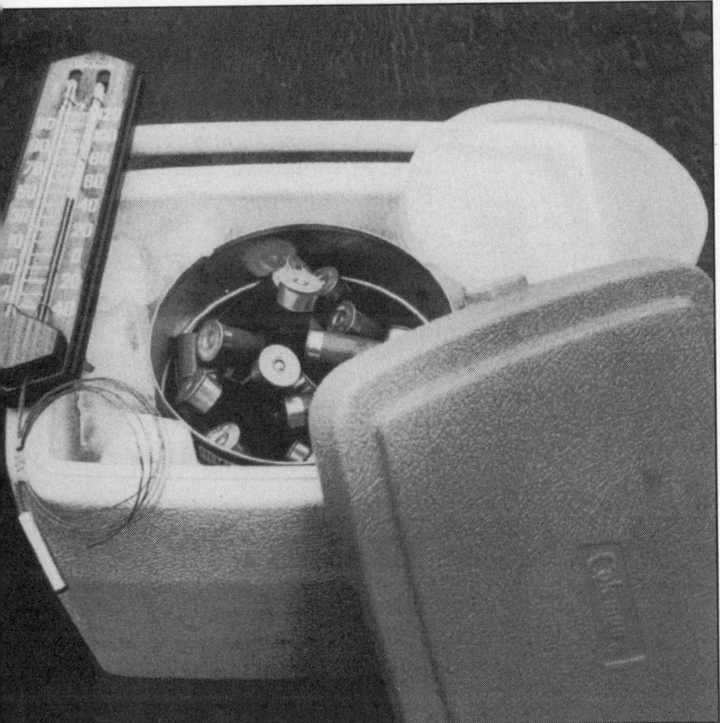

(Above) To achieve and maintain the shells at 32 degrees F., a small Coleman cooler provided the best results. The shells were placed in a sealed coffee can and the ice cubes were packed around the can.

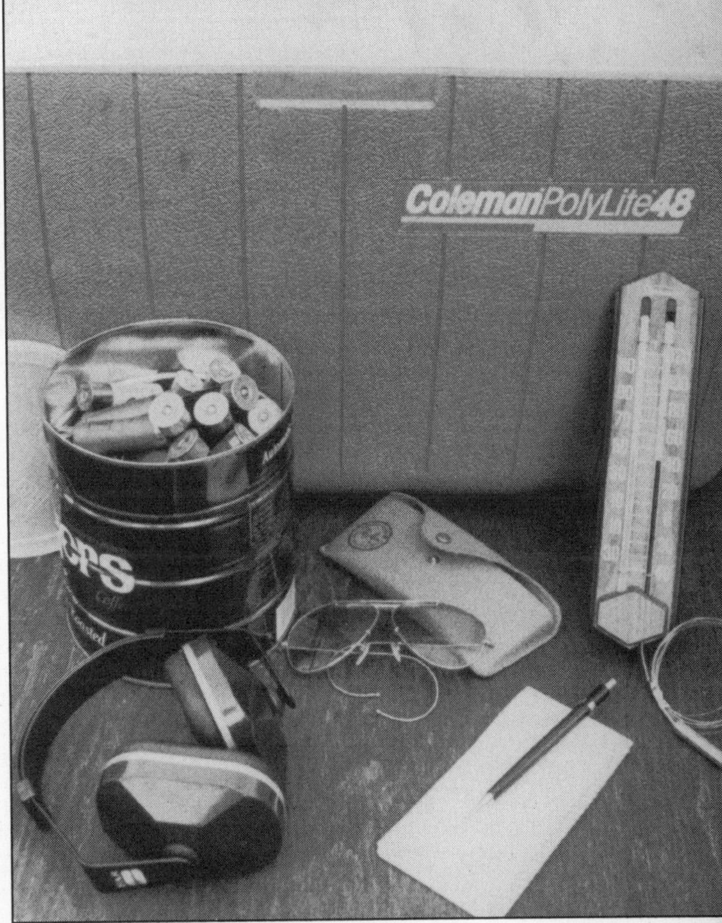


(Right) In order to achieve a temperature as low as 0 degrees F., dry ice was placed in a large Coleman cooler. An indoor/outdoor thermometer with a remote probe monitored the shells' temperature closely throughout the tests.

testing, the shells were fired in groups of three rounds, after which the barrel was allowed to cool to ambient temperature before repeat firings. My belief that shotgun barrel temperature would have little effect on velocity was somewhat confirmed when I did cursory checks for noticeable trends. Comparing the first round of the series with the last, no obvious velocity effects or patterns were detected.

To maintain the cold temperatures needed (0 and 32), insulated coolers were used. For 32 degrees, wet ice was used; dry ice was needed to achieve 0-degree temperature. Adjusting the distance between the dry ice and the shells allowed me to reach and maintain the desired level.

The 100-degree temperature was reached by using a warming oven. However, a trial run before the actual tests convinced me that a temperature as low as 100 degrees could not be adequately maintained without some modifications to the oven. Therefore, holes were drilled in the top to provide ventilation. Once I was assured that 100 degrees could be consistently maintained, the shotshells were placed in a glass oven pan with towels covering them bottom and top.

To constantly monitor the temperature at all ranges, an indoor/outdoor thermometer with a remote sensor was used. The thermometer probe was placed deep within the

**TABLE 1: MUZZLE VELOCITY AT 0 DEGREES F.**

| | Load Number | | | | | | | | |
|---|---|---|---|---|---|---|---|---|---|
| Round No. | No. 1 | No. 2 | No. 3 | No. 4 | No. 5 | No. 6 | No. 7 | No. 8 | No. 9 |
| 1 | 1197 | 1221 | 1174 | 1132 | 1134 | 1109 | 1094 | 1106 | 1053 |
| 2 | 1300 | 1215 | 1217 | 1094 | 1164 | 1079 | 1098 | 1093 | 1105 |
| 3 | 1254 | 1221 | 1186 | 1072 | 1150 | 1083 | 971 | 1161 | 1141 |
| 4 | 1241 | 1176 | 1209 | 1115 | 1118 | 1123 | 1099 | 1136 | 1007 |
| 5 | 1187 | 1234 | 1132 | 1097 | 1166 | 1177 | 1111 | 1144 | 1086 |
| 6 | 1239 | 1229 | 1164 | 1141 | 1180 | 1163 | 1084 | 1095 | 1095 |
| 7 | 1237 | 1201 | 1176 | 1109 | 1147 | 1185 | 997 | 1053 | 1073 |
| 8 | 1266 | 1183 | 1168 | 1134 | 1169 | 1201 | 1082 | 1140 | 1094 |
| 9 | 1305 | 1208 | 1177 | 1081 | 1154 | 1184 | 1136 | 1165 | 1096 |
| 10 | 1312 | 1212 | 1162 | 1160 | 1146 | 1194 | 1049 | 1128 | 1122 |
| Average Velocity | 1254 | 1210 | 1177 | 1114 | 1153 | 1150 | 1072 | 1122 | 1087 |

**TABLE 2: MUZZLE VELOCITY AT 32 DEGREES F.**

| | Load Number | | | | | | | | |
|---|---|---|---|---|---|---|---|---|---|
| Round No. | No. 1 | No. 2 | No. 3 | No. 4 | No. 5 | No. 6 | No. 7 | No. 8 | No. 9 |
| 1 | 1299 | 1208 | 1213 | 1101 | 1149 | 1219 | 1173 | 1165 | 1073 |
| 2 | 1223 | 1195 | 1171 | 1138 | 1221 | 1198 | 1174 | 1150 | 1060 |
| 3 | 1264 | 1173 | 1165 | 1171 | 1189 | 1269 | 1190 | 1153 | 1042 |
| 4 | 1207 | 1265 | 1167 | 1070 | 1166 | 1203 | 1134 | 1097 | 1108 |
| 5 | 1361 | 1259 | 1220 | 1042 | 1223 | 1188 | 1139 | 1165 | 1113 |
| 6 | 1231 | 1229 | 1166 | 1021 | 1167 | 1274 | 1118 | 1135 | 1142 |
| 7 | 1217 | 1214 | 1208 | 1059 | 1201 | 1136 | 1128 | 1145 | 1103 |
| 8 | 1104 | 1272 | 1137 | 1109 | 1259 | 1287 | 1161 | 1235 | 1115 |
| 9 | 1179 | 1225 | 1396 | 1089 | 1142 | 1207 | 1128 | 1130 | 1080 |
| 10 | 1201 | 1229 | 1219 | 1036 | 1188 | 1236 | 1147 | 1087 | 1129 |
| Average Velocity | 1229 | 1227 | 1206 | 1084 | 1191 | 1222 | 1149 | 1146 | 1097 |

**TABLE 3: MUZZLE VELOCITY AT 100 DEGREES F.**

| | Load Number | | | | | | | | |
|---|---|---|---|---|---|---|---|---|---|
| Round No. | No. 1 | No. 2 | No. 3 | No. 4 | No. 5 | No. 6 | No. 7 | No. 8 | No. 9 |
| 1 | 1385 | 1318 | 1296 | 1147 | 1299 | 1193 | 1288 | 1094 | 1207 |
| 2 | 1360 | 1291 | 1289 | 1158 | 1303 | 1167 | 1309 | 1212 | 1231 |
| 3 | 1384 | 1291 | 1300 | 1151 | 1287 | 1203 | 1288 | 1117 | 1179 |
| 4 | 1414 | 1306 | 1239 | 1147 | 1291 | 1153 | 1303 | 1125 | 1224 |
| 5 | 1359 | 1286 | 1260 | 1161 | 1308 | 1186 | 1289 | 1214 | 1189 |
| 6 | 1376 | 1163 | 1260 | 1149 | 1295 | 1141 | 1273 | 1125 | 1136 |
| 7 | 1416 | 1205 | 1254 | 1178 | 1208 | 1153 | 1281 | 1161 | 1204 |
| 8 | 1331 | 1182 | 1290 | 1138 | 1316 | 1127 | 1255 | 1149 | 1177 |
| 9 | 1427 | 1174 | 1209 | 1158 | 1320 | 1154 | 1273 | 1114 | 1175 |
| 10 | 1409 | 1246 | 1275 | 1156 | 1287 | 1120 | 1264 | 1100 | 1174 |
| Average Velocity | 1386 | 1246 | 1267 | 1154 | 1291 | 1160 | 1282 | 1141 | 1190 |

All rounds were shot in the order shown here beginning with round number one. During the 0 and 32 degree testing, the barrel was allowed to cool between each three rounds fired. At the higher temperature of 100 degrees, the rounds were fired one after another.

shell storage area. After the desired temperature was achieved, it was maintained for a minimum of one hour before beginning the actual firing tests. This helped ensure the shells were at a constant temperature throughout. Conditioning temperature fluctuations in the chambers were minimal. The greatest variations took place in the 100-degree testing. In this case, the temperature was maintained at ± 5 degrees. The 0-degree test chamber fluctuated ± 3 degrees, and at 32 degrees a level of ± 2 degrees was possible. Proper precautions were taken to ensure there was no danger of moisture contamination in the wet ice testings by sealing the shells in a moisture-proof container. During the three legs of testing, outside ambient temperature ranged from a low of 30 degrees to a high of 40 degrees F.

The firearms used were a Model 12 Winchester 20-gauge with a 28-inch Modified choke barrel and 2¾-inch chamber, and a 12-gauge Browning A5, 2¾-inch with a 28-inch Full choke barrel.

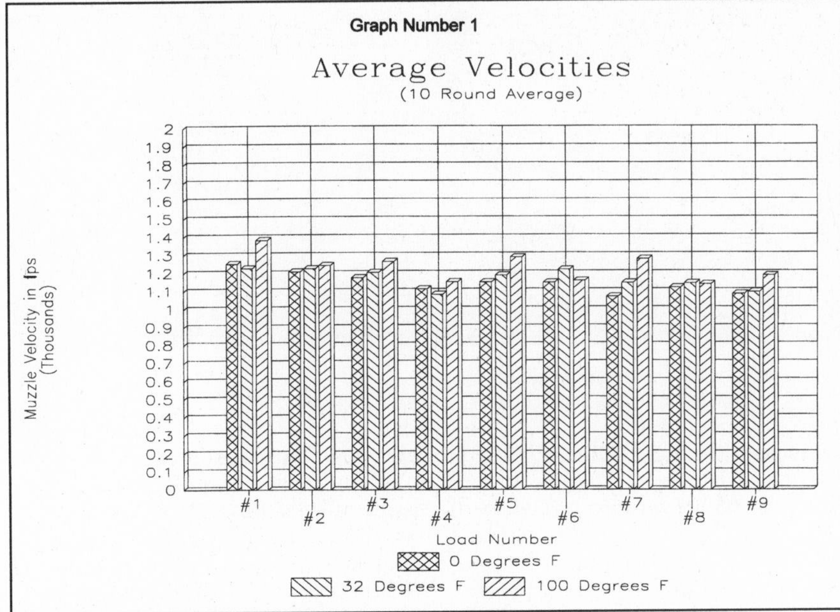


The average velocities are shown here for each of the loads tested. The averages were based on ten rounds of each particular load at the three temperature ranges. From left to right, the average velocities are shown for 0, 30 and 100 degrees Fahrenheit.

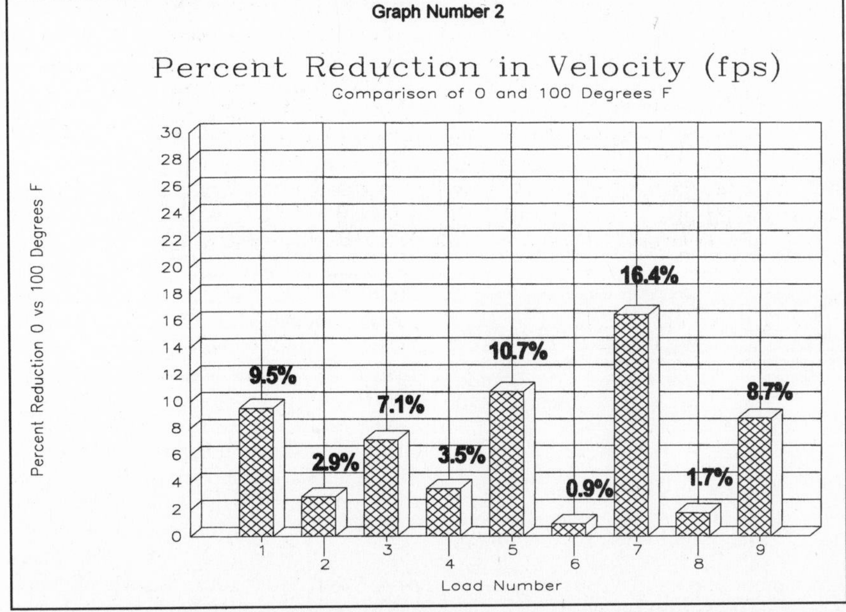


In each case, there was a demonstrated drop in muzzle velocity when the test rounds are compared at 0 degrees F. and 100 degrees F. The reduction varied substantially from load to load, yet the overall average of all nine types of rounds was 6.8 percent.

## Results

In all cases, shells functioned properly. There were no instances of what I believe to be inaccurate chronograph readings. There was one occasion during the 0-degree test that should be mentioned, however. When round three of the 20-gauge Remington shells (recorded velocity of 971 fps) was fired, it sounded different from the others. The report was high pitched, giving me the impression that not all of the powder had fully ignited, or at least not as well as it should have.

In addition, it should be noted that, when testing at the 100-degree level, variations in recoil were detected. In some cases, the recoil was quite heavy when compared to other rounds of the same type. When this was observed, the condition was always supported by a higher than normal recorded velocity. I also found during the high temperature tests that about one-third of the time the A5 Browning would fully eject the Federal Gold Medal Handicap hulls, even though the shotgun was set for heavy field loads.

In Tables 1 through 3, actual instrumental velocities (called muzzle velocities from here on) are shown, as well as the average velocity in feet per second. I am always a bit concerned about including the highest and lowest recorded velocities in an average, thinking that these could represent unusual or inaccurate data. In this case, however, after working the calculations, I found that this testing did not support such a hypothesis. Dropping these numbers out of the averaging calculations did not substantially change the results. Consequently, averages shown are for the entire ten rounds of each load.

It is quite obvious from a review of the data that in all cases there was a demonstrated effect based on the temperature of the shotshells. Graph 1 provides a quick summary of average velocities at each temperature level. A comparison is made in Graph 2 of muzzle velocity averages between the two temperature extremes (0 vs 100 degrees F). There were only a few cases where a significant level of velocity variation was not demonstrated. In particular, the two loads that showed the least effect between the two temperature extremes were Number 6 (Winchester AA Heavy Target 12-

Nine different types of ammunition made up the test ammo, six in 12-gauge and three in 20-gauge.

gauge) and Number 8 (Federal Game 20-gauge). A perplexing thing took place with Load Number 6, however. In this particular round, the average velocity *dropped* 62 fps at 100 degrees, when compared to the 32-degree rounds. This would indicate a reversal from what I would characterize as the normal trend.

The loads that showed the greatest difference for the two extreme temperatures were Load Number 5 (Federal Paper Gold Medal Handicap 12-gauge) at nearly 11 percent loss and Number 7 (Remington Express Long Range 20-gauge) at over 16 percent. As I said earlier, however, I believe the best conclusions that a reader can draw from this data may lie in looking at the tests as a group. If we calculate the overall averages, all inclusive of the nine different rounds at 0 and at 100 degrees, and compare these, we find a velocity reduction of 6.8 percent. In an attempt to put this figure into perspective, that calculates to a difference of over 80 feet per second in a load having a muzzle velocity of 1200 feet per second. Is this substantial enough to concern a shooter? This writer would have to respond, "absolutely."

## Ensuring Good Performance

If we agree that temperature can have an effect on shotshell velocity, and I think we have shown that here, can something be done to lessen these effects? It would seem logical that under cold conditions the effects can be moderated somewhat by protection of your shells. Rather than carrying your ammo exposed to the elements, for example in the shell loops of your hunting vest or sitting on the bench of your duck blind, it might be better to put them in an inside pocket of your hunting jacket. Body temperature can keep them warm. As the protected shells are used, they should be quickly replenished so you will always be shooting ammunition that has been protected from wintry temperatures.

It might be wise to give more thought to the use of different shells for different temperature conditions. Possibly the shell you use for early chukars and grouse is not the round you want when going after late-season pheasants, when the ground is frosted. Watch how your rounds perform at different temperatures and then match that performance to the conditions. If you find, as I did in the Horse Heaven Hills, that your performance seems to be less than usual, maybe its time to switch to a different shell.

Oh yeah, I never filled out that bag limit of chukars in the Horse Heaven Hills. I ran out of shells and it got dark on me. At least now I may have figured out the real reason why my performance was so pitiful. I'll never know for sure, but maybe it was because my shells just didn't have enough poop in them. I wish my ol' vizsla was still around so I could explain it to her. ●

### SHOTSHELL LOAD IDENTIFICATION

| Load No. | Shell (brand/type/length) | Gauge | Dram. Equiv. | Shot Charge (wgt. ozs./size) |
|---|---|---|---|---|
| 1 | Remington Express Long Range $2\frac{3}{4}$″ | 12 | $3\frac{3}{4}$ | $1\frac{1}{4}$/#6 |
| 2 | Federal Premium Hi-Brass $2\frac{3}{4}$″ | 12 | $3\frac{3}{4}$ | $1\frac{1}{4}$/#6 |
| 3 | Winchester Super-X High Brass $2\frac{3}{4}$″ | 12 | $3\frac{3}{4}$ | $1\frac{1}{4}$/#6 |
| 4 | Remington Premier Light Target $2\frac{3}{4}$″ | 12 | $2\frac{3}{4}$ | $1\frac{1}{8}$/#8 |
| 5 | Federal Paper Gold Medal Handicap $2\frac{3}{4}$″ | 12 | — | $1\frac{1}{8}$/#$7\frac{1}{2}$ |
| 6 | Winchester AA Heavy Target $2\frac{3}{4}$″ | 12 | 3 | $1\frac{1}{8}$/#$7\frac{1}{2}$ |
| 7 | Remington Express Long Range $2\frac{3}{4}$″ | 20 | $2\frac{3}{4}$ | 1/#$7\frac{1}{2}$ |
| 8 | Federal Game Load $2\frac{3}{4}$″ | 20 | $2\frac{1}{2}$ | $\frac{7}{8}$/#8 |
| 9 | Winchester Super-X High Brass $2\frac{3}{4}$″ | 20 | $2\frac{3}{4}$ | 1/#$7\frac{1}{2}$ |

*Copper-plated lead

Have you ever wondered why or how you should treat fired brass? Here's what you should know about...

# CASE INSPECTION AND PREPARATION

by NORMAN E. JOHNSON

CASE INSPECTION AND preparation need not be complicated nor involve a great deal of time, so long as we don't lose sight of what we want the cartridge to do. The cartridge is vital and must meet certain requirements, but the benefits of proper case inspection and preparation will serve the shooter in many ways.

A case must retain the primer, contain the powder, and hold the bullet firmly in proper alignment as it serves as a seal against gas pressure while shooting. To what mark of precision and level of safety all this is attainable is largely dependent upon us as we inspect, prepare and use the cartridges. While much of this treatise will deal with rifle cases, these procedures will apply to most metallic cases.

As handloaders and shooters, the level of precision as well as the number of cases we will be working with will vary greatly. Thus, we will want to maintain a level of precision as well as expediency as we go about our work. For example, the benchrest shooter must produce a case that is highly uniform in its entirety, while the prairie dog popper may consider volume production and efficiency of time more important. Of course, all must adhere to safe practices while selecting, inspecting and preparing cases.

### Selection Fundamentals

Regardless of the type of shooting we do or the number of cases we plan to prepare, we should use the same brand of cases for any given batch of those loaded. Different brands of cases often vary dimensionally and thus vary by weight as well as by metal alloy. Weight variance will be reflected in capacity, hence pressure, velocity and, of course, accuracy.

After segregating cases by brand, weigh them individually and set aside those that are significantly heavier or lighter than average. Place these in different boxes. An electronic scale makes this simple and fast. New cases should also be checked for weight, preferably after you have sized and trimmed them to proper dimensions. All cases should be cleaned prior to final selection, including the primer pockets. Sorting cases to within 2 or 3 grains will usually result in two or three lots from 100 cases. After that, simply keep them in their respective boxes.

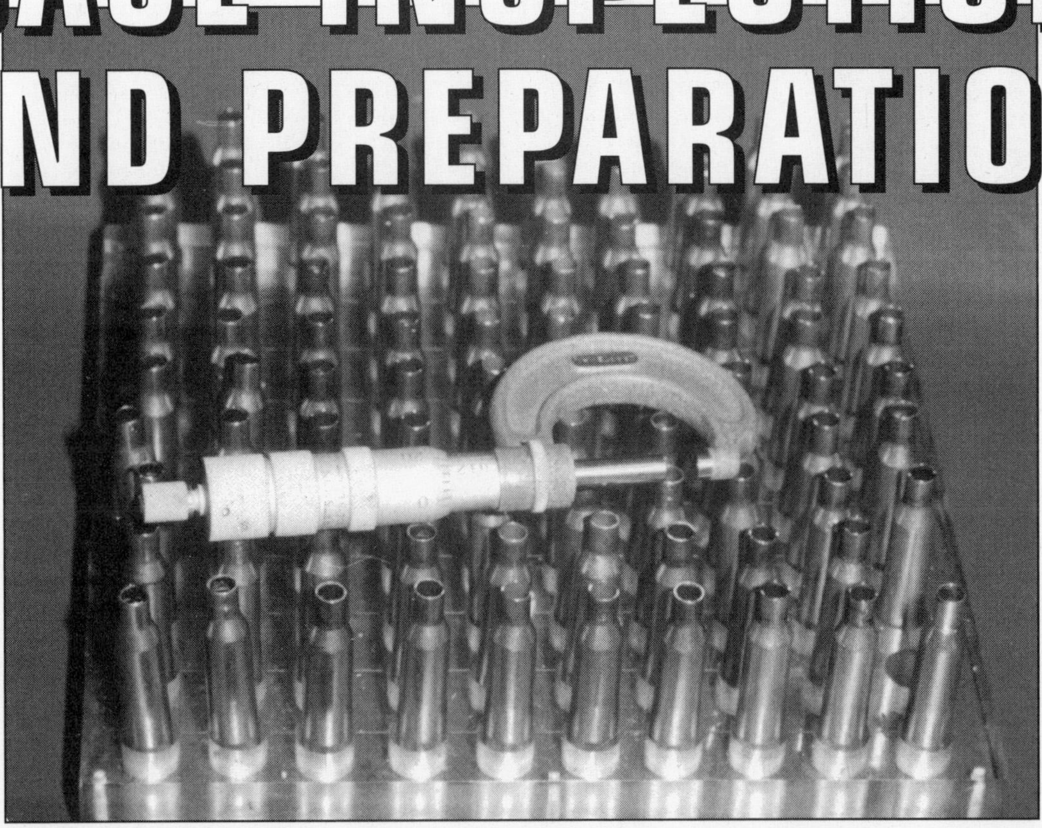

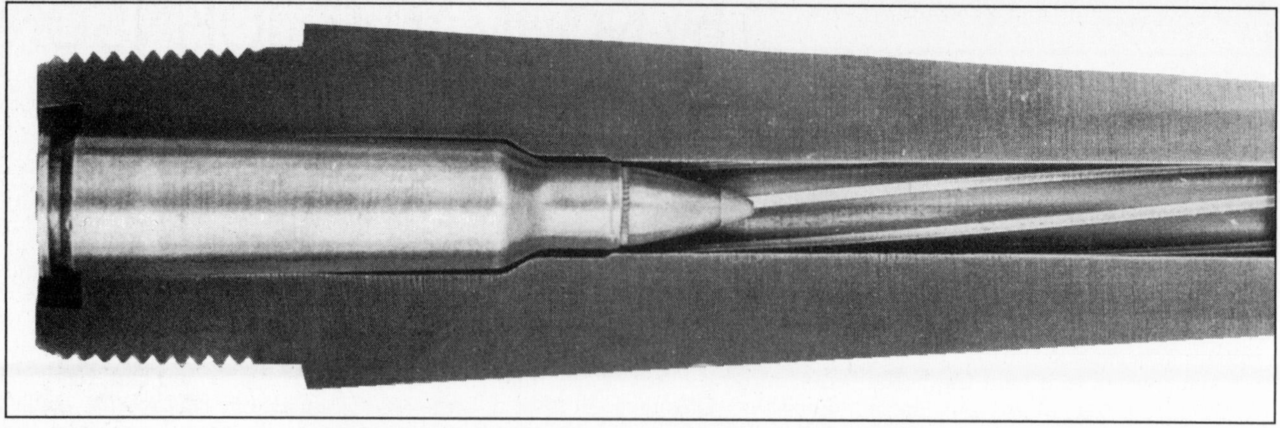

A cartridge in sectioned portion of barrel shows how a poorly fit case lies in the chamber.

Sectioned cases show the function of the cartridge case as it holds the bullet securely in alignment and contains the powder and primer ready for shooting.

Fired cases undergo changes that alter them structurally and dimensionally, and repeated firing increases any type of irregularity, so inspect them carefully for overall condition.

Prior to firing, a cartridge case is minutely smaller than the chamber, both in length and diameter. It must be, to be seated. On firing, gas pressure expands it to fill the chamber completely. This structural conformation produces a case that is fireformed to a given chamber, then the natural elasticity of the brass allows a small amount of spring-back, which makes extraction possible. However, the internal gas pressure causes cases to stretch as brass is forced outward and forward by the pressure. This effect is evident to some degree in all cartridges. This stretching sometimes causes cases to develop irregularities and defects that must be identified and dealt with. This is particularly true where there is repeated full-length sizing and firing in oversize chambers. Brass may become work-hardened and brittle, further reducing case life. Some cartridges are more susceptible than others in this respect, particularly if pressure is high and case taper is pronounced. The 220 Swift is among those in this category.

The question then begins to surface—just what should we look for as we inspect our cases? This partly depends on its intended purpose. Big game hunters may settle for a good sound case that is free of structural defects, while those concerned with extreme accuracy will search further for cases they can prepare to close tolerances.

With either goal, a close visual inspection of all cases should be performed. Here we must look intently for defects—especially in several-times-fired cases—for such things as a split or cracked neck or body, signs of an excessive load like a prominent pressure ring just above the web of the case, and any stretch ring that may indicate incipient head separation.

If the cartridges have been fired in other guns, such insidious problems may be inherited and must be identified. I once purchased some 243 cases, many of which had been weakened by firing in a rifle with excessive headspace. Had I not dis-

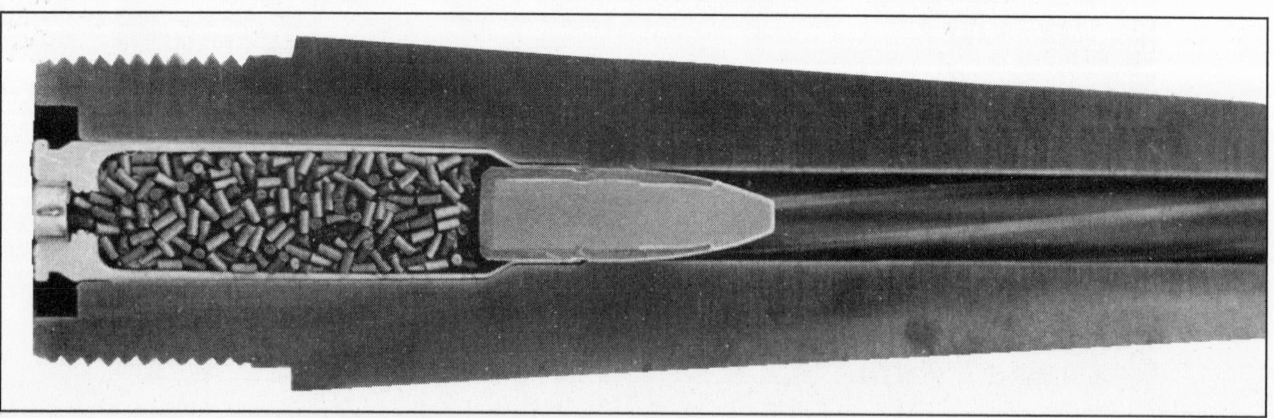

How a well-prepared case lies in the chamber.

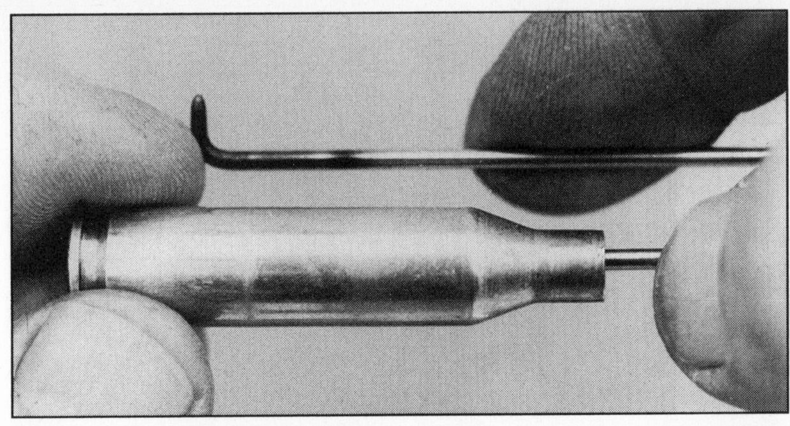

Incipient case head separation can be discovered by sliding a pointed and hooked wire inside the case wall. Note the outside stretch ring forward of the web. All cases showing this sign should be discarded.

Sectioned cases show a stretch ring ready to separate near the head. These internal grooves are readily detected using hooked wire.

covered this through close inspection, a dangerous condition could have resulted.

As you perform the visual inspection, look closely for protruding primers; they indicate the case didn't fit the chamber it was fired in. This can be a precursor to case stretching and weakening. Should you discover this defect in several cases, the remaining ones should be highly suspect.

Once you have done the visual inspection, the case must undergo further dimensional and mechanical inspection before it can be prepped. Here again, the intended use will determine its fitness. Inspection is best performed with gauges and measuring devices. Basic to this is a means of determining overall length and neck wall thickness. Later, after the primers are removed, a flash hole gauge should be used. This will be discussed in more detail later on.

At this point, the measurement and further inspection of the cases will show you what you need to do with them relative to your shooting needs. But first you should perform an internal inspection of any cases

Inspection reveals cracked or split necks—reason enough to discard cases.

(Above) Variations in case weight can affect pressures. The 220 Swift case on the left was several grains heavier than the center case, thus increasing pressure. The case on the right is unfired from a different lot.

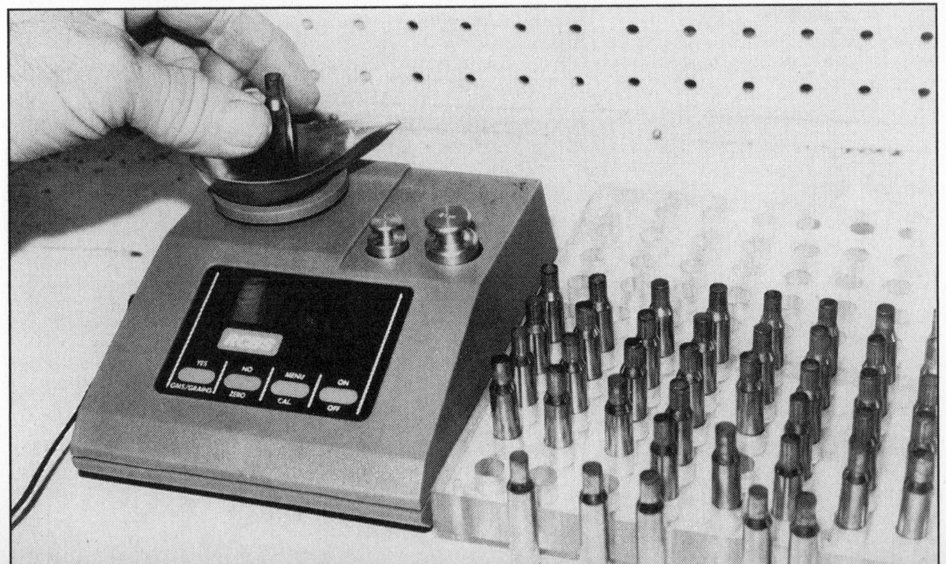

Segregating cases by weight leads to uniform pressures and velocities for more accurate shooting. The electronic scale is a great timesaver here.

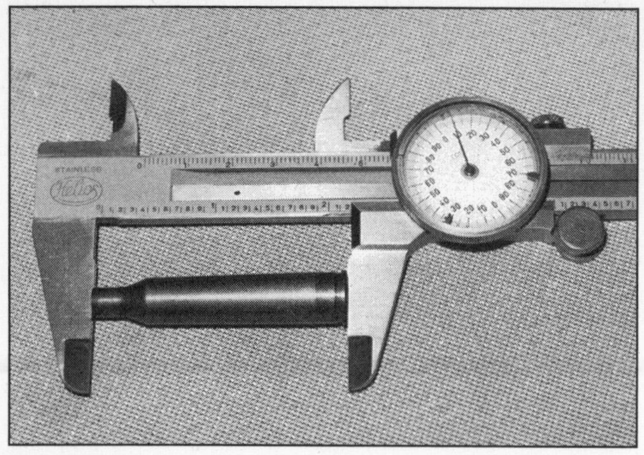

A machinist's dial caliper easily and accurately measures case length.

(Above) This handy gauge indicates whether a case needs trimming. It handles a number of common cases.

(Left) Using a Wilson trimmer gives cases the exact length desired.

The RCBS Trim Pro power case trimmer is set up on the author's bench.

that are suspect because of stretch rings. This is a simple test that can be performed with a hooked length of pointed wire. Just shove the hooked end inside the case, feeling the wall for irregularities near the web. Even minor groove-like depressions can be felt in this way, and this can alert you that the whole lot may be defective. Discard all suspect cases.

When you have a reasonable number of good cases to work with, they should be run through a sizing/decapping die before further inspection. If they are new, neck sizing only will suffice. If used, chances are they will require full-length sizing if they have been shot in a different rifle. Proper lubrication of the case neck or the entire case will be in order. Hunters often full-length size their cases to assure easy chambering, but most times there is no reason to overwork the brass, as this markedly shortens case life. After the case is sized and deprimed, further inspection can be better performed prior to the final steps in preparation.

## Final Inspection and Preparation

Consult a good reloading manual to determine maximum and "trim-to" case dimensions. Then, using a power or hand trimmer, trim all cases to the proper length. Following this, debur the outside of the case and chamfer the inside to facilitate bullet seating. The recent RCBS power case trimmer has a built-in feature that saves the handloader lots of time because the cases are trimmed and deburred in one operation. A number of other power and hand trimmers are available.

Before we get into neck preparation, a look at the primer pocket and flash hole is in order. Actually, inspection of the fired primer itself can provide important information. Smudged or blackened primers or primer pockets may signal an oversize, leaking pocket. This, along with primers that seat overly easy, are warnings that must not be overlooked. Cases in this condition should be discarded after smashing with a hammer to prevent "just one more loading." They serve as a caveat to reduce the powder charge. Primers should seat with a good, firm friction fit.

There are swaging tools on the market, as well as reamers, to remove the crimp from military-type primer pockets. Smooth, firm seating and uniform primer depth is our primary objective no matter what kind of priming tool is used. As one develops a feel for seating primers, a high degree of uniformity can be attained.

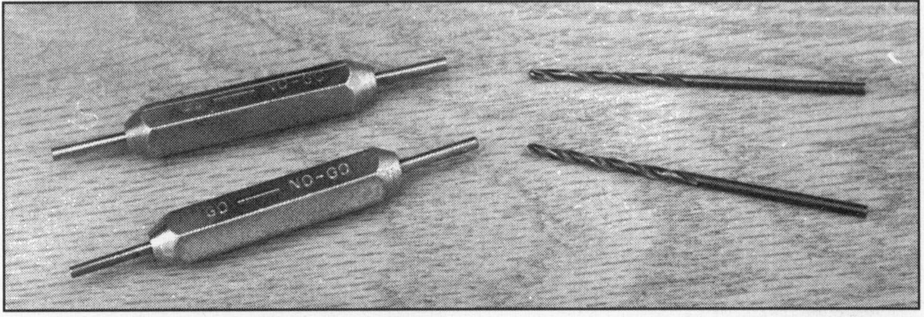

Flash hole gauges for large and small rifle and pistol cases along with appropriate drills for proper flash hole sizing. Cases with flash holes larger than the prescribed maximum should be discarded because this could result in extreme chamber pressures.

This prepared case is ready for priming with an RCBS priming tool.

RCBS' automatic primer feed head attaches to the press and automatically feeds primers from a tape into the feed system.

Fully as important to good priming is a pocket clear of debris and a uniform flash hole size. Cleaning primer pockets takes but seconds using a common square spade of correct size or one of the numerous power-driven tools.

In American-made cases, the flash holes are usually punched from the outside rather than drilled, and this often leaves a burr around part of the inner end of the hole. This is a random and inconsistent thing, and it can affect the way the primer's flame reaches the powder. Cutters—small tools that are inserted through the mouth of the case and rotated by hand—can remove these bits of metal. The idea is to just remove the ragged edge, not to weaken the head of the case, so use the correct tool for the job, such as those made by K&M, Russ Haydon and others.

Consistency of the flash hole diameter is also important to uniform ignition. There are gauges for checking this, usually go/no-go tools. For example, the gauge used for a 222 Remington may range from .080 to .088, minimum to maximum. This allows easy case segregation for those with extreme accuracy goals. Or you can standardize hole diameter by using an appropriate drill, so long as it doesn't exceed specified maximum diameter.

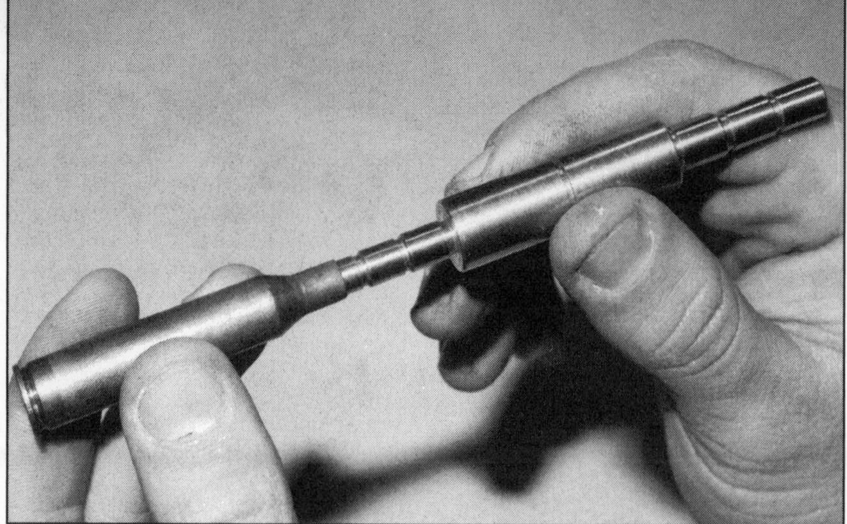

This special gauge designed and made by the author to exact bullet diameter helps determine if the fired case requires neck reaming or turning to prevent pinched bullets on chambering.

A case neck gauge invented by the author quickly and accurately determines neck wall thicknesses and variations.

### Case Neck Preparation

There are certain advantages to neck sizing cases, including extended case life and better case/bullet alignment in the chamber, for instance. And simple neck sizing also means a lot less work during case preparation. Most die manufacturers offer neck sizing dies along with a three-die set, or you can buy them individually. Thus, if handloads are to be fired in the same chamber as they were originally, neck sizing only is recommended.

Is it necessary to size the entire case neck when reloading? A quality neck-resizing die will provide precise bullet alignment and very adequate bullet retention with only partial neck resizing. But it is recommended that you size at least one bullet-diameter length of the case neck for uniform bullet pull during firing.

In a series of tests to determine if the degree of neck sizing influenced accuracy—involving three highly accurate benchrest rifles—no measurable difference was determined. However, when setting the sizing die in the press, be sure it is not set so deeply that the shoulder of the case is pushed back. This would produce excessive headspace in non-belted cases.

In a more vital area of case preparation, we get into neck reaming or turning. Case neck dimensions must be maintained for a number of reasons. Neck trimming—shortening cases to proper length—has already been discussed. Case neck walls need to be maintained at a proper and uniform thickness for two reasons. First, case necks stretch and thicken as a result of repeated firing, and if left this way, the thickened brass will contact the chamber neck before it can expand enough to fully release the bullet during firing. This can result in excessively high chamber pressure, so case necks must be monitored for this condition.

One simple test to check for thick necks is to try to insert the base of a bullet into a freshly fired case mouth. If the bullet enters easily you should be able to reload that case at least once more before further attention is devoted to neck turning or reaming. Ideally .002- to .004-inch is an acceptable clearance between the cartridge neck and the chamber—perhaps a bit greater for big game hunting cartridges.

You can also get a pretty good idea where you stand here by simply measuring the outside neck diameter of a loaded cartridge with a good micrometer and comparing this figure with the chamber neck diameter—assuming that you know it. If you don't, an accurate chamber cast can provide this information. I have also turned a brass rod to exact rifle chamber neck diameter to provide precise reference in this area. I then keep my case necks turned to within about .002-inch chamber neck clearance for my better rifles. This provides adequate clearance for bullet release. I have also made a special gauge of exact bullet diameter to insert into the mouth of a fired case as a basic test, as I have previously described, to take the place of a bullet for this purpose.

The second reason for reaming or turning case necks is to provide uniform case wall thickness. In most

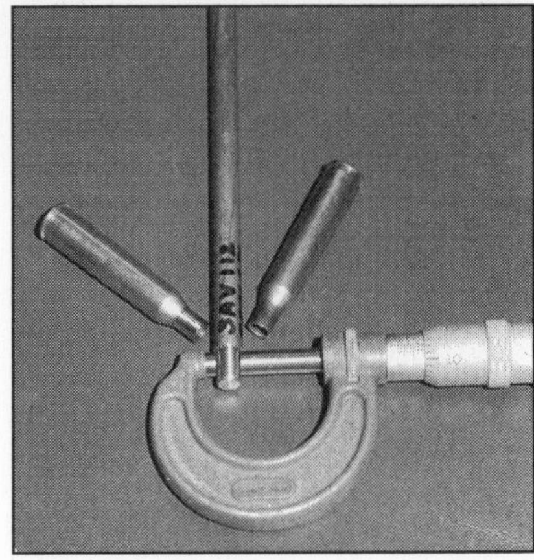

Tight case necks produced excessive chamber pressures by restraining the bullet when these cartridges were fired. One shows a markedly flattened primer (right), and the other a blown primer. These signs should warn the handloader of problems in this area.

(Above) A length of brass rod is turned to the exact chamber neck diameter to determine the exact case neck wall tolerance needed for precise shooting.

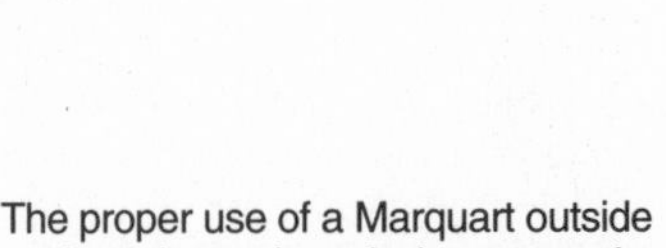

The proper use of a Marquart outside neck turning tool results in case necks of extremely uniform wall thickness.

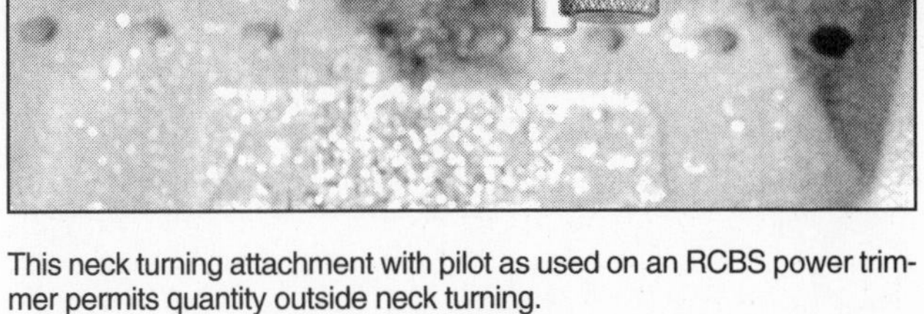

This neck turning attachment with pilot as used on an RCBS power trimmer permits quantity outside neck turning.

(Right) A case neck is being turned to exact wall thickness using a lathe and pilot.

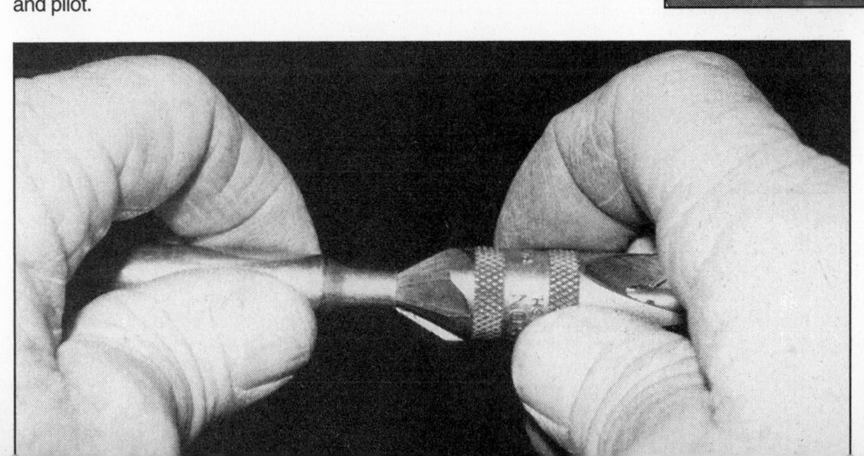

Wilson's dual-purpose chamfering tool deburrs both inside and outside of the case mouth.

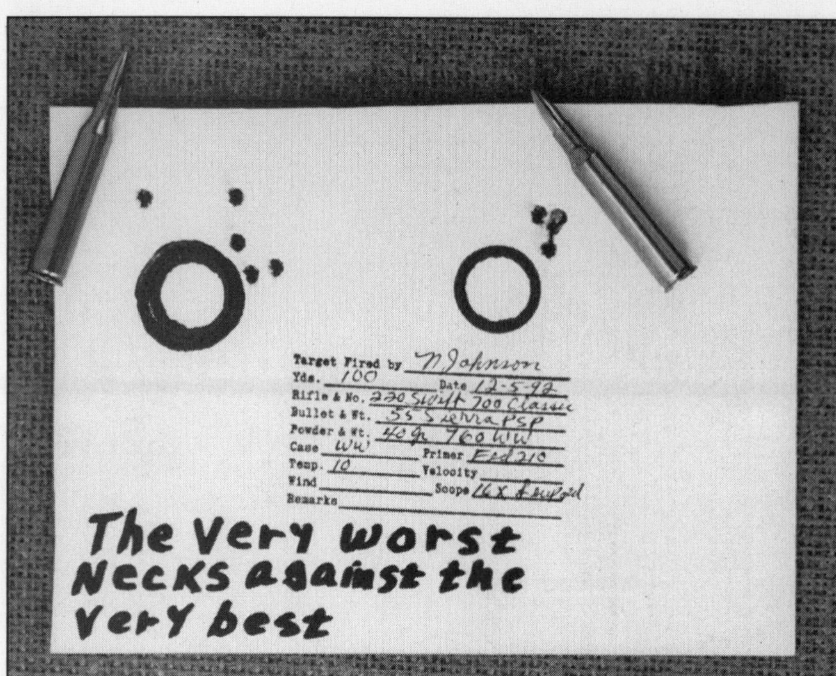


These 220 Swift groups were fired using the poorest case necks (left) and with necks of near-perfect wall thickness (right).

(Below) Groups using carefully turned case necks (top) against randomly selected necks with runout from .002- to .008-inch, with a 222 Magnum 40X Remington.

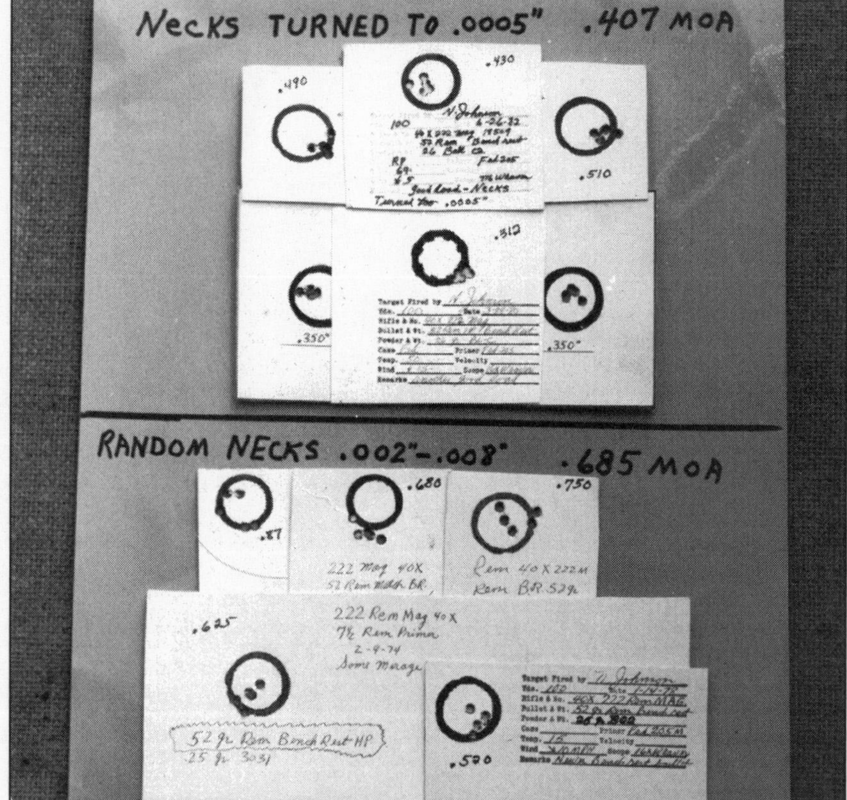


instances, a simple cleanup of the neck, removing but a couple thousandths of material, is sufficient. There remains little debate regarding the preferred method of doing this. Those truly interested in accuracy have largely abandoned neck reaming. Reaming simply doesn't produce as uniform a neck wall as turning metal from the outside of the case neck.

The benefits of neck turning were brought out more than thirty years ago in my article "Case Neck Variations and Their Effects on Accuracy" in *Gun Digest*, 20th Edition. I also had an article in the 1981 HANDLOADER'S DIGEST entitled, "Outside Is Better," dealing at length with the advantages of outside neck turning.

Different methods are used to turn case necks to uniformity as well as to the desired thickness. These include power turners and those used by hand. The principle is to use an inside-the-neck guide pilot with a cutter encircling the case neck set to remove a precise shaving of brass.

I have even used a lathe for this purpose, as well as a special mini-lathe I designed for the job. Sometimes two passes with the cutter will leave a more uniform finish where appreciable brass removal is required. The end result is a case neck turned to near-zero tolerance and to exact thickness.

Before turning case necks, the entire neck should be sized. This is necessary to prevent an excessive amount of brass being turned from the unsized larger-diameter portion of the neck nearer the shoulder. The small amount of lube remaining inside the case neck from sizing will usually provide enough lubrication for the neck turning spindle, but sometimes you have to add lube to it.

Properly selected and prepared cases will lead to concentric bullet seating and better bullet/case alignment. However, to take full advantage of your efforts, use a quality in-line bullet seating die. It will add further precision to your cartridge.

If you are among those who have settled for average shooting performance, the proper case inspection and preparation described above will be major steps toward safer and more accurate shooting. Further encouragement shouldn't be necessary. ●

by MIKE THOMAS

# 308 WINCHESTER STILL FIRST RATE WITH CAST BULLETS

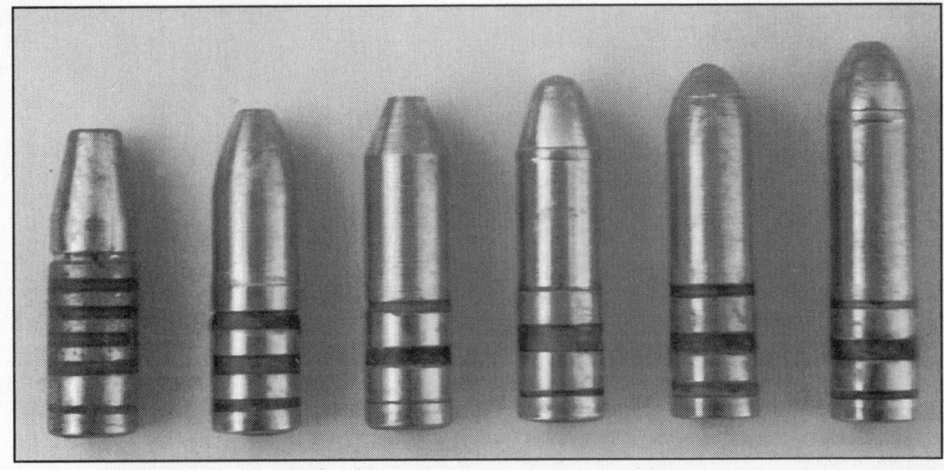

Cast bullets used in the author's testing (from left): Saeco #315, 169 grains; RCBS 30-180SP, 179 grains; Saeco #301, 189 grains; NEI 308-188-GC-DD, 193 grains; Lyman #311335, 205 grains; and the NEI 308-210-GC-DD, 221 grains. All bullets are fitted with Hornady gas checks and lubricated with Thompson Bear Cold lube.

PERHAPS SINCE ITS inception in the early '50s, the 308 Winchester has been noted as being a very accurate cartridge. No doubt this notoriety was gained exclusively with the use of jacketed bullets. The 308 was even used in formal benchrest competition for years and did well; that in itself says a great deal about the accuracy potential of the cartridge. Its use and subsequent success as an accurate cast bullet cartridge is not nearly as well known.

Even for a neophyte cast bullet enthusiast, the 308 Winchester comes highly recommended as a cartridge with which to learn the basics of the cast bullet game. Serious cast bullet shooters have an almost obsessive propensity for experimentation, and the 308 also serves well in this capacity for the intermediate and advanced enthusiast.

While it is true that many cast bullet benchrest competitors have gone to wildcat cartridges (based on shortened 308 cases in most instances), the standard 308 in an accurate rifle will still perform astonishingly well from an accuracy standpoint.

Quite a few cast bullet fans have a sincere interest in obtaining fine accuracy from their rifles. These same shooters, however, can't justify spending a large sum for a custom-actioned and -barreled rifle with which to shoot tiny groups. They don't want to invest $400 to $600 in a high-powered target scope either. And it is doubtful that they load their ammunition with benchrest hand dies using an arbor press. Why, these folks probably don't even have the equipment to square-up primer pockets or debur flash holes.

What they do have is run-of-the-mill handloading tools, dies, scales, measures, etc. Many also have a dial caliper and a micrometer. They buy new and used production rifles made by companies with names like Remington, Ruger, Savage, Winchester, and others. The same can be said of the scopes they use. These folks can actually do serious accuracy work with equipment they already have.

Loaded cast bullet 308 cartridges shown for comparison (from left): Saeco #315; RCBS 30-180SP; Saeco #301; Lyman #311335; NEI 308-188-GC-DD; and NEI 308-210-GC-DD.

The wide forend of the Remington Model 700VS rifle allows it to securely ride the front rest bag to ensure a steady hold for precision work.

## Gun and Scope

Since most earnest cast bullet shooters (including the author) probably belong to the above-described group, I have approached this article from that perspective. For a test rifle, I selected a new Remington Model 700VS (Varmint Synthetic) chambered in, of course, 308 Winchester.

This rifle is basically the old "Varmint Special" with several significant changes. It sports a 26-inch (1:10-inch twist) heavy barrel that has a muzzle diameter of about .800-inch. The barrel and action have a dull matte finish. The barrel is free floated in the charcoal-colored synthetic stock. An aluminum bedding block runs the full length of the receiver. The forend has a wide flat for added stability when shooting from a rest. And, finally, the barrel crown is cut in a concave fashion.

Using a Redfield base and rings, I mounted an older 20x Lyman LWBR scope equipped with a plain crosshair reticle atop the rifle. Precision work at 100 yards can easily be accomplished using any good quality scope of 10x or greater power. As with my Lyman, I strongly recommend a scope with a parallax-adjustable objective lens and target-type windage and elevation adjustments. Fine crosshairs are particularly helpful with the lower-powered scopes.

## Components

All loading data was developed using Remington brass, CCI 200 and CCI 250 large rifle and large rifle magnum primers, Hornady gas checks, and an alloy with a Brinell hardness of 15 to 16. This alloy is marketed as linotype, but it is actually the Lyman #2 mixture which has worked splendidly for me for a number of years.

### Bullet Moulds

I used six bullet designs, each of which has a proven accuracy reputation. Bullets cast from these moulds are rather easily capable of producing five-shot groups of 1.50 inches or less at 100 yards when used in selected loadings. All moulds are of the conventional double-cavity persuasion, with the exception of the one produced by NEI Handtools, Inc. This mould has two cavities, but each is cut for a different bullet.

(Above) The Remington Model 700VS (Varmint Synthetic) proved to be a fine out-of-the-box rifle for accurate cast bullet shooting. It's essentially the old Varmint Special with 26-inch barrel, synthetic stock, and a full-length aluminum bedding block under the receiver.

The author used an older model Lyman LWBR (Light Weight Bench Rest) 20x scope for all load development and testing with the Remington M700VS. The scope is equipped with precise, target-type adjustments.

**Saeco #301**: A bore-riding nose design. Bullets come from the mould measuring an average of .3131-inch and weigh 189 grains sized, lubricated, and gas-checked.

**Saeco #315**: A tapered "benchrest" design. Average as-cast diameter is .3122-inch. Bullets weigh 169 grains ready to load.

**Lyman #311335**: A bore-riding nose design. Measuring .3112-inch unsized, this bullet weighs 205 grains.

**RCBS 30-180SP**: A bore-riding nose design. This bullet averages .3116-inch and weighs 179 grains.

**NEI 308-188-GC-DD** (catalog #61) Measures .3113-inch unsized, with a weight of 193 grains, lubed and gas checked.

**NEI 308-210-GC-DD** (catalog #65A) Measures .3121-inch unsized, and weighs 221 grains ready to shoot.

The last two NEI bullet designs are fairly new and somewhat unconventional. A brief explanation is in order. Walt Melander, owner of NEI, developed his "dimensionally detailed" moulds in response to the ideas of experienced cast bullet shooters. These designs feature a one-caliber-long driving band with the forepart undersized for the bore diameter (about .002-inch). They have a fine centering ring just behind the bullet's meplat. According to Walt, this style will give the least friction. The "DD" style is available in all popular calibers. The 308-188-GC-DD, for instance, has one lube groove and two driving bands with a body slightly under bore diameter. The forward centering ring, just south of the nose, is slightly larger than bore diameter. The customer must specify the diameter of the centering ring. In 30-caliber, that can be from .301- to .303-inch.

### Powders

I used four. In the order of burning rates (from fast to slow) are Hercules Reloder 7, Accurate Arms 2015BR and 2230, and Hodgdon's H-4831. I see no point in examining each individual load in this text; the data tables are self-explanatory. However, I will touch on the high points as we progress.

The Remington Model 700VS has the typical 308 Winchester throat/chamber, which means that most long bullets will need to be seated deeply so the base of the bullet extends below the case neck. This is not always the detriment to accuracy that many shooters believe. Surprisingly accurate loads have been developed with deep-seated bullets. As for the bullets mentioned here, the Saeco #301, Lyman #311335, and NEI 308-210-GC-DD all must be seated with the base well below the case neck.

While on the subject of seating depth, all loads in the data table have the bullets seated out to a point where the bullet nose is at least slightly engraved by the rifling when the loaded cartridge is chambered. I have listed the seating depth for each bullet, but this figure will necessarily vary from rifle to rifle, at least minutely. The best rule of thumb is to seat a bullet as far out as possible, but just short of the point where a loaded round will "de-bullet" when the bolt is opened.

All bullets were sized and lubricated in a Redding (Saeco) sizer/lubricator. A .310-inch sizing die was used

## 308 WINCHESTER CAST BULLET LOADING DATA

| —Bullet— Wgt. Grs. | Type | Load (Grs./Powder) | MV (fps) | OAL (ins.) | Comments |
|---|---|---|---|---|---|
| 189 | Saeco #301 | 24.0/RL-7 | 1740 | 2.71 | accurate |
| 189 | Saeco #301 | 26.0/RL-7 | — | 2.71 | |
| 189 | Saeco #301 | 28.0/AA2015BR | 1855 | 2.71 | accurate |
| 189 | Saeco #301 | 29.0/AA2230 | 1880 | 2.71 | |
| 189 | Saeco #301 | 45.0/H-4831 | 2040 | 2.71 | |
| 189 | Saeco #301 | 45.0/H-4831 | 2130 | 2.71 | CCI 250 primer |
| 189 | Saeco #301 | 46.0/H-4831 | 2145 | 2.71 | poor |
| 169 | Saeco #315 | 24.0/RL-7 | 1800 | 2.72 | accurate |
| 169 | Saeco #315 | 25.0/RL-7 | — | 2.72 | |
| 169 | Saeco #315 | 26.0/AA2015BR | 1765 | 2.72 | accurate |
| 169 | Saeco #315 | 28.0/AA2015BR | 1880 | 2.72 | accurate |
| 169 | Saeco #315 | 27.0/AA2230 | — | 2.72 | |
| 169 | Saeco #315 | 29.0/AA2230 | 1920 | 2.72 | accurate; ten-shot group 1.25 inches |
| 169 | Saeco #315 | 44.0/H-4831 | 2010 | 2.72 | accurate |
| 169 | Saeco #315 | 44.0/H-4831 | 2010 | 2.72 | accurate; CCI 250 primer |
| 169 | Saeco #315 | 46.0/H-4831 | 2130 | 2.72 | poor |
| 205 | Lyman #311335 | 24.0/RL-7 | 1770 | 2.70 | |
| 205 | Lyman #311335 | 26.0/RL-7 | 1835 | 2.70 | |
| 205 | Lyman #311335 | 28.0/AA2015BR | 1840 | 2.70 | accurate |
| 205 | Lyman #311335 | 29.0/AA2230 | — | 2.70 | poor |
| 205 | Lyman #311335 | 30.0/AA2230 | 1885 | 2.70 | |
| 205 | Lyman #311335 | 43.0/H-4831 | 1990 | 2.70 | |
| 205 | Lyman #311335 | 43.0/H-4831 | 2005 | 2.70 | poor; CCI 250 primer |
| 179 | RCBS 30-180SP | 24.0/RL-7 | 1760 | 2.80 | |
| 179 | RCBS 30-180SP | 25.0/RL-7 | 1830 | 2.80 | |
| 179 | RCBS 30-180SP | 28.0/AA2015BR | 1865 | 2.80 | |
| 179 | RCBS 30-180SP | 28.0/AA2230 | 1805 | 2.80 | accurate |
| 179 | RCBS 30-180SP | 29.0/AA2230 | 1830 | 2.80 | accurate |
| 179 | RCBS 30-180SP | 44.0/H-4831 | 2015 | 2.80 | |
| 179 | RCBS 30-180SP | 44.0/H-4831 | 2010 | 2.80 | CCI 250 primer |
| 193 | NEI 308-188-GC-DD | 24.0/RL-7 | 1745 | 2.85 | accurate |
| 193 | NEI 308-188-GC-DD | 26.0/RL-7 | 1895 | 2.85 | |
| 193 | NEI 308-188-GC-DD | 28.0/AA2015BR | 1815 | 2.85 | |
| 193 | NEI 308-188-GC-DD | 29.0/AA2015BR | 1910 | 2.85 | |
| 193 | NEI 308-188-GC-DD | 29.0/AA2230 | 1820 | 2.85 | accurate |
| 193 | NEI 308-188-GC-DD | 30.0/AA2230 | 1880 | 2.85 | |
| 193 | NEI 308-188-GC-DD | 43.0/H-4831 | 1945 | 2.85 | |
| 193 | NEI 308-188-GC-DD | 44.0/H-4831 | 2030 | 2.85 | poor |
| 221 | NEI 308-210-GC-DD | 24.0/RL-7 | 1710 | 2.86 | poor |
| 221 | NEI 308-210-GC-DD | 26.0/RL-7 | 1815 | 2.86 | |
| 221 | NEI 308-210-GC-DD | 27.0/RL-7 | 1860 | 2.86 | poor |
| 221 | NEI 308-210-GC-DD | 28.0/AA2015BR | 1775 | 2.86 | |
| 221 | NEI 308-210-GC-DD | 29.0/AA2015BR | 1855 | 2.86 | MOA accurate |
| 221 | NEI 308-210-GC-DD | 29.0/AA2230 | 1805 | 2.86 | accurate |
| 221 | NEI 308-210-GC-DD | 30.0/AA2230 | 1840 | 2.86 | sub-MOA |
| 221 | NEI 308-210-GC-DD | 42.0/H-4831 | 1910 | 2.86 | |

Test rifle: Remington Model 700VS, 308 Winchester, 26-inch barrel.
Data compiled using Oehler 35P chronograph.
Ambient temperatures varied from 55 to 75 degrees F.
Components: Remington 308 brass, CCI 200 and CCI 250 primers, Thompson Bear Cold bullet lubricant, Hornady 30-caliber gas checks.
All bullets sized to .310-inch except for the Saeco #315 which was sized to .311-inch.
Alloy hardness: 15 to 16 BHN.
All groups five shots at 100 yards.
Velocity averages rounded to nearest 5 fps.
No fillers used in loads.
All loads tested were safe in the author's rifle.
Loads *should not be reduced* more than 5 percent to assure proper ignition and safety.

with all bullets except the Saeco #315. For some reason, this bullet was slightly more accurate when sized .311-inch. Perhaps in a different rifle this would not be the case. Bullets were lubricated with Thompson Bullet Lube "Bear Cold" lube.

This is rather hard lubricant that doesn't flow well through the Redding tool without applying heat to soften it. I have used Bear Cold extensively on cast rifle bullets with good results. LBT Blue is also worth trying. With bullets of proper diameter and hardness, leading is seldom, if ever, a problem with either of these lubricants. Other lubricants may also work well, but I can vouch for only those I have used.

All loads were assembled using RCBS dies in a Bonanza Co-Ax press. Brass was slighty belled to facilitate bullet seating.

I am reluctant to pick a "best" powder and "best" bullet. Bullets and powders were carefully selected, and all have the potential for fine accuracy. My testing involved a number of lengthy range sessions from which I learned a great deal. I offer the data to the reader and am confident that these loads will work well for others.

It is important to note that bullets were not weighed or segregated in any manner. Only a cursory visual inspection was made. This may account for unexplained flyers in some instances. The turning of case necks was mandatory for my rifle; however, this procedure may be totally unnecessary in another rifle.

H-4831 powder was the least useful of the propellants tested. Some horrible groups were shot with it. Nevertheless, it did well with the Saeco #315 bullet. Other powders also accounted for a poor group or two. All bullets were accurate in at least a couple of loadings.

The Saeco #301 bullet was slightly disappointing in that the best group size obtainable was 1.5 inches. I had anticipated somewhat better results with it. The Saeco #315, on the other hand, was capable of grouping inside of 1.25 inches. All groups were of five shots, with the exception of a very few ten-shot strings. One such group with this bullet stayed in the 1.25-inch realm using AA2230 powder. Lyman's #311335 did respectably well, but like the Saeco #301 was slightly disappointing. The bullet is still capable of consistently grouping in 1.5 inches or less.

Like the Saeco #315, the RCBS 30-100SP will shoot small groups without a great deal of load development. The NEI 308-188-GC-DD stayed within 1.25 inches with AA2230 and RL7 powders. The NEI 308-210-GC-DD is a very long bullet measuring 1.30 inches overall. The length forced me to use a short homemade top punch in my lubricator/sizer. At first glance, this bullet seems far too long for use in the 308 case. It's really not, however, and accuracy was excellent.

By the way, the centering ring on these two DD bullets measured .3035-inch. According to Walt Melander, a number of cast bullet competitors are using these bullets in matches. That's pretty high praise for any bullet. The NEI heavyweight turned in sub-MOA groups with AA2230 and AA2015BR powders. The lighter bullet was not quite as accurate in my testing, but still did quite well.

None of the loads in the tables are maximum. However, I would caution readers not to reduce powder charges by more than 5 percent, if that. Improper ignition and poor accuracy may result if charges are too light. Actually, it would be better to go to a faster burning powder rather than cut the listed charges to the point of inefficiency. It is important to remind ourselves that chamber pressure can be too low to fully expand case necks against the chamber when a round is fired.

In this situation, since there is no effective gas seal, powder gases can escape around the case to the rear of the action in the direction of the shooter's face. The blowby leaves cases particularly dirty, the neck and shoulder area covered with a heavy soot. The problem is effectively eliminated by gradually increasing the powder charge.

In the data tables comment column, "accurate" indicates one or more groups fired with a particular load that went into 1.5 inches or less.

There you have it. Good shooting. ●

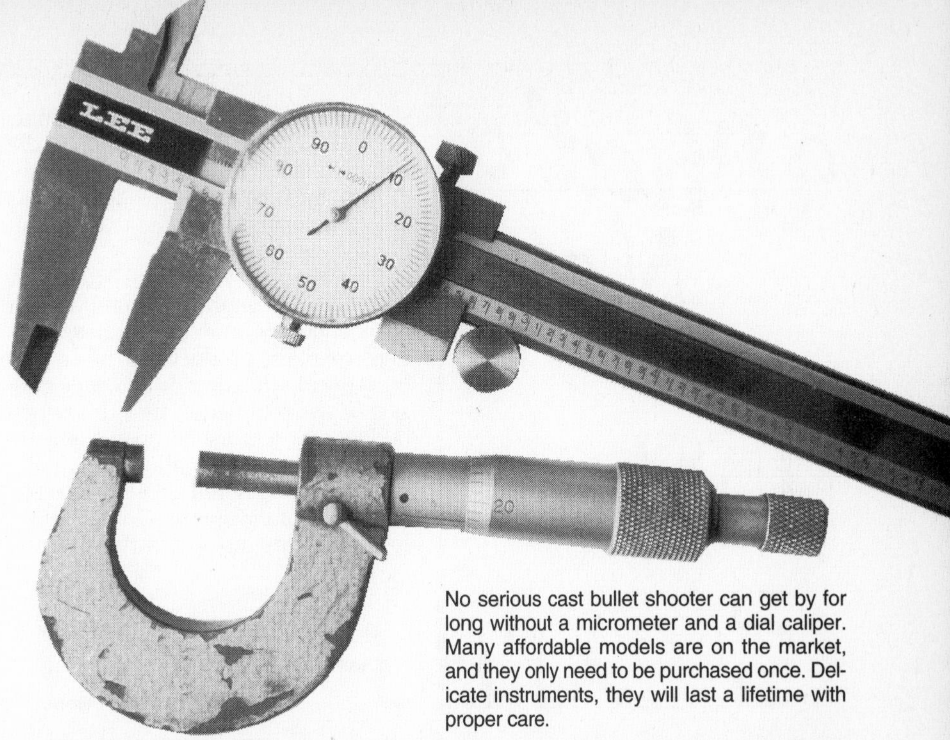


No serious cast bullet shooter can get by for long without a micrometer and a dial caliper. Many affordable models are on the market, and they only need to be purchased once. Delicate instruments, they will last a lifetime with proper care.

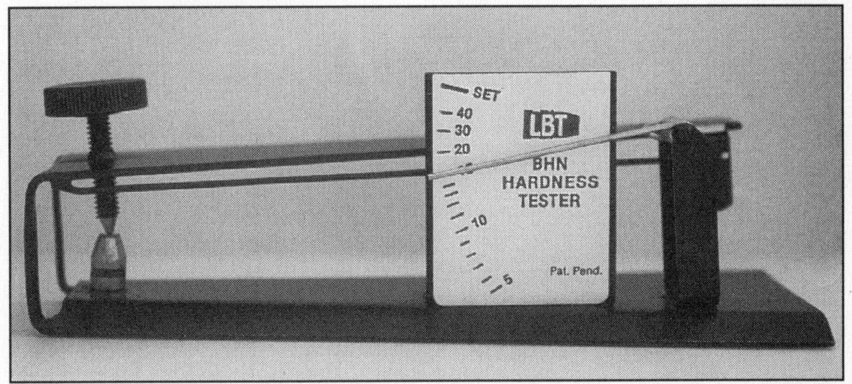


Bullet casters can't expect much more than mediocre results if alloy hardness is unknown from one batch to another. The LBT Hardness Tester is a no-nonsense instrument for measuring the Brinell hardness of a bullet. Redding also markets a tester.

# What's New IN COMPONENTS

by STEVE COMUS

THIS IS ONE of the most fascinating times on the firearms front in the recent history of Gundom. The pendulum may continue to swing, but not necessarily along the traditionally predictable path.

Put simply, there are quantum advances in sophistication, among both shooters and companies, that offer relevant products for us to use. Starting about a decade ago, an explosion in the number of "new" high-tech bullets was unleashed upon the market. Then came a smaller but equally significant blossoming in the number and kinds of powder available.

Such frantic activity cannot be sustained, nor would shooters really want it to be. Why? Because it takes time for the general shooting public to assimilate and put into everyday use any or all of a group of advancements. For example, some of the clean-burning, lower-heat, high-performance pistol and shotgun powders introduced during the past several years must be distributed throughout Gundom, and then shooters must have ample opportunity to try them to see what works best for their individual applications.

And so it goes with the extensive number of truly high-performance hunting and self-defense component bullets introduced during the past ten to fifteen years. It takes a number of yearly hunt cycles for shooters, in general, to be able to decide precisely what works best for them.

To a degree, this process continues. What this means is that, right now, companies are interested in offering the kinds of things that fill in the blanks. For example, following the rash of bullet and powder introductions over the past several years, now there is a parallel updating of reloading manuals to provide effective data so the handloaders can make best use of the products that now are available.

Among some of the more interesting introductions for this year, by manufacturer in alphabetical order, are these offerings:

### Alliant Techsystems

There is a lot of news this year from Alliant (formerly Hercules Powder Co.). The news includes everything

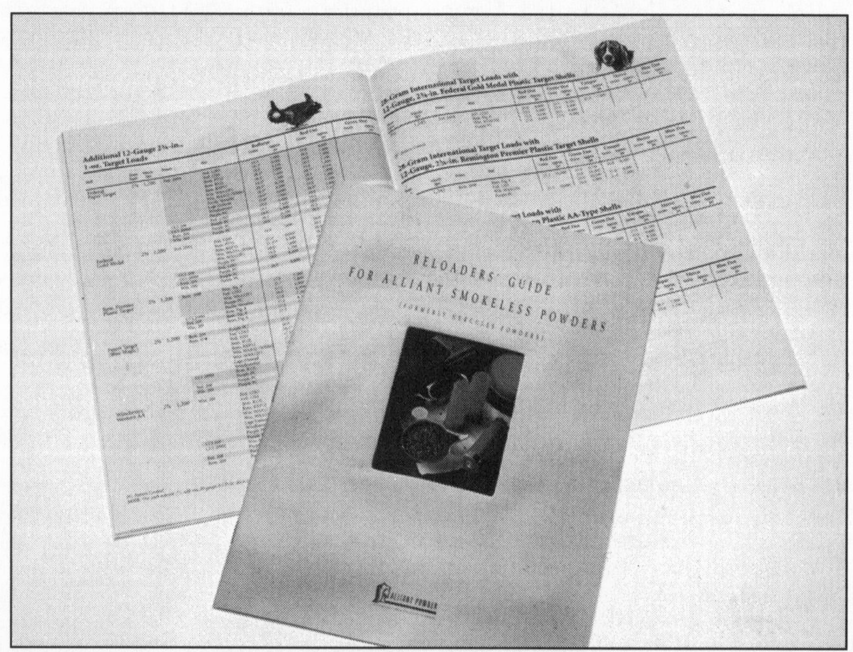


The *Reloaders' Guide for Alliant Smokeless Powders* has been redesigned.

from new packaging sizes for some of the powders to a new loading manual to a new guy to answer handloaders' questions on a computer website.

American Select shotgun powder is now available in an 8-pound plastic container. Previously, the product was offered only in 1- and 4-pound containers. The Reloder series of powders is now being offered in 8-ounce containers. Previously, Reloder powders were available only in 1- and 5-pound containers. The Reloder series comprises five smokeless powders for rifle cartridges. Series 7 is used in light rifle loads, series 12 and 15 are used in medium rifle loads, and series 19 and 22 are used in magnum rifle loads.

Alliant Techsystems has redesigned its *Reloaders' Guide for Alliant Smokeless Powders* to give it a new reader-friendly look and more information. The sixty-page booklet has been completely reformatted to an easier-to-read larger size and includes new data on American Select, Power Pistol, 357 SIG, 10mm, CCI SC primers, a variety of wad and primer combinations, and other loads as well as updated bushing charts. The publication also includes an eight-page insert that provides information on the history of Alliant powders and the company's new multi-million-dollar manufacturing facility in Richmond, Virginia. It also has a complete listing of Alliant powder products and their uses and characteristics.

Ben Amonette has been named technical service representative for Alliant. He is responsible for providing technical information to reloaders who inquire about Alliant powders through the company's toll-free assistance telephone line. Also, information about Alliant powders is now available on the Internet at http://reloading.ATK.com. Information includes subjects related to reloading and shooting, safety, shooting events, media and industry associations, and Alliant powders.

### Barnes Bullets

This year, the big news at Barnes is the introduction of five more kinds of their famous X-Bullets. Four of the new component bullets are for pistols, and the fifth is a 22-caliber.

Barnes is introducing the all-new Pistol X-Bullet line available in 44, 45 and 50 calibers. These include a 44-caliber .429-inch 200-grain XPB bullet with .172 ballistic coefficient and .155 sectional density, and 44-caliber .429-inch 225-grain XPB bullet with .195 BC and .175 SD. Also new is a 45-caliber .451-inch 250-grain XPB bullet with .188 BC and .176 SD, and a 50-caliber .500-inch 275-grain XPB bullet with .183 BC and .157 SD. The new 22-caliber X-Bullet is a .224-inch 50-grainer. Ballistic coefficient is .220, and it has a sectional density of .142.

There are two more items from Barnes that promise to be of interest to handloaders. Barnes Ballistics for Windows computer software allows the table, graph, gun information, sighting calculation, and note sections to be displayed and printed on one page for easy access and interpretation of the information. Other features include calculations for velocity, wind deflection, and striking velocities. It also helps in determining how altitude, temperature, uphill/downhill angles, wind and other factors affect bullet flight.

Also new from Barnes is their *Reloading Manual Number 2*, which features all-new graphics that compare bullet path and energies to help select the proper bullet for specific applications. There is an all-new section featuring articles by top authorities on subjects such as hunting in Africa, properly mounting scopes, accuracy from handloads, barrel cleaning tips and outdoor photography. Rounding out features of the manual are load data for all new Barnes bullets as well as ballistics tables that are easier to find and use.

### Federal Cartridge Co.

This year, Federal is offering two kinds of component brass cases: Premium Nickel-Plated and Gold Medal Brass.

Federal's Premium unprimed nickel-plated cases feature uniform grain structure and precise metallurgy that deliver strength, durability and excellent reloading capabilities. "Over the years, performance-minded hunters have recognized the consistency and quality of the proprietary brass that we use in our factory loads," says Dave Longren, vice president of engineering at Federal. "We're pleased to make these cases available."

Federal's Premium Brass cases are built to precise dimensional tolerances, which provide consistent case volume and ballistics. Their shoulders and necks are annealed to precise hardness for long life and easier loading, and the nickel-plating helps resist corrosion.

Premium cases available include the Remington 222, 223, 22-250, 7mm-08 and 7mm Magnum; the 30-06; the Winchester 270, 308 and 300 Magnum; the 45-70; and 7-30 Waters.

Also this year, Federal has brought back Gold Medal unprimed brass cases as components. They are available in 223, 308, 30-06, and 300 Winchester Magnum.

### Hawk, Inc.

Hawk, Inc., is offering its first-ever catalog. This custom bullet company offers calibers from 264 to 577, includ-

The Reloder series of powders from Alliant now comes in 8-ounce containers in addition to the 1- and 5-pound containers offered previously.

Hawk Precision Bullets are designed for real-world shooting. Here, 338 bullets recovered from a moose show (left) a diameter increase to .875-inch with 87-percent weight retention and (right) an increase to 1.05 inches with 90-percent weight retention.

ing hard-to-find sizes like 318, 348 and 411. The unique Hawk Precision Bullet has a "soft" jacket that delivers ferocious expansion, deep penetration and high weight retention. The catalog contains an explanation of the Precision Bullet and a section on terminal ballistics using a deer's chest area cross-section to show the extent of a bullet's damage, along with numerous photos. Other articles in the manual include "Hunting With Handguns" and "Muzzleloading." The remainder of the twenty-four-page catalog is full of unusual products and titles of books of interest to avid shooters and hunters.

### Hornady Manufacturing Co.

The biggest news from Grand Island, Nebraska, on the component front this year involves the sport of Cowboy Action Shooting. Hornady now is offering both loaded Frontier Cowboy Action ammunition and component bullets.

The lead in the bullets is swaged, not cast, to provide consistent, accurate performance. And the Hornady Cowboy bullet design is different. A special knurling system holds an even distribution of lubricating wax over the entire bearing surface. A grease ring at the rear of the bullet catches the wax as the bullet travels through the barrel. The result is significantly less leading in the barrel than with ordinary cast bullets with traditional grease grooves.

The bullet's authentic flatpoint design improves accuracy by moving the center of gravity back and assures proper positioning within authentic revolvers. This year, Hornady is offering two component Cowboy bullets. They are the 45-caliber (.454) 255-grain and 44-caliber (.427 for 44-40) 205-grain.

### Nosler

Nosler, Inc., is now offering its *Reloading Guide Number Four*, an all-new and greatly expanded book featuring freshly fired data for the entire line of Nosler Partition, Ballistic Tip and Handgun bullets.

This new guide, at 736 pages, is nearly 40-percent larger than Nosler's previous manual. And the actual loading data in this fourth edition represents a true departure from that found in other loading manuals. By presenting the load data in a graphic-format style, the guide gives the reader an at-a-glance comparison of velocities for each bullet weight. And there is a totally new ballistics table section.

### PMC (Eldorado Cartridge Co.)

This Boulder City, Nevada, operation is going great guns, so to speak, these days and is evolving as a much more major player in the firearms industry. For example, the extent and quality of PMC loaded ammunition is exploding, if we can use that word. And with this comes an attendant expansion in the number of component items from PMC.

For those who have not paid close attention, PMC has a lengthy record of offering component brass and bullets. But in the past, it has been more or less a hit-or-miss proposition. No longer. Now offerings are steady and expanding.

PMC offers 50 BMG unprimed brass cases in fifty-round boxes, seven boxes per case. Also offered are 660-grain FMJ bullets with cannelure. They come 100 bullets per plastic bag, six bags per case. Also available are 303 British unprimed brass cases in twenty-round boxes, twenty-five boxes per carton, as are cases for the 22-250 Remington and 243 Winchester. Finally, 9mm Luger 115-grain full-metal-jacket bullets come 500 bullets per bag, five bags per carton.

### Sierra

Four new bullets in three calibers are joining the Sierra line this year. Patterned after Sierra's 185-grain JHP, this new 45-caliber .451-inch 230-grain hollowpoint offers expansion while producing significant penetration. The momentum provided by the extra weight, combined with the bite of the cavernous hollowpoint, assures table-clearing performances in bowling pin matches. It is also designed for use in self-defense and hunting.

The 6.5mm .264-inch 107-grain MatchKing is intended for 200- and 300-yard shooting in both offhand and rapid-fire stages. It reportedly provides minimal recoil. The 6.5mm .264-inch 142-grain MatchKing is designed to be used for long-range matches fired at 600 to 1000 yards. It offers a blend of pin-point accuracy and optimum aerodynamic efficiency. Finally, the 7mm .284-inch 130-grain HPBT MatchKing is meant for competitive 7mm shooters. Sierra's new 130-grain MatchKing provides much less recoil

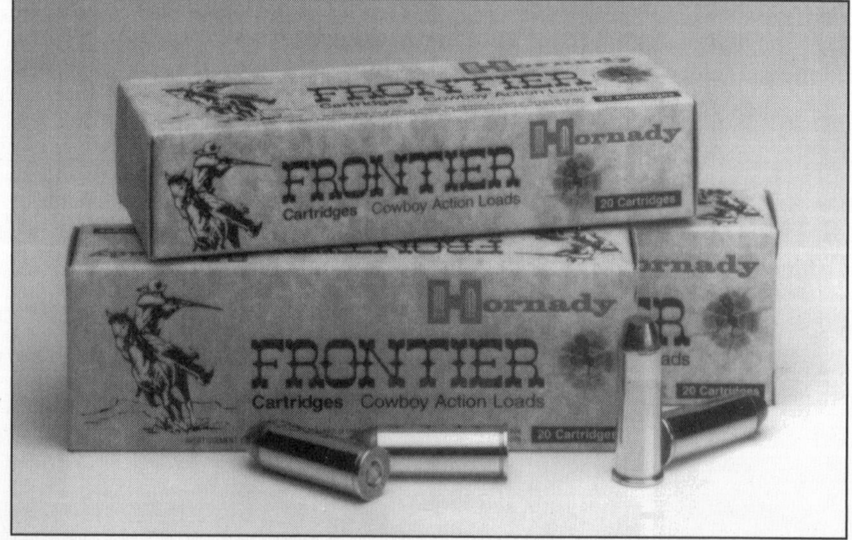


Hornady offers two new lead bullets for Cowboy Action Shooting—one 44-caliber and the other 45-caliber.

Nosler's *Reloading Guide Number Four* is now available.

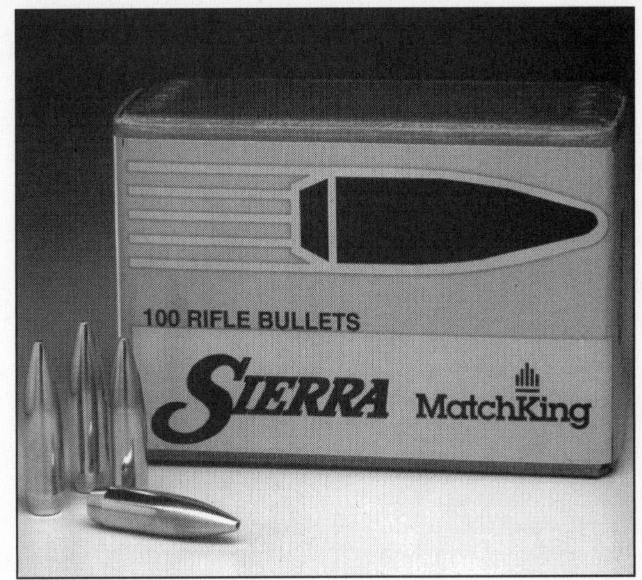


Sierra has introduced a 7mm/284 130-grain HPBT MatchKing bullet.

than the heavier 150- and 168-grain bullets used at longer ranges. Intended specifically for ranges out to 300 meters, the bullet is likely to find a home in the IHMSA and NRA Long-Range Handgun Silhouette fraternity, as well as in the various centerfire rifle disciplines.

### Speer

Speer has introduced two new component bullets this year—one a Gold Dot handgun bullet and the other a new Grand Slam rifle bullet. The new handgun bullet is a 200-grain hollowpoint for the 45 ACP. It also can be used in 45-caliber revolver cartridges. The new Grand Slam bullet is a 6.5mm 140-grain, intended for use in cartridges like the 6.5x55mm Swedish Mauser, 6.5x57mm Mauser, 6.5mm-06, 260 Remington, 264 Winchester Magnum and 6.5mm Remington Magnum.

### Winchester Ammunition (Olin)

Handgun hunting continues to evolve as a credible and quite serious sport. Within this specific kind of activity, there are two general kinds of firearm/ammo combinations. One involves single shot handguns that shoot what are essentially rifle cartridges, and the other uses more traditional handguns manifested in really powerful revolvers and autoloaders. Within the second grouping, the 454 Casull has for years been held as a standard by which powerful revolver cartridges are measured. Its major problem has been its wildcat status, which has limited its availability to a number of really pricey firearms. No longer. This year, the number of companies offering handguns that shoot the 454 Casull is growing.

Also, the 454 Casull cartridge and component brass are now being offered by a major ammo maker—specifically Winchester. Winchester initially is offering two factory loadings in the Super-X line. One is a 260-grain, and the other a 300-grain, both jacketed flatpoint designs. The two loaded offerings come fifty rounds to a box. Winchester's primed brass for the 454 Casull comes packaged 100 pieces to the box.

Winchester now offers the 454 Casull brass case as a component for reloaders.

Also new this year is the 15th edition of the *Winchester Ball Powder Propellant Reloading Manual*. This edition contains current information on loading pistol, rifle and shotgun ammunition using Winchester powders, including data for the 9x23mm Winchester and 454 Casull cartridges.

"New powder, bullet and cartridge developments along with related loading information are an ongoing process at Winchester," says Melanie Belt, associate production manager at Winchester. "In order to keep customers up to date on the latest information, we periodically update our ball powder manual." The latest version contains over 100 new loads, including information on Winchester's FailSafe rifle bullets and the new AA Plus shotshell powder. ●

by R.H. VANDENBURG, JR.

DEVELOPING LOADS that take a cartridge beyond its initial design is, for me, one of handloading's most rewarding efforts. To do so with a cartridge many consider limited in usefulness—the 30-30 Winchester—and with a gun many see as very limited—the M94 Winchester—simply heightens the pleasure.

In fairness, though, the perception of limited usefulness for the 30-30 is relatively recent. Introduced in 1895, the 30-30, then called the 30 Smokeless, began life with a metal-patched bullet of 160 grains. Other weights and styles followed quickly. The most popular hunting weights were, and are, 150 to 170 grains. But, prior to World War II, Peters offered both soft- and hollowpoint versions weighing 180 grains, and a varmint round of 110 grains was readily available.

In the early years of this century, the factories also loaded short-range or small game loads. I have in my collection 100- and 117-grain lead bullet samples loaded by Winchester. After the war, however, the light- and heavyweight offerings were dropped. It wasn't until the early 1980s that Federal introduced a 125-grain load and Remington brought out its Accelerator number with a saboted 55-grain 22-caliber bullet.

So it became the province of the handloader to develop and produce suitable lightweight varmint and small game loads. Actually, this had been going on all along, at least in some quarters. In his 1926 book, *Handloading Ammunition*, J.R. Mattern listed quite a number of 30-30 loads. Full-power loads, of course, but also reduced types for practice, light varmint and small game loads. Bullet weights included 90, 110, 115, 120, 125, 150, 160, 165 and 170 grains.

My own involvement was a gradual one. For years, I loaded standard-weight bullets for carbine use. Next came specialized ammo for handgun silhouette competition, and then a foray into heavy bullets, 180- and 190-grainers, for hunting heavier game than deer. Finally, a desire for a cast bullet practice load and a small game recipe brought me to the lighter bullets.

As I began to define my needs, it became evident I, too, was looking for two different things. First was an off-season load; one that was appropriate throughout the year, except for big game hunting season. Such a load should be suitable for taking varmints: lightweight, frangible bullets at relatively high velocity.

Why develop varmint loads for a 30-30 saddle carbine when so many better choices abound? The answer lies in lifestyle and making do with what you have. When traveling on horseback, it's hard to beat the convenience of the slab-sided lever gun. This is especially true if the gun is along "just in case," secondary to the work or play that prompted the ride. Likewise, such guns more or less permanently adorn the rack behind the driver's head in pickups throughout the West. Tractors and other farm or ranch vehicles frequently have among their stash a smooth-handling carbine as coyote or other varmint medicine. And finally for folks like me, as gunwriter Sam Fadala calls it, a "sidekick rifle" is a perfect companion afield. So I needed sidekick ammo for a sidekick rifle.

The second thing I needed was a small game load, generally developed for use on such critters as rabbits or mountain grouse where another load would result in too much meat damage. This load also would have plinking and young-shooter-training applicability. It would be equally suited for occasional use primarily on big game hunts, on dedicated small game hunts, or for general woods loafing in season.

### Improving Levergun Versatility

Though developing these loads involved testing several bullets with a variety of powders and consumed quite a bit of time, some interesting things were learned. But before we proceed, two safety lessons are in order. Lever-action guns with tubular magazines have their own unique manual of arms. Newer guns, including the Model 94 Winchester, often have crossbolt safeties, but millions of earlier examples do not. These guns all have exposed hammers and a blow to the hammer can result in the firing pin striking the primer of a chambered round, causing it to fire inadvertently. The principle is the same as with the older single-action revolvers. After some time afield with these guns, I have concluded that the best carrying mode is with the chamber empty, hammer down.

I keep the hammer down rather than back as some suggest because I usually hunt in timber, and a day with the hammer back will result in an action full of twigs, pine needles and, often, snow or rain. Levering a round into the chamber when needed, can, with practice, be as natural as raising the gun to the shoulder.

**If you want to use the all-time favorite deer rig on varmints, try...**

# LIGHT BULLETS

# in the 30-30

Varmint load choices for the 30-30 include (from left): Sierra 110-grain HP, Sierra 110-grain RN, Sierra 110-grain FMJ, Sierra 125-grain FN, Speer 110-grain SP, Speer 110-grain RN, Speer 110-grain FNHP, Hornady 100-grain SJ, Hornady 110-grain RN, Hornady 110-grain SP, Hornady 110-grain FMJ and Remington 125-grain SP.

Small game load choices for the 30-30 include (from left): .310-inch round ball, .311-inch 71-grain FMJ, 90-grain swaged SWC, 110-grain SP and 115-grain cast RN. Also, the Alex adaptor along with jacketed and cast 32 ACP loads.

The second safety lesson deals with the tubular magazine and the type of bullets used. Surely, this is old hat to many readers, but for our newer shooters, bear with me. Cartridges positioned in a tubular magazine rest with the point of one bullet against the primer of the one in front. If the point is sharp enough, such as a spitzer, or hard enough, such as a full metal jacket or a hollowpoint, the jarring recoil from firing the gun could cause sufficient sudden pressure to be applied to a primer to ignite it. The result would be most unpleasant, with cartridge brass, pieces of the magazine and splinters from the forend all acting as shrapnel from a grenade—with the shooter holding onto the part that just blew up.

Thus, you will note that I have, and will, refer to the single loading of cartridges with certain bullets. Single loading is, however, a misnomer. Actually, there are three acceptable methods of loading and using such cartridges. The first begins with an unloaded gun. You simply lever back the bolt and insert a cartridge into the chamber; the magazine is not used at all. In the second, a round is inserted into the magazine and left there until needed; then it is levered into the chamber before firing. In the third method, two cartridges are inserted into the magazine; when ready to shoot, one cartridge is chambered, leaving one in the magazine. Personally, I wouldn't use the third method when traveling in steep terrain where a fall could result in a sharp blow to the rifle butt, potentially setting off a primer if both rounds were in the magazine.

All shooting was done with a Winchester Model 94 carbine from a solid bench. The gun was held firmly at the forend and against my shoulder. My forward hand rested against a sandbag, as did each elbow. The gun shoots very good three-shot groups, but tends to spread its shots after that, unless it's cold out or shots are spaced quite a bit apart. All groups in the tests were five shots; weather was cool to cold, and shots were not hurried, but the barrel was allowed to cool completely only between strings. The gun is equipped with a Lyman peep rear sight. All varmint loads were tested at 100 yards; small game loads at 25.

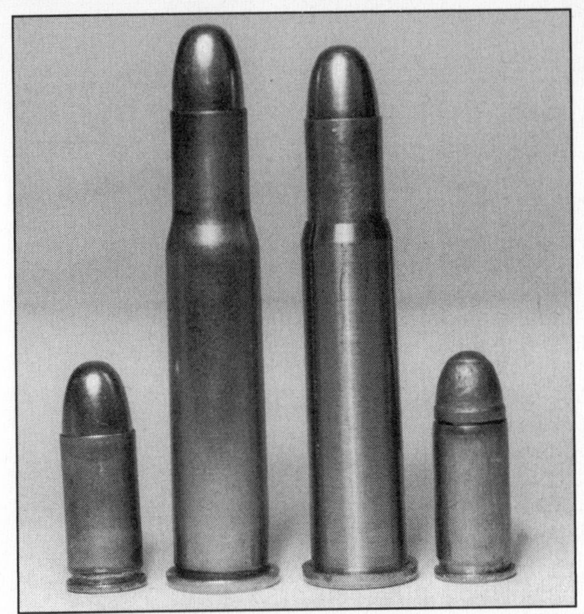

If you have an Alex adapter, you can shoot a pistol cartridge in your rifle (from left): a 30-30 case with a 71-grain 32 ACP bullet and a 32 ACP case with the same bullet in the Alex adaptor, flanked by 32 ACP jacketed and cast loads.

Probably what contributed most to my success was my choice of targets. When shooting at 100 yards, I used the International 300-meter target reduced to 300 yards. The target number is C3 available from such target companies as National in Rockville, Maryland; American in Denver, Colorado; and Rocky Mountain in Leesburg, Florida. The black on this target is 21.63 inches in diameter. Mounted at 100 yards, the black appears sufficiently larger than the bead front sight, allowing the shooter to center the bead. The eye will also center the bead in the rear aperture, making a very repeatable sight picture. The difference between this sight picture and some others tried was astounding. For example, using a six-o'clock hold on a 50-yard pistol center produced five-shot groups in excess of 5 inches. The same loads using the C3 target produces groups of 2 inches or so. In fact, I'm convinced that this carbine will make tighter groups than that, but unfortunately not without a scope if I have to shoot it. At 25 yards, the same principles held, but the target was a 25-yard pistol center. Best groups were under an inch.

### Off-Season or Varmint Loads

Developing varmint loads essentially begins and ends with bullet selection. Perhaps the best overall is the Speer 110-grain FNHP (flat-nose hollowpoint). This bullet is cannelured and designed for the 30-30, although it has a second cannelure for use in the 30 Carbine.

Full-metal-jacket round-nosed bullets are also offered by various companies. Again, the Hornady at .3075-inch is slightly smaller. These bullets would be subjected to single loading restrictions and would be best suited for taking furbearing animals where legal.

Speer and Hornady have 110-grain spirepoints. The Speer is of slightly heavier construction. Sierra offers a similar bullet but of hollowpoint design. These bullets would also be restricted to single loading, but all are excellent varmint types.

Several bullets in the 125- to 130-grain range are available. Speer has a 130-grain hollowpoint suitable for varmint use and a cannelured, flatpoint designed for the 30-30 but of game construction. It should be a good choice for antelope. Sierra has a 125-grain flat-nose, hollowpoint designed for the 30-30. It is of varmint construction, but may be ideal for coyotes or javalinas. Remington has a 125-grain PSP (pointed soft point); I am partial to it in the 30 Herrett, and it should be just as good in the 30-30.

Also worth considering are the Speer 100-grain Plinker and Hornady 100-grain semi-jacket. Others that I tested were 71-grain metal cased bullets for the 32 ACP, a 90-grain swaged semi-wadcutter, a 115-grain cast bullet and a .310-inch round ball.

The Speer 110-grain FNHP lived up to its billing. The combination of proper design for use in tubular magazines, suitability for varmint use and adequate accuracy make this an excellent off-season choice. With 37 grains of Scot 3032, it produced the highest velocity, the lowest extreme spead and the smallest group.

Spirepoint bullets were the most accurate. One very interesting thing to emerge was that the most accurate loads chronographed about 2600 fps. Results with bullets that clocked below 2500 fps or above 2700 fps were terrible. Above 2800 fps, groups were nonexistent. One memorable 9-inch example comes to mind! The best load of the series—35.0 grains of Scot 3032 with the Hornady 110-grain spirepoint at 2598 fps—put five shots in 2 inches, four in 1¼. For me and iron sights, that's as good as it gets.

The round-nose softpoints were the most interesting. They function easily through the magazine and are lightly constructed just enough to be suitable for varmint or plinking use. Again, 2600 fps proved significant. The Sierra offering won this time with 38 grains of Reloder 12 pushing it to 2609 fps with an extreme spread of 10 fps. Five shots went into 2⅛ inches.

The full-metal-jacket bullets have a more limited usefulness, it seems to me. For winter use on the occasional furbearer, they will probably do less pelt damage than the others. However, they may be illegal for small game or even varmints in some areas. Accuracy was good, but not quite the equal of the softpoint. Hornady won this one too, although the Speer wasn't tested. Velocity usually had to be over 2700 fps, regardless of diameter, for best results.

In testing the two 125-grain bullets, the Sierra FNHP and the Remington PSP, the former gave best results at about 2550 fps and the latter at about 2200 fps. The Sierra is designed for the 30-30 and deserves to be considered as a light bullet.

The two plinking bullets, the Hornady semi-jacket and the Speer Plinker, were tried. When fired at traditional 30-30 velocities of 2100 to 2200 fps, accuracy was quite acceptable. However, if velocities were raised, accuracy went south in a hurry.

### Small Game Loads

When it came time to look at small game loads, I really had to shift gears. In general, this round would be expected to perform at close range and low speeds, while utilizing the big game sight setting.

Over the years, for potting small game while hunting bigger stuff, I have carried a few round ball loads in a pocket. Consisting of a .310-inch round ball seated over 4 grains of Bullseye, I have loaded this in cases from the 30 Herrett to the 30-06 with

## TABLE I: VARMINT LOADS

| Bullet Wgt. grs. | Bullet Type | Case | Primer | Load (Grs./Powder) | O.A.L. (ins.) | Velocity (fps) | Remarks |
|---|---|---|---|---|---|---|---|
| 100 | Hornady SJ | R-P | CCI 250 | 36.0/W-748 | 2.435 | 2175 | Accurate |
| 100 | Hornady SJ | R-P | CCI 250 | 37.0/W-748 | 2.435 | 2235 | |
| 110 | Hornady RN | R-P | CCI 200 | 38.5/RL-12 | 2.530 | 2525 | |
| 110 | Hornady RN | R-P | CCI 200 | 39.5/RL-12 | 2.530 | 2611 | Best this bullet |
| 110 | Hornady RN | R-P | CCI 200 | 40.5/RL-12 | 2.530 | 2733 | |
| 110 | Hornady RN | R-P | CCI 200 | 41.5/RL-12 | 2.530 | 2801 | |
| 110 | Hornady FMJ | R-P | CCI 200 | 39.0/RL-12 | 2.550 | 2540 | |
| 110 | Hornady FMJ | R-P | CCI 200 | 40.0/RL-12 | 2.550 | 2674 | Best this bullet |
| 110 | Hornady FMJ | R-P | CCI 200 | 41.0/RL-12 | 2.550 | 2750 | |
| 110 | Hornady FMJ | R-P | CCI 200 | 42.0/RL-12 | 2.550 | 2847 | |
| 110 | Hornady SP | R-P | CCI 200 | 32.0/IMR-3031 | 2.585 | 2152 | |
| 110 | Hornady SP | R-P | CCI 200 | 33.0/IMR-3031 | 2.585 | 2372 | |
| 110 | Hornady SP | R-P | CCI 200 | 34.0/Scot 3032 | 2.585 | 2513 | |
| 110 | Hornady SP | R-P | CCI 200 | 35.0/Scot 3032 | 2.585 | 2598 | Most accurate load |
| 110 | Hornady SP | R-P | CCI 200 | 32.5/Scot 4197 | 2.585 | 2559 | |
| 110 | Hornady SP | R-P | CCI 200 | 41.0/RL-12 | 2.585 | 2811 | Inaccurate |
| 110 | Sierra RN | R-P | CCI 200 | 37.0/RL-12 | 2.550 | 2549 | |
| 110 | Sierra RN | R-P | CCI 200 | 38.0/RL-12 | 2.550 | 2609 | Best this bullet |
| 110 | Sierra RN | R-P | CCI 200 | 39.0/RL-12 | 2.550 | 2703 | |
| 110 | Sierra RN | R-P | CCI 200 | 36.0/Scot 3032 | 2.550 | 2659 | |
| 110 | Sierra RN | R-P | CCI 200 | 37.0/Scot 3032 | 2.550 | 2701 | |
| 110 | Sierra HP | W-W Super | CCI 200 | 37.0/RL-12 | 2.550 | 2459 | |
| 110 | Sierra HP | W-W Super | CCI 200 | 38.0/RL-12 | 2.550 | 2500 | |
| 110 | Sierra HP | W-W Super | CCI 200 | 39.0/RL-12 | 2.550 | 2596 | Accurate |
| 110 | Sierra HP | W-W Super | CCI 200 | 41.0/RL-12 | 2.550 | 2806 | Inaccurate |
| 110 | Sierra HP | W-W Super | CCI 200 | 32.0/Scot 4197 | 2.550 | 2606 | |
| 110 | Sierra HP | W-W Super | CCI 200 | 33.0/Scot 4197 | 2.550 | 2649 | |
| 110 | Sierra FMJ | R-P | CCI 200 | 38.0/RL-12 | 2.550 | 2541 | Best this bullet |
| 110 | Sierra FMJ | R-P | CCI 200 | 39.0/RL-12 | 2.550 | 2644 | |
| 110 | Sierra FMJ | R-P | CCI 200 | 32.0/Scot 4197 | 2.550 | 2606 | |
| 110 | Sierra FMJ | R-P | CCI 200 | 33.0/Scot 4197 | 2.550 | 2649 | |
| 110 | Speer RN | W-W Super | CCI 200 | 36.0/IMR-4064 | 2.550 | 2404 | |
| 110 | Speer RN | W-W Super | CCI 200 | 37.0/IMR-4064 | 2.550 | 2503 | Accurate |
| 110 | Speer RN | W-W Super | CCI 200 | 37.0/W-748 | 2.550 | 2478 | |
| 110 | Speer RN | W-W Super | CCI 200 | 38.0/RL-12 | 2.550 | 2577 | Very accurate |
| 110 | Speer RN | W-W Super | CCI 200 | 36.0/Scot 3032 | 2.550 | 2642 | |
| 110 | Speer RN | W-W Super | CCI 200 | 32.0/Scot 4197 | 2.550 | 2443 | |
| 110 | Speer RN | W-W Super | CCI 200 | 33.0/Scot 4197 | 2.550 | 2534 | |
| 110 | Speer SP | W-W Super | CCI 200 | 39.0/RL-12 | 2.550 | 2628 | Best this bullet |
| 110 | Speer SP | W-W Super | CCI 200 | 41.0/RL-12 | 2.550 | 2753 | Inaccurate |
| 110 | Speer SP | W-W Super | CCI 200 | 32.0/H-4198 | 2.550 | 2623 | |
| 110 | Speer SP | W-W Super | CCI 200 | 32.0/Scot 4197 | 2.550 | 2457 | Accurate |
| 110 | Speer FNHP | W-W | CCI 200 | 38.0/RL-12 | 2.435 | 2571 | Accurate |
| 110 | Speer FNHP | W-W | CCI 200 | 39.0/RL-12 | 2.435 | 2674 | Accurate |
| 110 | Speer FNHP | W-W | CCI 200 | 36.0/Scot 3032 | 2.435 | 2645 | |
| 110 | Speer FNHP | W-W | CCI 200 | 37.0/Scot 3032 | 2.435 | 2750 | Best this bullet |
| 125 | Remington | W-W | CCI 200 | 37.0/RL-12 | 2.435 | 2492 | |
| 125 | Remington | W-W | CCI 200 | 38.0/RL-12 | 2.435 | 2558 | |
| 125 | Remington | W-W | CCI 200 | 35.0/W-748 | 2.435 | 2167 | Accurate |
| 125 | Sierra FNHP | Win | CCI 200 | 36.0/RL-12 | 2.440 | 2354 | |
| 125 | Sierra FNHP | Win | CCI 200 | 37.0/RL-12 | 2.440 | 2557 | Accurate; best this bullet |

Notes: Firearm was Model 94 Winchester, 20-inch barrel, 1:12-inch twist, aperture rear, bead front sight. Range was 100 yards. OAL = overall cartridge length.

excellent results. I usually expand and bell the case mouth with a Lyman M die and seat the ball just over halfway into the mouth. A slight crimp will restore the mouth and hold the ball securely. A dab of lube or Liquid Alox helps to minimize leading. I have taken a lot of small game with this combination. Accuracy is more than adequate, but is best from a clean, or nearly so, barrel.

For these tests, I experimented with the Alex auxiliary cartridge for the 30-30. A throwback to earlier times, this is a cartridge-shaped device designed to allow the firing of 32 ACP ammo in a rifle chamber. While the accompanying directions specify Remington brand only, I cheated and tested Remington and Winchester factory ammo, as well as

## TABLE II: SMALL GAME LOADS

| —Bullet— Wgt. grs. | Type | Case | Primer | Load (Grs./Powder) | O.A.L. (ins.) | Velocity (fps) | Remarks |
|---|---|---|---|---|---|---|---|
| .310″ | Ball | W-W Super | CCI 200 | 4.0/Bullseye | N/A | 1314 | Accurate |
| 71 | REM FMJ | W-W Super | CCI 200 | 7.0/Unique | 2.383 | 1411 | |
| 90 | Horn SWC | W-W Super | CCI 200 | 7.0/Unique | 2.440 | 1361 | Very accurate |
| 90 | Horn SWC | W-W Super | CCI 200 | 12.0/SR 4759 | 2.440 | 1047 | |
| 110 | Sierra RN | W-W Super | CCI 200 | 7.0/Unique | 2.500 | 1185 | Very accurate |
| 110 | Sierra RN | W-W Super | CCI 200 | 12.0/SR 4759 | 2.500 | 1265 | |
| 110 | Sierra RN | W-W Super | CCI 200 | 12.0/AA 2400 | 2.500 | 1398 | Accurate |
| 110 | Speer FNHP | W-W Super | CCI 200 | 7.0/Unique | 2.435 | 1206 | |
| 115 | RCBS GL | R-P | CCI 200 | 7.0/Unique | 2.375 | 1288 | Accurate |
| 115 | RCBS GL | R-P | CCI 200 | 12.0/SR 4759 | 2.375 | 1185 | Very accurate* |

Notes: Firearm was Model 94 Winchester, 20-inch barrel, 1:12-inch twist, aperture rear, bead front sight. Range was 100 yards. OAL=overall cartridge length.

*SR 4759 did not burn completely at this low pressure, even when loads were highly accurate.

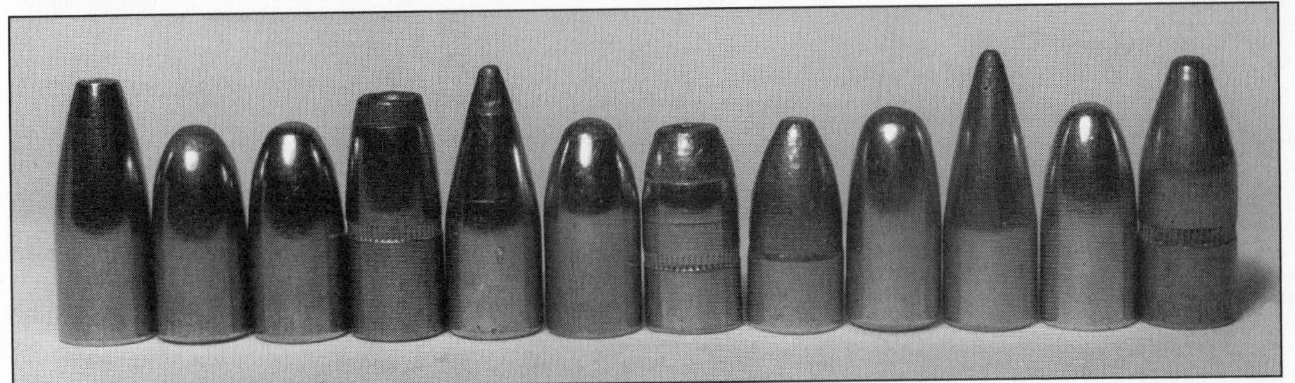

These varmint bullets were used in testing (from left): Sierra 110-grain HP, Sierra 110-grain RN, Sierra-110 grain FMJ, Sierra 125-grain FN, Speer 110-grain SP, Speer 110-grain RN, Speer 110-grain FNHP, Hornady 100-grain SJ, Hornady 110-grain RN, Hornady 110-grain SP, Hornady 110-grain FMJ and Remington 125-grain SP.

These small game bullets were used in testing (from left): Hornady .310-inch RB, Remington 71-grain 32 ACP FMJ, Hornady 90-grain swaged SWC, Sierra 110-grain RN, RCBS 115-grain cast and, used with the Alex adaptor, a 32 ACP with 71-grain FMJ and a 32 ACP with 77-grain cast RN.

cast and jacketed handloads. The factory loads worked satisfactorily, as did my handloads if the bullets were of .311-inch diameter. Sierra bullets, which are my choice for my 32 ACP pistol, are .312-inch in diameter. Ammo loaded with this bullet would not chamber in my carbine. Accuracy with the .311-inch diameter bullets, whether used in 32 ACP cases in conjunction with the auxiliary cartridge or loaded in 30-30 cases, was never the equal of the other bullets tried. Still, for the non-handloader, this is a viable option.

Hornady makes a .314-inch diameter swaged semi-wadcutter for the several 32-caliber revolver cartridges. It seemed ideal for a small game bullet except for diameter. I solved that by running it through a .309-inch sizing die. Results were exceptional.

A cast 115-grain gas check bullet from the RCBS 30-115 mould was next. This bullet can be driven much faster than called for as a small game round, but it performed well at any velocity, tying for the best group in the small game tests.

The Sierra round-nose softpoint was chosen as representative of the jacketed bullets for small game use. It worked very well, producing 1- to 1½-inch groups. The semi-jacketed 100-grain bullets were tried at small game velocities, but accuracy wasn't quite the equal of the others. In another rifle, one of these might make a great small game load.

In planning the small game loads, I attempted to keep velocities at about 1200 fps. This was to keep point of impact at close range reasonably close to point of aim while minimizing meat damage due to excess velocity. In practice, this worked. The most accurate loads ranged from about 1050 fps to 1400 fps.

In choosing a small game load, one must be careful to select a combination that can be instantly recognized, preferably by feel. This is especially true if they are to be carried while hunting bigger game. Because of the loss of accuracy of cast bullets when fired in a barrel fouled by jacketed

## TABLE III: FACTORY AND MISCELLANEOUS LOADS

| —Bullet— Wgt. Grs. | Type | Velocity (fps) | Remarks |
|---|---|---|---|
| 55 | Remington Accelerator | 3312 | Accurate |
| 60 | Winchester 32 ACP with Alex adaptor | 1062 | |
| 71 | Remington 32 ACP with Alex adaptor | 991 | |
| 71 | Remington 32 ACP (handload/2.5 grs. W-W 231) with Alex adaptor | 994 | |
| 77 | Cast 32 ACP (handload/2.4 grs. HP-38) with Alex adaptor | 1010 | Good |

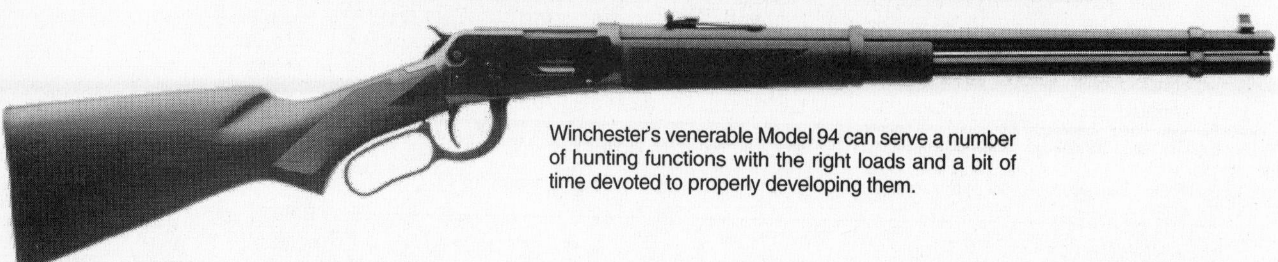

Winchester's venerable Model 94 can serve a number of hunting functions with the right loads and a bit of time devoted to properly developing them.

bullets, for most hunters the jacketed round-nose softpoint is probably the best choice. If, however, your big game bullet is cast, then either the 115-grain or 90-grain Hornady would be an excellent choice. This is all mitigated somewhat by the degree of care the gun receives. If you start out with a clean barrel and fire one or two shots at big game, and maybe one or two shots at small game, barrel fouling will not be a problem. If you do not keep your gun clean, mixing cast and jacketed bullets should be avoided.

### Conclusions

As you can see from the accompanying tables, several powders were used, six with the varmint loads and four with the small game loads. It would be difficult to rate them, except to say my best and most consistent varmint load results came from Reloder 12 and Scot 3032. The latter is not routinely available now, but is occasionally seen on dealers' shelves, and I had several pounds on hand when working on this article, so included it in my testing. It gave excellent results, so is worth snapping up if you happen across any. It's also worth noting that Lyman's latest reloading handbook, No. 47, recommends Reloder 12 above all others for the 30-30.

For the small game loads, I stumbled across something unusual. With every bullet, not counting the round ball load, 7 grains of Unique produced the best groups, with one exception. Even if you choose to adjust the velocity levels slightly, Unique is sure to produce good results.

While group sizes are not listed in the tables—pointless really, as your

Reloder 12 powder, now made by Alliant, is quite versatile in the 30-30 and other medium-size rifle cases.

guns and components will be different from mine—good varmint groups were 2 to $2^1/_2$ inches at 100 yards. The best small game loads were under an inch at 25 yards, and no group exceeded 2 inches.

You will also note from the tables that overall cartridge lengths did not generally exceed 2.55 inches. This was to ensure that all loads could be cycled through the magazine if desired. This left an ogive-to-lands gap of .065-inch with round-nose bullets in my gun; it would be larger with any of the other type of bullet. Spirepoints can be seated out further, as was the Hornady, and loaded directly into the chamber.

Crimping also merits comment, especially with regard to the non-cannelured bullets. All bullets were seated in one operation. Crimping, if done, was performed separately. Cannelured bullets were generally crimped with the standard seating die. Usually, non-cannelured bullets were carefully and lightly crimped with a Lee Factory Crimp die. Fairly extensive use of this die with a variety of bullet weights and styles in this caliber prompts me to recommend its use. As with any tool, improper use usually produces poor results. Bullets that are not going to be subjected to magazine carry obviously don't need crimping to ensure consistent overall length, but may benefit from it by holding bullet pull to a smaller tolerance, thereby assisting in a more consistent burning of powder. This may be more important in the 30-30 than other rifle calibers having traditionally thicker neck walls.

If all, or any, of this appeals to you, peruse the tables and select the bullet type that matches your needs. Try several different brands and I'll bet you will find, as I did, that a quick-stepping load for varmints and/or a load tailored for small game truly does expand the usefulness of the 30-30, a century-old favorite. ●

# Is a Larger Bore More Efficient?

***There are many ways to measure cartridge efficiency. Sometimes it comes down to the size of the hole in the barrel.***

by PAUL SCHIFFELBEIN, Ph.D.

IF CARTRIDGE EFFICIENCY were simply how many feet per second of muzzle velocity or foot-pounds of muzzle energy that you could get from each grain of powder used, it might interest only the academics and perfectionists among us. Consider the 30-06 cartridge, which has a usable case capacity of 67.6 grains of water. A recent listing[1] of 318 maximum loads for jacketed bullets weighing 110 to 250 grains shows powder charges ranging between 41 and 66 grains, with an average of 53 grains. A 1-pound can of powder will therefore load between 106 and 171 30-06 cartridges; the average is 132. At a retail price of roughly $15 per pound, that means you are spending between 9¢ and 14¢ per shot for powder (average 11¢). Even if cartridge efficiency were only half of what it is, the additional powder cost would be lost amid the other expenses associated with a typical hunting or target shooting excursion.

Cartridge efficiency is important because we are often trying to get the most performance out of an existing rifle, but are generally limited by case diameter or case length. We know that cartridge efficiency (measured as muzzle velocity per grain of powder used) decreases as case capacity increases[2]. That suggests that a larger bore should be more efficient than a smaller one when case size is restricted. Can you improve the efficiency of your firearm by simply increasing the bore diameter? I'll begin with a strict definition of efficiency and see where it takes us.

My dictionary defines efficiency as "the ratio of the effective or useful output to the total input in any system; especially, the ratio of the energy delivered by a machine to the energy supplied for its operation." That definition will help us evaluate the impact of bore diameter on cartridge efficiency. First, choose any cartridge as a starting point. Then progressively decrease and/or increase the neck diameter of that cartridge while leaving everything else about the cartridge—especially case capacity, the "energy supplied for its operation"—alone. I have, of course, just described the oldest wildcatting game around.

Table 1, while not attempting to be exhaustive, gives a good idea of just how many of our wildcat and commercial cartridges are simple neck-diameter alterations of previously existing cartridges.[3] Dates indicate commercial introduction (or adop-

[1] McPherson, M.L. *Metallic Cartridge Reloading*, 3rd Edition. Northbrook: DBI Books, 1996.

[2] Schiffelbein, Paul. "Overbore: Where Do You Draw the Line?," HANDLOADER'S DIGEST, 14th Edition. Northbrook, IL: DBI Books, Inc., 1994.

[3] Wildcat cartridges based on the 22 Hornet, 25-20 WCF, 30-30, 30-40 Krag, 303 British and 348 Winchester are mainly of historical interest and were omitted from the table. There are likewise entire series of cartridges based on the 222 Remington, 223 Remington, 224 Weatherby, 284 Winchester, 350 Remington Magnum, etc. Many of the cartridges listed exist in several versions. Commercial versions were favored over wildcat versions in the table. With the exception of the 375 Weatherby, I intentionally omitted "Improved" cartridges from the table. See Parker O. Ackley, *Handbook for Shooters and Reloaders* (Vol. I, 1962; Vol. II, 1966) and Frank C. Barnes, 1993, *Cartridges of the World*, 7th Edition, for additional information.

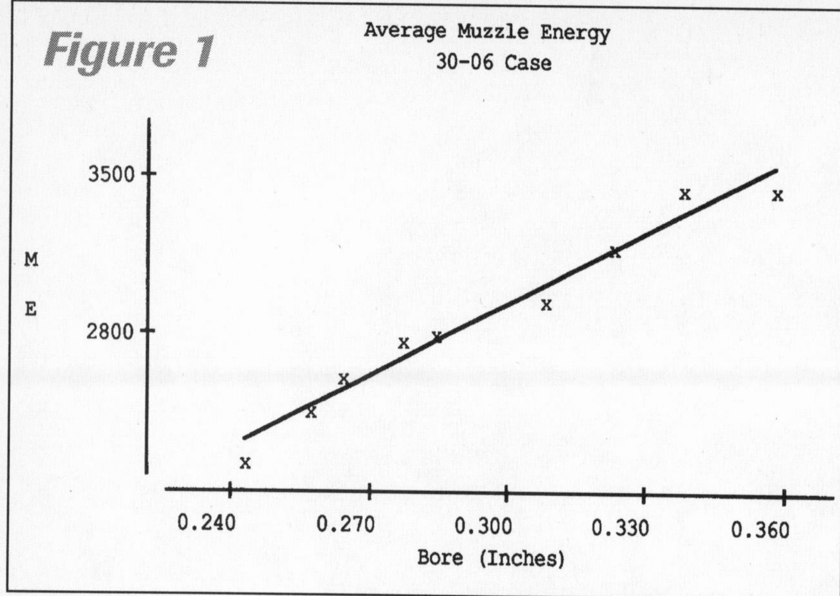


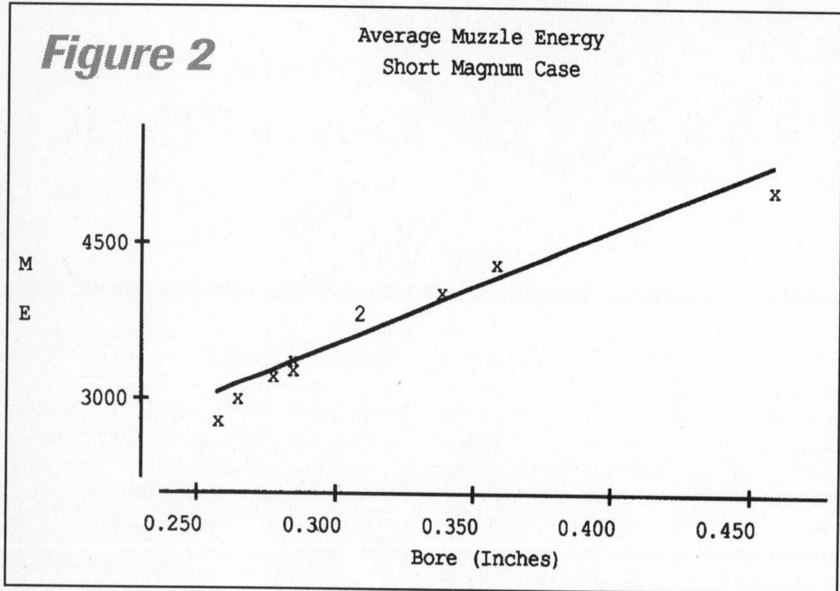


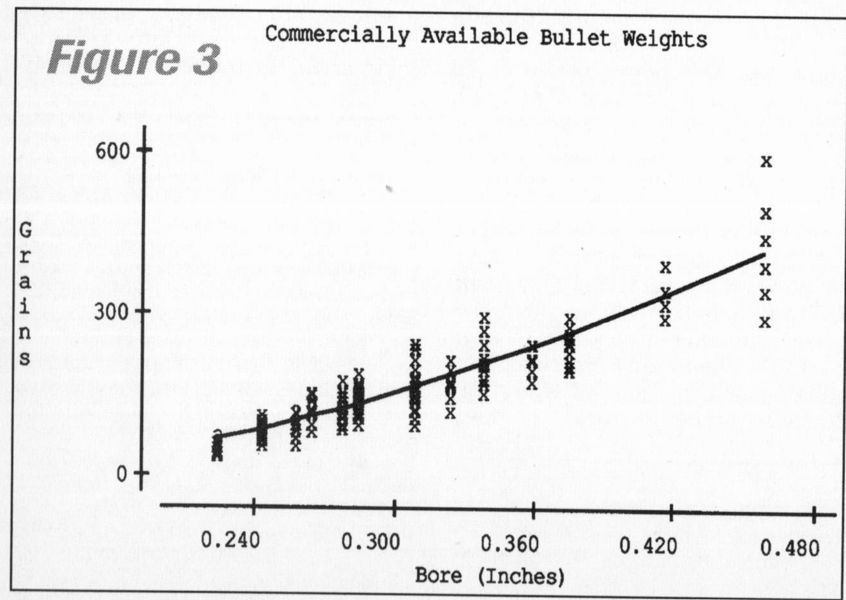


tion); actual development often predates commercial introduction by many years. (Incidentally, this table wouldn't have been much shorter if it were put together more than thirty years ago, when P.O. Ackley's books were published and Courtney Wills[4] stated that, "Once upon a time in the dear dead days of yore there was some excuse for wildcat cartridges." The surprising thing is that many of those same cartridges continue to be "invented" and renamed all these years later.)

Let's again use the 30-06 as an example and look at the relationship between muzzle energy and bore diameter (Figure 1). I don't have case capacity measurements for the wildcat cartridges, but the commercial cartridges have usable case capacities (grains of water) of 64.0 (25-06 Remington), 65.4 (270 Winchester), 67.7 (280 Remington), 67.6 (30-06) and 63.6 (35 Whelen). The average usable case capacity for this cartridge family is 65.7 grains, and none deviates from this average by more than 2.1 grains. Does a larger bore make for a more efficient cartridge? It certainly seems to. In fact, muzzle energy increases roughly 1000 foot-pounds for each 0.1-inch increase in bore size.

The same type of relationship is seen with other cartridge families. Figure 2 shows the muzzle energy versus bore relationship for the short magnum family (average usable case capacity 80.5 grains water). Muzzle energy increases roughly 1000 foot-pounds with each 0.1-inch increase in bore in this case as well.

You might wonder whether the relationships shown in Figures 1 and 2 are really caused by simple bore changes or are instead related to bullet weight. Larger calibers are associated with heavier bullets; in fact, that's often why we chose a larger caliber. While there is a lot of overlap in weights from one caliber to the next, Figure 3 shows that bullet weight increases on average about 145 grains for each 0.1-inch increase in bore diameter. Perhaps it is simply this increase in bullet weight that gives the larger calibers higher muzzle energy?

There is, in fact, a relationship between muzzle energy and bullet weight in any individual cartridge.

---

[4] Wills, Courtney. "Are There Any Good Wildcats?" *Gun Digest*, 20th Edition. Chicago: The Gun Digest Co., 1965.

**TABLE 1: PARENT AND OFFSPRING CARTRIDGES**

| Parent | Derivative |
|---|---|
| **250 Savage** (1915) | 22-250 (1965), 6mm-250, 270 Savage, 300 Savage (1920) |
| **8mm Mauser** (1888) | 22 Newton, 226 Barnes QT, 244 Remington (1955), 257 Roberts (1934), 6.5 Spence Special (6.5x57), 270-257, 7mm Mauser (1892) |
| **308 Winchester** (1952) | 22-243 Middlestead, 230 LLF, 243 Winchester (1955), 25 Souper, 263 Express, 270-308, 7mm-08 Remington (1980), 358 Winchester (1955) |
| **30-06 Springfield** (1906) | 22-06 Easling, 240 Super Varminter, 25-06 Remington (1969), 6.5mm-06, 270 Winchester (1925), 280 Remington (1957), 8mm-06, 333 OKH, 338-06, 35 Whelen (1987), 375 Whelen, 400 Whelen. |
| **458 Winchester Magnum** (1956) | 6mm Atlas, 257 Weatherby Magnum* (1948), 264 Winchester Magnum (1958), 270 Weatherby Magnum* (1948), 7mm Weatherby Magnum* (1948), 7mm Remington Magnum (1962), 300 Winchester Magnum (1963), 308 Norma Magnum (1960), 8x62 Durham Magnum, 333x61 Carlson Magnum, 338 Winchester Magnum (1958), 358 Norma Magnum (1959), 375 Durham Magnum, 400 Williams, 416 Taylor, 425 Express |
| **375 H&H Magnum** (1912) | 22 PMVF (CCC), 244 H&H Magnum, 258 Condor, 6.5 Critser Express, 270 Mashburn Magnum (long), 7mm Mashburn Magnum (long), 300 H&H Magnum (1925), 300 Weatherby Magnum (1948), 8mm Remington Magnum (1978), 333 Barnes Supreme, 340 Weatherby Magnum (1962), 350 Mashburn Super Magnum, Weatherby Magnum (1948), 416 Remington Magnum (1988), 450 Magnum (Ackley), 475 Magnum (Ackley) |
| **378 Weatherby Magnum** (1953) | 22 Eargesplitten Loudenboomer, 6.5-378, 30-378 Weatherby, 416 Weatherby Magnum (1989), 460 Weatherby Magnum (1958), 475 A&M Magnum, 495 A-Square, 500 A-Square |

* These cartridges were actually based on the necked down and blown out 300 H&H case. They are shorter than the parent case, however, so I have placed them with the "short" magnums.

**TABLE 2: MUZZLE ENERGIES FOR 30-06 CASE FAMILY**

| Cartridge | Bore (ins.) | Bullet (Wgt. Grs.) | ME (fpe) |
|---|---|---|---|
| 240 Super Varminter | .243 | 70 | 2103 |
| 240 Super Varminter | .243 | 75 | 2268 |
| 240 Super Varminter | .243 | 90 | 2283 |
| 240 Super Varminter | .243 | 100 | 2315 |
| 25-06 Remington | .257 | 87 | 2286 |
| 25-06 Remington | .257 | 90 | 2364 |
| 25-06 Remington | .257 | 100 | 2316 |
| 25-06 Remington | .257 | 117 | 2320 |
| 25-06 Remington | .257 | 120 | 2382 |
| 25-06 Remington | .257 | 122 | 2325 |
| 6.5mm-06 | .264 | 85 | 2460 |
| 6.5mm-06 | .264 | 100 | 2625 |
| 6.5mm-06 | .264 | 120 | 2680 |
| 6.5mm-06 | .264 | 140 | 2800 |
| 6.5mm-06 | .264 | 165 | 2920 |
| 270 Winchester | .277 | 100 | 2612 |
| 270 Winchester | .277 | 130 | 2702 |
| 270 Winchester | .277 | 135 | 2697 |
| 270 Winchester | .277 | 140 | 2685 |
| 270 Winchester | .277 | 150 | 2705 |
| 280 Remington | .284 | 100 | 2703 |
| 280 Remington | .284 | 120 | 2643 |
| 280 Remington | .284 | 140 | 2799 |
| 280 Remington | .284 | 150 | 2781 |
| 280 Remington | .284 | 160 | 2866 |
| 280 Remington | .284 | 165 | 2913 |
| 30-06 Springfield | .308 | 100 | 2818 |
| 30-06 Springfield | .308 | 125 | 2736 |
| 30-06 Springfield | .308 | 150 | 2820 |
| 30-06 Springfield | .308 | 152 | 2858 |
| 30-06 Springfield | .308 | 165 | 2872 |
| 30-06 Springfield | .308 | 168 | 2739 |
| 30-06 Springfield | .308 | 178 | 2924 |
| 30-06 Springfield | .308 | 180 | 2913 |
| 30-06 Springfield | .308 | 220 | 2837 |
| 8mm-06 | .323 | 170 | 3240 |
| 8mm-06 | .323 | 200 | 3260 |
| 8mm-06 | .323 | 225 | 3165 |
| 8mm-06 | .323 | 250 | 3240 |
| 338-06 | .338 | 200 | 3020 |
| 338-06 | .338 | 250 | 3730 |
| 338-06 | .338 | 275 | 3250 |
| 35 Whelen | .358 | 200 | 3177 |
| 35 Whelen | .358 | 250 | 3197 |
| 375 Whelen | .375 | 200 | 3265 |
| 375 Whelen | .375 | 235 | 3205 |
| 375 Whelen | .375 | 270 | 3400 |
| 375 Whelen | .375 | 300 | 2975 |
| 400 Whelen | .405 | 300 | 3415 |
| 400 Whelen | .405 | 350 | 3430 |

Data primarily from Barnes' *Cartridges of the World*; factory loadings used where possible.

Table 2 shows muzzle energies for cartridges in the 30-06 family. While it may take a few minutes of study to find the patterns in these data, muzzle energy is generally lowest for the lightest bullets in any caliber. Muzzle energy is pretty constant across the middle range of bullet weights. There appears to be a slight decrease in energy associated with the heaviest bullets.

An average[5] of the data in Table 2 shows the relationship between muz-

[5] The data were first scaled by subtracting the mean value and dividing by the standard deviation. The scaled sequences from each caliber were averaged and the results were smoothed.

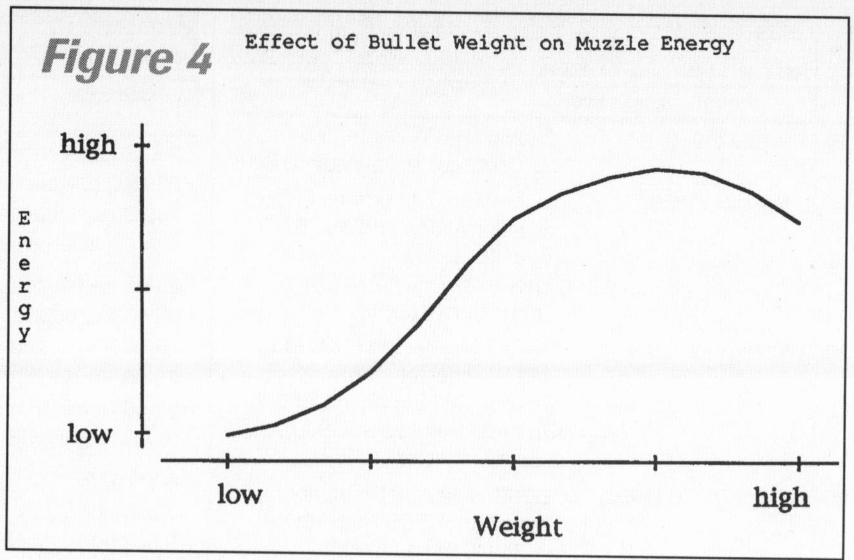


## Figures 5a-e

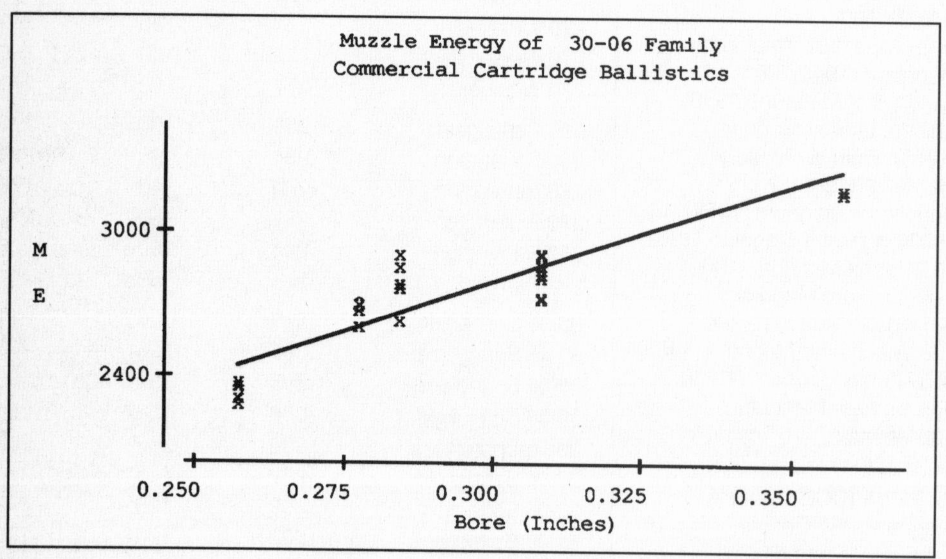


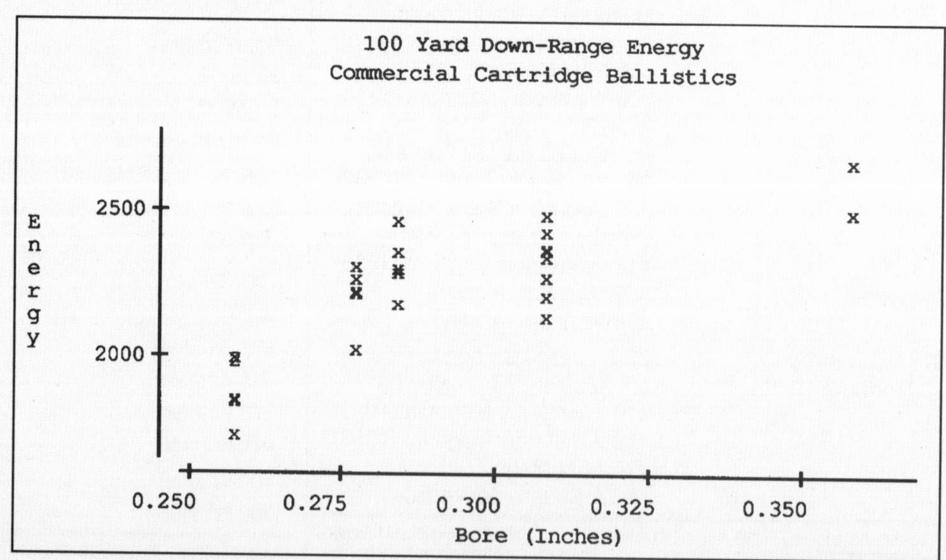

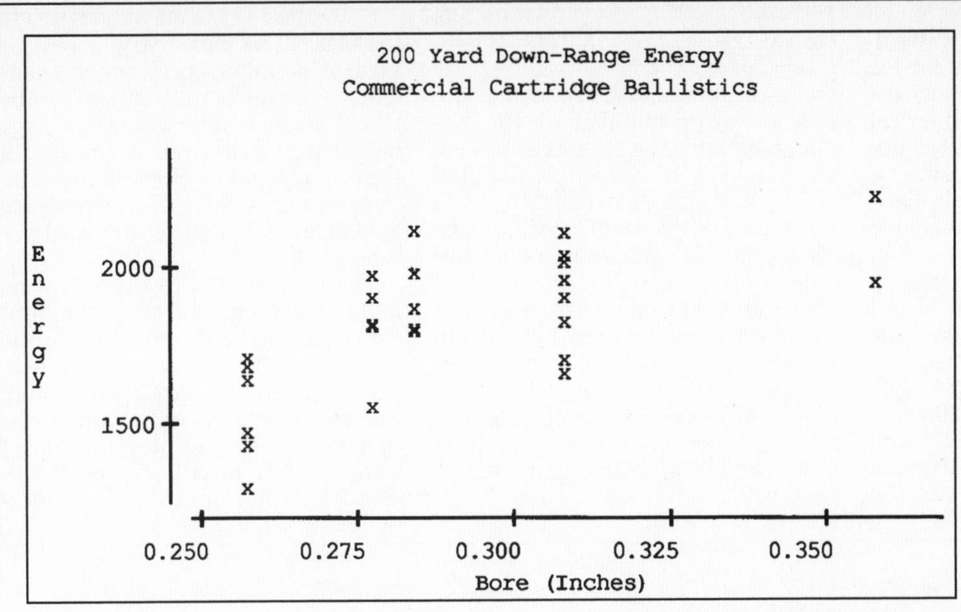
200 Yard Down-Range Energy
Commercial Cartridge Ballistics
Energy
2000
1500
0.250
0.275
0.300
0.325
0.350
Bore (Inches)

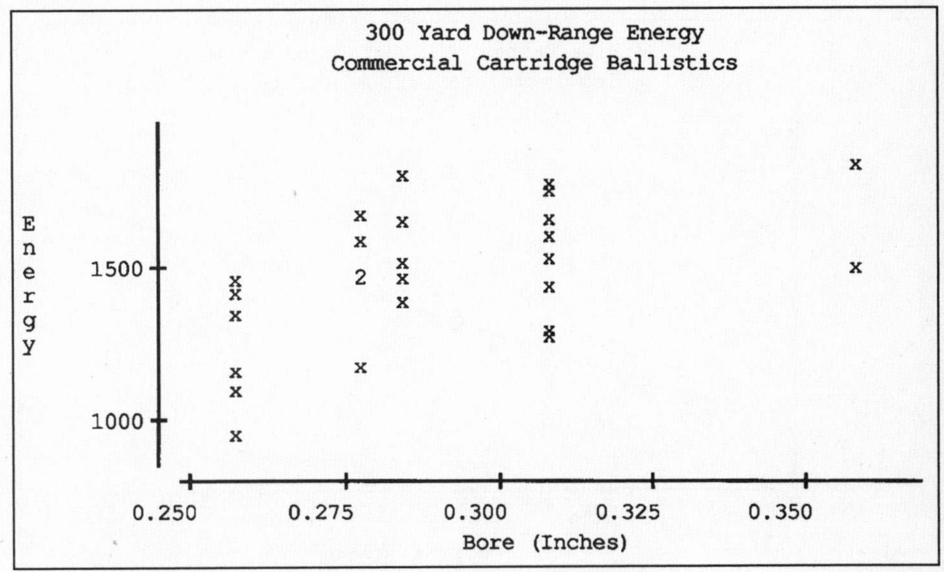
300 Yard Down-Range Energy
Commercial Cartridge Ballistics
Energy
1500
1000
0.250
0.275
0.300
0.325
0.350
Bore (Inches)

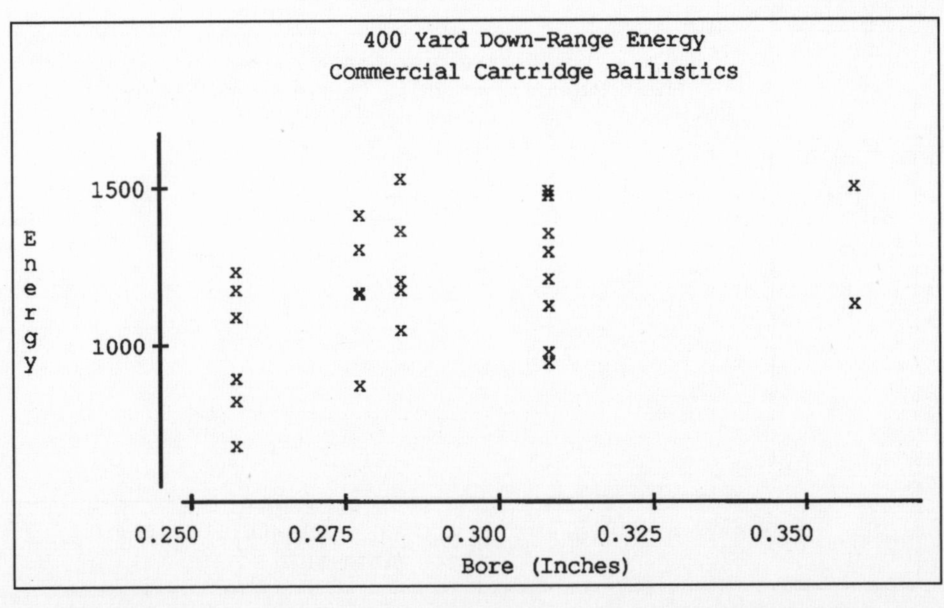
400 Yard Down-Range Energy
Commercial Cartridge Ballistics
Energy
1500
1000
0.250
0.275
0.300
0.325
0.350
Bore (Inches)

zle energy and bullet weight much more clearly (Figure 4). For any caliber, muzzle energy is lowest for the lightest bullets, then steadily increases with bullet weight. At the heaviest bullet weights, the energy dips slightly. Maximum energy in any caliber is seen with relatively heavy bullets, although not the heaviest available bullets. For any cartridge, bullet weight can affect muzzle energy by roughly 10 percent.

Now, what about the caliber effect? The 100-grain bullet, for instance, turns up in the 243, 257, 264, 277, 284 and 308 calibers. The 120-grain bullet turns up in 257, 264, 277 and 284 calibers; the 130- and 140-grain bullets in 264, 277, 284 and 308; the 150-grain in 277, 284, 308 and 323, etc. Muzzle energies in Table 2 definitely show a bore effect; muzzle energy increases with increasing bore size for any given bullet weight. The 100-grain bullet corresponds to muzzle energies of 2315 (.243), 2316 (.257), 2625 (.264), 2612 (.277), 2703 (.284) and 2818 (.308) foot-pounds. The upward trend is seen in the other bullet weights as well.

For any cartridge case, bore size can affect muzzle energy by approximately 30 percent. That is, given the ranges of bullet weights and bores in the 30-06 family of cartridges, bore is roughly three times as important as bullet weight in influencing muzzle energy.

So, to answer the question posed in the title of this paper, yes, increasing the bore definitely increases cartridge efficiency. But is that the end of the story? After all, it isn't muzzle energy but energy delivered at the target that is important. How do the relationships that we've been discussing hold up at 200-, 300- or 400-yard distances?

The data shown in the following plots are from Barnes' "Current American Rifle Cartridge Ballistics." Figure 5a is comparable to Figure 1 in its content, although Figure 5a contains only commercial cartridge data and plots all bullet weights individually for each caliber. The line represents the gener-

## Figures 6a-e

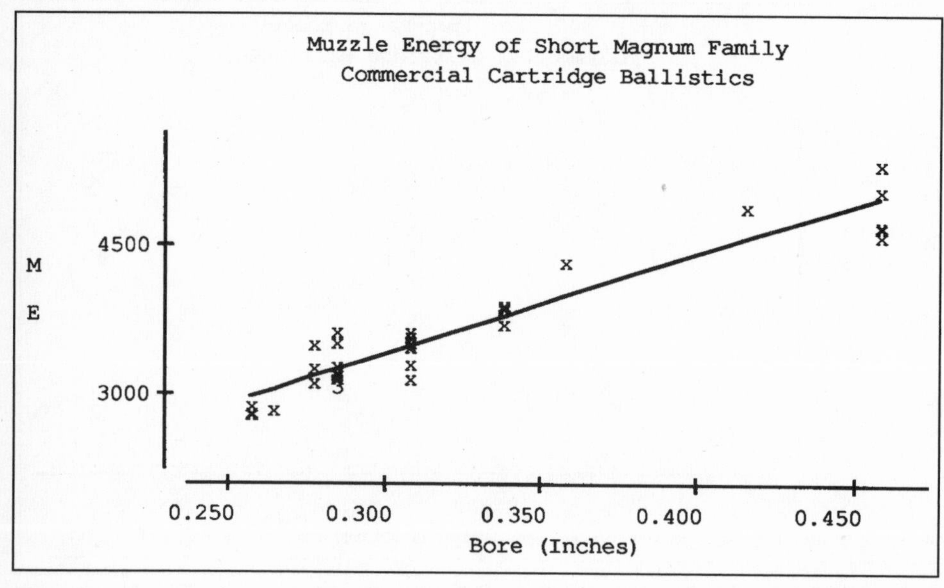


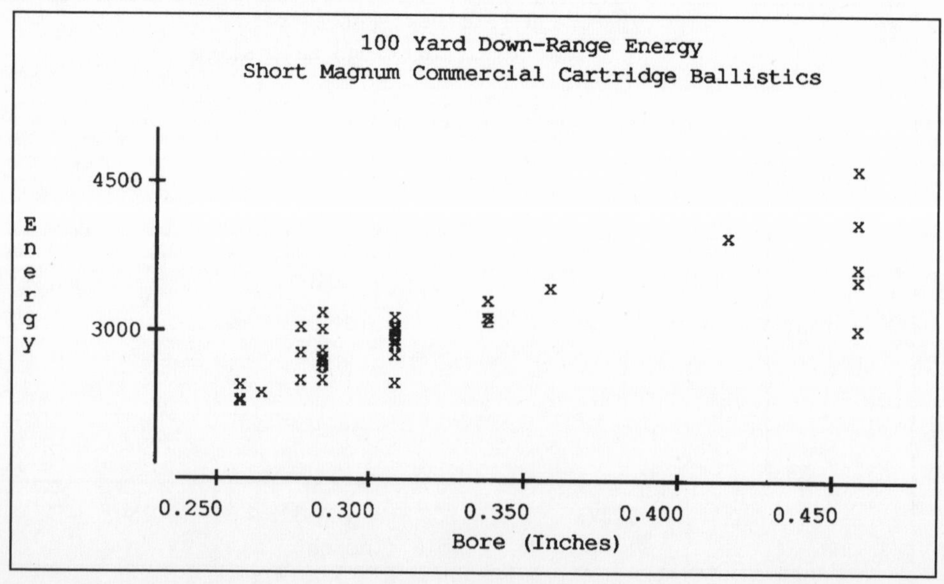

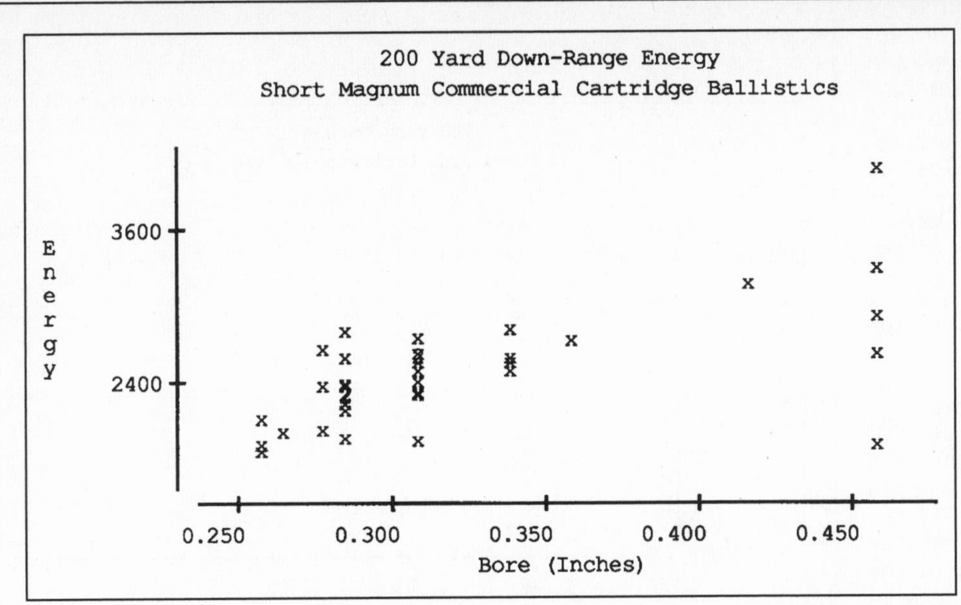
200 Yard Down-Range Energy
Short Magnum Commercial Cartridge Ballistics
Energy
3600
2400
0.250
0.300
0.350
0.400
0.450
Bore (Inches)

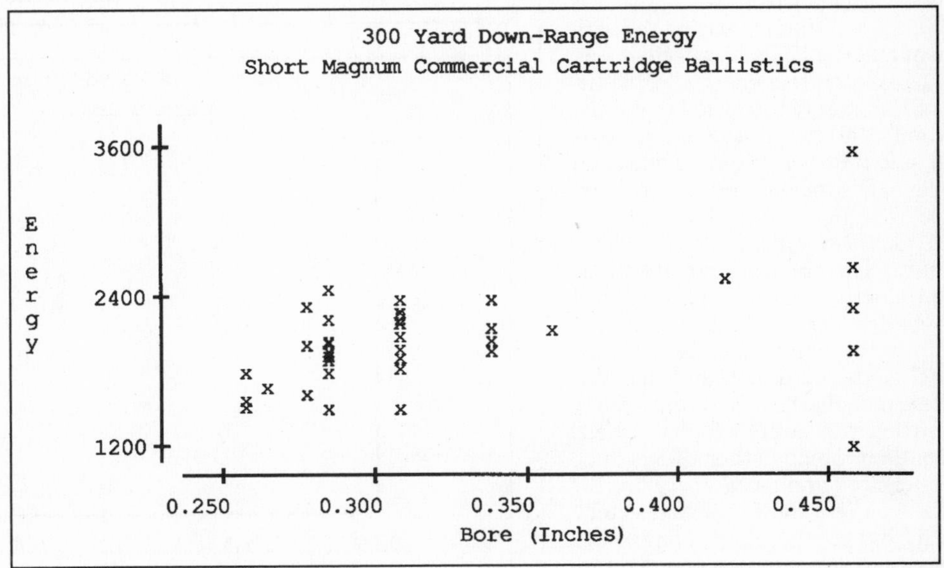
300 Yard Down-Range Energy
Short Magnum Commercial Cartridge Ballistics
Energy
3600
2400
1200
0.250
0.300
0.350
0.400
0.450
Bore (Inches)

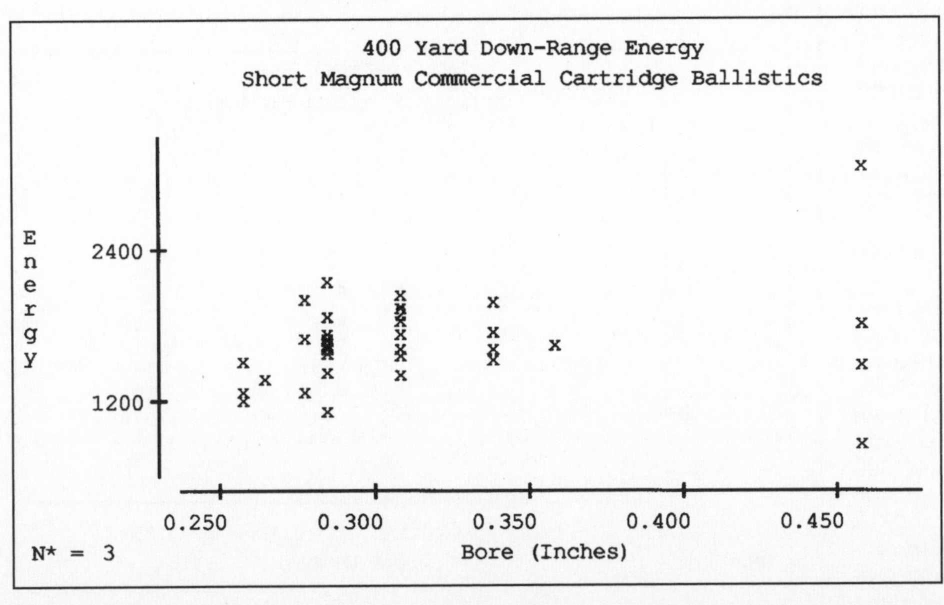
400 Yard Down-Range Energy
Short Magnum Commercial Cartridge Ballistics
Energy
2400
1200
0.250
0.300
0.350
0.400
0.450
N* = 3
Bore (Inches)

al trend, which corresponds to an increase of approximately 810 foot-pounds for each .1-inch increase in bore size. At 100 yards downrange, the slope of the energy-versus-bore relationship has flattened substantially (Figure 5b). At 200 yards and beyond (Figures 5c-e), the energy differences between the different calibers (243 excepted) have all but disappeared.

The story is the same for other cartridge families. Graphs for the short magnum family are shown in Figures 6a-e. Figure 6a contains similar information to Figure 5a. The trend represents a general increase of approximately 1000 foot-pounds for each 0.1-inch increase in bore size. Similar to the 30-06 family, energy differences between the cartridges—while dramatic at the muzzle—have largely disappeared at 200 yards downrange.

We've seen that increasing the bore size of a cartridge is an effective way to increase muzzle energy. While little of the energy increase is retained beyond 200 yards, the increase is real, and it doesn't require additional powder. The increase is not free, however.

My dictionary also states that "efficient implies proven capability based on productiveness in operation, and especially stresses ability to perform well and economically." When "efficient" is viewed in that broader context, it includes ease and consistency in hitting the target—factors which depend on, among other things, bullet trajectory and recoil.

Figures 7a-c show bullet trajectory (drop from bore) corresponding to the energy data in Figures 5c-e. Differences between the cartridges are not apparent at 100 yards, but become quite visible at 200 yards and beyond. Despite increased muzzle energy, the large caliber bullets drop more quickly. At 200 yards, each 0.1-inch increase in bore size is related to an additional 2.1 inches of drop. That difference becomes 7.5 inches at 300 yards, and more than 1 foot at 400 yards.

Trajectory of the various commercial bullets and calibers in the short magnum family are shown in Figures 8a-c. At 200 yards, each 0.1-inch increase in bore size is related to an additional 2.5 inches of drop. That difference becomes 8.5 inches at 300 yards, and well over 1 foot at 400 yards.

What is going on here? Quite simply, for bullets to share the same trajectory, they must have the same

## Figures 7a-c

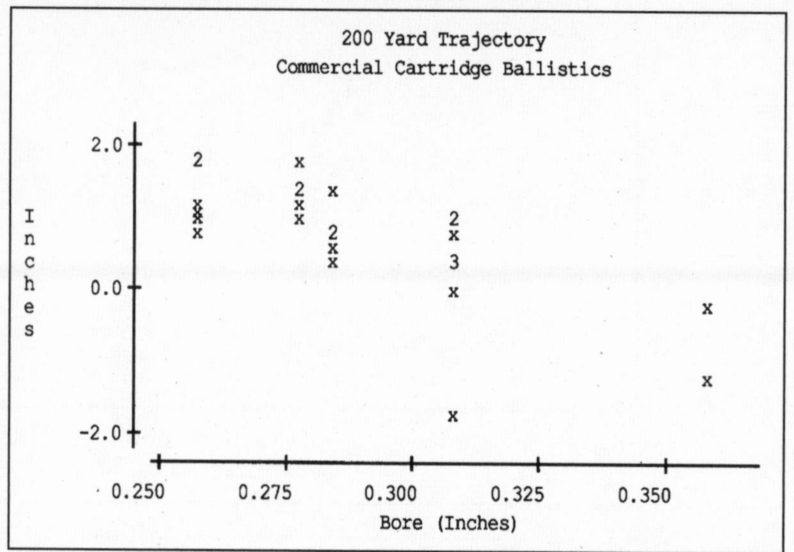


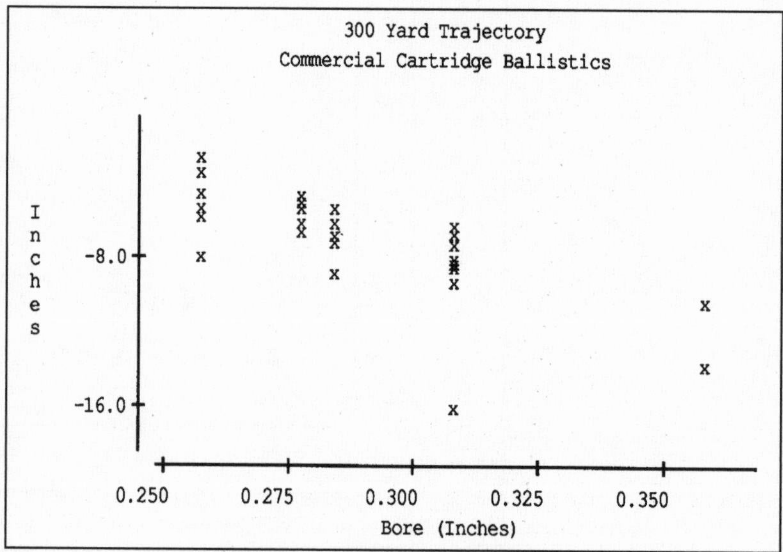


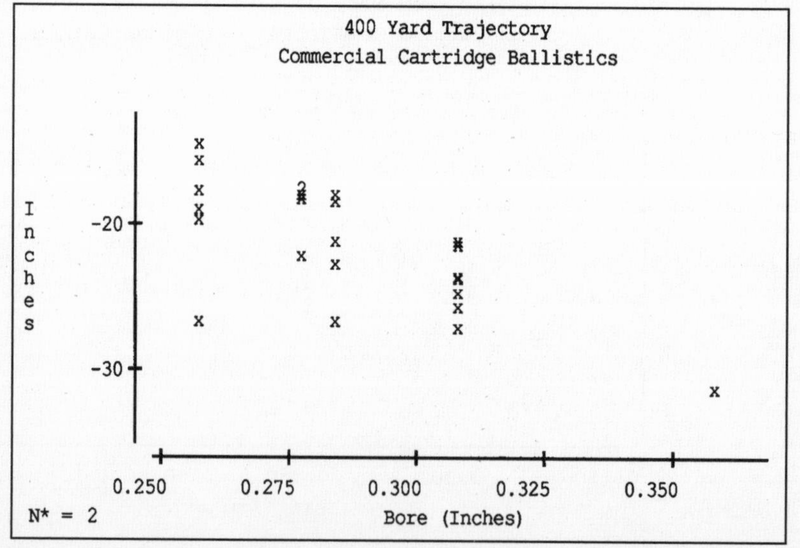

## Figures 8a-c

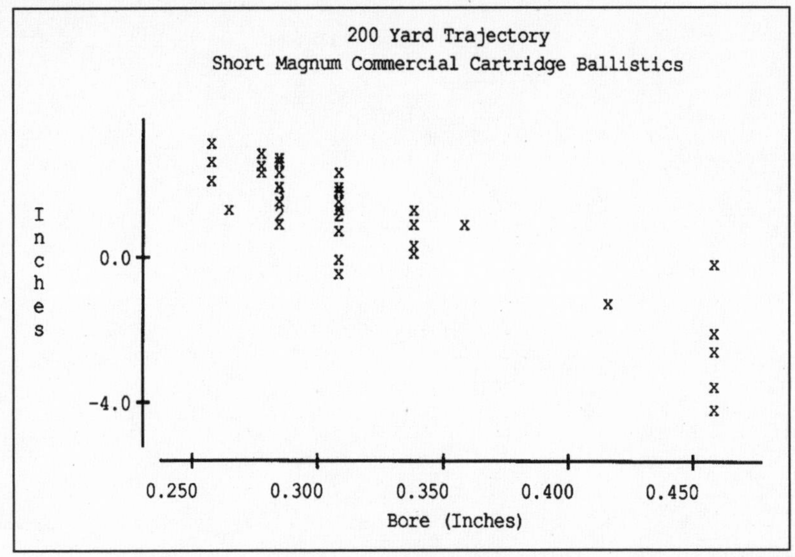


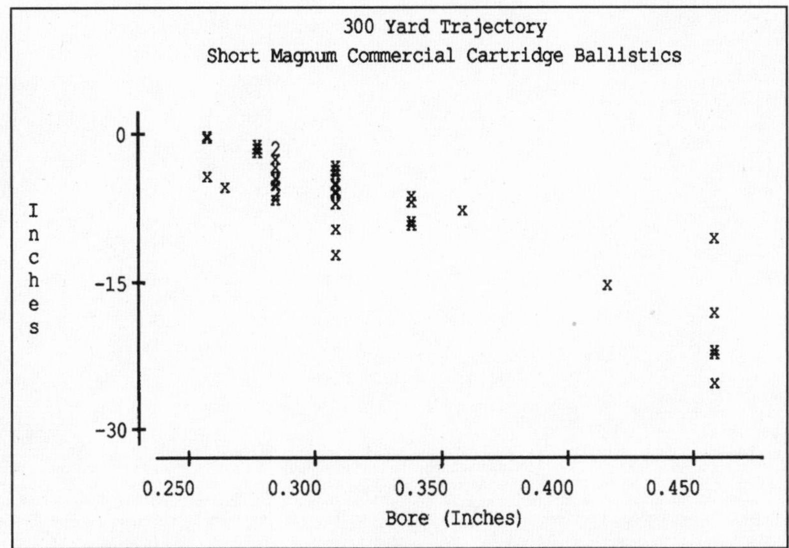


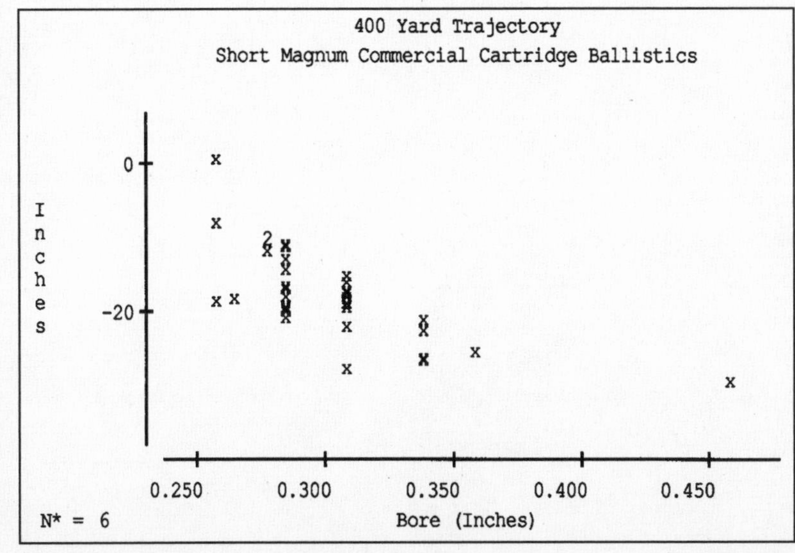


ballistic coefficient and start at the same velocity. While muzzle energy increases as bore size increases in any cartridge family, the energy doesn't increase fast enough to send bullets of equal ballistic coefficient out at the same velocity. As a result, trajectory suffers as bore increases.

Trajectory isn't the only characteristic that suffers when a cartridge is necked up; there is also the issue of recoil. Data presented by Paul Von Rosenburg[6] show that recoil is a function of bullet weight, powder weight, muzzle velocity and gun weight.[7] Recoil can actually be predicted quite well using only powder weight. Data from a widely reproduced page from the *Ideal Hand Book No. 17* (c. 1906) show that recoil can be explained very well using muzzle energy and velocity, with muzzle energy by far the most important predictor.[8] Since muzzle energy and powder weight are strongly related, these results aren't surprising. Quite simply, if you increase muzzle energy by 10 percent then recoil will also increase by 10 percent.

We've seen that increasing neck diameter is an easy way to increase muzzle energy in a cartridge. But whether the increase is an improvement or a handicap will depend on your needs. First, energy advantages at the muzzle are pretty much lost beyond 200 yards. The large diameter bullets in a cartridge family lose velocity more quickly and have consequently steeper trajectories. A flat trajectory is important for long shots, as it requires less accurate range estimation and holdover to place the shot. The relative importance of a flat trajectory depends on where you live and what you hunt. A larger bore with correspondingly heavier bullets might be a great tradeoff if you are primarily a woods hunter. A Western antelope hunter would likely prefer the flat trajectory of a smaller bore.

Of course, if you want heavier bullets *and* a flatter trajectory, you can always go to a bigger cartridge. But then that's another story.... ●

---

[6] Ackley, P.O. "A Few Notes on Sectional Density and Related Items," *Handbook for Shooters and Reloaders*, Vol. 1, 1962.

[7] The regression model is: Recoil (ft.-lbs.) = -24.8 + 0.206 Bullet Wgt. (grs.) + 0.371 Powder Wgt. (grs.) + 0.0182 Muzzle Vel. (fps) - 7.90 Gun Wgt. (lbs.)

[8] The relationship for smokeless powder is: Recoil (ft.-lbs.) = 2.82 + 0.00891 Muzzle Energy (ft.-lbs.).

AA
7/8 OZ.
Pat. Off. Marca Reg. Made in U.S.A.

## FOR LOW-COST AND LOW-RECOIL SHOTGUNNING, MASTER...

# THE SUBTLETIES OF THE TRAINING LOAD

BY DON ZUTZ

THE TERM "TRAINING loads" can be somewhat of a misnomer. We tend to equate it with beginners and milady because it smacks of a low-recoil level, but it goes further. For as we have been learning, the light 24-gram (about .84-ounce) and 7/8-ounce (about .875-ounce) shot charges in a 12-gauge gun can break their share of targets, providing low-recoil, low-cost practice for veteran shooters, too. We've been shown the way by those who compete in events sanctioned by the International Shooting Union (ISU), which has mandated loads no heavier than 24 grams for its tournaments, including the 1996 Olympics. These gunners have been breaking as many targets with 24-gram loads as they did with the old 1 1/8-ouncer, despite the fact that international forms of Skeet and trap are tougher than our stateside versions. Thus, it is possible that the training-load concept can be employed successfully for domestic clay shooting as well as for getting Junior and Sis started on hand-tossed clays behind Uncle Sig's barn.

(Inset) The newest wads around for light 12-gauge training reloads: Winchester's WAA12L "gray" wad, which was designed for 7/8-ounce (24-gram) reloads but can also take some 1-ouncers.

(Opposite page) For low-recoil and economical practice, nothing beats a so-called training load with its light, but effective, shot charge.

If there is a difference between the true training load that we'll cover here and the ISU 24-gram charges, it will be found in the velocity level. The international crowd likes 'em swift! The basic velocity for such loads as rolled stateside is 1325 fps, but overseas sources carry them to 1500 fps. So be it. The fact is that even these lighter loads give a recoil rap at elevated velocities, and beginners don't need that. Nor do we need such fast loads in American-style Skeet, trap and Sporting Clays, which are basically short-range games in which 1200 fps is an adequate starting velocity. In this article, I'll focus mainly on training reloads which operate between 1145 and 1250 fps for the practical purposes of low recoil and low cost.

We now come to the theoretical side of reloading training ammunition. There can be more to it than merely reducing the powder and shot charges. Both 24-gram and 7/8-ounce loads are quite light in a 12-gauge bore, and they are easily moved forward by the primer thrust and early powder gases. This quick payload movement, in turn, elongates the combustion chamber and holds down chamber pressures, which means that there isn't the same intense heat of a heavier charge. Lacking the heat of high chamber pressure, training reloads can suffer from inconsistent combustion, the result being inconsistent velocities and patterns. This is why lab technicians favor reloads with chamber pressures averaging 7000 psi or better. This seems to be a minimum for uniformity in pressure/velocity readings.

The problem is that most 24-gram and 7/8-ounce reloads for velocities of 1200 fps or less have chamber pressures below 7000 psi. If a reloader wants to use data reaching that level of velocity and pressure with that weight of shot in a 12-gauge loading, he'll have to search the files. Few such recipes exist. This one has worked out for me:

**HULL:** Remington Premier (RTL)
**PRIMER:** Federal 209A
**POWDER:** 18.5 grains of PB
**WAD:** Winchester WAA12SL
**SHOT:** 24.0 grams of lead
**PRESSURE:** 7100 psi
**VELOCITY:** 1200 fps
**NOTE:** Load data from IMR Powder Co. *Handloader's Guide for Smokeless Powders.*

For those who are working with recoil-sensitive beginners and are more concerned about ultra-low recoil than velocity spreads, the following recipe is both inexpensive and extremely mild:

**HULL:** Remington Premier (RTL)
**PRIMER:**Winchester 209
**POWER:** 15.0 grains of Hi-Skor 700-X
**WAD:** Claybuster CB1100-12
**SHOT:** 24.0 grams of lead
**PRESSURE:** 5300 psi
**VELOCITY:** 1140 fps
**NOTE:** Data also from IMR.

The above-mentioned 24-gram shot charge is a trifle lighter than the normal 7/8-ouncer. It converts to 370.3

grains, whereas a 7/8-ounce shot charge weighs 382.8 grains. The difference will be but a few pellets, but, scientifically speaking, the two individual measures of shot must be observed. At this writing, the main source of reloading information that I know about specifically related to 24-gram 12-gauge charges is the IMR Powder Co.'s *Handloader's Guide for Smokeless Powders* (1995 edition).

(Above) The new Winchester WAA12L wad will give a nice low-recoil result with just 19.5 grains of Super-Target Ball Powder under a 1-ounce shot charge.

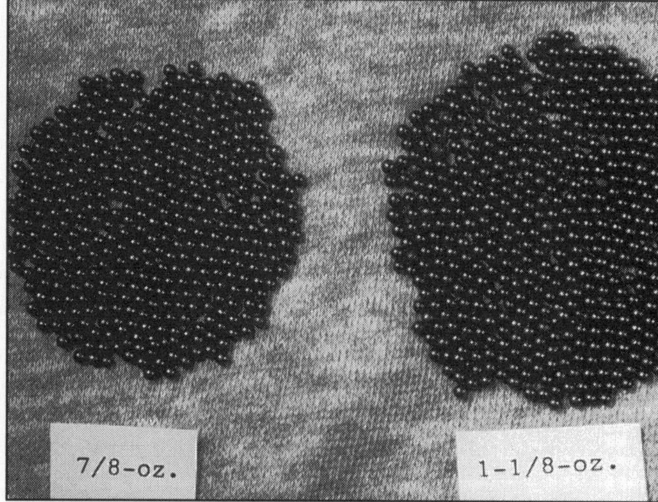


A 7/8-ounce charge of lead shot helps to lower the recoil in 12-gauge shotshells when held to low or moderate velocities. By some magic, the lighter 7/8-ounce load still manages to find the targets.

Americans are more likely to be interested in 7/8-ounce 12-gauge reloads. These are becoming more popular, and various sources—Hodgdon Powder Co., Winchester, Alliant (formerly Hercules)—are beginning to expand their manuals to include more such data. One of the first ever to publish data for 12-gauge, 7/8-ounce reloads was Hercules (now Alliant). The immediate problem then was getting such light charges to fill a 12-gauge case without an inward-angled crimp. Most wads at the time were designed for 1 1/8-ounce shot charges, although a few were intended for the 1-ounce load. In most of those early recipes, a .135 20-gauge nitro card was needed in the bottom of the shotcup to fill out the load. Often, this meant the upper layers of shot would be exposed to bore scrubbing, which meant deformed pellets. However, a few concepts put together reloads that didn't demand a nitro card filler. The following is an old favorite:

**HULL:** Winchester AA
**PRIMER:** Winchester 209
**POWDER:** 18.0 grains of Red Dot
**WAD:** Federal 12SO
**SHOT:** 7/8-ounce of lead
**PRESSURE:** 8000 psi
**VELOCITY:** 1200 fps

Some readers may question the use of a Federal 12SO wad in a hull with a tapered interior, believing that it was made for cases with cylindrical interiors. A close look, however, will prove that the F12SO wad does indeed have an adequate taper to tuck inside the Winchester AA hull and seat properly atop a full charge of Red Dot. The finished reload has a nice flat crimp.

While on the subject of wads, it must be noted that, as of this writing, only one wad has been produced to be a perfect match for the 7/8-ounce 12-gauge reloads. This is Winchester's WAA12L, alias the "gray wad." It has the length to fill a standard 12-gauge hull with light powder charges and the 24-gram or 7/8-ounce shot charge. Unfortunately, it is so new that most newer powder manuals do not have it listed. Perhaps those of the future will catch up. More unfortunate is the fact that Winchester's initial data sheet focuses mainly on the high-velocity ISU type of reload doing 1325 fps or better. For example:

**HULL:** Winchester AA
**PRIMER:** Winchester 209
**POWDER:** 22.0 grains of Win. Super-Target
**WAD:** Winchester WAA12L
**SHOT:** 7/8-ounce of lead
**PRESSURE:** 7900 psi
**VELOCITY:** 1325 fps

Can the new Winchester WAA12L interchange with the older Winchester WAA12SL wad? From the comparative data I've seen, it doesn't do so with the same ballistics. My early indications are that the WAA12L will run somewhat higher pressures by 1000 to about 1500 psi units (give or take a bit for individual reload variables). This may develop into just what the good doctor ordered, since a main problem with 24-gram and 7/8-ounce reloads is, as mentioned above, low chamber pressures. If we can increase the heat in those reloads cooking below 7000 psi, we just might find the velocities becoming more consistent. But always check reliable published reloading data before switching any component. Indeed, there should be a lot more information about the WAA12L wad by the time this edition of HANDLOADER'S DIGEST is printed.

While in the process of testing various 7/8-ounce training reloads, it is natural to find some that work out more consistently than others. I have listed my best findings in an append-

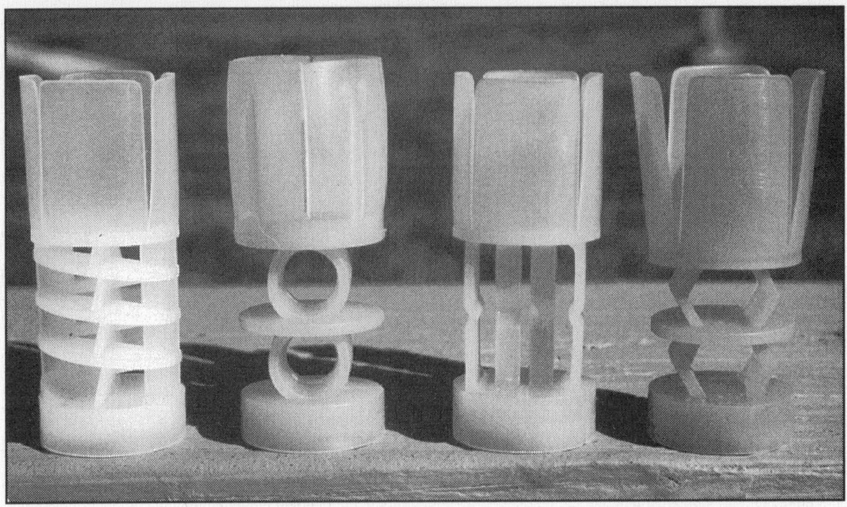

Long wads are needed in 12-gauge loads with light shot charges to fill out the capacity (from left): Federal's 12SO, Remington's TGT12, Winchester's WAAA12SL, and the Claybuster.

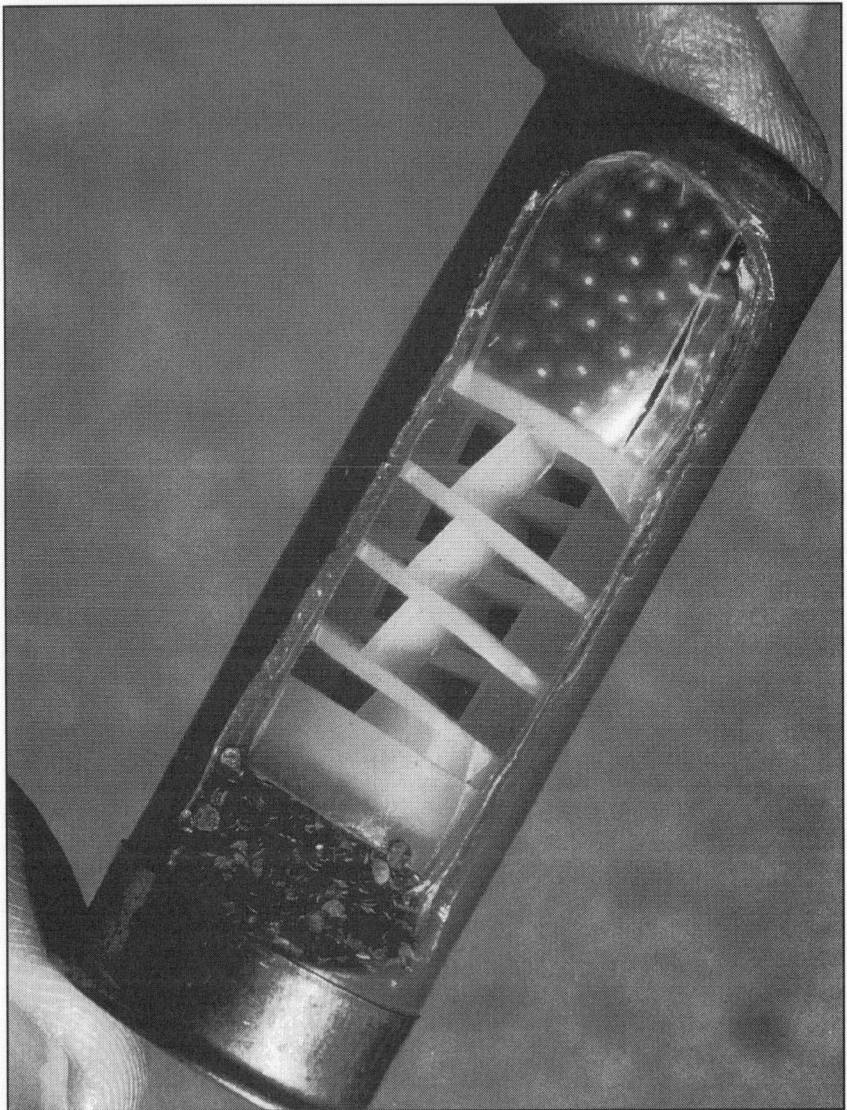

Sometimes it's difficult to fill out a case with just the 7/8-ounce shot charge unless there's a filler wad added. Not so with this combination of 18.0 grains of Red Dot in an AA hull case with the Federal 12SO. Yup, the 12SO *does* fit the AA case with ease—plus providing a stiffness for enhanced chamber pressures.

ed table. These tend to have pressures above 7000 psi, although they may be a bit faster than 1200 fps. My presentation has a variety of different velocity levels to give the reader a chance to experiment.

The 12 isn't the only gauge that can be given light training reloads, of course. A very popular beginner's gauge is the 20, which can be as gentle as a 28-gauge with just a 3/4-ounce training reload.

In general, the 20 doesn't present the same technical problems as the 12 when ultra-light shot charges are introduced. The narrower hulls and bores tend to build pressures faster than does the larger 12-bore, and that provides adequate chamber heat for enhanced uniformity. One look at the following recipes will prove that contention:

**HULL:** Remington 20-ga. Premier
**PRIMER:** Remington 209P
**POWDER:** 14.0 grains of Green Dot
**WAD:** Winchester WAA20
**SHOT:** 3/4-ounce of lead
**PRESSURE:** 10,500 psi
**VELOCITY:** 1200 fps
**NOTE:** Add two 1/8″ 410-bore card wads to bottom of wad.

**HULL:** Winchester 20-ga. AA
**PRIMER:** Winchester 209
**POWDER:** 14.0 grains of Green Dot
**WAD:** Winchester WAA41
**SHOT:** 3/4-ounce of lead
**PRESSURE:** 10,800 psi
**VELOCITY:** 1200 fps
**NOTE:** Add one 1/8″ 410-bore card wad to bottom of shotcup.

Those who might want to reduce recoil a little more can cut the above powder charges to 13.5 grains of Green Dot. The Alliant Powder Co.'s *Reloaders' Guide for Alliant Smokeless Powders* contains additional data for 3/4-ounce 20-gauge training reloads. Winchester's booklet also has some, although they are still based on the rapidly disappearing 452 and 473 Ball Powders.

If one wants *bona fide* 410 card wads to fill shotcups, he can find them at Ballistic Products, Inc., or perhaps at Precision Reloading, Inc. Both outfits send the first catalog free.

Despite the availability of light-kicking 20- and 28-gauge stuff, many parents still insist upon starting Junior with a 410. This is unfortunate for two reasons: First, 410s are generally so light that they are whippy and thus hinder a new shooter's progress. Secondly, 410s are normally Full-choked and make it difficult for a rank beginner to score. If the parent is determined to use the 410, however, it would be advisable for him to have the choke adjusted for wider Improved Cylinder patterns, as they'll suffice for the close-range clays thrown for starters. Also, even the 410 can be taken to a slightly lower velocity level for shaved recoil in a lightweight single or whatever. Winchester published this load:

**HULL:** Winchester 2½" 410 AA
**PRIMER:** Winchester 209
**POWDER:** 13.5 grains of 296 Ball
**WAD:** Winchester WAA41
**SHOT:** ½-ounce of lead
**PRESSURE:** 9100 lup
**VELOCITY:** 1150 fps

This reload will leave the bore a bit sooty, but there are no truly clean-burning 410 fuels. The velocity is certainly fast enough, as many scores of 200x200 have been broken at trap with 12-gauge loads clocking 1145 fps.

Which shot sizes for training reloads? If the person is indeed a beginner working on close-in clays, #8½ and #9 shot are recommended to fill out patterns with these lighter shot charges. On Skeet, #9s are perfect. Should training reloads be used on 16-yard traps, the heavier #8s and #7½s are suggested. For Sporting Clays, load #8s or #8½s.

Gun operation is a factor with training reloads. Many won't cycle autoloaders due to their low recoil impulse and/or their lack of powder gases. Likewise, some won't activate the inertial mechanism of doubles, which depend upon recoil energy to ready the second lock. Thus, be prepared to use training reloads in single shot situations.

A personal point is that training reloads are just that—practice fodder. Their low velocities and generally light patterns make them potential cripplers of fine game birds, and I'd advise against them afield. For whatever psychological reason(s), heavier loads aren't as disruptive and abusive when the shooter is swinging on game. His focal point is on the bird, not the gun, and he can get away with a harder-recoiling round under those thrilling, and more demanding, moments.

For extended periods of practice or instruction, however, the light training reloads are super stuff, letting the beginner or veteran enjoy himself while learning. •

## Selected 12-Gauge Training Reloads

**HULL:** Winchester AA
**PRIMER:** Winchester 209
**POWDER:** 16.5 grains of Red Dot
**WAD:** Winchester WAA12SL
**SHOT:** ⅞-ounce of lead
**PRESSURE:** 7300 psi
**VELOCITY:** 1200 fps
**NOTE:** Add one 20-ga. .135" card wad as filler.

**HULL:** Remington Premier (RTL)
**PRIMER:** Remington 209P
**POWDER:** 17.0 grains of Red Dot
**WAD:** Federal 12SO
**SHOT:** ⅞-ounce of lead
**PRESSURE:** 7200 psi
**VELOCITY:** 1200 fps

**HULL:** Federal plastic Gold Medal
**PRIMER:** Federal 209A
**POWDER:** 17.5 grains of Red Dot
**WAD:** Federal 12SO
**SHOT:** ⅞-ounce of lead
**PRESSURE:** 7600 psi
**VELOCITY:** 1200 fps

**HULL:** Remington Premier (RTL)
**PRIMER:** Winchester 209
**POWDER:** 15.9 grains of Clays
**WAD:** Winchester WAA12SL
**SHOT:** ⅞-ounce of lead shot
**PRESSURE:** 7100 psi
**VELOCITY:** 1200 fps

**HULL:** Winchester AA
**PRIMER:** Winchester 209
**POWDER:** 16.9 grains of Clays
**WAD:** Winchester WAA12SL
**SHOT:** ⅞-ounce of lead
**PRESSURE:** 7100 LUP
**VELOCITY:** 1200 fps
**NOTE:** Good Skeet reload with #9s.

**HULL:** Fiocchi (lilac)
**PRIMER:** Fiocchi 616
**POWDER:** 17.8 grains of Clays
**WAD:** Federal 12SO
**SHOT:** ⅞-ounce lead
**PRESSURE:** 7500 psi
**VELOCITY:** 1250 fps

**HULL:** Winchester AA case
**PRIMER:** Winchester 209
**POWDER:** 19.5 grains Win. Super-Target
**WAD:** Winchester WAA12L
**SHOT:** 1 ounce of lead
**PRESSURE:** 8500 psi
**VELOCITY:** 1200 fps

**HULL:** Winchester AA
**PRIMER:** Winchester 209
**POWDER:** 20.5 grains of Green Dot
**WAD:** Winchester WAA12SL
**SHOT:** ⅞-ounce of lead
**PRESSURE:** 8800 psi
**VELOCITY:** 1300 fps
**NOTE:** Green Dot tends to hold tight patterns despite higher velocity.

## Selected 16-Gauge Training Reloads

**HULL:** Winchester AA-type
**PRIMER:** Winchester 209
**POWDER:** 19.0 grains of Unique
**WAD:** Winchester WAA16
**SHOT:** 1-ounce of lead
**PRESSURE:** 9200 psi
**VELOCITY:** 1165 fps
**NOTE:** Shot charge can be cut to 15/16-ounce (408 grains) for reduced recoil.

**HULL:** Fiocchi plastic field
**PRIMER:** Fiocchi 616
**POWDER:** 17.5 grains of Green Dot
**WAD:** Winchester WAA16
**SHOT:** 1-ounce of lead
**PRESSURE:** 9400 psi
**VELOCITY:** 1165 fps
**NOTE:** Shot charge can be cut to 15/16-ounce (408 grains) for reduced recoil.

## Selected 20-Gauge Training Reloads

**HULL:** Federal plastic target
**PRIMER:** Federal 209A
**POWDER:** 15.0 grains of Green Dot
**WAD:** Federal 20S1
**SHOT:** ¾-ounce of lead
**PRESSURE:** 9000 psi
**VELOCITY:** 1200 fps

**HULL:** Remington Premier
**PRIMER:** Remington 209P
**POWDER:** 13.0 grains of Red Dot
**WAD:** Winchester WAA20
**SHOT:** ¾-ounce of lead
**PRESSURE:** 11500 psi
**VELOCITY:** 1200 fps
**NOTE:** May not operate semi-autos. Requires one ½" 410-bore card in shotcup as filler.

REMINGTON'S MODEL 700 ML/MLS falls into its own niche in the world of blackpowder shooting. It's an in-line modern muzzleloader by definition, but the familiar-handling bolt-action rifle is at home in a whitetail thicket, on a black timber elk mountain, in wild boar brush country, in willow creekbottom moose habitat, or anywhere else where shooting distances are on the short side. It's a rifle I've carried on general hunts where modern arms were allowed. Others had their bolt-action 30-06s and 300 Magnums, while I packed a 50-caliber M700 MLS firing a big conical lead bullet in front of a heavy dose of powder. Admittedly, I would get only one shot from a rifle that had to be loaded from the front, compared with the hunter packing his long-range cartridge-shooting repeater, but I was confident in the Remington's reliability, its ballistic authority, and its accuracy potential enhanced by a clear-as-mountain-air Zeiss 1.25-4x scope.

The Remington Model 700 MLS was used by the author to take this Maine black bear. Here, the rifle's designer, Nick Sachse, admires the results of his engineering efforts.

# LOADING REMINGTON'S MODEL 700 ML/MLS

by SAM FADALA

## This revolutionary new blackpowder gun is strangely familiar.

When the cards were laid on the table, the 700 MLS didn't hesitate to cash in. On one hunt, a big Maine black bear fell to a single 385-grain Remington Gamemaster lead bullet shoved out of the muzzle by 110 grains volume of Pyrodex RS powder. I was not surprised. Anything less than a one-shot show would have left me wondering.

So what is this rifle, the Model 700 ML/MLS, and how does a shooter go about getting the most from it in both handling and loads? The rifle comes by its name honestly. It is built on a Model 700 short action. ML stands for Muzzle Loader. MLS is the stainless steel version. The rifle carries the familiar Model 700 safety and trigger, along with standard open sights. It's scope-ready, too. There's a recoil pad and sling swivels. The barrel is 24 inches long, 1:28-inch twist. Overall length is 44.5 inches, weight a shade under 8 pounds. Length of pull is 13$^3/_8$ inches, drop at comb $^1/_2$-inch, drop at heel $^3/_8$-inch. The ML comes in 50-caliber only, the MLS in 50 or 54.

Muzzleloader appointments begin with a removable stainless steel breech plug. The plug is short, which promotes a fast lock time because the spark from the percussion cap doesn't have to travel very far to reach the main charge of powder in the breech. The face of the bolt is now a striker, shrouded to contain cap debris, and it rests but a short distance from a percussion cap seated on a hardened $^1/_4$-28 thread stainless steel nipple. Lock time was electronically gauged at 3.0 milliseconds, the

Here is the action of the Remington Model 700 MLS rifle. It must be called an action instead of a lock, because it is, in fact, identical to the short Model 700 centerfire version with the appropriate muzzleloader changes, of course. A standard scope mount is used for the Zeiss scope.

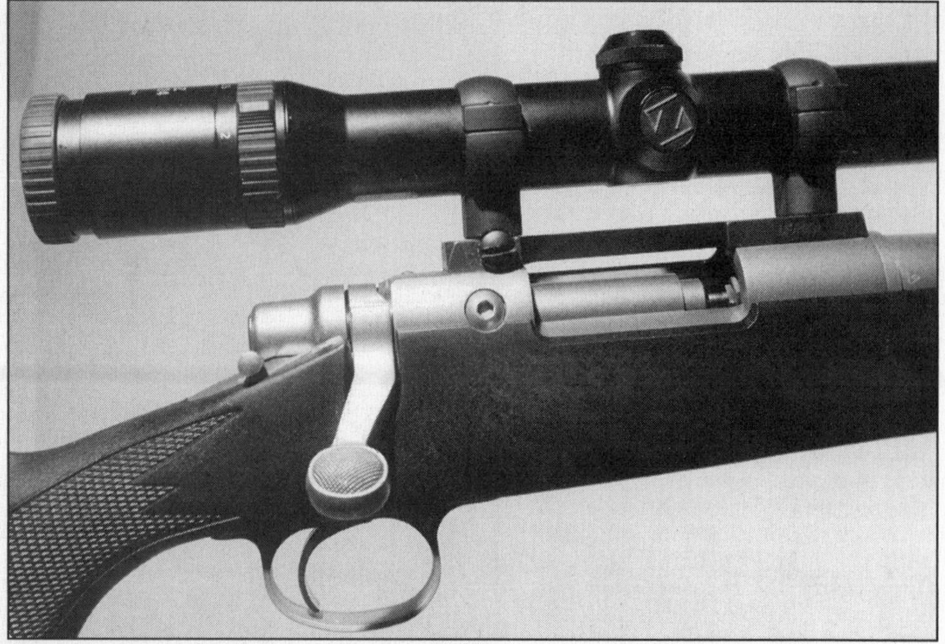

(Below) The bolt is removed from the Model 700 ML/MLS rifle with the use of one Allen wrench. When the bolt-stop screw is taken out, the bolt will slide free for maintenance of the rifle.

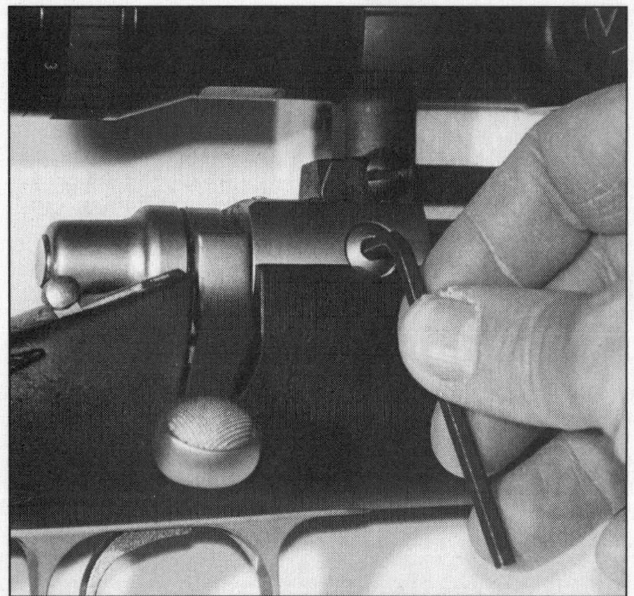

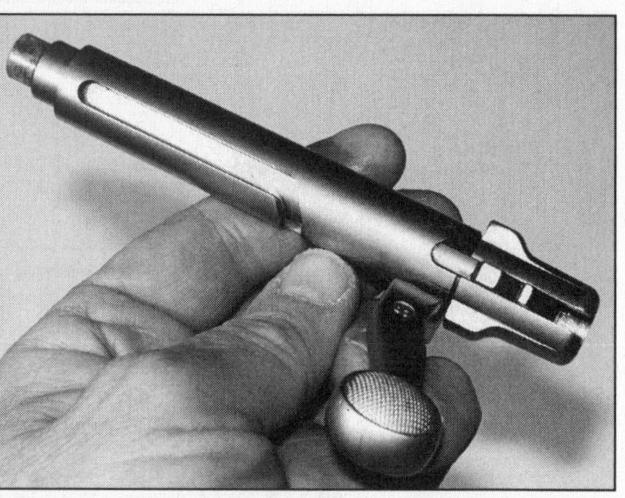

The bolt of the 700 ML/MLS required intelligent modification in order for it to function in the muzzleloader version of the rifle. The slot or groove is aligned with the bolt-stop screw hole when installing the bolt into the action of the rifle.

The face of the bolt was altered considerably to turn it into a striker without locking lugs. The shroud around the face of the bolt helps to contain cap debris.

same as the long-action Model 700 cartridge rifle. Beneath the barrel, a hard aluminum ramrod rests in a single thimble. This ramrod is special. It takes an extension piece plus a handle, which turn it into a true loading/cleaning rod.

The modified bolt is a touch of genius provided by Nick Sachse, the designer of the 700 ML/MLS. Nick knew that the recoil lugs of the original bolt were no longer necessary. The breech plug would hold the pressure generated by the powder charge. The bolt head was replaced with a shrouded striker. However, without bolt lugs, how would the bolt cam forward, engaging the trigger sear with the firing pin head and locking the bolt closed? Nick came up with the idea of a cam slot in the sidewall of the bolt body to interact with a follower inserted through the side of the receiver. The result is a bolt that can be removed from the action with a single Allen-head bolt-stop screw.

### Loads Like Any ML

To load the 700 ML/MLS, you follow the same basic procedure used with any muzzleloader. First, make certain that the rifle is not already loaded. This is accomplished by dropping the ramrod downbore. If there's a load in the chamber, the ramrod will protrude too far from the muzzle. Once you've settled on a favorite load, you can mark the ramrod where the rod and muzzle crown meet. By using that witness mark, the shooter always

In the cocked position, the striker is quite close to the cone of the nipple, so that there is minimal travel, which decreases lock time. The Remington Model 700 ML/MLS enjoys the same lock time associated with the Remington Model 700 long-action centerfire rifle.

This is the stainless steel breech plug shown with percussion cap in place. The shortness of the breech plug promotes the fast lock time of the 700 ML/MLS rifle. A little Wonder Lube or similar product is applied to the threads of the breech plug before installing it. This helps to free it later on for the cleaning process.

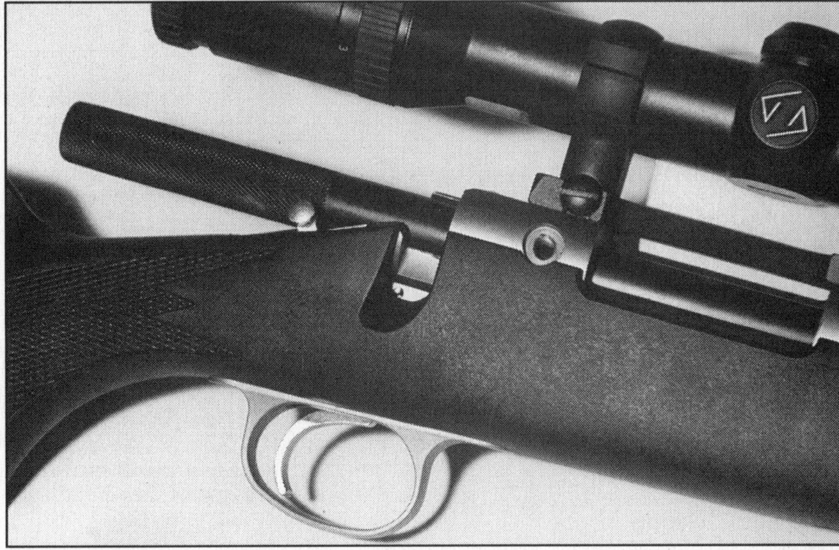

Here, the bore cleaning tube is shown installed. It simply threads into the barrel where the breech plug normally fits. It allows cleaning with solvent or water without getting either down into the action of the rifle.

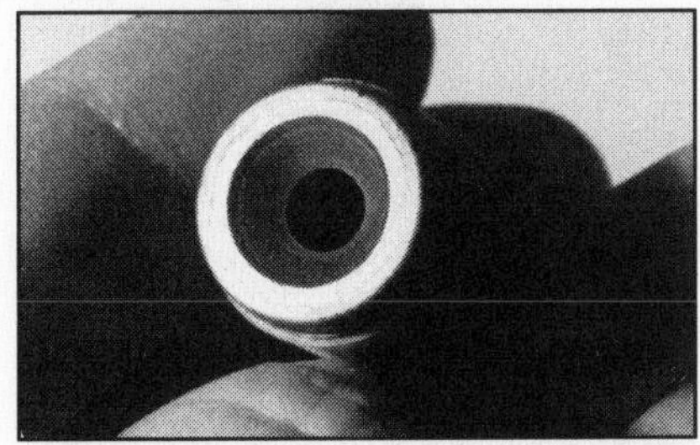

This is the face of the Model 700 ML/MLS breech plug. Powder, of course, goes into this beveled recess when the breech plug is mounted in the barrel. This end of the breech plug is kept grease-free for proper ignition.

knows that his load is properly seated downbore. With blackpowder arms, the projectile must be fully seated on the powder or dangerous pressure can result. Next, a cap or two is fired, with the muzzle of the unloaded rifle pointed at a lightweight object on the ground. The gas from the primer should blow the object aside, indicating a clear passage from the nipple through the breech plug, into the breech, and out the muzzle of the bore. If the object is not budged, that denotes an obstruction, perhaps in the nipple vent.

After popping caps, it's business as usual. With the safety engaged in the "On" position, a proper powder charge is dropped downbore followed by a projectile, which, with the Remington's 1:28 rate of twist, means a conical. A patched round ball shoots reasonably well, especially with lighter powder charges. During my initial field testing, I used patched round balls to down two wild boars with one shot each, but in spite of that, this rifle works best with conicals. With the projectile firmly seated on the powder charge, it's only a matter of placing a percussion cap on the cone of the nipple and you're ready to fire, as soon as the safety is disengaged. The trigger is adjustable, so I took my MLS to gunsmith Dale Storey who, in a few moments, had it set safe but reasonably light.

A weather shroud comes with the Model 700 muzzleloader for days when the weather is threatening. The shroud is placed on the end of the bolt assembly to protect the percussion cap from the elements. Speaking of the percussion cap, I had problems with Remington's No. 11 falling off the cone of the nipple. While it's difficult to get an exact micrometer reading across the open end of a malleable percussion cap, I tried, coming up with .180-inch diameter for the Remington cap, compared with .173 for RWS' and .176 for CCI's No. 11. That situation is now remedied. The next batch of caps to flow from Remington will be sized to fit the standard nipple cone more tightly.

The 700 ML/MLS is a paradox, in my opinion, because it fits two extreme ends of the spectrum. On one end, this modern in-line muzzleloader appeals to the newcomer who cares little to nothing about history, the romance of shooting yesteryear's guns, or any other traditional aspect of the muzzle-loading sport. He wants to partake of a special blackpowder-only hunt with a rifle that's a close match to the bolt-action centerfire he now owns. Everything about the 700 ML/MLS is familiar, except, of course, for its muzzleloader aspects. It feels like, looks like and handles like the cartridge version of the Remington Model 700.

On the other end of the spectrum is the veteran blackpowder shooter who has practiced the art for decades. I freely admit that I had a lot of trouble falling in love with the newfan-

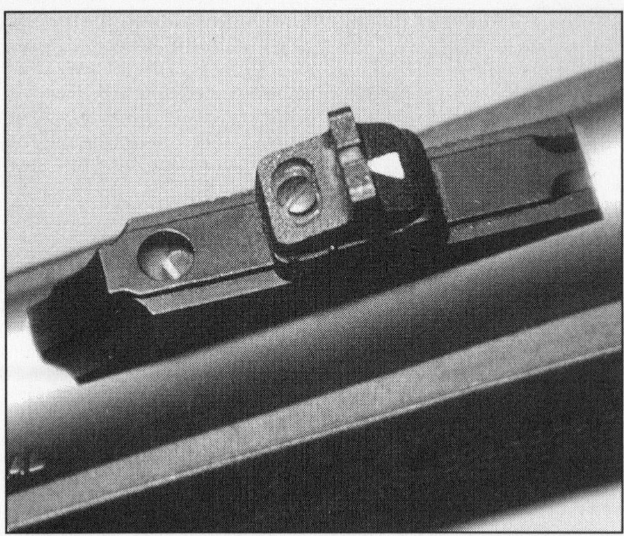

The rear sight of the 700 ML/MLS is factory-installed.

The front sight of the Model 700 ML/MLS rifle also is standard. Note the ramrod pipe (also called guide or thimble).

gled frontloader, and I still find no romance in shooting one. When I want to emulate the Eastern trail-blazer or Western mountain man, I'll carry a rifle that embodies the spirit of those men and times. But my M700 MLS fills a very different, and equally important, niche for me. It's a hardworking muzzleloader for any season.

M700 MLS may be cleaned just like its cartridge version. The bolt is removed via the single screw mentioned earlier. Then the nipple is screwed out using a special tool provided with the rifle. The other end of the same tool takes out the breech plug. Now you can look straight through the bore as with any other bolt-action rifle, and the rifle can be cleaned from the breech end, which is handy. Furthermore, a threaded tube is provided to keep water or solvent out of the action. This tube screws directly into the breech-plug seat. The cleaning rod now runs through the tube and into the bore. I tried flushing the bore with water, but abandoned that method for a solvent-only approach, using solvent with a bristle brush (essential for getting gunk out of the rifling grooves), followed by solvent-treated cleaning patches, dry patches, and so forth until the bore came clean.

Cleaning was further enhanced by the use of an "all-day" lube during shooting. In this instance, Ox-Yoke Wonder Lube did the trick, keeping fouling soft and removable, rather than allowing the residue to cake up and harden. Blackpowder leaves roughly half of itself behind after ignition, unlike smokeless powder, which goes from solid to gas much more completely. In part, the residue is composed of salts, which attract moisture, which in turn befriends that old gremlin called ferric oxide, commonly known as rust. By using Ox-Yoke Wonder Lube, followed by a good solvent/bristle brush/cleaning patch workout, the M700 ML/MLS cleaned up quickly and without fuss, a dream for the newcomer to smoke-pole shooting.

Also, the beginner can buy a kit that contains most of what he'll need to load and fire his new rifle. Remington's Black Powder Starter Kit contains a belt bag, short starter, screw (ball puller), adjustable powder measure, capper and pre-lubed patches. Remington also offers a Cyclone Quick Starter, the Black Out Flush Cleaning System, Wonder Lube, and more good stuff.

### Understand Instructions

That's a look at the 700 ML/MLS and what makes it tick. A complete reading and understanding of the *Instruction Book Model 700 In-Line Bolt Action Muzzleloading Rifle* booklet is absolutely essential to understand the rifle's workings and safety measures, but for now, you get the idea: Here is a truly modern muzzleloader, capable of dropping any big game animal on the continent with one shot. As for caliber, I consider the 50 a good all-around choice. However, if I were primarily interested in elk and larger game, I'd choose the 700 ML/MLS in 54-caliber for a bit heavier projectile. Remember, there is no such thing as high velocity in blackpowder shooting. If you want more punch, go to a heavier bullet.

As for projectiles, Remington recently brought out its own line in three categories: round ball, jacketed big game pistol bullet with sabot and lead conical. The Premier Golden Lead round ball from Remington is available in 32 to 58 calibers. Remington's Core-Lokt big game jacketed pistol bullet with sabot is offered in 45, 50 and 54 calibers, with actual bullet sizes being .357-inch and .429-inch caliber. The .357-inch bullet with sabot is for the 45-caliber muzzleloader. It weighs 165 grains. Two 44-caliber saboted pistol bullets fit the 50-caliber at 275 grains or 303 grains weight, the latter also usable in 54-caliber barrels. All of these pistol bullets are hollow-points.

Although I have never been a big fan of jacketed pistol bullets in big game muzzleloaders, I stand on shaky ground, because thousands of game animals have toppled to these projectiles, including the world-record muzzleloader elk, which was taken with a Sierra pistol bullet. Regardless, I still lean to the big lead conical over the lighter jacketed bullet. Remington's Gamemaster Pre-Lubed lead bullets are available for calibers 45, 50, 54 and 58, weighing respectively 285, 365, 400 and 535 grains. All are hollowpoints. There is another 50-caliber Gamemaster conical that runs 385 grains in a solid-nose version. It's the bullet I used to take the Maine bear mentioned earlier.

Rifles have their own personalities. You learn that after years of testing. Therefore, I was not surprised to find that my test rifle had a mind of its own when it came to bullet selection. While all bullets shot with sufficient

Here are two Remington blackpowder projectiles (from left): Remington's 303-grain Core-Lokt jacketed big game pistol bullet with sabot, shown in the sabot to the right, and a Remington Gamemaster 385-grain solid nose.

(Below) This is the nose of Remington's 303-grain Core-Lokt big game pistol bullet. One of these was used recently on a Kentucky whitetail deer hunt. It worked perfectly at close range from a treestand, dropping the deer in its tracks with one shot.

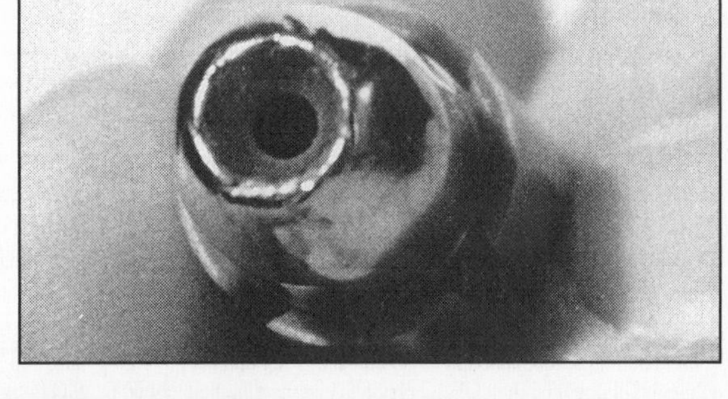

(Below) This is the new Buffalo Bullet Company SSB, Special Sabot Bullet, in the prototype form. The final bullet that will be on the market has a slightly smaller hollowpoint and a slightly sharper profile.

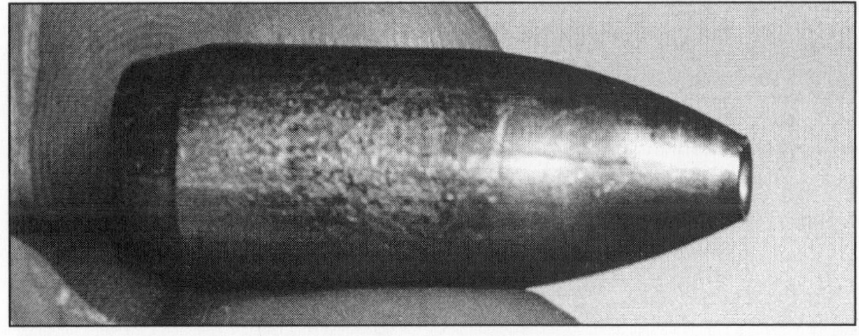

accuracy for big game hunting, a few shone brighter than the rest. I almost hesitate to mention them, because the reader might get the idea these are the only bullets he should try in his Model 700 ML/MLS. Let me say right away that when I tested a second rifle, it did not "like" the same bullets that my first rifle shot best. Nontheless, with a clear understanding that this is not necessarily a recommendation, the been-around-forever Thompson/Center 370-grain Maxi Ball grouped three shots into an inch at 100 yards like clockwork. The rifle did the same thing with a 400-grain bullet known as the Gamebuster, and again with a brand-new projectile from Buffalo Bullet Co. called the Buffalo Bullet SSB, which stands for Special Sabot Bullet.

This new Buffalo offering is a 45-caliber cast lead projectile in a 50-caliber sabot. It weighs 434 grains with a hollow point and a spitzer shape. It's quite unlike the usual blackpowder lead conical, and it will deliver improved downrange performance from its high retained velocity and energy. This is not a suggestion that we can "shoot far" just because a shapely bullet is available for muzzleloaders. I'm against the trend that seems to be afoot—that of convincing the blackpowder fan that he won't be all that handicapped with a muzzleloader, and that maybe he can turn his smokebelcher into a 30-06 after all. He cannot. Furthermore, if the hype and barnyard ballyhoo currently flung about becomes more convincing, game department officials might just take notice of it, saying, "Oh, I see. You can actually shoot at 200 yards with that muzzleloader? Then why do you need a special blackpowder-only season?"

Currently, the reason for allowing blackpowder guns where cartridge-shooters are not permitted is the fact that range is limited with the former. Remington warns that its Model 700 ML/MLS has a "Range More Than 1/2 Mile." That's a far cry from the extreme range of a modern big game cartridge, which can be several miles. On the other hand, within its range limitations, which I claim to be 125 yards when trajectory is considered, the 700 ML/MLS will drop big game with one shot—pronto. Remington's load data and mine matched closely, incidentally, which is not always the case with factory data due to variations between test guns and "real" firearms. For example, Remington shows a 385-grain 50-caliber bullet moving out at 1470 fps pushed by 120 volume FFg blackpowder. I used 120 by volume of Pyrodex RS with the same bullet and got 1491 fps 12 feet from the muzzle, which translates to over 1500 fps at the muzzle, essentially the same results printed by Remington.

### Round Ball Results

The only projectile that did not match up for me, either in muzzle velocity or accuracy, was the round ball. Remington got 2050 fps with 110

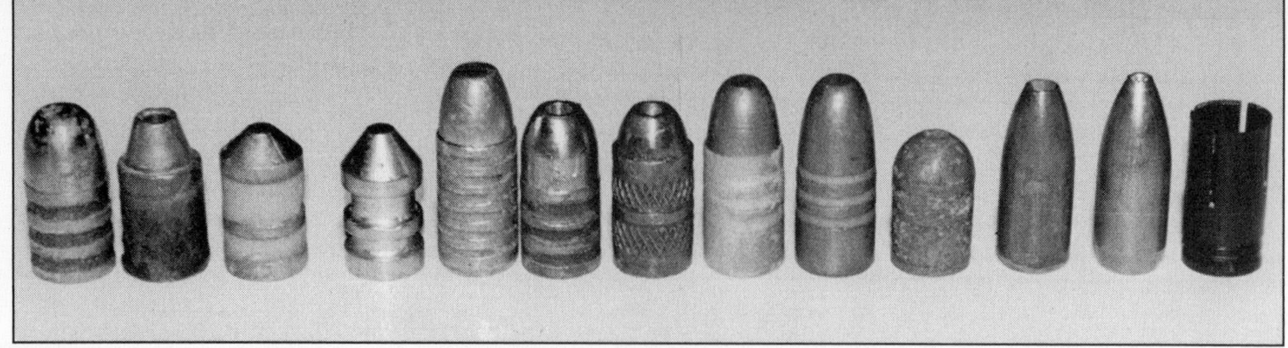

These are the bullets tested for this particular study of the new Remington Model 700 ML/MLS rifle (from left): 465-grain Gonic, 400-grain Gamebuster, 370-grain T/C Maxi Ball, 365-grain NEI, 600-grain White, 460-grain White, 490-grain Buffalo Bullet flat-base hollowpoint, 500-grain Parker Hyrda-Con paper-patched, the same bullet without paper-patching, 360-grain Mushroom Express (which weighed 340 grains), 434-grain prototype of the Buffalo SSB bullet, and finally the production version of the same bullet. On the far right is the sabot used for the SSB bullet. It is a full inch long.

grains of FFg blackpowder. My rifle produced a couple hundred fps less. Accuracy-wise, Remington claimed "good results" with the round ball. I would call my targets poor, with groups ranging 4 to 5 inches center to center at 100 yards. On the other hand, Remington's pistol bullet with sabot was reported to deliver fine accuracy, and it certainly did, especially in my second test rifle, where the 303-grain Core-Lokt consistently put five, not three, holes into less than an inch center to center at 100 yards. Incidentally, the 303-grain Core-Lokt gave 1530 fps in my test rifle, that velocity taken 12 feet from the muzzle to the middle screen of my Oehler Model 35P Proof chronograph, while Remington's tests showed the same bullet gave 1570 fps muzzle velocity. Remington's load was 120 volume FFg. Mine was 120 volume Pyrodex RS. Working back to the muzzle, my velocity would actually be slightly higher than Remington's.

I'm still testing bullets in my Model 700 MLS rifle. For this particular review, I tried the following: 465-grain Gonic, 400-grain Gamebuster, 370-grain T/C Maxi Ball, 365-grain NEI, 600-grain White, 460-grain White, 490-grain Buffalo hollowpoint flat-base, 500-grain Parker Hydra-Con flat-nose hollow-base paper-patched, the same bullet without paper-patching, the 360-grain Mushroom Express (my samples weighed 340 grains), the 434-grain Buffalo Bullet SSB prototype bullet, and the 434-grain Buffalo Bullet SSB spitzer in its final commercial form. Every projectile was tested with a top-end hunting load, and accuracy was best when only the base of the conical was treated with a dab of Wonder Lube before loading, leaving the sides of the bullet dry. This makes sense, as we wouldn't grease the shank of a modern bullet and expect best results.

I don't see the Remington Model 700 ML/MLS muzzle-loading rifle as a replacement for other muzzleloaders, at least not in my battery. When I want tradition, I'll turn to my custom Mulford longrifle or my Navy Arms Ithaca Hawken. In between, I'll grab my Storey Buggy Rifle, a sidehammer with old-time lines that breaks in the middle to fit into a 22-inch carrying space. The Buggy Rifle has a 19th century look, but it carries a 1:24-inch twist to handle conicals, plus it wears a recoil pad and sling. Some shooters fix up these short rifles with scopes, too, although mine has a peep sight. Then there's the in-line Remington, modern in design, but a muzzleloader through and through, offering the challenge of one shot, but with sufficient power for any big game where long-range shooting is not demanded. In summary, the M700 ML/MLS is a well-designed, well-built, contemporary blackpowder hunting rifle with good accuracy and power, very fast lock time, and a highly reliable ignition system. ●

**LOADS TESTED IN M700 MLS**

| —Bullet— Wgt. Grs. | Type | Load (Grs./Powder) | MV (fps) | ME (ft.-lbs.) |
|---|---|---|---|---|
| 360* | Mushroom Express | 2 Pyrodex Pellets (100/Pyrodex RS) | 1566 | 1852 |
| 365 | NEI Maxi-style Conical | 120/Pyrodex RS | 1577 | 2016 |
| 370 | T/C Maxi Ball | 120/Pyrodex RS | 1564 | 2010 |
| 400 | Gamebuster | 120/Pyrodex | 1522 | 2058 |
| 434 | Buffalo SSB | 2 Pyrodex Pellets (100/Pyorodex RS) | 1300 | 1629 |
| 434 | Buffalo SSB | 120/Pyrodex RS | 1405 | 1903 |
| 460 | White | 120/GOEX FFg | 1472 | 2214 |
| 465 | Gonic | 120/GOEX FFg | 1497 | 2314 |
| 490 | Buffalo | 120/GOEX Cartridge Grade | 1513 | 2491 |
| 500 | Hydra-Con (paper patched) | 120/GOEX Cartridge Grade | 1491 | 2469 |
| 500 | Hyrda-Con | 120/GOEX Cartridge Grade | 1496 | 2485 |
| 600 | White | 2 Pyrodex Pellets (100/Pyrodex RS) | 1300 | 2252 |
| 600 | White | 120/GOEX Cartridge Grade | 1388 | 2567 |

* Actual weight of test bullet was 340 grains

All chronographing was done with an Oehler Model 35P chronograph set up so that the muzzle of the rifle was 12 feet from the middle skyscreen, thus numbers are instrumentals rather than true muzzle velocities. Standard deviation from the mean velocity was low (excellent) for all loads, normally from around 9 to 15 fps. Elevation: 6000 feet above sea level. Temperatures: 60 to 75 degrees F. The exact average velocity was recorded, without regard for any other factors. Each load was chronographed at least twice for verification. Other Model 700 ML/MLS test rifles should produce very similar results, but are unlikely to produce identical results due to normal individual rifle variation.

# Looking BACKWARD

*Handloading memorabilia is interesting, evocative, possibly valuable and definitely instructive.*

by DON L. HENRY

LET'S SIT DOWN and sort through these boxes of boxes of old handloading stuff. The contents tell so many tales: stories of business ventures, loads and rifles, target groups, hunts, times gone by and friends—all worth recalling. Most who have seen this memorabilia, and others who imagine they have because they have similar boxes of stuff, remember experiences of their own like they happened yesterday. I'll bet you have recollections, too.

### Worth Saving

Several somebodys thought this stuff was worth saving. Let's see what's in this first box, the wood one, marked "Winchester, K2706C, 130 grain Hollow Point 4, 1000 Super Speed, .270 Winchester A38, Staynless, Non-Mercuric." Many memorable and a few remarkable shots came from this box, but those are tales for long trips and for around the fire in hunting camps. Now let's look at powder cans in the wooden shotshell cases underneath.

We'll use what we find as a kind of index to reloading history, and then see what we can discover about them in a set of HANDLOADER'S DIGEST and other gun books I've collected.

Milo Hill made bullets out of 22 rimfire cases in Caledonia, Ohio. It's been awhile since Ackley Controlled Expansion bullets were made in Trinidad, Colorado. Nosler Partitions used to be turret lathe-turned and came in a red box—actually two styles of red boxes. Speer's bullets once came in simple black-ink-on-white-paper boxes back when shooters bought boxes for the contents. Modern Gun Shop shipped bullets from Hollydale, California, in plain paper boxes. Arizona Bullet Co. supplied a lot of jacketed lead.

This is neat! Winchester No. 1 primers in plain gray cardboard with a blue label. I'd like to know if they still fire, but hate to diminish the collector value by breaking the seal. They must have come with this box of twenty-five Metal Patched Grooved bullets for reloading for the 1886 Winchester. And look, Winchester brass came in square boxes of twenty-five that had no room for the assembled cartridges. Way back when, folks used U.S. Primers No. 8, Winchester No. 3W, and Remington No. 1½ and 6½ primers. I'll bet these Winchester J. Goldmark percussion caps in this ten-tin roll were used with the blackpowder from cans in the next box.

Some of these turn-of-the-century blackpowder cans bring a C-note ($100) on the collectors' market. Remember the loading data published on SR-80, Pistol #5 and #6, Du Pont #1, and other canisters? And, who last saw an original Hi-Vel #2 reloading manual? And, here are four different Hi-Vel #2 cans!

There was a lot of shooting here, and history.

### When Handloading Was Young

Neal Knox was reminiscing:

Old component boxes, like old reloads rolling around the bottom of miscellaneous junk boxes and junk drawers, bring back fond memories to a graybeard such as me. And, they're also instructive.

While making a determined effort to clean up the mess a year or so ago, I ran across some old 38 loads in a box marked only "HOT—.357 ONLY." They had neither a date nor load data, but I knew exactly what they were. The bullet was a weird-looking almost-wadcutter that weighed around 155 grains; I had borrowed that old (in 1958) mould from a friend. The case was a heavy-walled G.I. RA-56 that a friend had given me as part of a GI can full of brass from the range at the then-new Dyess, Texas, AFB range. The charge was a stomping load of Unique.

Yeah, I know we're not supposed to do that kind of thing, but I had slowly worked up the load in a large-frame S&W, what the younger generation calls a Model 28. It wasn't safe to leave that kind of load around, for it could wreck some 38 Specials. So I did the prudent thing, I shot them up.

I didn't bother chronographing them, for they hadn't been chronographed at the time—several years before Ken Oehler introduced the Model 10, everyman's chrono. But it proved one thing: After over thirty-

"Winchester No. 1 Primers adapted to Pistol and Rifle Cartridges Using No. 1 Primers and Black Powders. Pat'd Oct. 1st, 1878." The paper-wrapped double wood-tray packet was sealed with shellac.

Wildcatting 22-calibers might have not been what it was without R.B. Sisk made-one-at-a-time bullets. Notice the "Wartime Bullets" label on the box at top. Some boxes are still sealed, and half-again to twice more valuable for it.

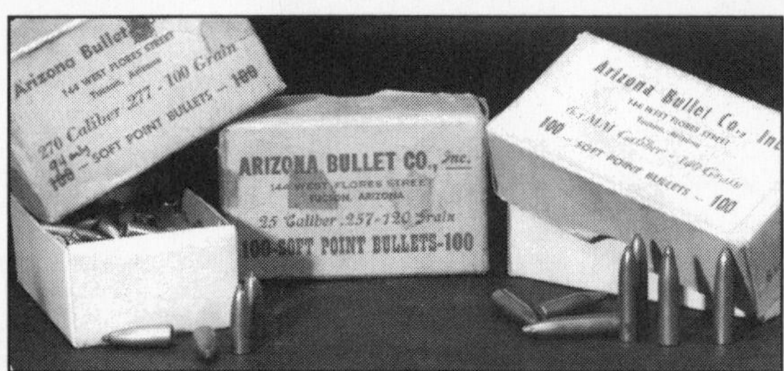


Arizona Bullet Co., Inc.'s, 257, 264 and 277 bullets still serve rifles with sights adjusted to a particular load.

Turret lathe-turned Nosler bullets first came from Ashland, Oregon, in red-labeled white boxes of fifty, before the factory moved to Bend.

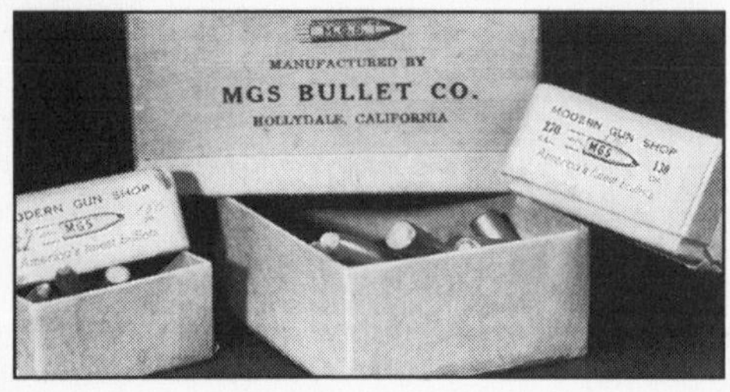


Modern Gun Shop labeled bullets with sealing tape.

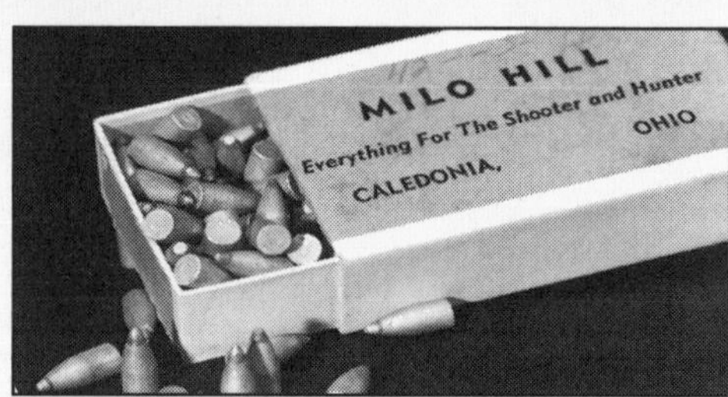


Milo Hill made jacketed 22 bullets from aluminum cartridge cases—probably in 1942.

five years, that ammunition was still mighty potent. Tell Senator Pat Monyihan that the nonsense he's heard about ammo having a five-year shelf life is just that; in polite company, nonsense.

As for old component boxes, and even components, they too are instructive. I've got some Federal round-head primers in white boxes with black printing, resting in wooden trays with grooves to keep the rows separate. Pre-OSHA, or DOT, or some other Uncle-will-protect-us law or regulation.

There's some very early Cascade Cartridge, Inc., primers, a firm started by Dick Speer, who single-handedly drove down the price of 100 primers from around $1.60 to 80 cents in the '50s. Remchester didn't like what handloading did to their ammo sales figures. We oldtimers loved CCI for what they had done for handloading.

And Dick Speer's brother, Vernon, had started making bullets with Joyce Hornady, using cleaned 22 rimfire hulls as jackets. I got a few of those Speer bullets with "H" stamped on the jacket by Winchester.

And I have some plain-brown boxes by another early bulletmaker, Ralph Sisk, who I knew well enough to be shown his darkest secret: his production line, which was a single long-handled press. Fact is, I was doing a bit of negotiation with R.B. about buying out his operation—mainly his brand name—back in 1966 when the folks at *Coin World* told me they were interested in putting out a gun newspaper, which we later named *Gun Week*.

Those old boxes and containers, like the Bullseye can still bearing the $2.80 price tag and the remnants of a 50-pound keg of 50-year-old salvage 4831 propellant that I got from Bruce Hodgdon for 50 cents a pound, bring back fond memories. But they do more than that. They tell us where we and reloading have been: simple, somewhat crude, innovative.

In 1947, Bob Bell bought a keg of IMR-4895, for $30 plus $5 freight, from B.E. Hodgdon. One-hundred-and-fifty pounds of it in a copper container with rubber-gasketed, bolt-locking round lid, the whole thing in a wooden box. "When I shoved the full length of my arm down in those cool gray kernels, I

Winchester brass for reloading came in square boxes of twenty-five, once priced at $2.36—that's $9.44 per 100.

This unopened box of Winchester 220 Swift bullets would be fun to load in the still-new, old Super-X brass.

"Patented December 14, 1886," a still-full box of 255-grain 38-55 bullets.

Ackley bullets were identified with black ink on gray paper boxes.

Early Vernon Speer bullets, black-on-white printing.

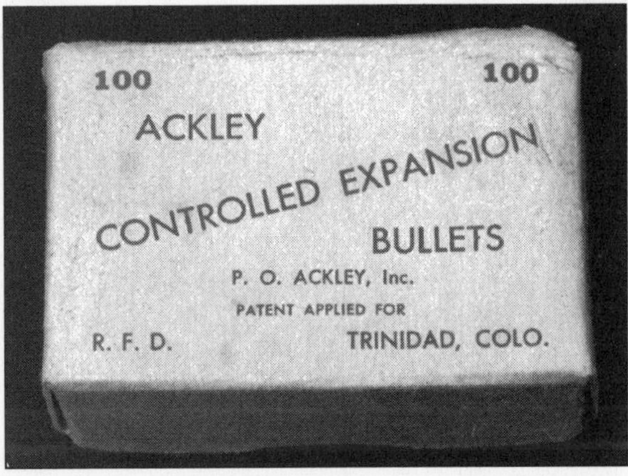

thought I was in heaven, set for life," he recalled. "But somehow, in some years, it was all gone except for a couple pounds."

Bob tested this last couple of pounds and wrote about the results in HANDLOADER'S DIGEST, 7th edition, in 1975, a quarter-century later. It was still remarkably accurate—it delivered quarter-minute groups. He concluded, "And I might say it leaves me with a sort of sinking feeling in my gut when I realize that old copper keg standing in the barn at home is finally—completely and forevermore—empty."

Fact is, assuming proper storage, most old equipment and components still work fine. Reminds me of the old lathe-turned Nosler 270 bullets I loaded over H-4831, using data published in the early Speer reloading manuals, of which I have a complete set, of course. As a young man who souped up cars, I figured that a published load could be pushed a little. I pushed.

Earl Roberts, he of gunstock fame, refused to enter the shooting tunnel in his Portland, Oregon, shop while I touched off a few rounds for benefit of the chronograph. Those 130-grain Noslers clocked the same speed as *advertised* 270 Weatherby loads, and held a tight group doing it. And, I am beginning to recall how one shot each put out the lights on several mule deer, a couple of black bear, and two 5x5 elk, one of the bulls out about 400 yards in the Wallowa Mountain wilderness. That, my first bull, is worth remembering; the whole critter and the wonderful hunt is all kept in one little Nosler bullet box.

Les Bowman said that Sisk bullets made it possible to develop the high-velocity 22-caliber cartridges. Old hands who played with wildcats like the 22 Hornet, 22 Hi-Power, Jerry Gebby's 22 Varminter (now called the 22-250) or 220 WOS (Wotkyns Original Swift) used Sisk bullets because in the 1920s and '30s there were few others.

### Memories in Boxes

Handloaders, especially old handloaders, have too many good memories to throw away even if they must be stored in empty boxes. Ethereal things must be collected and confined, lest they disperse and drift away.

Everything for the reloader was offered at a low price by Herter's. Grades of Herter's merchandise started at "Model Perfect" and went better from that. Many products from well-respected manufacturers were sold under the Herter's name. Although the packaging was monochromatic, catalog prose could grow mushrooms. How we either enjoyed or hated their catalog.

Blackpowder tins, usually painted yellow, orange or red for ease of retrieval, are colorful and artistic. A missing tear of the label suggests someone thought the Hercules leaf was too small.

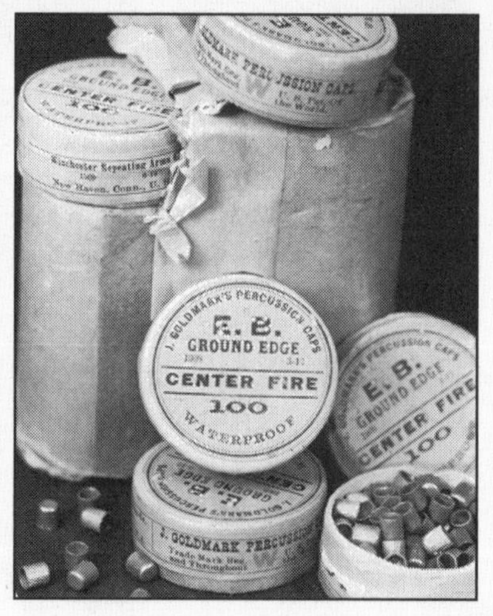


In 1909, Winchester marketed J. Goldmark's Percussion Caps in a ten-pack of tins to dealers. In this condition, these now trade at about $40 each tin.

Marion Hammer, NRA president, said, "Antique blackpowder cans, in addition to providing a historical perspective of the role of blackpowder in our nation's history, are actually works of art. Many of the early cans have lithographed labels that are intricately detailed designs depicting scenes of the time. They provide an entire segment of American history on their own."

Knowing my interest in loading memorabilia, Marion autographed and sent a copy of *Powder Horns in the Southern Tradition: Exhibition and Catalogue by Museum of Florida History*, in which three early cans from her collection are pictured. One of them, an orange "Hercules Black Powder Sporting" flask-shaped tin with belt-strap loop attached on the back, later sold for $800. Now there's something to justify saving old shooting stuff to the spouse.

### Yankee Ingenuity

Fred Barnes used to send his bullets in paper sacks. Bob Bell stopped to see him one weekend in the late '50s, outside of Grand Junction, Colorado. "Saw the machines, essentially handmade, that he made his bullets on, in his basement. He used rolls of pure copper tubing for jackets; pulled it through a 'sizer' fastened to the side of his house to get proper diameter—with his Cadillac."

Bob Hodgdon answered my call about wire-tab coffee bags marked 4831. "Dad began with pint cans, then discovered that double-lined coffee sacks were a good moisture barrier. We started using these about 1950 and continued through 1957. We went to the steel cans with the red and yellow label about 1958."

The survival rate on paper powder bags is probably very low, which is why they are interesting. The bag's extrinsic value is that it opened the fascinating and inspiring history of Hodgdon Powder Co., Inc. That story was told by Rick Hacker in the June 1981 issue of *American Rifleman*. You did save all of the back issues of *American Rifleman*, didn't you? The whole set in binders takes up only 30 linear feet of shelf space.

*Wiederladen*, a German reloading manual, calls America "the motherland of reloading and *wildkatz*."

Barnes and Sisk and Hodgdon were widely known, but are only

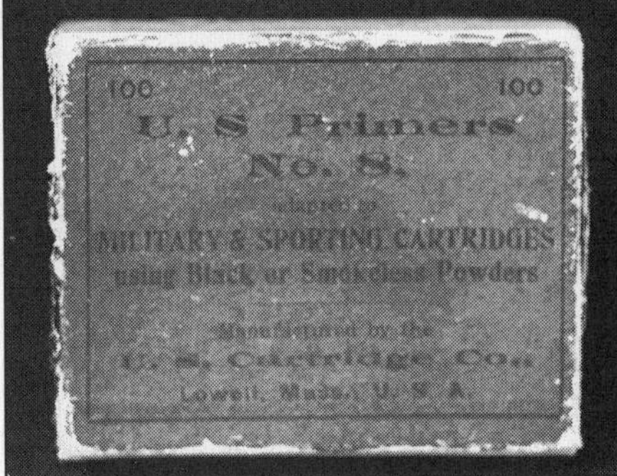


U.S. Cartridge Co. No. 8 primers.

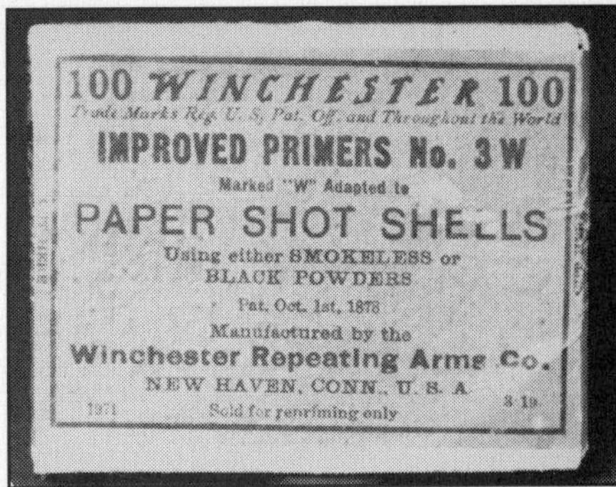


Patented October 1, 1878, Winchester No. 3W shotshell primers for paper hulls.

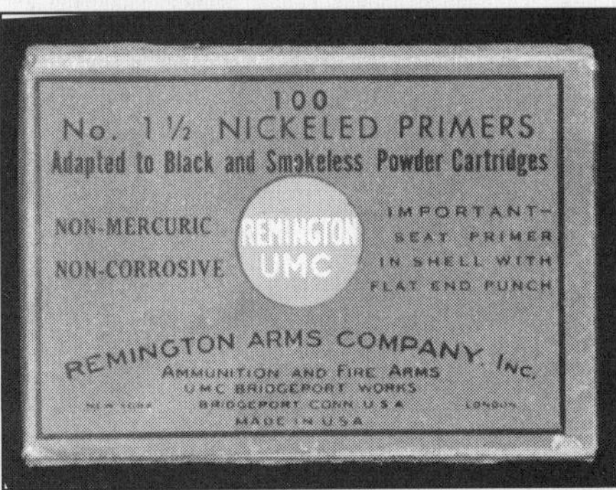


Green-and-red-label Remington UMC No. 1½ nickeled primers.

Remington No. 6½ primers were the "same size as No. 1½."

Three Remington percussion cap tins. These trade for $10 to $40 each, depending on condition and contents.

The Director of Civilian Marksmanship (DCM) sold Frankford Arsenal primers to NRA members inexpensively.

three of countless ingenious American reloaders. Does anyone remember Milo Hill, of Caledonia, Ohio, who made bullets out of *aluminum* "U"-headstamped 22 cases, presumably during WWII?

### Elegance in Black and White

Times were simpler—and better—then, when people communicated in black and white. Newspapers, and then television, and lessons about right and wrong were clear and understandable before shades of pastel packaging. Bullets came labeled simply: Milo Hill, P.O. Ackley, Dick and Vernon Speer, Joyce Hornady, Modern Gun Shop, Arizona Bullet Co.; even Remington and Winchester sent brass and bullets in black-lettered paper boxes. This was more than simply the era before affordable polychrome packaging. It was an era of integrity, when a manufacturer expected to earn sales through word-of-mouth advertising and keep customers by the quality of the contents instead of seducing a sale by coloring the package. There was a then unrecognized and now nearly forgotten elegance in plain black and white.

### Artifacts

The survival rate of combustibles, shootables, and packaging is low because most people throw stuff away. So, surprisingly often, memorabilia contains important artifacts. The object at hand might have been overlooked by many as junk, passed over by collectors of sporting memorabilia in search of "beautiful" objects, for beauty is, decidedly, in the eye of the beholder, and value . . . well, value is the worth of an object to the person who understands it.

Artifacts do speak. They have languages all their own. The kind of reloading memorabilia and ephemeralities—junk to some—we are considering here speaks of an era when self-sufficiency was tested more often than it seems to be today. They speak of a young technology and technological changes so vast that the antecedents are now strange to us. They speak of monetary values, but also of those types and amounts of values that societies place upon talent, resourcefulness, independence, work, beauty, patriotism, honor and numerous other facets of our culture, which would change beyond recogni-

Du Pont powder canisters draw attention and stimulate conversation wherever sportsmen gather. Improved Military Rifle powder had red, white and blue paper labels over soldered tins.

Du Pont Smokeless Shotgun Powder round tin with data for 28- to 10-gauge loads.

A pouring spout graced the wide-mouth canister of HiVel. That's an original loading manual, too.

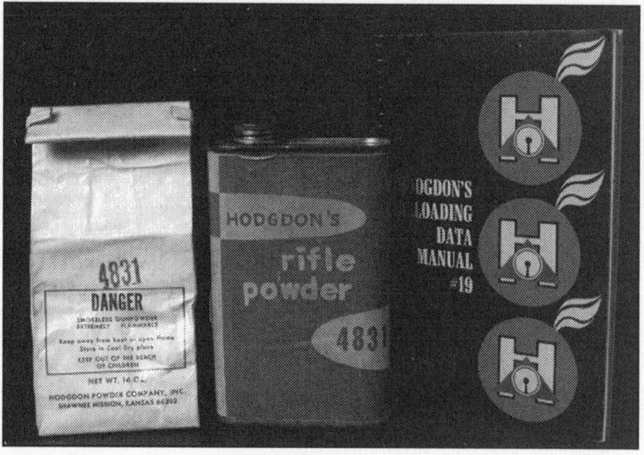


Hodgdon sold powder in coffee sacks until 1957 and then introduced the red-and-yellow-paper-labeled tin in 1958.

tion and would not be recalled were it not for those who save memories in boxes.

### A Place for History

When the NRA mounted a Museum in Microcosm exhibition of "The Single Action Army: Sam Colt's Legacy in Steel" for the 1996 NRA Annual Meetings in Dallas, Texas; for the First NRA Annual Gun Collectors Show in Nashville, Tennessee; and for exhibit at the new National Firearms Museum at NRA Headquarters in Fairfax, Virginia; I was dismayed to discover a great lack of firearms accouterments, memorabilia and ephemeralities needed to support the exhibit. Another member of the design team noticed that ammo for one of the guns was from the wrong period, and none of the correct vintage could be found. There is a safe-locked room at NRA Headquarters designed just to hold arms-related artifacts. Rows of archival shelves and drawers are nearly empty. Although the NRA collection contains over 3300 firearms, the related stuff in the collection could be packed into a pickup truck. After several phone calls, components to recreate the correct cartridges—primers, cases, and bullets—were found in the never-throw-anything-away accumulations of sundry graybeards so that exhibit authenticity was saved.

Few, in the past, seem to have understood that small objects and containers are important history. Too few understand that old cartridges, their boxes, firearms accessories, related books, and all the kinds of stuff we are now considering here is too important to throw away. Donations made to the National Firearms Museum qualify for tax credit and will benefit the national shooting community. Items in the NRA collection help researchers, writers, and photographers keep history alive. For more information, contact NFM Curator Doug Wicklund at NRA headquarters in Fairfax, Virginia.

### Bigger Boxes

Big boxes, in which little boxes and other stuff are stored, lie about—nay, decorate—my shop and office. Reminders of the 1950s and '60s when the sports department of Valley Hardware helped put me through college and graduate school, they serve

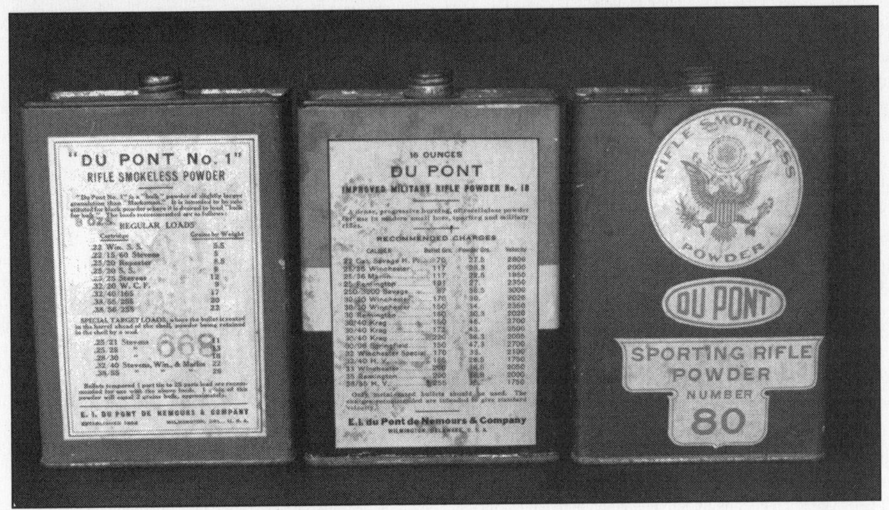


Du Pont powder canisters carried recommended charges for handloaders. Here are powders No. 1, No. 18 and No. 80.

This Laflin & Rand yellow metal pocket flask tin with paper label intact was manufactured in December, 1939.

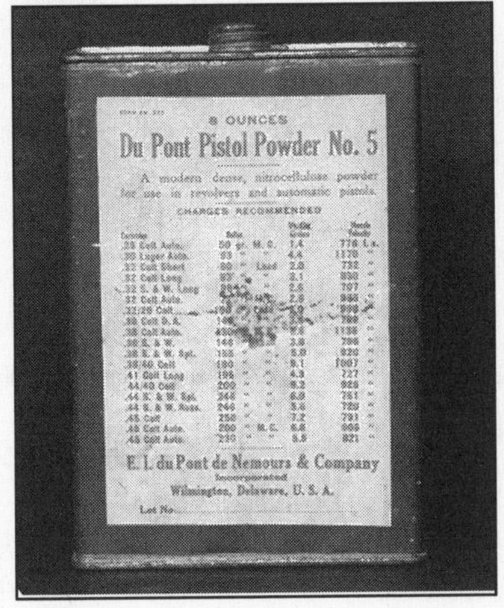


Pistol No. 5 loading data on the package.

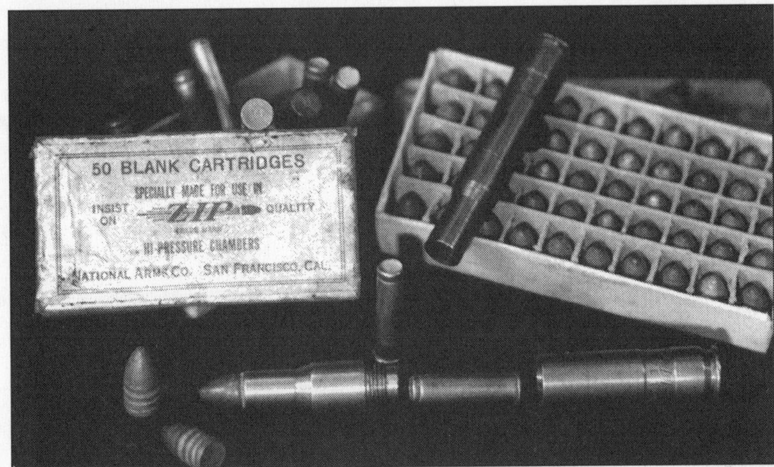


National Arms Co. ZIP auxiliary cartridges with a box of original special blanks and two boxes of original bullets. Cartridges are for the 30-40 Krag and 30-06 Springfield.

as ever-visible reminders of family, business, subsistence, sport. Now, the wooden Remington case for 30 Luger ammo holds fax messages and e-mail hard-copy; a Remington 45 Colt box that once held 2000 of those cartridges is a file for articles in progress; the Western World Champion Ammunition case for 3-inch 12-gauge loads holds computer software; and a near-dozen assorted shotshell crates hold folders and are "In," "Out" and "Pending" files. At the going collector's rate of $15 to $20 each, I could better afford a file cabinet; but I have seventeen file cabinets, none of which represents a golden age of shooting.

## Cartridges in Cartridges

Quick and easy low-power loads could be assembled in the field with auxiliary cartridges. These, unlike Townsend Whelen's squib loads, required no reloading tools. Popular for the first half of this century, examples include Marble's Auxiliary Cartridges, Winchester's Supplemental Chambers, and National Arms' ZIP Reload Chambers. The Marble and Winchester devices adapted standard pistol cartridges to rifle chambers so that, for example, a 32 S&W could be fired in a 30-caliber rifle. This allowed the owner of a 30-30, 30-40 or 30-06 rifle to carry a 32 pistol with ammo to serve both guns. ZIP used special blanks and bullets. The ZIP was least practical and successful, and is, therefore, the most scarce, interesting and instructive of all the types.

## Without End

There is no end of interesting things related to shooting history to collect, especially if one accumulates things not yet old. It is the scarcity of objects, and their low survival rate, that makes memo rabilia important and exponentially more valuable as time passes. A secret of pleasant and profitable collecting is to acquire interesting objects that others have no use for.

One need only look at the current price of usually discarded gun boxes, hang-tags and owner's manuals, from as recent as a few years ago, to understand the value of saving stuff. However, money is close to the poorest measure of wealth. History and happy recollections are beyond price. ●

I TRIED TO ignore the sharp bits of greenery sticking through my pants as I sprawled atop a broad stone wall, glassing the far corner of Henry's field of spring barley. The corner was 270 yards distant, and about 20 yards closer were four of the cottontails that had started enthusiastically chomping the barley shoots as soon as they appeared. My mission: to terminate them, with extreme prejudice....

During my apprenticeship as a varmint hunter, I hadn't actually hit any rabbits quite so far away before; around 220 yards had been my best shot to date. I knew that with my standard load, zeroed for 230 yards, another 20 yards represented a significant amount of bullet drop. In fact, the ballistics program on my PC said I should hold over by nearly an inch. The wind was gusting quite strongly from my right, and in the open I would not have attempted the shot. Up to that point, I'd missed plenty of long shots in windy conditions, so I was well acquainted with the wind drift to which small-caliber bullets are so prone. But I was aiming straight down the edge of the field, and my bullet would be shielded from the wind during most of its flight by a tall hedge-topped bank. The rabbits burrowed into the bank, rarely venturing more than a dozen yards from home.

Still, I thought, even a little wind drift can mean a miss on a small target at 250 yards; however, if those rabbits keep hopping around, pretty soon a couple will overlap, then I just shoot at the right-hand side of the windward rabbit, and I'll surely hit one of 'em. Optimistic maybe, but it was worth trying.

I snugged the Remington down on its bipod, cranked the Leupold up to 16x, tucked my left fist under the butt, and eased off the safety. Then I waited...and waited...'til one rabbit hopped from left to right, pausing behind another but not completely obscured; I put the crosshair on the shoulders of the front rabbit and gently squeezed the trigger. The blast of the 22-250 was followed a moment later by a hollow *Whop!* from downrange, and through my scope I observed the miniature eruption of dust and water droplets which I knew denoted a solid hit. I was puzzled, though, by the brief spectacle of a rabbit springing a couple of times into the air before disappearing from view: a varmint hit squarely by a 55-grain Nosler Ballistic Tip, which has departed one's rifle at over 3600 fps, does not jump around!

Building an accurate varmint load requires top-quality components.

In the end, a $^1/_4$-inch flatter trajectory over 300 yards couldn't convince the author that...

The remaining rabbits had scooted for their burrows, and I hadn't time to wait for them to reemerge, so I strolled down the field to investigate. By now the sun had risen clear above the hill behind me, brightly illuminating the scene of the varmints' illicit breakfast and revealing the answer to my puzzle: There lay the remains of the front rabbit, thoroughly shredded by the Nosler, but 15 inches beyond it lay a second rabbit—clearly the acrobat that had surprised me. This one was intact, but it had been effectively "shotgunned" by bullet and bone fragments exiting from the critter that took the initial impact.

After some self-congratulation in which I tended to compare myself with Daniel Boone, Davy Crockett and John Wayne, reason stepped in and I realized the amount of luck involved. OK, the first time I hit a small varmint at 250 yards I'd got two with one bullet, but might this be repeatable? I could spend years trying.

Nevertheless, it says something about your ammo if you calculate point of impact according to distance and everything pays off, as it did on this occasion and as things have often worked out subsequently at longer range; it tells a handloader

# The Grass Is Always Greener

by ANTHONY HARRISON

that he's finally doing a few things right, and he's got himself a load good enough for serious varminting.

I think I have a pretty fair varmint load, but recently I've been turning over in my mind the possibilities of developing it further, making it a "better" load. I find this makes me think carefully about the process whereby my load was developed and about what actually makes a good load.

Now, I regard myself as a reasonably experienced, sensible handloader, and my armory has included other rifles in 22-250 before the Remington. So I thought I didn't have to start from first principles. Developing a load for my rifle should have been a comparatively straightforward matter of modifying an existing load. I know it's widely believed that a good load often translates well from rifle to rifle, but at first, my experiences with the 22-250 didn't appear to confirm this.

In my previous Ruger MKII VBZ varminter, for instance, I had developed a load that sent Nosler's 55-grain Ballistic Tip downrange at quite a lick, in fact at a velocity I'm probably not allowed to mention, powered by a charge of VihtaVuori N150 slightly in excess of what the loading charts recommend as maximum. I'm not boasting here. I am absolutely not saying, "Heck, these book figures are for wimps! Real men go for serious velocity, and darn the consequences!" In fact, I would say I was *unwise*, and that although I like to make the most of the velocity potential of a hot caliber such as the 22-250, I am now more aware of the benefits to be had from holding powder charges down to recommended figures—like safety, for one, and not forfeiting much *in actual performance in the field*, for another. But at the time, I worked up my Ruger load using what I considered to be my usual degree of caution: increasing the powder charge in small increments, watching for signs of excessive pressure, and so on. I considered my load hot but safe.

Some gizmos are invaluable: the RCBS Precision Mic enables spot-on measurement of vital statistics such as headspacing and bullet seating.

Cutaway cases suggest one reason for the smaller powder capacity of the W-W case (left) over the R-P case. Note its significantly greater web thickness. Both flash holes are reamed to promote even powder ignition.

Then I sold the Ruger, reluctantly, after deciding its heavy non-adjustable trigger made it difficult for me to capitalize on the rifle's excellent potential for accuracy. I bought a rifle I'd admired for some while—a Remington Varmint Synthetic: sleek, functional and confidence-inspiring, and with a pretty good trigger.

Handloading considerations started with chamber measurements, using both a Stoney Point Chamber-All tool and the RCBS Precision Mic. I wanted a reference figure for the rifle's throat, so that I would be able subsequently to detect any significant throat erosion and alter my bullet seating accordingly.

I'm sold on the importance of seating depth and its contribution to accuracy. I also wanted to compare the Remington with the Ruger, so I could adjust my Forster Ultra seating die to give me the same amount of freebore in the new rifle—at least for my first firing trials, until I found out what amount of freebore it liked best.

The Precision Mic's "dummy bullet" system gave me a bolt face-to-lands figure that will act as a benchmark against which to measure throat erosion. The Chamber-

A 22-250 W-W case is pretty well filled by 42 grains of VihtaVuori N160, but to no advantage over a smaller charge of a faster powder, the author says.

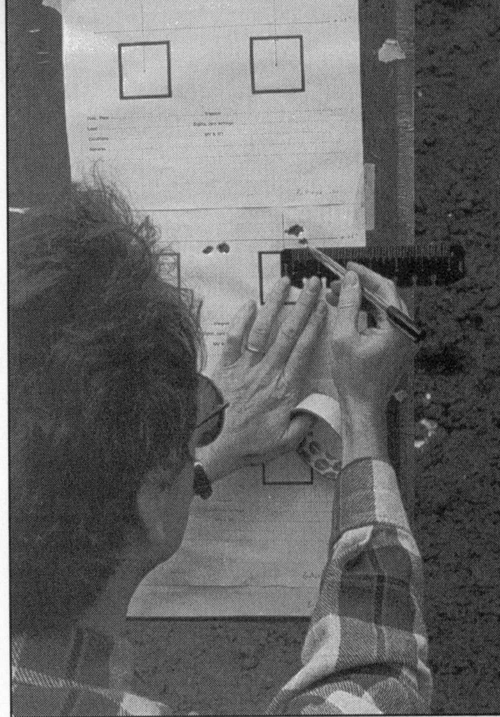

A fraction over a half-inch—pity about that flier....

All uses an actual bullet, and with the additional help of a bullet comparator and calipers, I found that ten measurements gave me an average figure of 2.733 inches. That's the OAL from the case head to a standard point on the ogive of a Nosler 55-grain Ballistic Tip, with the bullet in quite firm contact with the rifling. The equivalent figure in the Ruger had been 2.758 inches. I now knew that to get the same nominal .023-inch freebore that had worked well in the Ruger, I'd have to turn my seating die down by .025, the difference between the Chamber-All readings in the Remington and the Ruger. This sort of adjustment is a cinch using a micrometer-head die such as the Forster.

At the range, things didn't work out quite as I expected. Standard advice when changing one component of a load—in this case the rifle, which is in a real sense a load component—is to reduce the charge by 10 percent and work up again. But I found very quickly that load gave a level of pressure indications equivalent, it seemed, to the "hot" Ruger load—but I reached this stage at a much smaller charge weight, with a consequently lower MV.

The problem with chamber pressure for the average handloader is that without some fancy scientific equipment, or at least a highly accurate micrometer for checking case-head expansion (I don't feel competent to do this), shooters are making seat-of-the-pants judgments based on primer appearance after firing, chronographed velocities, and subjective assessments about relative ease of case extraction. Some might call this process *guessing*. Nevertheless, we have come to trust in our ability to apply this process in a consistent way. So what did I think when confronted by seeming evidence that two similar rifles could have quite radically different appetites for powder? I was baffled.

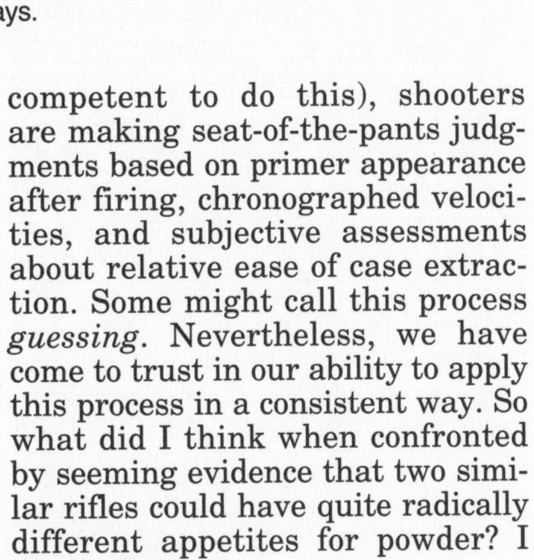

My original load (designated #07) in the Ruger gave me strikingly consistent velocities; the cases extracted effortlessly, showing primers fairly well flattened but with sufficient radius left to inspire confidence; and I'm still using the same cases. My new load (#08) in the Remington leaves primers looking much the same and feels no less potent, except that the chronograph tells a different story. Both rifles have 26-inch heavy barrels, and their headspace is identical to within .002. The .025-inch difference in the leade can probably not cause much pressure variation, though bore tightness/smoothness might be a factor, I guess. Both loads used the same brass and bullet, while powder (N150) and primers (Federal 210M) were from the same lot.

Given these objective similarities, I was forced to reconsider the reliability of my assessments concerning pressure. I suspect that if I were to run a side-by-side comparison of the Ruger load #07 with the Remington load #08, the former would prove to have achieved its superior performance at the expense of undesirably high pressure. In other words, my judgment was at fault when I put this load together. I placed too much reliance on the accuracy of what are essentially subjective judgments.

Perhaps I failed to make proper allowance for rifles having different handling characteristics. Before the Ruger, I'd owned a lightweight 22-250, so the Ruger's heavy barrel and laminated stock would have made a hot load seem tamer. It's perfectly feasible for a combination of design and manufacturing differences between the Ruger and the Remington to convey a superficially different response to the same load—or in the present case, an apparently *similar* response to radically *different* loads.

I suggest that no matter how safe we consider a given load to be, the point is to maintain a meaningful safety margin of pressure. We're reminded often enough that a top-end load can easily jump several thousand psi due to warmer weather or a big drop in the altitude of one's shooting location, putting it over the SAAMI pressure limit for its caliber. It's not worth it. Sure, it can be fun to achieve a MV in excess of factory ammo, but it's no longer true to say we handload in order to get higher velocities: The factory stuff is often right up there with the best (safe) handloads.

Am I just trying to rationalize the fact that my varmint load has lost a lot of oomph? No, I'm very happy with it in its present form; it does the business. My load #08 (W-W brass, Federal match primer, 36.7 grains of N150, Nosler 55-grain Ballistic Tip seated for a nominal .012-inch freebore) produces an average MV of around 3660 fps—very close to the figures quoted for some factory loads in 22-250 and for the faster handloads listed in, for example, *Speer Manual No. 12*. It does this consistently, too. In my first tests, fifteen consecutive rounds produced a maximum velocity variation of 28 fps, for a SD of between 6 and 7. I'm not the best shot around, in the field or off the bench, but for me this load consistently produces five-shot groups of 5/8-inch at a bit over 100 yards, and it probably would do better with a steadier hand on the rifle.

Like most shooters, I don't place total reliance on computer figures, but another reason for trusting this load is that my tests suggest it conforms very closely to the data produced by the Barnes Ballistics Program. I tried setting up the skyscreens of my PACT Model 1 chrono well downrange, to check velocity loss. After firing a couple of groups, I found the average velocity at 108 yards to be 3243 fps, within a few fps of the computer predicted figure. This further demonstrates that Nosler's stated BC for the 55-grain Ballistic Tip is pretty accurate. Nosler says .267; the Barnes program calculates around .28.

Another time, I set up a target at a carefully measured 250 yards and put three rounds into it from the Remington, off a bipod. They went into 1.63 inches and averaged .75-inch low, again almost exactly matching what the computer predicted for this load when zeroed at 230 yards.

To return to the original idea of refining my load, I was wondering if I could wring a bit more speed out of it without increasing pressure. My reasoning went like this:

First, I wonder why I get high pressure/velocity using only a modest charge of N150—a *smaller* charge weight than Speer No. 12 lists as maximum for a 55-grain bullet with N140, which is a *faster* powder; surely using the slower powder means I should have to drop in a bigger charge for results similar to N140?

Second, ah, but they say N150 is designed for calibers in the 30-06 class, i.e., larger-capacity cases than 22-250, and I've heard that igniting a given powder in larger or smaller cases can cause it to burn at a lesser or greater rate, in fact *altering its speed*. (I've tried using heavy charges of "slow" N160 in the 22-250, but I still got MVs around 3600, together with surprisingly strong pressure indications, plus noticeable blast and recoil.)

Third, I know Remington cases have slightly greater capacity than the W-W brass I normally use; perhaps an increased charge of N150 in the R-P case will prove a more efficient combination....

At this point, I sought expert advice and consulted VihtaVuori in Finland; Juhani Lumia of their Ammunition Research & Development Unit told me, "Because of the bigger (powder granule) dimensions, N150 is especially designed for calibers with a bigger case capacity. In most cartridges tested by us, a little bit higher velocity is reached using N150. This also means approximately 2 to 4 percent bigger charge weight. In some cartridges, especially with a smaller case capacity, no significant difference can be found between these two powders (N140 and N150)."

Which goes a long way toward explaining the results I got. I'd been right to conjecture that the medium-size 22-250 case might in effect be boosting the speed of N150 and giving me results I would have expected from similar charges of N140. Still, since N150 had proved to give top-class results in 22-250, I persisted with the experiment proposed above. A test confirmed that the Remington case/bigger charge combo would produce over 100 fps more velocity, with excellent accuracy, and without seeming—a big "seeming," at that—to increase pressure noticeably. The computer says this will give me a trajectory advantage of a whole 1/4-inch at 300 yards, compared with my trusty load #08.

So am I going to go for this "better load"? No. It's not worth it.

As I conclude this piece, it's exactly four hours since my varmint load proved its worth yet again, on a big dog fox in prime condition. I spotted him through the glasses at 7:10 on this dull, damp November morning, slinking down a hedgerow two fields away; after a couple of turns, he was crossing a field of winter wheat just across a shallow valley from my position, and when he paused broadside-on at 240 yards I nailed him. The Nosler hit square through the ribcage, and he dropped in his tracks. There was a tiny exit wound, nothing more. This is the trademark of the Ballistic Tip bullet, which fragments almost totally inside a predator, leaving just the solid base to zip on through.

As a keen handloader I'm always itching to tinker, but perhaps I'd better add another caliber to my armory and tinker with that; the 22-250 load stays the way it is. ●

A load built to zap small varmints at 300-plus yards is more than a match for a fox at 240 yards.

# THOUGHTS ON ENERGY

**This experimenter, dissatisfied with the numerous power ratings formulas, takes a new look at an old subject.**

by LEE SAUNDERS

"THREE THOUSAND foot-pounds of muzzle energy!....Carries a ton of energy at 300 yards!" You have all seen lines like these in the gun magazines. What do they mean? Do they mean anything? Well, words have meanings, and the term "foot-pounds" does have a definition. Check any dictionary. Or, for instance, the glossary of Speer's *Reloading No. 12 Manual*, where on page 711 it says: "Foot-pound: A unit of Kinetic Energy in the English system defined as the effort required to raise one pound to a height of one foot against the force of gravity." Numerous other references have the same definition, of course, and it's in every manual I've checked. So the literal meaning is that a bullet rated at 3000 foot-pounds will lift 3000 pounds 1 foot.

It doesn't.

This has always been a controversial subject. The results shooters see when a bullet strikes do not agree with a force of the magnitude and ability indicated by Kinetic Energy foot-pound ratings. For example, 3000 foot-pounds, if totally expended by the bullet stopping in the target, would theoretically lift (or push) a 150-pound deer 20 feet. It doesn't happen. An easier demonstration is to shoot into the end of a 20-pound wood block. When hit with 3000 foot-pounds, it should move 150 feet. Would you believe approximately 1 foot? Where do all those foot-pounds go? Or were they ever there?

When these things are pointed out (as they have been for generations), defenders of the Kinetic Energy formula respond with:

1. The energy force is of too brief a duration to actually move the weight;
2. Moving weight actually comes under the heading of Momentum, not energy;
3. Much of the bullet's energy is used up in penetration, bullet expansion and heat creation.

Dealing with these arguments in order:

1. *The energy force is of too brief a duration to actually move the weight.*

To claim that the force is present but too brief to produce the movement is fatuous. For an amount of energy to be credited with ability to move a stated weight, it has to move it. Period. The stated distance (1 foot) in whatever time period the energy exists. If it can't do it, it doesn't earn the label "foot-pounds."

2. *Moving weight actually comes*

These bullets were used in handloads for the author's tests (from left): Speer 200 JHP 45 ACP; Sierra 220 RN .308-inch; cast 200 SWC 45 ACP; Hornady 150 .323-inch; Remington 180 JHP .429-inch; Sierra 175 .323-inch; cast 250 .429-inch; Remington 185 .323-inch; cast 516 Minie .584-inch; Sierra 180 .308-inch; Speer 200 .323-inch; Remington lead 200 RN .357-inch; Hornady 220 .323-inch; cast 158 .357-inch; Hornady 170 FN .308-inch; Winchester 125 JHP .357-inch.

*under the heading of momentum, not energy.*

Moving weight may indeed belong in the Momentum category, but doesn't that require energy? And, to refer back, words having meaning, if energy can't lift or move weight, why label energy "foot-pound?" This defines energy in terms of weight-moving ability, which is misleading. Electricity, as an example, is energy obviously capable of doing work. It not only runs motors, it indirectly alters steel (welding). This energy is not commonly defined in terms of foot-pounds; it is labeled in terms of volts and watts, which do not sound like weight-moving terms. The point is that energy does not have to be labeled in foot-pound terms. The energy formula was devised as an attempt to quantify the energy force of a moving object. The originator knew that at a given velocity a heavier object has more force than a lighter one; that the faster an object travels, the more force it has. So the formula devised used mass times velocity times velocity. It seemed logical, but there were two problems.

The first problem is attaching the label foot-pounds with no way to prove that the indicated units really were foot-pounds. (Way back in junior high school science classes we were taught that a scientific principle was something that could be proven, and the proof could be checked by anyone who could perform the experiment. If it could not be proven, it was a theory not a principle.) The Kinetic Energy formula produces a number, a number which becomes larger with any increase in size of the factors that produce it—weight and velocity. If the result were assigned with a vague or amorphous unit label, it would be harder to pick apart; but instead it was given a term with a very definite meaning, a meaning that absolutely does not describe the amount of force present in any projectile whose energy is calculated by the formula. There is no calibration built into the formula that ensures the units are foot-pounds.

In this article, I will be using the term Linear Foot-Pounds (LFP). I wanted to document the weight-moving ability of projectiles, or lack of it. The foot-pound definition entails lifting weight. A way to shoot into objects in an upward direction, and then measure the lift, seems to be out of the league of the backyard experimenter. So my experiments were done by testing weight moved horizontally, thus "Linear Foot-Pounds." It's easier to push weight than to lift it, so results should, if anything, be higher than if weight were being lifted. Remember this when you see the low numbers for weight-moving capacity.

The Linear Foot-Pounds entry in Table I shows that bullets do not have the weight-moving ability indicated by the energy formula. Several hundred years ago, apparently the only way investigators could conceive to rate energy was by its ability to move weight. They had no way to know that there are many types of energy, and that moving objects could have two types at once. That led to the second problem—one formula that combined both Momentum and Impulse Energies, and accurately described neither.

3. *Much of the bullet's energy is used up in penetration, bullet expansion and heat creation.*

Another response is that most of the projectile's energy is used in penetrating the target and expanding the bullet. These actions obviously require energy. For example, the 8mm-06 175-grain bullet at 2777 foot-seconds has a Kinetic Energy of 2997 foot-pounds, theoretically enough to move 2997 pounds 1 foot; but as the chart shows, its Linear Foot-Pound rating is less than 14. This means that, if the traditional energy formula were correct, 99.5 percent of the bullet energy would be used up in penetration. If the bullet really had the ability to move 2997 pounds, and if the penetration of a 45-pound object was so difficult as to require 99.5 percent of that energy, the projectile would take the path of least resistance. It could literally bounce the object out of the way easier than penetrate it. The penetration is the result of the high velocity of the projectile, which is energy, but not energy of a type that can be expressed in weight-moving foot-pounds. "Impulse Energy" seems a better description. This term is used here to mean the ability to penetrate substances far beyond the expected ability of projectile material to perforate a harder material, simply as the result of sheer speed. ("Impulse" may have another meaning mathematically.)

### Hartley's Experiments

In Handloader's Digest, 11th Edition, Hal Hartley wrote of his experiments shooting at steel plates. He compared high-velocity centerfires such as the 220 Swift, 22-250, 243, 25-06 and 30-06. He used lightweight varmint soft-nose spitzers of the same brand in all cartridges but the 30-06, where the 180-grain softpoint was used. His first test was 1/4-inch steel plate. All calibers shot through it at 100, 200 and 300 yards. Then he tried 3/8-inch steel. A number of cartridges penetrated at 100 yards, but not at 200. The 30-06 was one that didn't succeed at 200 yards. The 220 Swift and 22-250 did perforate at 200 yards, but not at 300 yards.

The ability of these light, frangible bullets to penetrate more than the 180-grain 30-06 could not be explained by either the Kinetic Energy

The apparatus built to measure the Linear Foot-Pound ability of projectiles, as seen from the side with the Shooting Chrony chronograph in place.

or Momentum formulas. The 30-06 had more Kinetic Energy (foot-pounds) and nearly twice the Momentum at 300 yards than the Swift had at the muzzle. By the two traditional formulas, the 22 calibers were inferior to the 30-06 in every aspect of force and power. If the old ratings were true, there would be no way that the smaller cartridges could penetrate where the more powerful one failed. But they did.

Another time, he shot at 3/8-inch spring steel at less than 10 yards with the 458 Winchester Magnum. It dented the steel, no more. Then he tried the Swift. It shot completely through. Only the Swift's very high velocity could explain this. Apparently, if the speed was high enough, the bullet would punch through before it had time to disintegrate.

This is energy, but energy that cannot be defined in terms of Momentum or foot-pounds. Bullets obviously have two different types of force (at least)—one type from Momentum, the calculation of which includes weight and velocity; and the other from velocity alone, what I call Impulse Energy. The Momentum formula—(WxV)÷225,200—uses both bullet weight and velocity. The chart shows that Momentum ratings accurately indicate the relative positions of bullets and loads regarding weight-moving ability. They predict the order, but not the amount. The amount increases much faster than the Momentum rating, as velocity increases. With the 185-grain 8mm, increasing Momentum by 70 percent increased Linear Foot-Pounds by 206 percent. With the 180-grain 30-caliber, it was 33-percent Momentum increase versus 155-percent LFP increase. This might be the reason that led to velocity being squared in the Kinetic Energy formula. There would seem to be reason for factoring it in more than 1 to 1, but not to the point of squaring it, not if you want to call the results foot-pounds.

Energy is defined as the ability to perform work. Now, let's stipulate two projectiles and a steel plate. If we can agree that punching a hole through the plate is work, then it must require energy. If one bullet will penetrate and another will not, then the one that succeeds must by definition have more energy, or at least more of some kind of energy, than the one that fails. Consider our specific loads: The 30-caliber load has much more Momentum and Kinetic Energy than the 22-caliber load. If these formula ratings are correct and the only forms of projectile energy, then it is impossible for the 22-caliber to penetrate the plate if the 30-caliber won't. Of course the reality is that it will. So ballistic theory needs to change to match reality.

The only thing the 22-caliber has more of is velocity. So velocity must be some form of energy and the source of that bullet's ability to do what should be impossible if the formulas were correct. The next question is how to express this in a formula. But first it might be a good idea to show the earlier formulas:

| Momentum | Kinetic Energy |
|---|---|
| $\frac{WxV}{225,200}$ | $\frac{WxVxV}{450,400}$ |

Obviously, the KE formula is weighted toward velocity. Many people criticize this formula because velocity appears twice, but it is still not enough to describe Impulse Energy. It gives the 30/180/2700 much higher numbers than the 22/55/3690. To get the KE formulas, Newton (or whoever; I haven't researched it) added velocity another time to the starting point of the Momentum formula. He also added 225,200 to the Momentum divisor, thereby doubling it. We can only speculate that he was trying to keep the size of the result down. If he hadn't doubled the divisor, the KE figures would be twice what they are, and they were too high to begin with.

I decided to try taking the KE formula one step further, so I cubed velocity instead of just squaring it. And following the precedent of that formula, I increased the value of the divisor. Since inserting velocity the third time was a 50 percent increase over its appearance in the Kinetic formula, I increased the divisor 50 percent also. Not to have done so would have increased the results drastically. So my formula at this point was (WxVxVxV)÷675,600.

These guns were used in the author's test (from top): Model 870 Remington Special Field 12-gauge; Model 98 Mauser 8mm-06; 1898 Springfield 30-40 Krag; 1864 Springfield 58-caliber. Revolvers (from left): Ruger GP-100 357 Magnum; Ruger Super Redhawk 44 Magnum; Smith & Wesson 1917 45 AR/ACP.

It didn't work. The result was a nine-digit number, and it still rated the 30-caliber load higher than the 22-caliber load.

The more I looked at the Kinetic formula, the more I thought that the originator was trying to describe what I call Impulse Energy, although he used the label Kinetic Energy. Looking at it, I wondered how it would work without bullet weight. It reads (VxV)÷450,400 at this point. So I ran the figures and they seemed to describe Impulse Energy accurately. I knew there would be a problem separating bullet weight from an energy calculation (after all, bullet weight and velocity are combined in Momentum), but it appeared to be the only way that gave a realistic picture of Impulse Energy. It finally produced that elusive higher result for the 22/55/3680 (30 for the 22, 16 for the 30), thus matching reality. Think of Impulse Energy as describing a specific area or part of bullet energy. This is not to say that it would exist without the bullet, but it takes a picture of one characteristic of it. It also

## EDITOR'S NOTE

For as long as I can remember, hunters have been debating the validity of the Kinetic Energy formula, at least insofar as it was interpreted to predict killing power. Maybe it was never intended to be used that way, but after being published by ammo manufacturers and gun magazines for many decades, it was inevitable that's how it would be understood. It still is, by the vast majority of hunters.

But many of the more experienced ones have never accepted it. Some even tried to develop their own formulas, essentially to make predictions agree with actual results such as they had observed during many years in the field, killing hundreds—even thousands—of animals. Elmer Keith's Pounds-Feet formula comes quickly to mind, as does Warren Page's "Knockdown Nothing" approach, Charly Gullet's Universal Power Index, and old elephant-killer John "Pondoro" Taylor's famous KO (knockout) version. Even the IPSC, whose targets aren't alive, has their PF (power factor) for combat handgunners.

Even giving these shooters credit for their experience and efforts, their formulas have not been accepted by everyone. Probably no formula which has to deal with the infinite number of variables that exist in game shooting ever will be accepted universally. But individuals keep trying.

Which brings us to Lee Saunders, a self-described Vermont farmer and lifelong compulsive reader and nit-picker for whom the subject of foot-pounds became something to ponder while doing repetitive and boring chores around his one-man farm. So he sat down and wrote this article, his first. And then he blamed it on me! "As for my trying to write an article," he said in a letter to me, "you have only yourself to blame." In HD14 (1995), he pointed out, I'd invited submissions on deserving subjects. Which obligated me to read his thoughts, of course.

Now, I don't really expect this article will be the last word on energy. And advanced mathematicians have told me in loud superior tones that there are a dozen places they can tear it apart. Maybe they can. One claims, for instance, that in the higher levels of mathematics foot-pounds really has a different definition than the one that guys like me (and maybe you) have so long accepted. Which kind of suggests that they, too, have reservations about the KE formula. But anyway, I've asked them to submit an article that will explain the subject in terms that ordinary mortals can understand. Perhaps it will arrive one of these years. I doubt it, though. I don't remember reading any such piece in the last half-century, so have concluded that if anyone has a solid answer, he's keeping it to himself.

But in the meantime we have Saunders' effort. And I think it's worthwhile, because it at least shows original thinking.

*—Bob Bell*

These 3-inch, 12-gauge, 1-ounce slugs from Remington produced the highest Linear Foot-Pounds of any load tested.

has the virtue of producing small numbers, which I think is an advantage; large numbers produce unrealistic expectations.

## Only a Theory

Impulse Energy is indeed only a theory. If a way could be found to measure impulse (won't the electronics wizards have fun figuring that out—measuring impulse force without measuring Momentum; seems impossible to me, but never say never), formula numbers would undoubtedly be off. There isn't any built-in calibration in the formula, but I think it's realistic or I wouldn't propose it.

The Impulse Energy formula gives ratings as shown below that start to explain the results Mr. Hartley noted with his steel-plate experiments. Impulse is solely the result of velocity, regardless of bullet weight. Two widely different calibers, 22 and 45 for example, at exactly the same velocity, have exactly the same Impulse rating. Not the same Momentum, not the same Linear Foot-Pounds, but the exact same Impulse Energy available to perforate materials or expand the bullet.

**Impulse Ratings at Various Velocities**

| | |
|---|---|
| 700 fps = 1.088 | 2500 fps = 13.88 |
| 1000 fps = 2.22 | 3000 fps = 19.98 |
| 1500 fps = 4.99 | 3500 fps = 27.20 |
| 2000 fps = 8.88 | 4000 fps = 35.52 |

Let me stipulate at this point that ratings formulas are basically numbers arranged to give the results the originator is looking for. This applies to the Impulse Energy formula. But to me, it describes real circumstances. At 700 fps, the Impulse Energy rating is 1.088. At this velocity, even hollowpoint handgun bullets are unlikely to expand much, if at all. Increase the velocity to 1000 fps and the rating doubles, to 2.22. At this velocity, expansion has become fairly predictable. Move velocity up by 50 percent to 1500 fps and Impulse Energy doubles. This is the range where handgun hollowpoint performance becomes dynamic. Or take a rifle bullet made to expand at 2000 fps. Push it at 3000 and it blows up—a 50 percent velocity increase and an Impulse increase of 125 percent. It reflects results seen in Linear Foot-Pound testing; as velocity increases, energy increases progressively faster. It explains how with Mr. Hartley's steel plates higher velocity produced more Impulse Energy and corresponding ability to perform certain work. Not all work, but the ability to punch through thin metal barriers, and more energy for much more dynamic expansion. Impulse Energy accurately predicts what we see with high-velocity bullets and steel plates.

Regarding units of Impulse Energy, the formula produces units that are nominally pounds. But with so many formulas using pound units—Kinetic Energy, foot-pounds; Momentum, pound-seconds; Linear Foot-Pounds, etc.—I can't bring myself to use the unit again with Impulse Energy. I therefore propose that the Impulse Energy unit be known as the zerk. (If that sounds strange, compare it to volt, watt, therm, byte.)

Ratings of bullet weight-moving ability using the term foot-pounds can be reached only by testing and measurement. A study of the results in Table I indicates that Linear Foot-Pound ability increases progressively as velocity increases. Also, where the same bullet weight and velocity, which have the same Momentum, were tested in two or more calibers, the larger caliber produced more push in spite of the same Momentum rating. It may also be that length of penetration affects push by increasing the time of push. This can be affected by bullet construction. These factors make it impossible for any weight-velocity formula to give accurate results.

This is similar to the situation with ballistic coefficients. Bullets are usually listed with a single ballistic coefficient to simplify matters. In reality, the BC of a projectile changes as velocity changes. The higher the velocity, the greater the air resistance and the more important bullet shape is. The only truly accurate way to ascertain BC is to measure bullet velocity close to the muzzle and again downrange, then calculate the results. A similar procedure applies to obtaining Linear Foot-Pounds—test and calculate. Whether this is worthwhile to do is a valid question. The moderate level of real-world foot-pounds is not as exciting as the much higher numbers of the traditional energy formula. But these are the real numbers that go with the definition of foot-pounds.

## Two Types

So it can be summarized that ballistic energy is of two distinct types or characteristics: Impulse Energy and Momentum Energy. This is not a unique situation. For example, truck engines are rated on both horsepower and pounds of torque. It was discovered that the traditional engine rating of peak horsepower did not accurately describe performance under some conditions: starting off with heavy loads and in rough terrain. The result was the torque rating, which describes the engine's ability to maintain rpms under load. Two totally different ratings to describe one energy source.

To attempt to use energy ratings to ascertain stopping or killing power of cartridges is not realistically possible. The original Kinetic Energy formula was intended as an attempt to measure the energy of a moving object. It was never intended as a measure of killing power and never should have been used in that context. Impulse Energy and Momentum figures are more realistic, but are still of limited value in that area.

Energy is the source of the bullet's ability to do damage, the force that makes the bullet a moving projectile, not a motionless object. But the bullet is what does the damage. And damage is what counts.

On that subject, damage is the result of:

1. Bullet construction. This affects damage by:
   (a) Non-expanding (solid). Great penetration, bullet-diameter wound channel.
   (b) Expanding. Much wider wound channel at the expense of a substantial degree of diminished penetration. Rate of expansion can be controlled by bullet construction, from very fast (fragmenting) to much slower. A fast rate of expansion can extend the wound cavity much beyond bullet diameter by hydraulic pressure and create temporary cavity shock.

# WHAT DO BULLETS REALLY MOVE?

Like any shooter who has fired into plinking targets more substantial than tin cans, I knew that bullets wouldn't move much weight. But in order to have more definitive information for this article, I decided to experiment. I wanted to measure the ability of bullets to move weight horizontally. I called the results Linear Foot-Pounds.

My first test method was simply to put an 18-pound block of firewood on a smooth plywood surface and shoot into the end of it. The results were interesting and consistent, but it seemed possible to build a frame with a block suspended by rollers that would have less drag and be more accurate. A hardwood block was placed in the carriage as the bullet stopping point. The idea was that wood was soft enough for the bullet to penetrate without deflecting, but hard enough to stop the projectile in a short space, and offering resistance to get as much push as possible. Sand has been used in ballistic pendulums, but I wanted a lighter apparatus that could be taken apart and moved easily. Sand would also make the carriage very heavy, and I suspected the lighter calibers might produce so little movement as to be difficult to measure. Admittedly, wood-grain variations would mean that the blocks might not be as uniform as sand.

The blocks were replaced as necessary. After a number of shots, the block would begin to split, so another was inserted. Each block was weighed (while in the carriage) so the total amount of weight being moved could be used in the calculations. The weight of the carriage with various blocks ran from 42.3 to 48.0 pounds. A supply of bullets was placed in the carriage, and one was removed as each shot was fired to maintain a constant weight.

The method used to calculate Linear Foot-Pounds is the following formula:

A = Distance of movement of apparatus in inches.

B = Weight of apparatus with block being used.

(A÷12) x B = Linear Foot-Pounds.

These results were obtained with the bullets stopping in the apparatus, so all possible push was exerted on the block. In other targets with complete penetration, such as in hunting, the push often would not use up all the bullet force, so push movement would be less.

An apparatus scientifically engineered to eliminate all movement resistance would give slightly higher values. The difference between my first block-on-a-plywood-sheet and later carriage apparatus was in the 1 to 2 LFP range. Similar differences could be expected. This was a backyard experiment simply designed to show the vast discrepancy between energy foot-pound ratings and actual bullet abilities.

To digress for a moment, while doing the figures for the chart, I became aware of the following differences of opinion on numbers used in the momentum and energy formulas:

*NRA Handloading Guide*: Momentum = (WxV)÷225,200; Energy = (WxV$^2$)÷450,400.

*Lyman Handbook, 47th Ed.*: Momentum = (WxV)÷225,218; Energy = (WxV$^2$)÷450,436.

Several other reloading manuals: Momentum = (WxV)÷225,120; Energy = (WxV$^2$)÷450,240.

Only two centerfire rifles were available for testing, so a number of bullet weights and velocities were tested to cover as much area as possible. Some of the 8mm-06 loads approximate 30-06 handloads for Momentum. The 8mm 150-grain load gives velocity that will match both 308 and 30-06 factory loads at different downrange distances. The 8mm 175- and 185-grain loads match up with 180-grain 308 and 30-06 factory loads. The 30-40 Krag 170-grain FP matches the 30-30 Winchester 170-grain factory load at 80 yards from the muzzle.

It should be pointed out that comparisons between different diameter bullets may not be totally accurate. In this limited amount of testing, there is an indication that given the same bullet weight and velocity, or Momen-

The carriage and block seen from the end, as it looks when shooting for testing.

2. Velocity. This is the characteristic that enables softpoint bullets to expand and is an important factor in Momentum, thus penetration, bullet construction being up to it.
3. Bullet weight. Increasing weight in a given caliber increases:
   (a) Penetration
   (b) Momentum. Weight-moving ability or push.
4. Penetration. Must be sufficient to reach vital organs from whatever angle the shot is taken. Penetration past that point still increases damage by extending the wound cavity.
5. Bullet diameter. Has an effect by:
   (a) Increasing the cross-sectional size of the wound channel. With solid bullets, this is an important way to increase damage.
   (b) With any bullet weight at a given velocity, the larger caliber will have more push (LFP), by a small but definite amount, bullet construction being equal.

All of these together produce the total effect on target.

Sometimes the terms for the results can be misleading or confusing. Does "knockdown" refer to the target dropping from total damage or from sheer physical push? We've all seen the term used obviously referring to "push over" ability of various cartridges. In a literal sense, this ability is minuscule, as can be seen in the LFP chart, the legends of large-caliber elephant

tum, the larger diameter bullet will produce slightly more weight movement. Two load workups are shown to demonstrate how Linear Foot-Pounds and Impulse Energy increase as velocity increases with a given bullet.

Plainly, the Linear Foot-Pounds numbers are not overwhelming. Remember that 1 LFP is 1 pound moved 1 foot horizontally. Among the handguns, 45 ACP factory hardball produced 1.75 LFP, the heaviest 357 Magnum handload reached only 3 LFP, and the 44 Magnum loaded to the maximum reached 8 LFP. Clearly no handgun will knock down any human-size target from sheer push. Damage to the systems that keep the body upright is what is required. The long guns produced more movement, but nothing spectacular. The leader was the 12-gauge 1-ounce 3-inch magnum slug with 31 LFP.

Comparatively impressive, but...

Just to see how it compared, the block in the apparatus was punched with a gloved fist a number of times. Short sharp blows produced readings from 25 to 35 LFP. When a punch was thrown with follow-through, as if punching through the target, up to 61 LFP was achieved. With a 15-pound post maul, a short compact swing gave an average of 91 LFP. When tried with more swing to drive through the block, readings up 134 to 165 LFP were reached. It would certainly be interesting to test some big-bore rifles—the 458, etc—to see where in this range they would fit in. (Maybe later.)

In sum, the figures produced by the traditional Kinetic Energy formula absolutely do not denote foot-pounds. To earn the label, you have to do the work.

*—Lee Saunders*

**TABLE 1: VARIOUS WAYS OF EXPRESSING ENERGY**

| Caliber/Bullet | Velocity (fps) | Kinetic Energy (ft-lbs.) | Block Movement (ins.) | Momentum Rating | Linear Foot-Pounds | Impulse Rating |
|---|---|---|---|---|---|---|
| **12-gauge .715″** | | | | | | |
| 1 oz. slug, 3″ | 1540 | 2303 | 8.97 (4)* | 2.993 | 31.62 | 5.27 |
| 1 oz. slug, 2 3/4″ | 1459 | 2067 | 6.56 (2) | 2.834 | 24.33 | 4.72 |
| **8mm-06 cal. .323″** | | | | | | |
| 220 gr. | 2536 | 3139 | 4.73 (1) | 2.477 | 18.56 | 14.28 |
| 200 gr. | 2639 | 3093 | 4.27 (1) | 2.344 | 16.76 | 15.46 |
| 175 gr. | 2777 | 2997 | 3.69 (2) | 2.158 | 13.67 | 17.12 |
| 150 gr. | 2828 | 2663 | 2.54 (1) | 1.884 | 9.98 | 17.76 |
| 185 gr. | 2701 | 2997 | 3.69 (6) | 2.219 | 14.75 | 16.20 |
| 185 gr. | 2570 | 2714 | 3.44 (2) | 2.111 | 12.75 | 14.66 |
| 185 gr. | 2479 | 2525 | 3.08 (2) | 2.036 | 11.43 | 13.64 |
| 185 gr. | 2394 | 2353 | 2.73 (6) | 1.967 | 10.92 | 12.72 |
| 185 gr. | 2208 | 2002 | 2.38 (1) | 1.814 | 9.32 | 10.82 |
| 185 gr. | 1976 | 1603 | 2.10 (1) | 1.623 | 8.26 | 8.67 |
| 185 gr. | 1775 | 1293 | 1.65 (6) | 1.458 | 6.58 | 7.00 |
| 185 gr. | 1586 | 1033 | 1.23 (1) | 1.303 | 4.82 | 5.58 |
| **1864 Springfield .584″** | | | | | | |
| Cast Minie 516 gr. | 965 | 1063 | 3.33 (5) | 2.211 | 13.28 | 2.07 |
| **30-40 Krag cal. .308″** | | | | | | |
| 220 gr. | 1858 | 1686 | 2.23 (3) | 1.815 | 8.27 | 7.66 |
| 170 gr. | 1927 | 1401 | 1.42 (3) | 1.455 | 5.25 | 8.24 |
| 180 gr. | 2240 | 2006 | 2.63 (3) | 1.791 | 9.73 | 11.14 |
| 180 gr. | 2165 | 1873 | 2.46 (3) | 1.731 | 9.12 | 10.41 |
| 180 gr. | 2029 | 1645 | 2.17 (3) | 1.622 | 8.04 | 9.14 |
| 180 gr. | 1891 | 1427 | 1.73 (6) | 1.511 | 6.92 | 7.94 |
| 180 gr. | 1820 | 1323 | 1.55 (6) | 1.455 | 6.19 | 7.35 |
| 180 gr. | 1686 | 1135 | 1.03 (3) | 1.348 | 3.82 | 6.31 |
| **44 Magnum cal. .429″** | | | | | | |
| 255 gr. Cast | 1504 | 1281 | 2.04 (1) | 1.703 | 8.01 | 5.02 |
| 180 gr. | 1764 | 1243 | 1.71 (1) | 1.410 | 6.70 | 6.91 |
| **357 Magnum cal. .357″** | | | | | | |
| 200 gr. Cast | 1074 | 512 | .69 (1) | .954 | 2.70 | 2.56 |
| 158 gr. Cast | 1441 | 728 | .81 (1) | 1.011 | 3.01 | 4.17 |
| 125 gr. | 1525 | 645 | .38 (1) | .846 | 1.47 | 5.16 |
| **45 AR/ACP .452″** | | | | | | |
| 230 gr. FMJ | 845 | 363 | .44 (6) | .863 | 1.75 | 1.58 |
| 200 gr. JHP | 843 | 314 | .38 (1) | .749 | 1.47 | 1.58 |
| 200 gr. Cast | 759 | 255 | .21 (1) | .674 | .82 | 1.28 |

All figures are three-shot averages. Velocities measured at the block.
* Numbers in parentheses indicate the particular block (block and carriage total weight) used to test that load:
#1- 47.1 pounds
#2 and #3- 44.5 lbs.
#4- 42.3 lbs.
#5- 47.8 lbs.
#6- 48.0 lbs.
One Linear Foot-Pound is 1 pound moved 1 foot horizontally.

guns to the contrary. The damage done by the bullet to the body systems produces the "knockdown" effect. This is what many hunters mean by "power" in a cartridge, the ability to do damage on a scale that will get an animal off its feet in the shortest possible time. Plainly, the larger the animal, the more "power" is required. This is separate from killing power. (A 22 to the brain will kill instantly; a 22 through the heart will kill, but how fast?)

With so many factors involved, it can be seen that it's fruitless to attempt to measure target effect from energy alone. Energy is the force behind the damage, but it works only through the bullet. "Energy transfer," that well-loved term, takes place indirectly, not directly, only by the bullet creating damage.

A number of formulas have been devised to comparatively predict target effect, and to the extent that they include factors affecting wound cavity size, they work. More or less. They are most useful for helping hunters going after a size and type of game they have never hunted before to avoid totally inappropriate cartridge choice. Bullet choice is at least as important, and probably much more so. And the most overriding factor of all is location; that all-important damage needs to be done in the immediate location of vital organs. Which obviously requires the hunter to shoot straight. •

# My Love Affair with the FIREBALL

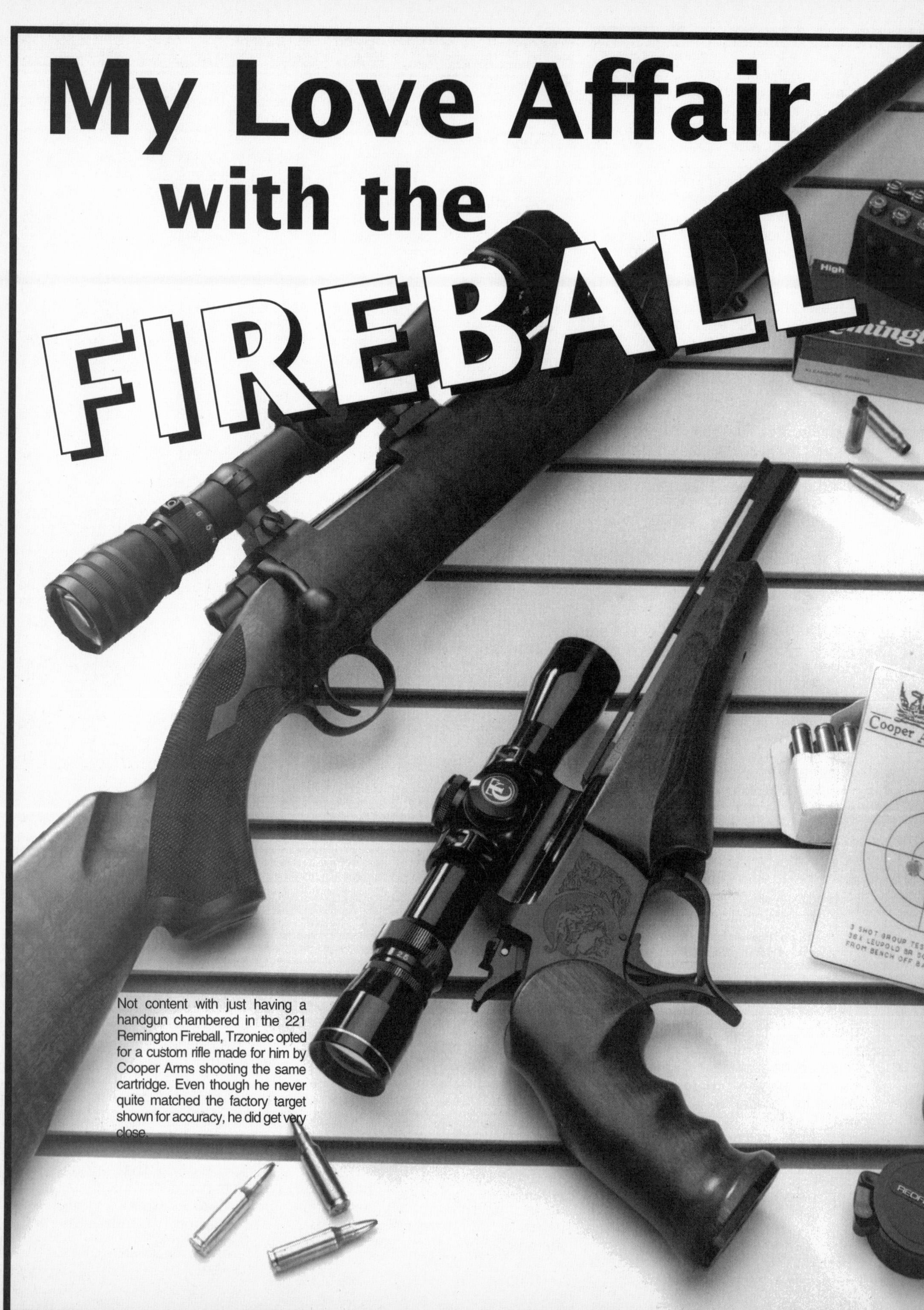


Not content with just having a handgun chambered in the 221 Remington Fireball, Trzoniec opted for a custom rifle made for him by Cooper Arms shooting the same cartridge. Even though he never quite matched the factory target shown for accuracy, he did get very close.

# The more the author worked with the 221 Fireball, the more he realized it's not just a handgun cartridge.

by STAN TRZONIEC

WHEN IT COMES to smallbore cartridges, nothing turns me on more than a good 22 centerfire. Not only are they pleasant on the shoulder, but even small 22s tend to be very accurate to at least 200 yards. Handloading these cartridges is always a joy, as the availability of components starts to outdistance the average human life span in bullet, powder and primer combinations. Finally, adding to the fact that all 22 cartridges tend to promote hunting at more times of the year than their bigbore counterparts simply translates to a better field hunter, no matter the game or distance. To help drive this point home, I'll never forget the words of a Montana guide who said, "Stan, give me a good varmint hunter anytime!"

Present times show a marked increase in 22 centerfire activity in both modern and resurgent (read nostalgic) cartridges. Major ammunition companies are producing special "varmint" loads that equal or surpass many of the more common home brews. And arms makers are starting to read their mail, as shown by Browning's recent entry of the 22 Hornet and Ruger's excellent No. 1 in 218 Bee. Other notables such as the 224 Weatherby—still one of my favorites but regrettably discontinued by the parent company—and the ill-fated 22 Remington Magnum, as well as the 219 Zipper, 220 Weatherby Rocket, 221 Remington Fireball and 225 Winchester, could all add up to much fun in the field.

### The Rifle and the Cartridge

While the Zipper, Rocket or the 225 seem to be something dreams are made of, the 221 Fireball is out there and surprisingly gaining on the smallbore populace. Granted, it's not on everyone's production list, but if you look hard enough, as I did, one can be had with little effort on your part. It's called the Model 21 rifle, and Cooper Arms can custom outfit you in a short period of time. More on them in a minute.

Interestingly, the 221 Fireball was introduced by Remington in 1963 and immediately chambered in the XP-100 pistol. This space-age pistol, as you may recall, had a DuPont Zytel brown-toned stock that closely resembled Buck Rogers' ray gun. It was really quite an accomplishment for Remington—this handgun thing I mean—as it was a first since their pocket automatics met their demise in 1935. With a 10½-inch barrel, Remington quoted ballistics for a factory round at about 2650 fps. Capable of dime-size groups out to the century mark, the 221 Fireball was dubbed as a "super-accurate" long-range pistol. I never owned a 221 Fireball in the XP-100, but a recent yen for the cartridge led me down the long road to acquiring not only one but two guns. My results with the Contender were in last year's HANDLOADER'S DIGEST; this time we move on to a rifle version.

This year's subject was made for me by Cooper Arms. My attraction to 22 centerfire varmint rifles got me interested in this little number at the SHOT Show last year. Talking with Doug Spencer, I found out that he chambers the Model 21 not only in 221 Fireball but also in the 17 Remington, 17 MACH IV, 22 PPC, 222, 223 and 222 Remington Magnum.

The Cooper rifle is a very handsome firearm that brings back memories of longarms used by hunters in the '40s and '50s. The M21's lines are pure American classic, the wood AAA or better, and custom options such as skeleton grip cap and buttplate, checkered bolt handle, special trigger and a fluted barrel can be added if your checkbook doesn't run dry. My basic rifle includes fancy wood, ebony forend tip, metal grip cap, fleur-de-lis checkering, thin rubber buttpad and special serial number.

For accuracy, the Cooper rifle has a medium barrel that was free-floated in its fancy stock. The scope is by Redfield and is matte finished to match the gun's metal work. Note the parallax adjustment—necessary on a full-blown varmint rig.

To add stiffness to this action, the rifle is a single shot. Here we note a round complete with a Hornady V-Max bullet ready for launch.

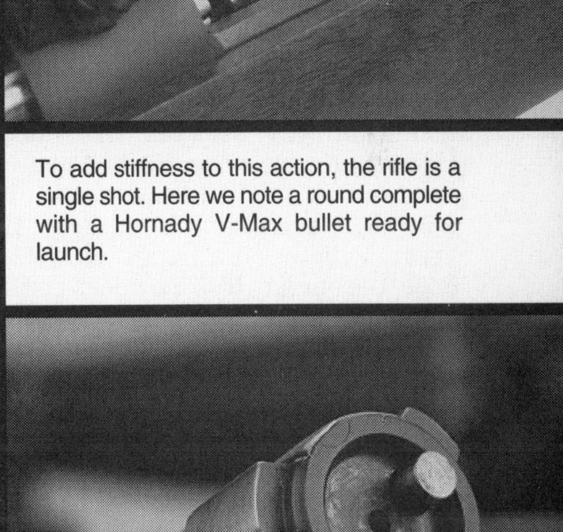

To complete the picture, Cooper Arms employs a three-lug locking-type bolt. Pay particular attention to the heft of all parts, including the ejector and extractor.

The rifle is tuned in to accuracy from the start. The match-grade 24-inch medium-heavy barrel tapers to .670-inch at the muzzle and is free-floated; it has a recessed target-type crown. The bolt, machined from 4140 bar stock, has a proprietary three locking-lug arrangement that, according to spokespeople at Cooper, distributes shear forces more equally than those incorporating only twin lugs. The receiver is drilled and tapped for scope mounts, and I installed Leupold rings/bases and a Redfield 4-12x matte-finished scope. Complete, the outfit weighed 7½ pounds. By the time I sighted-in at 100 yards, I was starting to get itchy. A great fire-forming load was a 50-grain bullet over 16 grains of Accurate Arms 1680 and the CCI BR-4 primer. Cartridge overall length was 1.820-inch. Velocity was not recorded.

So why did I lean toward the 221 Remington Fireball? Personal reasons aside, we note the following comparisons, all with a 52-grain, .224-inch bullet.

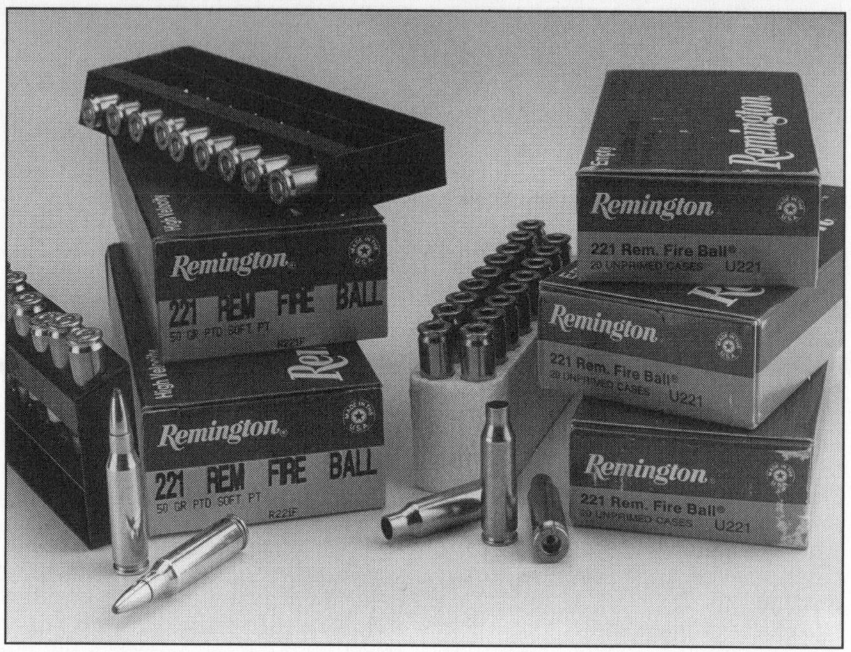

Currently, there is an adequate stock of 221 Remington brass. However, the parent company is not listing the cartridge at this time, so if you have the urge to acquire a rifle in this caliber, stock up now.

**52-GRAIN BULLET VELOCITIES**

| Cartridge | Gun Used | MV (fps) |
|---|---|---|
| 22 Hornet | Browning Low Wall | 2387 |
| 221 Fireball | Cooper Arms | 2987 |
| 222 Rem. | Model 700 Custom | 3102 |
| 220 Swift | 40X-BBR | 3714 |

The 221 Fireball obviously falls about midway between the small Hornet and the large Swift. For the hunter who might like to tailor his gun to the terrain he is hunting, it's great. Fellows on a budget (the 221 does use much less powder) could base their decision on this factor, but in grains of powder expended versus custom firearm cost this would seem remote. Bottom line? This shooter just thinks the 221 Fireball is one extraordinary cartridge not getting its due.

### Reloading the 221 Fireball

Handloading the 221 Fireball really follows basic procedures that we are all used to in daily life. Components are all out there in spades, especially so in 22-caliber. Remington still stocks 221 brass, and if your dealer doesn't have it on his shelf, it's easily obtainable through normal channels, packed twenty rounds to the box. Strongly request the same lot number throughout your entire order. Factory ammunition has been discontinued, although I've found some—albeit buried in dust—at a few dealers. Make an offer, they will take it! When the supply dries up, cases can be made from 222 or 223 Remington brass. Pay attention to neck thickness and reaming.

Primers also ran pretty standard. Since most shooters want the best in accuracy with a minimum of effort, settle on the various benchrest primers made by Remington or CCI. For this article, CCI BR-4 small rifle primers got the nod. Prior experience showed these to be excellent in both the Contender and Cooper. They are very uniform in performance and easily obtainable at just about any gun shop in the country.

Powder choices were a bit more difficult. Not so much in the short-barreled Contender where propellants such as 2400, Winchester 680, H-110 or IMR-4227 fared very well, but more so in the rifle. Of course, the 221 Fireball was never touted as a rifle cartridge. After checking many manuals, five powders surfaced as suitable for the Fireball—IMR-4227, AA1680, IMR-4198, AA2015BR, and Reloder 7. All seemed to work quite well. With a case that holds roughly 21 grains of water, most did their job well in the 24-inch tube. All powder charges noted in this article were culled from up-to-the-minute handloading guides and personal recommendations from folks in the shooting industry. None of the loads listed go over the working maximums allowed in velocity or CUP (copper units of pressure) for this particular cartridge, but of course everyone should start low and work up while watching for signs of excess pressure.

The bullets shown on the chart pretty well represent most of the heavy hitters in the industry with regard to brand, weight, and design that match this cartridge and its ability to perform at both short- (reduced loads) and long-range distances. Lighter weight bullets can be used on small game at closer distances, while slightly heavier projectiles are my favorite when the wind kicks up, the varmints get larger, and the distances start to stretch out.

Over the course of many months, the rifle was taken out to the range for sighting-in, breaking in, and fire-forming brass for serious handloading sessions. With enough brass formed, I sat at the bench to start the accuracy trials.

I like to neck-size only in my varmint rifles. When big game hunting, I follow the practices used for any big-bore rifle by full-length sizing all my cases simply because I want to avoid possible problems in the field with chambering or follow-up shots. Students and followers of the Trzoniec philosophy note that I like to monitor neck-sizing via smoking with a candle. Smoke on the shoulder and neck of the case is the simplest way of checking this and probably the most accurate of any routine around.

Like all 22 centerfires, the 221 Fireball uses bullets in the .224-inch class.

For 50-yard loads, Trzoniec used a .224-inch "BEE" selection. That hollowpoint should be an instant success story at short distances given the velocity they travel.

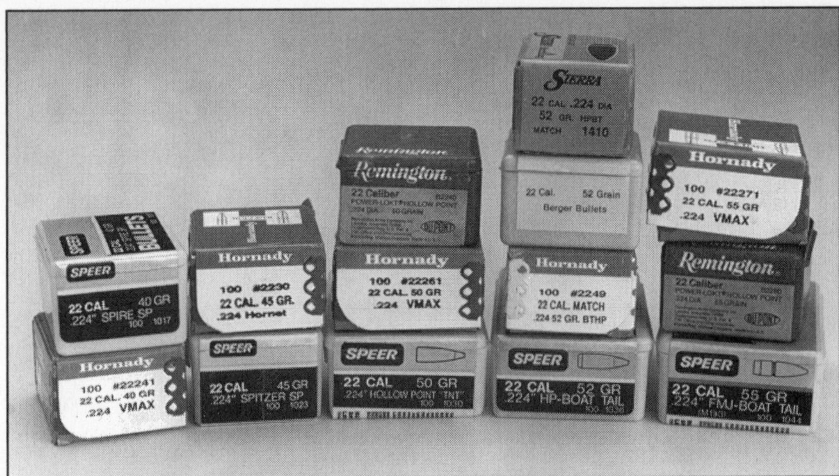

In testing, the author tried for a cross-section of bullet makes, types and weights. Shown here is the entire selection, complete with names and stock numbers.

The propellants shown here gave the best results with the 221 Fireball. The strips shown in the foreground are part of the new RCBS APS system for priming both pistol and rifle cases.

For first-timers, it goes like this: Insert the sizing die, minus the decapper, into your press. Screw it down until it bottoms out on the shellholder. Back it off about four turns. The reason for not including the decapper is just to make life easier, because without the decapper the shell gets a smoother ride up and inside the die; this allows better control with regard to a more precise setting without the jolt associated with the operation of expanding the neck.

*Be positive no powder or primers are nearby*. Lube the case and hold it over a lighted candle until smoke coats both the neck and shoulder. Because the 221 Fireball case is small, it tends to get warm, so holding it with a pair of pliers is not a bad idea. Let it cool and place it into the shellholder.

Screw the sizing die in about a half-turn at a time until you start to get contact with the case. Soon you'll see the progress of the die as it works its way down the neck. As it approaches the neck-shoulder juncture limit your adjustment to 1/8-turn or less. We want the die to barely touch the shoulder. Remember, we are neck-sizing only; the rest of the case should remain untouched. When you are satisfied with the adjustment, hold the die and tighten the lock ring. Try the case in the rifle (keeping in mind that it should feel snug as the bolt is turned down). If it chambers OK, replace the decapper in the die and size the remainder of your cases.

A brief word should be mentioned about inside neck lube, especially on small-capacity cases. Over the years, I've found that the less lube you use, the better, as the number of collapsed shoulders only rises as the amount of case lube increases. I've come to lube only about one in five cases, and at that very sparingly, with a touch of case lube at the very end of a Q-Tip. To finish, wipe each case with a dry towel, then squirt a bit of lighter fluid on another towel to rid the case of any remaining lubricant. Chamfer the mouth both inside and out, check the primer pocket and move on.

All cases were primed on the new RCBS APS Priming Tool using BR-4 primers. Develop a regular procedure. I've found that if you advance this machine too fast, malfunctions can occur and damaged primers might show up in your cases.

Seating bullets is always a challenge. With light bullets of 40 to 45 grains, I try to get at least one bullet diameter seated into the case. This seems preferable to trying to seat the bullet near the lands. I favor a solidly seated bullet to one just perched on the very top of the mouth; it seems to perform better at the terminal end, possibly due to the increased resistance causing better powder combustion. Heavier bullets are seated just shy of the barrel lands, of course.

You'll also notice that, with some of the bullets in the loads listed, overall length exceeds the 1.830 inches given in most manuals. This is no need for concern in the Cooper rifle. These

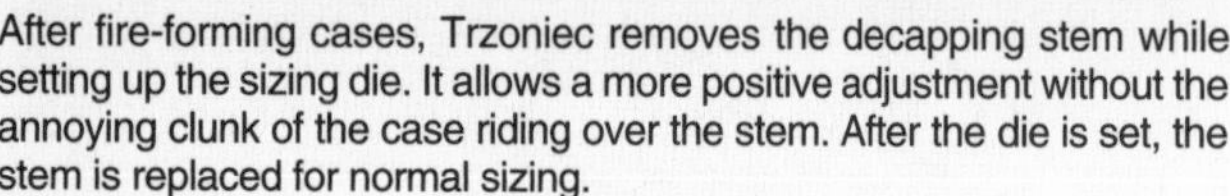

After fire-forming cases, Trzoniec removes the decapping stem while setting up the sizing die. It allows a more positive adjustment without the annoying clunk of the case riding over the stem. After the die is set, the stem is replaced for normal sizing.

Being a big advocate of neck-sizing only on varmint-type cases, the author first smokes a case with a candle. In this way, you can see the progress of the die as it moves down the neck. Here, this is noted by the clear area near the mouth; the shoulder is yet untouched.

(Below) Too much lube does no one any good, especially on smaller cases. Only a small amount is needed. The author uses a cotton swab, applying it to every fifth case.

bullets have a very streamlined profile and extend into the bore without contact. A dummy round of each load was made, and tried for fit and function, before actual loading began.

To get good test results, accuracy at the loading bench is a must, especially with smaller cartridges like the 221 Fireball. Drop charges as you usually do, but do it to within .5-grain of the final charge. Use a powder trickler to bring the charge up to the desired weight. For reduced loads, a tiny (0.1- to 0.2-grain) pinch of ordinary cotton was used to keep the powder against the primer for consistent results. The only two loads that even came close to being "compressed" were Number 3 with 18 grains of IMR-4198 and Number 14, which filled the case halfway up the neck with 19 grains of AA2015BR. Other than these two examples, powder charging went on without a hitch.

### The Envelope, Please!

The day of reckoning came just before a storm marched in. Weather was perfect for 22 centerfire testing; temperature was in the mid-50s, absolutely no wind and overcast—great for velocity readings over a chronograph. One tip here—before you go out for serious testing, contact the weather department at your local television affiliate; they can tell you when the best time is for wind or other conditions that can make or break a good range session.

Testing was divided into two parts. The first consisted of a large selection of working loads (textbook generated) and was fired at 100 yards. These were intended for varmints out to 200 yards. The second part, the smallest, was tested at 50 yards, where you might be hampered by thick cover or hunting in heavy wood lots. The interval between groups was three to five minutes, longer as the barrel warmed up. I might say here that the barrel on the Cooper never really became hot to the touch—warm, yes, but not hot. This probably helped the groups.

If you want the last foot-second of velocity, note that, with 45-grain bullets, AA1680 was the winner. With 50-grain bullets, trusted IMR-4227 was high man; 52-grain bullets showed a preference for IMR-4198; finally, the heavier 55-grain projectiles went to AA2015BR, but not by much with a slight accuracy loss. Actually, there was little velocity spread with the different powders. Keep in mind this is a 221 Remington Fireball. It's small. If you want to get more velocity, don't pack more powder in, just move up to another cartridge. As far as the best groups went, there was a tie between IMR-4227 and AA1680. IMR-4198 came in third. So if you are on a budget, cases loaded with IMR-4227 or AA1680 should give you plenty choice as far as bullet weight and velocity.

### Getting Down to the Nitty-Gritty

Almost always, my best groups came when overall length was greater than the factory specification of 1.830 inches. With bullets of not more than 45 grains, load Number 3 proved best when loaded with a Hornady softpoint. This particular offering was seated at 1.860 inches with a slightly compressed charge of 18 grains of IMR-4198.

The priming of all cases follows sizing, depriming, cleaning and trimming, if necessary. This is the new RCBS APS (Automatic Priming System) in use.

While the APS system is fast, don't try to set any records! The case on the left has a normal primer installed, while the primer on the right is deformed—the result of going too fast. Remember, consistency is the key to accuracy.

With a velocity of 3140 fps and a group size at 100 yards of only .625-inch, this one was definitely the hands-down winner.

Moving up to the 50-grain selections, the best one here was again the one that was seated out to 1.900 inches. This time, the new Hornady V-Max bullet with 15.8/IMR-4227 delivered the goods at nearly 3000 fps. Giving half-inch groups, this one would be my choice with this weight bullet. The slightly heavier 52-grain bullets gave near-instant satisfaction with two offerings. The first with a Berger bullet ahead of 17.5 grains of Reloder 7 pushed 2842 fps with average groups of .6875-inch. However, my choice would be the Sierra boattail hollowpoint (match) with 16/IMR-4227. With an overall length just under factory specs (1.825 inches), it almost reached that magical 3000 fps with a group size of a most impressive .312-inch. This would be my choice for an all-around varmint load in the 221 Remington Fireball.

Finally, the 55-grain Hornady V-Max seated out to 1.900 inches went into a half-inch with 17/AA1680. Velocity was 2840 fps. Factory-loaded Remington ammunition consisted of a 50-grain Pointed Soft Point, and in my Cooper rifle, it delivered .75-inch groups at almost 2900 fps. Not too shabby!

At 50 yards, I used the Hornady 45-grain "BEE" hollowpoint as a standard. All were charged with ascending weights of 2400 powder, starting at 10 grains and working up to 14 grains. As with the other loads, CCI BR-4 primers were used and all were loaded to 1.700 inches. The chart shows 12 grains was the winner with a .25-inch group and 2751 fps. It is interesting to note, again, if you're limited to but a few propellants, good ol' 2400 will deliver the goods at nearly 3000 fps with relative ease. Food for thought, I'm sure.

**TESTING THE 221 FIREBALL**

| Load Number | —Bullet— Wgt. Grs. | Type | Load (Grs./Powder) | OAL (ins.) | MV (fps) | Group (ins.) |
|---|---|---|---|---|---|---|
| 1. | 40 | Speer SP | 18.0/AA1680 | 1.750 | 3225 | 1.00 |
| 2. | 40 | Horn. V-Max | 18.0/AA1680 | 1.840 | 3158 | 1.125 |
| 3. | 45 | Horn. SP | 18.0 (C)/IMR-4198 | 1.860 | 3140 | 0.625 |
| 4. | 45 | Speer Spitz | 16.0/IMR-4227 | 1.810 | 3092 | 1.00 |
| 5. | 50 | Horn. V-Max | 15.8/IMR-4227 | 1.900 | 2999 | 0.50 |
| 6. | 50 | Rem. PLHP | 17.5/AA1680 | 1.810 | 2956 | 0.625 |
| 7. | 50 | Speer TNT | 17.8/RE-7 | 1.840 | 2884 | 1.00 |
| 8. | 52 | Berger HP | 17.5/RE-7 | 1.830 | 2842 | 0.687 |
| 9. | 52 | Horn. BTHP | 17.7/IMR-4198 | 1.860 | 3079 | 1.125 |
| 10. | 52 | Sierra BTHP | 16.0/IMR-4227 | 1.825 | 2987 | 0.312 |
| 11. | 52 | Speer BTHP | 17.0/IMR-4198 | 1.850 | 2946 | 1.00 |
| 12. | 55 | Horn. V-Max | 17.0/AA1680 | 1.900 | 2840 | 0.50 |
| 13. | 55 | Rem. HP | 17.6/IMR-4198 | 1.820 | 2818 | 0.75 |
| 14. | 55 | Speer FMJ | 19.0 (C)/AA2015BR | 1.860 | 2844 | 1.250 |
| 15. | 50 | Rem. PSP | Factory load | 1.830 | 2893 | 0.75 |
| 16.* | 45 | Horn. HP | 10.0/2400 | 1.700 | 2336 | 0.75 |
| 17.* | 45 | Horn. HP | 12.0/2400 | 1.700 | 2751 | 0.25 |
| 18.* | 45 | Horn. HP | 14.0/2400 | 1.700 | 2997 | 0.375 |

Notes: Loads noted with an * were tested at 50 yards, all others at 100, with Cooper Arms Model 21 Classic; (C) denotes a compressed charge.

### Downrange Stats

Shooting the Fireball shows that it falls in line with most of its peers. For instance, if we take my choice load (Number 10) of the Sierra 52-grain BTHP at 2987 fps (3000 fps for comparison purposes) and zero it at 100 yards, 200-yard bullet drop will be roughly 3.6 or 3½ inches. If you have the range to do it on, sighting the same load at 200 yards will show a bullet rise of 1.8 inches at 100 yards, followed by a drop of about 9 inches at 300 yards. There's no point in checking longer ranges, for at 300 yards you are working with 1900 fps and only 422 foot-pounds of energy.

In conclusion, the 221 Remington Fireball is a very interesting cartridge to work with in a rifle and is destined to be one of my favorites. Surely this 22-caliber offering is not going to set the world on fire, but as group sizes with many loads and bullets show, the Fireball is competitive with others in its class. The Cooper rifle performed like a charm. You simply can't ask for more, except that possibly a production riflemaker (Remington, Ruger, Browning, Winchester take note) might adopt it and bring the cost down for more shooters.

This varmint hunter is happy. Very happy! •

# Some Idle Thoughts On THE LAST USEFUL WILDCAT

I WOULD HAVE passed up the shot if our slim-pickin's hunt had not been winding down. The four-point bull was carrying the mail. Worse yet, he was pushing the 200-yard distance to which I (then a recent convert) try to limit my shots on any game larger than antelope. Not to worry!

Thanks to a lot of assistance from Lady Luck, the elk dropped at my second shot. The first, a near-miss, had turned him, offering a broadside shot. There would be no need to trail him. He had simply slid along in the snow as far as his momentum and the BLM drift fence along the continental divide had allowed.

My 250-grain Barnes had done massive damage to both his heart and the off elbow, and my new 8mm-06 was now blooded.

As I thawed my numbed fingers against a steaming coffee cup, stocking feet cozied up to Pop Hickel's sheepherder stove, Pop gave a couple of deep pulls on his pipe before asking, "How did the new rifle work?"

"Great."

"Leave a blood trail?"

"For as far as he went."

Pop had served as "gun" during a four-year biological study of a large elk herd. He knew a great deal about elk hunting and a lot about what it takes to bring one down.

Though he subscribed to the "where" rather than the "with which" rifle theory, he did not consider the 270 or, for that matter, the 30-06 good elk rifles. Experience had made him a great believer both in blood trails and the 35-caliber holes that he thought it took to make them.

Pop had seen the soured carcasses of far too many mortally wounded elk that had been found a day too late. He had a low opinion of hunters who tried shots upward of 200 yards on the bigger game, i.e. elk and moose, with the above-mentioned rifles, and an even lower opinion of gunwriters advocating such shots. Any conversation with him was an experience long sorely missed.

All too soon, the whine of straining gears reached us as the remaining members of our party brought in my elk, and as happened on far too many occasions, our pleasant, slow-paced and (for me) educational conversation was placed on hold; but I have digressed.

In the 1966 *Gun Digest*, one Courtney Wills, in an article as entertaining as it was informative, ranked the 25-06, 8mm-06 and the 35 Whelen as "the few useful wildcats." With Remington having long since recognized the virtues of the 25-06 and, more recently, the 35 Whelen, we are left with only the 8mm-06 among his wildcat candidates. Wills also wrote, "Anyone getting a new rifle built for the 8mm-06 would be laying himself open to the suspicion that he had lost his marbles."

### That Would Be Me

I may qualify as runner-up for the lost-marbles award. My second 8mm-06, a homegrown job, was made up in the early 1960s. Its FN commercial Mauser action and new Czech-made Iranian Mauser barrel were purchased from *American Rifleman* ads. The myrtle wood stock blank came from Herter's.

I'd set aside my 270, not because it had failed me on elk, but rather because of a string of near-failures resulting from ill-advised long-range shots at big mule deer.

Getting back to the missing-marbles award, the hands-down winner here has to be Col. Charles Askins. The colonel had *three new custom-made rifles* chambered for the 8mm-06 cartridge.

In his article, "The 8mm-06 Still Packs a Punch" (Nov. 1981 *American Rifleman*), Askins, after praising the 25-06 and 35 Whelen as had Courtney Wills, wrote ". . . there is still another wildcat which impresses me immensely with its goodness, made up like the others on the '06 casing, and this is the 8mm-06." Askins' article also covered the building of the

three rifles and their ". . . like gangbusters" performance in Africa.

The colonel included the 8mm-06 among "Askins' Best Rifles" in the July 1986 *Rifleman*, as well. He went on to comment about extractors and made it obvious that he preferred the '98 Mauser type on a rifle for dangerous game, rather than one built into the bolt face (a feeling I share even though I have had no trouble at all with the more modern design). He also has nothing good to say about featherweight rifles, claiming "unless the rifle weighs something over 8½ lbs. it simply will not hold steady for me."

Of the "improved" chambering, which he had tried, Askins in the earlier article wrote, "I have yet to detect that this contributes anything more than a cosmetic effect."

It should be noted here that the colonel, an inveterate wildcatter, had put together a variety of combinations over the years. For example, if my old memory serves (no guarantees!), his first effort, covered in an article he wrote back in the mid-1930s, was the conversion of a Colt Woodsman from rimfire to

The original stock and barrel of the author's second 8mm-06 are now paired with a VZ 24 action. Below is the author's first 8mm-06, a WWI military Mauser rebarreled and sporterized in Germany between the wars. It now sports a Bishop stock and Williams Guide rear sight. Early ring trouble with its Echo QD mount was corrected with oversized screws.

Its original myrtle wood replaced by a Ram-Line composition stock, the author's 8mm-06 now serves as a foul-weather backup rifle to his 280 and 35 Whelen. The latter was built on the FN deLuxe commercial action pulled from the author's second 8mm-06.

(Above) All of the bullets shown here shoot well in both rifles, even the old Grand Junction-produced 250-grain Barnes, which are a far cry from those made today. Though we have not yet used the Barnes .323-inch X-Bullet on game, it should perform like gangbusters, as those used in the 35 Whelen have shown.

The "last useful wildcat" is not a finicky eater. In addition to all of the powders shown here, H-414 and RL-19 perform well with a wide variety of bullets.

a straight-sided 22-caliber centerfire cartridge.

### The Influence of the 318

One reason for Askins' phenomenal success in Africa was his exceptional marksmanship. A second is to be found in the performance of a ballistic twin of the 8mm-06—the 318 Westley Richards. In his *Cartridges of the World*, Frank Barnes shows 62 grains of 4831 pushes the 250-grain Barnes bullet at a muzzle velocity of 2410 fps in the 8mm-06, while the 318's 250-grain bulleted factory load travels at 2400 fps.

John Taylor in his 1948 classic, *African Rifles and Cartridges*, wrote of the 318 Westley Richards: ". . .a splendidly satisfactory general purpose weapon, provided it is not abused by being taken alone against dangerous game at close quarters . . . it is a delightful little weapon to use, whilst its trajectory is as flat as you are ever likely to want in Africa." Taylor, here, was commenting upon the factory load using the 250-grain bullet.

**FAVORITE 8MM-06 LOADS**

| Bullet Wgt. Grs. | Load (Grs./Powder) | MV (fps) |
|---|---|---|
| 150 | 55.0/4064 | 2986 |
| 170 | 54.0/4064 | 2755 |
| 200 | 53.0/4064 | 2721 |
| 220 | 58.0/4350 | 2515 |
| 250 | 59.0/4831 | 2392 |

New Frankford Arsenal cases and Winchester primers used in all loads; ambient temperature 64 degrees F; Oehler Model 33 Chronotach. Loads used were based on current data. No attempt was made to "fine-tune" any of the above loads for accuracy or velocity.

With the author's Redfield 12x Metallic Silhouette scope mounted on the VZ 24-actioned rifle, all loads showed excellent hunting accuracy. Some three-shot cloverleaf groups were produced at 100 yards with all weights from 150 to 220 grains.

Some commercial brass will show slightly lower velocities with the above loads.

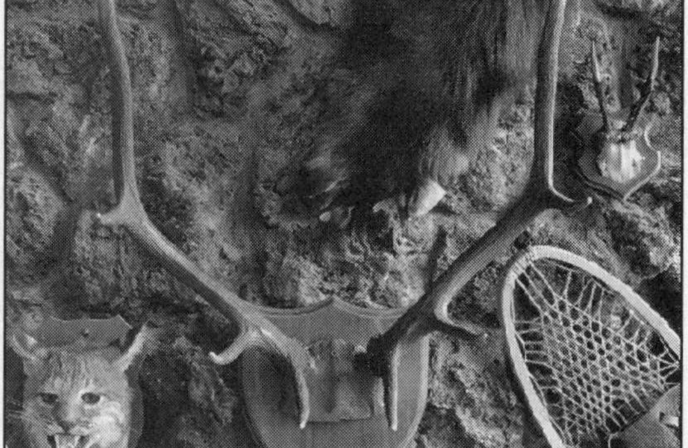

Though often close to being turned into stag grips, this mediocre elk rack has survived as a souvenir of a lucky moment.

My thirty-five-year interest in the 8mm-06 was fostered by Taylor's reflections on the 318. It was furthered by the excellent downrange ballistic figures then listed for 8x57 loads in Norma's tables in *Gun Digest* (which it exceeds) and the excessive headspace (as evidenced by set back primers) that led to the rechambering of my sporterized WWI Mauser.

The 8mm-06 is an easy cartridge to reload. It is easy on cases—some of my G.I. match cases (now retired) show no stress after a dozen full-load firings; new '06 cases are both easy to come by and inexpensive; and a wide variety of excellent bullets is available, ranging in weight from 125 to 250 grains (including a 220-grain Barnes solid). George L. Herter—a man not given to praising others' wildcat cartridges—said it all in an old Herter's manual: "It makes a fine big game cartridge, which is both efficient and flexible."

None of the above should be construed as meaning that the handloader pushing for the last foot-second of velocity can not run afoul of pressure curves. Nor does it alter the fact that the extra "muscle" comes *fully* into play only when the heavier bullets are used. This is seen in the excellent downrange (200- and 300-yard) energy figures of the 200-grain and heavier bullets.

Muzzle velocities of the 150- and 170-grain loads listed in my old Herter's, Hornady and Speer manuals average considerably faster than those in the later manuals. The hitch here is that, with most loads, breech pressures crowd or exceed the 50,000-pound level. Since 8mm-06 users (of necessity, handloaders) are likely to be skilled hunters, they will find that muzzle velocities running below those of the old max loads will be adequate to their needs.

In closing be warned: My experience has been that the incognizant (a polite word for ignorant) will look down their noses upon learning that your rifle is an 8mm-06. They will be suitably impressed, however, some even showing envy, and Col. Askins will receive his due if they are told that it is a 323 Askins Express. •

# Loading The 45 Springfield

**This century-old blackpowder rifle is anything but an antique—it's a high-tech weapon capable of amazing accuracy...if you know what you're doing.**

by C. RODNEY JAMES

AFICIONADOS OF THE Allin cam-lock (Trapdoor) Springfield must possess a certain degree of masochism to maintain their stubborn love affair with this rifle. So much abuse has been heaped upon this model—nearly all of it an unjust accretion of ignorance.

Those who have kept the faith and their Springfields (in good condition) have reason to rejoice in the republication of J.S. and Pat Wolf's *Loading Cartridges for the Original .45-70 Springfield Rifle and Carbine*. This second revised edition of the Wolfs' book at over 200 pages offers far more than information on reloading. In fact, a better title might be "Loading and Shooting the 45 Springfield." The volume contains a plethora of valuable information on buying a rifle, cleaning and maintenance, adjusting sights, using the sling while shooting, troubleshooting mechanical problems, history and development of the ammunition, a reading list for Springfield collectors—about everything needed to master this often misunderstood rifle. This new edition contains essential pressure data, plus information not found in the first edition on loading for the 45 Colt SAA. It is also indexed for easy fact-finding.

About the only fault I could find was the absence of some boldface type and a timely "Follow these instructions exactly!" reminder. The Wolfs share their experiences in mastering the 45, which struck a sympathetic chord with me and should do the same with countless others. But where most of us gave up trying and consigned our Springfields to the closet, wall-rack or sales table, the Wolfs doggedly pursued the quest for accurate shooting results.

My interest in the rifle came from my grandfather, who used one as a soldier in the West in the 1880s. I recall his telling me of shooting them to 1000 yards with a fair degree of accuracy and that they were hard kickers. My first big-bore rifle was a Model 1873 45 that was later stolen. My second and third examples were Model 1888s with the rod bayonet, which perhaps were the best shooters because of the additional weight out front. However, early-model (M1881, M1884) rod-bayonet rifles were not all that accurate, owing to a poor locking system at the front allowing the bayonet to vibrate against the barrel, causing vertical stringing of shots. Most of today's competition shooters use rod bayonet models with the bayonet removed.

### Double Charge

My second M1888 was damaged through an accidental overload—a double charge of Unique—when a phone call disrupted my concentration and I failed to notice the additional powder before seating a 486-grain bullet. Always use a loading block! I have often wondered if that load would destroy another type of action. I don't know, but it was well over a listed maximum for the 458 Winchester with that bullet. (See "Anatomy of a Blackpowder Blowup," *Guns Illustrated, 1996*). Fortunately, the rifle stayed together. The receiver cracked, but the breechblock did not disengage, and though shaken, I suffered no injury—a testament to the rifle's sound engineering.

Neither M88 shot well with anything I put through it. The best I got with cast bullets were 7- to 10-inch groups at 100 yards. I hung it up at that point, which was in 1980. Yet there were those annoying reminders of Springfield performance—Townsend Whelen referring to it as "...a very sterling, accurate, and reliable arm."[1] In his book, *Our Rifles*, Chas. W. Sawyer stated that Springfields could average 5-inch ten-shot groups at 200 yards, and one with a good barrel could do much better than that. In the anecdote that followed, Sawyer described squelching a Doubting Thomas by placing three consecutive shots in a 2-foot circle at a measured distance of 1123 yards.[2]

---

[1]Townsend Whelen, "My Single Shot Rifles." *Gun Digest, 7th Ed.*, 1953, p.82.

[2] Chas. W. Sawyer, *Our Rifles*, The Cornhill Co., Boston, 1920, p.186.

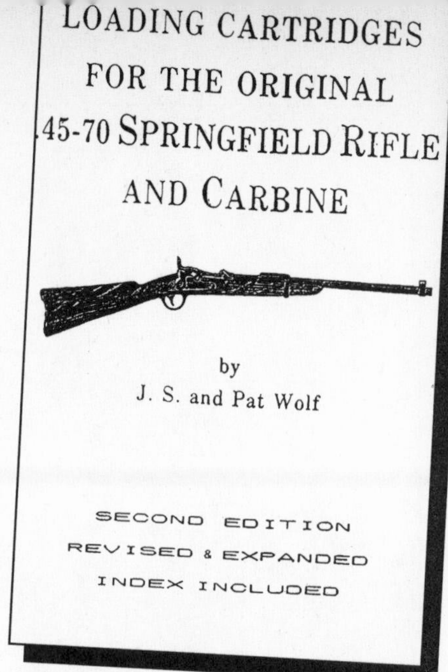


The book everyone who plans to shoot the Allin Springfield should read.

Obviously something was wrong in the performance department, and like most dissatisfied customers, I faulted the rifle. Occasionally, I heard of people using groove-diameter bullets from custom moulds that, by virtue of their being cast .462- to .464-inch, often required reaming of the chamber to accommodate the enlarged cartridge. Also, the bullets grew tail fins when they passed through .452-.454 bores. Obviously, this wasn't the answer.

The Wolfs began a three-year research project shooting their way through hundreds of pounds of lead to discover or *rediscover* what the

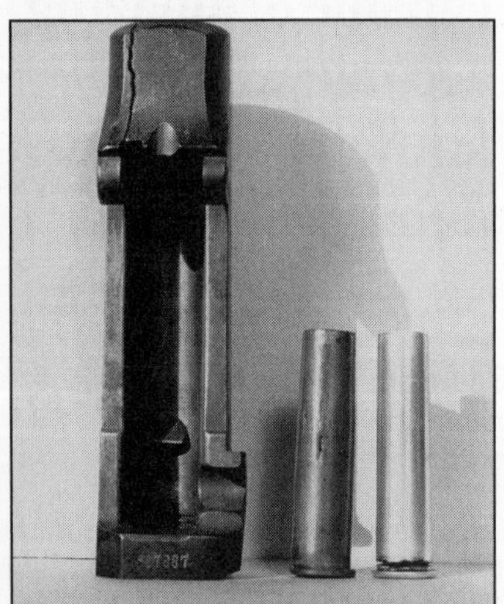

Cracked by a double charge of Unique behind a 486-grain bullet, the receiver and breechblock held, sparing the shooter any injury. The action would appear to be more robust than previously thought. The old semi-balloon case (left) was a poor choice for reloading. The modern case (right) was fired with mercuric primers and suffered a nearly complete head separation.

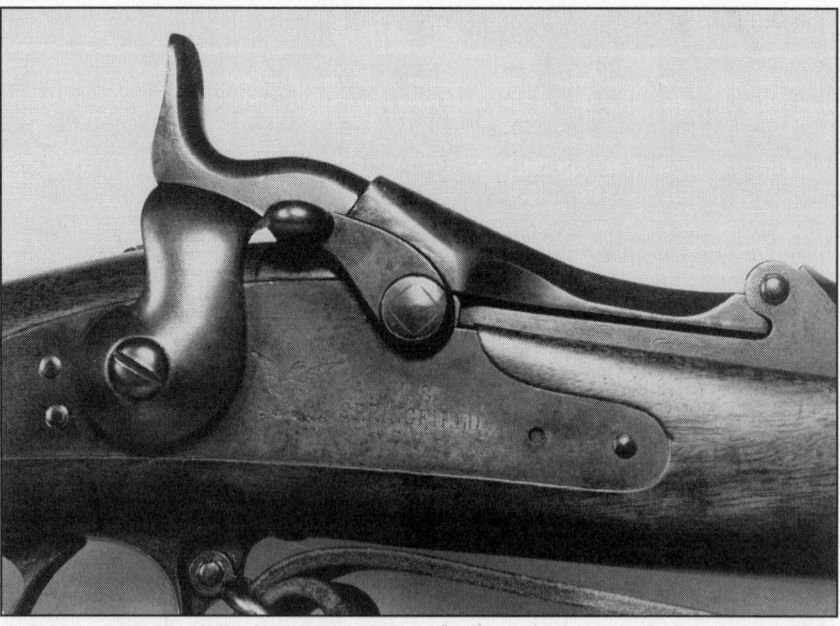

The Trapdoor Springfield was an excellent design in its day, and even had large gas escape vents to deflect the blast away from a shooter's eyes if a cartridge case failed. Properly loaded, it's still an effective gun.

Various bullets for the 45-70 (from left): Model 1873 405-grain; the same bullet turned to show the hollow base; modern Lee and Lyman 405-grain 45s; the modern jacketed 405-grain; Lyman #457125 500-grain from an old mould; Model 1881 500-grain.

(Below) The proper alloy is critical to good accuracy. The left bullet is right from the mould. The fired bullet (center) has fully expanded to take rifling properly. The right bullet is badly gas cut and leaded the bore. It failed to expand because of a too-hard alloy.

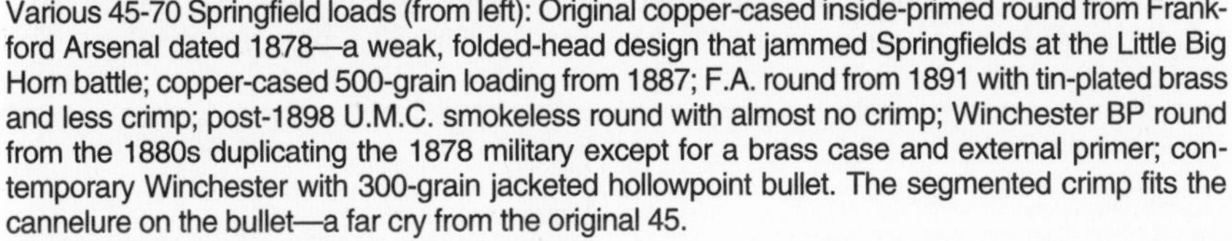

Various 45-70 Springfield loads (from left): Original copper-cased inside-primed round from Frankford Arsenal dated 1878—a weak, folded-head design that jammed Springfields at the Little Big Horn battle; copper-cased 500-grain loading from 1887; F.A. round from 1891 with tin-plated brass and less crimp; post-1898 U.M.C. smokeless round with almost no crimp; Winchester BP round from the 1880s duplicating the 1878 military except for a brass case and external primer; contemporary Winchester with 300-grain jacketed hollowpoint bullet. The segmented crimp fits the cannelure on the bullet—a far cry from the original 45.

The original Springfield flash hole was .097-inch. The case on left is drilled .096 (a No. 41 bit does the job) to Wolf's specifications. At right is an unaltered case.

guys at Frankford Arsenal had learned by the same method over a century ago. By poring over arsenal records, testing and breaking down old ammunition for examination, they discovered that, contrary to popular belief, the Allin Springfield was not simply a clunker/relic of a time when rifles had yet to be perfected, but a weapon that legitimately can be described as a high-tech, blackpowder, long-range rifle.

While it is true that there were stronger contemporary actions, the Springfield bested competitors in government trials by virtue of being more reliable and equally accurate in the torture tests these arms must endure to be accepted. Unlike the Sharps, Winchester and a host of other contenders, the first motion in the ejection process of the Springfield's action is *away* from the case head and not across it—a major jamming point in arms with sticky cases. That these actions jammed at the battle of the Little Big Horn is now accepted as the fault of the copper-case, folded-head cartridges, which stuck in hot, dirty guns, probably because the rims were thinned by excessive polishing to remove corrosion.

### High-Tech Aspects

The high-tech aspects of the Springfield were hidden in a rifle built to please the general officers who demanded an arm that looked "military"—their idea of "military" being a Civil War Springfield. This attitude, it might be added, prevailed up to the time the M-16 was adopted. The high-tech elements of the 45 were in the rifling, ammunition and sights, as armorers in the Springfield and Frankford Arsenals sought to draw the last ounce of performance and accuracy from the 45-70 cartridge.

The 45-70 had its beginning during the Civil War when it became obvious that a smallbore weapon was more accurate and maintained velocity over longer ranges better than a larger bore with a bullet of equal weight.[3] For the next two-plus decades, experimentation evolved a number of loadings—the best known being the 70-grain blackpowder 405-grain bullet for the Models 73 and 79 rifle and carbine, and the 500-grain loading for

[3]An experimental Frankford Arsenal cartridge from the 1860s with a .455 bullet looking much like a heel-crimped 45-70 is pictured on page 145 in Chas. R. Suydam, *The American Cartridge*.

the Models 84 and 88 rifles. Both are discussed in detail in the Wolfs' book, along with other lesser-known target, guard and practice loads.

To maintain accuracy and power, Frankford Arsenal engineers came up with a system that featured an undersize bullet—.458- to .459-inch—of nearly pure lead with enough tin to harden it to withstand velocities and pressures of 1350-1425 fps and 17,600-25,600 psi respectively. The 405-grain bullets had a hollow base, the 500-grainers a dished base, designed to expand to groove diameter *as they left the case*. For maximum power and expansion, the powder was compressed to get 70 grains into the 2.1-inch case. To efficiently burn this powder, the flash hole was made .097-inch diameter. It was filled with a primer having a long burn time to break up and properly ignite the compressed charge. A heavy crimp at the case mouth held the bullet in place until bullet-expanding pressure was achieved. This system had the advantage of burning blackpowder more completely and thus more cleanly than with a loose charge. The deep-groove rifling assured a good grasp on the bullet, which was maintained with minimal drag even as the grooves filled with fouling. Each bullet, since it started out undersize, expanded to fill the *existing* groove space—a custom fit for each bullet. The Springfield was thus able to fire many more accurate shots, without cleaning, than other rifles of the time, before bore fouling degraded accuracy, which was a clear advantage under battle conditions. Bullets were of a deep-cannelure design to hold plenty of lubricant to keep fouling soft and prevent leading of the bore.

### Why the Mystery?

Well it might be asked: Why was this knowledge lost and why do today's loading books offer nothing more than reduced charges for "Trapdoor" Springfields as compared to other 45-70s? The story is probably like this: The perfection of the long-range 500-grain-bullet loading came around 1881. Within a few years, the 30-caliber military rifle with its high-velocity, smokeless-powder cartridge appeared on the scene. Interest in blackpowder arms and shooting rapidly waned. An 1898 smokeless load was produced for the Allin Springfield. It gave excellent results, but as a military arm the Springfield was obsolete. As black and semi-smokeless loadings gave way to smokeless powder, commercial manufacturers found that a harder bullet (later a jacketed bullet) sized to the new standard of .457- to .458-inch, shallower grooves, a smaller flash hole (.081 compared to .097), a different crimp and a cooler-burning primer gave higher velocities with lighter bullets. Also achieved were flatter trajectories, less recoil, lower pressures and equal accuracy.

Thus, modern 45-70 ammunition, while it bears the headstamp .45-70 GOVT, is *really* made to the standards of 45 Winchester, Remington and Marlin sporters, and is for all intents and purposes a different cartridge. The original government-made cartridges were discontinued in the early part of this century as government arsenals undertook production of 30-40 and 30-06 rifle ammunition.

When the 45 Springfields became obsolete, they were dumped on the market at bargain prices—at times, less than a dollar apiece. With surplus ammunition readily available and cheap, few if any shooters bothered to reload. By the 1950s, surplus ammunition was pretty well used up, interest in handloading for the 45 Springfield was minimal, and the chief concern for publishers of reloading manuals was safety with this cartridge in the Springfield action, not performance. Thus, no attempt was made to distinguish the military from the 45-70 sporter cartridge.

While .457-inch jacketed bullets work in the Springfield, accuracy is mediocre and barrel erosion soon occurs, ruining accuracy. In recreating the original ammunition, the Wolfs developed special moulds to reproduce the original bullets. These are offered by Wolf's Western Traders. The 1873 bullet mould by Lee is available from Wolf. NEI also offers a 405-grain mould. The 1881 mould is offered by Rapine. Bullets from Mt. Baldy Bullets sell at this writing at $11 per hundred for the

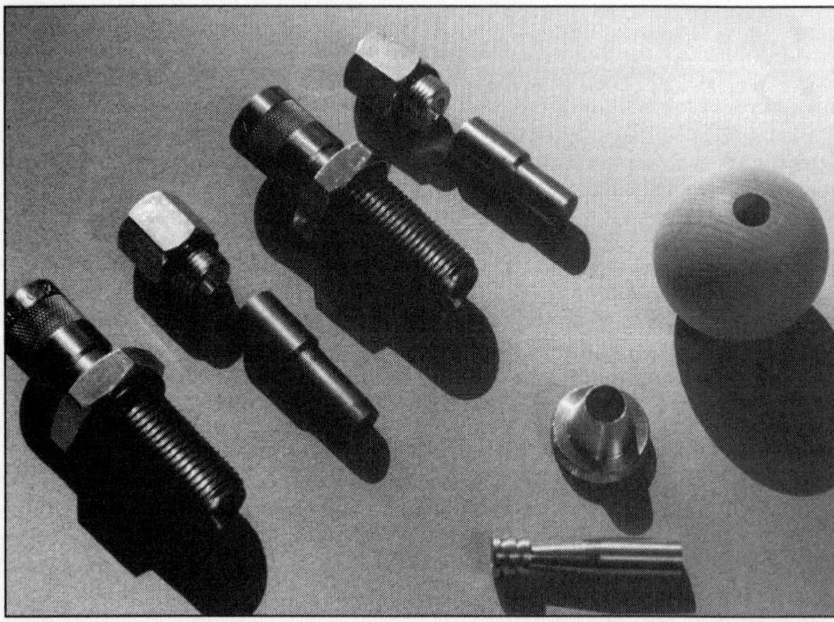

A case expansion die (left) and powder compression die (right) are necessary to reproduce original ammunition. Lyman dies can be used for crimping, but better results can be had with the crimping die Wolf offers. The ball handle, brass guide and jag form the basis of an original, military cleaning rod. The buyer supplies a dowel rod available from Wolf. Dies are by Lee and available only from Wolf.

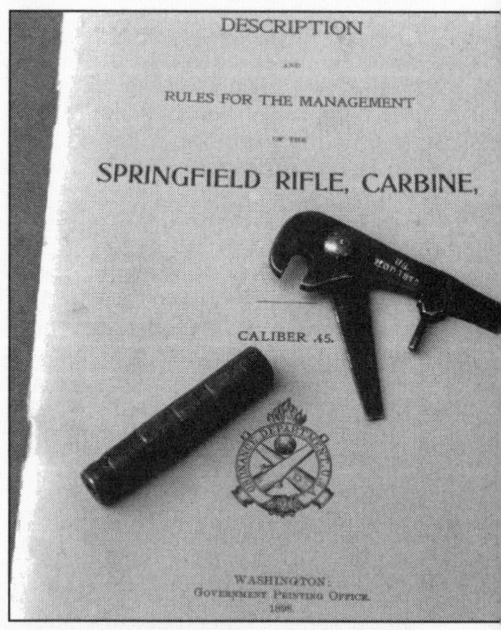


Reprints of original manuals and original accoutrements, including this headless shell extractor and Model 1879 takedown tool, are available from Wolf.

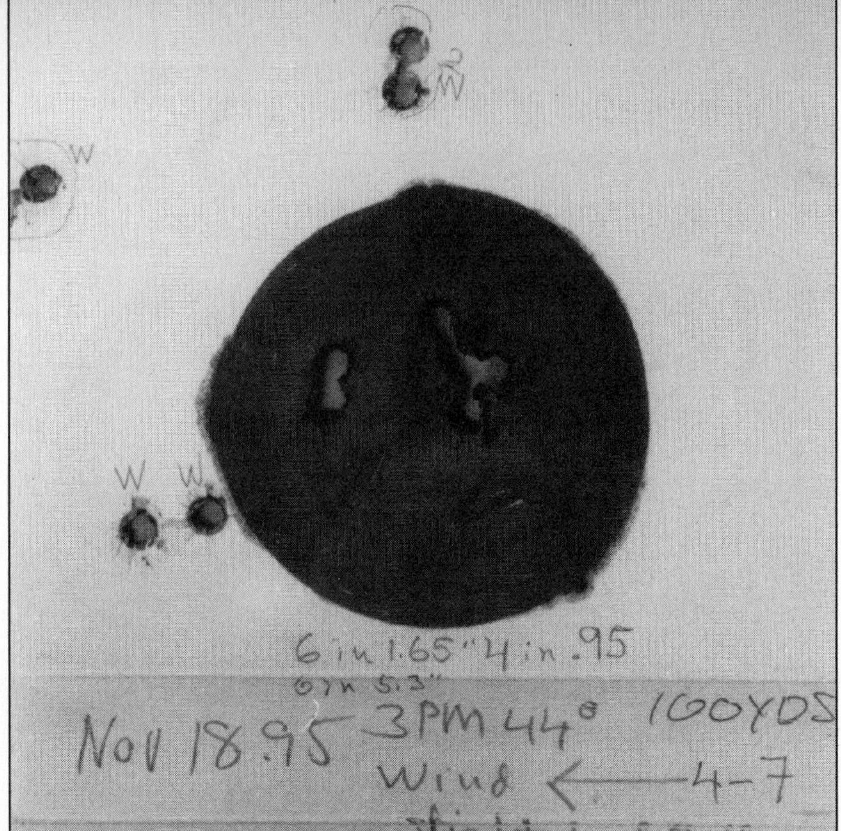


These two groups were fired from the author's M1884 Springfield at 100 yards using an M1881 bullet from a Rapine mould, sized .459-inch. The group in the white measures 5.3-inch, in the black 1.65. The large group was 40.5 grains, the small 41 grains of Accurate Arms 2495BR.

500-grain and $15 for the 405-grain. According to Doug Schoniger, single- and double-cavity moulds for the 500-grain M1881 bullet, cut by SAECO, are available *only* from Mt. Baldy. Special expansion, compression and crimping dies made by Lee are available from Wolf.

### Follow Instructions

Fabricating one's own Springfield ammunition is *advanced reloading*, and the instructions in the Wolfs' book must be followed *carefully*. That means follow *all* the steps and procedures in the *exact* order. In this respect, the Springfield is like a computer—very unforgiving. It works fine if you operate it properly. Deviate just a little bit and the Springfield tends to work *not at all*, as opposed to 45-70 sporters, which may work to some degree with variations in powder type, charge and bullet alloy.

My first inkling of this was when I cooked up the required 20 to 1 lead and tin alloy for the bullets. I used lead plumbing pipe and tin from beer-keg-tap tubing, both recommended by Philip Sharpe in his massive *Complete Guide to Handloading*. There was evidently a small amount of contamination in my components from arsenic, antimony or whatever because, even though the bullets were very soft and cast well, they failed to expand properly in the rifle and piled up lead in the bore.

Two shots with the wrong alloy is all it takes to put a lot of lead in the first 8 inches of barrel, ruining accuracy until it is completely removed. The deep-groove Springfield bore holds such lead very well. Often, this leading is invisible by virtue of being burnished through repeated application of a brush. Even with the proper ammunition, this bore leading will strip bullets and tumble them in flight unless it is completely removed. Brushing and the use of tight patches well saturated with a metal-fouling solvent will eventually remove such lead, but Outers' "Foul Out" electrochemical system is easier. Pure metals are a must! The same is true of lubricants, either commercial or formulated. Those that don't work cake in the barrel and cause leading.

For the modern Springfield shooter, the Wolfs have researched and developed both duplex loads and those using IMR-3031 and SR 4759, which duplicate black and early smokeless loads, without the cleanup problems. In terms of accuracy, results are excellent. I get groups of less than 4 inches and often below 2 inches at 200 yards, which is well within arsenal specifications. With an iron-sighted rifle, that's about as good as I can get.

### Not All Guns Safe

Readers may be wondering at this point about pressures generated using the magnum primers and the .096-inch flash hole they recommend. The answer is yes, pressures are higher, but in line with the specs generated by Frankford Arsenal. In generating their data, the Wolfs had Tom Armbrust of McHenry, Illinois, do the pressure testing on the loadings. In duplicating the 1898 smokeless load, the Wolfs use 40 grains of IMR-3031 for 1425 fps. With the .081-inch flash hole, the average (CUP) was 21,200 with a peak of 25,600. With the .096-inch flash hole, the average was 21,600, the peak 26,700. This was with the smaller-capacity Federal case in a universal receiver, so it tends to reflect higher readings than would probably be generated in an actual rifle. Nevertheless, these are above what many writers recommend as safe limits for the Allin Springfield. The Wolfs noted that *not all guns may be safe with this data*, urging, as does this writer, that the shooter have *any* Springfield he is planning to fire checked by a competent gunsmith first. Guns damaged through corrosion or other abuse may not be serviceable. After all, the newest of these rifles and carbines are a century old!

My own first success using the Wolfs' data came on a miserably cold December afternoon. With 40 grains of IMR-3031 behind a 500-grain Rapine bullet, I put five shots into 3.5 inches at a measured 100 yards before mist, dark and a need for new glasses made further shooting impossible. If you are willing to craft the right ammunition, the Wolf system works.

Ever since the burning of the library of Alexandria, human history has been a story of information discovered, lost, then rediscovered. We can thank Spencer and Pat Wolf for their zest in ballistic archeology in retrieving the original Springfield ammunition from obscurity, and with it the opportunity for today's shooters to enjoy the full potential of these fine old military rifles. With over half a million 45 Springfields produced, there are still quite a few around in good shooting condition. ●

#### Author's Note

Spencer Wolf died in September 1993 after a hard battle with cancer.

*With almost all the author's deer shots coming under 200 yards, why should he lug a big gun? He settled for...*

# THE 30 BENCH REST

## A Most Useful Cartridge

I HAVE A weakness for things compact and efficient. Things well designed. I like sports cars, especially those with smaller engines that are on the cutting edge of design and deliver high horsepower relative to weight, and at the same time just sip gasoline. Ditto for general aviation aircraft. Many go fast, but few do it on a small engine and modest gallons-per-hour fuel consumption. The same basic situation can be found in the world of ballistics. Any bullet in any caliber can be driven at high velocity. Doing it efficiently cuts the field considerably.

Never really having been a magnum person, I started out handloading for rifles years ago with a 308 Winchester in the Ruger M77. The 308 gets much bang for the buck. I bagged a lot of deer with it over the years. When I changed calibers a few years ago, I didn't move up in power, I moved down—to a 250 Ackley Improved. That is a very efficient number that breathes right on the heels of the 257 Ackley Improved and the 25-06, and does it with considerably less powder. Extended barrel life comes along with the package at no extra charge.

What I found from shooting both the 308 and the 250 AI was that they were both excellent long-range cartridges. High-mountain "plinking" at 600 to 1200 yards left me glad not to be on the receiving end of a combination like this at even such extreme distance. I also found that 90 percent of my shots at deer were taken at less than 200 yards, whether in the open spaces here in Colorado or the mesquite country of southern Texas. And as I shoot more, I find myself less interested in even taking shots beyond about 200 yards at big game, even though I do a lot of practice shooting at longer distances. That philosophy gives more clean kills in the long run.

So, here I was with two excellent long-range deer rifles and most of my game shooting at less than 200 yards—and more often less than 100. The 250 AI is a good choice at the shorter ranges, too, because the Nosler Partition bullet tends to bloodshoot less meat. With the 308, I took the chance of losing both shoulders if I wasn't very careful with bullet placement. I began to look for a less powerful 30-caliber replacement for the 308.

(As a side note, early in WWII the German military came to the same conclusion concerning the average

Here pictured second from the left is the 30 BR with its competition (from left): 308 Winchester (7.62 Nato), 7.62x39 Russian and 223 Remington (5.56 NATO).

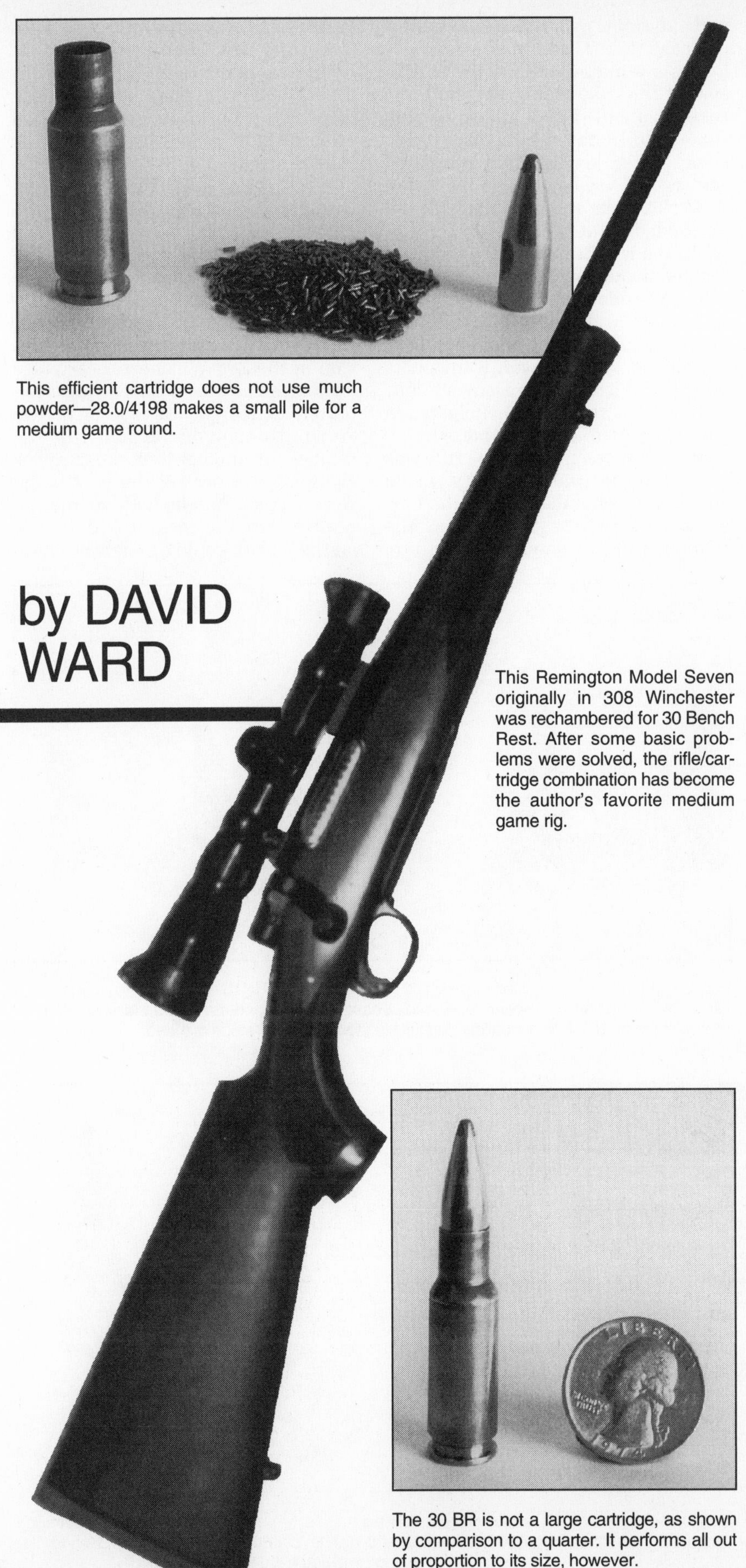

This efficient cartridge does not use much powder—28.0/4198 makes a small pile for a medium game round.

by DAVID WARD

This Remington Model Seven originally in 308 Winchester was rechambered for 30 Bench Rest. After some basic problems were solved, the rifle/cartridge combination has become the author's favorite medium game rig.

The 30 BR is not a large cartridge, as shown by comparison to a quarter. It performs all out of proportion to its size, however.

soldier in the average firefight. Most exchanges occurred at less than 300 meters, and the standard battle cartridge had more power than needed. It was also heavier than necessary, as was the standard battle rifle, and recoil was excessive. They went to the 7.92x33mm Kurz for various uses in 1941, and the rest is, as they say, history.)

My conclusions and requirements seemed to parallel those of most of the military world, so I started in that area with my search. The 7.92 Kurz is, of course, no longer around, and if it were, it would probably be considered underpowered for big game with its short 1.32-inch case. Just not enough room for powder. The Russian answer to the German cartridge, the 7.62x39mm, is of larger capacity and is becoming popular in this country. I seriously considered a Ruger Mini-30 and that would have satisfied my needs quite well, except for one problem. I wanted a short, light, bolt-action rifle.

Here is where things got sticky. The Russian cartridge is offered, or was, in the Mini-Mark X from Interarms. I tried one. It just wasn't the right rifle for me, mostly due to the small size of the bolt handle, so I continued my search. There wasn't much else out there for the Russian.

I looked about for another cartridge that might fill the bill and remembered a writeup about the 308x1.5 or 308 Short. Designed by Frank Barnes in 1961 and chambered in very light rifles, it got rave reviews for performance on varmints and medium game. For my purposes, it had two other major factors going for it—it offered a standard head size and it could be formed easily from 7mm BR brass currently available over the counter. (Actually the 7mm BR brass measures 1.52 inches but loading data for the 30 BR and 308x1.5 are identical.)

I was immediately attracted to the 308 Short because of my penchant for things compact and efficient. According to Barnes, velocities of 2500 could be reached with a 150-grain bullet and 2600 fps with the 125-grain, all from a dinky 27 or 28 grains of 4198 powder. Wonderful! Those velocities were approaching the 300 Savage's. It seemed almost too good to be true...and that was exactly the case. Barnes' velocities were measured in a 24-inch barrel. Hardly an ultralight, compact rifle there. I was thinking more along the lines of 18 inches or so for the barrel.

Where would that length leave those velocities?

There was only one way to find out.

I ordered up a Remington Model Seven in 308 Winchester and got to work. The 30 BR dies are available as a standard item from RCBS, and since I have never had anything less than the finest quality from that company, I ordered a set. They arrived promptly, which was good, because a conversation with the people at Clymer Manufacturing Co. informed me that the 30 BR reamer was not a standard item with them and so would have to be made up from scratch. Could I please send them a loaded round so they could take the dimensions from it. No problem.

I quickly formed fifty cases. I say quickly because it is just that. Run the 7mm BR case over a neck expander and through the sizing die and out comes a 30 BR case. Chamfer the case mouth and you're ready to load. As a matter of fact, the expansion of the case mouth shortens the case to about 1.495 inches, giving some additional time before trimming. After loading five rounds, I sent two off to Clymer, and they went to work on the reamer. Meanwhile I proceeded to load a batch for use when the rifle was ready, which now seemed about two light-years away.

The reamer finally arrived (much to Clymer's credit it did not take nearly as long as it seemed) and both it and the Model Seven went off to 300 Gunsmith here in Denver. They do fine work and have participated in a number of projects with me over the years. A few weeks later, the rifle was ready. All that was necessary was to shorten the chamber end of the barrel a half-inch or so and run the reamer in. Easy enough? Not quite. When I picked it up, I luckily brought ten of the new cartridges to testfire. Every one of the cases came out with a neat little ring just down the neck from the mouth. It had expanded ever so slightly more behind the ring than in front.

After some head scratching and chin rubbing, we came up with the answer. Clymer, using the loaded round, made up the reamer to cut the case neck dimension of .3335-inch (that loaded round measures .3320-inch at the neck). From my Speer Reloading Manual, the neck dimension of the 308 Winchester cartridge for which the Model Seven was originally chambered was .343-inch. The gunsmith thought he had run the reamer far enough to make sure the shoulder and neck of the new round were correct. And he had. We did not realize that the case neck diameter on the 30 BR would be slightly small-

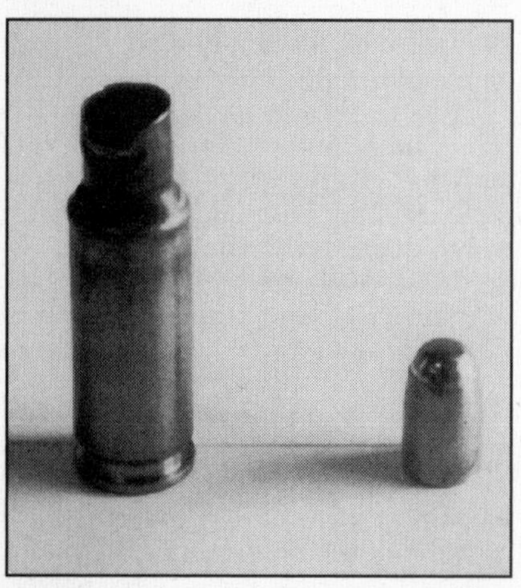

The hazards of working with a sharply square-based bullet like the Mauser 86-grain. Even chamfering does not ensure against case mouth collapse and loss of the case.

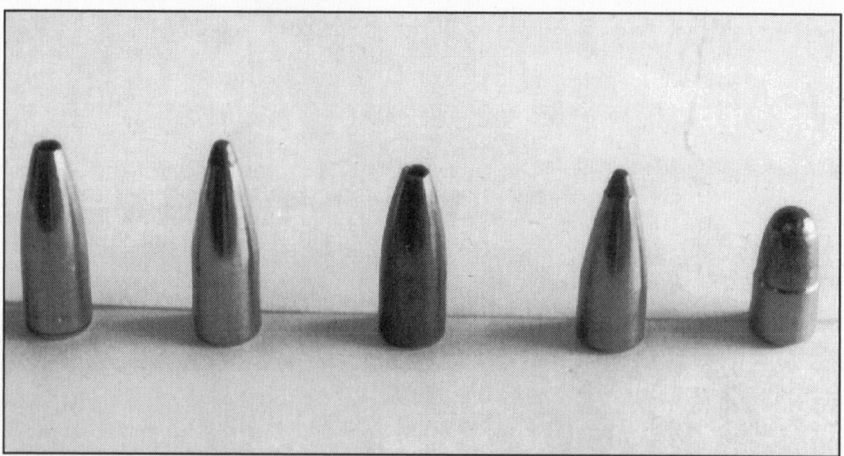

Bullets used for testing (from left): Speer 130 HP, Hornady 130 SP (Single Shot Pistol), Sierra 110 HP, Hornady 110 SP and Speer 100 Plinker. These bullets all perform well at the velocities possible with the 30 BR. Heavier bullets with thicker jackets are not recommended.

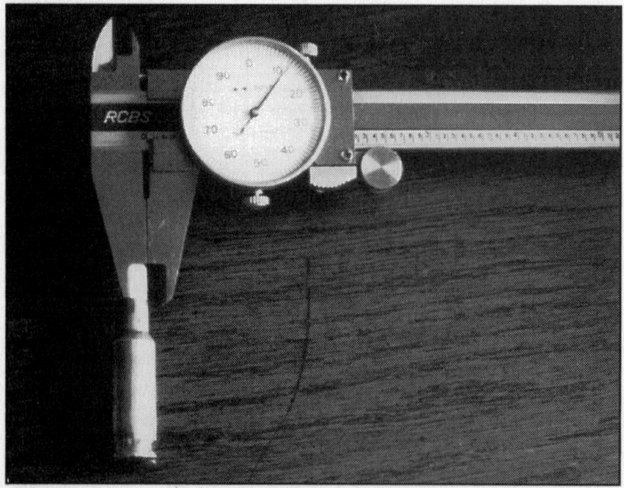


The 30 BR brass is relatively thin, measuring .012-inch at the mouth. That means extra care is required during bullet seating to make sure that case mouths and shoulders do not collapse.

Case forming is a simple process. Run the 7mm BR case (left) through the 30 BR sizer die and you have a 30 BR case (center). Chamfer the case mouth, prime, load and you have the final product.

A look at the correct position of the rear of the 222 Remington magazine spring on the floorplate that will ensure proper feeding. The author used small amounts of masking tape to hold springs, follower, etc., in their proper positions. A more permanent method of attachment will be decided upon later, possibly silicone caulk or glue.

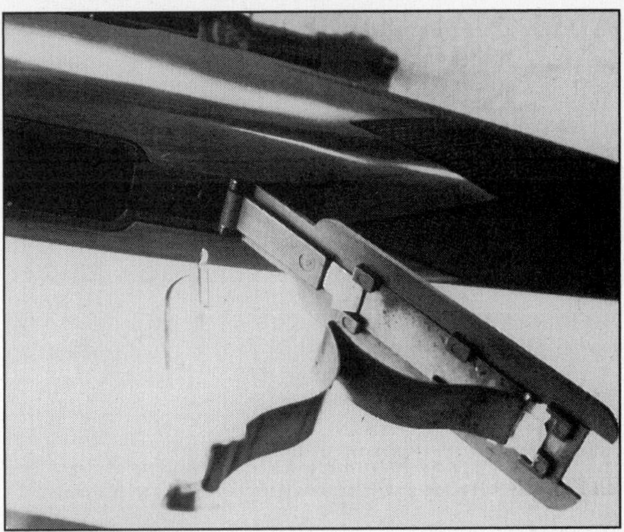

A small fold of masking tape at the front of the magazine spring helps assure no forward movement, which would affect proper feeding.

The 308 Winchester magazine follower had to be shortened about 1/2-inch (from the rear of the follower only) so that the 222 magazine spacer would fit into the magazine well behind it. Don't forget to file it smooth so that it slides easily up and down against the spacer.

er because the Bench Rest brass is thinner than standard 308 Winchester brass. My batch of Bench Rest brass measures .012-inch in thickness as opposed to the .015-inch of Winchester brass. The problem was easily solved: We ran the reamer in as far as was necessary to remove all traces of the old neck and trimmed and threaded the barrel, and everything was fine. Fortunately, there was enough bulk at the chamber end of the barrel to do so. With that problem taken care of, I mounted a Redfield Golden Five Star Compact variable 2-7x scope in Redfield mounts on the little Remington and was off and shooting. I have always found Redfield scopes and products to be of excellent quality, so I stuck with what I knew. The final length on the barrel was 17.5 inches with an overall length of 36.75 inches, making this one compact rifle. And considering that the muzzle diameter of the barrel is only .545-inch, the gun shoots very well. But I'll get to that in a minute.

In developing loads for the 30 BR, I started with Frank Barnes' original 308x1.5-inch loads. He used a number of powders including 3031, 4198, 4064, Ball C and H-380. I eliminated 3031, H-380 and 4064, because they did not seem to give efficient results, but added AA 2230 and H-335. I could not lay my hands on any Reloder 7 or AA 1680, which I would have liked to include in the testing, especially since AA 1680 was developed specifically for the 7.62x39.

Barnes' loads, which are listed in both his book, *Cartridges of the World*, and in P.O. Ackley's *Handbook for Shooters and Reloaders* Vol. I, show the best performance by far with 4198. A load of 27 grains bumps the 150-grain bullet along at 2532 fps, and 28 grains moves the 125-grain slug at 2641 fps from his 24-inch barrel. I feel that the 150-grain bullet is more weight than is necessary for the type of shooting that this cartridge is designed for. Besides, expansion is a question at velocities in the low 2000s or less at impact. Consequently, I concentrated my work on bullet weights in the 110-130-grain range. They do not take up as much powder space and perform nicely, especially those designed for use in the big single shot pistols.

I started my work with 4198, and sure enough, it was a good performer. With the 150-grain Speer BT (for reference) and 27 grains of powder I got

2308 fps. Not bad for 17.5 inches of barrel. Working with Hornady's 130-grain Single Shot Pistol bullet, my max load was 28.5 grains of 4198, one-half grain more than Barnes. Velocity was 2442 fps, just 31 fps more than the Barnes max load of 28 grains. Not really worth the trouble, so I stuck with the 28-grain load. Coincidentally, that load gave the best accuracy, settling in right at 2 inches at 100 yards (remember that skinny barrel). The 110-grain Sierra HP stepped along at a sparkling 2535 fps with a max load of 28.5 grains of 4198. Case head expansion indicated that Barnes was right on with that load, too.

Almost no pressure test results are available for non-standard cartridges, so I testfired all my max loads eight times per case. There were no signs of excess pressure on any of the cases—no expanded primer pockets, no indication of imminent case head separation, no stretching.

The author settled on two loads, one with the 130-grain Hornady SP bullet designed for single shot pistols and 28.0/4198 for big game, and the Sierra 110-grain HP and 37.2/H-335 for varmints.

Right here I need to stop and discuss the only serious problem encountered with the 30 BR, and it will occur with any conversion based on a short, fat case: proper cartridge feeding. The case would not feed with the standard 308 follower. I called Tim McCormick at Remington's custom shop, because they had made a brief run of Model Sevens in 7mm BR. Bad news. They essentially stopped making the rifle in that caliber because they could not consistently make it feed properly.

I knew that the first thing needed was a 222 Remington magazine spacer to shorten the length of the magazine. But then the 308 follower would not fit, nor would the longer magazine spring. A bit of cut and patch was going to be necessary. Tim was kind enough to help me round up some extra springs of both sizes (222 and 308) and the magazine block. I got to work.

First, I shortened the 308 follower (from the back, not the front) so it would fit into the magazine with the spacer installed. I smoothed the edges where it had been cut. Then I cut off about 1/2-inch of the 308 magazine spring and put the whole thing together with the spacer tucked in the back. If I inserted more than one round in the magazine, the loads would dip either forward or to the rear and would not feed. I went ahead with testing, loading each round singly, but meanwhile reminding myself that a rifle that does not function is not worth much.

I took the assembly apart and put it back together at least a dozen times. Then the 222 springs arrived and into the rifle one went. I could get the thing to feed a full magazine once, sometimes. Progress, but not much. Part of the problem was that the spacer would slip down with the first group of cartridges, and that fouled things up. A wad of masking tape solved that problem. Take it apart. Put it together. Load the magazine. Unload. Take it apart. I felt like I was in the Marine Corps again.

Then I saw it. The spring was moving in both the follower and the floorplate. If it moved too far forward in either place, the backs of the cartridges in the magazine did not get enough support, sagged downward and did not feed. More masking tape was applied, and suddenly it all worked! With the rear of the spring flush with the back of the follower and about 1/4-inch to the front of the brackets at the back of the floorplate, the rifle would feed perfectly every time. And has ever since.

In order to more permanently attach the spring and the spacer, I'm going to try clear silicone caulk or maybe glue of some type. The point is that, with everything in its proper place, it feeds perfectly. One other thing. Now that you know what to do, the whole process of filing, fitting and attaching described above will take

**30 BENCH REST LOAD DATA**

| —Bullet— Wgt. Grs. | Type | Powder | Max./Load (grs.) | Velocity (fps) |
|---|---|---|---|---|
| 86 | Mauser | 4198 | 28.2 | 2701 |
| 100 | Speer Plinker | 4198 | 28.5 | 2594 |
| 110 | Sierra HP | 4198 | 28.5 | 2535 |
| | | H-335 | 37.2 | 2493 |
| | | BLC-2 | 37.0 | 2402 |
| | | AA 2230 | 35.5 | 2497 |
| 130 | Hornady SP | 4198 | 28.0 | 2411 |
| | | H-335 | 36.5 | 2444 |
| | | BLC-2 | 36.5 | 2358 |
| | | AA 2230 | 34.0 | 2394 |
| 150 | Speer SPBT | 4198 | 27.0 | 2308 |

All velocity measurements taken 10 feet from muzzle with a Competition Electronics Pro-Tach chronometer, and are an average of two five-shot strings. Remington cases. CCI 400 primers. Temperature approximately 81 degrees F.

The author with the completed Model Seven. It is an accurate, lightweight, handy rifle suitable for varmints and medium game.

you less than thirty minutes. There is no brain damage involved, just some fine tuning.

Back to the loading of the 30 BR.

I could have stopped right where I was because the performance was everything that I was looking for, but I wanted flexibility in powder selection. In addition, I couldn't believe that 4198 was the only powder that would give top velocities in the 30 BR. Besides, I like to handload. That's the point, right? The accompanying chart shows that the other powders tested were right up there with 4198 in performance. With both bullet weights, maximum velocities ran surprisingly close with any powder. It becomes more of a choice based on which powder/bullet combination your particular rifle prefers for best accuracy. I settled on the 130-grain Hornady and 28 grains of 4198, and the 110 Sierra HP and 37.2 grains of H-335. The latter load delivers 2493 fps and groups in just under 2 inches. Loads for lighter-weight bullets are listed in Barnes' data, and I did some preliminary work with an 86-grain Mauser bullet. It shot very well with 28.2 grains of 4198, but loading the sharply square-based bullet was a nightmare. Even with a good case-mouth chamfering, the bullet did not want to seat straight, and I lost several of the thin-walled BR cases when the case mouth collapsed. The 100-grain Speer Plinker with its rounder bottom corners would work well, but it is close enough to the Sierra HP that I didn't bother with it. I tend to be a one- or two-load person for a hunting rifle, preferably with an obviously different-looking bullet for the second load. That way there is never any confusion as to which load I am shooting. Besides, round-nosed bullets aren't as efficient.

Two-MOA groups are more than acceptable for a hunting rifle, especially for an under-7-pound rifle with a pencil-thin barrel. But the 30 BR has an accuracy potential which I feel is going to waste here. Down the road a bit, I intend to put an 18-inch medium-weight barrel on the Model Seven and see just how well it really can shoot.

Meanwhile, as I finish writing this, I have just returned from a pronghorn hunt. The little 30 BR does perform. A neck shot taken at about 125 yards dropped a nice buck like a sack of potatoes. A several-hundred-yard stalk to make the shot brought out the best in Remington's lightweight rifle. It didn't weigh me down or catch on the sagebrush as I crawled the last 50 yards. As a matter of fact, it is fast becoming my favorite hunting rifle and will be attending the November mule deer hunt this year in lieu of the 250 Ackley.

If you think you might like to try an efficient little cartridge that delivers a lot of bang for the buck, take a shot at the 30 Bench Rest. ●

**B**IG-BORE RIFLES were popular in the late 19th and early 20th centuries, but after WWII no lever guns larger than 35-caliber were manufactured. The concept that "faster is better" became quite popular, with Roy Weatherby probably the leading advocate of this school of thought. As one who has taken a lot of game with Weatherby calibers, I can't deny they give me an edge on extremely long shots. In fact, that is why I selected the 300 Weatherby for certain Western hunts. But I am from Pennsylvania, and most of our shots throughout the East are not more than 100 yards, so this is "lever gun country."

In the mid-'60s to fill what was a void in big-bore lever-action cartridges, Marlin introduced a new "stretched out" big bore by adding almost an inch to the 44 Magnum case and keeping its mouth diameter the same. The new cartridge was called the 444 Marlin, and the rifle to handle it the Model 444; it was basically their long-popular M336.

What made this combination special? Marlin marketed it as the most powerful lever action ever made, pointing out that it had $1\frac{1}{2}$ tons of energy at the muzzle with its 240-grain bullet. They also stated that it was intended for hunting any North American game. However, its 240-grain "handgun" bullet quickly became a problem as it was not designed for the velocity this rifle was capable of delivering.

Nevertheless, it attracted attention. For instance, in the *Hodgdon Data Manual No. 26,* it says: "Few of our pure woods rifles qualify as suitable for hunting all big game from deer to elk and moose with factory loaded ammunition. The 444 Marlin is one that does." That alone says a lot!

In 1972, Marlin went a step further in big-bore cartridges and chambered the old reliable 45-70 Government in another modified 336 action, marketing it as the Model 1895. Most agreed it was a good idea to revive the 45-70, but this cartridge became the major competitor of Marlin's own 444, so their action in this situation seems rather strange.

I became acquainted with the 444 in 1969. After some familiarity shooting with it and because I prefer optics on a hunting rifle, I mounted a Bausch & Lomb 2.5-8x, which I still have on it today. It was easy to install, a statement that can't be

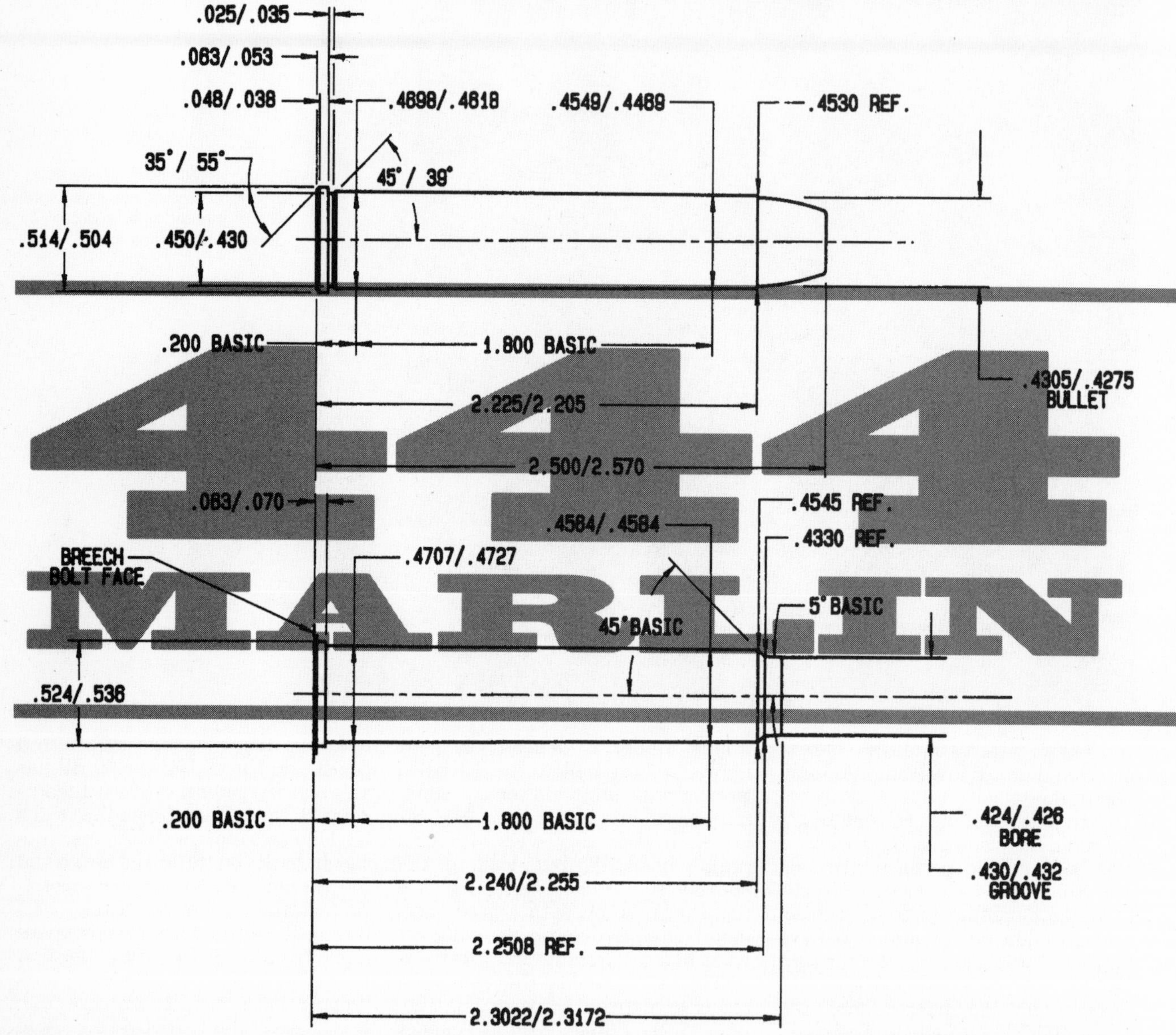

On my first hunt at White Oak Plantation in Alabama, I harvested this buck with the 444 Marlin rifle at about 125 yards. One shot with the Hornady 265-grain bullet brought him down.

# A HARD-HITTER IN RIFLE OR HANDGUN

by DR. GEORGE E. DVORCHAK, JR.

The Marlin 444 (top) sports a 24-inch barrel; the handgun is the SSK T/C Contender with a 14-inch barrel.

made about an earlier powerful lever action, the top-ejecting M71 348 Winchester. The scope made me quickly realize the 444 was an accurate woods cartridge.

One problem in the 444's early days, as previously alluded to, centered on its 240-grain frangible handgun bullets. Out of a rifle barrel, these bullets averaged about 2300 fps, while the same projectile from a 7½-inch 44 Magnum produced about 1400 fps. This big difference ultimately affected the field performance of the bullet, which had been designed for the lower velocity.

Hornady came to the rescue by producing a 265-grain flatpoint with their efficient Interlock design. It was specifically intended for the faster velocity of the new cartridge in the 444 Marlin rifle. Later, Hornady and Speer both added 300-grain bullets. These two heavyweights have two cannelures, and the forward one should be used for crimping, so OAL cartridge length is OK in the rifle's action. All have flat points, which are more efficient at rifle velocities than hollowpoints that tend to shatter and cause shallow wounds.

(A spitzer bullet, although it would work safely in a single shot handgun, was out of the question since the 444 Marlin uses a tubular magazine. Obviously, placing a cartridge with a pointed bullet against the primer of another would not be safe. With recoil, that primer could be detonated to create a chain reaction, which could result in injury or death to the shooter.)

Few will deny that the 444 in a rifle is a fine woods outfit for deer, bear and moose. Some went further. They saw the potential of the 444 Marlin in a handgun, specifically the Thompson/Center Contender.

### The SSK Hand Cannons

A few years after the 444's introduction, my good friend J.D. Jones, who heads SSK Industries, realized the potential of this case as a basis for other cartridges. In 1978, he developed his most popular big game wildcat, the 375 JDJ. He did this by necking down a 444 Marlin case. No fire-forming was necessary. Other cartridges formed from 444 Marlin brass would soon follow. Called the SSK Hand Cannon Cartridges, they are the 309, 8mm, 338 #2, 358, 9.3mm, 375, 411, 416 and the now-obsolete 430.

Some handgunners commented that big-bore revolvers already were available in the standard 41 and 44 Magnums, so why a handgun in a

The 44 Magnum (from left) and two other cartridges using the 44-caliber bullet: the 445 Super Mag (made from 30-40 Krag brass) and a factory Remington 240-grain 444 Marlin.

The 300-grain Speer (left) comes with two cannelures. When using it in the 444 Marlin, you should crimp into the top cannelure (right). The one in the middle was crimped into the wrong cannelure; this makes the cartridge too long to be chambered properly.

444-based cartridge? Well, anyone who prefers a handgun with power that goes beyond what the above two are safely capable of producing will find the single shot the best option. For these people, Thompson/Center offers rugged and accurate guns in a wide variety of calibers. If you want a big wildcat, an SSK Hand Cannon in 444 Marlin is an excellent selection. It's accurate and powerful, and has controllable recoil if fitted with an SSK Arrestor Brake. After a quarter-century of experience with this cartridge in a rifle and for the past eight years in a Hand Cannon, I can truly

The 444 bullets used to gather the data (from left): a Hornady 200-grain HP and 265-grain FP, a Speer 300-grain Plated SP and a Freedom Arms 300-grain JFP.

To load the 444 Marlin, a three-die set is required. The second-stage die is used to open up the case mouth so the bullet will not crush the case.

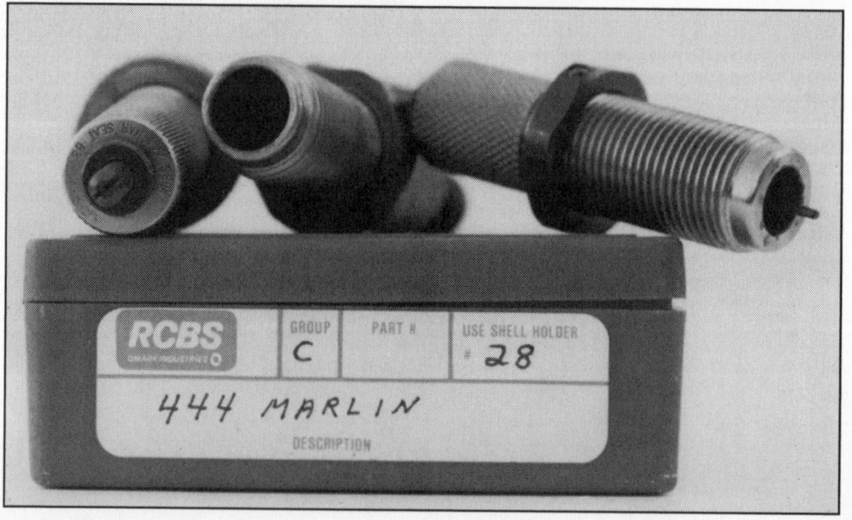

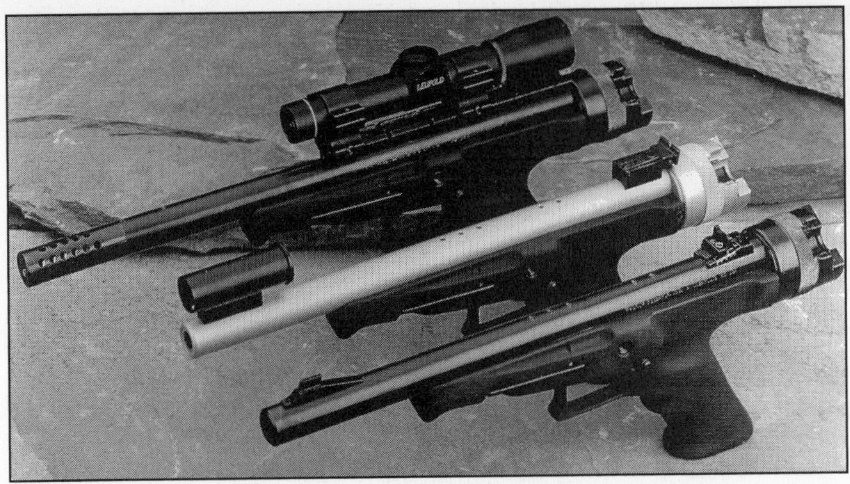


The other 444 Marlin handgun worth noting is the single shot Lone Eagle from Magnum Research. All new guns come with a threaded muzzle, so if the owner desires a recoil-reducing device, highly recommended and shown on the scoped handgun, then pick up one from the dealer and screw it onto the factory-threaded barrel.

say that this is an excellent choice in either.

The 444 Marlin cartridge is not available in the Contender from the T/C factory or their custom shop at Fox Ridge Outfitters. To get one, you must place an order with J.D. Jones at SSK.

According to J.D., the 444 Marlin is a popular chambering, so barrel delivery is only a few weeks. If for any reason that chambering is depleted, it will take J.D.'s craftsmen six to eight weeks to make one up on a Shilen barrel blank. In today's world, that is still not bad time.

The basis for a custom 444 Marlin pistol is the Contender's well-designed and versatile frame. It takes only a minute to change barrels on it, essentially giving you a new handgun. I recommend a 14-inch barrel for the 444 chambering. It gives a bit more velocity, and the extra weight steadies the gun and dampens recoil. This length is also closer to what the 444 was originally intended for as a rifle cartridge. SSK uses only premium-grade barrels with the lug welded on by an electron-beam process. The lug is then heat-treated by the same process T/C uses at their factory. I urge you to have the barrel fitted with an SSK Arrestor. Without this, a 444 Contender's recoil is brutal.

## Lone Eagle

I had one of the first Lone Eagle single shot handguns from Magnum Research to test in this caliber. It's a beautifully built gun and provides another option for hunters to consider. However, it did not have a brake, and after only two or three shots my hand hurt. With an arrestor, which is available, recoil is cut about in half, so it's not difficult to shoot. Also, you should be aware that when you order, say, a 14-inch barrel with arrestor, you are getting 14 inches of barrel but only 13 inches with rifling, because the last inch with those little holes to vent gases is also an expansion chamber. I remind purists who would prefer a true 14-inch tube that the loss of 1-inch of rifling translates into only a few foot-seconds decrease in velocity. The game will never notice the difference, but your arm will.

## Ballistics and Sights

With the load I settled on for my 444 SSK T/C Contender, 45.0 grains of H-4198 with a 265-grain Hornady bullet and Federal 210 primer, I get a velocity of about 1866 fps. With a 100-yard zero, this bullet drops only 5 inches at 150 yards and about 14 at 200. At 300 yards, it prints more than 4 feet below the point of aim. Obviously, this load is most effective within 200 yards.

The same load in the rifle drops some 3 inches at 150 yards, 10 at 200. At 250, drop is 22 inches (6 inches less than the handgun). Here, the rifle's energy decreases to about 924 fpe, and the handgun is down to 750. At 300 yards, the 265-grain bullet from the rifle drops 39 inches and from the handgun plummets about 51.

With these numbers embedded in your brain, the only thing left is to hold properly and squeeze the trigger when the opportunity comes up. Remember—unlike a flat-shooting 300 Weatherby, the heavy 444 bullet drops off very quickly beyond 150 yards.

To accurately place a bullet, good sights are a must. I highly recommend optics on any handgun or rifle used for hunting. With optics, you can see the game better, as well as any obstruction along the bullet's path. For some time now, I have been using a Bausch & Lomb 2-6x. It works fine.

At top power, the eye relief of some handgun variables sometimes suffers. The B&L has a constant eye relief of 20 inches. Other good handgun variables I have used are available from Simmons, Weaver, Burris and Redfield, and doubtless there are others. The nice thing about a variable is that it can be carried on the lowest setting for a fast, close shot, then with the twist of a ring you have higher power for a long chance.

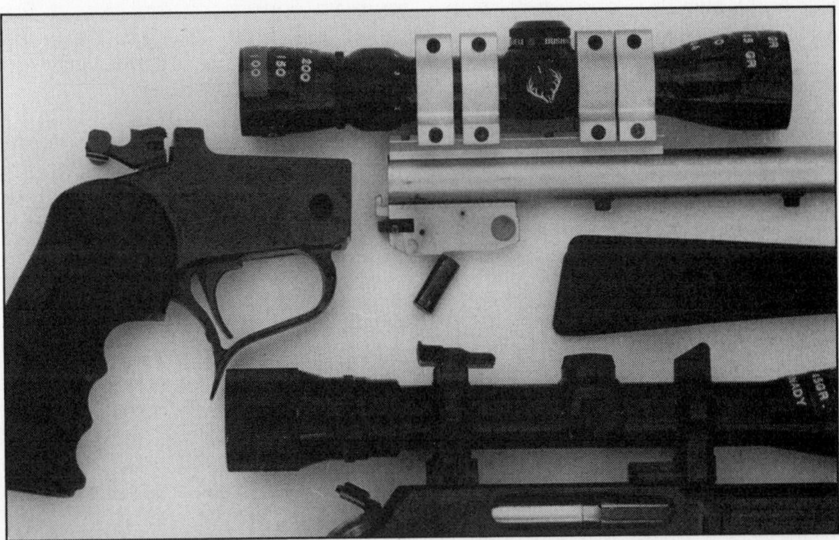

To give support to and hold it on a big-bore handgun, three or four scope rings are recommended. Shown is the SSK T'SOB mount and four rings. On the Marlin is the Scope-Site system available from Millett. With it you have a set of open sights over the scope that are quite accurate.

At Hamilton's range, I used an Oehler 35-P chronograph to measure velocities from the rifle and handgun. (Photo by Steve Hamilton)

Without good mounts, scopes can be unreliable. On the SSK T/C 444 Marlin, I used and liked SSK's T'SOB mount. It is securely fastened to the barrel and takes up to four scope rings. It's a good answer for heavy recoiling handguns.

### Ammo

The three-shot groups listed in Table 1 were fired at 90 yards. The Marlin rifle has a 24-inch barrel, the SSK T/C Contender a 14-inch including a 1-inch arrestor. Chronograph was an Oehler 35-P, and temperature about 40 degrees Fahrenheit.

Be aware that using one company's bullet with another's loading data could result in excess pressure for a load. For example, Speer info for their bullets lists a diameter of .429, and Hornady gives .430. Both are for the 444 Marlin, but they are different diameters. Not much, but possibly enough to cause trouble with some loads. So check your components and data carefully, and stick to loads from current manuals.

I have been using 45.0 grains of H-4198 with a Federal 210 primer and 265-grain Hornady bullet. I have charged 100 cases up to eight times each with no problem except for minor stretching. Once a case exceeds 2.225, all should be trimmed back to 2.115, which I have done.

It's also important to adhere to the manuals' maximum cartridge length. If the bullet is not seated deeply enough and properly crimped, the cartridge will not completely chamber. When this happens and you try to extract it, the bullet will usually stick in the leade and the powder will probably dump into the action. That's enough to make anyone say nasty words, especially on a dark cold December morning, so check things out at your loading bench, early.

In my rifle, the above load produces about 2150 fps, and in the 14-inch handgun, approximately 1850. I recommend that you stick with the 265- or 300-grain bullets in the handgun. The 300-grain works fine in some rifles, but not all, due to the slow (1:38) twist. I'm fortunate because it's accurate in mine—usually about 2½ inches, often 1½, on my 90-yard setup. J.D. Jones told me he usually uses 1:18 or 1:20 twist, depending on the bullet weight a customer intends to use.

The 444 Marlin in either rifle or handgun is an excellent woods cartridge for most of North America's big game species. I found it to be accurate and, in the SSK Contender, of tolerable recoil so long as an Arrestor was fitted. Without such a brake, recoil can be quite unpleasant. Another positive feature is that factory loaded ammo is available from Remington, if needed.

**TABLE 1: 444 MARLIN LOADS**

| Firearm | —Bullet— Wgt. Grs. | Type | Load (Grs./Powder) | Primer | Velocity (fps) | Group (ins.) |
|---|---|---|---|---|---|---|
| Marlin | 240 | Remington factory | — | — | 2235 | 1.75 |
| T/C | 240 | Remington factory | — | — | 2016 | 2.5 |
| Marlin | 265 | Hornady | 45.0/H-4198 | Fed 210 | 2150 | 2.0 |
| T/C | 265 | Hornady | 45.0/H-4198 | Fed 210 | 1866 | 1.75 |
| Marlin | 300 | Speer | 55.0/H-335 | CCI 200 | 1933 | 2.0 |
| T/C | 300 | Speer | 55.0/H-335 | CCI 200 | 1758 | 2.5 |
| Marlin | 300 | FA | 57.5/BLC-2 | CCI 200 | 2080 | 3.0 |
| T/C | 300 | FA | 57.5/BLC-2 | CCI 200 | 1910 | 2.5 |
| Marlin | 200 | Hornady* | 56.0/AA1680 | CCI 200 | 2590 | 2.0 |
| T/C | 200 | Hornady* | 56.0/AA1680 | CCI 200 | 2261 | 2.0 |

*Note: The last load with the Hornady 200-grain hollowpoint is recommended only for varmints such as coyotes or groundhogs, not for deer or larger game. Bullets of this weight and style, due to the comparatively high velocity obtainable in this cartridge, often fragment violently without penetrating.

# 6mm Bullet Effectiveness

by THOMAS SMITH

**Despite the accuracy and light recoil of various 6mm-chambered hunting rifles, they are often considered 50-percent deer guns...unless you use the right bullet.**

THE TWO MOST popular 6mm cartridges have been on the American hunting scene for forty-plus years now. Very few cartridges have enjoyed such acceptance and widespread use as the 243 Winchester. The 6mm Remington, although not quite as popular as the 243, certainly has its advocates, as does the 240 Weatherby. All in all, it's hard to argue that 6mms aren't popular with hunters.

But that doesn't mean that everything is all roses with these relative smallbores. In spite of widespread successful use, many hunters of experience acknowledge that the 6mms at times do not perform as intended.

Over the years, I've used 6mm cartridges fairly extensively. I've also observed the effects of their use by many other hunters. Much of my experience comes from observation of factory ammunition and reloads with conventionally constructed bullets. Sometimes the 6s' effect is immediate and dramatic, and sometimes it is considerably less so.

In recent years, many new 6mm bullets have been made available to the hunter. These are of modern design and construction, and are claimed to offer significant improvements in bullet performance. Because of the impetus provided by the availability of these newer bullets, I decided to test a number of the readily available 6mm bullets—both new and traditional designs—under standard conditions. I hoped to be able to measure performance differences among them. In turn, I hoped the results would help identify which, if any, would be expected to be more effective in the field.

## Measuring Effectiveness Difficult

How quickly a bullet kills is determined solely by the amount and kind of body tissue it destroys or interferes with. A lot of factors have an influence on this. Bullet expansion, penetration, location of the wound, and the species of animal are important, but are not the only parameters that affect killing effectiveness.

Measuring bullet effectiveness is very difficult. Not only are there many variables, but the expense of a reasonably thorough undertaking is considerable. The ideal test material is live animal tissue of the kind the bullet is designed for. However, it's obviously difficult to shoot enough animals to collect an appropriate number of measurements. Domestic animal carcasses are a possibility, but there are readily apparent difficulties getting these also.

The best alternative is a substitute material that behaves enough like live animal tissue to provide valid comparisons. Ballistic gelatin is widely used in industry circles for bullet testing. It's probably the best artificial material available, in part no doubt because it is derived from animal tissue itself. While fairly expensive, its biggest drawback is that, unless you have somewhat sophisticated facilities, it is difficult to work with.

Because of the ease of handling, availability, and small expense, water-soaked paper materials have long been used by amateur experimenters. Water-soaked newsprint is heavy but fairly easy to manage and transport, and bullets fired into it

These three hunting rifles are popular 6mm-chambered choices, but without the right bullet, they may be marginal for big game (from top): Winchester Model 70 Classic Featherweight, Weatherby Mark V Deluxe and Ruger Model 77 Mark II All-Weather Stainless.

are easily recovered. A uniform texture and composition can be easily maintained, and this helps ensure comparable test conditions and repeatability.

Telephone directories were used for all tests reported here. Directories were submerged in water for at least six hours to ensure saturation. Bullets fired into wet paper can be easily recovered by just removing some books or pages. The saturation level and paper compression were kept as uniform as possible, and the paper was replaced frequently.

I gathered samples of twenty-eight different bullets ranging from 75 to 105 grains. They were selected because of their known or advertised suitability for big game, as opposed to varmints. All those reported on are available either in factory ammunition and/or as separate components. Granted, some are much more readily obtainable than others. The data presented are based on averages of five bullets. From a statistical standpoint, larger sample sizes would be desirable, but I seriously doubt if the results would change significantly. The data presented here show an accurate comparison of the performance of one bullet relative to the others.

Muzzle velocity is important, but impact velocity more directly affects bullet performance. Obviously, due to velocity differences, a bullet will have a different effect on a game animal at short range rather than long. All other factors being equal, differences in performance are almost entirely attributable to impact velocity. Average bullet impact velocities for 80/85-grain, 90/96-grain and 100-grain bullets at 100 yards were typical of the caliber and were measured or estimated to be 3120, 3028 and 2870 fps respectively. At 200 yards, these same groups of bullets were estimated to have velocities of 2816, 2782 and 2675 fps. Velocities for the 75- and 105-grain bullets were proportionately higher and lower.

### Construction Important

Of particular importance in determining how well a bullet performs, however, is how it is constructed and what it is constructed of. Hunting bullets historically and typically have a relatively soft lead-alloy core and a copper-alloy jacket. Depending on the manufacturer and, of course, the use the bullet is designed for, bullet cores range from pure lead to those hardened with antimony and other elements, or perhaps by heat treatment. Jacket alloys vary from manufacturer to manufacturer and may include various amounts of zinc, tin and nickel, but the basic ingredient remains the same, copper. Bonded cores and jackets, divided or partitioned cores, bullet tip inserts, thickened jackets, features which help lock the jacket and core, homogeneous composition, and combinations of these features are all used by different manufacturers.

As part of my investigations, jacket and core weights for each bullet were obtained and compared with penetration, weight retention and expansion. In order to do this, the cores and jackets must be separated. Fortunately, there are relatively easy processes for doing this. In my tests, I used a dilute solution of nitric acid to dissolve the jacket, leaving the lead core. Check with your chemist friend or go to the library before handling acids. With nitric or any other acid, you run the risk of violent splattering, potentially into your eyes, face, clothes and other unwanted places. Other experimenters have separated jackets and cores by using a torch to melt out the lead. I haven't tried this, but it sounds like a workable approach. With this method, it may be more difficult to measure jacket thickness, though.

Some judgement and subjectivity must be used in measuring jacket thickness because of the tapering configurations of at least some bullet jackets. In my tests, I attempted to measure at a location just forward of the cannelure, if present, or just forward of the base of the core in bullets with abbreviated cores like the Jensen, Hirtenberger and Trophy Bonded. In others, the approximate midpoint of the bullet was used.

In determining and evaluating bullet performance, retained weight and penetration are important. Retained weight gives some measure of a bullet's ability to hold together under the tremendous stresses it is subjected to upon and subsequent to impact. Weight retention also usually translates to greater penetration. Within reason, penetration is a desirable attribute in a game bullet and of considerable importance in its ultimate effectiveness. Construction of a bullet is important in that at a given velocity a bullet that loses the least weight will "hold together," overcome more resistance and penetrate farther than one that doesn't.

Another element is even more telling and of potentially greater value in evaluating a bullet's performance. That factor is the size, location, shape and configuration of the wound cavity, and the adjacent tissue damage created by the expanding bullet. Measuring these wound channels, and the associated tissue damage, is difficult in the extreme. I've fiddled around with this to a certain degree, but let me tell you, however it's done, it's imprecise and messy.

One measurement that gives some insight into wound channel characteristics and hence killing performance, especially when used in conjunction with retained weight and penetration, is bullet expansion. This can be defined as the cross-sectional area of the nose of a bullet recovered after impact. As a bullet expands, it causes progressively more tissue damage. As its frontal area increases, however, resistance to it also increases as penetration is slowed or reduced. In practical field terms, the ideal is a bullet that will provide maximum expansion along with maximum weight retention and penetration on the category of game it was designed for.

Cross-sectional areas of recovered bullets are presented in Table 1. While not all bullets expand to perfect "mushrooms," for purposes of comparison all bullets were assumed to expand to form a circle, the diameter of which was obtained by averaging three or more cross-sectional measurements of each bullet. The area of this circle was calculated from the average diameters. While perhaps not ideal, I feel this method of calculating frontal area is reasonable because even the tissue in the area between the various parts of "petals" of the expanding bullet is undoubtedly subjected to considerable injury and stress. In addition, the resulting tissue damage is probably comparable to that created by bullets exhibiting more closely classic mushroom-shaped expansion.

## Timing is Everything

One thing that cannot be measured without extremely sophisticated facilities and equipment, which needless to say I do not possess, is the timing of the bullet expansion and, as alluded to earlier, the shape of the resulting cavity or wound channel. Since bullet measurements can conveniently be taken only on recovered bullets, the measurements are, in effect, those at the end of the expansion action and at the end of the wound channel. But did expansion take place in the first inch of penetration or in the last inch? Was it uniform or did it begin or stop after a certain period? In other words, what is the transitional configuration of the bullet as it penetrates to successive depths? This is immensely important in determining the shape and configuration of the wound channel. These factors have a profound effect on the animal. A bullet that expands rapidly in the first bit of penetration and continues on without further expansion would be expected to produce a different result than one that expands uniformly throughout its path and reaches maximum expansion near the end of its travel.

The cross-sectional area of an unexpanded 243 bullet is .046-inch. Comparing this figure with those shown in the table can give an idea of the relative expansion of each bullet.

The interpretation of penetration, weight retention and expansion data has to be done and viewed with a clear understanding of their limitations and weaknesses. The data or values as presented are best viewed as indicators rather than actual measures of bullet performance. The measurements presented do, however, allow the comparison of bullets tested under standard conditions, and this can be of value in predicting or anticipating how a bullet will behave or perform under actual field situations.

It's important to remember that ultimately the measure of a bullet's effectiveness is its ability to quickly disable a game animal to the point of immobility and/or quick death.

## The Results

I was a little surprised the 90-grain Speer didn't show any better penetration than it did, since others have reported on the suitability of this bullet for game animals. From my data, it would appear that it is better suited to varmints than deer.

The Nosler Ballistic Tip design is representative of a new application of a familiar pattern. Structurally, it's comparable to the older Remington Bronze Point and the newer Jensen. With the 95-grain version, penetration was comparable to conventionally jacketed bullets such as those offered by most major bullet manufacturers. Weight retention at 100 yards was generally better than most other bullets of conventional design, and surprisingly, weight retention at 200 yards was quite high at over 70 percent. In comparison, although penetration was definitely greater, weight retention of the proven 95-grain Nosler Partition at 200 yards was 6 percent less. If rapid expansion coupled with reasonable weight and excellent accuracy are needed, the 95-grain Ballistic Tip is definitely a bullet to consider.

Another Nosler bullet that characteristically showed fine performance was their 85-grain Partition. Penetration and proportional weight retention of this bullet at 100 and 200 yards was measurably greater than most conventionally constructed bullets. Expansion with this bullet was quite good, exceeding that of the proven 95- and 100-grain Partitions. This greater expansion is probably related to the substantially higher muzzle and impact velocities of the lighter bullet. For those who use small-capacity 6mm cartridges, or wish to achieve maximum velocities, this bullet would be a prime candidate.

The Hirtenberger ABC, along with the 96-grain offering from RWS, were, to my knowledge, the only bullets of foreign manufacture tested. The Hirtenberger gave an excellent performance, especially in the weight retention category. Except for the 100-grain Barnes X at both 100 and 200 yards, and the Trophy Bonded Bear Claw at 200 yards, this Austrian bullet retained proportionally more weight than any other. Penetration was slightly less with the Hirtenberger than with some others, no doubt because of its excellent expansion characteristics. At both 100 and 200 yards, only the heavier Trophy Bonded expanded more than this bullet. The only other bullet to exceed the Hirtenberger's expansion was, curiously, the 105-grain Remington Extended Range. Major drawbacks with the Hirtenberger are availability and frightfully prohibitive cost (at last look $79—that's right 79 American dollars—per hundred).

The 95-grain Nolser Partition showed excellent performance and, in practical terms, is fully the equal of any 100-grain bullet currently available, in my opinion.

The 80-grain Jensen J26 is another lighter weight bullet offering excellent performance in terms of weight retention and penetration. The streamlined form of both the 80- and 100-grain Jensens offers enhanced trajectories. While the 80-grain version should appeal to those looking toward small-capacity cases or high velocity, the 100-grain J26 is an even better performer in all categories. At the 100-yard range, only the 100-grain Barnes X retained more weight than the Jensen, and few showed better penetration. At 200 yards, only the 100-grain Trophy Bonded and the 100-grain Barnes X retained more weight. Penetration at 200 yards was comparable to the better performing bullets.

The lightest of the bullets tested was the 75-grain Barnes X. Constructed of solid copper alloy, this bullet shows real game-taking potential for those desiring ultra-high velocity. Penetration and proportional weight retention were indeed very good, easily exceeding most heavier and more conventionally constructed game bullets. Besides those reported on here, other lightweight 6mm bullets are not in the same league as or remotely comparable to the Barnes. As good as this bullet appears to be, I'm going to have to test them more before I would say it was the best of the lighter bullets. In the tests I've done, there appears to be a definite tendency for the petals of the expanding bullet to break off, thus limiting final expansion and weight retention. However, as will be mentioned later, this apparently does not significantly affect this bullet's performance on game.

The 90-grain Barnes X appears to have mixed performance characteristics. This bullet showed the most penetration, equaling or exceeding that of the heavier 100-grain Barnes X. On the other hand, expansion and proportionate weight retention more closely approximated the lighter 75-grain X. With this bullet, there was also a tendency to lose part of its expanding front section. It appears the higher velocity of the 90-grain bullet results (at least with the lot of bullets I tested) in it opening more forcefully, thus causing the expanding copper petals to break off; this, in turn, results in a smaller final expanded diameter. Evidently, velocity is high enough with the resulting smaller diameter to overcome the resistance of the test material, and thus at 200 yards or comparable ranges, penetration is greater than with the 100-grain X.

### Too Much of a Good Thing?

When driven at top velocities, the 75- and 90-grain X-Bullets are perhaps too much of a good thing. In other words, these bullets *may* react better (i.e. retain more weight and destroy more tissue) at lower velocities. On the other hand, at least one other writer has reported on these lightweight bullets when driven at ultra-high velocities from extremely large capacity cases. His experience indicates they can be very effective in taking smaller big game species even though he reported that, like my observations, the test bullet shed its petals also. I can report on firsthand experience with 257-caliber 85-grain Barnes X-Bullets on deer and antelope when driven at 25-06 velocities. Penetration on chest cavity shots has been complete at all ranges to 350 yards (the longest distance experienced), and at less than 100 yards the effect of all shots can be accurately described as lightning bolt-like. Any disintegration or breakage of the petals in reality apparently does not produce a measurable decrease in performance on game.

Not much can be said about the 100-grain Barnes X that isn't complimentary. Penetration at 100 yards was as good or better than that of any other bullet tested, and at 200 yards it was greater than any other bullet except the 90-grain X, 95- and 100-grain Nosler Partitions, and the 96-grain RWS. Weight retention was effectively 100 percent with an average loss of only .6-grain for both ranges. In addition, expansion was top notch, being exceeded by few other bullets, and then only by a small amount. Since I did my tests, Barnes has apparently discontinued this bullet and replaced it with one of 95 grains.

The 100-grain Speer Grand Slam and the 96-grain RWS Cone Point outwardly have fairly conventional construction—lead cores encased in a copper alloy jacket. These jackets are heavier than those of most conventionally constructed bullets; this in turn accounts for the smaller percentage of core material when compared with offerings from Hornady, Sierra, Federal, Remington, Winchester, and even other Speers. One interesting aspect of the Speer Grand Slam, which it shares with the 100-grain Hornady, is an inner ring or belt on the jacket that serves to lock in the core. In the Grand Slams, the core is actually made up of two parts, the front one having $1^1/_2$ percent antimony, the rear one 5 percent, which makes it much harder and ensures penetration. The inner jacket ring holds the rear core in place, and the front part is poured onto it via Speer's Hot Core process, in effect melting them

Fired and unfired bullets (from left): 75-grain Barnes X, 80-Grain Jensen and 85-grain Hirtenberg.

together where they interface. This, of course, is a more complex procedure than that of conventional bullets, which they outperform.

### Conventional Bullets

Weight retention and penetration of the 105- and 100-grain Speer and Hornady SPs and RNs were judged to be adequate, but not exceptional. In all these bullets, weight retention and penetration were substantially less than that of the 95- and 100-grain Nosler Partitions, 100-grain Speer GS, 96-grain RWS, 100-grain Jensen, 100-grain Trophy Bonded and all the Barnes Xs. The 100-grain Sierra SP and Semi-SP were not exceptional either. In addition to mediocre penetration, both of the Sierras showed a tendency to come apart to a greater degree than the others. The Federal 100-grain Hi-Shok was also unspectacular in its performance.

In looking at the penetration and retained weight data presented in the table, it can be concluded that, as a generalization, conventional boattail varieties are not the best choice for game-taking applications. Although boattails retain velocity and energy better at longer ranges and may be more accurate, those possible attributes do not necessarily compensate for the reduced weight retention and penetration shown in these tests. These characteristics appear to be inherent with the design since the 100-grain Sierra, Hornady and Speer boattails all showed poorer performance than their flat-base counterparts. Jacket thickness no doubt influences this, but more probably the internal tapered base plays a major role since the core has no mechanism for being held in the jacket. In my opinion, while conventional 6mm boattails are OK for game taking, careful shot placement, in the chest cavity only, should be considered the rule.

That said, the boattail design of the Jensen is worth comment. The results with the 100-grain Jensen show how construction rather than bullet shape is the major factor in determining how a bullet reacts on impact. None of the Jensen bullets I tested showed any tendency to separate or otherwise come apart. Warren Jensen said it very clearly when he pointed out that terminal performance has little to do with ballistic shape and a lot to do with engineering and internal structure.

Based on earlier field experience, I anticipated the 100-grain Remington Core-Lokt would perform better than it did. While weight retention was adequate, penetration was no better than that of many others. Cross-sectional area at 200 yards was the second largest recorded and helps explain the average penetration. The Core-Lokts have a good reputation when it comes to game-taking performance. Against this reputation, the superior performance of many other bullets as reported here really demonstrates those other bullets' quality.

### Heaviest Bullets

At 105 grains, the Remington Extended Range offering, along with the 105-grain Speers, were the heaviest bullets tried in these tests. For the most part, everything about this bullet's jacket thickness, penetration and retained weight appear to be similar if not identical to the older Pointed Soft Point Core-Lokt. Penetration at 100 and 200 yards was also judged to be adequate but not exceptional. Expansion measurements at 100 yards and, to a slightly lesser extent, at 200 yards were among the highest obtained and may in part explain the good reputation Remington PSPCL and, by inference, ER bullets have in actual field use.

Similarly, Winchester Power Points performed quite well. While penetration was only average, weight retention and bullet frontal area at 200 yards were among the highest. Practically speaking, I would expect this bullet to do an excellent job on deer-size game.

Unfortunately, the same good performance was not seen from the newer Winchester Silvertip boattail bullet. Although of seemingly similar construction, the Silvertip did not perform as well as the older design. While the trimmer shape of the new Silvertip may offer some advantages in terms of trajectory and striking energy, as discussed earlier, its boattail design and seemingly thinner jacket apparently does nothing to promote weight retention and penetration.

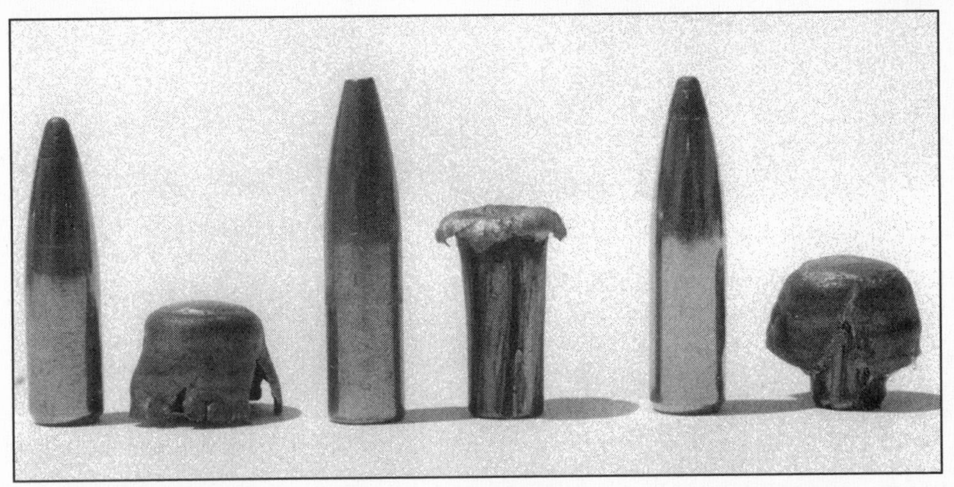

Fired and unfired bullets (from left): 85-grain Nosler Partition, 90-grain Barnes X and 95-grain Nosler Partition.

Among the heavier bullets tested, it was no surprise that the 100-grain Nosler Partition came out on top or at least very close to it. Penetration at both 100 and 200 yards was, in practical terms, as good as any other. Although Nosler Partitions exhibited a tendency to lose that portion of the core and jacket forward of the partition, they nonetheless showed excellent weight retention. At 100 yards, of the bullets with lead cores weighing 95 grains or more, only the 96-grain RWS and the 100-grain Jensen and Trophy Bonded retained more weight, and at 200 yards, weight retention was comparable to or better than most.

The Trophy Bonded Bear Claw was quite clearly one of the best performers of any of the bullets tested. With this bullet, not only was penetration as good as any and better than most, weight retention was

Fired and unfired bullets (from left): 96-grain RWS, 100-grain Barnes X and 100-grain Nosler Partition.

Fired and unfired bullets (from left): 100-grain Trophy Bonded, 100-grain Jensen, 100-grain Speer GS.

comparable to or better than that of other controlled-expansion designs. The main attribute of the Trophy Bonded is its ability to reach this high level of weight retention and penetration while at the same time showing marvelous expansion. In all my tests, few others came close to and none exceeded the Trophy Bonded in measured terminal expansion. These bullets are very stoutly constructed. When fired into the recovery media at 20 yards, these bullets still retained an average of over 93 percent of their weight. This is a severe test of bullet "toughness" and shows that a hunter using Trophy Bondeds does not have to worry about this bullet coming apart on game. While I haven't tried this with the 100-grain Barnes X, I doubt if it would retain as much weight due to petal breakoff.

### What Does It Mean?

A number of conclusions might be drawn from all this data. One obvious thing my tests show is that, clearly, conventionally constructed bullets with soft lead-alloy cores and relatively thin copper alloy jackets do not show as good performance as do other non-conventional bullets. The table also shows how similar in performance conventional patterns are. But as with most things, there are possible exceptions. In this case, the 96-grain RWS and 100-grain Speer GS are apparent...if they are considered "conventional" in the first place. These bullets showed penetration, weight retention and expansion more comparable to designs considered to be "premium."

Another thing my tests show is that bullet weight is less important than design, construction and structure. Several lighter weight bullets—including the 75-grain Barnes X, 80-grain Jensen J26, and 85-grain Hirtenberger ABC and Nosler Partition—clearly outperformed heavier bullets of more conventional structure. This could prove to be a definite advantage in small cartridge case applications. Properly used and considering inherent energy and momentum limitations, these lighter bullets should be completely effective in bagging game.

Somewhat the converse of what I indicated before, it is clear that "modern" 6mm big game bullet designs of heavier weight (i.e. 95 to 100 grains) can be expected to provide superior performance. In this modern group, I would place the 95- and 100-grain Nosler Partitions; the 100-grain Jensen J26, Trophy Bonded Bear Claw and Barnes X; and arguably the 96-grain RWS Cone Point and 100-grain Speer Grand Slam. These have shown clear performance advantages over most if not all others.

Of bullets that had at least some lead core, the 85-, 95- and 100-grain Nosler Partitions; the 80- and 100-grain Jensen J26s; the 85-grain Hirtenberger ABC; the 95-grain Nosler Ballistic Tip; the 96-grain RWS Cone Point; the 100-grain Trophy Bonded Bear Claw; and the 100-grain Speer Grand Slam had core weights that comprised less than 60 percent of the total bullet weight. These bullets were also found to be among the best performers. When viewed with the data from the Barnes X-Bullets, these results show clearly that the trend in big game bullet design toward an increased percentage of copper alloys has had a positive effect in improving bullet performance and impact characteristics.

Which bullet you choose depends on several things. Personally, while I have used light bullets, I don't advocate and can't recommend them ex-

**TABLE 1: 6MM BULLET CONSTRUCTION AND PERFORMANCE MEASUREMENTS**

| —Bullet— Wgt. Grs. | Type | Jacket Thickness (ins.) | Core Weight (percent of total) | Expanded Cross-Sectional Area (square inches) (100 yds.) | (200 yds.) | Penetration (ins.) (100 yds.) | (200 yds.) | Retained Weight (percent) (100 yds.) | (200 yds.) |
|---|---|---|---|---|---|---|---|---|---|
| 75 | Barnes X | — | — | .147 | .203 | 14 | 13 | 82.1 | 84.5 |
| 80 | Jensen J26 | .061 | 15.2 | .147 | .160 | 13 | 13 | 80.1 | 85.6 |
| 85 | Hirtenberger ABC | .075 | 12.0 | .214 | .206 | 13 | 11 | 87.1 | 93.1 |
| 85 | Nosler Partition | .035 | 54.9 | .188 | .162 | 14 | 12 | 67.3 | 71.9 |
| 90 | Barnes X | — | — | .133 | .120 | 16 | 16 | 82.5 | 85.1 |
| 90 | Speer SP | .020 | 68.0 | .110 | .092 | 10 | 9 | 37.0 | 35.9 |
| 95 | Nosler Ball. Tip | .023 | 57.1 | .209 | .203 | 11 | 12 | 57.1 | 70.4 |
| 95 | Nosler Partition | .030 | 57.0 | .139 | .133 | 16 | 14 | 71.9 | 65.9 |
| 96 | RWS Cone Point | .030 | 55.0 | .144 | .158 | 13 | 14 | 80.2 | 74.2 |
| 100 | Barnes X | — | — | .214 | .204 | 16 | 14 | 99.5 | 99.3 |
| 100 | Federal Hi-Shok | .023 | 74.6 | .152 | .176 | 11 | 11 | 32.9 | 50.2 |
| 100 | Hornady BT | .022 | 65.0 | .181 | .109 | 10 | 10 | 47.7 | 40.6 |
| 100 | Hornady RN | .022 | 69.0 | .140 | .139 | 11 | 12 | 50.5 | 52.2 |
| 100 | Hornady SP | .022 | 68.0 | .120 | .126 | 12 | 11 | 49.2 | 69.6 |
| 100 | Jensen J26 | .060 | 14.2 | .185 | .197 | 15 | 13 | 86.4 | 82.2 |
| 100 | Nosler Partition | .030 | 57.0 | .131 | .128 | 16 | 15 | 71.2 | 67.3 |
| 100 | Remington CL | .022 | 67.0 | .133 | .232 | 11 | 12 | 56.0 | 64.2 |
| 100 | Sierra BT | .018 | 68.0 | .142 | .124 | 10 | 11 | 45.5 | 42.0 |
| 100 | Sierra SSP | .023 | 67.0 | .126 | .140 | 11 | 11 | 47.6 | 58.1 |
| 100 | Sierra SP | .024 | 65.0 | .141 | .116 | 12 | 11 | 43.1 | 50.3 |
| 100 | Speer BT | .027 | 76.0 | .125 | .118 | 10 | 10 | 36.1 | 38.8 |
| 100 | Speer Grand Slam | .034 | 58.1 | .194 | .158 | 13 | 13 | 67.6 | 72.6 |
| 100 | Trophy Bonded BC | .050 | 23.0 | .262 | .247 | 16 | 13 | 79.9 | 94.6 |
| 100 | Winchester PP | .029 | 64.0 | .177 | .209 | 13 | 12 | 64.3 | 77.0 |
| 100 | Winchester ST | .023 | 66.1 | .203 | .173 | 12 | 11 | 51.9 | 44.8 |
| 105 | Remington ER | .022 | 70.1 | .226 | .202 | 12 | 11 | 57.8 | 60.0 |
| 105 | Speer RN | .027 | 67.0 | .177 | .124 | 12 | 12 | 49.5 | 57.0 |
| 105 | Speer SP | .026 | 69.0 | .133 | .165 | 12 | 11 | 45.9 | 55.4 |

cept for perhaps emergency or specialized applications. They are often capable of bagging game, but they do offer less performance than heavier weights. I think their application to big game hunting situations is marginal and should be limited to careful and calculating riflemen who thoroughly know the limitations of their ability and equipment.

After that, it becomes a little bit of personal taste and a lot of how a bullet performs. Right now I'd be inclined to say that the 100-grain Jensen would be the best for me, largely because of its superior and consistent accuracy in my rifle. In another rifle, it could well be different. I would have to rate the Trophy Bonded as potentially the best of the lot based on its wonderful combination of penetration, weight retention, and expansion. After all, the fact still remains that bigger wound channels and greater tissue damage help to bag game, and the Trophy Bonded obviously has shown the maximum combination of expansion and penetration.

### In the Field

In terms of game-taking experience, the Noslers have a record extending over several decades that can't be faulted. Rightfully so, they're the standard against which all other bullets are compared, and it's a high standard at that. In terms of consistent penetration and weight retention, it's likely that there can be much improvement over them.

The Barnes X-Bullets, particularly the 100-grain, appear to offer the greatest retained weights, coupled with excellent expansion. Any tendency of the expanding petals to break off and lessen effectiveness is probably much less of a real disadvantage than a theoretical one. Their relatively large length-to-weight ratio would seem to offer some ballistic advantage at longer ranges. Other positive factors of the Barnes are their availability and relatively low cost.

The RWS and the Speer GS certainly have many things going for them performancewise. On the downside for the RWS are higher cost and extremely limited availability. The Speer is readily available and competitively priced, and has shown an ability to perform. I would have little reservation about using it.

Ultimately, I think the choice between any of these bullets—particularly the 95- and 100-grain Nosler Partitions, as well as the 100-grain Barnes X, Jensen and Trophy Bonded—can be distilled down, first, to accuracy in your gun and, second, velocity. Availability is a consideration, but availability can be very transient. Assuming adequate velocity in the first place, I would simply select the bullet that shoots best for you. That way you would be almost certainly guaranteed of having the most accurate, least likely to fail bullet and load combination possible. If you know your bullet will penetrate, expand, hold together and do the job it was intended to, and if your rifle will put the bullet where you aim it, what more could any rifleman and hunter ask. If it doesn't work out, he knows the fault was his and not that of his equipment.

If there is a fault with 6mms on game it is that they don't provide much margin for error. As any hunter of experience knows, human error—in sighting, range judgement, taking a marginal shot—is commonplace. If the rifleman/hunter does his part, eliminates the error and puts the bullet in a vital spot, modern 6mm bullets can and will perform. ●

*In Norse mythology, Thor is the god of thunder. This Oklahoman says he's getting more boom out of him now*

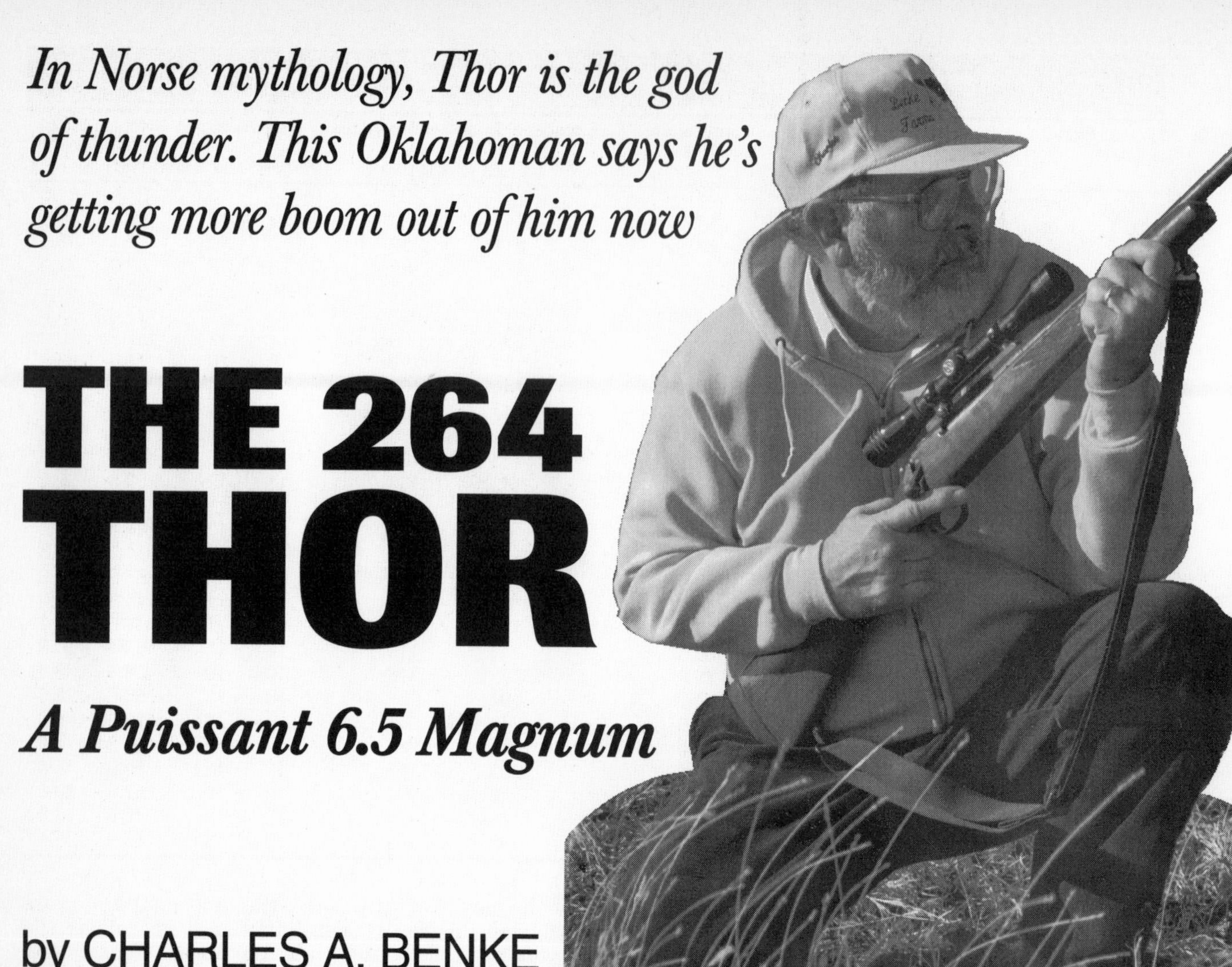

# THE 264 THOR

## *A Puissant 6.5 Magnum*

by CHARLES A. BENKE

SOME YEARS BACK, my decades-long passion for 6.5mm cartridges led me to a king-size one, the 264 Thor. The Thor is a strong belted case of good capacity, basically a necked-down, sharp-shouldered 8mm Remington Magnum. It gives impressive velocities—like 3700 fps with 100-grain bullets, up to 3500 using 120-grainers, and almost 3400 with 140s. To say that such ballistics will handle long-range shots at pronghorns, deer, sheep, caribou, etc., seems to be belaboring the obvious.

The Thor isn't the first 6.5mm magnum, of course. Back before World War II, Schuler necked down the big beltless 8x68 case to 6.5, and RWS brought it out about 1939 with 93- and 127-grain Cone Point bullets, the former, according to advertised specs, at 3950 fps and the latter at 3450. Hirtenberger's two best-selling factory loads contain the 105-grain Nosler Partition and the 123-grain ABC. CIP specs call for a twist of 1:11 inches, which makes this cartridge most usable with projectiles weighing 140 grains or less. The 6.5x68 has slightly less powder capacity than the Thor. I've had a 6.5x68 for years, and it has performed well on lots of antelope and open-country deer.

Slightly bigger is the belted 264 Winchester Magnum. (Measured externally, the 6.5x68mm has more powder room, but RWS and Hirtenberger brass is thicker than Winchester's.) Col. Charles Askins took the American load to Africa in 1959, but it was the summer of 1960 before the 264 Model 70 could be found in gun stores. This necked-down 338 Winchester Magnum offspring suffered bad press from the start. It continues. The *Lyman 47th Reloading Handbook* (1992) says: "Due to short barrel life few hunters would select this round over the 270 Winchester which offers similar performance." That's bad press for a big belted magnum cartridge!

For an article in *Handloader* No. 160, I used six 264 Winchester Magnum rifles. Two of them would crowd 3200 fps with a carefully prepared handload featuring Winchester's old 140-grain two-diameter Power Point bullet, so designed to keep pressure lower. So any 6.5mm wildcat cartridge designed to compete with these two factory magnums would have to clearly exceed 3200 fps with a 140-grain bullet.

Winchester laboriously documented their development of the 264 Winchester Magnum. It is so well done, one suspects the copy was put together after the cartridge was introduced. Nowhere in that copy does it mention that several experimenters were already getting good results from the 7x61 Sharpe & Hart belted case necked down to 6.5mm. (The 7x61 S&H, incidentally, was based on an early experimental French military rimless case, with variants in 6.5mm. The 6.5mm Sharpe & Hart experiments simply brought this case development full circle.)

(Opposite page) The 264 Thor makes a terrific long-range rifle for pronghorns, deer, sheep, caribou, etc., and has plenty of punch.

Left to right: 264 Winchester Magnum, 264 Thor, and the beltless 6.5x68.

One such experimenter was Wichita Falls, Texas, gunsmith Bill Mowrey (later of blackpowder Mowrey Rifle Co. fame). Bill necked down the 7x61 S&H and called his creation the 6.5mm Bearcat. Bill told me that his biggest problem in the mid-1950s was trying to find slow-burning powders suitable for the cartridge. Today, that's not a problem.

While mid-size 6.5mm magnums were more popular, there have existed some really powerful 6.5mm magnums. The 6.5 Gipson Magnum, based on the scarce 275 Holland & Holland belted case, supposedly produced 3350 fps with a 130-grain bullet. I don't know the barrel length, but this case also was said to push a 150-grain bullet to 3116 fps with IMR-4350.

Oklahoma City gunsmith Art Mashburn shortened the 300 H&H case to 2.6 inches to create his 6.5 Super Mashburn, while the 6.5 Critser Express kept the case at its full 2.8 inches.

Col. Paul Wright used the 300 Weatherby case for a cartridge named the 6.5/300 Weatherby-Wright-Hoyer Magnum, which was used for impressive 1000-yard match shooting. The Hodgdon lab fired this cartridge at over 3400 fps with a heavy charge of H-202 powder behind a 139-grain match bullet, at 55,000 psi. Hodgdon carried this experiment further and built a 6.5/378 Weatherby. It was concluded that this behemoth case would not produce more than 3400 fps with bullets of 140 grains, so it was no improvement on the smaller case.

In more recent years, experimentation with 6.5mm magnums languished. At the 1995 SHOT Show in Las Vegas, I was greeted at the Clymer Manufacturing Co. booth by Dave Manson, a Clymer employee, and Mark Pinkston, of Kailua Custom Guns in Coquille, Oregon. Mark moved to Oregon from Hawaii where he had full production capabilities, including manufacture of his own composite stocks. These two worthies teamed up to create a 6.5mm magnum based on the full-length 8mm Remington Magnum case, and they dubbed it the "264 Thor." Pinkston had built several hunting rifles for the cartridge, and it had already proved successful on elk by the time I got my hands on one.

The 264 Thor can be described graphically as the 6.5mm-8mm Remington Magnum 35-Degree Improved. The first sizing die was so marked. Before apoplexy sets in contemplating such a huge container pushing a 6.5mm bullet, I remind you of the recent success of the very similar 7mm Shooting Times Westerner, and the even larger 7mm ICL and 7mm Dakota. A fired 264 Thor case holds just a tad less powder than does a fired 7mm STW case. As I measure it with Oklahoma well water, the 264 Thor holds 93.1 grains of water to the base of the neck, my 7mm STW case holds 94.3 grains to the same spot, while a Super-X 264 Winchester Magnum case holds but 79.7.

The rifle Mark Pinkston shipped me for evaluation is a Remington 700 with 26-inch C.P. Donneley barrel and Mark's own PPRS muzzlebrake. This muzzlebrake is currently being evaluated by a major U.S. rifle manufacturer. The stock is out of one of Mark's old moulds from Hawaii. Included was a set of loading dies from Dave Daveson (4-D Custom Die Co.) of C-H Tool & Die. The rifle came with Redfield mounts and rings, and I installed a Simmons 44 Mag scope.

The rifle was shipped with twenty-five fire-formed cases. Pinkston and Manson thought the 6.5mm wildcat would need a longer neck than the 8mm Remington parent case, so they moved the shoulder back a tiny distance. Pinkston tells me the cases I received from him were formed by scrunching the parent case in a 300 Winchester Magnum die, a 7mm Remington Magnum die, followed by a 264 Thor full-length die, then fire-formed using 25 to 28 grains of Bullseye powder with no bullet. It obviously worked. I grabbed several 300 Weatherby Magnum brass and sized them in the 264 Thor seater die first, then full-length sized them in the sizer die, and fire-formed them with 28 grains of Bullseye. I noticed no significant difference between his formed cases and mine.

The 264 Thor, like the parent 8mm Remington Magnum brass, is 2.84 inches in length. A loaded round of 3.66 inches functions through this Remington Model 700. A rifle's magazine dictates maximum loaded length, but 3.66 inches is probably typical. Unless or until factory 7mm STW brass becomes more widely available, 8mm Remington Magnum and 300 Weatherby Magnum brass will continue to be the parent cases for this cartridge. The 7mm STW brass converts to 264 Thor with one pass through the sizer die.

The shooting began. Since the 264 Winchester Magnum's 3200 fps with 140-grain bullet was my beginning threshold, I created a table for the very slow powders that would achieve that initial velocity from the 264 Thor. (See Table 1.)

This table belies its true usefulness. I do not consider any powder burning faster than H-1000 to be suited for full-power loads in this cartridge. For instance, 67/IMR-4831 indeed yields 3200 fps, but 68 grains of the same powder will lock the bolt. Since a carefully prepared handload in a select 264 Winchester Magnum rifle will produce the same velocity, there's not much merit in using the "faster" ultra-slow powders in this cartridge.

Appropriate powders for the 264 Thor are those designed for the 50 BMG and the various 20mm and 25mm rounds. Several companies market these ultra-slow powders through gun periodicals and retailers, but reloading information is scarce. I'll describe some of my components.

VV 24N41 is VihtaVuori Oy's extruded powder for the 50 BMG. The granules are smaller and shorter

(Left) Benke's test rifle is a Remington long action with 26-inch Donneley barrel and PPRS muzzlebrake. It was furnished by gunsmith Mark Pinkston.

Pinkston's PPRS muzzlebrake is just over 2 inches long and has 1/2-inch holes to vent gases. It is very efficient.

than those of IMR-5010. VihtaVuori considers this a canister powder; the canister weighs 8 pounds. Its burning rate (in the Thor) is between H-1000 and IMR-5010. VV 24N41 appears to be useful in other cartridges, such as the 6.5mm Gibbs and the 25-06 Remington.

H-570 is a very old surplus powder. It is an extruded powder that Hodgdon sold in bulk many years ago. In 1988, some readers reported that their supplies of this powder were beginning to deteriorate. My own small lot of H-570 came in 1-pound white paper sacks packaged and sold by Hodgdon. The powder remaining in my sacks does not yet show signs of deterioration.

IMR-5010 is an extruded powder with very large granules. I'm not sure if DuPont (or IMR) ever sold this powder in canisters. All lots I have seen have been repackaged. The labels on some containers have "IMR" as part of the powder's name; many do not. Hogdgon sells a version called H-5010. By whatever name, 5010 is one of the best powders in the 264 Thor with 120- and 140-grain bullets.

TCCI 5050 is a spherical powder that looks much like H-870, burning

VihtaVuori 24N41 and IMR-5010 are both extruded powders and very well suited for use in the 264 Thor.

**TABLE 1:
264 THOR EQUIVALENT LOADS**

| —Load— | |
|---|---|
| Grains | Powder |
| 67 | IMR-4831 |
| 70 | MR 3100 (bulk) |
| 70 | RL-22 |
| 71 | IMR-7828 |
| 72 | AA 3100 |
| 72 | VV 165 |
| 76 | H-1000 |
| 77 | VV 24N41 |
| 77 | MR 8700 |
| 78 | H-570 |
| 79 | H-870 |
| 80 | IMR-5010 |
| 81 | TCCI 5050 |
| 85 | RVO-70 |

CCI 250 primers, fire-formed R-P 8mm Remington Magnum brass, 140-grain Hornady Interlok bullets. Velocities are 3200 to 3225 fps with these charges.

**Warning!** Do not interpret this chart as a bona-fide powder burn-rate chart of the ultra-slow powders. As chamber pressure increases, some of these powders change position slightly. Many "surplus" propellants are not canister grade and other lots may vary significantly in burning rate.

just slightly slower. Surplus powder labeled as pulled from the 20x102mm Vulcan round burns much like TCCI 5050 in this cartridge. They differ visually, as TCCI 5050 is totally spherical while the surplus Vulcan powder has an occasional tail on the spheres.

The slowest powder I found usable in this cartridge is called RVO-70 by its distributor, River Valley Ordnance Works, in Harvester, Missouri. This extruded RVO-70 (also known as HC 30) was manufactured for 25mm ammo and is slightly slower burning than most lots of IMR-5010. A heavily compressed load of 87 grains of this powder under a 140-grain Nosler in the 264 Thor produces about 3265 fps, and the case literally falls out of the chamber when the bolt is worked. That same charge under the Barnes 140-grain X Bullet produces 3390 fps, but extraction is sticky. RVO-70 is also good with the 155-grain Sierra match bullet.

Bill Mowrey couldn't find them in Wichita Falls, Texas, forty years ago, but there are powders on the market today that are too slow for even the 264 Thor. Accurate Arms sells a powder they call AA 8700, and River Valley Ordnance Works sells one they call RVO Super-Slow. Both are too slow for most small-arms applications.

I tested some little-known projectiles. The Armfield Bullet Co. swages plain and bonded bullets in most calibers and weights. I used their 90-grain hollowpoint and their 120-grain bonded bullet in these trials.

The HT bullet does not contain lead. It is made from homogeneous stock, similar to the Barnes X Bullet. The body of the HT bullet is smaller, and only the driving bands contact the lands of the barrel. Such a design is said to reduce chamber pressure because only the driving bands are engraved. The ballistic coefficients of these bullets are among the highest in the industry. These bullets are extremely long for their weight. The 120-grain HT bullet is longer than most 140-grain conventional bullets.

### 264 THOR LOAD DATA

| Bullet Wgt. Grs. | Bullet Type | Load (Grs./Powder) | Velocity (fps) | Comments |
|---|---|---|---|---|
| 90 | Armfield | 82/IMR-7828 | 3828 | |
| 90 | Armfield | 85/H-1000 | 3873 | |
| 100 | Nosler Ballistic Tip | 83/H-1000 | 3710 | |
| 100 | Barnes X | 88/H-870 | 3687 | Compressed |
| 100 | HT | 88/VV 24N41 | 3727 | Compressed |
| 105 | Nosler Partition | 88/IMR-5010 | 3673 | Compressed |
| 120 | Sierra | 76/H-1000 | 3342 | |
| 120 | Nosler Ballistic Tip | 79/VV 24N41 | 3367 | |
| 120 | Armfield | 84/H-570 | 3434 | |
| 120 | HT | 84/H-870 | 3491 | |
| 120 | Sierra HPBT | 84/IMR-8700 | 3433 | |
| 120 | Speer | 85/IMR-5010 | 3440 | |
| 120 | Barnes X | 85/IMR-5010 | 3505 | |
| 120 | Remington | 87/TCCI 5050 | 3468 | |
| 125 | Nosler Partrition | 85/IMR-5010 | 3481 | |
| 129 | Hornady | 85/IMR-5010 | 3421 | |
| 138 | Lapua | 78/VV 24N41 | 3297 | |
| 139 | Norma SP | 85/TCCI 5050 | 3342 | |
| 140 | Speer | 80/H-570 | 3286 | |
| 140 | Hornady | 84/H-870 | 3364 | |
| 140 | Sierra HPBT | 83/IMR-5010 | 3309 | Compressed |
| 140 | Nosler Partition | 87/RVO-70 | 3267 | Heavily compressed |
| 140 | Barnes X | 87/RVO-70 | 3390 | Heavily compressed |
| 144 | Lapua | 86/RVO-70 | 3213 | Heavily compressed |
| 155 | Sierra HPBT | 83/RVO-70 | 3073 | Compressed |
| 160 | Hornady | 83/RVO-70 | 2992 | |

All heavier bullets were seated to an overall length of 3.66 inches to function through the magazine. **Warning**: Do not capriciously interchange bullets of the same weight. Some projectiles are so long that they decrease case capacity drastically when seated to function through the magazine. Components: Fire-formed R-P 8mm Remington Magnum brass, CCI 250 primers.

Temperature: 50 to 90 degrees F.

Test Rifle furnished by Mark Pinkston: M700 Remington, 26-inch C.P. Donneley barrel, with Pinkston's own composite stock and PPRS muzzlebrake.

The 138-grain Lapua bullet actually weighs 138.8 grains on my Lyman electronic scale. Both the 138- and the 144-grain Lapua bullets are of match design and have recently become available through precision-shooting supply houses.

After about 200 shots, I removed Mark Pinkston's muzzlebrake. Field artillerymen will instantly recognize this bulbous suffix on the barrel. It has the same profile as the bore evacuator found on 155mm artillery pieces. This brake matches the barrel on the outside at .654-inch. It is 2.115 inches long with two 1/2-inch holes drilled at right angles to the bore. The holes are .222-inch apart, forming two 90-degree planes for the escaping gases to blow against. One-half-inch of the end of the barrel is reduced to .500-inch and threaded. The muzzlebrake can be unscrewed with the fingers, although I can't imagine anyone removing it. It works well.

With muzzlebrake in place, an eleven-year-old boy unleashed a 140-grain projectile at 3300 fps and declared the experience "fun." Unscrew that brake and the perceived "kick" and noise levels go up. This same phenomenon occurs with other muzzlebrakes. The shooter ranks noise and recoil as tolerable. Anyone standing to the side gets pounded by those gases. This muzzlebrake, like most others, would be a nuisance at a public firing range.

That's enough technical information. How do I rate the Thor overall? It's what most of us thought we were getting when we bought our first 264 Winchester Magnum. This cartridge, in this rifle, produces about 5 percent more velocity than will the very best 264 Winchester Magnum. The Winchester Magnum, with a select 140-grain handload, in a select rifle, will reach 3200 fps. This 264 Thor puissant magnum will almost reach 3400 fps with that same 140-grain bullet.

An extra 200 fps with the 140-grain bullet does not alter trajectory much, but it does increase striking energy considerably. A few cynics still label the 264 Winchester Magnum as "marginal" for elk. The 264 Thor is not "marginal." The quickest way to get a 264 Thor is to rechamber a 264 Winchester Magnum built on the M700 Remington or similar long action. Several years ago, I spent good money to set the barrel back on a 264 Winchester Magnum that had a bad chamber. I'd never do that today. I'd simply rechamber it to the 264 Thor. ●

# ANOTHER LOOK AT REMINGTON'S 41 MAGNUM

*Sometimes, as the author points out, the middle of the road is the best.*

by JAMES W. TANK

IF I WERE ASKED to name a revolver cartridge that is big on performance but short on popularity, Remington's 41 Magnum would be the first to come to mind. Being caught between the slightly more powerful 44 Magnum on one end and the lighter 357 Magnum on the other, many shooters felt the 41 was merely an exercise in redundancy. However logical such reasoning may seem, it wanes rapidly in view of the 41's virtues. Before I get into the actual handloading, let's take a brief look at the 41's history, coupled with some comparisons between the 357, 41 and 44 that are not only interesting, but also help answer some questions. Why is there a 41 Magnum, and now that we have it, what good is it? What niche, if any, does this cartridge fill?

The 41 Magnum was introduced in the spring of 1964 as a police cartridge, through the urgings of such firearms notables as Elmer Keith, Bill Jordan and Skeeter Skelton. These fine gentlemen envisioned a revolver/cartridge combination that would provide the non-reloading police officer with a choice of two bullet types driven at two different velocities. First, a 210-grain lead semi-wadcutter driven at 850-1000 fps for "everyday" use; and second, a 210-grain jacketed soft-nose traveling at 1300-1500 fps for use against vehicles or barricades. Remington produced the ammo and Smith & Wesson provided two revolvers: the fixed-sight 4-inch Model 58, intended for police use, and the adjustable-sight Model 57, which, except for caliber, is the same as the Model 29 in 44 Magnum. Everything was going according to plan until an unexpected logistical problem occurred.

Instead of the low-velocity lead load, the first lots of ammunition shipped out by Remington were the higher-velocity soft-nosed type. The

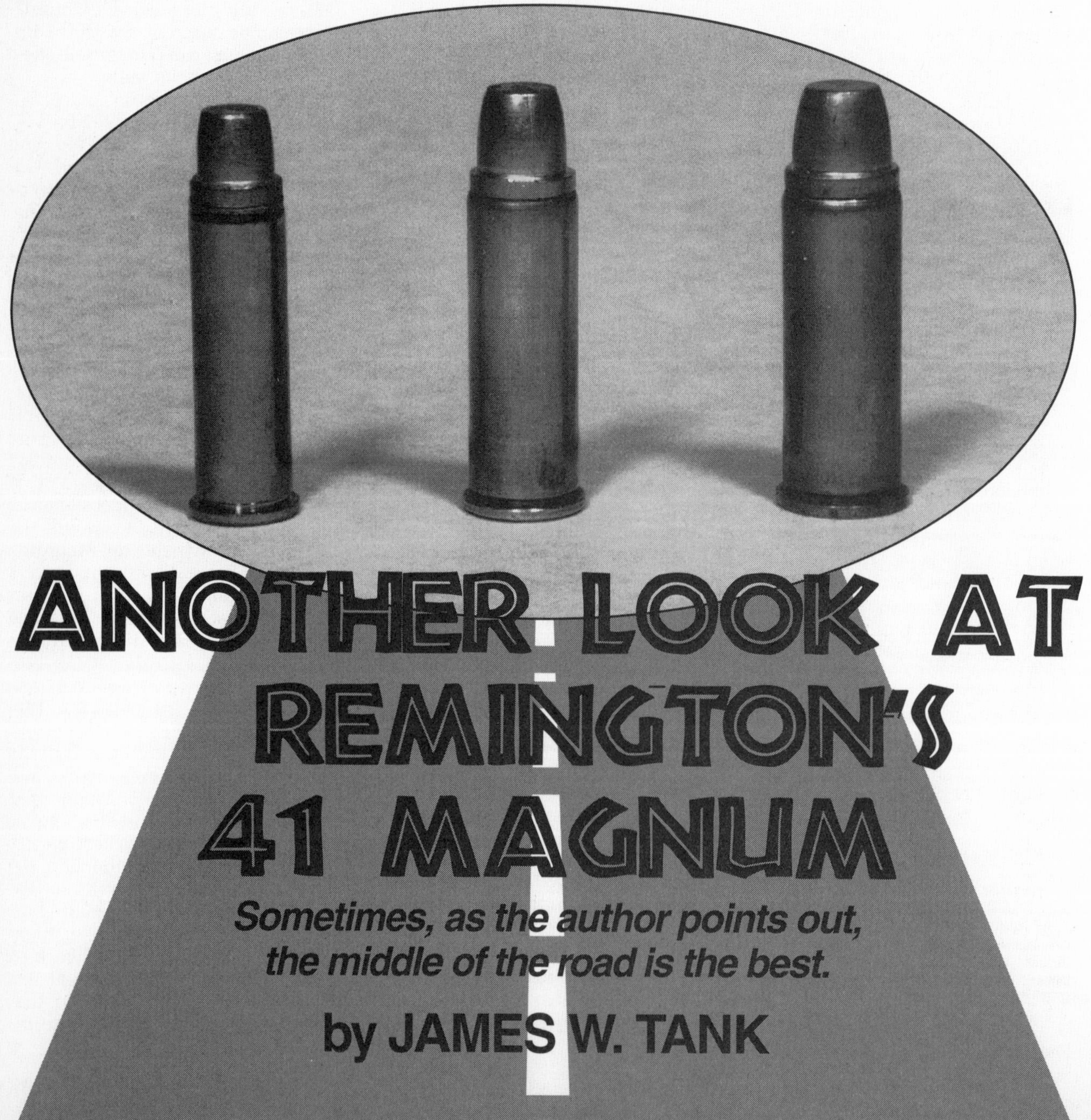

The three most common revolver magnums (from left): 357, 41 and 44 Magnums. Each of these cast bullets is crimped on the crimping groove.

Cast semi-wadcutter bullets such as the WCC 210, Ohaus #611 210 K, and Lyman 220-grain #4410459 cover a velocity range from 750-1400 fps.

12.5 foot-pounds of recoil generated by this loading was simply too much for most law officers to handle in rapid-fire tests, and consequently rapid-fire scores plummeted. For the most part, so did fondness for the new revolver/cartridge concept. Given their choice, those officers who could do so happily returned to their 357 Magnums. Some departments hung on to the 41, but they were few indeed. Today, more and more police officials are adopting high-capacity semi-automatics in such calibers as 9mm, 10mm and 40 S&W, making it reasonable to say that those departments retaining the 41 Magnum are all but non-existent.

These Lyman #410459 SWCs weigh 220 grains when cast from Lyman #2 alloy. As the final steps prior to loading, the bullets will be sized to .410-inch and lubed. Visual inspection of all bullets is a must.

Although the 41 Magnum didn't really "catch on" as a police cartridge—through no fault of its own, I might add—it remains one fine hunting cartridge. Often referred to in various shooting publications as "the middle magnum" or "almost a 44," these comments shouldn't be taken in a negative sense. When the three most commonly known revolver magnums are compared, the 41 is the middle magnum, although its power lies closer to the 44. Keep in mind, however, that the 41 isn't a 44, and it was never intended to be. Compare these 357, 41 and 44 Magnum factory ballistics:

**FACTORY BALLISTICS FOR MAGNUM REVOLVER LOADS**

| Caliber | Bullet Wgt.Grs.. | Bullet Type | Bbl. Length (ins.) | Velocity (fps) | Energy (fpe) | Recoil (fpe) |
|---|---|---|---|---|---|---|
| 357 | 158 | JSP | 8 3/8 | 1550 | 845 | 6.3 |
| 41 | 210 | JSP | 8 3/8 | 1500 | 1050 | 12.5 |
| 44 | 240 | JSP | 6 1/2 | 1470 | 1150 | 16.5 |

If the 44 test gun also had an 8 3/8-inch barrel, another 70 fps could be added to its velocity, giving it 1540 fps; speed approximating the 357. Energy figures would increase to 1270 foot-pounds, and recoil energy would also experience a slight increase. This table gives a fairly good comparison of velocities and recoil, but for those who use energy as the sole factor for determining killing power, a word of caution. In the nearby chart, bullet weight and speed were used to determine energy. A very important factor, bullet diameter, has been ignored.

Assuming a bullet diameter of .357 for the 357 Magnum and .410 for the 41 Magnum, we have a difference of .053-inch in favor of the 41, which I consider rather significant. The difference shrinks to .020 when the diameters of the 41 and 44 Magnums are compared.

When the original factory bullet weights are examined among the 357, 41 and 44, the following facts become apparent. The 41 Magnum's 210-grain bullet is 52 grains heavier than the 357's 158-grain bullet, and only 30 grains lighter than the 44 Magnum's 240-grain bullet.

Bullet weight and diameter should be major considerations for anyone wishing to hunt game the size of deer and black bear. Drive these bullets as fast as you safely

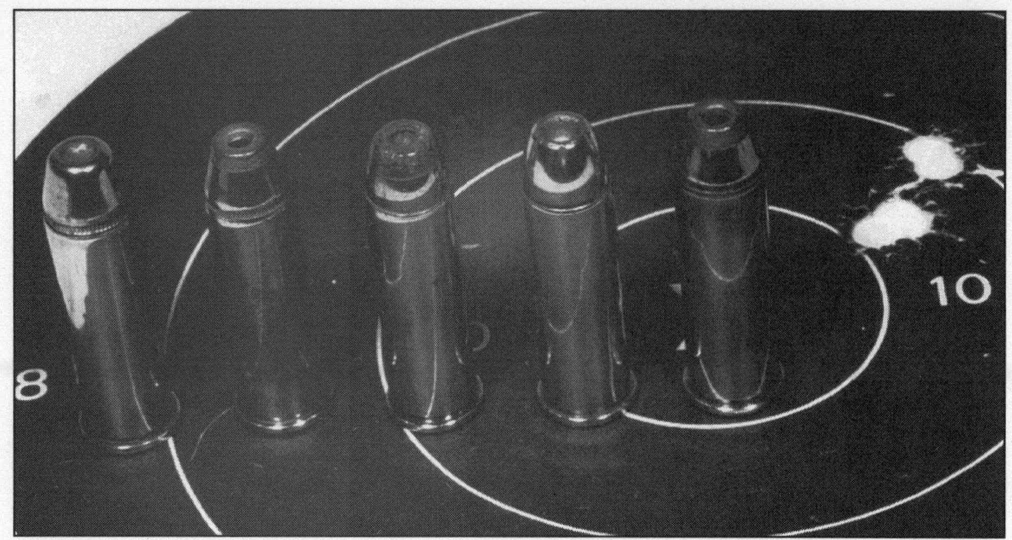


A number of 41 Magnum loads (from left): the Sierra 220 Silhouette, Sierra 210 JHC, Hornady 210 JHP, Hornady 210 XTP, Sierra 170 SHC. The five-shot group was fired from a Ruger Bisley loaded with 24/H-110/170 JHC.

can, while still maintaining what you consider acceptable accuracy. Yes, deer- and bear-size animals have been successfully taken with smaller calibers, but my personal preference runs to the 40s. The additional weight and diameter of the larger magnums make bigger holes to "let air in and blood out," as Elmer Keith once wrote.

You can see from the table of factory loadings that recoil of the 41 and 44 is substantially more than that generated by the 357. This is where the 41 Magnum is unique.

The recoil of any 41 Magnum factory load is not nearly as punishing as that of 44 factory loadings, yet it still launches a bullet that is almost half an inch in diameter, weighs over 200 grains, and does so at magnum velocities. The 41 Magnum is a fine choice for those handgunners who feel uncomfortable with the recoil of the 44 Magnum, but still want a 40-caliber magnum handgun.

I shoot my Ruger 41 at least twice weekly; 99 percent of the time I'm shooting handloads, and about 85 percent of that time they're loaded with cast bullets. Though the factory ammunition offerings are good, handloading is not only an economic necessity, but it also affords me the opportunity to load and shoot various bullet styles and weights at various speeds and power levels.

All of the loads listed in my 41 Magnum Load Data chart are under maximum, but some are close. Check handloading books such as the *Lyman Cast Bullet Handbook* for maximum load listings. Be on the safe side and start your tests at least 10 percent under what I have listed, and work up in 1/2-grain increments.

All of the bullets in my 41 Magnum handloads are crimped. I discovered years ago with my first RCBS three-die set that it is easier to set the crimp once and simply adjust the bullet seating stem to compensate for differences in bullet lengths. This system has worked fine for me over the years, first with my RCBS Jr. press, and now with my Dillon RL-450 progressive. Only one bullet type, the 210-grain Hornady jacketed hollowpoint (JHP) bullet, experiences slight nose flattening during the seating/crimping process. Accuracy is not adversely affected. Flattening doesn't occur when I load Hornady 210-grain Extreme Terminal Penetration (XTP) bullets, which have replaced the old JHP style.

The 41 Magnum headspaces on the rim, and, therefore, case length is not as critical as it is for cases that headspace on the case mouth. I prefer to stress uniformity as much as possible in my handloading as the primary way of eliminating variables, so when my cases reach 1.29 inches in length, I trim them to 1.28 inches.

All of the jacketed bullets I load in the 41 Magnum are crimped on the cannelure, and the cast bullets are crimped in the crimping groove. Overall length has never been a problem.

For those reloaders who don't use cast bullets, jacketed bullets are offered by the various bullet makers in weights ranging from 170 to 220 grains. Coupled with the right components, some satisfying handloads can be achieved.

If game up to the size of fox and coyote are being hunted, the 170-grain Sierra jacketed hollow cavity (JHC) should fit the bill nicely. Loaded in front of 24.0 grains of Hodgdon H-110, the bullet leaves the muzzle of my Ruger at 1365 fps with moderate recoil and good accuracy, but with a noticeable muzzle flash. This particular bullet would have great self-defense potential if loaded to 1000-1100 fps with a faster powder like Unique. Such a moderate recoiling load would allow for faster recoil recovery during double-action shooting, provide good bullet expansion without the problem of overpenetration, and eliminate muzzle flash. The H-110 load, however, remains my choice for hunting. Many rounds consisting of the 170-grain JHC with 24.0 grains of H-110 were chronographed at 1440 fps from a friend's 7 1/2-inch 41 Magnum Ruger Bisley, which, as an added bonus with the same load, can shoot 25-yard, five-shot clusters that average less than an inch. The added barrel length combined with an extremely tight cylinder-to-barrel gap were responsible for the velocity increase over what could be achieved with my 6 1/2-inch Ruger.

The bullet weight most commonly associated with the 41 Magnum is, of course, the 210. The Sierra 210-grain JHC and Hornady 210-grain JHP have always been my choices, although I have no doubt that the Nosler and Speer offerings in this weight are also good performers. During the annual Wisconsin deer season, I keep five chambers in my old 41 Ruger loaded with either the Sierra or Hornady bullets and 19.5 grains of Winchester 296 when I'm in a treestand covering an area of 50 yards or less. Just a safety reminder: When using the older single actions that do

| **41 REMINGTON MAGNUM LOAD DATA** | | | | | | | |
|---|---|---|---|---|---|---|---|
| **Bullet** Wgt.Grs. | Type | **Load** (Grs./Powder) | Primer | **MV** (fps) | **Group** (ins.) | **Comments** |
| **Jacketed** | | | | | | |
| 170 | Sierra JHC | 24.0/H-110 | CCI 350 | 1365 | 1 3/8 | |
| 210 | Hornady JHP Sierra JHC | 20.5/IMR-4227 | CCI 300 | 1282 | 2 3/4 | near max. |
| 210 | Hornady JHP Sierra JHC | 20.5/H-110 | CCI 350 | 1175 | 2 | |
| 210 | Hornady XTP Sierra JHC | 19.5/W-296 | CCI 350 | 1200 | 1 3/16 | |
| 220 | Sierra Sil. | 20.0/W-296 | CCI 350 | 1100 | 1 3/4 | near max. |
| **Cast** | | | | | | |
| 210 | Green Bay SWC | 10.0/Unique | CCI 300 | 1208 | | Very accurate |
| 210 | Ohaus #611 210 K | 8.0/Unique | CCI 300 | 1032 | | |
| 210 | Ohaus #611 210 K | 19.0/2400 | CCI 300 | 1430 | 1 3/4 | ten-shots at 25 meters |
| 220 | Lyman #410459 SWC | 4.5/Bullseye | CCI 300 | 758 | | Target load |
| **Cast With Soft Gas Checks** | | | | | | |
| 220 | Lyman #410459 SWC | 18.0/H-110 | CCI 300 | 1120 | 1 3/8 | |
| 220 | Lyman #410459 SWC | 8.5/Unique | CCI 300 | 1054 | 1 3/4 | best all-round load |

Test gun: Ruger Blackhawk Old Model (three-screw), 6 1/2-inch barrel.
Remington cases. Oehler Model 12 chronograph with 5-foot screen spacing; first screen 10 feet from the muzzle. All groups are four-target, five-shot averages.

not have a transfer bar, load only *five* rounds. Keep the hammer down on an *empty chamber*!

The game of metallic silhouette shooting brought about demands for heavier 41-caliber bullets in solid form, and the bullet companies responded with 220-grain flatpoint solids. These early bullets had a fully jacketed flatpoint, and the jacket was crimped into the base of the bullet. The rest of the base was exposed lead. In the past several years, the bullet companies have opted to reverse the jacket design by putting the solid portion of the jacket at the base of the bullet and ending the jacket by folding it over a very small portion of the exposed lead at the flatpoint. The lead at the point visibly indents, but not enough that it could be mistaken for a hollowpoint. This design change was supposedly made because the original flatpoint solids could penetrate body armor. Properly stoked, these "originals," if you can find any, will also provide your sixgun with optimum penetration capability, which can be very comforting in dangerous game country. A Sierra 220 Silhouette bullet pushed by 20.0 grains of 296 will topple those 50-pound, 200-yard IHMSA rams with regularity. This proved to me that the design switch didn't detract from what that bullet was designed to do in the first place, knock over metallic silhouette targets.

With the 210-grain bullet weight, IMR-4227 powder gives the highest velocity, beating 296 by 82 fps. However, I am willing to sacrifice the added velocity for the better accuracy of 296. H-110 gave the lowest velocity, 1175 fps, and accuracy with 210-grain jacketed bullets was not as good as I got with 296 handloads.

IMR-4227 and H-110 both displayed their own particular accuracy problems with the 210-grain bullets tested.

H-110 would often group three shots, touching, then two more shots would open the group to over 2 inches. These flyers didn't occur in any special order, nor did groups settle down as I began to approach maximum loads.

None of my IMR-4227 loads would group acceptably. I define acceptable accuracy as five shots into 1 3/4 inches at 25 yards.

During the jacketed bullet tests, IMR-4227 preferred standard primers, while the more difficult-to-ignite H-110 and 296 required magnum primers for best results.

I have used cast bullets for most of my shooting over the past twenty-two years. I didn't cast my own when I first started reloading; I bought 210-grain SWC cast bullets from the Green Bay Bullet Co. I preferred the plain-base design, but if the gas-check version was all that was available, I would use it. Both types seemed to shoot equally well with the same load of 10 grains of Unique and CCI standard primers. This produced velocities of 1208 fps, with moderate recoil and excellent accuracy.

I eventually bought an Ohaus #611 210 K, 41-caliber bullet mould. Its shape is somewhat different from what we are accustomed to seeing in the semi-wadcutter design. The body is longer than normal and is topped off with a small flatpoint.

This long body is enough to restrict powder space when using the more bulky powders, as I discovered when loading IMR-4227. I had not yet reached the maximum load when I could no longer seat the bullets to the crimping groove, even with the powder charge heavily compressed. Due to its spaghetti-like shape, IMR-4227 takes up more space in the case than any of the other powders I used.

The front driving band on this particular Ohaus design is narrow and has a tendency to not always fill out completely when cast. Even when the mould and the metal are at the proper temperature, each bullet must be inspected for overall uniformity, with special attention paid to the driving band. Bad bullets do show up and must not be allowed to mix with the good ones.

I cast bullets from linotype, lubed and sized to .410-inch in a Lyman 450 lubricator/sizer.

I had two favorite loads for these semi-wadcutters, a light-to-medium load consisting of 8.0 grains of Unique, which chronographs at 1032 fps; and a heavy-hitting load of 19.0 grains of 2400 that sends bullets zipping out the barrel at 1430 fps. I have shot 25-meter, ten-shot groups that measured 1 3/4 inches, attesting to this hot handload's accuracy.

(Above) Progressive reloading presses such as this Dillon RL-450 allow for faster reloading as compared to single-stage presses.

Leaving the muzzle at 1200 fps, 210-grain Green Bay SWC bullets in front of 10.0/Unique printed this five-shot group, shot offhand at 50 feet. Note the full caliber holes caused by the sharp shoulders incorporated in the semi-wadcutter design.

Unfortunately, the bolt holding the sprue plate to the old Ohaus mould broke several years back, about the same time that my source of linotype metal dried up. I retired that mould in favor of a Lyman #410459 double-cavity. Weighing 220 grains when cast from Lyman's #2 bullet alloy, the slugs are lubed and sized to .410-inch.

My target load is 4.5 grains of Bullseye, which gives a muzzle velocity of 758 fps. It is very accurate and pleasant to shoot, and I often use this load at our club's 50-foot indoor range. It's great for offhand practice. Recoil is very mild, making this bullet/powder combination ideal for double-action shooting.

My other two loads with this bullet—18.0 grains of H-1110, 8.5 grains of Unique—both utilize soft gas checks (SGCs). (See Handloader's Digest, 13th Edition, "Soft Gas Checks.") These loads shoot well, and the SGCs keep my bore free of leading. I shoot the Unique load much more than the other because my Dillon is set to throw 8.5 Unique, which is what I use with the 250-grain SWC and SGC in my Model 629 44 Magnum. One charge setting satisfies two calibers. My powder measure stays set as it is, and I weigh all other charges on a powder scale.

When I discussed primer/powder preferences for jacketed bullets earlier in this article, I noted that H-110 would perform well with magnum primers only. With cast bullets, however, H-110 shows a marked preference for the standard version.

Although I enjoy casting and shooting my own bullets, casting time seems to be getting more scarce, resulting in my buying Wisconsin Cartridge Co. (WCC) cast bullets on a more frequent basis. Although I haven't chronographed these 210-grain, bevel-base SWC bullets, a charge of 19.0 grains of 2400 lit by CCI standard primers should give velocities around 1350 fps. I carry five of these in the cylinder of my old Ruger when I'm driving for deer in thick woods and swamps, where the shooting is notoriously fast and close. These 210s have ample velocity and penetrate deeply into, if not completely through, a whitetail, which is the performance I want for this type of hunting situation.

The WCC bullets are cast from an alloy that is much harder than Lyman #2, making them adaptable to my 19.0/2400 load without leading the barrel. When this charge pushes my Lyman 220s, however, inaccuracy and barrel leading result.

During my tests, I didn't find one 41 Magnum load that gave its best accuracy with a maximum powder charge. Usually, groups would transform into patterns and recoil would increase dramatically with max loads. Couple this with the added pounding the gun was exposed to, and it didn't take me long to realize that I was deriving no benefits from the continued use of these heavy charges.

The 41 Remington Magnum can be handloaded to give performance levels ranging from 750 fps target loads to full-blown 1400 fps hunting loads. This gives flexibility to the cartridge, enabling it to handle different types of shooting situations, and handle them well. This is, indeed, a fine cartridge. ●

# HOW TO BARREL LAP

by C.E. HARRIS

## Don't give up on that rough, fouled barrel. There's still something you can do.

I'M NO EXPERT on lapping barrels, as I've only done a couple of dozen, rather than hundreds like those who do such things for a living. Hand lapping is the best way to clean a rough, fouled barrel, but it requires patience and common sense. Fire lapping, as advocated by Merrill Martin, has been tried by many people over the years. I don't agree with a lot which has been written about fire lapping, but it might be OK to try on a barrel you don't care much about. I would never attempt it with an expensive match-grade barrel or a collector piece that you couldn't replace.

Fire lapping, in my opinion, is the impatient man's way and does not do as good a job because most of the abrasive action takes place in the throat, during the first few inches of bullet travel. In hand lapping, you can work on the whole surface of the bore.

Barrel maker Boots Obermeyer told me there is no point in using abrasive finer than 240-grit. If you use too fine a compound, you will accentuate the loose spots. Essentially, what you are doing is aggressive cleaning and ensuring uniform dimensions. If you are lapping a drilled and reamed barrel prior to rifling, in order to remove reamer marks and to bring the bore up to size, you would use a heavier grit like 200, or even 180. Then after rifling, you give it a few passes with finer compound like 220 or 240 to knock off the wire edges from the cutter.

### Lap Before Cutting

A new barrel should be lapped before the ends have been cut off, chambered and crowned. If you want to lap a finished barrel, you have to go about it differently to keep from enlarging the muzzle. Here's how to clean up a nice old rifle with a salt-and-pepper bore, putting it back into shooting shape.

**Step One**: Strip the rifle to its barreled action and remove the bolt or breechblock.

**Step Two**: Brush the bore well with a brush and bore cleaner, wipe it dry with patches, and degrease it with mineral spirits.

**Step Three**: Preheat a lead pot and dipper filled with soft, pure lead.

**Step Four**: Clamp the barreled action in a padded vise, sights down.

**Step Five**: Use a polished, one-piece steel cleaning rod. Fit a worn bore brush to it and impale a patch over the brush, pulling it three-quarters of the way down the brush. The lap should be at least four bullet diameters long, when formed onto the brush section. The patch forms a dam to keep the lead from running down the rod.

**Step Six**: Insert the rod and brush in the bore from the chamber end and run it up to within 1/2-inch of the muzzle.

**Step Seven**: When the lead has melted, lightly oil the outside of the muzzle to keep the lead from sticking, then pour molten lead over the barrel until it runs off the barrel without solidifying.

**Step Eight**: When the muzzle is hot, turn the bore upright and carefully pour hot lead from the dipper down into the bore and up to the muzzle. Let the lead overflow and keep pouring as the lead solidifies so you will get a well filled out casting.

**Step Nine**: When the lap hardens, *gently* tap it partly out of the muzzle, but not completely; then trim off the ragged end with a sharp knife or side cutters. Swab the hot lap with AA Clover paste or 240-grit emery paste, let the grease base melt and run back into the bore, and then, while grasping the rod firmly in both hands with the barrel securely clamped, slowly pull the lap back into the bore.

**Step Ten**: Clamp the barreled action in a horizontal position in the vise so that when you push the lap out the muzzle it will exit about 1-inch before it hits a stop. This keeps the lap from enlarging the bore, but will keep it snug as it bumps gently against the stop on each stroke.

**Step Eleven**: At first you may be able to work the lap only in short strokes near the muzzle. You want to work it back toward the breech as soon as you can and do most of your work there, working in 6-inch strokes and then taking a full stroke the length of the bore every second or third pass.

**Step Twelve**: After about a dozen passes, the lap will become loose. Push it all the way out, apply some more compound, rotate it over one groove, pull it back again and repeat the process so you are not always running the grit in the same "tracks." This will take some effort. If you are unable to pull the old lap back into the bore, don't sweat it. Just tap it back out, melt it off in the pot, preheat the muzzle again, and cast another one. It shouldn't take more than twelve to twenty strokes at maximum to do the job. Otherwise, you are overdoing it.

**Step Thirteen**: Afterward, do a really thorough cleaning, being especially careful to get all the grit out of the lug seats.

**Step Fourteen**: After cleaning and reassembly, take your favorite loads and go to the range to enjoy the fruits of your labor. The bore may still not look like new, but it will probably shoot better. ●

by DARREL G. DENNIS

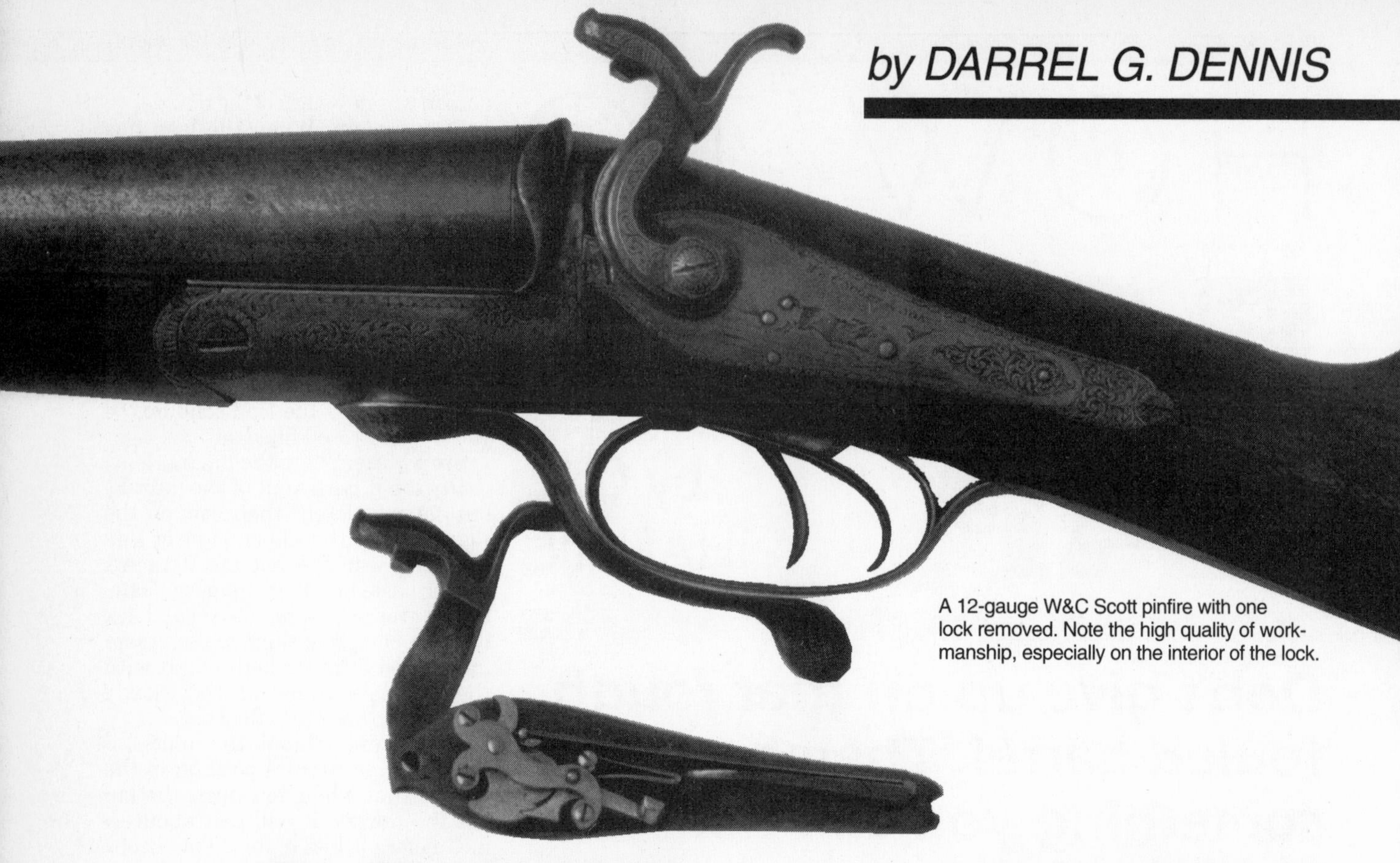

A 12-gauge W&C Scott pinfire with one lock removed. Note the high quality of workmanship, especially on the interior of the lock.

# To Shoot My PINFIRE

SEVERAL YEARS AGO, a friend who knew I was interested in double guns brought a W&C Scott pinfire shotgun to my house and asked me to find a buyer for it. The gun was a 12-gauge back-action sidelock of high quality and was in very good mechanical condition.

After a number of unsuccessful attempts to sell it, I suggested to my wife Marjorie that it would make a nice Christmas present. She obliged, and on Christmas Day I removed the locks and found that the internal parts were exquisitely fitted. The lock parts were nickel-plated, and the hammers cocked with a crisp click as if the internal parts were as hard and smooth as glass.

Since my preference is for guns that are usable, as well as collectible and attractive, I attempted to acquire some shells. Turner Kirkland of Dixie Gun Works offered original 20-gauge pinfire cartridges for sale but I was unable to find any number of 12-gauge shells except for the occasional specimens at gun shows.

After other sources were explored without success, I decided to manufacture my own using a variation of the method outlined in Boothroyd's book.[1] Basically, I drilled a hole in a deprimed shotshell battery cup; drilled appropriately located holes in shells of Activ or Eclipse manufacture; and by using a nail, No. 11 percussion cap and aluminum duct tape I was in business, at least in a rather primitive and perhaps dangerous way.

The results were never entirely satisfactory from a ballistics standpoint, since hangfires were frequent. In addition, I was plagued by the safety question: Does one prime a shell already loaded with blackpowder and risk an explosion, or does one load a primed shell with the pin in place and risk similar unpleasantries perhaps of an even more spectacular nature?!!

Despite my enthusiasm for pinfire shooting, I valued my eyes and trigger finger and therefore let the project languish after a few experimental shells and one bagged cottontail rabbit.

I believe that reading too much about shooting pinfires by authors such as Roger Barlow kept up my enthusiasm, and the essentially unusable pinfire that hung over the fireplace continued to haunt me. Occasionally, I'd ponder the problem of loading safer and better cartridges. Eventually I decided that a turned brass rod to replace the battery cup should improve ignition since the percussion cap would be directly immersed in the powder charge. On the day I decided to manufacture the rods with a slot to hold the percussion cap, it was not possible to locate an appropriately sized end mill, so the project ground to another halt.

As I looked at the piece of brass in the lathe, I thought that boring the rod in the side to hold a small pistol primer with an open end directly contacting the powder charge might work. I wasn't sure that the gun would adequately fire pistol primers, but in about twenty minutes I had

[1]Boothroyd, G. 1985. *The Shotgun History and Development*. A. and C. Black Ltd., 35 Bedford Row., London.

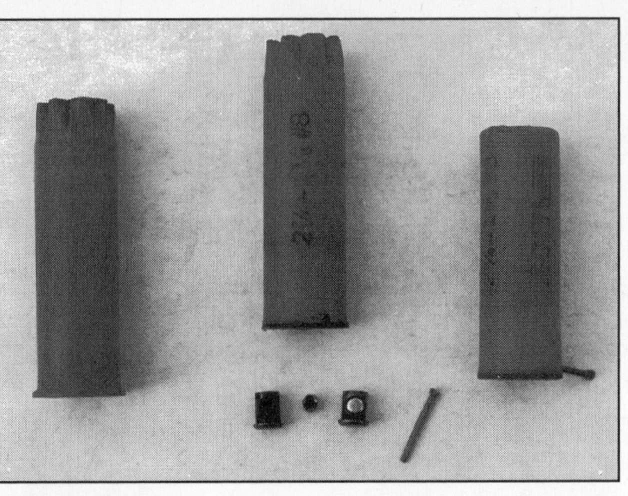

Pinfire cartridge components during three stages of development (from left): unmodified Activ empty case; modified case, brass holder, small pistol primer, primed brass holder and modified finishing nail (pin); loaded shell.

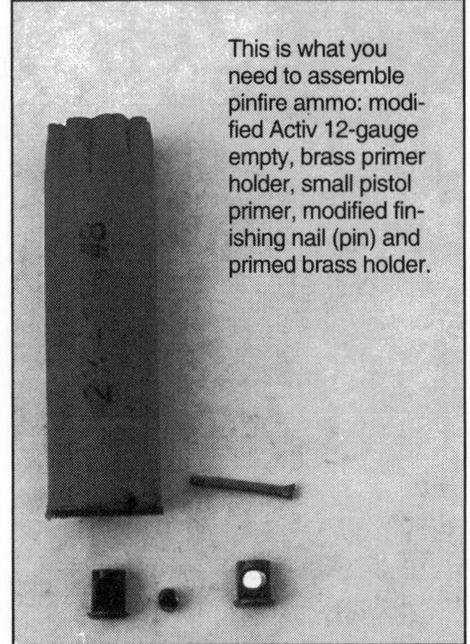

This is what you need to assemble pinfire ammo: modified Activ 12-gauge empty, brass primer holder, small pistol primer, modified finishing nail (pin) and primed brass holder.

two experimental primer holders produced and ready to try. The Scott fired the primers six times in a row, using cut-off 1½-inch finishing nails for pins. I was ecstatic! It was now late afternoon, and I quickly seated the primer holders in two shells, loaded them with 3 drams FFFg and 1⅛ ounces of shot, drove to my friend Sam Millard's house in the country, and with the two shots broke two hand-thrown clay targets into tiny pieces. The loads were crisp and fast.

Later, twenty-four more brass holders were produced on my Maximat VIOP combination lathe-milling machine. The production rate was approximately eight holders per hour.

To produce the holders, I turned a piece of 0.375-inch brass rod to a diameter of 0.244 with a thin rim left at 0.318 to resemble a regular shotshell battery cup. Overall length was 0.325-inch. These were drilled with a No. 2 center drill held in the tail stock until a chamfer was cut in the front end of the holder to equal approximately 80 percent of the holder's diameter. I suspect that the chamfer is not necessary, but after the early experiences with hangfires I decided to do everything possible to help ignition.

For production efficiency, each end of the rod is turned and bored appropriately and then each holder is held in a drill press vise and drilled to hold the primer using a No. 2 center drill. The primer pocket in the side of the holder is finished with a 4.5mm drill, with the end ground square. This leaves the primer a loose fit in the holder so that it can be readily pried from the holder after firing. Depths are approximately 0.135-inch so that the primer will seat deeply enough to clear the shell as the holder is inserted.

I found that less tool changing was required if primer holders were turned on each end of two rods, so that the four holders could be drilled in the drill press at the same time and then all four could be cut off in the lathe. Shells are best manufactured by turning the rim of Activ plastic shells to 0.8-inch in diameter. Activs are preferable to other makes because of a steel reinforcing plate in the head that prevents the firing pin from pulling through the back of the shell. All modern centerfire shells must have the rim trimmed to enable the cartridges to chamber in pinfire guns.

Holes for the pin are drilled immediately inside the steel liner with a No. 47 drill which measures 0.078, so that adequate clearance is provided for the 0.075 pins and binding and subsequent hangfires do not occur. The length of the pins should be adjusted so that a maximum of 0.125-inch of travel is left before the hammers bottom on the barrels after contacting the pins. In addition, the primer must be carefully aligned with the pin hole in the shell when it is primed.

All the above work can be readily accomplished by any basement machinist with a lathe and a drill press. I decided to continue to use finishing nails for pins rather than brass rod because the nails were more likely to fire modern primers. Nails are considerably harder than brass rod and are potentially more likely to damage soft hammers; however, the increased surface area of the nail head lessens the impact on soft hammer steel and largely compensates for increased hardness.

Primers are easily seated by placing the primer, compound side up, near the edge of a wooden block, positioning the holder opening over the primer and pressing gently down. Several attempts may be required, but with a bit of practice, primers will be easily and quickly seated. Fired primers can be removed from the holder by inserting a blunt nail through the front hole in the holder and levering the primer out the side.

After producing twenty-six shells, I shot a round of Skeet, and broke eighteen targets. That could be an all-time record for Skeet shot with a pinfire! There were several misfires that fired the second time I cocked the hammer on the left side of the Scott and one cartridge that would not fire. Later investigation showed that a minor adjustment in the hammer position on the Scott cured the misfires, and the shell that wouldn't fire was a result of the primer being oriented 180 degrees out of line with the pin.

The chief merits of the present system are safety in loading and excellent ignition. My shells were loaded on a MEC 250 with a moveable shellholder. The completed shell may be safely carried in pockets, whereas original pinfires were unsafe if they were dropped or otherwise mishandled. I do not insert the firing pin into the shells until the gun is loaded, something that would be totally impractical as well as dangerous with other systems.

A word of caution: unlike my Scott, many pinfires have thin barrels and only very light loads should be used. The use of guns with deeply pitted barrels should be avoided entirely.

I'm looking forward to hunting with the Scott this fall and will definitely try to better my record at Skeet. Since the gun weighs 9 pounds, the hunting will likely be limited to decoying ducks and maybe a few pheasants. In any event, there is a lot of satisfaction in using the old gun in a safe and effective fashion. In addition, its lack of utility no longer haunts me as it hangs over the fireplace! ●

# HANDLOADER'S MARKETPLACE

SHOWCASING
SELECTED PRODUCTS
FOR THE RELOADER

## NEW RIFLE POWDER

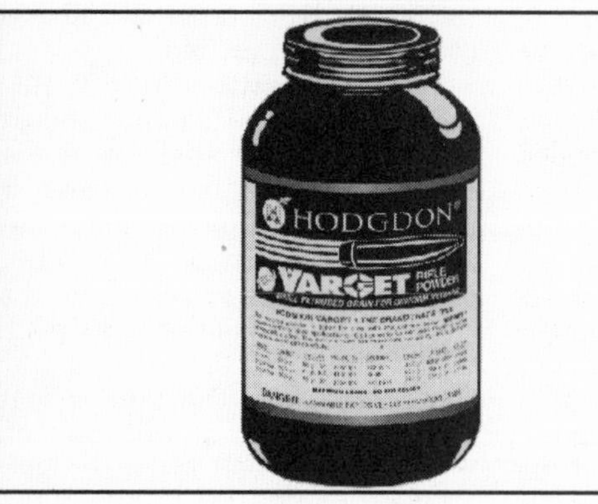


Hodgdon's versatile rifle powder Varget® was developed to give improved performance and velocities in many popular rifle cartridges.

Varget's small extruded grains meter more uniformly through powder measures and the powder lacks the sensitivity to temperature of other powders. These two characteristics produce more consistent velocities and pressures in varying weather conditions. In some caliber/bullet combinations this high-energy powder provides superior performance such as 4135 fps in the 22/250 with a 40-grain bullet.

The burning rate of Varget falls between H380® and H4895® and is similar to, though not interchangeable with, 4064. Load data for Varget is available in Hodgdon's complimentary *1997 Basic Reloaders Manual.*

**HODGDON POWDER CO., INC.**

## BULLET SEATING DEPTH SYSTEM

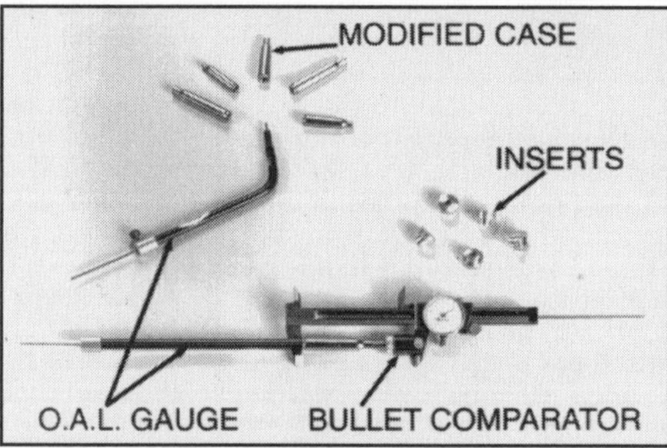


Small changes in the clearance between the bullet and the rifling can make a dramatic difference in accuracy. By fine-tuning the bullet seating depth of handloads, you can often cut group size in half. Stoney Point offers a versatile and affordable two-gauge system which precisely regulates the clearance between the bullet and rifling. Using any bullet of choice and the O.A.L. Gauge, you can, in about one minute, produce an accurate model of your chamber. Then, caliper measurement from case base to ogive determines the precise seating depth needed for the bullet to contact the rifling. This gauge system makes it easy to set your seating die for the exact bullet jump you desire. Modified Cases are available to fit any chamber size, including wildcats. Dealer program available.

**STONEY POINT PRODUCTS, INC.**

## RIFLE, PISTOL AND SHOTSHELL POWDERS

Accurate Arms offers a full line of pistol, rifle and shotshell propellants for handloaders. Whether reloading for hunting, competition or just practice, Accurate Arms propellants have been formulated to meet your needs. Their disc, flake, ball and extruded powders offer burning speeds for all popular cartridges as well as some of the more esoteric. Four burning speed formulations are available for shotshell plus four for pistol reloaders and twelve more geared specifically to the rifle-class cartridge. For the rifle cartridge reloader, two types of propellants are available—ball propellants, including the popular Accurate 2230, and the X-truded™ line, from XMP-5744 to XMR-4350. For more information, to place an order or for a free copy of their reloading booklet, call their toll-free Customer Service Line or write them direct.

**ACCURATE ARMS COMPANY, INC.**

## NYLON COATED GUN CLEANING RODS

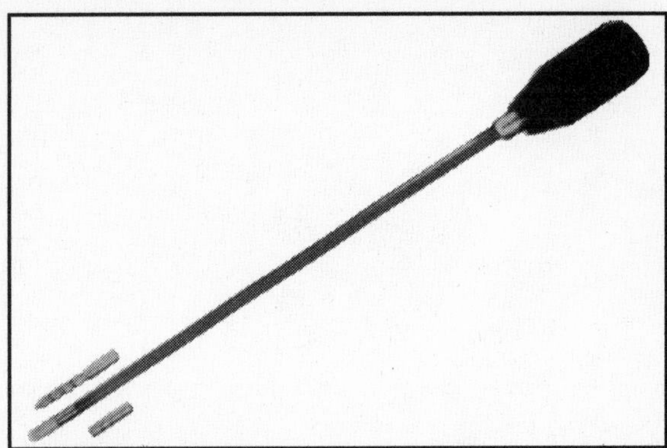

J. Dewey cleaning rods have been used by the U.S. Olympic shooting team and the benchrest community for over 20 years. These one-piece, spring-tempered, steel-base rods will not gall delicate rifling or damage the muzzle area of front-cleaned firearms. The nylon coating eliminates the problem of abrasives adhering to the rod during the cleaning operation. Each rod comes with a hard non-breakable plastic handle supported by ball-bearings, top and bottom, for ease of cleaning.

The brass cleaning jags are designed to pierce the center of the cleaning patch or wrap around the knurled end to keep the patch centered in the bore.

Coated rods are available from 17-caliber to shotgun bore size in several lengths to meet the needs of any shooter. Write for more information.

**J. DEWEY MFG. CO., INC.**

## FOLDING BIPODS

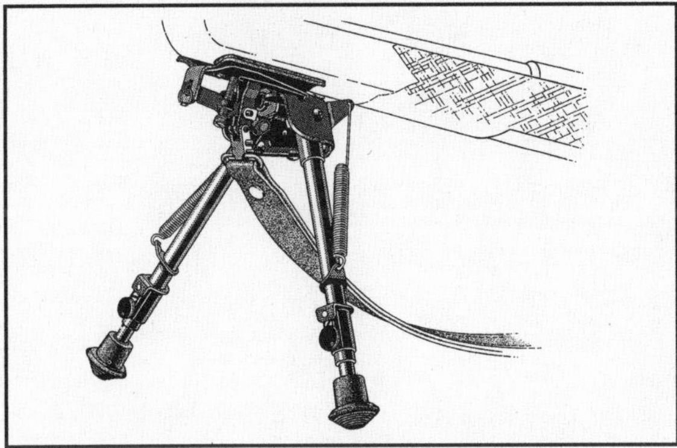

Harris Bipods clamp securely to most stud-equipped bolt-action rifles and are quick-detachable. With adapters, they will fit some other guns. On all models except the Model LM, folding legs have completely adjustable spring-return extensions. The sling swivel attaches to the clamp. This time-proven design is manufactured with heat-treated steel and hard alloys and has a black anodized finish.

Series S Bipods rotate 45° for instant leveling on uneven ground. Hinged base has tension adjustment and buffer springs to eliminate tremor or looseness in crotch area of bipod. They are otherwise similar to non-rotating Series 1A2.

Thirteen models are available from Harris Engineering; literature is free.

**HARRIS ENGINEERING, INC.**

## SHOTGUNNER'S CATALOG

For over 20 years Ballistic Products has provided the world's shotgunners with custom components for reloading high-performance shotshell ammunition. They provide the makings for 10-gauge, sporting Clays and target, small bore, bismuth, steel shot, benchrest and slug ammunition, as well as a library of loading guides and ballistics information.

Ballistic Products invites you to get to know their knowledgable technicians, commitment to R&D and after-the-sale support. They are a great source for fine shotgun ammunition products. Call their toll-free order line between 9:00 AM and 5:00 PM CST. Mention *Handloader's Digest* and receive a free catalog subscription.

**BALLISTIC PRODUCTS INC.**

## BULLET ULTRA™ SEATER

Forster Products has been providing quality-conscious shooters and reloaders with precision equipment since 1939. Their complete line of tools, equipment and accessories has set the standard of quality in the industry for 58 years.

From case trimmers and reamers to their exclusive Co-Ax© Press, Forster's reloading products are among the best on the market. For optimum rifle accuracy, Forster offers their precision Bench Rest© seater and sizing dies as well as their Ultra™ micrometer bullet seater. Forster's expanding line of handgun reloading equipment holds true to this same tradition of excellence. In addition, gunsmiths, armorers and blackpowder enthusiasts will find a broad selection of quality tools and supplies.

**FORSTER PRODUCTS**

## PREMIUM BULLET MOULDS

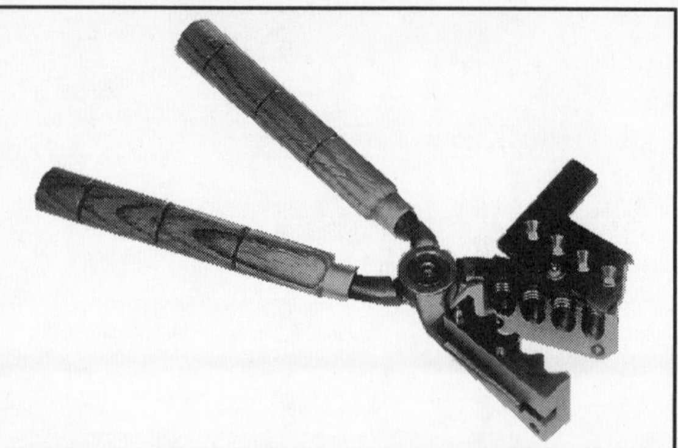

SAECO has long been regarded as one of the premier names in production bullet moulds by knowledgeable casters.

Several years ago, Redding Reloading purchased the remains of the old SAECO Reloading Company and is now producing the SAECO bullet mould line.

Redding has been constantly refining and adding to the lineup of sizes and styles to choose from and offers two-cavity and four-cavity blocks as standard items. Single-, three-, six- and eight-cavity moulds are also available on special order.

When you write or call Redding Reloading for a free catalog of SAECO products, be sure to mention you read about the SAECO lineup in *Handloader's Marketplace*.

**REDDING RELOADING EQUIPMENT**

## NEW BRASS CASE POLISH

Iosso's new Case Polish simplifies the cleaning of brass cases. Working as an additive to tumbling media, it cleans and restores the brass to a high luster finish. In addition to removing powder fouling, residue, oxidation, tarnish and discoloration, it also protects casings from tarnishing once cleaned.

Simply adding two tablespoons of polish to each pound of tumbling media will reduce tumbling time, give brass casings a like-new finish, and effectively clean and polish casings for the lifetime of the tumbling media.

For soiled casings approximate tumbling time is just one hour; 30 minutes for cases pre-cleaned with Iosso Case Cleaner.

Iosso Case Polish is available in 8-oz., 32-oz., 1- and 5-gallon containers. The 8-oz. size retails for $10.30.

**IOSSO PRODUCTS**

## RIFLE, PISTOL AND SHOTSHELL POWDERS

Accurate Arms offers a full line of pistol, rifle and shotshell propellants for handloaders. Whether reloading for hunting, competition or just practice, Accurate Arms propellants have been formulated to meet your needs. Their disc, flake, ball and extruded powders offer burning speeds for all popular cartridges as well as some of the more esoteric. Four burning speed formulations are available for shotshell plus four for pistol reloaders and twelve more geared specifically to the rifle-class cartridge. For the rifle cartridge reloader, two types of propellants are available—ball propellants, including the popular Accurate 2230, and the X-truded™ line, from XMP-5744 to XMR-4350. For more information, to place an order or for a free copy of their reloading booklet, call their toll-free Customer Service Line or write them direct.

**ACCURATE ARMS COMPANY, INC.**

## ADJUSTABLE BORE SAVER ROD GUIDES

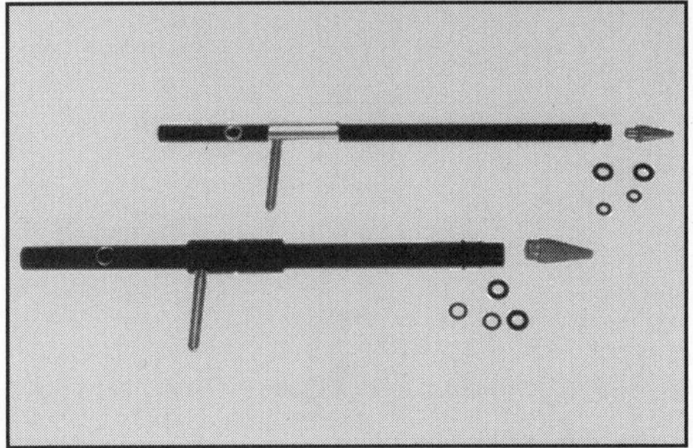

The Dewey Bore Saver cleaning rod guide replaces the bolt in your action while cleaning. The cleaning rod enters the bore straight, without harming the chamber or throat. Made from anodized aluminum in six bore sizes, the aluminum rod guide collar with threaded brass adjustment pin allows for quick adjustment to any bolt length. Chamber-sealing O-rings prohibit solvents from entering the action, trigger and magazine areas.

The guide can be used with all cleaning rods; all models fit .695- to .700-inch bolt diameter rifles. All guides allow brush clearance through tube I.D. and come with solvent port, spare O-rings and O-ring assembly tool. Weatherby and Sako models available. Write or fax J. Dewey Mfg. Co., Inc. for more information.

**J. DEWEY MFG. CO., INC.**

## RIFLE POWDERS

Finnish manufacturer VihtaVuori Oy offers American reloaders a full line of rifle powders for benchrest, varmint and hunting purposes.

VihtaVuori's 100 series single base powders are the cylindrical type for clean burning, consistent performance and top accuracy. These powders include the fastest burning N110, followed by N120, N130, N133, N135, N140, N150, N160, N165 and the slowest burning, N170.

VihtaVuori's High Energy 500 series is formulated to gain higher muzzle velocities without increasing chamber pressures.

All VihtaVuori rifle powders come packaged in 2-pound canisters. Reloading data is available in their free reloading guide. Write, call or fax their importer, Kaltron-Pettibone, for more information.

**VIHTAVUORI OY**

## NEW BULLET LUBES

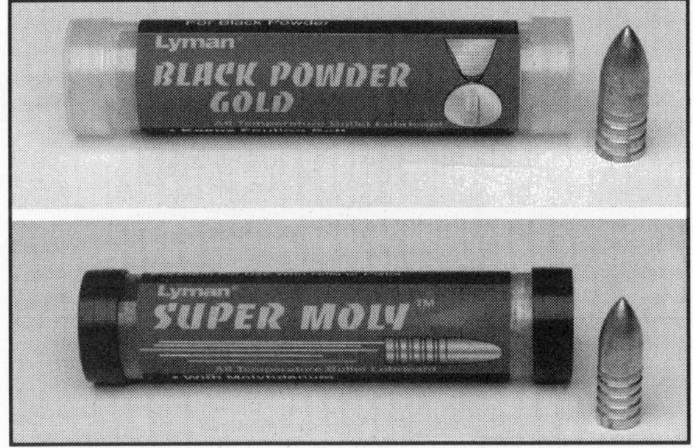


Lyman Products Corporation announces two new lubes for cast bullet shooters. Black Powder Gold, their match-proven high-performance lube, was developed specifically for the blackpowder cartridge shooter and was used in competition at the 1996 Black Powder Silhouette Championship at Ratone, New Mexico, finishing twice in the Top Ten. Lyman's new Super Moly is an all-purpose, high temperature bullet lubricant designed for any kind of cast bullet shooting. The special formulation includes the addition of Molybdenum Disulfide which helps increase bullet velocity and improve accuracy by coating the rifle or pistol barrel with a fine film to prevent leading. Both lubes will not melt up to 130°, yet are soft enough to be applied to bullets by hand. For more information, call or write Lyman Products.

**LYMAN PRODUCTS CORPORATION**

## NEW SHOTGUN SLUGS WITH SABOTS

Lyman's new 12- and 20-gauge Shocker Shotgun Sabots allow any shotshell reloader to load slugs without any special tools.

Shocker Slugs are designed to fit into standard one-piece shotgun wads and can be fold crimped like standard shotshells. Their special wasp-waist design provides controlled expansion and energy transfer without any sacrifice in accuracy.

On impact the hollow rear section of the slug folds up and outward, which proves devastating on big game up to 100 yards. The 12-gauge slug weighs 525 grains; the 20-gauge, 350 grains.

Call or write Lyman Products Corporation for more information.

**LYMAN PRODUCTS CORPORATION**

# HANDLOADER'S MARKETPLACE

## PRECISION RELOADING DIES

REDDING has built a reputation equal to the quality of the reloading gear they produce, and they continue to expand their line of reloading dies.

Their newest introduction is a line of bushing-style neck sizing dies with interchangeable sizing bushings in .001″ increments from 17 through 30-caliber.

The latest catalog from REDDING lists dies for over 400 different calibers and a whole host of special-purpose dies. There are competition seating and neck-sizing dies, special purpose crimping dies, trim dies, custom-made dies and a section on case-forming that lists everything you need to form one caliber from another.

Write, call or fax REDDING to receive their latest catalog.

**REDDING RELOADING EQUIPMENT**

## COMPETITION POWDER MEASURES

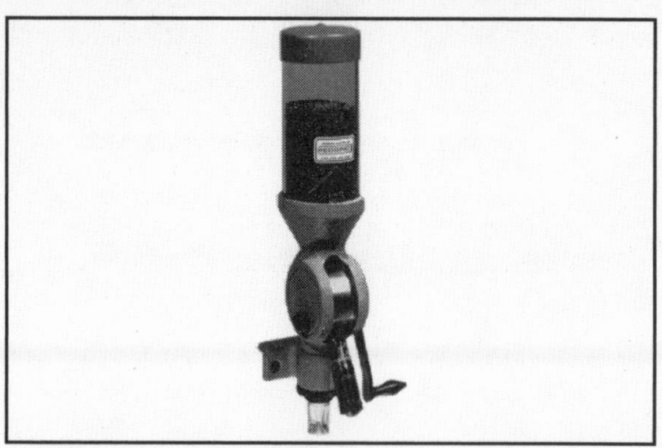

REDDING powder measures have earned a well-deserved and dedicated following among benchrest shooters. Close tolerances, hand-fitted drums and super-accurate micrometer adjustments are a REDDING trademark.

Two new competition models have recently been introduced. Both feature reduced diameter, "test tube" shaped metering chambers to minimize irregular powder settling and enhance charge-to-charge uniformity.

The Competition BR-30 has a charge range of 10 to 50 grains and was designed specifically for benchrest competition reloaders.

The Competition 10X-Pistol measure, with a charge range of approximately 1 to 25 grains, was created as the ideal pistol powder measure. Write, call or fax REDDING for their latest catalog.

**REDDING RELOADING EQUIPMENT**

## HANDLOADER'S MARKETPLACE MANUFACTURERS' ADDRESSES

**ACCURATE ARMS COMPANY, INC.**
*(Pg. 197, 198)*
Dept. HDM17
5891 Hwy. 230 W.
McEwen, TN 37101
Phone: 800-416-3006
Fax: 615-729-4211

**BALLISTIC PRODUCTS INC.**
*(Pg. 197)*
Attn: Dept. HM'17
Box 293
20015 75th Avenue North
Corcoran, MN 55340
Phone: 888-273-5623 (orders) or
612-494-9237 (other)
Fax: 612-494-9236

**J. DEWEY MFG. CO., INC.**
*(Pg. 197, 199)*
Attn: Dept. HM'17
P.O. Box 2014
Southbury, CT 06488
Phone: 203-264-3064
Fax: 203-262-6907

**FORSTER PRODUCTS**
*(Pg. 198)*
Attn: Dept. HM'17
82 E. Lanark Ave.
Lanark, IL 61046
Phone: 815-493-6360
Fax: 815-493-2371

**HARRIS ENGINEERING INC.**
*(Pg. 197)*
Attn: Dept. HM'17
999 Broadway
Barlow, KY 42024

**HODGDON POWDER CO., INC.**
*(Pg. 196)*
Attn: Dept. H90697
P.O. Box 2932
Shawnee Mission, KS 66201
Phone: 913-362-9455
Fax: 913-362-1307

**IOSSO PRODUCTS**
*(Pg. 198)*
Attn: Dept. HM'17
1485 Lively Blvd.
Elk Grove Village, IL 60007
Phone: 847-437-8400
Fax: 847-437-8478

**KALTRON-PETTIBONE**
*(Pg. 199)*
Attn: Dept. HM'17
1241 Ellis Street
Bensenville, IL 60106
Phone: 800-683-0464
Fax: 708-350-1606

**LYMAN PRODUCTS CORPORATION**
*(Pg. 199)*
Attn: Dept. 344-5
475 Smith Street
Middletown, CT 06457-1541
Phone: 860-632-2020 or
800-225-9626
Fax: 860-632-1699

**REDDING RELOADING EQUIPMENT**
*(Pg. 198, 200)*
Attn: Dept. HM'17
1098 Starr Road
Cortland, NY 13045
Phone: 607-753-3331
Fax: 607-756-8445

**STONEY POINT PRODUCTS, INC.**
*(Pg. 196)*
Attn: Dept. HM'17
P.O. Box 234
New Ulm, MN 56073-0234
Phone: 507-354-3360
Fax: 507-354-7236

**VIHTAVUORI OY**
*(Pg. 199)*
Attn: Dept. HM'17
1241 Ellis Street
Bensenville, IL 60106
Phone: 800-683-0464
Fax: 708-350-1606

# HANDLOADER'S DIGEST
17th Edition

# CATALOG

# LOADEX

**An alphabetical listing of all the products in the HANDLOADER'S DIGEST catalog by manufacturer name and product.**

## A



## B

## C



## D

## E



## F



## G



## H

## I



## J



## K



## L

## M



## N



## O



## P

## Q, R

## S

PART 1 2 3 4 5 6 7

# METALLIC CARTRIDGES
## TOOLS & ACCESSORIES

# Section 1: Metallic Cartridges

**C-H/4-D Heavyweight Champion**

**Frame:** Cast iron
**Frame Type:** O-frame
**Die Thread:** 7/8-14 or 1-14
**Avg. Rounds Per Hour:** NA
**Ram Stroke:** 3 1/4″
**Weight:** 26 lbs.
**Features:** 1.185″ diameter ram with 16 square inches of bearing surface; ram drilled to allow passage of spent primers; solid steel handle; toggle that slightly breaks over top dead center. Includes universal primer arm with large and small punches. From C-H Tool & Die/4-D Custom Die.
**Price:** . . . . . . . . . . . . . . . . . . . . . . **$220.00**

**C-H/4-D No. 444**

**Frame:** Aluminum alloy
**Frame Type:** H-frame
**Die Thread:** 7/8-14
**Avg. Rounds Per Hour:** 200
**Ram Stroke:** 3 3/4″
**Weight:** 12 lbs.
**Features:** Two 7/8″ solid steel shaft "H" supports; platen rides on permanently lubed bronze bushings; loads smallest pistol to largest magnum rifle cases and has strength to full-length resize. Includes four rams, large and small primer arm and primer catcher. From C-H Tool & Die/4-D Custom Die.
**Price:** . . . . . . . . . . . . . . . . . . . . . . **$214.50**

**C-H/4-D No. 444-X Pistol Champ**

**Frame:** Aluminum alloy
**Frame Type:** H-frame
**Die Thread:** 7/8-14
**Avg. Rounds Per Hour:** 200
**Ram Stroke:** 3 3/4″
**Weight:** 12 lbs.
**Features:** Tungsten carbide sizing die; Speed Seater seating die with tapered entrance to automatically align bullet on case mouth; automatic primer feed for large or small primers; push-button powder measure with easily changed bushings for 215 powder/load combinations; taper crimp die. Conversion kit for caliber changeover available. From C-H Tool & Die/4-D Custom Die.
**Price:** . . . . . . . . . . . . . . . . **See chart for pricing.**

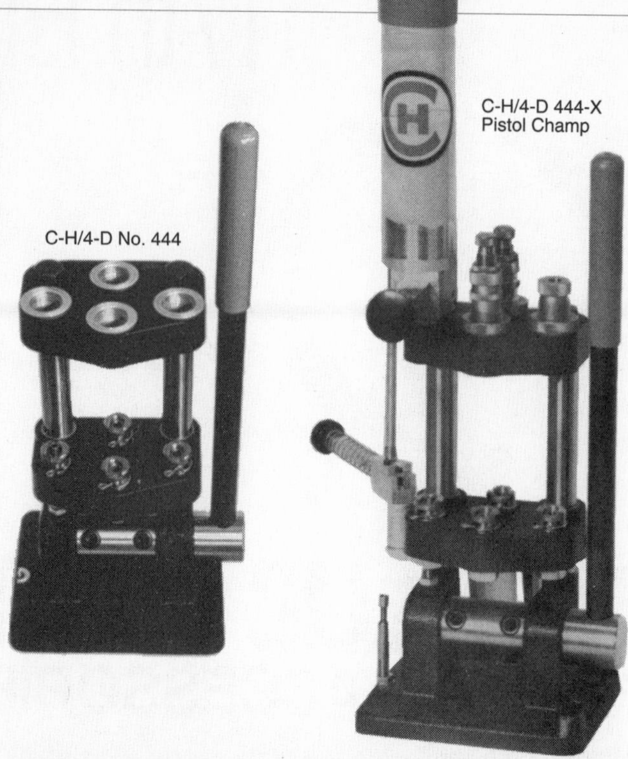

C-H/4-D No. 444

C-H/4-D 444-X Pistol Champ

| C-H/4-D | | | | |
|---|---|---|---|---|
| | No. 444 Pistol Champ | | 444-X Conversion Kit | |
| Caliber | Carbide Sizer | Steel Sizer | Carbide Sizer | Steel Sizer |
| 10mm/40 S&W | $308.50 | $292.00 | $92.50 | $62.80 |
| 30 M1 Carbine | 316.50 | 292.00 | 92.50 | 62.80 |
| 32 S&W/H&R Mag. | 308.50 | 292.00 | 84.50 | 62.80 |
| 38 Spl/357 Mag. | 308.50 | 292.00 | 84.50 | 62.80 |
| 41 Magnum | 308.50 | 292.00 | 84.50 | 62.80 |
| 44 Magnum | 308.50 | 292.00 | 84.50 | 62.80 |
| 45 ACP | 308.50 | 292.50 | 84.50 | 62.80 |
| 45 Colt | 308.50 | 292.00 | 84.50 | 62.80 |
| 9mm Luger | 308.50 | 292.00 | 84.50 | 62.80 |

**FORSTER Co-Ax Press B-2**

**Frame:** Cast iron
**Frame Type:** Modified O-frame
**Die Thread:** 7/8-14
**Avg. Rounds Per Hour:** 120
**Ram Stroke:** 4″
**Weight:** 18 lbs.
**Features:** Snap-in/snap-out die change; spent primer catcher with drop tube threaded into carrier below shellholder; automatic, handle-activated, cammed shellholder with opposing spring-loaded jaws to contact extractor groove; floating guide rods for alignment and reduced friction; no torque on the head due to design of linkage and pivots; shellholder jaws that float with die permitting case to center in the die; right- or left-hand operation; priming device for seating to factory specifications. "S" shellholder jaws included. From Forster Products.
**Price:** . . . . . . . . . . . . . . . . . . . . . . **$294.00**
**Price:** Extra shellholder jaws . . . . . . . . . . . **$24.00**

**HOLLYWOOD Jr. Press**

**Frame:** Aluminum
**Frame Type:** H-frame
**Die Thread:** 7/8-14
**Avg. Rounds Per Hour:** 50-100
**Ram Stroke:** 6 1/2″
**Weight:** 17 lbs.
**Price:** . . . . . . . . . . . . . . . . . . . . . . **$200.00**

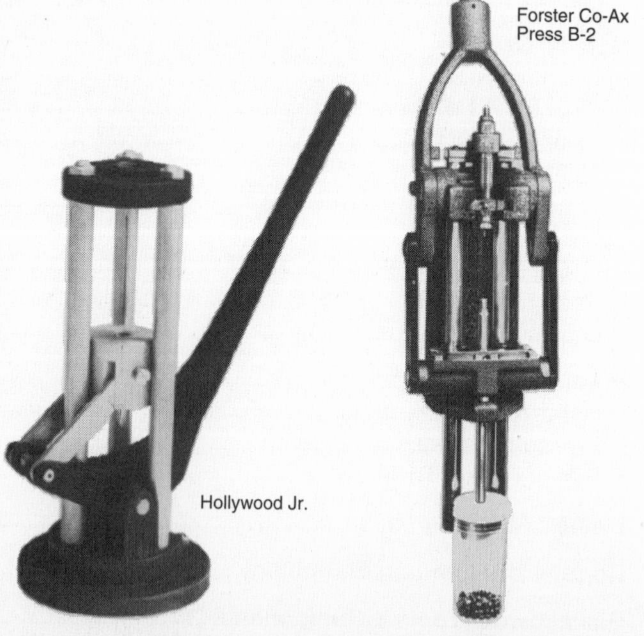

Hollywood Jr.

Forster Co-Ax Press B-2

METALLIC PRESSES/Single Stage

Hollywood Senior

Hollywood Senior Turret

| FORSTER | |
|---|---|
| Co-Ax "S" and "LS" Shellholder Calibers | |
| PISTOL | |
| 22 Rem. Jet | 25 Auto |
| 30 Luger | 38 Special |
| 32 Auto | 351 Win. |
| 32 Colt N.P. | 25-20 Win. |
| 32 S&W | 351 Win. S.L. |
| 9mm Luger | 32-20 Win. |
| 38 Special | 41 Rem. Mag. |
| 380 Auto | 44-40 Win. |
| 32 Short Colt | 45 Auto |
| 32 Long Colt | 45 Colt |
| 9mm Win. Mag. | 45 Win. |
| 32 Rem. | 38-40 Win. |
| 30 Rem. | 303 Savage |
| 38 Auto | 45 Auto Match |
| 38 Short Colt | 44 Rem. Mag. |
| 38 Long Colt | 10mm |
| RIFLE | |
| 17 Rem. | 7mm Wea. |
| 218 Bee | 280 Rem. |
| 221 Rem. | 284 Win. |
| 222 Rem. | 300 Savage |
| 222 Rem. Mag. | 30-30 Win. |
| 223 Rem. | 30-40 Krag |
| 5.6x50 | 300 Win. Mag. |
| 30 Carbine | 303 British |
| 32-20 Win. | 307 Win. |
| 219 Zipper | 308 Win. |
| 22 Savage | 308 Nat'l M |
| 224 Wea. | 308 Norma |
| 220 Swift | 30-06 |
| 22-250 Rem. | 300 H&H |
| 225 Win. | 300 Wea. |
| 240 Wea. | 8mm Rem. Mag. |
| 243 Win. | 8mmx57 |
| 6mm Rem. | 8mmx68S |
| 6mm PPC | 32 Win. |
| 25-06 Rem. | 32-20 Win. |
| 250 Savage | 38-40 Win. |
| 25-35 Win. | 338 Win. |
| 257 Roberts | 340 Wea. |
| 257 Wea. | 35 Rem. |
| 264 Win. Mag. | 350 Rem. Mag. |
| 6.5x54 Mann.-Schoe. | 356 Win. |
| | 358 Win. |
| 6.5 Rem. Mag. | 358 Nor. Mag. |
| 6.5 Swede | 375 Wea. |
| 270 Win. | 375 H&H |
| 270 Wea. | 38-55 Win. |
| 7x64 Brenneke | 444 Marlin |
| 7mm-08 | 44-40 Win. |
| 7mmx57 | 458 Win. Mag. |
| 7mm BR | 375 Win. |
| 7mm Rem. | 32-40 Win. |

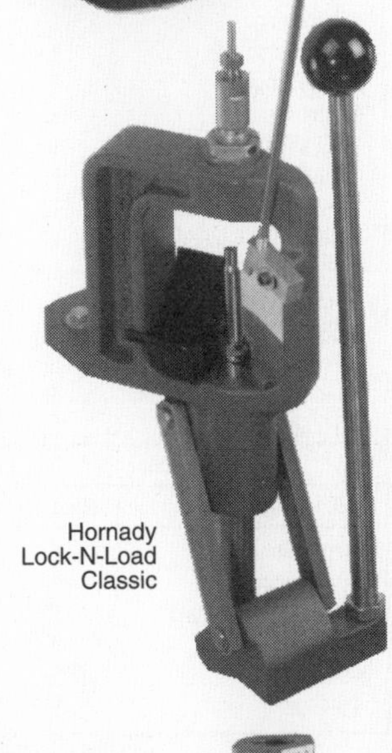

Hornady Lock-N-Load Classic

Huntington Compac Tool

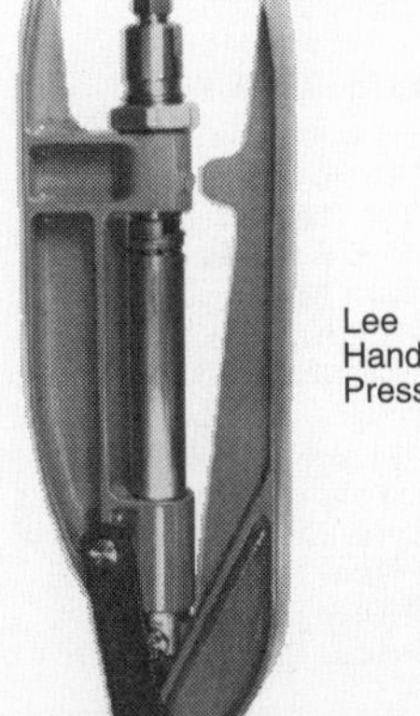

Lee Hand Press

**HOLLYWOOD Senior Press**

**Frame:** Ductile iron
**Frame Type:** O-frame
**Die Thread:** 7/8-14
**Avg. Rounds Per Hour:** 50-100
**Ram Stroke:** 6$^1/_2$″
**Weight:** 50 lbs.
**Features:** Leverage and bearing surfaces ample for reloading cartridges or swaging bullets. Precision ground one-piece 2$^1/_2$″ pillar with base; operating handle of 3/4″ steel and 15″ long; 5/8″ steel tie-down rod for added strength when swaging; heavy steel toggle and camming arms held by 1/2″ steel pins in reamed holes. The 1$^1/_2$″ steel die bushing takes standard threaded dies; removed, it allows use of Hollywood shotshell dies. From Hollywood Engineering.
**Price:** . . . . . . . . . . . . . . . . . . . . . . **$500.00**

**HOLLYWOOD Senior Turret Press**

**Frame:** Ductile iron
**Frame Type:** H-frame
**Die Thread:** 7/8-14
**Avg. Rounds Per Hour:** 50-100
**Ram Stroke:** 6$^1/_2$″
**Weight:** 50 lbs.
**Features:** Same features as Senior press except has three-position turret head; holes in turret may be tapped 1$^1/_2$″ or 7/8″ or four of each. Height, 15″. Comes complete with one turret indexing handle; one 1$^1/_2$″ to 7/8″ die hole bushing; one 5/8″ tie down bar for swaging. From Hollywood Engineering.
**Price:** . . . . . . . . . . . . . . . . . . . . . . **$600.00**

**HORNADY Lock-N-Load Classic**

**Frame:** Die cast heat-treated aluminum alloy
**Frame Type:** O-frame
**Die Thread:** 7/8-14
**Avg. Rounds Per Hour:** NA
**Ram Stroke:** 3$^5/_8$″
**Weight:** 14 lbs.
**Features:** Features Lock-N-Load bushing system that allows instant die changeovers. Solid steel linkage arms that rotate on steel pins; 30° angled frame design for improved visibility and accessibility; primer arm automatically moves in and out of ram for primer pickup and solid seating; two primer arms for large and small primers; long offset handle for increased leverage and unobstructed reloading; lifetime warranty. Comes as a package with primer catcher, PPS automatic primer feed and three Lock-N-Load die bushings. Dies and shellholder available separately or as kit with primer catcher, positive priming system, automatic primer feed, three die bushings and reloading accessories. From Hornady Mfg. Co.
**Price:** Classic Reloading Package . . . . . . . . . . **$99.95**
**Price:** Classic Reloading Kit . . . . . . . . . . . **$239.95**

**HUNTINGTON Compac Tool**

**Frame:** Aircraft aluminum
**Frame Type:** NA
**Die Thread:** 7/8-14
**Avg. Rounds Per Hour:** NA
**Ram Stroke:** NA
**Weight:** 37 oz.
**Features:** Small and lightweight for portability; performs all standard reloading operations; sufficient leverage to full-length resize, decap military brass and case-form. Accepts standard shellholders. Is bench mountable. Dimensions: 3$^1/_2$″ x 9″. From Huntington Die Specialties.
**Price:** . . . . . . . . . . . . . . . . . . . . . . **$74.98**

**LEE Hand Press**

**Frame:** ASTM 380 aluminum
**Frame Type:** NA
**Die Thread:** 7/8-14
**Avg. Rounds Per Hour:** 100
**Ram Stroke:** 3$^1/_4$″
**Weight:** 1 lb., 8 oz.
**Features:** Small and lightweight for portability; compound linkage for handling up to 375 H&H and case forming. Dies and shellholder not included. From Lee Precision, Inc.
**Price:** . . . . . . . . . . . . . . . . . . . . . . **$22.98**

**LEE Challenger Press**

**Frame:** ASTM 380 aluminum
**Frame Type:** O-frame
**Die Thread:** 7/8-14
**Avg. Rounds Per Hour:** 100
**Ram Stroke:** 3 1/2"
**Weight:** 4 lbs., 1 oz.
**Features:** Larger than average opening with 30° offset for maximum hand clearance; steel connecting pins; spent primer catcher; handle adjustable for start and stop positions; handle repositions for left- or right-hand use; shortened handle travel to prevent springing the frame from alignment. Dies and shellholders not included. From Lee Precision, Inc.
**Price:** . . . . . . . . . . . . . . . . . . . . . . . . **$43.00**

**LEE Loader**

Kit consists of reloading dies to be used with mallet or soft hammer. Neck sizes only. Comes with powder charge cup. From Lee Precision, Inc.
**Price:** . . . . . . . . . . . . . . . . . . . . . . . . **$19.98**

**LEE Reloader Press**

**Frame:** ASTM 380 aluminum
**Frame Type:** C-frame
**Die Thread:** 7/8-14
**Avg. Rounds Per Hour:** 100
**Ram Stroke:** 3"
**Weight:** 1 lb., 12 oz.
**Features:** Balanced lever to prevent pinching fingers; unlimited hand clearance; left- or right-hand use. Dies and shellholders not included. From Lee Precision, Inc.
**Price:** . . . . . . . . . . . . . . . . . . . . . . . . **$24.98**

**LEE Turret Press**

**Frame:** ASTM 380 aluminum
**Frame Type:** O-frame
**Die Thread:** 7/8-14
**Avg. Rounds Per Hour:** 300
**Ram Stroke:** 3"
**Weight:** 7 lbs., 2 oz.
**Features:** Replaceable turret lifts out by rotating 30°; T-primer arm reverses for large or small primers; built-in primer catcher; adjustable handle for right- or left-hand use or changing angle of down stroke; accessory mounting hole for Lee Auto-Disk powder measure. Optional Auto-Index rotates die turret to next station for semi-progressive use. Safety override prevents overstressing should turret not turn. From Lee Precision, Inc.
**Price:** . . . . . . . . . . . . . . . . . . . . . . . . **$69.98**
**Price:** With Auto-Index . . . . . . . . . . . . . . . **$83.98**
**Price:** Extra turret . . . . . . . . . . . . . . . . . . **$10.98**

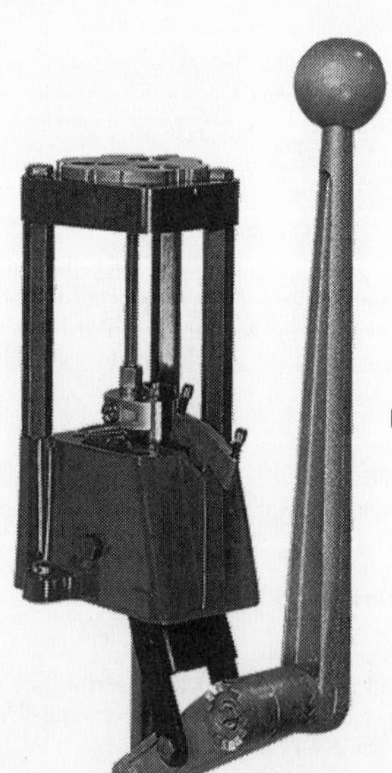

Lee Turret

Lee Reloader

**LYMAN 310 Tool Die Sets**

| Cartridge | Handle Size |
|---|---|
| **RIFLE** | |
| 222 Rem. | S |
| 223 Rem. | L |
| 222 Rem. Mag. | L |
| 243 Win. | L |
| 6mm Rem. | L |
| 270 Win. | L |
| 30 M1 Carbine | S |
| 30-30 Win. | L |
| 30-06 | L |
| 7.62mmx63 | L |
| 300 Savage | L |
| 308 Win. | L |
| 38-40 | S |
| 44-40 | S |
| 45-70 Gov't. | L |
| **PISTOL** | |
| 9mm Luger | S |
| 38 Auto | S |
| 38 Spl./357 Mag. | S |
| 44 Rem. Mag. | S |
| 45 ACP | S |
| 45 Colt | S |

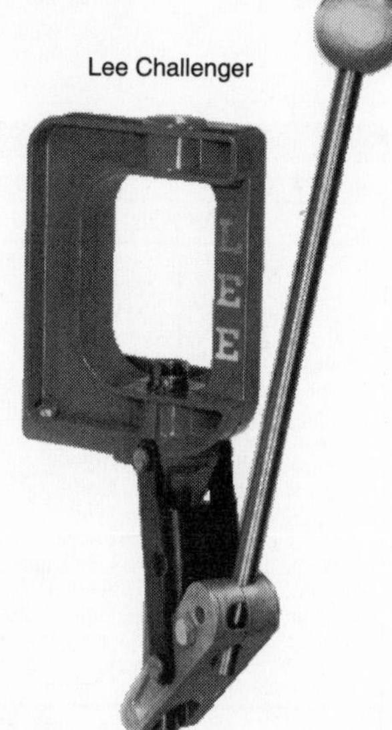


Lee Challenger

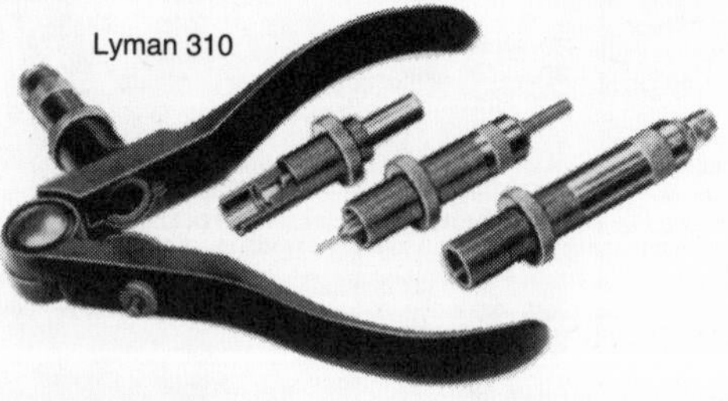

Lyman 310

**LYMAN 310 Tool**

**Frame:** Stainless steel
**Frame Type:** NA
**Die Thread:** 7/8-14
**Avg. Rounds Per Hour:** NA
**Ram Stroke:** NA
**Weight:** 10 oz.
**Features:** Compact, portable reloading tool for pistol or rifle cartridges. Adapter allows loading rimmed or rimless cases. Die set includes neck resizing/decapping die, primer seating chamber; neck expanding die; bullet seating die; and case head adapter. From Lyman Products Corporation.
**Price:** Dies . . . . . . . . . . . . . . . . . . . . **$36.00**
**Price:** Press . . . . . . . . . . . . . . . . . . . **$36.00**
**Price:** Carrying pouch . . . . . . . . . . . . . . . **$9.95**

Turret handle disconnector

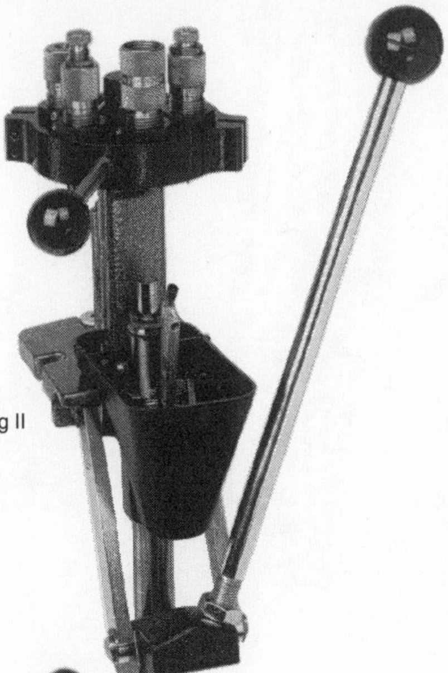

Lyman T-Mag II

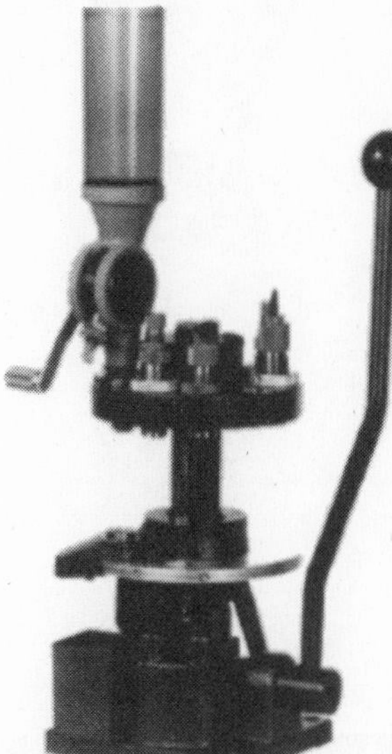

Ponsness/Warren Metal-Matic P-200

Lyman Orange Crusher II

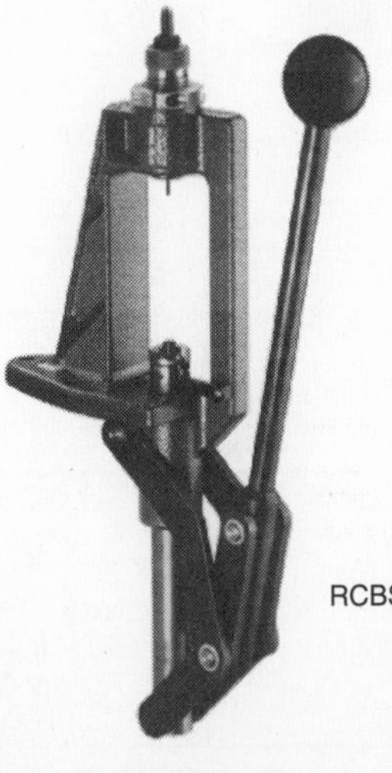

RCBS Partner

**LYMAN AccuPress**

**Frame:** Die cast
**Frame Type:** C-frame
**Die Thread:** 7/8-14
**Avg. Rounds Per Hour:** 75
**Ram Stroke:** 3.4″
**Weight:** 4 lbs.
**Features:** Reversible, contoured handle for bench mount or hand-held use; for rifle or pistol; compound leverage; Delta frame design. Accepts all standard powder measures. From Lyman Products Corporation.
**Price:** . . . . . . . . . . . . . . . . . . . . . . . **$32.00**

**LYMAN Orange Crusher II**

**Frame:** Cast iron
**Frame Type:** O-frame
**Die Thread:** 7/8-14
**Avg. Rounds Per Hour:** 75
**Ram Stroke:** 3 7/8″
**Weight:** 19 lbs.
**Features:** Reloads both pistol and rifle cartridges; 1″ diameter ram; 4 1/2″ press opening for loading magnum cartridges; direct torque design; right- or left-hand use. New base design with 14 square inches of flat mounting surface with three bolt holes. Comes with priming arm and catcher. Dies and shellholders not included. From Lyman Products Corporation.
**Price:** . . . . . . . . . . . . . . . . . . . . . . . **$108.00**

**LYMAN T-Mag II**

**Frame:** Cast iron with silver metalflake powder finish
**Frame Type:** Turret
**Die Thread:** 7/8-14
**Avg. Rounds Per Hour:** 125
**Ram Stroke:** 3 13/16″
**Weight:** 18 lbs.
**Features:** Reengineered and upgraded with new turret system for ease of indexing and tool-free turret removal for caliber changeover; new flat machined base for bench mounting; new nickel-plated non-rust handle and links; and new silver hammertone powder coat finish for durability. Right- or left-hand operation; handles all rifle or pistol dies. Comes with priming arm and primer catcher. Dies and shellholders not included. From Lyman Products Corporation.
**Price:** . . . . . . . . . . . . . . . . . . . . . . . **$149.95**
**Price:** Extra turret . . . . . . . . . . . . . . . . . . **$34.95**

**PONSNESS/WARREN Metal-Matic P-200**

**Frame:** Die cast aluminum
**Frame Type:** Unconventional
**Die Thread:** 7/8-14
**Avg. Rounds Per Hour:** 200+
**Weight:** 18 lbs.
**Features:** Designed for straight-wall cartridges; die head with 10 tapped holes for holding dies and accessories for two calibers at one time; removable spent primer box; pivoting arm moves case from station to station. Comes with large and small primer tool. Optional accessories include primer feed, extra die head, primer speed feeder, powder measure extension and dust cover. Dies, powder measure and shellholder not included. From Ponsness/Warren.
**Price:** . . . . . . . . . . . . . . . . . . . . . . . **$175.00**
**Price:** Extra die head . . . . . . . . . . . . . . . . **$39.95**
**Price:** Powder measure extension . . . . . . . . . . **$19.95**
**Price:** Primer feed . . . . . . . . . . . . . . . . . . **$34.95**
**Price:** Primer speed feed . . . . . . . . . . . . . . **$11.50**
**Price:** Dust cover . . . . . . . . . . . . . . . . . . **$18.95**

**RCBS Partner**

**Frame:** Aluminum
**Frame Type:** O-frame
**Die Thread:** 7/8-14
**Avg. Rounds Per Hour:** 50-60
**Ram Stroke:** 3 5/8″
**Weight:** 5 lbs.
**Features:** Designed for the beginning reloader. Comes with primer arm equipped with interchangeable primer plugs and sleeves for seating large and small primers. Shellholder and dies not included. Available in kit form (see Metallic Presses—Accessories). From RCBS.
**Price:** . . . . . . . . . . . . . . . . . . . . . . . **$52.25**

# Section 1: Metallic Cartridges



### RCBS AmmoMaster Single

**Frame:** Aluminum base; cast iron top plate connected by three steel posts.
**Frame Type:** NA
**Die Thread:** $1^{1}/_{4}$″-12 bushing; $^{7}/_{8}$-14 threads
**Avg. Rounds Per Hour:** 50-60
**Ram Stroke:** $5^{1}/_{4}$″
**Weight:** 19 lbs.
**Features:** Single-stage press convertible to progressive. Will form cases or swage bullets. Case detection system to disengage powder measure when no case is present in powder charging station; five-station shellplate; Uniflow Powder measure with clear powder measure adaptor to make bridged powders visible and correctable. 50-cal. conversion kit allows reloading 50 BMG. Kit includes top plate to accommodate either $1^{3}/_{8}$″ x 12 or $1^{1}/_{2}$″ x 12 reloading dies. Piggyback die plate for quick caliber change-overs available. Reloading dies not included. From RCBS.
**Price:** . . . . . . . . . . . . . . . . . . . . . . . **$178.38**
**Price:** Single-to-auto kit . . . . . . . . . . . . . . . **$245.13**
**Price:** 50 conversion kit . . . . . . . . . . . . . . . **$71.00**
**Price:** Piggyback/AmmoMaster die plate . . . . . . . **$22.00**
**Price:** Piggyback/AmmoMaster shellplate . . . . . . **$25.29**
**Price:** Press cover . . . . . . . . . . . . . . . . . . **$7.13**

### RCBS Reloader Special-5

**Frame:** Aluminum
**Frame Type:** 30° offset O-frame
**Die Thread:** $1^{1}/_{4}$-12 bushing; $^{7}/_{8}$-14 threads
**Avg. Rounds Per Hour:** 50-60
**Ram Stroke:** $3^{1}/_{16}$″
**Weight:** 7.5 lbs.
**Features:** Single-stage press convertible to progressive with RCBS Piggyback II. Primes cases during resizing operation. Will accept RCBS shotshell dies. From RCBS.
**Price:** . . . . . . . . . . . . . . . . . . . . . . . **$100.13**

### RCBS Rock Chucker

**Frame:** Cast iron
**Frame Type:** O-frame
**Die Thread:** $1^{1}/_{4}$″-12 bushing; $^{7}/_{8}$-14 threads
**Avg. Rounds Per Hour:** 50-60
**Ram Stroke:** $3^{5}/_{16}$″
**Weight:** 17 lbs.
**Features:** Designed for heavy-duty reloading, case forming and bullet swaging. Provides 4″ of ram-bearing surface to support 1″ ram and ensure alignment; ductile iron toggle blocks; hardened steel pins. Comes standard with Universal Primer Arm and primer catcher. Can be converted from single-stage to progressive with Piggyback II conversion unit (see Metallic Presses—Accessories). From RCBS.
**Price:** . . . . . . . . . . . . . . . . . . . . . . . **$128.63**

### REDDING Model 25 Turret Press

**Frame:** Cast iron
**Frame Type:** Turret
**Die Thread:** $^{7}/_{8}$-14
**Avg. Rounds Per Hour:** NA
**Ram Stroke:** 3.4″
**Weight:** 23 lbs., 2 oz.
**Features:** Strength to reload pistol and magnum rifle, case form and bullet swage; linkage pins heat-treated, precision ground and in double shear; hollow ram to collect spent primers; removable turret head for caliber changes; progressive linkage for increased power as ram nears die; slight frame tilt for comfortable operation; rear turret support for stability and precise alignment; six-station turret head; priming arm for both large and small primers. Also available in kit form with shellholder, primer catcher and one die set. From Redding Reloading Equipment.
**Price:** . . . . . . . . . . . . . . . . . . . . . . . **$289.50**
**Price:** Kit . . . . . . . . . . . . . . . . . . . . . **$324.00**

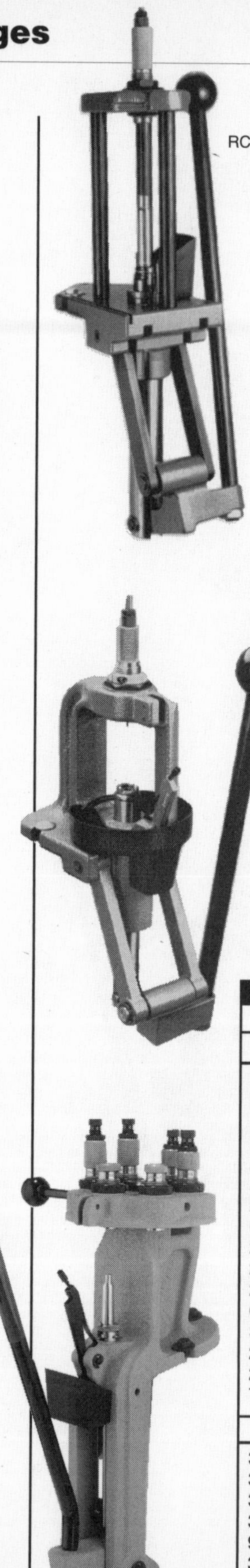

RCBS Ammo Master Single

RCBS Rock Chucker

Redding Model 25

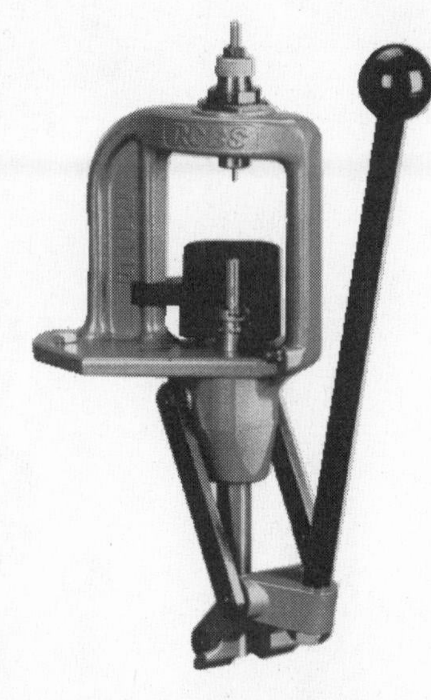


RCBS Reloader Special-5

| REDDING Series AA Die Press Kits | |
|---|---|
| **RIFLE** | |
| 221 Rem. Fire Ball | 7mm Rem. Mag. |
| 22 Hornet | 7mmx57 Mauser |
| 220 Swift | 280 Rem. |
| 222 Rem. | 284 Win. |
| 22-250 Rem. | 7.62x39 |
| 223 Rem. | 30-30 Win. |
| 243 Win. | 30-40 Krag |
| 6mm Rem. | 30-06 Sprfld. |
| 250 Savage | 300 Wea. Mag. |
| 25-06 Rem. | 300 Win. Mag. |
| 257 Roberts | 308 Win. |
| 6.5mmx55 | 303 British |
| Swed. Mauser | 8mmx57 Mauser |
| 264 Win. Mag. | 338 Win. Mag. |
| 270 Win. | 35 Rem. |
| 7mm-08 Rem. | 375 H&H Mag. |
| **PISTOL** | |
| 30 M1 Carbine | 38 Spl./357 Mag. |
| 32 S&W Long | 41 Mag. |
| 32 H&R Mag. | 44 Spl. |
| 380 Auto | 44 Mag. |
| 9mm Luger | 44-40 Win. |
| 38 Spl. | 45 ACP & AR |
| 357 Mag. | 45 Colt |

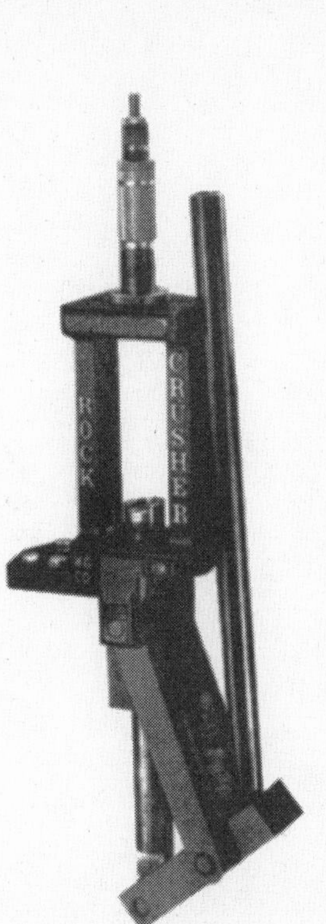


Rock Crusher

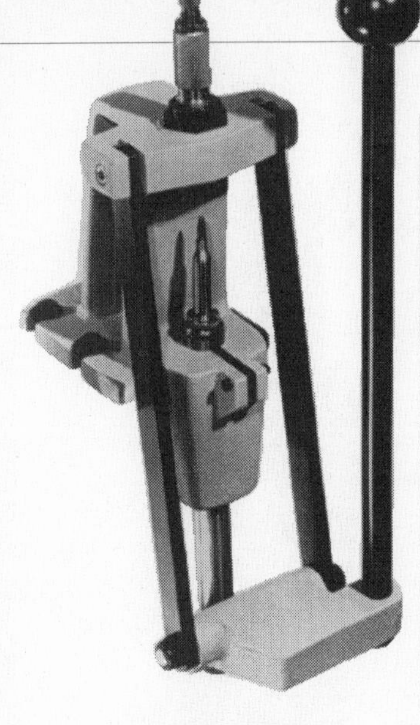

Redding Ultramag

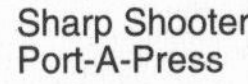

Sharp Shooter
Port-A-Press

### REDDING The Boss

**Frame:** Cast iron
**Frame Type:** O-frame
**Die Thread:** $\frac{7}{8}$-14
**Avg. Rounds Per Hour:** NA
**Ram Stroke:** 3.4″
**Weight:** 11 lbs., 8 oz.
**Features:** 36° frame offset for visibility and accessibility; primer arm positioned at bottom of ram travel; positive ram travel stop machined to hit exactly top-dead-center. Also available in kit form with shellholder and set of Redding A dies. From Redding Reloading Equipment.
**Price:** . . . . . . . . . . . . . . . . . . . . **$129.00**
**Price:** Kit . . . . . . . . . . . . . . . . . . **$165.00**

### REDDING Ultramag

**Frame:** Cast iron
**Frame Type:** Non-conventional
**Die Thread:** $\frac{7}{8}$-14
**Avg. Rounds Per Hour:** NA
**Ram Stroke:** $4\frac{1}{8}$″
**Weight:** 23 lbs., 6 oz.
**Features:** Unique compound leverage system connected to top of press for tons of ram pressure; large $4\frac{3}{4}$″ frame opening for loading outsized cartridges; hollow ram for spent primers. Kit available with shellholder and one set Redding A dies. From Redding Reloading Equipment.
**Price:** . . . . . . . . . . . . . . . . . . . . **$289.50**
**Price:** Kit . . . . . . . . . . . . . . . . . . **$324.00**

### ROCK CRUSHER Press

**Frame:** Cast iron
**Frame Type:** O-frame
**Die Thread:** $2\frac{3}{4}$-12 with bushing reduced to $1\frac{1}{2}$-12
**Avg. Rounds Per Hour:** 50
**Ram Stroke:** 6″
**Weight:** 67 lbs.
**Features:** Designed to load and form ammunition from 50 BMG up to 23x115 Soviet. Frame opening of $8\frac{1}{2}$″ x $3\frac{1}{2}$″; $1\frac{1}{2}$″x12″; bushing can be removed and bushings of any size substituted; ram pressure can exceed 10,000 lbs. with normal body weight; 40mm diameter ram. Angle block for bench mounting and reduction bushing for RCBS dies available. Accessories for Rockcrusher include powder measure, dies, shellholder, bullet puller, priming tool, case gauge and other accessories found elsewhere in this catalog. From The Old Western Scrounger.
**Price:** . . . . . . . . . . . . . . . . . . . . **$785.00**
**Price:** Angle block . . . . . . . . . . . . . . . **$57.95**
**Price:** Reduction bushing . . . . . . . . . . . . **$21.00**
**Price:** Shellholder, 50 BMG, 12.7, 55 Boyes . . . . . **$36.75**
**Price:** Shellholder, 23 Soviet . . . . . . . . . **$65.00**
**Price:** Shellholder, all others . . . . . . . . . **$47.95**
**Price:** Priming tool, 50 BMG, 20 Lahti . . . . . . **$65.10**

### ROSS & WEBB Benchrest Press

**Frame:** Aircraft aluminum hardened tool steel
**Frame Type:** C-frame
**Die Thread:** $\frac{7}{8}$-14
**Avg. Rounds Per Hour:** NA
**Ram Stroke:** 2″
**Weight:** 4.5 lbs.
**Features:** Precision-made benchrest quality press. Small, 9″ tall, portable and made to extremely tight tolerances. Standard shellholders must be machined to fit ram. Comes with base for easy set-up and take-down. From Hoehn Sales, Inc.
**Price:** . . . . . . . . . . . . . . . . . . . . **$179.00**

### SHARP SHOOTER Port-A-Press

**Frame:** 6061 aluminum
**Frame Type:** O-frame
**Die Thread:** $\frac{7}{8}$-14
**Avg. Rounds Per Hour:** NA
**Ram Stroke:** $2\frac{1}{2}$″
**Weight:** 8 lbs.
**Features:** Lightweight, compact three-station turret press; measures 12″ high, 5″wide and $6\frac{1}{2}$″ deep; built-in bench clamp to attach to any bench; removable turret. From Sharp Shooter Supply.
**Price:** . . . . . . . . . . . . . . . . . . . . **$225.00**
**Price:** Extra turret . . . . . . . . . . . . . . **$10.50**

Redding The Boss

### DILLON AT 500

**Frame:** Aluminum alloy
**Frame Type:** NA
**Die Thread:** 7/8-14
**Avg. Rounds Per Hour:** 200-300
**Ram Stroke:** 3 7/8″
**Weight:** NA
**Features:** Four stations; removable tool head to hold dies in alignment and allow caliber changes without die adjustment; manual indexing; capacity to be upgraded to progressive RL 550B. Comes with universal shellplate to accept 223, 22-250, 243, 30-06, 9mm, 38/357, 40 S&W, 45 ACP. Dies not included. From Dillon Precision Products.
**Price:** . . . . . . . . . . . . . . . . . . . . . . **$179.95**

### DILLON RL 550B

**Frame:** Aluminum alloy
**Frame Type:** NA
**Die Thread:** 7/8-14
**Avg. Rounds Per Hour:** 500-600
**Ram Stroke:** 3 7/8″
**Weight:** 25 lbs.
**Features:** Four stations; removable tool head to hold dies in alignment and allow caliber changes without die adjustment; auto priming system that emits audible warning when primer tube is low; a 100-primer capacity magazine contained in DOM steel tube for protection; new auto powder measure system with simple mechanical connection between measure and loading platform for positive powder bar return; a separate station for crimping with star-indexing system; 220 ejected-round capacity bin; 3/4-lb. capacity powder measure. Height above bench, 35″; requires 3/4″ bench overhang. Will reload 120 different rifle and pistol calibers. Comes with one caliber conversion kit. Dies not included. From Dillon Precision Products, Inc.
**Price:** . . . . . . . . . . . . . . . . . . . . . . **$298.95**
**Price:** Instruction manual . . . . . . . . . . . . . . . **$5.95**

### DILLON RL 1050

**Frame:** Ductile iron
**Frame Type:** Platform type
**Die Thread:** 7/8-14
**Avg. Rounds Per Hour:** 1000-1200
**Ram Stroke:** 2 5/16″
**Weight:** 62 lbs.
**Features:** Eight stations; auto case feed; primer pocket swager for military cartridge cases; auto indexing; removable tool head; auto prime system with 100-primer capacity; low primer supply alarm; positive powder bar return; auto powder measure; 515 ejected round bin capacity; 500-600 case feed capacity; 3/4-lb. capacity powder measure. Loads all pistol rounds as well as 30 M1 Carbine, 223 and 7.62x39 rifle rounds. Height above the bench, 43″. Dies not included. From Dillon Precision Products, Inc.
**Price:** . . . . . . . . . . . . . . . . . . . . . **$1,079.95**

### DILLON Square Deal B

**Frame:** Zinc alloy
**Frame Type:** NA
**Die Thread:** None (unique Dillon design)
**Avg. Rounds Per Hour:** 400-500
**Ram Stroke:** 2 5/16″
**Weight:** 17 lbs.
**Features:** Four stations; auto indexing; removable tool head; auto prime system with 100-primer capacity; low primer supply alarm; auto powder measure; positive powder bar return; 170 ejected round capacity bin; 3/4-lb. capacity powder measure. Height above the bench, 34″. Comes complete with factory adjusted carbide die set. From Dillon Precision Products, Inc.
**Price:** . . . . . . . . . . . . . . . . . . . . . . **$227.95**

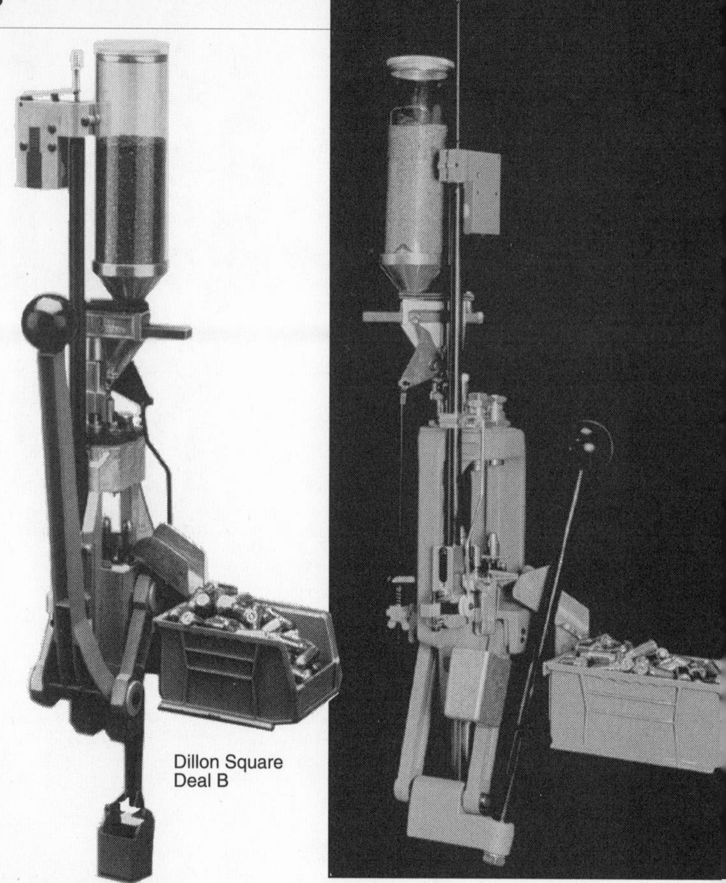

Dillon Square Deal B

Dillon RL 550B

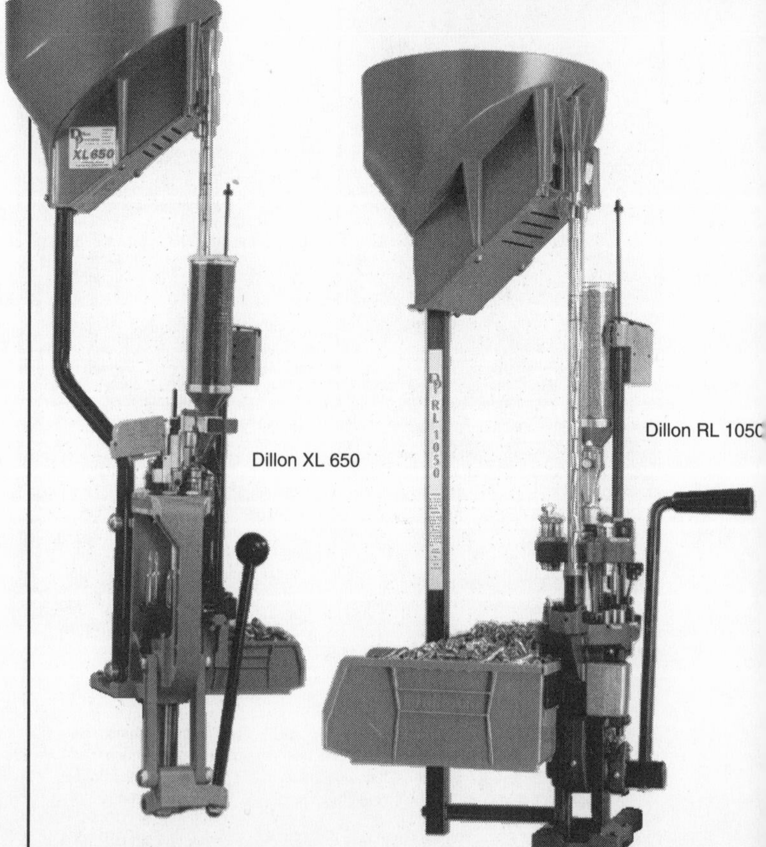



Dillon XL 650

Dillon RL 1050

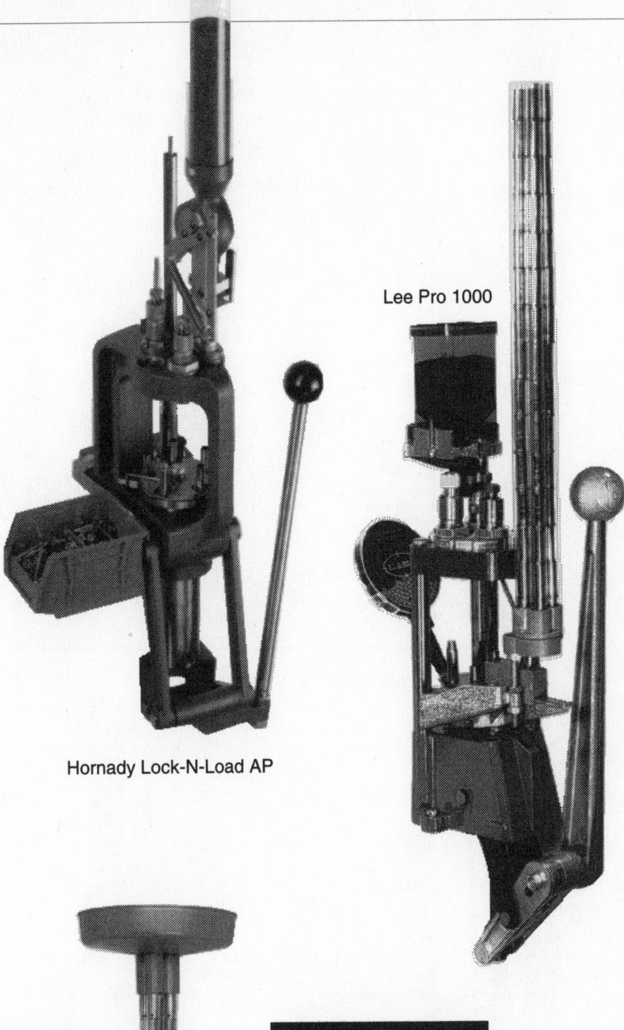

Lee Pro 1000

Hornady Lock-N-Load AP

Lee Load Master

| LEE |
|---|
| Load-Master Pistol Calibers |
| 32 S&W Long |
| 32 H&R Magnum |
| 9mm Luger |
| 380 Auto |
| 38 Special |
| 357 Magnum |
| 40 S&W |
| 10mm Auto |
| 44 Special |
| 44 Magnum |
| 45 ACP |
| 45 Colt |

| LEE |
|---|
| Load Master Rifle Calibers |
| 222 Rem. |
| 223 Rem. |
| 22-250 |
| 243 Win. |
| 6.5x55 |
| 270 Win. |
| 30-30 Win. |
| 308 Win. |
| 30-06 |

### DILLON XL 650

**Frame:** Aluminum alloy
**Frame Type:** NA
**Die Thread:** $^7/_8$-14
**Avg. Rounds Per Hour:** 800-1000
**Ram Stroke:** $4^9/_{16}$″
**Weight:** 46 lbs.
**Features:** Five stations; auto indexing; auto case feed; removable tool head; auto prime system with 100-primer capacity; low primer supply alarm; auto powder measure; positive powder bar return; 220 ejected-round capacity bin; $^3/_4$-lb. capacity powder measure; 500-600 case feed capacity with optional auto case feed. Loads all pistol/rifle calibers less than $3^1/_2$″ in length. Height above the bench, 44″; $^3/_4$″ bench overhang required. From Dillon Precision Products, Inc.
**Price:** . . . . . . . . . . . . . . . . . . . . . . . . **$398.95**
**Price:** Instruction manual . . . . . . . . . . . . . . . **$5.95**

### HORNADY Lock-N-Load AP

**Frame:** Die cast heat-treated aluminum alloy
**Frame Type:** O-frame
**Die Thread:** $^7/_8$-14
**Avg. Rounds Per Hour:** NA
**Ram Stroke:** $3^3/_4$″
**Weight:** 26 lbs.
**Features:** Features Lock-N-Load bushing system that allows instant die changeovers; five-station die platform with option of seating and crimping separately or adding taper-crimp die; auto prime with large and small primer tubes with 100-primer capacity and protective housing; brass kicker to eject loaded rounds into 80-round capacity cartridge catcher; offset operating handle for leverage and unobstructed operation; 2″ diameter ram driven by heavy-duty cast linkage arms rotating on steel pins. Comes with five Lock-N-Load die bushings, shellplate, deluxe powder measure, auto powder drop, and auto primer feed and shut-off, brass kicker and primer catcher. Lifetime warranty. From Hornady Mfg. Co.
**Price:** . . . . . . . . . . . . . . . . . . . . . . . . **$349.95**

### LEE Load-Master

**Frame:** ASTM 380 aluminum
**Frame Type:** O-frame
**Die Thread:** $^7/_8$-14
**Avg. Rounds Per Hour:** 600
**Ram Stroke:** $3^1/_4$″
**Weight:** 8 lbs., 4 oz.
**Features:** Available in kit form only. A $1^3/_4$″ hard chrome diameter ram for handling largest magnum cases; loads rifle or pistol rounds; five-station press to factory crimp and post size; auto indexing with wedge lock mechanism to hold one ton; auto priming; removable turrets; four-tube case feeder with optional case collator and bullet feeder (late 1995); loaded round ejector with chute to optional loaded round catcher; quick change shellplate; primer catcher. Dies and shellholder for one caliber included. From Lee Precision, Inc.
**Price:** Rifle . . . . . . . . . . . . . . . . . . . . **$320.00**
**Price:** Pistol . . . . . . . . . . . . . . . . . . . . **$330.00**
**Price:** Case collator . . . . . . . . . . . . . . . . **$14.98**
**Price:** Adjustable charge bar . . . . . . . . . . . . **$9.98**

### LEE Pro 1000

**Frame:** ASTM 380 aluminum and steel
**Frame Type:** O-frame
**Die Thread:** $^7/_8$-14
**Avg. Rounds Per Hour:** 600
**Ram Stroke:** $3^1/_4$″
**Weight:** 8 lbs., 7 oz.
**Features:** Optional transparent large/small or rifle case feeder; deluxe auto-disk case-activated powder measure; case sensor for primer feed. Comes complete with carbide die set (steel dies for rifle) for one caliber. Optional accessories include: case feeder for large/small pistol cases or rifle cases; shell plate carrier with auto prime, case ejector, auto-index and spare parts; case collator for case feeder. From Lee Precision, Inc.
**Price:** . . . . . . . . . . . . . . . . . . . . . . . . **$199.98**

## PONSNESS/WARREN Metallic II

**Frame:** Die cast aluminum
**Frame Type:** H-frame
**Die Thread:** 7/8-14
**Avg. Rounds Per Hour:** 150+
**Ram Stroke:** NA
**Weight:** 32 lbs.
**Features:** Die head with five tapped 7/8-14 holes for dies, powder measure or other accessories; pivoting die arm moves case from station to station; depriming tube for removal of spent primers; auto primer feed; interchangeable die head. Optional accessories include additional die heads, powder measure extension tube to accommodate any standard powder measure, primer speed feeder to feed press primer tube without disassembly. Comes with small and large primer seating tools. Dies, powder measure and shellholder not included. From Ponsness/Warren.
**Price:** . . . . . . . . . . . . . . . . . . . . . . **$299.00**
**Price:** Extra die head . . . . . . . . . . . . . . . **$42.50**
**Price:** Primer speed feeder . . . . . . . . . . . . **$11.50**
**Price:** Powder measure extension . . . . . . . . . **$19.95**
**Price:** Dust cover . . . . . . . . . . . . . . . . . **$27.95**

## RCBS Auto 4x4

**Frame:** Cast iron
**Frame Type:** O-frame
**Die Thread:** 7/8-14
**Avg. Rounds Per Hour:** 500
**Ram Stroke:** 3″
**Weight:** 27 lbs.
**Features:** Four-station press for high volume reloaders. Loads medium-length rifle or pistol cartridges. Can be used as a single-stage tool and has the strength to form wildcat cases or swage bullets. Comes with powder measure adaptor and assembly; depriming tube; large and small automatic primer feed assemblies; ammunition catch box and base; hex key wrenches; cleaning brush; resizing lubricant; primer tray; deprime bottle and cap. From RCBS.
**Price:** . . . . . . . . . . . . . . . . . . . . . . **$388.50**
**Price:** Shellplate . . . . . . . . . . . . . . . . . **$26.25**

## RCBS AmmoMaster-Auto

**Frame:** Aluminum base; cast iron top plate connected by three steel posts.
**Frame Type:** NA
**Die Thread:** 1 1/4-12 bushing; 7/8-14 threads
**Avg. Rounds Per Hour:** 400-500
**Ram Stroke:** 5 1/4″
**Weight:** 19 lbs.
**Features:** Progressive press convertible to single-stage. Features include: 1 1/2″ solid ram; automatic indexing, priming, powder charging and loaded round ejection. Case detection system disengages powder measure when no case is present in powder charging station. Comes with five-station shellplate and Uniflow powder measure with clear powder measure adaptor to make bridged powders visible and correctable. Piggyback die plate for quick caliber change-over available. Reloading dies not included. From RCBS.
**Price:** . . . . . . . . . . . . . . . . . . . . . . **$394.63**
**Price:** Auto-to-single kit . . . . . . . . . . . . . **$71.00**
**Price:** Piggyback/AmmoMaster die plate . . . . . . . **$22.00**
**Price:** Piggyback/AmmoMaster shellplate . . . . . . **$26.25**
**Price:** Press cover . . . . . . . . . . . . . . . . **$10.25**

## STAR Universal Rifle Press

**Frame:** Cast iron with aluminum base
**Frame Type:** Unconventional
**Die Thread:** 7/8-14
**Avg. Rounds Per Hour:** 300
**Ram Stroke:** NA
**Weight:** 30 lbs.
**Features:** Same as pistol press but has length of stroke to handle most popular large rifle calibers. Shellplate and expander plug included, dies not included. Comes completely assembled. From Star Machine Works.
**Price:** . . . . . . . . . . . . . . . . . . . . . . **$1,500.00**

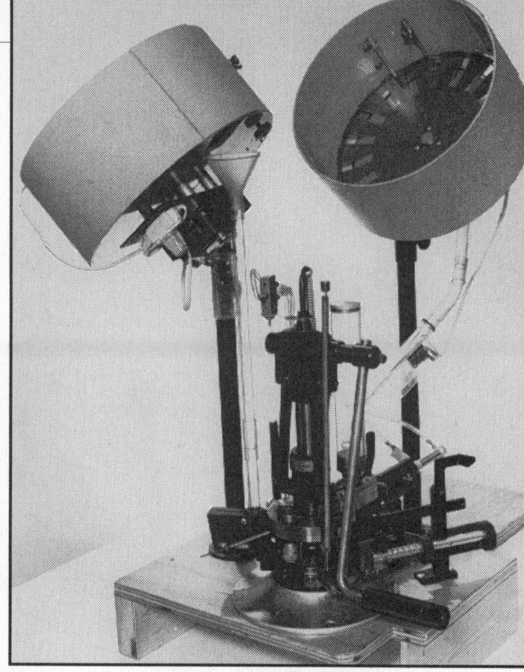
Fully-automated Star Universal

RCBS AmmoMaster

RCBS Auto 4x4

## STAR Universal Pistol Press

**Frame:** Cast iron with aluminum base
**Frame Type:** Unconventional
**Die Thread:** 11/16-24 or 7/8-14
**Avg. Rounds Per Hour:** 300
**Ram Stroke:** NA
**Weight:** 27 lbs.
**Features:** Four or five-station press depending on need to taper crimp; handles all popular handgun calibers from 32 Long to 45 Colt. Comes completely assembled and adjusted with carbide dies (except 30 Carbine) and shellholder to load one caliber. From Star Machine Works.
**Price:** With taper crimp . . . . . . . . . . . . . **$947.00**
**Price:** Without taper crimp . . . . . . . . . . . . **$925.00**
**Price:** Extra tool head, taper crimp . . . . . . . **$367.00**
**Price:** Extra tool head, w/o taper crimp . . . . . . **$345.00**

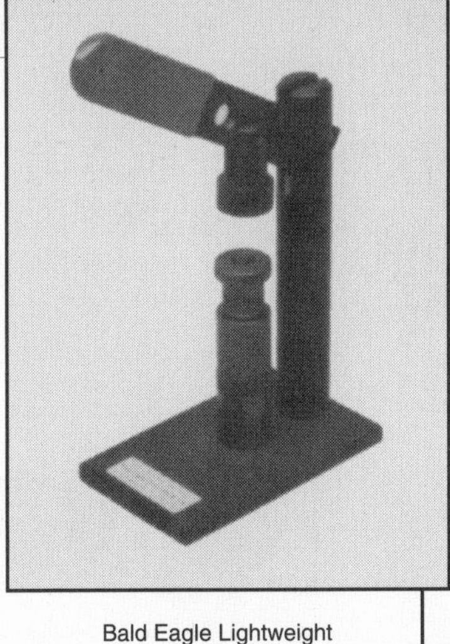

Bald Eagle Lightweight

B-Square Super Mag Arbor

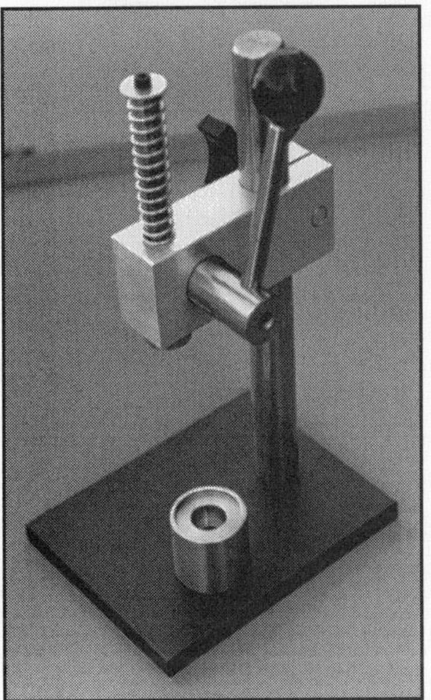

Sinclair Arbor Press

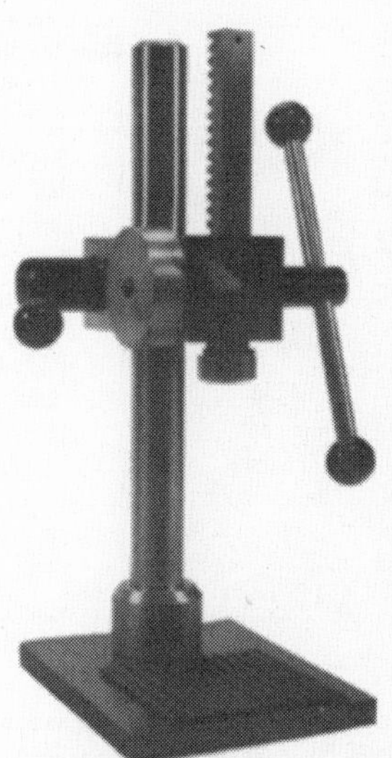

Hart Arbor Press

Jones Arbor Press

K&M Services Arbor Press

**BALD EAGLE Lightweight Press**

**Frame:** 2024-T6 aircraft aluminum
**Mechanical Advantage:** 1:5
**Weight:** 1.25 lbs.
**Features:** Spring-loaded plunger which elevates and returns handle to original position. Uses Wilson-style seater die. Main support is 6 5/8″ high; base is 3″x5″. Finish is black hardcoat. From Bald Eagle Precision Machine Co.
**Price:** . . . . . . . . . . . . . . . . . . . . . . . . **$60.00**

**B-SQUARE Super Mag Arbor Press**

**Frame:** Stress-proof steel with 60/61T6 aluminum base and head
**Ram Stroke:** 1 1/2″
**Weight:** 8 1/2 lbs.
**Features:** Features twin posts for "no-spring"; capability to full-length size up to 30-06 in Wilson die; fully adjustable press head; spring return ram and replaceable brass caps; 4 1/2″ handle adjustable for right- or left-hand use. Dimensions: height, 12″; width, 4″. From B-Square Company.
**Price:** . . . . . . . . . . . . . . . . . . . . . . . . **$99.95**

**HART Arbor Press**

**Frame:** Steel and aluminum
**Ram Stroke:** 3.5″
**Weight:** NA
**Features:** Bronze bushings; vertical adjustment from 1″ to 7″; handle offers 2″ stroke per revolution; locking handle for securing vertical adjustments. Deluxe version available with spring return on ram. From Robert W. Hart & Son, Inc.
**Price:** . . . . . . . . . . . . . . . . . . . . . . . . **$110.95**
**Price:** Deluxe press . . . . . . . . . . . . . . . . . . **$129.95**

**JONES Arbor Press**

**Frame:** Aluminum alloy
**Ram Stroke:** NA
**Weight:** 4 lbs.
**Features:** Hardened and polished steel guide post; adjustable head; open base for catching spent primers; adjustable for right- or left-hand use; easy takedown for transportation and storage. From Neil Jones Custom Products.
**Price:** . . . . . . . . . . . . . . . . . . . . . . . . **$135.00**
**Price:** 50-caliber . . . . . . . . . . . . . . . . . . . **$155.00**

**K&M Arbor Press**

**Frame:** Aluminum
**Ram Stroke:** .900″
**Weight:** 42 oz.
**Features:** T-bar and rectangular bar constructed for strength. Ram adjustment made by socket head cap screws which allows sliding ram unit on T-Bar. Overall height 9 1/2″ with 3 3/4x5″ rectangular base. Portable press for home or range designed to be used with hand dies. Toggle link/crankshaft design provides smooth operation. Ram bushings of Oilite bronze. From K&M Services.
**Price:** . . . . . . . . . . . . . . . . . . . . . . . . **$64.00**

**SINCLAIR Arbor Press**

**Frame:** Stainless steel with steel base
**Ram Stroke:** 3 1/2″
**Weight:** 4 1/2 lbs.
**Features:** Designed for use with hand dies; compact and portable; steel base eliminates need to clamp down for use. From Sinclair International, Inc.
**Price:** . . . . . . . . . . . . . . . . . . . . . . . . **$88.00**

## BULLET SWAGING SUPPLY

**Conversion Unit**

Converts RCBS Rock Chucker, Lyman Orange Crusher and Pacific 007 presses into swaging press. Consists of modified ram for swaging, a punch holder and ejector pin. One hole must be drilled in base of press for ejector pin. Includes BSS 3-die set. From Bullet Swaging Supply, Inc.

**Price:** . . . . . . . . . . . . . . **$75.00**
**Price:** With 3-die set . . . . . . **$325.00**
**Price:** For RCBS Big Max . . . . **$350.00**

## C-H/4-D

**"H" Ram**

Can be used with any Hollywood or Dunbar press and will accept any universal shellholder head. Available with standard 5/16" center hole or 3/8" center hole used at priming station and H-Mag press. Does not include shellholder. From C-H Tool & Die/4-D Custom Die.

**Price:** . . . . . . . . . . . . . . **$7.65**

**Press Top Bushing**

Designed to work with most O- and C-type presses to allow use of dies threaded larger than 7/8-14. From C-H Tool & Die/4-D Custom Die.

**Price:** 1 1/4"-12x7/8"-14 . . . . . . **$12.95**
**Price:** 1 3/8"-12x7/8"(or 1")-14 . . . . **$13.95**
**Price:** 1 1/2"-12x7/8"(or 1")-14 . . . . **$14.95**

**Shellholder Adaptor**

Fits all Herters and Lachmiller presses which use one or two set-screws to hold shellholder. Adapts them to standard snap-in shellholder. From C-H Tool & Die/4-D Custom Die.

**Price:** . . . . . . . . . . . . . . **$14.25**

**Shellholder Extension**

For use when trimming short cases in file trim die. Extends shellholders 3/4". From C-H Tool & Die/4-D Custom Die.

**Price:** . . . . . . . . . . . . . . **$12.05**

**Universal "C" Press Ram**

Features relieved clearance for primer and floating shellholder action for alignment. Shellholder not included. From C-H Tool & Die/4-D Custom Die.

**Price:** . . . . . . . . . . . . . . **$16.45**

**Universal Shellholders**

Detachable shellholders to fit all popular presses. From C-H Tool & Die/4-D Custom Die.

**Price:** . . . . . . . . . . . . . . **$6.05**

## DAKOTA

**Shellholders**

Shellholders for Dakota Arms proprietary cartridges, 7mm, 300, 330, 375, 416 and 450 Dakota. From Dakota Arms.

**Price:** . . . . . . . . . . . . . . **$12.50**

## DILLON

**AT 500 Auto Eject Upgrade**

To upgrade AT 500 press to RL 550B. Includes cartridge chute/bracket and cartridge bin. From Dillon Precision Products.

**Price:** . . . . . . . . . . . . . . **$12.95**

**AT 500 Auto Powder Upgrade**

To upgrade AT 500 press to RL 550B. Accurate to within 0.1-grain. Magnum rifle powder bar optional. From Dillon Precision Products.

**Price:** . . . . . . . . . . . . . . **$59.95**
**Price:** Magnum rifle bar . . . . . **$17.00**

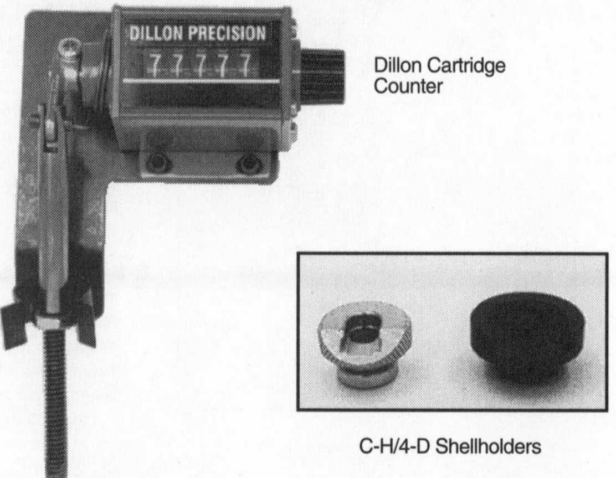


Dillon Cartridge Counter

C-H/4-D Shellholder Extension

C-H/4-D Shellholders

Dillon 550B Conversion Kit

| DILLON RL 1050 Caliber Conversion Kits |
|---|
| 32 S&W |
| 380 Auto |
| 9mm |
| 9x25 Dillon |
| 38 Super |
| 38/357 Mag. |
| 40 S&W |
| 10mm |
| 41 Magnum |
| 44 Magnum |
| 45 ACP |
| 45 Long Colt |
| 223 |
| 30M1 Carbine |
| 7.62x39 |

| DILLON Square Deal B Caliber Conversion Kits |
|---|
| 32 S&W |
| 380 ACP |
| 38 Special |
| 357 Magnum |
| 38 Super |
| 9mm |
| 40 S&W |
| 10mm |
| 41 Magnum |
| 44 Spl. |
| 44 Magnum |
| 44-40 Win. |
| 45 ACP |
| 45 Colt |

**DILLON RL 550B Caliber Conversion Kits**

| RIFLE | | | | PISTOL |
|---|---|---|---|---|
| 17 Rem. | 257 Wea. Mag. | 32 Rem. | 6mm Rem. | 30 Mauser |
| 218 Bee | 25 Rem. | 32 Win. Special | 6.5-06 | 30 Luger |
| 219 Zipper | 264 Win. Mag. | 33 Win. | 6.5x52 Carcano | 32 S&W Mag. |
| 219 Donaldson | 270 Win. | 338 Win. | 6.5x54 Mann.-Sch. | 32 H&R Mag. |
| 220 Swift | 270 Wea. Mag. | 340 Wea. Mag. | 6.5x55 Swedish | 32 Short Colt |
| 221 Rem. Fireball | 280 Rem. | 348 Win. | 6.5 Jap. | 32 ACP |
| 222 Rem. | 284 Win. | 350 Rem. Mag. | 6.5 Rem. Mag. | 380 ACP |
| 22-250 | 30 M1 Carbine | 356 Win. | 6mm PPC | 9mm |
| 222 Rem. Mag. | 300 Win. Mag. | 357 Herrett | 7mm-08 | 38 S&W |
| 223 Rem. | 30-06 | 358 Win. | 7.62x39 Russian | 38AMU |
| 224 Wea. Mag. | 300 H&H | 358 Norma Mag. | 7.65x53 Mauser Rim. | 38 Super |
| 225 Win. | 300 Savage | 35 Rem. | 7.62x54 Russ. | 38/357 Mag./Max. |
| 22 Hornet | 300 Wea. Mag. | 35 Win. | 7mmx57 Mauser | 10mm/40 S&W |
| 22 Rem. Jet | 303 British | 35 Whelen | 7x64 Brenneke | 41 AE |
| 22 Sav. Hi-Power | 30-30 Win. | 375 Win. | 7.7 Japanese | 41 Mag. |
| 240 Wea. Mag. | 30-338 Win. | 375 H&H Mag. | 7mm BR | 44 Special |
| 243 Win. | 30-40 Krag | 375 Super Mag. | 7mm Express | 44 Mag. |
| 244 Rem. | 307 Win. | 375 Wea. Mag. | 7mm Int'l. | 45 ACP |
| 250 Savage | 308 | 38-40 Win. | 7mm Rem. Mag. | 45 Auto Rim |
| 25-06 | 308 Norma Mag. | 38-55 Win. | 7mm Merrill | 455 Webley |
| 25-20 Win. | 30 Herrett | 416 Rem. Mag. | 7mm Int'l Rimmed | 45 Long Colt |
| 25-35 Win. | 30 Merrill | 444 Marlin | 7mm TCU | 45 Win. Mag. |
| 256 Win. Mag. | 30 Rem. | 44-40 Win. | 7mm Wea. Mag. | 454 Casull |
| 257 Roberts | 32-20 Win. | 45-70 Gov't. | 8mm Mauser | 50 AE |
| 257 Ackley Imp. | 32-40 Win. | 458 Win. Mag. | 8mm Rem. Mag. | |

## DILLON

**AT 500 Auto Prime Upgrade**
To upgrade AT 500 press to RL 550B. Includes priming housing and shield; large and small primer slides; large and small pickup tubes, tube lips and magazine tubes; operating rod; primer track bearing; housing screws; spring retaining pin. From Dillon Precision Products.
**Price:** . . . . . . . . . . . . . . **$59.95**

**AT 500 Early Warning Primer Upgrade**
To upgrade AT 500 press to RL 550B. Features easy slip-on attachment. From Dillon Precision Products, Inc.
**Price:** . . . . . . . . . . . . . . **$15.00**

**Accessory Roller Handle**
Accessory press handle for Dillon XL 650, RL 550B and AT 500. From Dillon Precision Products, Inc.
**Price:** . . . . . . . . . . . . . . **$24.95**

**Auto Powder Measure System**
For RL 550B and XL 650 presses. Powder measure to fit extra tool head allowing for quick caliber changeovers. From Dillon Precision Products, Inc.
**Price:** . . . . . . . . . . . . . . **$49.95**

**Bench Wrenches**
Has all correct sizes for Dillon dies, powder systems and press adjustments. From Dillon Precision Products, Inc.
**Price:** . . . . . . . . . . . . . . . **$4.95**

**Cartridge Counter**
Attaches to all Dillon presses or any "crimp only" crimp die. Counts number of rounds of loaded ammo. From Dillon Precision Products, Inc.
**Price:** . . . . . . . . . . . . . . **$15.95**

**Low Powder Sensor**
Provides audible and visual signal when powder level in reservoir drops to 1000 grains. Made of clear polycarbonate with LED light. Two AAA batteries included. From Dillon Precision Products, Inc.
**Price:** . . . . . . . . . . . . . . **$29.95**

**Machine Mount**
Heavy gauge steel mount for RL 550 and XL 650 presses designed to spread the weight load across the reloading bench and raise the reloading press to optimum working level. From Dillon Precision Products, Inc.
**Price:** . . . . . . . . . . . . . . **$29.95**

**Press Covers**
Packcloth nylon machine cover for all Dillon presses. Features D-ring for locking, heavy-duty zipper and optional master lock. From Dillon Precision Products, Inc.
**Price:** RL 550B/Square Deal B with lock . . . . . . . . . . **$22.90**
**Price:** RL 550B/Square Deal B cover only . . . . . . . . . . **$19.95**
**Price:** RL 1050/XL 650 with lock . . **$37.90**
**Price:** RL 1050/XL 650 cover only . . **$34.95**

**RL 550B Caliber Conversion Kits**
Contains shellplate, powder funnel and locator buttons. See chart for available calibers. From Dillon Precision Products, Inc.
**Price:** All calibers . . . . . . . . **$27.95**
**Price:** 50 AE . . . . . . . . . . . **$39.95**

**RL 1050 and XL 650 Powder Check System**
Automatically checks cases for over or under powder charges. From Dillon Precision Products, Inc.
**Price:** . . . . . . . . . . . . . . **$49.95**

RL 1050/XL 650 Powder Check System

Dillon Tool Head Assembly

**DILLON XL 650**
**Caliber Conversion Kits**

| RIFLE | Price | RIFLE | Price |
|---|---|---|---|
| 17 Rem. | $49.95 | 308 Norma Mag. | $100.00 |
| 22 Hornet | 49.95 | 256 Win. Mag. | 49.95 |
| 7.62x39 | 49.95 | 8mm Rem. Mag. | 100.00 |
| 22 Rem. Jet | 49.95 | 257 Roberts | 49.95 |
| 218 Bee | 49.95 | 338 Win. Mag. | 100.00 |
| 7.62x54 | 100.00 | 257 Ackley Imp. | 49.95 |
| 220 Swift | 49.95 | 340 Wea. Mag. | 100.00 |
| 30M1 Carbine | 49.95 | 257 Wea. Mag. | 100.00 |
| 30-06 | 49.95 | 6mm Rem. | 49.95 |
| 222 Rem. | 49.95 | 350 Rem. Mag. | 100.00 |
| 300 Wea. Mag. | 100.00 | 6.5 Rem. Mag. | 100.00 |
| 222 Rem. Mag. | 49.95 | 375 H&H Mag. | 100.00 |
| 300 Win. Mag. | 100.00 | 6.5x55 | 49.95 |
| 22-250 | 49.95 | 38-40 WCF | 49.95 |
| 300 H&H Mag. | 100.00 | 264 Win. Mag. | 100.00 |
| 30-338 Win. Mag. | 99.95 | 444 Marlin | 49.95 |
| 32-20 | 49.95 | 270 Wea. Mag. | 100.00 |
| 223-5.56mm | 49.95 | 44-40 WCF | 49.95 |
| 303 British | 49.95 | 270 Win. | 49.95 |
| 224 Wea. Mag. | 49.95 | 458 Win. Mag. | 100.00 |
| 30-30 Win. | 49.95 | 7mm Rem. Mag. | 100.00 |
| 243 Win. | 49.95 | 45-70 Gov't. | 100.00 |
| 308-7.62 Nato | 49.95 | 7mm Wea. Mag. | 100.00 |
| 25-06 | 49.95 | | |
| **PISTOL** | **Price** | **PISTOL** | **Price** |
| 221 Rem. Fireball | 49.95 | 7mm TCU | 49.95 |
| 30 Luger | 49.95 | 44 Mag. | 49.95 |
| 30 Mauser | 49.95 | 9x21 | 49.95 |
| 38 Super | 49.95 | 45 ACP | 49.95 |
| 32 ACP-7.65mm | 49.95 | 9mm | 49.95 |
| 38/357 Mag. | 49.95 | 45 AR | 49.95 |
| 32 H&R | 49.95 | 9x18 Makarov | 49.95 |
| 10mm/40 S&W | 49.95 | 454 Casull | 49.95 |
| 32 Short Colt | 49.95 | 9x25 Dillon | 49.95 |
| 41 Mag. | 49.95 | 45 Long Colt | 49.95 |
| 32 S&W | 49.95 | 380 ACP | 49.95 |
| 44 Special | 49.95 | 45 Win. Mag. | 49.95 |

## DILLON

**RL 1050 Caliber Conversion Kits**

Includes dies (optional), shellplate, locator buttons, swage backup rod/expander, case feed adapter, case feed plunger and powder funnel. See chart for available calibers. From Dillon Precision Products, Inc.

**Price:** With dies . . . . . . . . . **$124.90**
**Price:** No dies . . . . . . . . . . **$74.95**
**Price:** 9x25, 223 with carbide dies . . . . . . . . . **$159.95**
**Price:** 30 M1 with carbide dies . . . **$137.00**

**Square Deal B Conversion Kits**

Carbide sizer die, expander/powder funnel, seat die, crimp die, shellplate and locator buttons. See chart for available calibers. From Dillon Precision Products, Inc.

**Price:** . . . . . . . . . . . . . . **$59.95**

**Tool Head Conversion Assembly**

A separate stand-alone unit used in conjunction with Dillon caliber conversion kit to change calibers easily on Dillon progressive presses. **RL 550B Assembly:** Includes toolhead, powder measure, powder die, cartridge counter and tool head stand; dies optional. **RL 1050 Assembly:** Comes with tool head, powder measure and cartridge counter. **XL 650 Assembly:** Tool head, tool head stand, powder measure and cartridge counter. From Dillon Precision Products, Inc.

**Price:** RL 550B without dies . . . . **$77.45**
**Price:** RL 1050 . . . . . . . . . **$165.95**
**Price:** XL 650 . . . . . . . . . **$78.45**

**Tool Heads**

For Dillon RL 550B, Square Deal B and XL 650 progressive presses for caliber changeovers. Keeps dies in alignment to eliminate time-consuming die adjustment when changing calibers. Tool head stand extra. From Dillon Precision Products, Inc.

**Price:** RL 550B . . . . . . . . . **$11.45**
**Price:** Square Deal B . . . . . . **$19.95**
**Price:** XL 650 . . . . . . . . . **$13.95**
**Price:** Tool head stand . . . . . . **$5.00**

**Universal Mounting Hardware**

Designed for use with all Dillon presses for bench mounting press. Includes four Grade 5 hex bolts, four lock nuts, four flat washers and two wood screws. From Dillon Precision Products, Inc.

**Price:** RL 550B . . . . . . . . . **$3.25**

**XL 650 Caliber Conversion Kits**

Comes complete with shellplate, locator buttons, powder funnel and casefeed adapter parts. See chart for available calibers. From Dillon Precision Products, Inc.

**Price:** . . . . . . . . . . . . **See chart.**

**XL 650 Case Feed Assembly**

To change to large pistol, small pistol, large rifle or small rifle. Comes with case feed bin, case feed tube and attachment bar. From Dillon Precision Products, Inc.

**Price:** . . . . . . . . . . . . . **$154.95**
**Price:** Extra case feed plate . . . . **$28.50**

**XL 650 Powder Dies**

Designed for the XL 650 press. Allows moving powder measure from tool head to tool head without changing the "belling" adjustment. From Dillon Precision Products, Inc.

**Price:** . . . . . . . . . . . . . . **$4.95**

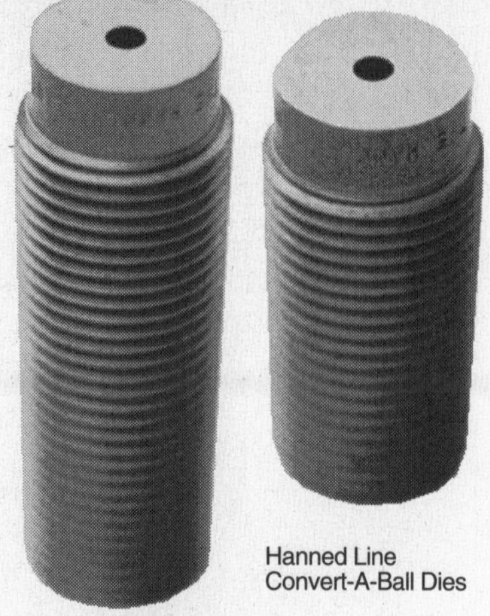

Hanned Line Convert-A-Ball Dies

Forster Conversion Kit

## FORSTER

**"E-Z Just" Shellholder/Primer Conversion Kit**

For Co-Ax presses manufactured prior to 1983. Converts old shellholder/primer system to the current "S" jaw/primer catcher system. From Forster Products.

**Price:** . . . . . . . . . . . . . **$38.40**

## HANNED LINE

**Convert-A-Ball Die**

Converts military ammo with FMJ bullets into flat tips. Standard thread allows use with any standard reloading press. Two versions available: short version for 7.62x39 or 308 NATO; long version for 7mm Mauser, 7.62x54R Russian, 303 British, 30-06, 7.65x54mm French and 8mm Mauser. From The Hanned Line.

**Price:** Short . . . . . . . . . . **$32.50**
**Price:** Long . . . . . . . . . . **$36.60**

## HOLLYWOOD

**Auto Primer Feed**

Fits Hollywood Senior Turret press for automatic priming of cases. Available for standard rifle/pistol cases as well as 50-caliber and shotgun primers. From Hollywood Engineering.

**Price:** Rifle/pistol . . . . . . . . **$35.00**
**Price:** 50-cal./shotgun . . . . . . **$45.00**
**Price:** Primer tube with spring . . . **$15.00**
**Price:** Tube only . . . . . . . . **$10.00**
**Price:** Primer tube spring . . . . . **$5.00**

Hollywood Auto Primer Feed

## HOLLYWOOD

**Priming Rod**

For use with shellholder extension and Universal shellholder and button inserts. Height will depend on combination of use. Specify press, small or large, flat or oval, pistol or rifle. For all Hollywood presses. From Hollywood Engineering.

**Price:** . . . . . . . . . . . . . **$25.00**
**Price:** 50 BMG . . . . . . . . . **$30.00**
**Price:** 20mm . . . . . . . . . . **$40.00**
**Price:** Shotgun . . . . . . . . . **$30.00**

**Senior and Universal Turret Head Plates**

Turret head plates for the Hollywood Senior press can be ordered in four configurations: eight, 1½-12 threaded holes for large dies; four 1½-12 threaded holes; four, ⅞-12 holes; or eight, ⅞-14 holes. Turret plates are also available for the old Hollywood Universal press. Available as standard turret or solid aluminum 10-hole turret threaded 1½-12 for use with all large dies. From Hollywood Engineering.

**Price:** Senior . . . . . . . . . . **$90.00**
**Price:** Senior Turret . . . . . . **$100.00**
**Price:** Universal, standard . . . . **$110.00**
**Price:** Universal, 10-hole . . . . **$200.00**

**Shellholder Extension**

Shortens stroke on Hollywood presses. Makes loading small cartridges easier and assists in case forming and heavy press work. Must have special priming rod. From Hollywood Engineering.

**Price:** . . . . . . . . . . . . . **$15.00**

**Universal/Standard Shellholder**

Will accept all button inserts. Must have Hollywood priming rods for use on Hollywood presses. From Hollywood Engineering.

**Price:** Standard calibers . . . . . . **$7.00**
**Price:** Universal shellholder . . . . **$10.00**
**Price:** Shellholder inserts . . . . . **$7.00**
**Price:** 50 BMG . . . . . . . . . **$30.00**
**Price:** 20mm . . . . . . . . . . **$40.00**
**Price:** Shotgun . . . . . . . . . **$25.00**

## HORNADY Shellplates

**SHELLPLATE NO. 1**
5.6x57
22/250
240 Wea.
243 Win.
244/6mm
6mm Int.
6mm/284
6mm BR
250 Sav.
25-06
257 Rbts.
25-284
6.5-06
6.5x57
270 Win.
7x57 (7mm Mau.)
7mm-08
7mm Rem BR
7x64
7mm Exp./280
284 Win.
300 Sav.
308 Win.
30-06
7.7 Jap.
8mm Mau.
8mm-06
8x60S
35 Whelen
358 Win.
9.3x57
9.3x62
44 Auto Mag.
45 ACP/WM

**SHELLPLATE NO. 2**
219 Zipper
5.6x52R
22 Sav. HP
25/35 Win.
30-30 Win.
30 Herrett
32 Win. Spl.
8.15x46R
357 Herrett
375 Win.
7x30 Waters
32-40

**SHELLPLATE NO. 3**
22 Hornet
22 K-Hornet

**SHELLPLATE NO. 4**
220 Swift
225 Winchester
7mm Merrill
30 Merrill

**SHELLPLATE NO. 5**
257 Wea.
6.5 Rem. Mag.
264 Win. Mag.
270 Wea.
7mm Rem. Mag.
7mm Wea.
300 H&H
300 Win. Mag.
300 Wea.
308 Norma Mag.
8mm Rem. Mag.
338 Win. Mag.
340 Wea.
350 Rem. Mag.
358 Norma Mag.
375 H&H
416 Rem. Mag.
458 Win.

**SHELLPLATE NO. 6**
22 PPC
22 Rem. Jet
256 Win.
6mm PPC
7.62x39
38 Spl.
357 Mag.
357 Max.

**SHELLPLATE NO. 8**
30 Luger
9mm Luger
38 Super Auto

**SHELLPLATE NO. 10**
10mm Auto
40 S&W

**SHELLPLATE NO. 11**
303 British

**SHELLPLATE NO. 14**
33 Winchester
378 Wea.
460 Wea.
45-70 Gov't.
416 Wea.

**SHELLPLATE NO. 16**
17 Rem.
17/222
17/223
221 Rem.
222 Rem.
222 Rem. Mag.
5.6x50 Mag.
223 Rem.
6mm/223
6x47 Rem.
6.5mm TCU
7mm TCU
7mm/223 Ingram
7x47 Helm
380 Auto
6mm TCU

**SHELLPLATE NO. 22**
30 M1 Carbine
32 ACP

**SHELLPLATE NO. 26**
35 Rem.

**SHELLPLATE NO. 29**
41 Mag.

**SHELLPLATE NO. 30**
6.5x68
7.5 Swiss
357/44 Bain & Davis
44 Spl.
44 Mag.

**SHELLPLATE NO. 32**
45 Long Colt

**SHELLPLATE NO. 36**
32 S&W Long
32 S&W Short
32 H&R

Hornady Shellholder

Hornady Lock-N-Load Bushing System

## HORNADY

**Accessory Pack**

Reloading accessories minus the press and shellholder. Includes deluxe powder measure; magnetic scale; nonstatic Universal powder funnel; Universal reloading tray; primer turning plate; Unique case lube; chamfer/debur tool; three case neck brushes; large and small primer pocket cleaners; accessory handle; abridged *Hornady Handbook*; reloading video. From Hornady Mfg. Co.

**Price:** . . . . . . . . . . . . . . **$195.95**

**Auto Primer Shutoff**

Standard on the Hornady Lock-N-Load AP press, primer shutoff also available as accessory. Allows removing primer tubes from auto primer feed without spilling primers. Weight: 4 oz. From Hornady Mfg. Co.

**Price:** . . . . . . . . . . . . . . **$10.55**

**Automatic Primer Feed**

For Lock-N-Load Classic and 0-7 single-stage presses. Comes with large and small primer tubes. Weight: 1 lb. From Hornady Mfg. Co.

**Price:** . . . . . . . . . . . . . . **$19.95**
**Price:** Extra primer tubes . . . . . **$6.95**

## HORNADY

**Brass Kicker**

Accessory for Hornady Lock-N-Load AP press to automatically eject loaded round with each stroke of the press handle. From Hornady Mfg. Co.

**Price:** . . . . . **Contact manufacturer.**

**Case Activated Powder Drop**

Progressive press accessory for Hornady, RCBS and Redding powder measures. Allows powder to be dispensed automatically with each pull of the lever only when a case is present in the station. No adjustments needed when changing powder measures. Uses Lock-N-Load bushing system. From Hornady Mfg. Co.

**Price:** . . . . . . . . . . . . . . **$29.95**

**Large Cartridge Catcher**

Holds one-third more reloaded cartridges than standard catcher on Lock-N-Load AP press. Capacity for over 100 rounds. Weight: 1 lb. From Hornady Mfg. Co.

**Price:** . . . . . . . . . . . . . . **$5.25**

**Lock-N-Load Bushings**

Unique bushing system to allow quick caliber changeovers on press. Threaded $^7/_8$-14 to house and store any die or powder measure. Bushing with die or measure lock solidly into Hornady Classic or AP press. A press conversion bushing for use with other brands of reloading presses using $1^1/_4$-12 bushings also available. From Hornady Mfg. Co.

**Price:** 2 pack . . . . . . . . . . **$8.95**
**Price:** 3 pack . . . . . . . . . . . **$12.95**
**Price:** Press conversion bushing . . **$10.95**

**Lock-N-Load Classic Kit**

Includes Lock-N-Load Classic single-stage press; three die bushings; primer catcher; auto prime system; auto prime feed; deluxe powder measure; magnetic scale; primer turning plate; large and small primer pocket cleaners; accessory handle; three case neck brushes; powder funnel; chamfer/debur tool; die wrench; loading block; Unique case lube; and the abridged *Hornady Handbook*; and *Hornady Handbook of Cartridge Reloading* video tape. From Hornady Mfg. Co.

**Price:** . . . . . . . . . . . . . **$239.95**

**Shellholder 007 and L-N-L Classic**

Machined from solid steel. Available for all popular calibers. Fits Hornady and most other standard presses. Weight: $^1/_4$-lb. From Hornady Mfg. Co.

**Price:** . . . . . . . . . . . . . . **$5.25**

**Shellholder Extension**

Used for forming long cases into short cases. Fits all rams designed for universal shellholders. Extension shellholder number corresponds with standard, removable-head shellholder number. Available in #1, #2 and #16. Weight: $^1/_4$-lb. From Hornady Mfg. Co.

**Price:** . . . . . . . . . . . . . . **$9.95**

**Shellplates Pro-Jector and L-N-L AP Press**

Retainer spring shellplate to hold cases in place during loading operation. Available for over 170 calibers. From Hornady Mfg. Co.

**Price:** . . . . . . . . . . . . . . **$25.95**

Hornady Case Activated Powder Drop

## HOWELL

**Rotary Bullet Feeder**

For most standard progressive reloading presses. Feeds 22-, 25-, 30-, 33-, 9mm, 38-, 41- or 45-caliber bullets, nose or base first, at a rate of 100 bullets per minute. Capacity for 700 to 900 bullets. 14", 16" and 20" bowls available. Powered by 110-volt completely enclosed assembly. Comes set up and ready to run for one or two calibers. From Howell CNC & Machine.

**Price:** 14", one size base first . . . **$995.00**
**Price:** 14", two sizes base first . . **$1,225.00**
**Price:** 14", one size nose first . . **$1,150.00**
**Price:** 14", two sizes nose first . . **$1,375.00**
**Price:** 14", one size nose or base first . . . . . . . . **$1,475.00**
**Price:** 14", two sizes nose or base first . . . . . . . . **$1,750.00**
**Price:** 16", one size base first . . **$1,350.00**
**Price:** 16", two sizes base first . . **$1,625.00**
**Price:** 16", one size nose first . . **$1,500.00**
**Price:** 16", two sizes nose first . . **$1,750.00**
**Price:** 16", one size nose or base first . . . . . . . . **$1,750.00**
**Price:** 16", two sizes nose or base first . . . . . . . . **$2,150.00**
**Price:** 20", one size base first . . **$2,375.00**
**Price:** 20", one size nose first . . **$2,673.00**

## HUNTINGTON

**Aluminum Primer Catcher**

Designed for RCBS reloading presses to replace plastic primer catcher standard on Rock Chucker, Jr. or Reloader Special-5. Cast from aluminum and designed to attach to press with rubberband. From Huntington Die Specialties.

**Price:** . . . . . . . . . . . . . **$9.98**

**Aluminum Wedge Block**

For the old RCBS Jr. press. Allows the press to be tipped back at a more comfortable angle. From Huntington Die Specialties.

**Price:** . . . . . . . . . . . . . **$9.98**

## KLEINENDORST

**Expand-Iron**

Smooths and rounds case mouth or, with next larger caliber size mandrel, expands 22 case to 6mm, 6mm to 25 or 7mm to 30. Fits all standard threaded presses. Stop screw at end of plug adjusts to contact inside web of case head to prevent damage to case neck or shoulder. Pilots for 17- through 30-caliber available. Comes complete for one caliber. From Bob Pease Accuracy.

**Price:** . . . . . . . . . . . . **$15.50**
**Price:** Extra pilots . . . . . . . . **$9.00**

## LEE

**Anniversary Reloading Kit**

Includes Lee Challenger press; Lee Perfect powder measure; Lee Safety scale; powder funnel with powder data manual; case cutter and lock stud for trimming cases; chamfer tool; tube of sizing lube; Lee Auto-Prime tool with shellholders for over 115 cartridges; primer pocket cleaner. From Lee Precision, Inc.

**Price:** . . . . . . . . . . . . **$99.98**

**Bullet Feed Kit**

Designed for use on the Lee Pro 1000 or LoadMaster progressive presses to automatically feed bullets in line with case mouths for seating and crimping. Available in eight sizes from 30-caliber to 45. Comes complete for one caliber. From Lee Precision, Inc.

**Price:** . . . . . . . . . . . . **$29.98**
**Price:** Feed die and fingers for additional calibers . . . . . . **$14.98**

## LEE

**Case Collator**

For use with Load-Master or Pro 1000 presses. Made of durable plastic, the collator fills the four case feed tubes. From Lee Precision, Inc.

**Price:** . . . . . . . . . . . . . **$14.98**

**Case Feeder**

For the Lee Pro 1000 and Load-Master presses. Transparent four-tube case feeder for large or small pistol and rifle cases. Large pistol case feeder will handle 38 Special, 357 Magnum, 41 Magnum, 44 Special, 44 Magnum, 45 ACP, 45 Colt, 10mm Auto and 7.62x39 Russian cases. Small feeder handles 9mm Luger, 380 Auto, 32 Auto, 32 S&W Long, 32 H&R Magnum, 38 Auto and 38 Super. Rifle feeder takes 222, 223 and 30 M1 cases. Extra case feeder tubes available. From Lee Precision, Inc.

**Price:** All sizes . . . . . . . . . **$25.00**
**Price:** Extra tubes, 7-pack . . . . . **$7.98**

**Challenger Press Kit**

Includes Lee Challenger press; ram prime; powder funnel; case sizing lube; dies for one caliber with shellholder; powder dipper and load data. Available in 2-die rifle sets or 3-die carbide pistol sets. Special kit price with purchase of Lee die set. From Lee Precision, Inc.

**Price:** 2-die kit . . . . . . . . **$66.98**
**Price:** 3-die kit . . . . . . . . **$73.98**
**Price:** With Lee die set . . . . . . **$39.98**

**Deluxe Pistol Reloading Kit**

Includes Lee Turret press; Auto Disk powder measure; Safety scale; primer pocket cleaner; cutter and lockstud for trimming cases; chamfer tool. From Lee Precision, Inc.

**Price:** 2-die kit . . . . . . . **$115.98**

**Hand Press Kit**

Includes hand press; ram prime; powder funnel; case sizing lube; dies for one caliber and shellholder; powder dipper; and load data. Available in 2-die rifle sets or 3-die carbide pistol sets. Special kit price with purchase of Lee die set. From Lee Precision, Inc.

**Price:** 2-die set . . . . . . . . **$59.98**
**Price:** 3-die set . . . . . . . . **$65.98**
**Price:** With Lee die set . . . . . . **$32.98**

Lee Case Feeder

## LEE

**Load-Master Pistol Kit**

Comes with Lee Load-Master press, carbide die set for one caliber, Pro Auto-Disk powder measure and a case feeder. Comes factory set up for one caliber. From Lee Precision, Inc.

**Price:** . . . . . . . . . . . . . **$330.00**

**Load-Master Rifle Kit**

Includes Lee Load-Master press, Lee Pace-Setter dies, Perfect powder measure, Universal charge die and case inserter. Comes factory set up for one caliber. From Lee Precision, Inc.

**Price:** . . . . . . . . . . . . . **$320.00**

**Load-Master Shellplate**

Five-station shellplate for Lee Load-Master. From Lee Precision, Inc.

**Price:** . . . . . . . . . . . . . **$29.98**

**Load-Master Turret**

Five-station turret for Lee Load-Master press with 20 locking lugs for quick caliber changeover. From Lee Precision, Inc.

**Price:** . . . . . . . . . . . . . **$14.98**

**Load-Master Loaded Round Catcher**

Accessory for Lee Load-Master. Made of tough plastic. Capacity for 100 45 ACP rounds. From Lee Precision, Inc.

**Price:** . . . . . . . . . . . . . **$14.98**

**Multi-Tube Adapter**

Designed for use with Lee Bullet Feed Kit. High-capacity 100-round magazine supplies Lee Bullet Feeder during reloading operation. Unit includes adaptors for large and small bullets and comes with four large and small feed tubes. From Lee Precision, Inc.

**Price:** . . . . . . . . . . . . . **$25.00**

**Pro 1000 Shell Plate Carrier**

To change calibers entire shellplate carrier can be replaced. Includes shellplate, Auto Prime, case ejector, Auto Index and spare parts. From Lee Precision, Inc.

**Price:** . . . . . . . . . . . . . **$53.98**

**LEE**
**Challenger Press Kit Calibers**

| RIFLE | PISTOL |
|---|---|
| 223 | 9mm Luger |
| 243 | 38 Spl. |
| 270 | 357 Mag. |
| 30-30 | 44 Spl. |
| 308 | 44 Mag. |
| 30-06 | 45 ACP |

These are Lee PaceSetter dies with crimp die.

**LEE**
**Hand Press Kit Calibers**

| RIFLE | PISTOL |
|---|---|
| 223 | 9mm Luger |
| 243 | 38 Spl. |
| 270 | 357 Mag. |
| 30-30 | 44 Spl. |
| 308 | 44 Mag. |
| 30-06 | 45 ACP |

These are Lee PaceSetter dies with crimp die.

Lee Load-Master Shellplate

| LEE | |
|---|---|
| **Shellplate Carrier Calibers** | |
| **SHELLPLATE #** | **CALIBER** |
| 1 | 38 Spl., 357 Mag. |
| 2 | 45 ACP |
| 4 | 222, 223, 380 Auto, 32 S&W Long, 32 H&R Mag. |
| 7A | 30 M1 Carbine |
| 9 | 41 Mag. |
| 11 | 44 Spl., 44 Mag., 45 Colt |
| 19 | 40 S&W, 9mm Luger, 38 Super, 38 Auto, 41 AE |
| 19L | 10mm Auto |

| LEE |
|---|
| **Turret Kit Calibers** |
| **PISTOL** |
| 9mm Luger |
| 38 Spl. |
| 357 Mag. |
| 41 Mag. |
| 44 Spl. |
| 44 Mag. |
| 45 ACP |
| 45 Long Colt |
| 223 (with rifle charge die) |

Lee Hand Press Kit

Lee Load-Master Turret

Lee Deluxe Pistol Reloading Kit

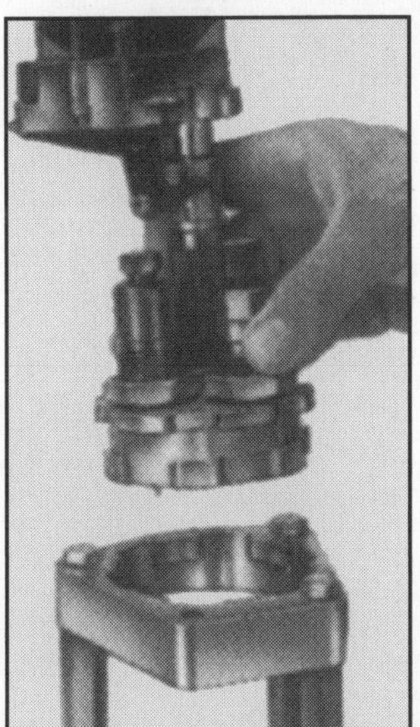

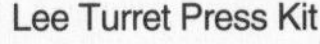

Lee Turret Press Kit

## LEE

**Pro 1000 Shellplates**

Three-station shellplates for Lee Pro 1000. If converting to caliber of different primer size, Pro 1000 primer attachment must be ordered. From Lee Precision, Inc.

**Price:** . . . . . . . . . . . . . . **$20.00**

**Pro 1000 Turret**

Turret for the Lee Pro 1000 press. From Lee Precision, Inc.

**Price:** . . . . . . . . . . . . . . **$10.98**

**Ram Prime**

Primes on press up-stroke. Includes punches for large and small primers. From Lee Precision, Inc.

**Price:** . . . . . . . . . . . . . . **$11.98**

**Shellholder Box**

Plastic transparent box to hold eleven shellholders. From Lee Precision, Inc.

**Price:** . . . . . . . . . . . . . . **$2.60**

**Shellholder Set**

Eleven shellholders to fit over 115 of the most popular cartridges. From Lee Precision, Inc.

**Price:** . . . . . . . . . . . . . . **$19.98**

**Turret Press Kit**

Includes Lee Turret press; Auto-Index with factory installed and adjusted carbide dies for one caliber; shellholder. From Lee Precision, Inc.

**Price:** . . . . . . . . . . . . . . **$102.98**

Lee Pro 1000
Shellplate Carrier

Lee
Shellholder Set

## Section 1: Metallic Cartridges

### LYMAN

**AccuLine Starter Kit**
Includes AccuPress, AccuScale, case lube kit, ram prime die, deburring tool, powder funnel, primer tray, loading block and *Metallic Reloading User's Guide.* From Lyman Products Corporation.
**Price:** . . . . . . . . . . . . . . **$99.95**

**Auto-Primer Feed**
For T-Mag II and Orange Crusher presses. Specify older presses when ordering. Comes with two tubes, large and small. Weight: 3 lbs., 1 oz. From Lyman Products Corporation.
**Price:** . . . . . . . . . . . . . . **$18.25**

**Bench Wrench**
Steel combination wrench designed to fit all Lyman die lock nuts and T-Mag II turret support post. Also fits new style Lyman and RCBS 7/8x14 nuts. From Lyman Products Corporation.
**Price:** . . . . . . . . . . . . . . **$3.75**

**Detachable Shellholder**
Precisely machined and hardened for Orange Crusher, O-Mag, T-Mag II or Special-T presses. From Lyman Products Corporation.
**Price:** . . . . . . . . . . . . . . **$5.75**

**Crusher II Pro Kit**
Kit contains Orange Crusher press; Model 505 powder scale; case lube kit; loading block; powder funnel; primer tray; *Lyman 47th Edition Reloading Handbook*. Weight: 25 lbs. (500 scale); 24 lbs. (AccuScale). From Lyman Products Corporation.
**Price:** . . . . . . . . . . . . . . **$149.95**

**Primer Catcher**
Heavy-duty plastic. Locks securely to Orange Crusher, T-Mag II, Special-T and Spar-T presses. From Lyman Products Corporation.
**Price:** . . . . . . . . . . . . . . **$5.50**

**Deluxe Reloaders Pro Kit**
Kit contains Accupress; Pro 505 powder scale; Accutrimmer with nine pilots; ram prime die; deburring tool; powder funnel; Quick Spray case lube; four popular shellholders; *Lyman 47th Reloading Handbook*. From Lyman Products Corporation.
**Price:** . . . . . . . . . . . . . . **$132.50**

**Expert Kit**
Includes choice of T-Mag II or Orange Crusher press; Universal case trimmer with expanded pilot multi-pack; M-500 reloading scale; #55 powder measure; Universal priming arm; primer tray; auto primer feed; detachable shellholder; primer catcher; quick-release turret system (T-Mag only); deburring tool; case lube kit; powder funnel; extra decapping pins; 7/8-14 adaptor for mounting powder measure; instructions; and *Lyman Reloading and Cast Bullet Guide*. T-Mag kit available with or without dies and shellholder. T-Mag Rifle Set includes rifle die set (223, 22-250, 243, 270, 308, 30-30, 30-06) and shellholder to load one cartridge, 30 lbs; Carbide Pistol Set includes carbide 3-die set (9mm, 38/357, 10mm/40 S&W, 44 Mag., 45 ACP) and shellholder to load one caliber, 31 lbs. Orange Crusher Expert Kit comes in no-cal. version only and does not include dies or shellholder. From Lyman Products Corporation.
**Price:** T-Mag rifle set . . . . . . **$360.00**
**Price:** T-Mag pistol set . . . . . **$378.95**
**Price:** T-Mag no-cal. . . . . . . **$339.95**
**Price:** Crusher II no-cal. . . . . **$299.95**

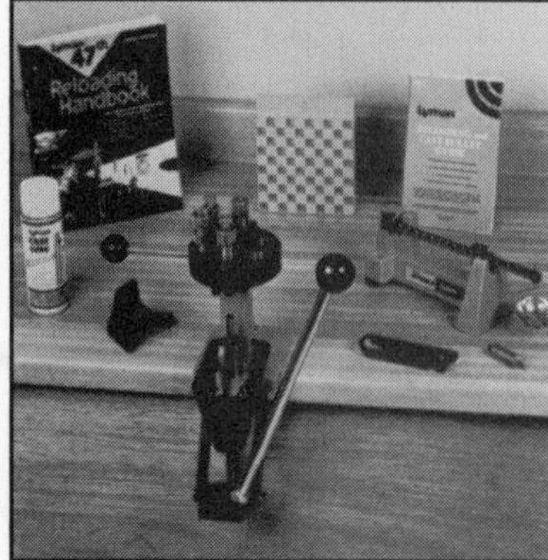

Lyman T-Mag II Pro Kit

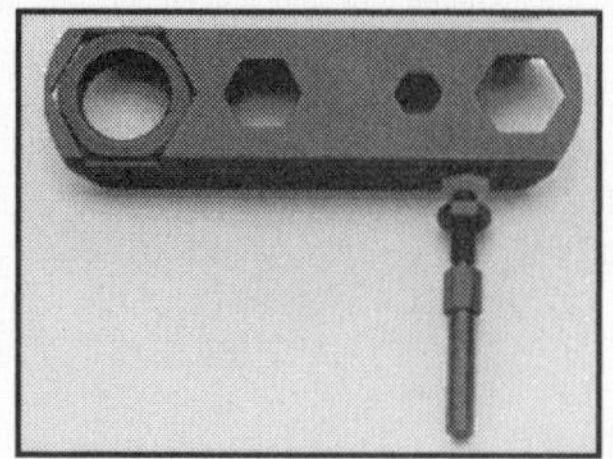

Lyman Bench Wrench

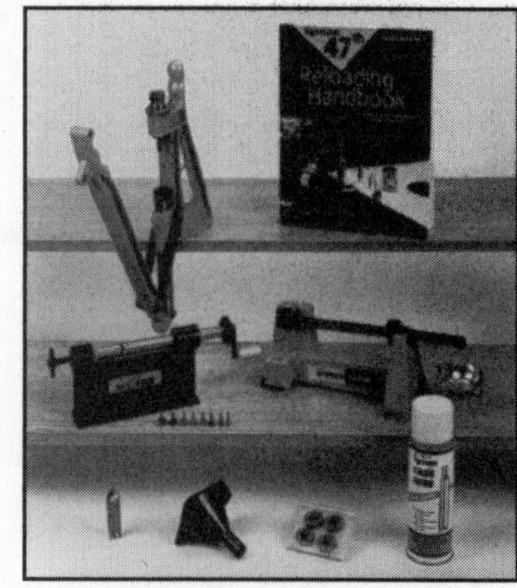

Deluxe Pistol Reloaders Kit

Lyman Shellholder Set

### LYMAN

**Shellholder Set**
Includes 12 standard shellholders for most popular pistol/rifle cartridges in organizer/storage box. From Lyman Products Corporation.
**Price:** . . . . . . . . . . . . . . **$23.95**

**J to X Shellholder Adaptor**
Adaptor available to allow use of X shellholder with older Lyman presses using J-type shellholders. From Lyman Products Corporation.
**Price:** Adaptor . . . . . . . . . **$8.25**

**T-Mag II Pro Kit**
Includes T-Mag II press; Pro 500 powder scale, loading block, deburring tool, spray case lube, powder funnel and *Lyman 47th Edition Reloading Handbook*. From Lyman Products Corporation.
**Price:** . . . . . . . . . . . . . . **$210.00**

**310 Tool Set Pouch**
Rugged nylon camouflage pouch with military-type belt clip holds 310 tool handles and dies for field use. From Lyman Products Corporation.
**Price:** . . . . . . . . . . . . . . **$9.95**

**T Priming Punch**
Required when using J to X shellholder adaptor to seat primers in older style presses. Includes both large and small punches and sleeves. From Lyman Products Corporation.
**Price:** . . . . . . . . . . . . . . **$6.75**

**Universal Priming Arm**
Seats all sizes and types of primers. Supplied with two priming sleeves, large and small. From Lyman Products Corporation.
**Price:** . . . . . . . . . . . . . . **$8.75**

Lyman Orange Crusher Starter Kit

Lyman Expert Kit

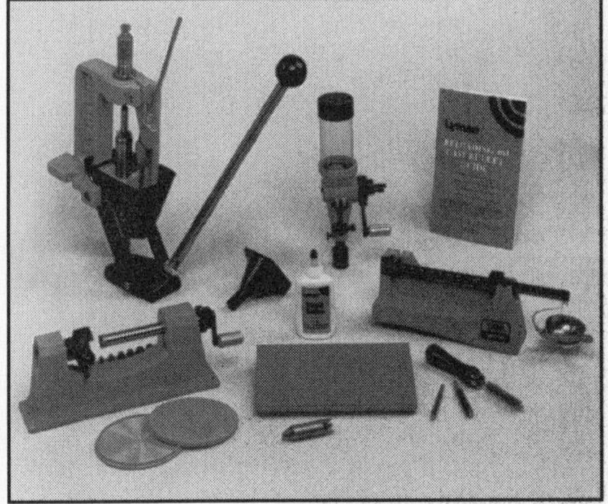

M-A Systems Easy Case Feed

M-A Systems Easy Loader

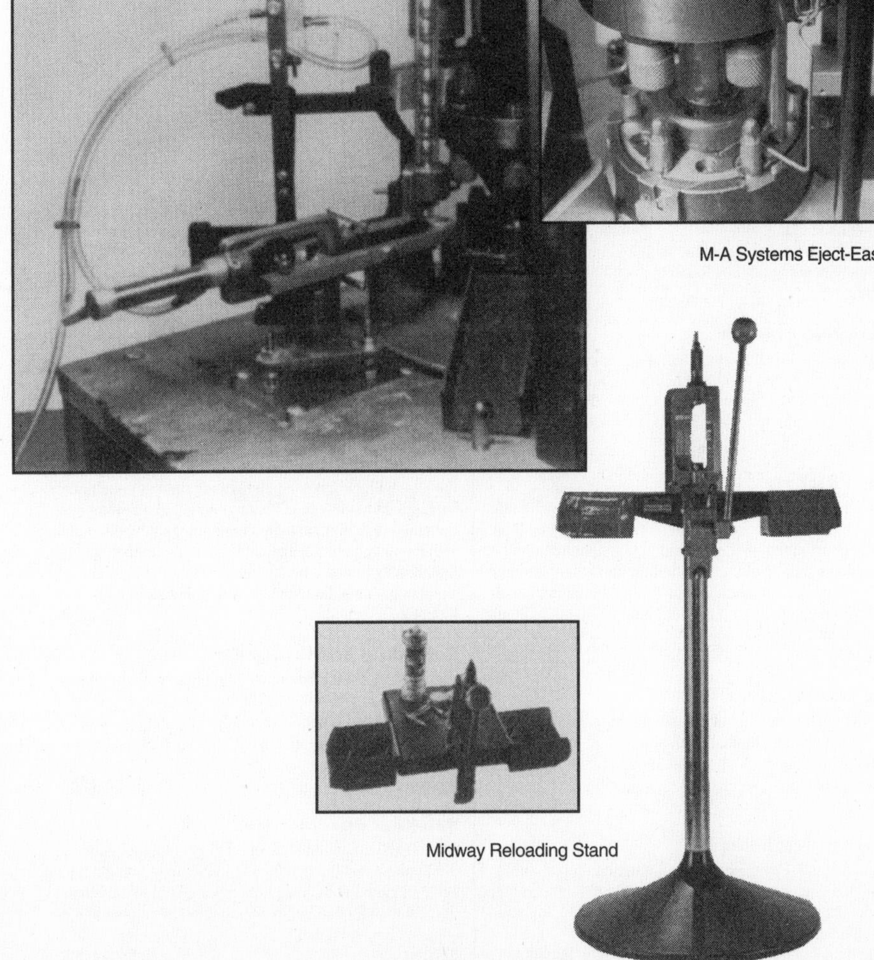

M-A Systems Eject-Ease

Midway Reloading Stand

## M-A SYSTEMS

**Easy Case Feeder for Star Press**

Feeds cases automatically. Adjusts for 9mm through 45 Colt; special feed tube available for 380 Auto. Includes two supply tubes 36″ long and will adapt to most case collators. Two push rods stabilize self-lubricating nylon case shuttle bar to reduce operating force and wear. Weight: 2 lbs. From M-A Systems.

**Price:** . . . . . . . . . . . . . . **$164.50**

**Easy Loader**

Mounts to Star, Dillon RL 1000 and C-H/4-D Die Inline to feed bullets base down at rate of 2500 per hour. Operates automatically in sequence with press from regulated 50-60 psi air source. Accepts all flat-based bullets, some hollow base, round-nose, wadcutters and semi-wadcutters. Comes complete for 9mm through 45-caliber with two sizes of bullet supply tubes, four feed tubes and two sets of bullet grippers. 223 and 380 Auto require special grippers; 223-caliber requires special feed tubes. Weight: 4 lbs. From M-A Systems.

**Price:** Star . . . . . . . . . . **$410.00**
**Price:** Dillon . . . . . . . . . **$465.00**

**Eject-Ease for Star Press**

Side-ejects loaded 30- through 45-caliber rounds at taper crimp station. Round held securely in shellplate taper crimp pocket, eliminating side crimp and case crushing. As tool head moves up, the spring wire ejector moves case out of shellplate and clear of press. No press modification required. Comes complete with installation instructions. Weight: 1-lb. From M-A Systems.

**Price:** . . . . . . . . . . . . . . **$45.00**

**Roller-Ease Handle for Star Press**

Replacement handle for Star press. Operating arm of steel; roller handle 1″ diameter aluminum, medium knurled for non-chafing grip surface. Increases effective fulcrum without increasing length of stroke. Weight: 1-lb. From M-A Systems.

**Price:** . . . . . . . . . . . . . . **$24.95**

**Roto-Ease for Star Press**

Designed for the Star press to automatically advance shellplate, increasing reload rate from 400 to 800 rounds per hour. Operates with all calibers. Cam operation controls acceleration and deceleration of shellplate. Operating hook pulls in plane with shellplate and mounts to right rear of press. No press modification required. Weight: 2 lbs. From M-A Systems.

**Price:** . . . . . . . . . . . . . . **$169.50**

## MIDWAY

**Reloading Stand**

Portable lightweight stand to mount reloading press. Features drilling template for stand top with hole positions for mounting most popular presses. Comes with two accessory bins that clip to edge of stand and hold components and tools. From Midway Arms, Inc.

**Price:** . . . . . . . . . . . . . . **$39.99**
**Price:** Extra top . . . . . . . **$14.99**
**Price:** Extra bin . . . . . . . . . **$3.29**

## PONSNESS/WARREN

**Dust Covers**

Sturdy canvas cover for Metallic II and Metal-Matic presses. From Ponsness/Warren.

**Price:** Metallic II . . . . . . . . **$27.95**
**Price:** Metal-Matic . . . . . . . **$20.95**

## PONSNESS/WARREN

**Metallic II Die Head**

Extra die heads for changing and mounting a different caliber. From Ponsness/Warren.

**Price:** . . . . . . . . . . . . . . **$42.50**

**Metallic II Powder Measure Extension**

Raises powder measure above dies. Complete with housing, spring and large and small primers. From Ponsness/Warren.

**Price:** . . . . . . . . . . . . . . **$19.95**

**P-200 Die Head**

Extra die heads for changing and mounting a different caliber. From Ponsness/Warren.

**Price:** . . . . . . . . . . . . . . **$39.95**

**P-200 Primer Feed**

Fits all Metal-Matic presses. Includes large and small primer tubes and steel primer tube shield. From Ponsness/Warren.

**Price:** . . . . . . . . . . . . . . **$34.95**

**P-200/M-II Primer Speed Feeder**

Feeds primers to primer feed. Available for large or small primers. From Ponsness/Warren.

**Price:** . . . . . . . . . . . . . . **$11.50**

## PRIME RELOADING

**Hydro Punch**

Hydro punch for removing Berdan or Boxer primers from crimped or non-crimped cases. Available for over 120 calibers from 22 Hornet to 55 Boyes. Body constructed of brass, integral reservoir of non-ferrous metal. For rare or vintage calibers, send two sample fired cases. From H.J. Kohne.

**Price:** . . . . . **Contact manufacturer.**

## RCBS

**Accessory Base Plate-2**

Heavy .820″ thick aluminum casting measuring $9^{7}/_{8}$″x$5^{1}/_{2}$″ with holes drilled and pre-tapped for mounting reloading tools. For use with RCBS rotary case trimmer, powder measure stand, Lube-a-Matic, Reloader Special-5 press, Rock Chucker, Partner press, auto and standard priming tools. Fasteners included. From RCBS.

**Price:** . . . . . . . . . . . . . . **$22.63**

**Ammo-Crafter Kit**

Accessory kit without press. Includes: Trim-Pro manual trimmer; case trimmer kit; Primer Tray-2; *Speer Reloading Manual*; 5-0-5 scale; Uniflow powder measure; case loading block; deburring tool; case lube kit; and powder funnel. From RCBS.

**Price:** . . . . . . . . . . . . . . **$253.38**

**APS Priming System**

Revolutionary new priming system utilizing preloaded flexible primer strips that are automatically indexed with each pull of the handle. The APS tool can be bench mounted or press mounted. The 25-capacity primer strips are color coded by primer type and can be hooked together for continuous feeding. The bench-mounted tool is a free-standing unit with its own handle while the press-mounted tool fits into conventional presses. From RCBS.

**Price:** Bench-mounted tool . . . . **$80.63**
**Price:** Press-mounted tool . . . . . **$51.50**

**APS Primer Strips**

Available as fully loaded color-coded strips with 25 primers per plastic strip or empty, ready for use with the APS Primer Strip Loader. From RCBS.

**Price:** . . . . . **Contact manufacturer.**

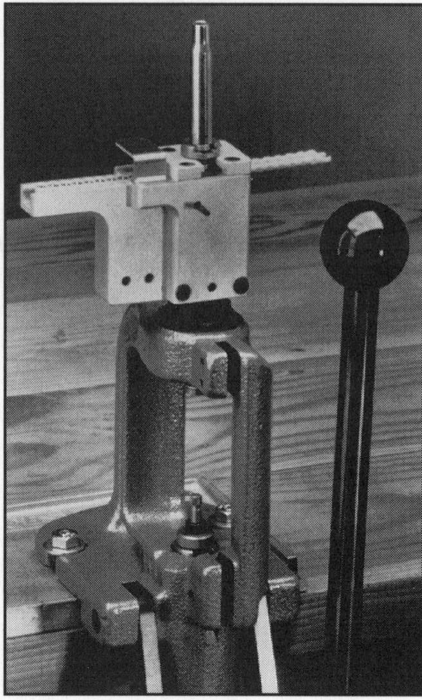

RCBS APS Press Mounted Priming System

Redding Shellholder

RCBS Cartridge Counter

## RCBS

**APS Primer Strip Loader**

For loading primers into empty APS plastic strips for reuse. Each push of the handle orients and seats 25 primers into the strip. Compact in size for easy storage. From RCBS.

**Price:** . . . . . . . . . . . . . . **$20.84**

**Cartridge Counter**

Attaches to Uniflow powder measure and counts each powder charge thrown, up to four digits. For use with RCBS AmmoMaster auto, PiggyBack II or with powder measure alone. From RCBS.

**Price:** . . . . . . . . . . . . . . **$17.63**

**Case Kicker**

For use with RCBS Jr., Reloader Special and Rock Chucker presses. An ejector spring assembly that mounts on right side of press and pushes the case out of the shellholder into a box mounted on left side of press. Includes primer deflector to catch decapped primers and direct them to container on floor. From RCBS.

**Price:** . . . . . . . . . . . . . . **$21.63**

**Lock-Out Die**

Detects a no-powder or double charge condition in the progressive reloading process and locks up or halts ram travel at the case mouth. For use with pistol calibers. From RCBS.

**Price:** . . . . . . . . . . . . . . **$36.63**

**Partner Reloading Kit**

Comes with Partner press. Includes: 5-0-2 scale; case loading block; case lube kit; Primer Tray-2; deburring tool; powder funnel; and *Speer Reloading Manual*. From RCBS.

**Price:** . . . . . . . . . . . . . . **$143.25**

## RCBS

**Piggyback II**

Converts RCBS Rock Chucker, Reloader Special-3 and Reloader Special-5 single-stage presses to progressive units. Features automatic indexing, priming, powder charging and loaded round ejection. Case detection system disengages powder measure when no case is present in powder charging station. Comes with clear powder measure adaptor to view and correct bridged powders. Five-station shellplate, reloading dies and powder measure not included. From RCBS.

**Price:** . . . . . . . . . . . . . . **$157.88**

**Powder Checker**

For use with progressive presses to confirm each case receives the correct powder charge. A moving rod indicates the presence of powder and provides a quick visual comparison for the amount of powder dropped. Located between the powder charging and bullet seating stations. Black oxide finish. From RCBS.

**Price:** . . . . . . . . . . . . . . **$23.50**

**Reloading Accessory Kit**

Includes: Powder measure/Piggyback stand; powder trickler; primer pocket brushes for large and small pockets; case loading block; stainless steel dial caliper; small and medium case neck brush. From RCBS.

**Price:** . . . . . . . . . . . . . . **$89.75**

**Reloader Special-5 Kit**

Comes with Reloader Special-5 press. Includes: 5-0-5 scale; case loading block; case lube kit; Primer Tray-2; powder funnel; and *Speer Reloading Manual*. Dies and shellholders must be purchased separately. From RCBS.

**Price:** . . . . . . . . . . . . . . **$231.13**

## RCBS

**Shellholder Rack**

Durable plastic rack measures 5-3/4"x6-7/8". Features 32 numbered pegs for each size shellholder and pull-out reference table listing proper shellholder for popular rifle/pistol calibers. Can be mounted on bench or wall. From RCBS.

**Price:** . . . . . . . . . . . . . **$14.88**

**Shellholders**

**Price:** . . . . . . . . . . . . . . **$5.50**
**Price:** Extended shellholder . . . . **$7.88**
**Price:** Shellholder ram, C press . . **$18.88**
**Price:** Adaptor, H press . . . . . **$12.75**
**Price:** Adaptor, Herters . . . . . **$14.63**

**Shotshell Die**

Compatible with Rock Chucker and Reloader Special 3/5 and AmmoMaster presses. Transforms metallic press to 10-, 12-, 16- or 20-gauge shotshell press. Designed for compression-formed plastic hulls with appropriate wad column. Can use with high brass hulls and up to 3" magnum loads. Die set includes shot measure, case holder and 6- and 8-point case crimper. From RCBS.

**Price:** . . . . . . . . . . . . . **$56.88**

**Rock Chucker Reloading Kit**

Comes with Rock Chucker press. Includes: 5-0-5 reloading scale; Uniflow powder measure; *Speer Reloading Manual*; Trim-Pro manual trimmer; case trimmer kit; hex key set; case loading block; case lube kit; automatic primer feed; Primer Tray-2; powder funnel; and deburring tool. From RCBS.

**Price:** . . . . . . . . . . . . . **$355.25**

## REDDING

**Boss Pro-Pak**

Contains Boss reloading press; Model #2 powder/bullet scale; powder trickler; set of Series A reloading dies; pad-style case lube kit; deburring tool for cases from 17- to 45-caliber; Model #18 case preparation kit; powder funnel; and *Hodgdon Loading Data Manual*. From Redding Reloading Equipment.

**Price:** . . . . . . . . . . . . . **$336.00**

**Competition Shellholder Sets**

Five-piece set in .002" increments (+.002", +.004", .006", +.008" and +.010") allows headspace control adjustments on press. Finished in black oxide and clearly marked. From Redding Reloading Equipment.

**Price:** . . . . . . . . . . . . . **$45.00**

**Model No. 11 Shellholder**

Universal snap-in design precision machined and heat-treated. From Redding Reloading Equipment.

**Price:** . . . . . . . . . . . . . **$7.95**

**Extended Shellholders**

Required when trimming short cases under 1-1/2" OAL. From Redding Reloading Equipment.

**Price:** . . . . . . . . . . . . . **$12.00**

**Reloading Press Kits**

Each Redding press available in kit form to include the press, choice of one set of Series A reloading dies and matching shellholder. From Redding Reloading Equipment.

**Price:** Boss press kit . . . . . . **$165.00**
**Price:** Turret press kit . . . . . **$324.00**
**Price:** Ultramag press kit . . . . **$324.00**

## ROCK CRUSHER

**Shellholders**

Shellholders for Rock Crusher press for 50 BMG, 55 Boyes rifle, 12.7mmx107 Russian, 20mm Lahti, 20mm Solothurn, 20mm Vulcan, 20mm Hispana, 20mm Oerlikon, 23mmx115 Soviet. From The Old Western Scrounger.

**Price:** 50 BMG, 12.7, 55 Boyes . . . **$36.75**
**Price:** 14.5 Russian, 20 Lahti, 20 Vulcan, 20 Oelikon, 20 Hispana . . . . **$47.25**
**Price:** 23 Soviet . . . . . . . . **$65.00**

## SLAP

**Powder Buddy**

Accurate trip meter fitted to any powder measure or progressive/semi-progressive press to show a count from 1 to 99,999 of each powder throw. Helps prevent double charging or no powder charge. All-metal construction. From SLAP Industries.

**Price:** . . . . . . . . . . . . . **$29.95**

## THOMPSON

**Tool Mount**

Interlocking steel plates allow use of multiple reloading tools from a single mounting point. The base plate is permanently affixed to the reloading bench while the accessory plate is attached to the tool in use—powder measure, case trimmer, lubrisizer, etc. The plates are 1/8" thick, 5-3/8" long and 2-1/2" wide. Complete installation instructions included. From Thompson Tool Mount.

**Price:** . . . . . . . . . . . . . **$25.00**

## VEGA TOOL

**Re-Manufactured Shellholders**

Shellholders or shellholder adaptors to fit obsolete reloading presses. Shellholder adaptors for Herters, Lyman, Wells and Hollywood presses accept universal shellholders. Re-manufactured shellholders available in most popular calibers for Lyman J2 type, Hollywood and Herters presses. From Vega Tool Co., Inc.

**Price:** Shellholders . . . . . . . **$16.20**
**Price:** Adaptors . . . . . . . . . **$16.20**

## WILSON/SINCLAIR

**Hand Die Reloading Kit**

Includes Sinclair arbor press and die base, Wilson bullet seater, neck die and neck die bushing. Optional kit with micrometer attachment also available. From Sinclair International, Inc.

**Price:** . . . . . . . . . . . . . **$180.30**
**Price:** With micrometer attachment . **$210.05**

Vega Tool Re-Manufactured Shellholders

Redding Competition Shellholder

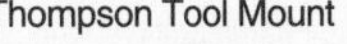

Thompson Tool Mount

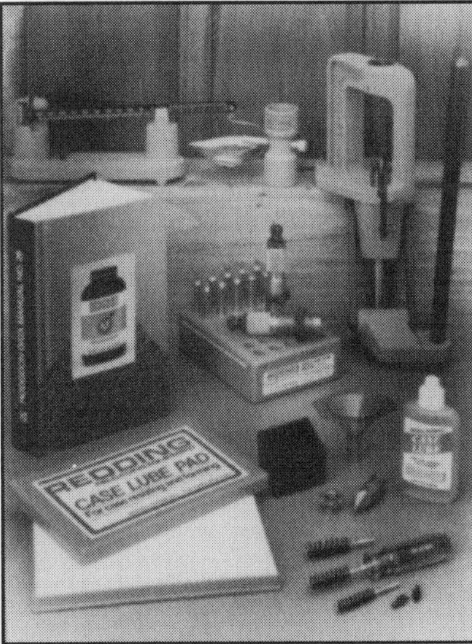


Redding Boss Pro-Pack

## BALD EAGLE

**Unchambered Die Bodies**

Stainless steel $\frac{7}{8}$-14 short, medium, long, and tong tool dies. These unchambered sizing dies accept Wilson sizing bushings for adjusting neck tension on loaded rounds. Concentric inside and out. From Bald Eagle Precision Machine Company.

**Price:** . . . . . . . . . . . . . . . **$60.00**

## BRUNO

**310 Tool Neck-Size Die**

Size die for 6mm BR and PPC and 308. Accepts Wilson bushings. Bushing not included. From Bruno Shooters Supply.

**Price:** . . . . . . . . . . . . . . . **$93.00**

## CARBIDE DIE & MFG.

**Pistol Dies**

Carbide single- and two-stage sizing dies for handgun calibers. Threaded $\frac{7}{8}$-14 for standard loading presses and $\frac{11}{16}$-24 for the Star Universal Pistol press. Single-stage dies: 38 Spec., 38 ACP, 380 Auto, 32 S&W, 357 Magnum, 32 Auto, 38 S&W, 41 Magnum, 44 S&W, 44 Magnum, 45 ACP, 45 Auto Rim, 45 Colt, 9mm and 10mm/40 S&W. Two-stage dies with two carbide rings: 38 Spec., 38 ACP, 45 ACP and 44 Spec. Come with decap pin and set screw. From Carbide Die & Mfg. Co., Inc.

**Price:** Single-stage dies . . . . . **$43.00**
**Price:** Single-stage, 9mm . . . . . **$65.00**
**Price:** Two-stage dies . . . . . . **$65.00**

## C-H/4-D

**20mm Lahti Dies**

Dies threaded $1\frac{1}{2}$-12 with expander for use with U.S. 20mm projectiles. Expander for original projectiles available. Shellholder with $\frac{5}{8}$-18 thread and priming tool also offered. From C-H Tool & Die/4-D Custom Die.

**Price:** . . . . . . . . . . . . . . **$385.00**
**Price:** Shellholder . . . . . . . . **$40.00**
**Price:** Priming tool . . . . . . . **$60.00**

**50 BMG Bushing Neck Sizer Die**

Neck size die with bushings in .001″ increments in sizes from .538 to .552. Bushings interchangeable with Neil Jones arbor die. Comes complete with one bushing. From C-H Tool & Die/4-D Custom Die.

**Price:** . . . . . . . . . . . . . . **$210.00**
**Price:** Neck sizer and seater . . . **$400.00**
**Price:** Bushing . . . . . . . . . **$15.00**

**50 BMG Dies**

Chrome-plated steel two-die set threaded $1\frac{1}{2}$-12 for reloading 50 BMG caliber. Set includes full-length size and crimp seater. From 4-D Custom Die.

**Price:** . . . . . . . . . . . . . . **$214.50**
**Price:** Shellholder . . . . . . . . **$15.00**

## C-H/4-D

**50 BMG Straight Line Seater**

Features sliding sleeve to hold bullet in alignment with case with normal run-out of .002″-.004″. From C-H Tool & Die/4-D Custom Die.

**Price:** . . . . . . . . . . . . . . **$210.00**
**Price:** Neck sizer and seater die combo . . . . . . . . . . . . **$400.00**

**Blank Crimping Die**

Crimp die for loading blank cartridges. Straight-walled cases need only one die. Rimless calibers require shoulder to control headspace thus require shoulder die. Dies available for most popular calibers; odd calibers at extra cost. From C-H Tool & Die/4-D Custom Die.

**Price:** . . . . . . . . . . . . . . **$79.95**
**Price:** Shoulder die, 9mm, 45 ACP . **$19.95**

**Bullet Sizing Die**

Custom $\frac{7}{8}$-14 threaded die to size down oversize bullets in .004″ increments. From C-H Tool & Die/4-D Custom Die.

**Price:** . . . . . . . . . . . . . . **$54.95**

**Bushing Neck Sizer Die**

Bushing neck size die with bushings in .001″ increments. Available in three body lengths: short (1″ to $1\frac{1}{2}$″ shoulder); medium ($1\frac{1}{2}$″ to 2″ shoulder); long (2″ to $2\frac{1}{2}$″ shoulder). Bushings available from .239″ to .400″. From C-H Tool & Die/4-D Custom Die.

**Price:** . . . . . . . . . . . . . . **$49.95**
**Price:** Body only . . . . . . . . . **$30.00**
**Price:** Bushing . . . . . . . . . . **$10.00**

Bald Eagle Unchambered Die Bodies

## C-H/4-D

**Custom Reloading Dies**

Die sets, forming dies, trim dies, etc. are stocked for hundreds of calibers or can be made to order for an additional tooling charge. Die groups A through H standard $\frac{7}{8}$-14 thread; groups J and K, 1-14 thread; group N dies $1\frac{1}{2}$-12 threading. All dies except N are for use with shellholders or shellplates having industry standard dimension of 0.125″ from case head to top of shellholder. From C-H Tool & Die/4-D Custom Die.

**Price:** . . . . . . . . . . . . **See chart**

**Expander Die Bodies**

Available in any length and top thread. Specify length, top thread, body diameter and minimum inside diameter. From C-H Tool & Die/4-D Custom Die.

**Price:** $\frac{7}{8}$-14 O.D. . . . . . . . . **$11.00**
**Price:** 1-14 O.D. . . . . . . . . . **$22.00**

**"M"-Type Expander Plugs**

Designed for loading cast bullets or jacketed bullets. Expander has plug .001″ smaller than bullet diameter and a taper to bell case mouth slightly to prevent "lead shaving." From C-H Tool & Die/4-D Custom Die.

**Price:** To 45-cal. . . . . . . . . . **$11.00**
**Price:** 46-50-cal. . . . . . . . . . **$16.50**
**Price:** 51-70-cal. . . . . . . . . . **$22.00**

**Speed Seater Die**

To facilitate seating of wadcutter-type bullets. Die opening is larger in diameter than main body, gradually tapering to seating stem. From C-H Tool & Die/4-D Custom Die.

**Price:** . . . . . . . . . . . . . **$16.00**

**Small Base Die Sets**

For reloading cartridges to minimum dimensions. Available for 223 Remington, 30-06 and 308 Winchester. From C-H Tool & Die/4-D Custom Die.

**Price:** Set . . . . . . . . . . . **$35.00**
**Price:** Sizer die . . . . . . . . . **$19.25**

**Taper Crimp Die (Pistol)**

Precision-honed, hardened and polished inside with non-glare satin finish outside. For autoloading calibers that headspace off the case mouth. Available in all C-H/4-D calibers. From C-H Tool & Die/4-D Custom Die.

**Price:** . . . . . . . . . . . . **See chart.**

**Taper Crimp Die (Rifle)**

Available in all C-H/4-D die offerings. Eliminates case trimming and is useful for handloading semi-auto rifle ammo. From C-H Tool & Die/4-D Custom Die.

**Price:** . . . . . . . . . . . . **See chart.**

**C-H/4-D Custom Die Prices**

| DIES | GROUP A | B | C | D | E | F | G | H | J | K | N | S |
|---|---|---|---|---|---|---|---|---|---|---|---|---|
| Die Set | $35.00 | $37.00 | $40.00 | $44.00 | $57.20 | $60.50 | $83.60 | $119.90 | $130.90 | $141.90 | $214.50 | $385.00 |
| Neck Size Die | 23.15 | 16.15 | 26.25 | 29.05 | 28.00 | 39.60 | 55.00 | 77.00 | 99.00 | 99.00 | 143.55 | 257.65 |
| Seating Die | 19.25 | 17.35 | 22.00 | 24.40 | 21.90 | 29.70 | 40.70 | 55.00 | 71.50 | 71.50 | 107.25 | 192.50 |
| File Trim Die | 29.70 | 29.70 | 29.70 | 29.70 | 29.70 | 29.70 | 40.70 | 55.00 | 71.50 | 71.50 | 104.50 | 187.55 |
| Case Form Die | 29.70 | 29.70 | 29.70 | 29.70 | 29.70 | 29.70 | 40.70 | 55.00 | 71.50 | 71.50 | 104.50 | 187.55 |
| Taper Crimp Die* | 12.00 | 12.00 | 12.00 | 12.00 | 12.00 | 22.00 | 29.70 | 41.80 | 52.80 | 52.80 | 66.00 | 118.45 |
| Taper Crimp Die** | 12.00 | 14.00 | 16.00 | 20.00 | 36.50 | 36.50 | 49.50 | 66.00 | 88.00 | 88.00 | 126.50 | 227.05 |
| Reamer Die/Reamer | 77.00 | 77.00 | 77.00 | 77.00 | 77.00 | 77.00 | 88.00 | 99.00 | 110.00 | 110.00 | 143.00 | 265.00 |

*Straight Wall; **Bottleneck/Straight Taper

## C-H/4-D

### Tapered Expanders

Gradual taper for expanding the case neck to larger caliber. Will expand neck .050" to .060". Sizes through 45-caliber, fits any expander body with 9-16 top thread. Larger sizes require special die bodies. From C-H Tool & Die/4-D Custom Die.

**Price:** To 45-cal. . . . . . . . . . **$10.00**
**Price:** 46-50-cal. . . . . . . . . . **$15.00**
**Price:** 51-70-cal. . . . . . . . . . **$25.00**

### Titanium Nitride Die Coating

Titanium nitride coating makes die harder than carbide with low coefficient of friction and requires less sizing effort. Available in any C-H/4-D standard die offerings. From C-H Tool & Die/4-D Custom Die.

**Price:** Per die . . . . . . . . . . **$30.00**

### Universal Decapping Die

Comes in two sizes—large and small. Small die decaps calibers 22 Hornet through 6mm-06. Larger die accommodates all calibers from 25-20 to 50-110 Winchester and with 1/4" diameter decap rod and .070" decap rod will decap military 308 and 30-06 cases with crimped-in primers. From C-H Tool & Die/4-D Custom Die.

**Price:** 7/8-14 . . . . . . . . . . **$17.95**
**Price:** 1-14 . . . . . . . . . . **$26.95**

## DAKOTA

### Dakota Dies

Reloading dies for the Dakota Arms proprietary cartridges, 7mm, 300, 330, 375, 416 and 450 Dakota. From Dakota Arms, Inc.

**Price:** . . . . . . . . . . . . **$75.00**

Forster Ultra Bullet Seater Die

Dillon's Dynamic Carbide Pistol Dies

## DILLON

### Custom Carbide Rifle Dies

Three-die carbide sets include size/decap, seater and crimp die. Design features include radiused carbide mouth; long tapered carbide ring; heavy headed decap pin; vented seating stem. All have large radiused mouths and wrench hex adjustments. Rifle die calibers: 223 Remington, 30 Carbine and 308 Winchester. Pistol die calibers: 380 Auto, 9mm, 38 Super, 38/357, 10mm/40 S&W, 41 Mag., 44 Spec., 44 Mag., 45 ACP, 45 LC and 9x25 Dillon. From Dillon Precision Products, Inc.

**Price:** 223 . . . . . . . . . . **$103.95**
**Price:** 308 Win. . . . . . . . . . **$113.95**
**Price:** Size die . . . . . . . . . . **$79.95**
**Price:** Extra decap pins, 10 . . . . . **$3.50**

### Dynamic Carbide Rifle/Pistol Dies

Die sets with sizer/decap and seat die. Crimp die available separately. Carbide sizer and decapper feature larger lead-in radius for smoother reloading and a floating decap assembly with snap ring for release of spent primers. Seater die and crimp die allow disassembly without loosing adjustment. Seating die "flip-flop" stem allows changing bullet nose configuration without removal of die from press. Die sets do not include expander die; designed to work with a powder-through expander. Die calibers: 380 Auto, 9mm, 38 Super, 38/357, 10mm/40 S&W, 41 Mag., 44 Spl./44 Mag., 45 ACP, 45 Long Colt and 9x25 Dillon. From Dillon Precision Products, Inc.

**Price:** Rifle . . . . . . . . . . **$103.95**
**Price:** 308 Win. . . . . . . . . . **$113.95**
**Price:** 223, 30 Carbide size die only . **$79.95**
**Price:** 308 Win. size die only . . . . **$89.95**
**Price:** Pistol . . . . . . . . . . **$49.95**
**Price:** 9x25 Dillon . . . . . . . . **$103.95**

### Three Die Rifle Set

Includes sizing/depriming seating and taper crimp dies. Size die features full-length to minimum tolerances, carbide expander ball and stuck case remover. For calibers 223 Rem., 308 Win., 30-06 Springfield and 7.62x39. From Dillon Precision Products, Inc.

**Price:** . . . . . . . . . . . . **$49.95**

## FORSTER

### Bench Rest Die Set

Two-die set that includes both the Bench Rest Sizing die and Bench Rest Seater die. From Forster Products.

**Price:** . . . . . . . . . . . . **$69.50**

### Bench Rest Seater Die

Straight-line, chamber-type, non-crimping style die that holds bullet and case in alignment in close fitting channel. Adaptable to standard loading presses. From Forster Products.

**Price:** . . . . . . . . . . . . **$39.00**

### Bench Rest Sizing Die

Precision die with polished interior. Special attention given to headspace taper and diameter. The new expander button floats on the stem near the stem top to allow the expander to enter the case neck while it is in the neck sizing portion of the die to assure alignment. From Forster Products.

**Price:** . . . . . . . . . . . . **$32.20**

### Ultra Bullet Seater Die

Bullet seating die with micrometer seating depth adjustment. Head is graduated in .001" increments with .025" bullet movement per revolution. Available in 51 calibers. Kit to upgrade Forster Bench Rest seater die available. From Forster Products.

**Price:** Ultra Seater Die . . . . . . **$57.30**
**Price:** Upgrade kit . . . . . . . **$40.00**
**Price:** Die set with seater die . . . **$86.00**

### Weatherby Bench Rest Die Set

Two-die Bench Rest set, sizer and seater die, for Weatherby magnum calibers from 224 to 340. From Forster Products.

**Price:** . . . . . . . . . . . . **$76.50**

Forster Benchrest Die

### FORSTER PRODUCTS
### BENCH REST DIE SETS

| CARTRIDGE | | |
|---|---|---|
| 17 Remington | 250 Savage (250/3000) | 30 Herrett |
| 22 Hornet | 257 Ackley (40°) | 7mm T.C.U. |
| 22 BR Remington | 257 Roberts | 30-30 Winchester |
| 22 P.P.C. Sako | 257 Weatherby Magnum | 300 Winchester Mag. |
| 221 Fireball | 264 Winchester | 300 Weatherby Mag. |
| 222 Remington | 6.5x57 Mauser | 303 British |
| 222 Remington Magnum | 6.5x55 Swedish | 308 Winchester |
| 223 Remington | 6.5x55 SKAN | 308 Nat'l. Match |
| 5.6x50 Rimmed | 270 Winchester | 30-06 |
| 220 Swift | 7x64 Brenneke | 30-06 Ackley (40°) |
| 22/250 Remington | 7mm-08 | 8mm Remington Mag. |
| 243 Winchester | 7x57 Mauser | 8x57 Mauser |
| 6mm BR Remington | 7mm BR Remington | 8x68S |
| 6mm P.P.C. Sako | 7mm Remington Mag. | 338 Winchester Mag. |
| 6mm Remington (224) | 7mm STW | 340 Weatherby Mag. |
| 224 Weatherby Magnum | 270 Weatherby Mag. | 357 Herrett |
| 240 Weatherby Magnum | 7mm Weatherby Mag. | 375 H&H |
| 25/06 Remington | 280 Remington | |

## FREEDOM ARMS

**454 Casull Dies**

RCBS Carbide 3-die set for .452″ bullets. From Freedom Arms, Inc.

**Price:** . . . . . . . . . . . . . **$53.00**

## FREMONT

**Seating Die**

A 7/8-14 non-crimping, straight-line bullet seating die using a spring-loaded sliding sleeve to align case neck and shoulder with bullet. Bullet chamber cutaway allows insertion of bullet directly into sliding sleeve. Dies are universal and can seat bullets in any case of same caliber. Short cases require use of Fremont extended shellholder. Available in 17, 224, 6mm, 25, 270, 6.5mm, 7mm, 30, 338 and 35 calibers. From Fremont Tool Works.

**Price:** . . . . . . . . . . . . . **$32.50**
**Price:** Extended shellholder . . . . **$7.50**

## GOODWIN

**Reloading Dies**

Precision machined steel reloading dies made in England by James Goodwin for unusual and hard-to-find calibers. Reloading dies threaded 7/8-14. Special shellholders available. From Jack First, Inc.

**Price:** Die set . . . . . . . . . . **$110.00**
**Price:** Shellholder . . . . . . . . **$12.00**

## HARRELL'S PRECISION

**Vari-Base Sizing Die**

410 stainless steel resizing die that incorporates interchangeable screw-in neck and base reforming buttons that allow reforming fired PPC cases to concentric, near chamber dimensions. From Harrell's Precision.

**Price:** . . . . . . . . . . . . . **$100.00**
**Price:** Die and one bushing . . . . **$75.00**
**Price:** Base buttons . . . . . . . **$12.50**

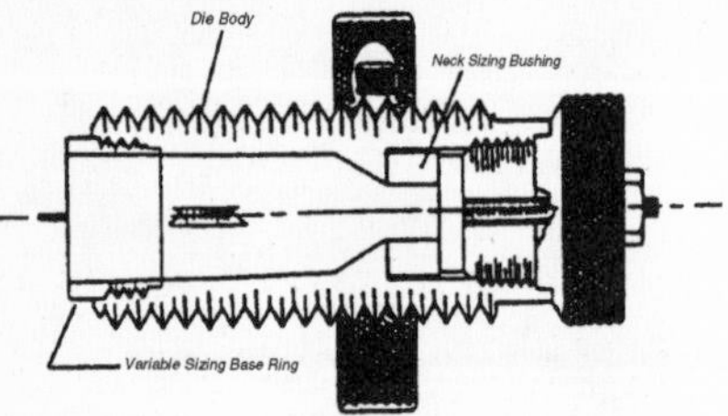


Harrel's Precision
Vari-Base Reloading Die

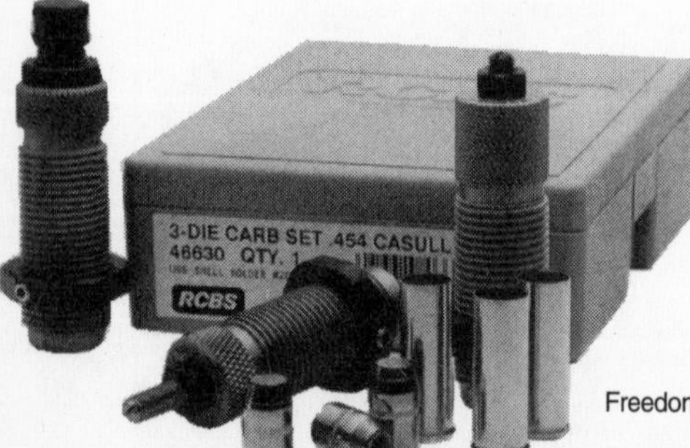


Freedom Arms 454 Casull Dies

## HOLLYWOOD

### STANDARD PISTOL/RIFLE STEEL DIES

**3-DIE SETS**

| | | | |
|---|---|---|---|
| 22 Jet CF | 32 S&W | 38 Long Colt | 44 Webley |
| 221 Rem. | 32 S&W Long | 38 Spl. | 44-40 Rev. Old |
| 25 ACP | 32 Short Colt | 357 Mag. | 44-40 Rev. New |
| 256 Win. | 32 Long Colt | 38-40 Rev. | 45 ACP |
| 30 Mauser | 32-20 Rev. | 41 Short Colt | 45 Long Colt |
| 7.63 Mauser | 9mm Short | 41 Long Colt | 44 Auto Rim |
| 7.65 Mauser | 9mm Luger | 41 Mag. | 455 Webley |
| 7.65 Luger | 380 ACP | 44 American | 45 Colt Blank |
| 7.7 Jap. Nambu | 38 Super Auto | 44 S&W Spl. | 45 Colt Short |
| 31 Jap. | 38 S&W | 44 Mag. | |
| 32 ACP | 38 Short Colt | 44 Russian | |

**2-DIE SETS**

| | | | |
|---|---|---|---|
| 22 Hornet | 25 Mag. Belted Cut. | 7x64-06 Case | 338 Win. |
| 22 K-Hornet | 25-6mm Donaldson | 7x65mm Mauser | 340 Wea. Mag. |
| 218 Bee | 25-06 | 7.35mm | 348 Win. |
| 218 Bee CCC | 25-06 CCC | 7.5mm Swiss | 348 CCC |
| 218 Mashburn | 25-06 Imp. | 7.5mm Schmidt Rubin | 348-8mm Alaskan |
| 22 Lovell | 25-20 Repeater | 7.7mm Japanese | 35 Rem. |
| 22 R2 Lovell | 25-20 Single Shot | 7.7-06 Case | 35 Newton |
| 221 Rem. | 25-35 Win. | 7.62 NATO | 35 Newton |
| 222 Rem. | 250-3000 Savage | 7.62mm Russian | 35 Whelen |
| 222 Rem. Mag. | 250-3000 CCC | 7.92mm German Sht. | 35 Whelen Imp. |
| 219 Zipper | 250 Donaldson | 30 M1 Carbine | 35 Ackley Mag. |
| 219 Zipper Imp. | 250 Ackley Mag. | 30 Rem. | 35 Win. S.L. |
| 219 Gib. Wasp | 256 Newton | 30 Newton | 350 K&K |
| 219 Don. .404 | 256 Japanese | 30 Newton Special | 350 Rem. Mag. |
| 219 Don. .407 | 256 Spencer | 30 CP Newton Belted | 351 Win. |
| 22 Sav. High-Power | 256 Win. | 30 Ackley Mag. | 358 Norma |
| 22 Sav. High-Power CCC | 256 Mag. QT | 30-30 Win. | 358 Win. |
| 22 Varminter | 257 Roberts | 30-30 CCC | 9x56mm Mann.-Schn. |
| 22 Varminter CCC | 257 Roberts CCC | 30-30 Krag CCC | 9x57mm Rim. |
| 22 Arrow | 257 Imp. Roberts | 30-40 Krag | 9.3x62mm |
| 22-06 CCC | 257 Wea. Mag. | 30-06 | 9.3x72mm Rim. |
| Lindahl Std. Chuck | 6.5mm Rem. Mag. | 30-06 CCC | 9.3x74-357 Rim. |
| Lindahl Super Chuck | 6.5mm Mann.-Schoen. | 30-06 Ackley Imp. | 9.3x74-367 |
| 22 Gebby Jr. Var. | 6.5mm Japanese | 30-06 8mm Ackley Imp. | 9.3x74mm Rim. Imp. |
| 22 Gebby Sr. Var. | 6.5mm Carcano | 30-06 8mm Standard | 9.5mm |
| 22 Rhetts | 6.5mmx53 Rim. | 300 Savage | 9.5x57mm Mann.-Schn. |
| 220 Swift | 6.5mmx55 Krag | 300 H&H Mag. | 375 Mag. CCC |
| 220 Swift CCC | 6.5mmx55 Mauser | 300 H&H CCC | 375 Mag. |
| 220 Wea. | 6.5mmx57mm | 300 Wea. Mag. | 375 Mag. Flanged |
| 220 Imp. | 6.5mmx68mm | 300 Win. Mag. | 375 Mag. Wea. |
| 22 Mag. CCC | 264 Win. | 303 British | 375-06 CCC |
| 223 Rem. Mag. | 270 Win. | 303 Savage | 376-357 Imp. Flanged |
| 224 Wea. Mag. | 270 CCC | 308 Norma | 375-9mm Flanged |
| 225 Win. | 270 Mag. CCC | 308 Win. | 375-9.3mm Imp. Flngd. |
| 228 Ackley | 270 Ackley Mag. | 32 Win. Spl. | 38 WCF |
| 240 Gebby Super Var. | 270 Wea. Mag. | 32 Rem. | 38-55 |
| 240 Gebby Var. Belted | 280 Ross | 32-20 Win. | 38-56 |
| 240 Cobra | 284 Rem. | 32-40 | 401 Win. Auto |
| 243 Win. | 284 Win. | 8mm Mauser .318 | 405 Win. |
| 6mm Rem. | 7mm Mauser | 8mm Mauser .323 | 44 WCF |
| 244 Gibson | 7mm CCC | 8mm Lebel | 444 Marlin |
| 244 Rem. | 7mm Mag. CCC | 8x56mm Mann.-Schn. | 45-70 |
| 244 H&H | 7mm Rem. Mag. | 8x57mm Mauser Rim. | 45-90 |
| 25 Rem. | 7mm Wea. Mag. | 8x57mm Rimless | 458 Win. Mag. |
| 25 Souper | 7mm Cradle | 8x57mm Jr. Mauser | 458 MCW Mag. |
| 25 Donaldson Ace | 7x57mm Mauser | 8x60 Rim. | 50-110 |
| 25 Krag CCC | 7x57mm Rim. | 8x68mm | 11mm (43 Mauser) |
| 25 Barr Belted Mag. | 7x61mm Sharp & Hart | 8.15x46mm Rim. | |
| | 7x64mm German | 33 Win. | |

| HOLLYWOOD Carbide Pistol/Rifle Dies | | |
|---|---|---|
| Caliber | Die Type | Price |
| **DECAP RODS/TAPER CRIMP/NECK SIZER** | | |
| Standard | Decap rod, no carbide ball | $20.00 |
| 50 | Decap rod, no carbide ball | 55.00 |
| Standard | Decap rod, carbide ball to 30-cal. | 30.00 |
| 50 | Decap rod, carbide ball | 60.00 |
| Standard | Decap rod, carbide ball 30-cal. and over | 60.00 |
| 22-30 | Taper crimp | 50.00 |
| 30-50 | Taper crimp | 80.00 |
| All | Neck Sizer | 97.00 |
| **FULL-LENGTH SIZER(HOLLYWOOD, RCBS, DILLON, STAR)** | | |
| 25 ACP, 32 ACP, 380 ACP, 38 S&W Short | | 65.00 |
| 30 M1, 32 S&W Long, 38/357, 38 Super ACP, 38 Special, 41 Mag., 44 Spl. Mag., 44 Rem. Mag., 45 ACP, 9mm Luger | | 75.00 |
| 10mm, 45 Long Colt | | 80.00 |
| 44 Auto Magnum | | 120.00 |
| 45-70 | | 140.00 |
| **FULL-LENGTH BOTTLENECK SIZER (HOLLYWOOD, RCBS, DILLON, STAR)** | | |
| 223, 308, 22-250, 38-40, 44-40 | | 150.00 |
| 25-20 SS, 25-20 WCF, 32-20 | | 130.00 |
| 30-06, 25-06, 7mm | | 155.00 |
| 50-caliber | | 425.00 |
| **FULL-LENGTH DIE SET (HOLLYWOOD)** | | |
| 25 ACP, 32 ACP, 380 ACP, 38 S&W Short | | 50.00 |
| 30 M1,, 32 S&W Long, 38/357, 38 Super ACP, 38 Spl., 41 Mag., 44 Spl. Mag., 44 Rim. Mag., 45 ACP, 9mm | | 95.00 |
| 10mm, 45 Long Colt | | 100.00 |
| 44 Auto Magnum | | 155.00 |
| 45-70 | | 160.00 |
| **FULL-LENGTH BOTTLENECK DIE SETS(HOLLYWOOD)** | | |
| 223, 308, 22-250, 38-40, 44-40 | | 170.00 |
| 25-20 SS, 25-20 WCF, 32-20 | | 150.00 |
| 30-06, 25-06, 7mm | | 175.00 |
| 50-caliber | | 520.00 |

**POR:Price on request.**

| GOODWIN DIES *Die Sets* | | |
|---|---|---|
| Dies | | |
| 240 Flanged | 400-360 | 45-75 Win. |
| 242 Vickers | 360-2½″ NE* | 45-90 Win. |
| 6mm Lee Navy | 360 #2 NE* | 450 3¼″ NE |
| 244 Holland | 369 Purdey* | 500-450 3¼″ |
| 255 Rook | 9.3x62 Mauser | 500-450 #2 |
| 6.5x68 | 9.3x64 | 577-450 Martini Henry* |
| 26 BSA | 9.3x72R | 455 Colt |
| 280 Ross* | 9.3x74R | 455 Webley* |
| 30 Newton | 375-2½″ NE | 455 Webley Auto |
| 300 Sherwood | 375 Flanged* | 461 #1 Gibbs |
| 7.62 Nagant Rev. | 9.5x56 | 461 #2 Gibbs |
| 351 Win. SL | 38-56 | 500-465 NE |
| 375-303 | 38-72 | 470 3¼″ |
| 310 Cadet | 40-60 Win. | 475 NE |
| 318 Richards | 40-82 Win. | 475 #2 |
| 7.65 French Long* | 400 Purdey | 476 NE |
| 8mm Lebel Rev. | 400-375 | 50-70 |
| 8mm Lebel Rifle* | 450-400 3″* | 50-95 Win. |
| 8x50R | 450-400 3¼″ NE* | 50-110 Win. |
| 8x57S | 401 Win. SL | 50-140 Win. |
| 8x60R Port. | 10.75x68 Mauser | 500 Jeffrey |
| 8x68S | 10.75x73 Jeffrey* | 500 3″ NE |
| 8.15x46.5R | 405 Win. | 577-500 Magnum |
| 32 Win. Spl. | 416 Rigby | 505 Gibbs |
| 33 Win.* | 425 Westley Richards | 577 Snider* |
| 333 Jeffre | 11 Gras | 577 2¾″ |
| 9x56 | 43 Egyptian | 577 3″ NE |
| 35 Win. | 11 Mauser* | |
| 400-350 | 45-60 Win. | |

*Shellholder available.

## HOLLYWOOD

### 38-45 Dies

Comes as a complete set for reloading and case-forming or each die separately. A tungsten carbide sizer die is also available. From Hollywood Engineering.

**Price:** Complete set . . . . . . **$140.00**
**Price:** Reloading die set . . . . . **$65.00**
**Price:** Case-form die set . . . . . **$75.00**
**Price:** Carbide size die . . . . . **$150.00**

### 50-Caliber Seater/Necksizer Die

Hardened steel and plated die threaded 1½-12. Comes complete with seater die, necksizer bushing, seater plug, inside lock nut, wrench for lock nut. From Hollywood Engineering.

**Price:** . . . . . . . . . . . . **$150.00**

### Carbide Die Sets

Hollywood offers carbide decap rods, taper crimp dies and neck sizer dies for all their standard die calibers. They also offer full-length carbide sizer dies, full-length bottleneck sizer dies, full-length carbide sets and full-length bottleneck carbide sets for Hollywood, RCBS, Dillon and Star presses. From Hollywood Engineering.

**Price:** . . . . . . . . . . . **See chart.**

### Machine Gun Dies

Hardened steel and plated dies to fit any press with 1½-12 threaded holes. Available for 50-caliber and 20mm. From Hollywood Engineering.

**Price:** 50-cal. . . . . . . . . . **$200.00**
**Price:** 20mm . . . . . . . . . **$290.00**

### Standard Pistol/Rifle Die Sets

Two- and 3-die sets in most popular calibers. Dies made of steel and threaded 7/8-14. From Hollywood Engineering.

**Price:** . . . . . . . . . . . . **$45.00**

### Vickerman Seater Die

Steel die for standard and large pistol/rifle calibers and 50 BMG. Threaded 7/8-14 and 1½-12. From Hollywood Engineering.

**Price:** Standard, 7/8″ . . . . . . . **$60.00**
**Price:** Large, 1½″ . . . . . . . **$170.00**
**Price:** 50 BMG . . . . . . . . **$170.00**

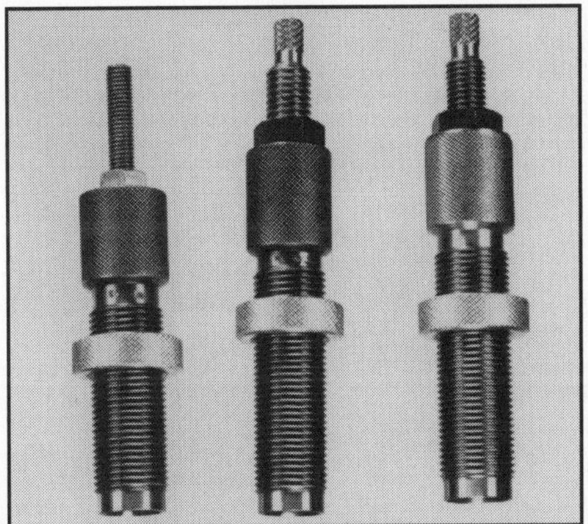

Goodwin Reloading/Case-Form Dies

## Hornady

### RIFLE/PISTOL DIES

| Cartridge | Die Group | Shellholder | Cartridge | Die Group | Shellholder | Cartridge | Die Group | Shellholder |
|---|---|---|---|---|---|---|---|---|
| **RIFLE** | | | | | | | | |
| 17 Rem. | III | 16 | 6.5x55/Scan. | I | 19 | 300 Wea. | I | 5 |
| 17/222 | IV | 16 | 6.5/06 | IV | 1 | 308 Norma Mag. | IV | 5 |
| 17/223 | IV | 16 | 6.5mm TCU | III | 16 | 7062 Russian | IV | 23 |
| 218 Bee | III | 7 | 6.5 Rem. Mag. | IV | 5 | 705 Swiss | III | 30 |
| 219 Zipper | IV | 2 | 6.5 Mann. | IV | 20 | 32/20 Win. | III | 7 |
| 221 Rem. | III | 16 | 6.5 Carc. | IV | 21 | 7.62x39 | I | 6 |
| 222 Rem. | I | 16 | 6.5 Japanese | IV | 34 | 7.7 Japanese | III | 1 |
| 222 Rem. Mag. | III | 16 | 6.5x57 | IV | 1 | 303 British | I | 11 |
| 22 Hornet (.224) | I | 3 | 6.5x68 | IV | 30 | 7065 Beig. | III | 24 |
| 22 K-Hornet (.224) | IV | 3 | 264 Win. Mag. | I | 5 | 32 Win. Spl. | III | 2 |
| 22 RCFM-Jet (.224) | IV | 6 | 270 Win. | I | 1 | 32/40 Win. | IV | 2 |
| 22 PPC (.224) | IV | 6 | 270 Wea. | III | 5 | 8mm Mauser | I | 1 |
| 5.6x50 Mag. (.224) | IV | 16 | 7x30 Waters | III | 2 | 8mm/06 | IV | 1 |
| 5.6x52R (.227) | IV | 2 | 7x57 (7mm Mauser) | I | 1 | 8mm Rem. Mag. | III | 5 |
| 5.6x57 (.224) | IV | 1 | 7mm/08 | I | 1 | 8x60 S | IV | 1 |
| 223 Rem. (.224) | I | 16 | 7mm Rem. Mag. | I | 5 | 8x68 S | IV | 30 |
| 22/250 | I | 1 | 7mm Rem. BR | III | 1 | 8.15x46 R | IV | 2 |
| 220 Swift | I | 4 | 7mm TCU | I | 16 | 338 Win. Mag. | I | 5 |
| 22 Savage HP | IV | 2 | 7mm Merrill | IV | 4 | 33 Win. | IV | 14 |
| Wea. | IV | 17 | 7x65 R | IV | 13 | 340 Wea. | I | 5 |
| 225 Win. | III | 4 | 7mm Wea. | I | 5 | 348 Win. | IV | 25 |
| 240 Wea. | III | 1 | 7x64 | IV | 1 | 35 Rem. | I | 26 |
| 243 Win. | I | 1 | 7mm/223 Ingram | IV | 16 | 35 Whelen | I | 1 |
| 244/6mm | I | 1 | 7x47 Helm | IV | 16 | 357/44 B&D | IV | 30 |
| 6mm Int. | IV | 1 | 7x61 S&H | IV | 35 | 350 Rem. Mag. | IV | 5 |
| 6mm/223 | III | 16 | 7mm Express/280 | I | 1 | 357 Herrett | III | 2 |
| 6mm/PPC | I | 6 | 284 Win. | III | 1 | 358 Win. | III | 1 |
| 6mm TCU | III | 16 | 7.35 Carc. | IV | 21 | 358 N. Mag. | IV | 5 |
| 6mm/284 | IV | 1 | 30/30 Win. | I | 2 | 375 H&H | III | 5 |
| 6x47 Rem. | IV | 16 | 300 Savage | I | 1 | 378 Wea. | IV | 14 |
| 250 Savage | III | 1 | 30 Luger | III | 8 | 9.3x74 R | IV | 13 |
| 25/06 | I | 1 | 30 Merrill | IV | 4 | 9.3x57 | IV | 1 |
| 257 Roberts | I | 1 | 30 Herrett | III | 2 | 9.3x62 | IV | 1 |
| 25/20 Win. | IV | 7 | 303 Savage | IV | 33 | 10.3x60 | IV | 25 |
| 25/35 Win. | III | 2 | 308 Win. | I | 1 | 416 Rem. Mag. | IV | 5 |
| 256 Win. | IV | 6 | 30/40 Krag | III | 11 | 416 Rigby | IV | 38 |
| 257 Wea. | III | 5 | 30/06 | I | 1 | 416 Wea. | IV | 14 |
| 25 Rem. | IV | 12 | 300 H&H | III | 5 | 460 Wea. | IV | 14 |
| 25/284 | IV | 1 | 300 Win. Mag. | I | 5 | | | |
| **PISTOL** | | | | | | | | |
| 25 ACP | II | 37 | 38 Smith & Wesson | IV | 28 | 44 Auto. Mag. | IV | 1 |
| 30 M1 Carbine | I | 22 | 38-357-357 Max. | II | 6 | 44/40 Win. | IV | 9 |
| 32 ACP | II | 22 | 357 Win. | I | 2 | 444 Marlin | II | 27 |
| 32 S&W Long/ShortH&R Mag. | II | 36 | 10mm Auto.-40 S&W | II | 10 | 45 Auto. Rim | II | 31 |
| **9x18 Makarov** | | | 38/40 Win. | IV | 9 | 45 ACP/AR/WM | II | 1 |
| 9mm Luger/9x21 | II | 8 | 41 Action Express | IV | 8 | 45 Long Colt | II | 32 |
| 380 Automatic | II | 16 | 41 Mag. | II | 29 | 45/70 Gov't | I | 14 |
| 38 Super Automatic | II | 8 | 44 Spl/44 Mag. | II | 30 | 458 Win. | I | 5 |

Hornady Custom Grade New Dimension Dies

**HORNADY**
**Custom New Dimension Die Prices**

| DIE SERIES | 2-DIE RIFLE | 3-DIE RIFLE | CUSTOM PISTOL |
|---|---|---|---|
| **Series I Set** | $26.95 | $28.50 | |
| Full-Length Die | 17.70 | 22.55 | |
| Seat Die | 14.00 | 14.00 | |
| Expander | 6.50 | 7.55 | |
| **Series II Set** | | | 37.75 |
| Full-Length Die | | | 22.55 |
| Seat Die | | | 17.20 |
| Expander | 6.50 | | 7.55 |
| **Series III Set** | 32.15 | | |
| Full-Length Die | 24.75 | | |
| Seat Die | 14.00 | | |
| Expander | 6.50 | | |

## HORNADY

**50-BMG Die Set**

New Dimension specialty two die set threaded 1½-12. From Hornady Mfg. Co.

**Price:** . . . . . . . . . . . . . . . **$260.00**
**Price:** Shellholder . . . . . . . . . **$25.50**
**Price:** Lock ring . . . . . . . . . **$13.00**

**50 BMG File-Type Trim Die**

New Dimension specialty trim die threaded 1½-12. From Hornady Mfg. Co.

**Price:** . . . . . . . . . . . . . . . **$117.00**

**Micro-Just Seating Stem**

Micro-adjustable seating stem to fit any Hornady New Dimension Seating die. Allows precise bullet seating depth in .001″ increments. From Hornady Mfg. Co.

**Price:** . . . . . . . . . . . . . . . **$14.95**

**Neck-Size Die**

Steel die finished in hard satin chrome. Resizes only the case neck. Standard 7/8-14 thread with blued steel lock ring. Interior heat-treated and polished. Weight: 1 lb. From Hornady Mfg. Co.

**Price:** . . . . . . . . . . . . . . . **$16.25**

**Custom Grade New Dimension Series I, II, III, IV Dies**

Benchrest quality dies made of high-quality hand-inspected steel. Dies are lathed to industry-established dimensional tolerances for maximum cartridge size; inside surface hand polished and protective coating applied. Features redesigned and improved one-piece expander spindle for improved alignment and lock assembly for more precise fit; elliptical expander to reduce friction and case neck stretch; stronger, all-steel construction; in-line bullet seating system with floating sleeve and stem and bult-in crimper; hardened steel decap pin; no-lube Titanium Nitride pistol size die; and wrench flats. Available in most standard rifle/pistol calibers (Series I, II, III). Custom dies (Series IV) also offered on special order. From Hornady Mfg. Co.

**Price:** . . . . . . . . . . . . **See chart.**

**Taper Crimp Die**

All steel and precision engineered. Add to three-die pistol set to apply crimp to autoloading pistol cases. Available for 9mm, 38, 9x21, 10mm, 40 S&W, 45 ACP, 45 Auto Rim, 45 Winchester Magnum. Weight: 1 lb. From Hornady Mfg. Co.

**Price:** . . . . . . . . . . . . . . . **$12.20**

Hornady Micro-Just Seating Stem

**HORNADY**
**New Dimension Series I, II, III Dies**

| SERIES I 2-DIE | SERIES I 3-DIE | SERIES III 2-DIE | SERIES II 3-DIE |
|---|---|---|---|
| 22 Hornet | 30 M1 Carbine | 17 Rem. | 25 ACP |
| 222 Rem. | 375 Win. | 218 Bee | 32 ACP |
| 223 Rem. | 444 Marlin | 221 Rem. | 32 S&W Long/Short |
| 22/250 | 45-70 Gov't. | 222 Rem. Mag. | H&R Mag. |
| 220 Swift | 458 Win. | 225 Win. | 9mm Luger |
| 243 Win. | | 240 Wea. | 9x18 |
| 244/6mm Rem. | | 6mm/223 | 9x21 |
| 6mm PPC | | 6mm TCU | 380 Auto |
| 25-06 | | 6mm Rem. BR | 38 Super Auto |
| 257 Roberts | | 25-35 Win. | 38/357 |
| 6.5x55 Scan. | | 250 Savage | 357 Maximum |
| 264 Win. Mag. | | 257 Wea. | 10mm Auto/40 S&W |
| 270 Win. | | 6.5mm TCU | 41 Mag. |
| 7x57 | | 270 Wea. | 41 Action Exp. |
| 7mm Exp./280 | | 284 Win. | 44 Spl. |
| 7mm-08 | | 7x30 Waters | 44 Mag. |
| 7mm Rem. Mag. | | 7mm Rem. BR | 45 ACP |
| 7mm TCU | | 30 Herrett | 45 Win. Mag. |
| 7mm Wea. | | 7.5 Swiss | 45 Auto Rim |
| 30-30 Win. | | 30 Luger | 45 Long Colt |
| 300 Savage | | 30-40 Krag | |
| 300 Wea. | | 300 H&H | |
| 308 Win. | | 7.7 Japanese | |
| 30-06 | | 7.65 Belgian | |
| 300 Win. Mag. | | 32 Win. Spl. | |
| 303 British | | 32/20 Win. | |
| 7.62x39 | | 8mm Rem. Mag. | |
| 8mm Maus. (8x57 JS) | | 357 Herrett | |
| 338 Win. Mag. | | 358 Win. | |
| 340 Wea. | | | |
| 35 Rem. | | | |
| 35 Whelen | | | |
| 375 H&H | | | |

## JONES

**Micro-Adjustable Bullet Seating Hand Die**

A straight-line seating die with bushings available in .001″ increments to precisely support and align the neck of the case. Adjustable threaded cap and stem allow depth adjustment increments of .00125″ and .050″ per revolution. Manufactured of steel with black oxide finish. Die and bushings available for all popular calibers including wildcats. State loaded neck dimension of cartridge for proper bushing size. Comes with one bushing. From Neil Jones Custom Products.

**Price:** . . . . . . . . . . . . . **$80.00**
**Price:** 17-cal. and +30-cal., add . . . **$12.00**

**Micro-Adjustable Neck Sizing Hand Die**

A precision neck sizing die that features an adjustable cap threaded to provide .050″ of movement per revolution and scribed increments of .00125″. Used with Jones neck/shoulder bushings, the case neck is sized and the shoulder moved back in precisely controlled steps as case is forced into die. Shoulder bushings available in all sizes and shoulder angles including wildcats. Made of steel with black oxide finish. Tension adjustable decapping punch suitable for all calibers from 22 on up. For use on arbor press and with Jones bushing style No. 2. Comes with bushing and die base for arbor press use. From Neil Jones Custom Products.

**Price:** . . . . . . . . . . . . . **$80.00**
**Price:** 17-cal. and +30-cal., add . . . **$12.00**

Jones Micro Form Die

## JONES

**Micro Form Die**

Case-forming system consisting of micro-adjustable die body and a series of forming bushings. Bushings are manufactured with a larger lead angle than regular sizing bushings to reduce neck diameters and/or move the case shoulder. Number of bushings required depends on the caliber and if the shoulder is moved. Price does not include No. 6 style bushing. From Neil Jones Custom Products.

**Price:** . . . . . . . . . . . . . **$80.00**
**Price:** Bushing . . . . . . . . . **$12.00**

**Threaded Neck-Sizing Die**

Designed for use in conventional reloading press. Manufactured with standard 7/8-14 thread but uses interchangeable hardened steel bushings available in increments of .001″ for precision neck-sizing. Single die with proper bushings will accommodate all cartridges with same head diameter. Expansion mandrels to open up case necks to larger caliber also available. Price does not include No. 2 style bushing. From Neil Jones Custom Products.

**Price:** . . . . . . . . . . . . . **$80.00**
**Price:** 17-cal. and +30-cal., add . . . **$12.00**
**Price:** Extra bushing . . . . . . . **$10.00**
**Price:** Expansion mandrel . . . . **$14.00**
**Price:** Decap punch . . . . . . . **$10.00**

**Threaded Seating Die**

For use in conventional reloading press. Same design features as Jones micro-adjustable seating die with direct in-line alignment of case neck and floating seating punch adjustable in increments of .001″. Available in most calibers and cartridges. Comes with one No. 5 style bushing. From Neil Jones Custom Products.

**Price:** . . . . . . . . . . . . . **$90.00**
**Price:** 17-cal. and +30-cal., add . . . **$12.00**

# Section 1: Metallic Cartridges

## LEE

### Carbide Factory Crimp Die

For handgun ammunition. Carbide sizer sizes cartridge during crimping operation. Adjusting-screw sets desired amount of crimp. Trim length is not critical. From Lee Precision, Inc.

**Price:** . . . . . . . . . . . . . **$17.98**
**Price:** 9mm . . . . . . . . . . . **$19.98**

### Carbide Speed Die

For use in single-station press. Eliminates need to change dies between operations. Comes with shellholder, powder dipper and load data for one cartridge. Available for 9mm Luger, 38 Special, 357 Magnum, 44 Magnum, 45 ACP. From Lee Precision, Inc.

**Price:** . . . . . . . . . . . . . **$19.98**

### Carbide/Steel Pistol Dies

Three-die pistol sets. Carbide dies contour ground to provide stepless sizing. Set includes sizer/decapper, powder-through-expander and bullet seater. Each die has enlarged mouth to align with cases, even damaged cases. Steel dies have same features as carbide except case must be lubricated. Come with free shellholder. From Lee Precision, Inc.

**Price:** Carbide . . . . . . . . . **$36.98**
**Price:** Steel . . . . . . . . . . **$27.98**

### Collet Rifle Dies

No-lube necksize-only dies. A collet squeezes case neck against precision mandrel with minimum run-out. Not recommended for autoloaders, slide- or lever-action firearms. See chart for available calibers. From Lee Precision, Inc.

**Price:** . . . . . . . . . . . . . **$34.98**

### Decapping Die

No-lube decap die removes crimped-in primers on press. One size fits all cases. From Lee Precision, Inc.

**Price:** . . . . . . . . . . . . . . **$9.98**

### Factory Crimp Die

Standard with Lee PaceSetter die sets. Crimps the bullet in place without possibility of case buckling. From Lee Precision, Inc.

**Price:** . . . . . . . . . . . . . **$11.98**

### Limited Production Rifle Dies

Limited Production two-die set includes full-length sizer, bullet seater/roll crimper, shellholder, powder dipper and load data for single cartridge in transparent storage container. This set does not include a factory crimp die. See chart for available calibers. From Lee Precision, Inc.

**Price:** . . . . . . . . . . . . . **$29.98**

### PaceSetter Rifle Die Set

Three-die rifle set includes full-length sizer, bullet seater/roll crimper, factory crimp die, shellholder, powder dipper, load data and instructions for single cartridge in transparent storage container. Two price levels—one for standard stocked die sets and another for Ltd. production die sets. See chart for available calibers. From Lee Precision, Inc.

**Price:** Standard . . . . . . . . **$27.98**
**Price:** Limited Production . . . . . **$29.98**

### RGB Series Rifle Die Set

Rifle two-die set with full-length sizer and bullet seater/roll crimper only with load data for one cartridge in transparent plastic storage container. See chart for available calibers. From Lee Precision, Inc.

**Price:** . . . . . . . . . . . . . **$17.98**

## LEE

### RIFLE DIES

| Caliber | RGB Series | PaceSetter 3-Die | PaceSetter Ltd. | Limited Production | Collet Necksize | Factory Crimp | Taper Crimp |
|---|---|---|---|---|---|---|---|
| **RIFLE** | | | | | | | |
| 17 Rem. | NA | NA | NA | A | A | NA | NA |
| 22 Hornet | NA | NA | A | NA | A | A | NA |
| 218 Bee | NA | NA | A | NA | NA | A | NA |
| 22 PPC | NA | NA | NA | A | A | NA | NA |
| 221 Fireball | NA | NA | NA | A | NA | NA | NA |
| 222 Rem. | A | A | NA | NA | A | A | A |
| 223 | A | A | NA | NA | A | A | A |
| 22-250 | A | A | NA | NA | A | A | NA |
| 220 Swift | NA | NA | NA | A | A | A | NA |
| 243 Win. | A | A | NA | NA | A | A | NA |
| 6mm PPC | NA | NA | NA | A | A | NA | NA |
| 6mm Rem. | NA | NA | A | NA | A | A | NA |
| 25-20 | NA | NA | A | NA | NA | A | NA |
| 25-35 | NA | NA | NA | A | NA | NA | NA |
| 250 Savage | NA | NA | NA | A | A | A | NA |
| 257 Roberts | NA | NA | A | NA | A | A | NA |
| 25-06 | NA | NA | A | NA | A | A | NA |
| 260 Rem. | NA | NA | NA | A | NA | NA | NA |
| 264 Win. Mag. | NA | NA | NA | A | NA | NA | NA |
| 6.5 Carcano | NA | NA | NA | A | NA | NA | NA |
| 6.5 Japanese | NA | NA | NA | A | NA | NA | NA |
| 6.5 Rem. Mag. | NA | NA | NA | A | NA | NA | NA |
| 6.5x55 | A | A | NA | NA | A | A | NA |
| 270 Wea.. | NA | NA | NA | A | NA | NA | NA |
| 270 Win. | A | A | NA | NA | A | A | NA |
| 7mm BR | NA | NA | NA | A | A | NA | NA |
| 7mm TCU | NA | NA | NA | A | NA | NA | NA |
| 7-30 Waters | NA | NA | NA | A | NA | A | NA |
| 7x57 Mauser | NA | NA | A | NA | A | A | NA |
| 7x64 Brenneke | NA | NA | NA | A | NA | NA | NA |
| 7mm-08 | NA | NA | A | NA | A | A | NA |
| 7mm Express | NA | NA | A | NA | A | A | NA |
| 7mm Rem. Mag. | A | A | NA | NA | A | A | NA |
| 284 Win. | NA | NA | NA | A | NA | NA | NA |
| 7mm Wea. | NA | NA | NA | A | NA | NA | NA |
| 7.35 Carcano | NA | NA | NA | A | NA | NA | NA |
| 7.5 Schmidt Rubin | NA | NA | NA | A | NA | NA | NA |
| 7.5X54 MAS | | | | | | | |
| 7.62x39 Russian | A | A | NA | NA | NA | A | A |
| 7.62x54 Russian | NA | NA | A | NA | NA | A | NA |
| 30 Herrett | NA | NA | NA | A | NA | NA | NA |
| 30/40 Krag | NA | NA | A | NA | NA | A | A |
| 30-30 Win. | A | A | NA | NA | A | A | A |
| 303 Savage | NA | NA | NA | A | NA | NA | A |
| 308 Win. | A | A | NA | NA | A | A | A |
| 300 Savage | NA | NA | A | NA | NA | A | NA |
| 30-06 | A | A | NA | NA | A | A | A |
| 300 Win. Mag. | A | A | NA | NA | A | A | NA |
| 300 H&H | NA | NA | NA | A | A | NA | NA |
| 300 Weath. Mag. | NA | NA | A | NA | A | A | NA |
| 7.65 Arg. Mauser | NA | NA | A | NA | NA | A | A |
| 7.7 Japanese | NA | NA | A | NA | NA | A | A |
| 303 British | A | A | NA | NA | A | A | A |
| 32-20 | NA | NA | NA | A* | NA | A | NA |
| 32-40 | NA | NA | NA | A | NA | NA | NA |
| 32 Win. | NA | NA | NA | A | NA | NA | NA |
| 33 Win. | NA | NA | NA | A | NA | NA | NA |
| 8mm Rem. Mag. | NA | NA | NA | A | NA | NA | NA |
| 8x57 Mauser | A | A | NA | NA | A | A | NA |
| 8mm Lebel | NA | NA | NA | A | NA | NA | NA |
| 338 Win. | NA | NA | A | NA | A | A | NA |
| 348 Win. | NA | NA | NA | A | NA | A | NA |
| 350 Rem. Mag. | NA | NA | NA | A | NA | NA | NA |
| 356 Win. | NA | NA | NA | A | NA | A | NA |
| 358 Win. | NA | NA | NA | A | NA | A | NA |
| 35 Rem. | NA | NA | A | NA | A | A | NA |
| 35 Whelen | NA | NA | NA | A | A | NA | NA |
| 38-40 | NA | NA | NA | A* | NA | A | NA |
| 38-55 | NA | NA | NA | A* | NA | A | NA |
| 38-56 | NA | NA | NA | A | NA | NA | NA |
| 375 H&H | NA | NA | A | NA | A | A | NA |
| 375 Win. | NA | NA | NA | A* | NA | A | NA |
| 416 Rem. | NA | NA | NA | A | NA | A | NA |
| 43 Mauser | NA | NA | NA | A | NA | NA | NA |
| 43 Spanish | NA | NA | NA | A | NA | NA | NA |
| 44-40 | NA | NA | NA | A* | NA | A | NA |
| 444 Marlin | NA | NA | NA | A* | NA | A | NA |
| 45-70 Gov't. | NA | NA | NA | A* | NA | A | NA |
| 458 Win. Mag. | NA | NA | NA | A* | NA | A | NA |

A:Available; NA:Not available. *Special Order. **Custom die $30.00.

METALLIC DIES/Pistol & Rifle

# LEE

## PISTOL DIES

| Caliber | RGB Series | PaceSetter 3-Die | PaceSetter Ltd. | Limited Production | Collet Necksize | Factory Crimp | Taper Crimp |
|---|---|---|---|---|---|---|---|
| **PISTOL** | | | | | | | |
| 25 ACP | A | NA | NA | A* | A* | NA | NA |
| 30 M1 Carbine | A | NA | NA | A | A | A | NA |
| 30 Luger | NA | A | NA | NA | A | NA | NA |
| 30 Mauser | NA | A | NA | NA | A* | NA | NA |
| 7.62 Tokarev | NA | A | NA | NA | A | NA | NA |
| 32 ACP | A | NA | NA | A | A | NA | NA |
| 32 S&W Long | A | NA | NA | A | A | A | NA |
| 32 H&R Magnum | A | NA | NA | A | A* | A | NA |
| 32-20 | NA | A | NA | NA | A* | NA | A** |
| 38-40 | NA | A | NA | NA | A* | NA | A** |
| 9mm Luger | A | A | A | A | A | A | A |
| 9mm Makarov | A | NA | NA | A | A | NA | NA |
| 38 Colt N.P. | NA | NA | NA | A | A* | NA | NA |
| 38 Super/38 ACP | A | NA | NA | A | A | A | |
| 380 Auto | A | NA | NA | A | A | A | A |
| 38 S&W | A | NA | NA | A | A* | NA | NA |
| 38 Special | A | A | A | A | A | A | A |
| 357 Magnum | A | A | A | A | A | A | A |
| 40 S&W | A | NA | NA | NA | NA | NA | A |
| 10mm Auto | A | NA | NA | A* | A* | A | A |
| 41 AE | NA | NA | A | A* | NA | NA | NA |
| 41 Magnum | A | NA | NA | A | A | A | NA |
| 44 Special | A | A | NA | A | A | A | A |
| 44 Magnum | A | A | A | A | A | A | A |
| 44-40 | NA | A | NA | NA | A* | NA | A** |
| 45 Colt | A | NA | NA | A | A | A | A |
| 45 ACP | A | A | A | A | A | A | A |
| 45 Auto Rim | A | NA | NA | A | A* | A | NA |
| 455 Webley MII | A | NA | NA | A | A* | A | NA |
| 45 Win. Mag. | A | NA | NA | A | A | A | A |
| 454 Casull | A | NA | NA | A | A | A | A |
| 45 HP Italian | A | NA | NA | A | A* | A | A |

A:Available; NA:Not available. *Special Order. **Custom die $30.00.

## LEE

**Rifle Charging Die**

For use on standard threaded presses to charge small-capacity rifle cases using Lee Auto-Disk powder measure. Similar in operation to powder-through-expanding die, except does not expand case mouth. From Lee Precision, Inc.

**Price:** . . . . . . . . . . . . . . **$11.98**

**Steel Rifle Dies**

All Lee dies feature one-piece reaming, wrench flats, collet held decapper, finger adjustable bullet seater, elevated expander, O-ring locks. Dies offer unbreakable decapper, floating bullet seater, heat-treated to maximum hardness and progressively machine-honed inside surface. Lee dies come in five configurations: RGB, PaceSetter, PaceSetter Ltd., Limited Production and Collet dies. From Lee Precision, Inc.

**Price:** . . . . . **See individual listings.**

**Taper Crimp Die**

Hardened steel die designed to overcome crimp problems caused by incorrect bullet seater dies. See chart for available calibers. From Lee Precision, Inc.

**Price:** . . . . . . . . . . . . . . **$9.98**

**Universal Charging Die**

Charges both rifle and pistol cases. Includes connecting rod and adaptors to actuate measure with the case. Measure positively resets when ram fully lowered. Comes with drop tubes for most cartridges from the 380 ACP to the 300 Winchester Magnum. Does not expand case mouth. From Lee Precision, Inc.

**Price:** . . . . . . . . . . . . . . **$24.98**

## LYMAN

**AA Rifle 2-Die Sets**

All-steel die set consists of full-length resizing die, with decapping stem and neck expanding button, and a bullet seating die. Best for reloading jacketed bullets in bottlenecked cases. For reloading cast bullets, add a neck expanding die. From Lyman Products Corporation.

**Price:** . . . . . . . . . . . . . . **$24.95**

### LYMAN AA Rifle 2-Die/ Small Base Die Parts

| DIE/DIE PART | PRICE |
|---|---|
| 2-Die Set | $24.95 |
| Sizing die body | 15.50 |
| Decapping rod | 2.00 |
| Expanding die body | 10.00 |
| Expanding button | 3.95 |
| Expanding plug | 5.00 |
| Seating die body | 13.50 |
| Seating screw | 3.95 |
| Decapping rod | 2.00 |
| Decapping pin lock nut | .25 |

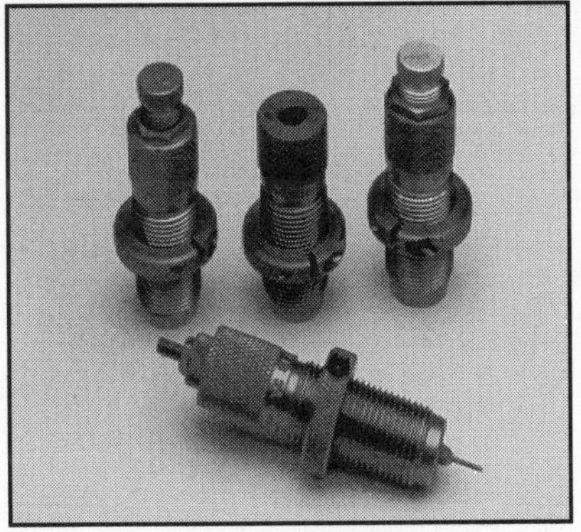

Lyman Carbide 4-Die Pistol Set

### LYMAN AA Standard Rifle 3-Die Parts

| DIE/DIE PART | PRICE |
|---|---|
| AA Standard 3-Die Set | $32.00 |
| Sizing die body (steel) | 15.50 |
| Sizing die body (carbide) | 22.95 |
| Decapping rod | 2.00 |
| Neck expanding die body | 10.00 |
| Expanding plug | 5.00 |
| Seating die body | 13.50 |
| Bullet seating screw | 3.95 |

### LYMAN AA Standard Pistol 3-Die Parts

| DIE/DIE PARTS | PRICE |
|---|---|
| AA Standard Pistol 3-Die Set | $28.50 |
| Sizing die body | 15.50 |
| Deacapping rod | 2.00 |
| Neck expanding die body | 10.00 |
| Expanding plug | 5.00 |
| Seating die body | 13.50 |
| Bullet seating screw | 3.95 |

Lee Carbide Factory Crimp Die

# Lyman

## RIFLE/PISTOL DIES

| Cartridge | Die Group | Shellholder | Cartridge | Die Group | Shellholder | Cartridge | Die Group | Shellholder |
|---|---|---|---|---|---|---|---|---|
| | | —RIFLE— | | | | | —PISTOL— | |
| 17 Rem. | AA-2 | 26 | 30 M1 Carbine | AA-3 | 19 | 45-70 Gov't | AA-3 | 17 |
| 22 Hornet | AA-2 | 4 | 30-30 Win. | AA-2 | 6 | 50-70 Gov't | AA-3 | 22 |
| 222 Rem. | AA-2 | 26 | 30-06 | AA-2, SB-2 | 2 | 25 ACP | S-3 | 32 |
| 222 Rem. Mag. | AA-2 | 26 | 308 Win. | AA-2, SB-2 | 2 | 7mm TCU | S-3 | 26 |
| 223 Rem. (5.56mm) | AA-2, SB-2 | 26 | 300 Sav. | AA-2 | 2 | 30 Luger | S-3 | 12 |
| 22-250 | AA-2 | 2 | 300 Wea. Mag. | AA-2 | 13 | 30 Mauser | S-3 | 12 |
| 220 Swift | AA-2 | 5 | 300 Win. Mag. | AA-2, SB-2 | 13 | 32 ACP | C-4, C-3, S-3 | 23 |
| 5.6mmx50R | MR-2 | 1 | 7.62x39mm | AA-2 | 3 | 32 S&W Long | C-4, C-3, S-3 | 9 |
| 243 Win. | AA-2, SB-2 | 2 | 7.62x54 Russian | AA-2 | 17 | 32 H&R Mag. | C-4, C-3, S-3 | 9 |
| 6mm Rem. | AA-2, SB-2 | 2 | 303 British | AA-2 | 7 | 380 Auto | C-4, C-3, S-3 | 26 |
| 25-06 Rem. | AA-2 | 2 | 7.65mm Arg. Maus. | AA-2 | 2 | 38 S&W | C-4, C-3, S-3 | 21 |
| 250 Sav. | AA-2 | 2 | 32-20 Win. | AA-3 | 10 | 38 Super Auto | C-4, C-3, S-3 | 12 |
| 257 Roberts | AA-2 | 2, 8 | 32 Win. Spl. | AA-2 | 6 | 9mm Luger | C-4, C-3, S-3 | 12 |
| 25-20 Win. | AA-3 | 10 | 8mmx57 Maus. | AA-2 | 2 | 38 Special | C-4, C-3, S-3 | 1 |
| 6.5mmx55 SCAN | AA-2 | 27 | 8mm Rem. Mag. | AA-2 | 13 | 357 Rem. Max. | C-4, C-3, S-3 | 1 |
| 6.5mmx57 Maus. | MR-2 | 2 | 338 Win. Mag. | AA-2 | 13 | 9mm Makarov | C-3 | 12 |
| 6.5mmx57R Maus. | MR-2 | 14B | 35 Rem. | AA-2 | 8, 2 | 9x23 Win. | C-3 | 12 |
| 6.5mmx55Swed. Maus. | AA-2 | 27 | 35 Whelen | AA-2 | 2 | 40 S&W | C-4, C-3 | 15 |
| 270 Win. | AA-2, SB-2 | 2 | 358 Win. | AA-2 | 2 | 10mm Auto | C-4, C-3 | 15 |
| 7mm STW | AA-2 | 13 | 9.3mmx62 | MR-2 | 2 | 41 Mag. | C-4, C-3, S-3 | 30 |
| 7mm TCU | ND-2 | 26 | 9.3mmx64 | MR-2 | 30 | 41 Action Exp. | C-4, C-3, S-3 | 12 |
| 7mm Rem. Mag. | AA-2, SB-2 | 13 | 9.3mmx72R | MR-3 | 30 | 44 Mag. | C-4, C-3, S-3 | 7 |
| 7mmx57 Maus. | AA-2 | 2 | 9.3mmx74R | MR-2 | 14B | 44 Spl. | C-4, C-3, S-3 | 7 |
| 7mmx57R Mauser | AA-2 | 14B | 375 H&H | AA-2 | 13 | 445 Super Mag. | C-4, C-3, S-3 | |
| 280 Rem. | AA-2 | 2 | 375 Win. | AA-3 | 6 | 44-40 Win. | AA-3 | 14B |
| 7mm-08 Rem. | AA-2 | 2 | 38-55 Win. | AA-3 | 6 | 45 ACP | C-4, C-3, S-3 | 2 |
| 7x30 Waters | AA-2 | 6 | 40-65 | AA-3 | 17 | 45 Win. Mag. | C-4, C-3, S-3 | 2 |
| 7mm Wea. Mag. | AA-2 | 13 | 416 Rigby | AA-2 | 17 | 45 Colt | C-4, C-3, S-3 | 11 |
| 7mmx64 Brenn. | MR-2 | 2 | 44-40 Win. | AA-3 | 14B | 50 AE | C-4 | 7 |
| 7mmx65R Brenn. | MR-2 | 14B | 444 Marlin | AA-3 | 14B | | | |

AA-2:2-die set for bottleneck cases; AA-3:3-die rifle set for straight-wall cases; MR-2:Metric rifle 2-die set; MR-3:Metric rifle 3-die set; SB-2:Small base 2-die set for jacketed bullets; C-4:4-die carbide set; C-3:3-die carbide set; S-3:Standard AA 3-die set.

### LYMAN

**AA Rifle 3-Die Set**

For reloading straight-wall cases. Full-length sizing die with decapping stem, AA two-step neck expanding (M) die and bullet seating die. Also good for loading cast bullets. From Lyman Products Corporation.

**Price:** . . . . . . . . . . . . . **$32.00**

**Carbide Pistol 3-Die Set**

Tungsten carbide full-length resizing and decapping die, two-step neck expanding die and bullet seating chamber and screw. Comes with extra seating screws for loading all popular bullet designs for given caliber. Two-step expander prevents cast bullet distortion and assures precise case neck tension. Loads both magnum and special length cases. Resizing ring eliminates need for case lubing. From Lyman Products Corporation.

**Price:** . . . . . . . . . . . . . **$38.95**

**Carbide Pistol 4-Die Set**

Features one-piece decapping rod design made of hardened tool steel. Includes separate taper crimp die for reloading semi-auto cartridges; powder charge/expanding die with special hollow expander plugs for two-step neck expansion and powder charging. Top of expand/powder die threaded to accept Lyman #55 powder measure, AccuMeasure or any other brand threaded measure. Neck size die and seating die make up the quartet. From Lyman Products Corporation.

**Price:** . . . . . . . . . . . . . **$49.95**

### LYMAN

**Metric Rifle 2-Die Set**

For reloading metric calibers with jacketed bullets. From Lyman Products Corporation.

**Price:** . . . . . . . . . . . . . **$24.95**

**Multi-Expand/Powder Charge Die**

Simultaneously expands case mouth and drops powder charge from measure. Includes expander/powder drop tubes for 32, 9mm, 38/357, 10mm/40 S&W, 41, 44 and 45 Auto plus non-expanding universal drop tube. Works with all presses and powder measures with standard die thread. From Lyman Products Corporation.

**Price:** . . . . . . . . . . . . . **$22.00**

**Neck Size Rifle 2-Die Set**

Works only neck of case to retain fireformed dimensions. Includes special sizing die with decapping stem and expander button and a standard bullet seating die. From Lyman Products Corporation.

**Price:** . . . . . . . . . . . . . **$28.50**

**Ram Prime Die System**

Designed for primer feeding on top of press. Standard die threading to fit all presses. Includes large and small primer punches. From Lyman Products Corporation.

**Price:** . . . . . . . . . . . . . **$12.95**

### LYMAN

**Small Base Rifle 2-Die Set**

Designed for loading jacketed bullets in cartridges sized to minimum dimensions. Set includes special small base full-length resizing die with decapping stem and expander button and a standard bullet seating die. From Lyman Products Corporation.

**Price:** . . . . . . . . . . . . . **$28.50**

**Standard Pistol 3-Die Set**

Includes same features as carbide 3-die set except resizing die is steel. From Lyman Products Corporation.

**Price:** . . . . . . . . . . . . . **$28.50**

**Specialty Die Sets**

Die sets for 475 Wildey and 50 Action Express. Four-die sets for both calibers include taper crimp die; case forming set for 475 Wildey allow cases to be formed from 284 Winchester cases. From Lyman Products Corporation.

**Price:** Die set . . . . . . . . . **$49.95**
**Price:** 475 case form die set . . . . **$99.95**

**Taper Crimp Die**

Applies proper crimp to pistol and rifle cases. Heat-treated to R50 minimum surface hardness and interior hand polished to 8 rms finish. From Lyman Products Corporation.

**Price:** . . . . . . . . . . . . . **$13.25**

## LYMAN

**Two-Step Expanding (M) Die**

Designed for cast and jacketed bullet loads. Prevents case stretching to extend case life. Expands inside of case neck to just under bullet diameter then expands case mouth to bullet diameter or slightly over. From Lyman Products Corporation.

**Price:** . . . . . . . . . . . . . **$11.75**

**Universal Decapping Die**

For all calibers 22 through 45 except 378 and 460 Weatherby. Solid one-piece construction of hardened tool steel. Works well for military crimped primers. From Lyman Products Corporation.

**Price:** . . . . . . . . . . . . . **$10.75**

## N.D.F.S

**Die Service for Obsolete Cartridges**

This English company manufactures custom three-die sets with standard threading for obsolete blackpowder cartridges. From N.D.F.S.

**Price:** . . . . . **Contact manufacturer.**

## RCBS

**50 BMG Dies**

Two-die set contains a full-length sizer and seater die with built-in roll crimper. Dies are produced in two diameters: 1 3/8"-12 for use with Big Max press and AmmoMaster 50 kit; 1 1/2"-12 for use with AmmoMaster 50 kit and other presses. Trim die and neck sizer die also available. From RCBS.

**Price:** Die set . . . . . . . . . **$387.24**
**Price:** Trim die . . . . . . . . . **$209.00**
**Price:** Neck sizer die . . . . . . **$209.00**

**Carbide Rifle/Pistol Dies**

RCBS **Group B** and **Group C** three-die sets include: carbide sizer die with decapping assembly, expander die, and seater die. Tungsten carbide inner ring resizes without the need for case lubing. From RCBS.

**Price:** . . . . . . . . . . . . . **See chart.**

**Neck Expander Die**

For use when reloading cast bullets. Die expands case neck and slightly flares case mouth to prevent lead shearing. From RCBS.

**Price:** . . . . . . . . . . . . . **$19.63**
**Price:** Die body . . . . . . . . . **$14.88**
**Price:** Plug . . . . . . . . . . . **$7.13**
**Price:** Plug rod . . . . . . . . . **$3.25**
**Price:** Lock ring 1/4"-28 . . . . . **$2.13**

**Case-Forming Dies**

Contact RCBS for extensive listing of available case-form dies. From RCBS.

**Price:** . . . . . **Contact manufacturer.**

**Competition Rifle Dies**

Two die sets feature: full-length sizer with raised expander ball for extra leverage and smooth neck expansion; maximum concentricity between die neck and body; seater die with micrometer bullet-seating head with 0.001" click adjustments; side window with sliding guide for bullet insertion and alignment; bullet-seating sleeve for correct alignment; extended shellholder for shorter rounds; and black oxide finish. Sets come with set-screw wrench, hexagonal lock rings. From RCBS.

**Price:** . . . . . . . . . . . . . **See chart.**

**Lube Die**

Decaps and lubes cases in one step. Designed for progressive presses but also works in single-stage reloaders. Four sizes for 45 calibers. From RCBS.

**Price:** . . . . . . . . . . . . . **$27.13**

## RCBS

### RIFLE/PISTOL DIES

| Caliber | Die Group | Shellholder/ Shellplate # |
|---|---|---|
| 17 Rem. | A | 10 |
| 218 Bee | D | 1 |
| 22 Hornet | A, Comp. | 12 |
| 22K-Hornet | D | 12 |
| 22 PPC | D | 32 |
| 22 Rem. Jet | D | 6 |
| 22 Sav. High-Power | D | 2 |
| 22-250 | A, Comp., RS | 3 |
| 220 Swift | A | 11 |
| 221 Rem. Fire Ball | A | 10 |
| 222 Rem. | A, Comp., RS | 10 |
| 222 Rem. Mag. | D | 10 |
| 223 Rem. | A, Comp., RS | 10 |
| 224 Wea. Mag. | D | 27 |
| 225 Win. | D | 11 |
| 5.6x50 Rimmed | D | 6 |
| 240 Wea. Mag. | D | 3 |
| 243 Win. | A, Comp., RS | 3 |
| 6mm PPC | D | 32 |
| 6mm Rem. | A | 3 |
| 25 Auto | B | 29** |
| 25-06 | A | 3 |
| 25-20 Win. | D | 1 |
| 25-35 Win. | D | 2 |
| 250 Sav. | A | 3 |
| 256 Win. Mag. | D | 6 |
| 257 Roberts | A | 3,11 |
| 257 Roberts Improved | D | 3,11 |
| 257 Wea. Mag. | D | 4 |
| 264 Win. Mag. | A | 4/26 |
| 6.5 Rem. Mag. | D | 4 |
| 6.5mm T/CU | D | 10 |
| 6.5mm-06 | D | 3 |
| 6.5x50 Japanese Arisaka | D | 15 |
| 6.5x52 Carcano | D | 9 |
| 6.5x54 Mannlicher-Scho. | D | 9 |
| 6.5x55 Swedish Mauser | A, Comp., RS | 2 |
| 6.5x57 | D | 3 |
| 270 Wea. Mag. | A | 4 |
| 270 Win. | A, Comp., RS | 3 |
| 280 Rem. | A | 3 |
| 284 Win. | D | 3 |
| 7mm BR Rem. | A | 3 |
| 7mm Rem. Mag. | A, Comp., RS | 4/26 |
| 7mm T/CU | A | 10 |
| 7mm Wea. Mag. | A | 4 |
| 7mm-08 Rem. | A, Comp. | 3 |
| 7mmx57 Mauser | A | 11/3 |
| 7mmx64 Brenneke | A, Comp. | 3 |
| 7mmx65 Rimmed | D | 26 |
| 7-30 Waters | A | 2 |
| 30 M-1 Carbine | C | 17 |
| 30 Herrett | D | 2 |
| 30 Luger | D | 16 |
| 30 Mauser | D | 16 |
| 30 Rem. | D | 19 |
| 30-06 Springfield | A, Comp., RS | 3 |
| 30-30 Win. | A, RS | 2 |
| 30-338 Win. Mag. | D | 4 |
| 30-40 Krag | A | 7 |
| 300 H&H Mag. | A | 4 |
| 300 Sav. | A | 3 |
| 300 Wea. Mag. | A | 4 |
| 300 Win. Mag. | A, RS | 4/26 |
| 303 British | A, RS | 7 |
| 303 Sav. | D | 21 |
| 307 Win. | A | 2 |
| 308 Norma Mag. | D | 4 |
| 308 Win. | A, Comp., RS | 3 |
| 7.5mm Schmidt-Rubin | D, Comp. | 2 |
| 7.62x39 | A, RS | 32 |
| 7.62x54R Russian | A | 13* |
| 7.65x53 Belgian Mauser | D | 3 |
| 7.7x58 Japanese Arisaka | D | 3/2 |
| 32 Automatic | B | 17 |
| 32 H&R Mag. | B | 23 |
| 32 S&W Long | B | 23 |
| 32 Win. Special | A | 2 |
| 32-20 Win. | B | 1 |
| 32-40 Win. | D | 2 |
| 8mm Rem. Mag. | D | 4 |
| 8mm-06 | D | 3 |
| 8mmx57 Mauser | A, Comp., RS | 3 |
| 8mmx68S Mag. | D | 34* |
| 33 Win. | D | 14* |
| 338 Win. Mag. | A | 4 |
| 340 Wea. Mag. | D | 4 |
| 348 Win. | A | 5* |
| 35 Rem. | A | 9 |
| 35 Whelen | A | 3 |
| 350 Rem. Mag. | D | 4 |
| 356 Win. | A | 2 |
| 357 Herrett | D | 2 |
| 357 Mag. | B | 6 |
| 357 Rem. Maximum | B | 6 |
| 358 Norma Mag. | D | 4 |
| 358 Win. | A | 3 |
| 9mm Luger | B | 16 |
| 9mm Makarov | B | 16 |
| 9mmx21 | B | 16 |
| 9.3x62 Mauser | D | 3 |
| 9.3x72R | F | 30 |
| 9.3x74R | D | 4 |
| 375 H&H Mag. | A | 4 |
| 375 Win. | C | 2 |
| 378 Wea. Mag. | D | 14* |
| 38 Colt Super Auto | B | 39 |
| 38 S&W | E | 6 |
| 38 Special | B | 6 |
| 380 ACP | B | 10 |
| 38-40 Win. | E | 35* |
| 38-55 Win. & Ballard | F | 2 |
| 40 S&W | B | 27 |
| 10mm Auto | B | 27 |
| 41 Action Express | B | 16 |
| 41 Mag. | B | 30 |
| 416 Rem. Mag. | D | 4 |
| 416 Rigby | D | 37* |
| 44 Mag. | B | 18 |
| 44 Special | B | 18 |
| 444 Marlin | C | 28 |
| 44-40 Win. | B | 35* |
| 45 ACP | B | 3 |
| 45 Auto Rim | B | 8* |
| 45 Colt | B | 20 |
| 45 Win. Mag. | E | 36* |
| 45-70 Gov't. | C | 14* |
| 458 Win. Mag. | C | 4 |
| 460 Wea. Mag. | D | 14* |
| 50 Action Express | E | 33* |
| 50-70 U.S. Government | F | 31** |

Comp.:Competition Dies; RS:Reloader Special Dies.
* Auto 4x4 shellplate not available.
** Auto 4x4 and five-station shellplates not available.
When two shellholder numbers are shown, the most popular is shown first.

## RCBS

### Powder Checker Die

Confirms powder charge during press operation and provides visual comparison of powder charge from case to case. From RCBS.

**Price:** . . . . . . . . . . . . . . **$23.50**

### Precision Dies

RCBS **Group A, E and F** two- or three-die sets featuring: sizing dies with strict tolerances; satin matte finish; fine body knurling for non-slip adjustment; hardened die body; and thread adjustable expander-decapping assembly that locks in place. From RCBS.

**Price:** . . . . . . . . . . . . **See charts.**

### Reloader Special Dies

For loading ammunition that exceeds factory specifications. Made with one-piece reamer construction and hardened steel. Features include: non-slip separate collet that holds expander-decapping pin in place and on center; wrench flats and body knurling for easy adjustment; steel hex lock rings with set screws. From RCBS.

**Price:** . . . . . . . . . . . . **See chart.**

### Shotshell Die

Designed to load modern compression-formed plastic hulls with appropriate wad column on RCBS metallic presses—Rock Chucker, Reloader Special-3 and -5, and AmmoMaster single. Use with high brass hulls with up to 3″ magnum loads. Set includes shot measure, case holder and 6- or 8-point crimper. Available for 10-, 12-, 16-, or 20-gauge. From RCBS.

**Price:** . . . . . . . . . . . . . . **$56.88**

### Universal Decap Die

Precision machined die to decap uncleaned, unlubed cases from 22- to 45-caliber. Includes die body, decap assembly with lock nut, die lock ring and plastic storage box. From RCBS.

**Price:** . . . . . . . . . . . . . . **$10.70**

RCBS Competition Rifle Dies

**RCBS Group A Dies**

| DIE/DIE PART | PRICE |
|---|---|
| Full-Length Die Set | $29.00 |
| Full-Length Sizer Die | 23.00 |
| Neck Die Set | 30.50 |
| Neck Sizer Die | 23.00 |
| Small Base Die Set | 30.00 |
| Small Base Sizer Die | 23.00 |
| Seater Die | 19.50 |
| Expander-Decapping Unit | 5.20 |
| Expander Ball | 3.33 |
| Expander-Decapping Rod | 1.75 |
| Decapping Pin (5) | 1.75 |
| Guide Bushing | 1.75 |
| Seater Plug | 4.13 |
| Trim Die | 19.50 |

**RCBS Group C Dies**

| DIE/DIE PART | PRICE |
|---|---|
| 3-Die Carbide Set, Roll or Taper Crimp | $56.00 |
| 3-Die Set, Roll/Taper Crimp | 37.13 |
| Carbide Sizer Die | 42.00 |
| Sizer Die | 19.63 |
| Expander Die | 13.88 |
| Seater Die, Roll/Taper Crimp | 17.88 |
| Decapping Unit | 5.59 |
| Decapping Pin Holder | 2.75 |
| Decapping Rod | 1.75 |
| Decapping Pin (5) | 1.75 |
| Expander Assembly | 5.53 |
| Guide Bushing | 1.75 |
| Seater Plug | 4.13 |

**RCBS Group E Dies**

| DIE/DIE PART | PRICE |
|---|---|
| 3-Die Set | $53.13 |
| Sizer Die | 30.88 |
| Expander Die | 18.63 |
| Seater Die | 24.50 |
| Decapping Unit | 5.59 |
| Decap Pin Holder | 2.75 |
| Decapping Rod | 1.75 |
| Decapping Pin (5) | 1.75 |
| Expander Assembly | 5.53 |
| Guide Bushing | 1.75 |
| Seater Plug | 4.13 |

**RCBS Competition Dies**

| DIE/DIE PART | PRICE |
|---|---|
| Full-Length Die Set | $85.88 |
| Full Length Sizer Die | 28.75 |
| Seater Die | 53.63 |
| Extended Shellholder | 8.75 |
| Expander-Decap Assembly | 6.58 |
| Guide Bushing | 3.18 |
| Expander-Decap Rod | 3.18 |
| Expander Ball | 3.05 |
| Decapping Pin Holder | 2.75 |
| Decapping Pin (5) | 1.75 |
| Seater Plug Assembly | 7.38 |
| Bullet Guide | 5.13 |

**RCBS Group B Dies**

| DIE/DIE PART | PRICE |
|---|---|
| 3-Die Carbide Set | $39.63 |
| 3-Die Set, Roll/Taper Crimp | 29.63 |
| Carbide Sizer Die | 28.88 |
| Sizer Die | 16.38 |
| Expander Die | 11.75 |
| Seater Die, Roll/Taper Crimp | 15.50 |
| Decapping Unit | 5.59 |
| Decapping Pin Holder | 2.75 |
| Decapping Rod | 1.75 |
| Decapping Pin (5) | 1.75 |
| Expander Assembly | 5.53 |
| Guide Bushing | 1.75 |
| Seater Plug | 4.13 |
| Trim Die | 19.50 |

**RCBS Group D Dies**

| DIE/DIE PART | PRICE |
|---|---|
| Full-Length Die Set | $48.50 |
| Full-Length Sizer Die | 34.00 |
| Neck Die Set | 55.75 |
| Neck Sizer Die | 39.88 |
| Seater Die | 26.75 |
| Expander Decapping Unit | 5.20 |
| Expander Ball | 3.33 |
| Expander Decapping Rod | 1.75 |
| Decapping Pin (5) | 1.75 |
| Guide Bushing | 1.75 |
| Seater Plug | 4.13 |
| Trim Die | 35.38 |

**RCBS Group F Dies**

| DIE/DIE PART | PRICE |
|---|---|
| 3-Die Set | $61.25 |
| Sizer Die | 42.50 |
| Expander Die | 22.38 |
| Seater Die | 27.63 |
| Decapping Unit | 5.59 |
| Decapping Pin Holder | 2.75 |
| Decapping Rod | 1.75 |
| Decapping Pin (5) | 1.75 |
| Expander Assembly | 5.53 |
| Guide Bushing | 1.75 |
| Seater Plug | 4.13 |

**RCBS Reloader Special**

| DIE/DIE PART | PRICE |
|---|---|
| Die Set | $17.00 |
| Expander-Decapper Unit | 4.18 |
| Expander Ball | 2.80 |
| Expander Decapping Rod | 1.75 |
| Decapping Pin (5) | 2.00 |
| Collet | 1.86 |
| Collet Closer | 1.86 |
| Seater Plug | 3.94 |

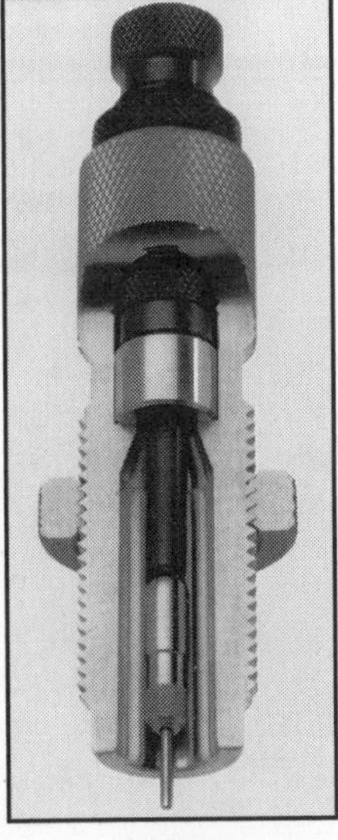
Redding Type S

| REDDING Competition Die Calibers | |
|---|---|
| 221 Rem. | 260 Rem. |
| 222 Rem. | 6.5/284 Win. |
| 223 Rem. | 6.5x55 Swedish |
| 22 PPC | 264 Win. Mag. |
| 22 BR Rem. | 270 Win. |
| 22-250 Rem. | 7mm IHSMA |
| 22-250 Rem. Imp. 40° | 7mm TCU |
| 220 Swift | 7mm BR Rem. |
| 6mm PPC | 7mm-08 Rem. |
| 6mm BR Rem | 7mmx57 Mauser |
| 6mm TCU | 280 Rem. |
| 243 Win. | 280 Rem. Imp. 40° |
| 243 Win. Imp. 40° | 284 Win. |
| 6mm Rem. | 7mm Rem. Mag. |
| 6mm/284 Win. | 7mm STW |
| 250 Savage | 308 Win. |
| 257 Roberts | 30-06 Spfd. |
| 257 Rob. Imp. 40° | 300 Win. Mag. |
| 25-06 Rem. | 30-338 Win. Mag. |
| 6.5/308 Win. | 300 Wea. Mag. |

**REDDING Pistol/Rifle 2-Die Prices**

| DIE SET/DIE PART | SERIES A | SERIES B | SERIES C | SERIES D |
|---|---|---|---|---|
| Full-Length Set | $42.00 | $60.00 | $75.00 | $87.00 |
| Deluxe Set | 69.00 | 94.50 | 117.00 | 135.00 |
| Neck Size Die | 30.00 | 39.00 | 48.00 | 55.00 |
| Full-Length Size Die | 30.00 | 39.00 | 48.00 | 55.00 |
| Decap Rod Assembly | 9.00 | 9.00 | 9.00 | 9.00 |
| Decap Rod | 6.00 | 6.00 | 6.00 | 6.00 |
| Size Button | 5.00 | 5.00 | 5.00 | 5.00 |
| Seating Die | 24.90 | 34.50 | 42.00 | 49.50 |
| Seat Plug | 6.00 | 6.00 | 6.00 | 6.00 |
| Form & Trim Die | 27.00 | 36.00 | 42.00 | 49.50 |

**REDDING Pistol/Rifle 3-Die Prices**

| DIE SET/DIE PART | SERIES A | SERIES B | SERIES C | SERIES D |
|---|---|---|---|---|
| 3-Die Set | $42.00 | $60.00 | $75.00 | $87.00 |
| Sizing Die | 24.00 | 31.50 | 37.50 | 45.00 |
| Decap Rod Assembly | 9.00 | 9.00 | 9.00 | 9.00 |
| Decap Rod | 6.00 | 6.00 | 6.00 | 6.00 |
| Seating Die | 21.90 | 30.00 | 36.00 | 42.00 |
| Seat Plug | 6.00 | 6.00 | 6.00 | 6.00 |
| Expander Die | 16.50 | 22.50 | 27.00 | 31.50 |
| Expander | 7.50 | 7.50 | 7.50 | 7.50 |
| Trim Die | 27.00 | 36.00 | 42.00 | 49.00 |

Redding Benchrest Competition Resizing Die

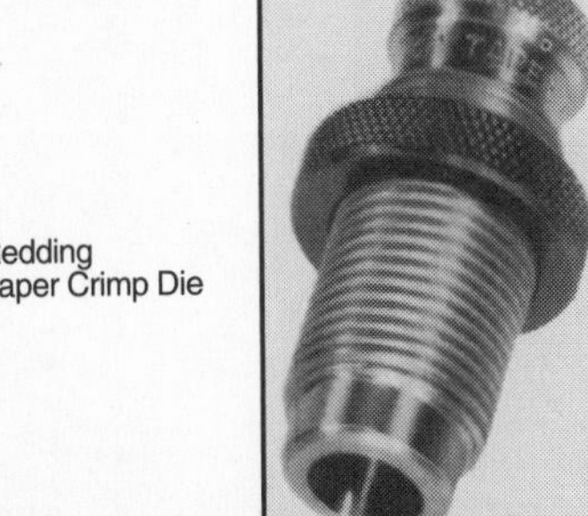

Redding Taper Crimp Die

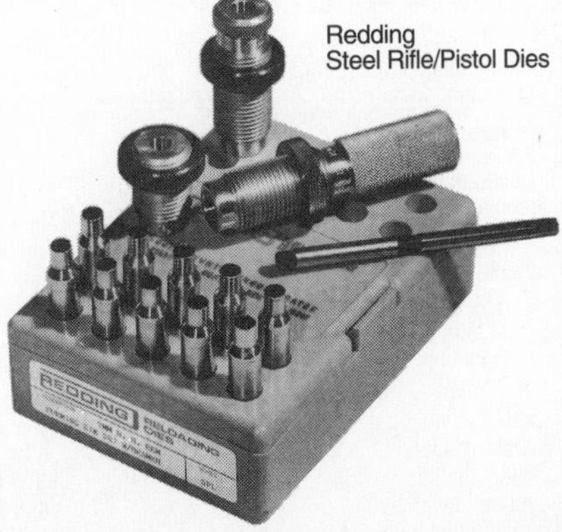

Redding Steel Rifle/Pistol Dies

## REDDING

### Bushing-Style Neck-Sizing Die

Designed to control amount of neck sizing for precision reloading. Two models available, Type S or Benchrest Competition. Both models will accept interchangeable sizing bushings that come in .001″ increments and cover a size range from .235 to .340 or 22-caliber through 30. The dies are available in 42 calibers without the bushings and have an adjustable decapping rod to allow positioning of the bushing to resize only a portion of the neck length if desired. The Benchrest Competition die features micrometer adjustments. Bushings are of steel or titanium nitrite treated steel. From Redding Reloading Equipment.

**Price:** Type S neck sizing die . . . **$48.00**
**Price:** Benchrest competition die . . **$89.50**
**Price:** Steel bushing . . . . . . . **$12.50**
**Price:** Titanium nitrite steel bushing **$19.50**

### Bushing-Style Body Dies

Designed to full-length resize the case body only and bump the shoulder position for proper chambering without disturbing the case neck. No internal parts and intended for use only to resize cases which chamber with difficulty after repeated firings. From Redding Reloading Equipment.

**Price:** . . . . . . . . . . . . . **$24.00**

### Case Forming Dies

Made on a custom basis only to form brass cases from one caliber to another. From Redding Reloading Equipment.

**Price:** . . . . . . **Contact manufacturer.**

### Competition Bullet Seating Die

Straight-line bullet seater with seating depth micrometer. Seating stem precision ground to exactly match bullet diameter. Micrometer calibrated in .001″ increments for precise seating depth and has a "zero" set feature to zero micrometer to specific rifle. From Redding Reloading Equipment.

**Price:** . . . . . . . . . . . . . **$96.00**

### Custom Made Dies

Die sets for cartridges not listed can be custom made by Redding; send them chamber reamer drawing or dimensions and shoulder angle or cartridge for price quote. From Redding Reloading Equipment.

**Price:** 2-die set . . . . . . . . **$103.50**
**Price:** 2-die set with tapered expander . . . . . . . . . **$109.50**
**Price:** Full-length sizer or neck sizer **$67.50**
**Price:** Deluxe die set . . . . . . **$159.00**
**Price:** Deluxe set with tapered expander . . . . . . . . . **$165.00**
**Price:** 3-die set . . . . . . . . **$114.00**
**Price:** Taper crimp die . . . . . . **$49.50**
**Price:** Form die . . . . . . . . . **$49.50**
**Price:** Trim die . . . . . . . . . **$60.00**

### Form & Trim Dies

Made to chamber dimensions to eliminate resizing when file trimming. Pistol trim dies require extended shellholder. From Redding Reloading Equipment.

**Price:** Series A . . . . . . . . . **$27.00**
**Price:** Series B . . . . . . . . . **$36.00**
**Price:** Series C . . . . . . . . . **$42.00**
**Price:** Series D . . . . . . . . . **$49.50**

### Neck Sizing Die

Designed for bottleneck cases to neck size only. Available individually or come standard in Deluxe die set. From Redding Reloading Equipment.

**Price:** . . . . . . . . . . . . **See chart.**

## REDDING

### RIFLE/PISTOL DIES

#### RIFLE

| Caliber | Die Group | Shellholder |
|---|---|---|
| 17 Rem. | B | 10 |
| 17 Mach IV | D | 10 |
| 218 Bee | B | 3 |
| 219 Zipper | C | 2 |
| 219 Donaldson Wasp | D | 2 |
| 22 Hornet | A | 14 |
| 22 K Hornet | B | 14 |
| 22 B.R. Rem. | C | 1 |
| 22 Rem. Jet | D | 12 |
| 22 Savage H.P. | C | 2 |
| 220 Swift | A | 4 |
| 22-250 Rem. | A | 1 |
| 22-250 Imp. 40 | C | 1 |
| 221 Rem. | A | 10 |
| 222 Rem. | A | 10 |
| 222 Rem. Mag. | C | 10 |
| 223 Rem. | A | 10 |
| 224 Wea. Mag. | D | 12 |
| 225 Win. | C | 4 |
| 5.6x50 R Mag. | CM | 12 |
| 5.6x57 RWS | CM | 1 |
| 5.7MM Johnson (22 Spitfire) | CM | 22 |
| 240 Wea. Mag. | C | 1 |
| 243 Win. | A | 1 |
| 243 Win. Imp. 40° | D | 1 |
| 243 Imp. 30° | CM | 1 |
| 6mm Rem. | A | 1 |
| 6mm Rem. Imp. 40° | D | 1 |
| 6mm TCU | B | 10 |
| 6mm Wasp | CM | 2 |
| 6mm BR Rem. | B | 1 |
| 6mm PPC Rem. | B | 12 |
| 6mm/223 Rem. | C | 10 |
| 6mm/284 Win. | C | 1 |
| 6mmx47(6mm-222 Rem. Mag.) | C | 10 |
| 25 Rem. | D | 5 |
| 25-06 Rem. | A | 1 |
| 25-06 Rem. Imp. 40° | D | 1 |
| 25-20 Win. | B | 3 |
| 25-35 Win. | C | 2 |
| 25/284 Win. | D | 1 |
| 250 Sav. | A | 1 |
| 250 Sav. Imp. 40° | D | 1 |
| 256 Win. Mag. | B | 12 |
| 257 Roberts | A | 1 |
| 257 Roberts Imp. 40° | B | 1 |
| 257 Wea. Mag. | B | 6 |
| 264 Win. Mag. | A | 6 |
| 6.5mm BC | CM | 1 |
| 6.5 Rem. Mag. | D | 6 |
| 6.5mm TCU | CM | 10 |
| 6.5mm-06 | C | 1 |
| 6.5mmx50 Japanese | C | 4 |
| 6.5mmx52 Curano | C | 1 |
| 6.5mmx54 Mann. | C | 24 |
| 6.5mmx55 Swed. Mauser | A | 1 |
| 6.5mmx57 Mauser | D | 1 |
| 6.5mmx68S | D | 19 |
| 6.5mm/257 Roberts | CM | 1 |
| 6.5mm/257Roberts Imp. 40° | CM | 1 |
| 6.5mm/284 Win. | D | 1 |
| 6.5mm/300 Wea. Mag. | D | 6 |
| 270 Win. | A | 1 |
| 270 Win. Imp. 40° | D | 1 |
| 270 Wea. Mag. | B | 6 |
| 270-257 Roberts Imp 40° | CM | 1 |
| 280 Rem. | A | 1 |
| 280 Rem. Imp. 40° | C | 1 |
| 284 Win. | A | 1 |
| 7mm Rem. Mag. | A | 6 |
| 7mm B.R. Rem. | B | 1 |
| 7mm TCU | B | 10 |
| 7mm INT-R | C | 2 |
| 7mm IHMSA | C | 1 |
| 7mm Wea. Mag. | B | 6 |
| 7mm STW | D | 6 |
| 7mm-08 Rem. | A | 1 |
| 7mm-08 Rem. Imp. 40° | D | 1 |
| 7-30 Waters | B | 2 |
| 7mmx47(7mm-222 Rem. Mag.) | CM | 10 |
| 7mmx57 Mauser | A | 1 |
| 7mmx57 Imp. 40 | D | 1 |
| 7mmx61 Sharp & Hart | D | 6 |
| 7mmx64 Brenn. | C | 1 |
| 7mm/300 Wea. Mag. | C | 6 |
| 7mm-350 Rem. Mag. | CM | 6 |
| 7.5mm Schmidt Rubin(Swiss) | C | 2 |
| 7.62x39 | A | 12 |
| 7.62 Russian (7.62x54R) | B | 15 |
| 30 Herrett | D | 2 |
| 30 Rem. | D | 5 |
| 30-06 | A | 1 |
| 30-06 Imp. 40° | C | 1 |
| 30-20 TC | C | 3 |
| 30-30 Win. | A | 2 |
| 30-30 Imp. 40° | D | 2 |
| 30-40 Krag | A | 8 |
| 30-338 Win. Mag. | C | 6 |
| 30-8mm Rem. Mag.(30 Super) | CM | 6 |
| 300 H&H Mag. | B | 6 |
| 300 Sav. | C | 1 |
| 300 Win. Mag. | A | 6 |
| 300 Wea. Mag. | A | 6 |
| 303 Sav. | B | 21 |
| 308 Win./307 Win. | A | 1, 2 |
| 308 Norma Mag. | B | 6 |
| 308x1.75 | CM | 1 |
| 7.65mmx53 Mauser(Belgian) | B | 1 |
| 7.7mmx58 Japanese | C | 1 |
| 303 British | A | 8 |
| 32 Win. Spl. | B | 2 |
| 32 Rem. | C | 5 |
| 32-40 Win. | B | 2 |
| 7.92mmx33 Kurz Mauser | D | 1 |
| 8mm Rem. Mag. | C | 6 |
| 8mm Lebel | CM | 26 |
| 8mm-06 | D | 1 |
| 8mm-06 Imp. 40° | D | 1 |
| 8mmx56 Mann. | D | 1 |
| 8mmx57 Mauser | A | 1 |
| 8mmx60S | D | 1 |
| 8mmx64S Brenn. | D | 4 |
| 8mmx68S | C | 19 |
| 8.15x46R | D | 2 |
| 33 Win. | D | 18 |
| 338 Win. Mag. | A | 6 |
| 338-06 | C | 1 |
| 338-06 Imp. 40° | D | 1 |
| 338/284 Win. | CM | 1 |
| 340 Wea. Mag. | B | 6 |
| 348 Win. | C | 20 |
| 35 Rem. | A | 1 |
| 35 Win. | C | 8 |
| 35 Whelen | B | 1 |
| 35 Whelen Imp. 40° | D | 1 |
| 350 Rem. Mag. | B | 6 |
| 357 Herrett | D | 2 |
| 358 Win./356 Win. | B | 1,2 |
| 358 Norma Mag. | B | 6 |
| 358 STA | CM | 6 |
| 9mmx56 Mann. | CM | 1 |
| 9mmx57 Mauser | C | 1 |
| 9.3mmx62 Mauser | C | 1 |
| 9mmx74R | D | 6 |
| 375 H&H Mag. | A | 6 |
| 375 H&H Mag. Imp. 40° | D | 6 |
| 375 Wea. Mag. | D | 6 |
| 378 Wea. Mag. | D | 18 |
| 416 Rem. Mag. | C | 6 |
| 416 Wea. Mag. | D | 18 |
| 460 Wea. Mag. | D | 18 |

#### PISTOL

| Caliber | Die Group | Shellholder |
|---|---|---|
| 25 ACP (25 Auto) | D | 27 |
| 270 REN | CM | 14 |
| 30 M1 Carbine | A | 22 |
| 30 Luger | C | 13 |
| 30 Mauser | B | 13 |
| 32-20 Win./30-20 TC | C | 3 |
| 32 Short Colt | CM | 10 |
| 32 Long Colt | CM | 10 |
| 32 ACP | B | 22 |
| 32 S&W (Short) | CM | 10 |
| 32 S&W (Long) | A | 10 |
| 32 H&R Mag. | A | 10 |
| 32 S&W/32 H&R Mag. | A | 10 |
| 32-20 Win. | B | 3 |
| 38 Super Auto. | B | 5 |
| 380 Auto. | A | 10 |
| 9mm Luger | A | 13 |
| 351 Win. S.L. | D | 5 |
| 357/44 Bain & Davis | CM | 19 |
| 38 S&W | D | 12 |
| 38 Spl. | A | 12 |
| 357 Mag. | A | 12 |
| 38 Spl./357 Mag. | A | 12 |
| 357 Maximum | C | 12 |
| 40 S&W | B | 5 |
| 10mm Auto. | B | 5 |
| 40 S&W/10mm Auto. | B | 5 |
| 38-40 Win. | C | 9 |
| 375 Win. | B | 2 |
| 38-55 Win. & Ballard | C | 2 |
| 38-56 Win. | D | 18 |
| 41 Long Colt | C | 1 |
| 40-65 Win. | D | 18 |
| 40-82 Win. | D | 18 |
| 401 Win. S.L. | D | 2 |
| 405 Win. | D | 8 |
| 41 Mag. | A | 21 |
| 41 Action Exp. | D | 13 |
| 44 Russian | C | 19 |
| 44 Special | A | 19 |
| 44 Mag. | A | 19 |
| 44 Spl./44 Mag. | A | 19 |
| 44-40 Win. | A | 9 |
| 444 Marlin | B | 19 |
| 45 ACP & AR | A | 1, 17 |
| 45 Win. Mag. | D | 7 |
| 45 Colt | A | 23 |
| 455 Webley | C | 6 |
| 45-70 U.S. Gov't | B | 18 |
| 45-90 Win. | D | 18 |
| 458 Win. Mag. | B | 6 |

## REDDING

**Taper Crimp Dies**

For handgun cartridges that headspace on case mouth and conventional roll crimp is undesirable. Also available for some revolver cartridges. Rifle calibers include: 223 Remington, 7.62x39, 30-30, 308 Winchester and 30-06. From Redding Reloading Equipment.

**Price:** . . . . . . . . . . . . . **$24.90**

**Pistol/Rifle Steel Dies**

Two- and three-die sets carefully machined to close and uniform tolerances and finish machined on precision lathes. All die parts made of high-grade steel alloy. Knurled outside surface allows hand adjustments. Standard (2-die) and Deluxe (3-die) sets are for bottleneck cases, the Deluxe set containing a separate neck size die. Three-die sets are for straight wall cases and include an expander die. Series A dies are pistol and rifle die sets for most popular calibers; Series B, die sets for slightly less popular calibers; Series C, popular wildcats and less popular rifle/pistol calibers; Series D, represent obsolete calibers and wildcats. Redding will also manufacture custom dies upon request. From Redding Reloading Equipment.

**Price:** . . . . . . . . . . . . . **See chart.**

**Profile Crimp Die**

For handgun cartridges that do not headspace on case mouth. Provides tighter more uniform roll-type crimp. From Redding Reloading Equipment.

**Price:** . . . . . . . . . . . . . **$24.90**

**Titanium Carbide/Pro Series Pistol Dies**

No-lube standard three-die set available also in Pro Series for progressive reloading presses. Pro Series bullet seating die designed for bullet seating only with no crimping. A Profile crimp die is supplied for final crimp except for cartridges that headspace on the case mouth. For these a taper crimp die is substituted. All Pro Series dies have large radius at mouth for easy case entry. From Redding Reloading Equipment.

**Price:** Titanium carbide die set . . . **$79.50**
**Price:** Titanium sizer die . . . . . **$59.50**
**Price:** Pro Series die set . . . . . **$79.50**
**Price:** 9mm, either set add . . . . **$10.00**

## PONSNESS/WARREN

**Bullet Seating Die**

Die body threaded 7/8-14 to fit all presses. Uses retaining sleeve to seat bullets precisely. Sleeves available in diameters .224″ through .358 to handle calibers 22 through 35. From Ponsness/Warren.

**Price:** Die body . . . . . . . . . . **$22.95**
**Price:** Sleeve . . . . . . . . . . . **$9.25**

Ponsness/Warren Bullet Seating Die

## ROCK CRUSHER

**File Trim Die**

For the 50 BMG has same features as reloading dies. From The Old Western Scrounger.

**Price:** . . . . . . . . . . . . . **$124.20**

**Reloading Dies**

Specifically designed for the Rock Crusher press. Precision honed, hardened and mirror finish polished with non-glare outside satin finish. Die sets available for 50 BMG, 55 Boyes rifle, 12.7x107 Russian, 20mm Hispano, 20mm Oerlikon, 20mm Lahti, 20mm Solothurn, 20mm Vulcan, 23x115 Soviet. From The Old Western Scrounger.

**Price:** 50 BMG . . . . . . . . **$254.00**
**Price:** 55 Boyes . . . . . . . . **$403.00**
**Price:** 12.7mm Russian . . . . . **$403.00**
**Price:** 20mm Vulcan . . . . . . **$452.00**
**Price:** 20mm Oerlikon . . . . . **$452.00**
**Price:** 20mm Hispano . . . . . . **$452.00**
**Price:** 20mm Lahti, Solothurn . . **$467.00**
**Price:** 23mmx115 Soviet . . . . . **$795.00**
**Price:** Shellholder . . . . **$36.75-$65.00**

## SKIP'S MACHINE

**Custom Steel Die**

Shoulder set-back die for benchresters or varmint shooters for forming wildcat cases. From Skip's Machine.

**Price:** . . . . . . . . . . . . . **$75.00**

## SCOTT

**Benchrest Dies**

Precision-made titanium nitride full-length resize dies for the benchrest shooter. Come in 6mm PPC or 6mm-22 BR calibers. From Dwight Scott.

**Price:** . . . . . . . . . . . . . **$125.00**

## STAR

**Carbide Pistol Dies**

Precision machined four and five carbide die sets threaded 11/16-24 to fit the Universal Star press. Available in most popular calibers. One set standard with press. From Star Machine Works.

**Price:** . . . . . . . . . . . . . **$31.50**

## WHITETAIL DESIGN

**Bushing for L.E. Wilson Neck Size Die**

Carbide bushing available in 6mm only. Soon will be offered in 22-caliber. From Whitetail Design and Engineering Ltd.

**Price:** . . . . . . . . . . . . . **$30.00**

## WILSON

**Full-Length Sizing Die**

Designed for use on heavy-duty arbor press. Non-adjustable, straight-line die for reforming and resizing cases which have been fired numerous times. Available in most hunting and benchrest calibers. From Sinclair International, Inc.

**Price:** . . . . . . . . . . . . . **$19.95**

**Neck Sizing Die**

Precision hand die used with either small mallet or arbor press to control and/or change incrementally cartridge case neck reduction through a series of interchangeable bushings. Bushings available in increments of .001″, from .236″ through .343″. All neck dies size neck to 3/16″ from mouth end. Available with or without one bushing. From L.E. Wilson, Inc.

**Price:** With bushing . . . . . . . **$62.50**
**Price:** Without bushing . . . . . . **$50.00**
**Price:** Bushing . . . . . . . . . **$12.50**

Rock Crusher Reloading Dies

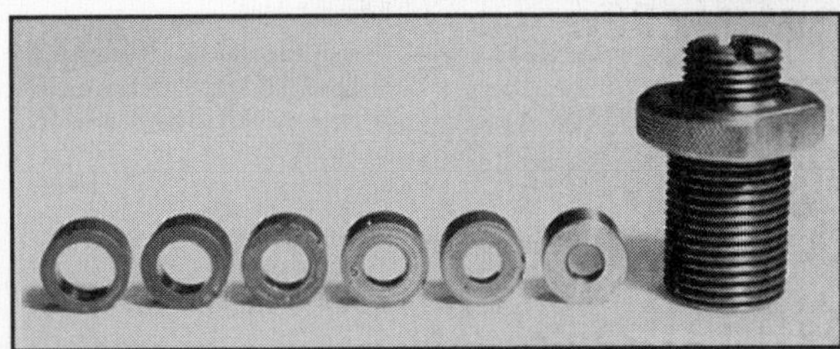

Skips Machine

## ALEX

**Stuck Case Extractor**
Removes stuck cases separated above the case head from reloading dies. One extractor will work on nearly all cartridges of the same caliber. Available in calibers 22, 6mm (243), 25, 7mm (270), 30, 338, 35, 375, 44. From Alex, Inc.
**Price:** . . . . . . . . . . . . . . . **$18.00**

## C-H/4-D

**Die Boxes**
Plastic see-through boxes for die storage. Available in two sizes: 5x4¼x1½ or 5x4¼x1½. From C-H Tool & Die/4-D Custom Die.
**Price:** Small . . . . . . . . . . . . **$.99**
**Price:** Large . . . . . . . . . . . **$2.00**

**Die Wrench**
Tightens 1-1⅛″ die hex lock ring on any progressive loading press. From C-H Tool & Die/4-D Custom Die.
**Price:** . . . . . . . . . . . . . . . **$7.95**

**Lock Ring**
Solid steel lock ring with nylon ball lock for ease of loosening. Fits all makes of dies with ⅞-14 threads. From C-H Tool & Die/4-D Custom Die.
**Price:** ⅞″ . . . . . . . . . . . **$2.25**
**Price:** 1½x12″ . . . . . . . . . . **$6.00**
**Price:** ½x20″ . . . . . . . . . . **$1.25**
**Price:** 9/16x18″ . . . . . . . . . . **$1.35**
**Price:** ⅝x18″ . . . . . . . . . . **$1.45**
**Price:** ¾x16″ . . . . . . . . . . **$1.55**
**Price:** 1x14″ . . . . . . . . . . **$5.00**
**Price:** 1¼x14″ . . . . . . . . . . **$6.00**

**Stuck Case Puller**
Removes stuck cases from sizing dies. From C-H Tool & Die/4-D Custom Die.
**Price:** . . . . . . . . . . . . . . . **$7.65**

**Titanium Nitride Expander Ball**
Coated expander ball eliminates need for case neck lubrication. Available in 22, 243/6mm, 270, 284/7mm, 308 and 323/8mm. 7mm and larger have 10-32 inside threads; others have 8-32 threads. Also fits RCBS, Redding, Hornady dies. From C-H Tool & Die/4-D Custom Die.
**Price:** . . . . . . . . . . . . . . . **$8.95**

## FORSTER

**Lock Ring**
Cross-bolt design for easy tightening and loosening with a screwdriver. From Forster Products.
**Price:** . . . . . . . . . . . . . . . **$3.60**

**Stuck Case Remover**
Works on any sizing die and will extract cases which have the decap rod and expander ball stuck in die. Includes two extractor nuts, two punch rods and washer to protect top of die. From Forster Products.
**Price:** . . . . . . . . . . . . . . **$18.30**

## HORNADY

**Die Wrench**
Fits flats on New Dimension die spindle assembly, lock rings and die body. From Hornady Mfg. Co.
**Price:** . . . . . . . . . . . . . . . **$5.00**

**Lock-N-Load Bushings**
Bushings threaded ⅞x14 for Hornady Classic and AP Lock-N-Load presses or conversion bushing for use with other brands of reloading presses. From Hornady Mfg. Co.
**Price:** 2 pack . . . . . . . . . **$8.95**
**Price:** 3 pack . . . . . . . . . **$12.95**
**Price:** Press conversion bushing . . **$10.95**

## HORNADY

**MicroJust Seating Stem**
Incremented in .001″ for precision bullet seating depth. Replaces standard seating depth adjustment stem of any New Dimension seating die. From Hornady Mfg. Co.
**Price:** . . . . . . . . . . . . . . **$14.95**

**RCBS-Type Carbide Expander**
Designed to fit RCBS dies. Includes carbide expander, elliptical expander, spindle, deprime pin and collar lock. Weight: 1 lb. From Hornady Mfg. Co.
**Price:** . . . . . . . . . . . . . . **$23.00**

**Stuck Case Remover**
Consists of #7 drill and ¼″-20 tap and remover body that fits shellholder on any standard press. Weight: ¼-lb. From Hornady Mfg. Co.
**Price:** . . . . . . . . . . . . . . **$13.65**

**Sure-Loc Lock Rings**
Solid steel rings threaded ⅞-14 lock solid without touching die threads. Weight: 4 oz. From Hornady Mfg. Co.
**Price:** . . . . . . . . . . . . . . . **$2.49**

## LYMAN

**New Style ⅞-14 Hex Nut**
Designed for use with the Lyman bench wrench. From Lyman Products Corporation.
**Price:** . . . . . . . . . . . . . . . **$2.25**

**⅞-14 Adapter**
Used to mount small diameter 310 and obsolete Tru-Line dies to modern presses. From Lyman Products Corporation.
**Price:** . . . . . . . . . . . . . . . **$5.75**

**AA Die Boxes**
Tough plastic box for individual dies with snap lock hinged cover. Also available to hold two- or three-die die sets. From Lyman Products Corporation.
**Price:** . . . . . . . . . . . . . . . **$2.00**
**Price:** . . . . . . . . . . . . . . . **$2.50**

**Die Rack Organizer**
Plastic rack that holds four die sets with shellholder and unloaded cartridge for checking overall length. From Lyman Products Corporation.
**Price:** . . . . . . . . . . . . . . . **$8.75**

**Hex Nuts**
Heavy-duty die check nut. Must be used with other brands of standard threaded dies when used in Spar-T press. From Lyman Products Corporation.
**Price:** . . . . . . . . . . . . . . . **$2.00**

**Split-Lock Ring**
Steel split ring fits all standard threaded dies. From Lyman Products Corporation.
**Price:** . . . . . . . . . . . . . . . **$2.50**

## MARMIK

**50 BMG Stuck Case Remover**
Steel fixture to remove stuck cases from resizing die and used in combination with drill bit, tap and cap screw. From MarMik, Inc.
**Price:** . . . . . . . . . . . . . . . **$4.00**

**50 BMG Steel Polishing Plug**
Case-shaped plug to polish and/or enlarge interior of 50 BMG die bodies. From MarMik, Inc.
**Price:** . . . . . . . . . . . . . . . **$5.00**

## MTM

**Multiple Set Die Box**
Holds four rifle or pistol die sets with space provided for shellholders and last round loaded with each set of dies. Label on inside of box lid. From MTM Moulded Products Company.
**Price:** . . . . . . . . . . . . . . **$10.20**

## RCBS

**Die Storage Box**
Thick plastic box with built-in cradle to hold from one to three dies. From RCBS.
**Price:** . . . . . . . . . . . . . . . **$3.63**

**Die Wrench**
Heat-treated steel construction die wrench with pivoting handle. From RCBS.
**Price:** . . . . . . . . . . . . . . . **$3.00**

**Stuck Case Remover**
Williams-type tool removes stuck cases from sizing dies. Case head is drilled and tapped, stuck case remover placed over die and hex head screw is turned with wrench until case is freed. Comes with drill, tap and wrench. From RCBS.
**Price:** . . . . . . . . . . . . . . **$13.25**

**Stuck Case Remover-2 Kit**
Extracts cases from dies with removable guide bushings or dies with raised expander ball. Kit contains two extractor nuts and two punch rods. From RCBS.
**Price:** . . . . . . . . . . . . . . . **$5.38**

## REDDING

**Carbide Size Button Kit**
Upgrade die sets with carbide size button kit. Available for bottleneck cartridges 22- through 30-caliber. Die button free floating on decap rod allowing it to self-center in case neck. Includes: carbide size button, retainer and spare decapping pin. From Redding Reloading Equipment.
**Price:** . . . . . . . . . . . . . . **$21.00**

**Die Spacer Kit**
For use with combination die sets and reloading dies to compensate for case length or make no-crimp adjustment without removing lock ring. Kit includes three spacers: .062″ for no-crimp or partial resizing; .125″, 44 Spl./44 Magnum spacer; .135″, 38 Spl./357 Magnum spacer. From Redding Reloading Equipment.
**Price:** . . . . . . . . . . . . . . . **$7.80**

**Stuck Case Removal Kit**
Williams-type device to drill and tap case head. Place remover over die, turn hex head screw with wrench until case pulls free from size die. From Redding Reloading Equipment.
**Price:** . . . . . . . . . . . . . . **$16.50**

**Tapered Size Buttons**
To expand necks of bottleneck cartridges up to desired size. Available in 6mm, 25, 6.5, 270, 7mm, 30, 8mm, 338, 35 and 375. From Redding Reloading Equipment.
**Price:** Button only . . . . . . . **$12.00**
**Price:** Decap rod assembly with tapered button . . . . . . . **$16.50**

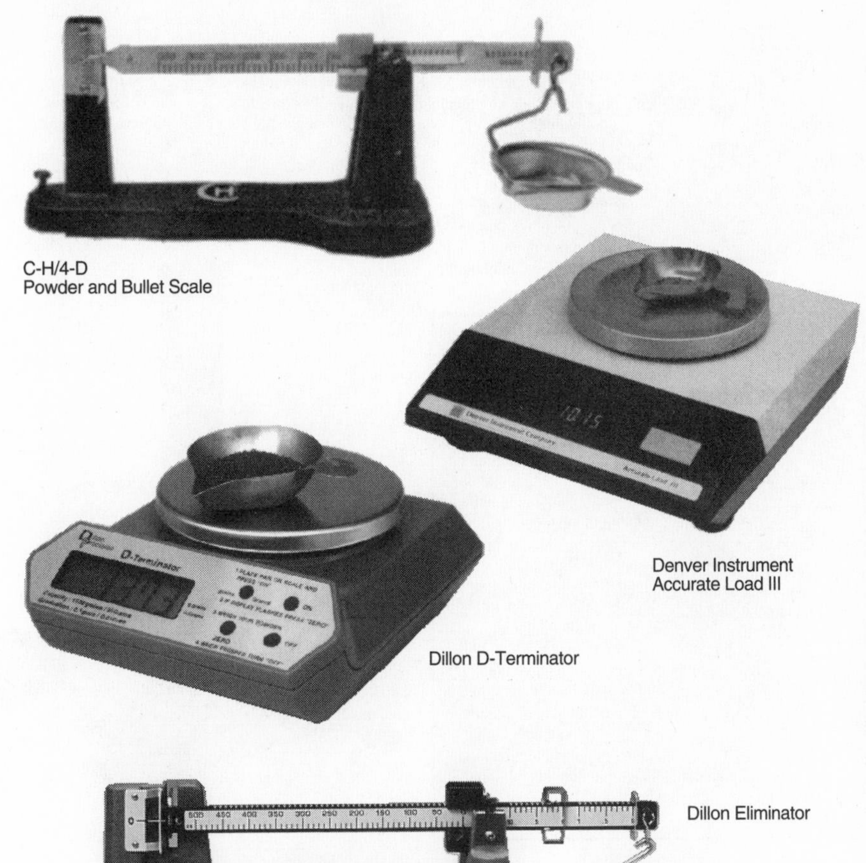
C-H/4-D
Powder and Bullet Scale

Denver Instrument
Accurate Load III

Dillon D-Terminator

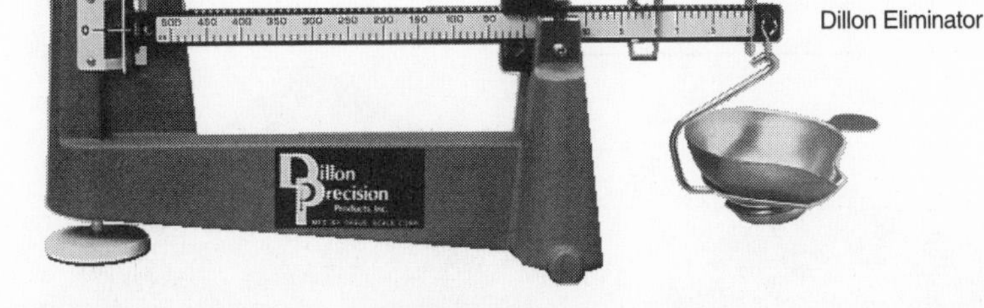
Dillon Eliminator

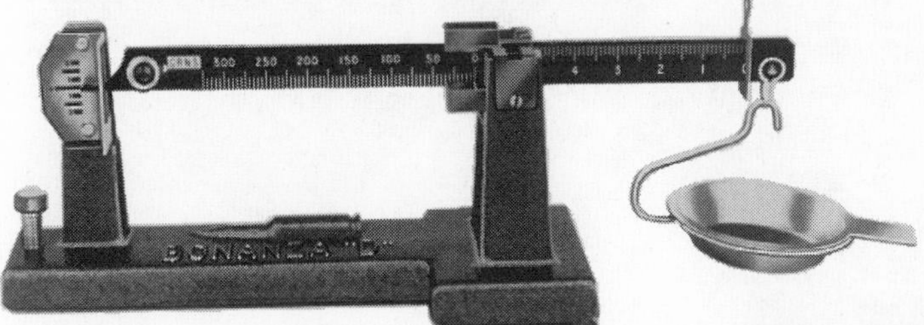
Forster "D" Powder/Bullet Scale

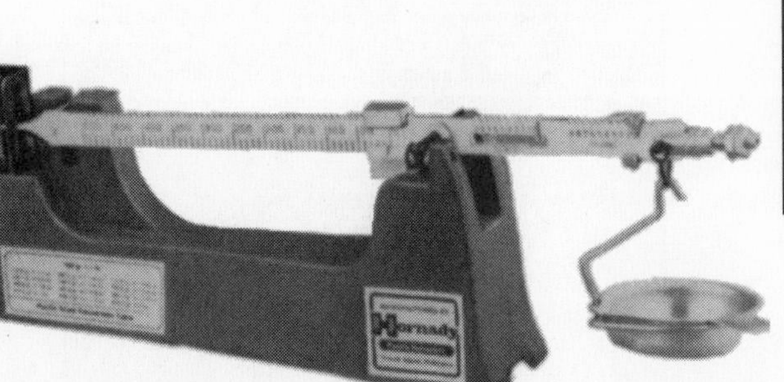
Hornady Magnetic Scale

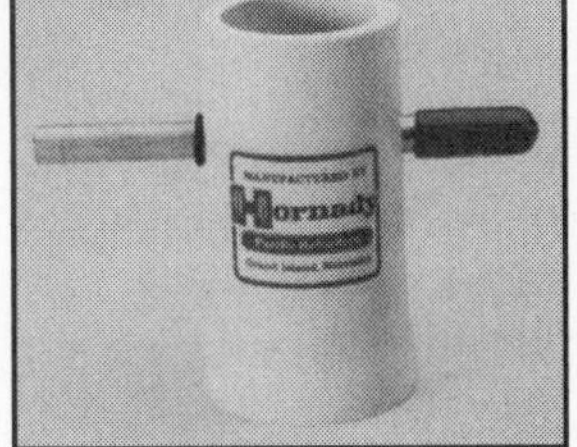
Hornady Powder Trickler

## C-H/4-D

**Powder and Bullet Scale**

All metal powder and bullet scale. Features magnetic damping, 510-gr. capacity and beam graduated in 10-grain, 1-grain and .1-grain increments; leveling screw on base. From C-H Tool & Die/4-D Custom Die.

**Price:** . . . . . . . . . . . . . . **$54.45**

**Powder Dripper**

Features extra large base with insert for weighting with shot or bullets for extra stability; knurled knob. From C-H Tool & Die/4-D Custom Die.

**Price:** . . . . . . . . . . . . . . . **$7.15**

## DENVER INSTRUMENT

**Accurate Load III**

Electronic scale with 1500-grain capacity and precision weighing to +/-0.1-grain. Response time of 2 seconds. Full range TARE function and flourescent display. Made of cast aluminum. Optional battery pack allows portability. Weight: 12 lbs. From Denver Instrument Co.

**Price:** . . . . . . . . . . . . . **$399.00**

## DILLON

**D-Terminator Scale**

Electronic scale accurate to within 0.1-grain/0.01-grain. Features 1500-grain/9.5-gram capacity and large LCD readout. Uses one 9-volt battery and comes with AC adaptor. From Dillon Precision Products, Inc.

**Price:** . . . . . . . . . . . . . **$149.95**

**Eliminator Scale**

Accurate to 0.1-grain and employs triple-poise balance beam with magnetic damping. From Dillon Precision Products, Inc.

**Price:** . . . . . . . . . . . . . **$43.95**

## FORSTER

**"Big Red" Powder Trickler**

Two-piece construction trickler with ballast for additional stability. From Forster Products.

**Price:** . . . . . . . . . . . . . . **$12.50**

**"D" Powder/Bullet Scale**

Die-cast aluminum base scale with epoxy hardcoat finish. "V" agate bearings at fulcrum reduce friction. Capacity to 330 grains with accuracy to $1/10$-grain and sensitivity to $1/20$-grain. From Forster Products.

**Price:** . . . . . . . . . . . . . . **$56.00**

## HORNADY

**Magnetic Scale**

Two models available, one to weigh in grains (Model M), the other in grams (Model G). Features magnetic damping; $1/10$-grain accuracy; 510-grain capacity; conversion table for grains to ounces. Weight: 3 lbs. From Hornady Mfg. Co.

**Price:** . . . . . . . . . . . . . . **$51.95**
**Price:** With trickler . . . . . . . **$56.95**

**Powder Trickler**

Features large-capacity plastic reservoir with lead counterweight to prevent tipping, brass tube and cushioned knob. Weight: $1/2$-lb. From Hornady Mfg. Co.

**Price:** . . . . . . . . . . . . . . . **$5.95**

**Scale Plus Kit**

Includes Hornady magnetic scale, powder trickler and powder funnel. Weight: $3^3/4$ lbs. From Hornady Mfg. Co.

**Price:** . . . . . . . . . . . . . . **$56.95**

## LEE

**Safety Scale**

Features 110-grain capacity; magnetically dampened approach to weight; razor blade pivot for sensitivity; sensitive and readable to $^{1}/_{20}$-grain; tough phenolic resin beam. From Lee Precision, Inc.

**Price:** . . . . . . . . . . . . . **$29.98**

## LYMAN

**Autoscale**

Electronic powder scale that uses optoelectronics to sense the position of the balance arm, eliminating friction-caused weighing errors. Powder is dispensed through two barrels. High-speed barrel controls rapid feeding up to 10 grains per second; final load is controlled by the slow barrel with accuracy to $+^{1}/_{20}$-grain. 9-volt transformer fits any household outlet. Designed for large grain rifle powder only. From Lyman Products Corporation.

**Price:**110V . . . . . . . . . . **$296.00**

**Price:** 220V . . . . . . . . . . **$300.00**

**Auto Powder Trickler**

Push-button operation dispenses powder evenly and consistently. Features built-in vertical and horizontal height adjustments for adapting to various scale designs. Handles all conventional ball, stick or flake powder types. Reservoir removes for cleaning. Comes in 110- and 220-volt. From Lyman Products Corporation.

**Price:** . . . . . . . . . . . . . **$37.50**

**Conversion Chart**

Ounce-to-grain metal conversion chart with adhesive backing for mounting. From Lyman Products Corporation.

**Price:** . . . . . . . . . . . . . . **$2.00**

**Electronic Scale Carry Case**

Moulded carry case for storing or transporting. Separate compartments for adaptor, powder pan and calibration weight. From Lyman Products Corporation.

**Price:** . . . . . . . . . . . . **$22.00**

**Dust Covers**

Nylon dust covers for Lyman 1000, 500, Pro 1000, Pro 500, Accuscales and Universal case trimmer. Hard see-through cover available for LE-1000 and RCBS 500-gr. scale. From Lyman Products Corporation.

**Price:** Nylon . . . . . . . . . . . **$5.00**

**Price:** Hard . . . . . . . . . . . . **$4.00**

**LE-300 Electronic Scale**

Offers 300-grain weight capacity. Converts to metric gram mode. Small and compact. From Lyman Products Corporation.

**Price:** . . . . . . . . . . . . . **166.50**

**LE-500 Electronic Scale**

Features 650-grain working capacity; auto-touch calibration; accuracy to .1 grain; grain or gram readout; compact size, $3^{1}/_{2}$ x $5^{3}/_{8}$″. Comes with powder pan, four AAA batteries and storage/carry case. From Lyman Products Corporation.

**Price:** . . . . . . . . . . . . . **$183.25**

**LE-1000 Electronic Scale**

Offers 1,000-grain weight capacity with digital display. Converts to metric (gram) mode. Compact frame for storability and transportability. Powered by AC power adaptor or 9-volt battery. Calibration weight and dust cover included along with power adaptor. Optional carrying case available. 220-volt version for same price. From Lyman Products Corporation.

**Price:** . . . . . . . . . . . . . **$259.95**

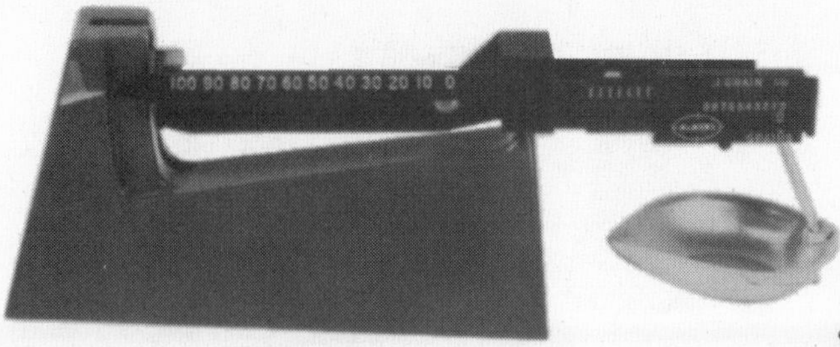

Lee Safety Scale

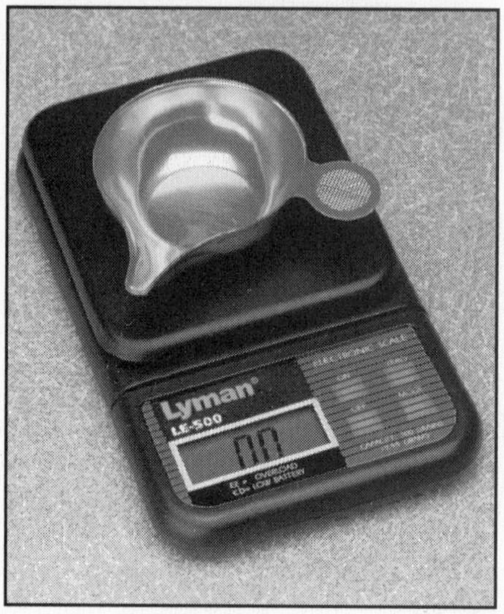

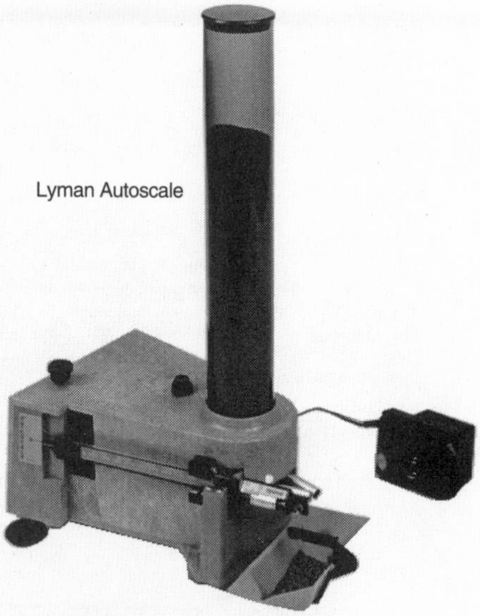

Lyman Autoscale

Lyman LE-500 Scale

Lyman LE-1000 Electronic Scale

Lyman LE-300

Lyman Auto Powder Trickler

## LYMAN

**Model 500 Powder Scale**

Provides 505-grain capacity and accuracy to 1/10-grain. Features positive pan positioning and magnetic damping. Also available in 32-gram capacity metric model. Dust cover and conversion chart available separately. Weight: 2 lbs. From Lyman Products Corporation.

**Price:** . . . . . . . . . . . . . **$63.25**
**Price:** Metric scale . . . . . . . **$75.00**

**Model 1000 Scale**

Large capacity scale holds up to 1,005 grains and is accurate to 1/10-grain. Features magnetic damping, precision ground knife edge on agate bearings and positive pan positioning. Comes with conversion table and dust cover. From Lyman Products Corporation.

**Price:** . . . . . . . . . . . . . **$92.95**

**Powder Dribbler**

Features large powder reservoir and tip-free base. From Lyman Products Corporation.

**Price:** . . . . . . . . . . . . . **$10.25**

**Pro 500**

Features high impact styrene base with built-in compartment for storage of check weights; large leveling wheel; large damper for fast zeroing; improved scale pan platform; 505-gr. capacity; accuracy to 1/10-grain. Weight: 12 oz. From Lyman Products Corporation.

**Price:** . . . . . . . . . . . . . **$39.95**

**Pro 1000**

Features high impact styrene base with built-in compartment for counter weight; large leveling wheel; large damper for fast zeroing; improved scale pan platform; 1005-gr. capacity; accuracy to 1/10-grain. Weight: 1 lb. From Lyman Products Corporation.

**Price:** . . . . . . . . . . . . . **$56.00**

**Scale Weight Check Set**

To check scale accuracy. Deluxe 10-piece set has 210.5 grains total weight. Shooters weight set totals 60.5 grains. From Lyman Products Corporation.

**Price:** Deluxe set . . . . . . . . **$26.50**
**Price:** Shooters set . . . . . . . **$19.00**

## PACT

**BBK Scale**

Features 750-grain, 50-gram capacity for powder or bullet weighing; accuracy to .1-grain to 300 grains, .2-grain from 300 to 750 grains. Includes two precision check weights, powder pan and one 9-volt battery. From PACT.

**Price:** . . . . . . . . . . . . . **$89.99**
**Price:** Carry case . . . . . . . . **$14.99**

**Electronic Scale**

Features 750-grain/50-gram working capacity; auto-touch calibration; accuracy to .1-grain up to 300 grains, .2-grain from 300 to 750 grains. Comes with powder pan, one 9-volt battery and two precision check weights. From Midway Arms, Inc.

**Price:** . . . . . . . . . . . . . **$89.99**

**Digital Precision Powder Dispenser**

Delivers exact powder charges to PACT digital scale with simple keyboard charge entry. Infrared data port allows communications between dispenser and scale for exact calibration. From PACT.

**Price:** . . . . . . . . . . . . . **$179.99**

**Digital Scale**

Features 1500-gr. or 100-gram capacity for powder or bullet weighing; accuracy to .1-gr.; automatic error detection software; large LCD readout. Comes with two precision calibration weights and AC adapter. Now available with infra-red data port to allow printing data and to drive a new Electronic Trickler. From PACT.

**Price:** Deluxe set . . . . . . . . **$149.99**
**Price:** Powder pan . . . . . . . . **$3.99**
**Price:** Storage case . . . . . . . **$16.99**
**Price:** Infra-Red Data Port . . . . **$25.00**

## RCBS

**5-0-2 Scale**

505-grain capacity single-beam scale with die cast metal base. Features two-poise design: large poise reads up to 500 grains in 5-grain increments; the small poise to 5 grains in 0.1-grain increments. Magnetic damping system works on force-field principle so beam stops with minimal pointer swing. Weight: 1 1/2 lbs. From RCBS.

**Price:** . . . . . . . . . . . . . **$53.25**
**Price:** Scale cover . . . . . . . . **$6.13**

**5-0-5 Powder Scale**

The 5-0-5 features a three-poise system. Calibrations on left side of beam are in 10-grain increments; two poises on right side adjust in 1- and 0.1-grain increments. Scale is magnetically damped; self-aligning agate bearings support hardened steel beam pivots with a guaranteed sensitivity of 1/10-grain. Capacity is 511 grains. Ounce-to-grain conversion table on the base for shotgun reloaders. Available in metric. Weight: 1 1/2 lbs. From RCBS.

**Price:** . . . . . . . . . . . . . **$72.50**
**Price:** Metric . . . . . . . . . . **$87.13**
**Price:** Scale cover . . . . . . . . **$6.13**

**304 Powder Scale**

Direct-dial powder charges to 0.1-grain. Front beam graduated in 10-grain increments to 100 grains; back beam in 100-grain increments to 1,000 grains. Features two poises, hardened steel knives, agate bearings, magnetic damping, oversized aluminum pan and adjustable powder trickler stand. Capacity, 1,110 grains. From RCBS.

**Price:** . . . . . . . . . . . . . **$348.75**

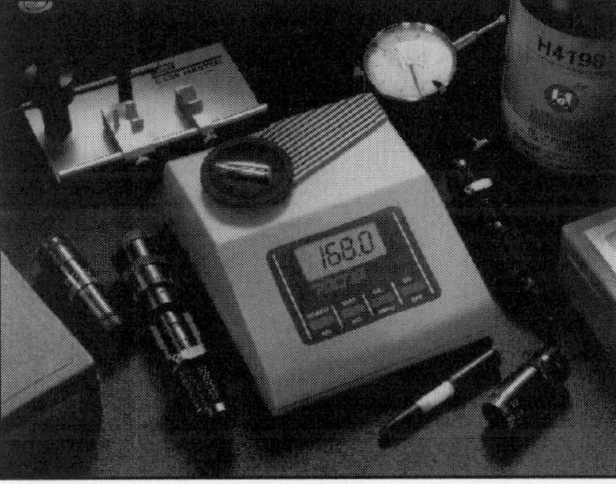


PACT Digital Scale

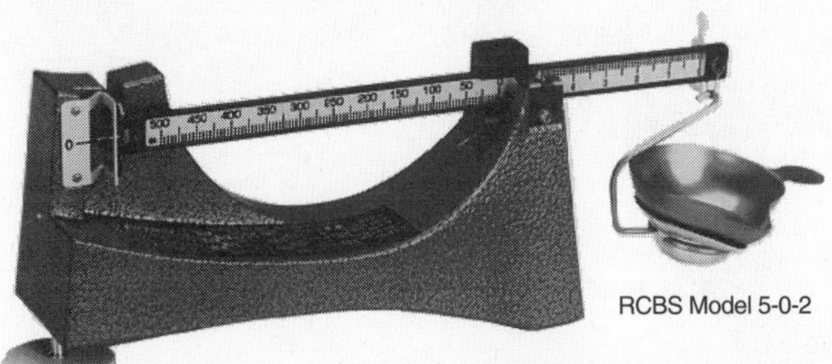

RCBS Model 5-0-2

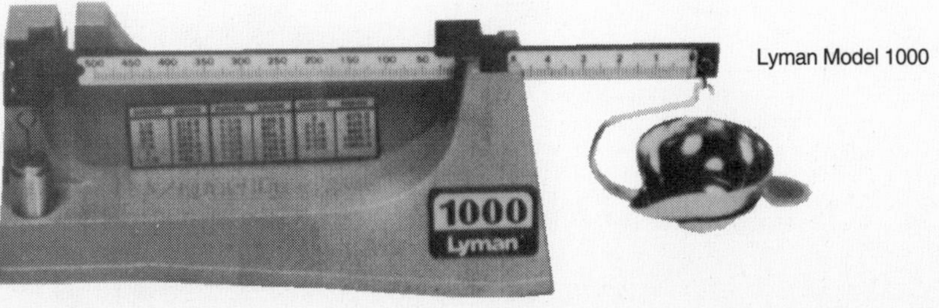


Lyman Model 1000

POWDER TOOLS/Scales & Accessories

## RCBS

### 10-10 Powder Scale

Features a lockable micrometer poise for settings of 0.1 to 10 grains; approach-to-weight system to help avoid overloads; magnetic damping; non-stick/non-spill aluminum pan; self-aligning agate bearings; hardened steel pivot knives and plastic cover. Capacity is 1,010 grains. Attachment weight is included. From RCBS.

**Price:** . . . . . . . . . . . . . **$115.13**

### Partner Digital Scale

Compact, lightweight design featuring 750-grain capacity; 0.1-grain accuracy from 0-350 grains, 0.2-grain from 350-750 grains; four-digit LED readout; measures in grams or grains. Comes with 9-volt battery. From RCBS.

**Price:** . . . . . . . . . . . . . **$146.25**

### PowderMaster Electronic Trickler

Features wireless infrared data transfer system to calibrate trickler with RCBS Powder Pro digital scale; rubber push-button charge weight data entry; dual feed augers; accuracy to 0.1-grain; clear plastic powder reservoir; specail hopper design to eleminate static and powder bridging. From RCBS.

**Price:** . . . . . . . . . . . . . **$214.00**

### Powder Pro Electronic Scale

Four digit LCD readout scale that features weight readout in .1-gr. increments up to 999.9 grains and in 1-gr. increments from 1000 to 1500 grs. Measures in grams or grains; pushbutton automatic zeroing. Compact design with recessed platform designed to accommodate trickler. Comes with scale pan, two calabration weights and AC transformer.

**Price:** 110 . . . . . . . . . . **$203.38**
**Price:** 220 . . . . . . . . . . **$209.63**

### Powder Trickler

All-metal trickler with knurled plastic knob. Wide base to prevent tipping. From RCBS.

**Price:** . . . . . . . . . . . . . **$11.25**

### RangeMaster Electronic Scale

Featues laboratory grade 4" stainless steel platen; extra large LCD display; programmable battery shut-off; 1500-grain capacity; 0.1-grain accuracy; low battery indicator; non-stick, non-spill aluminum pan. Operates on AC power or single 9-volt battery. From RCBS.

**Price:** 120 . . . . . . . . . . **$220.38**
**Price:** 220, 240 . . . . . . . . **$264.88**

### Scale Check Weights

For testing the accuracy of scale read-outs. Comes as standard set of 60.5 grains for powder charges (2x20, 1x10, 1x5, 2x2, 1x1 and 1x.5); or deluxe set of 510.5 grains for bullets, cases and powder (1x200, 2x100, 1x50, 2x20, 1x10, 1x5, 2x2, 1x1, 1x.5, 1 forceps). From RCBS.

**Price:** Standard . . . . . . . . **$19.38**
**Price:** Deluxe . . . . . . . . . **$36.75**

RCBS Powder Pro

RCBS PowderMaster

RCBS RangeMaster

RCBS Partner

Redding Model No. RS-1

## REDDING

### Model No. 2 Powder/Bullet Scale

Features magnetic dampened beam swing; hardened and ground knife edges that ride in milled stainless steel bearing seats; 505-grain capacity; accuracy to 1/10-grain; pour spout pan; two counterpoise system; 1/10-grain over/under graduations. From Redding Reloading Equipment.

**Price:** . . . . . . . . . . . . . **$75.00**

### No. 5 Powder Trickler

Solid all-metal trickler with metal tube and knurled knob. Features low center of gravity for stability. Weight: 1-lb. From Redding Reloading Equipment.

**Price:** . . . . . . . . . . . . . **$19.80**

### Model No. RS-1 Powder/Bullet Scale

Two counterpoise system with 1/10-grain over/under graduations and sensitive to less than 1/20-grain. Capacity for 380 grains and comes with pour spout pan. From Redding Reloading Equipment.

**Price:** . . . . . . . . . . . . . **$49.50**

## VIBRASHINE

### Electric Powder Trickler

Features clear dispensing tube; push button switch; adjustable height and position on dispensing tube. Handles all conventional ball, stick or flake powders. From VibraShine, Inc.

**Price:** . . . . . . . . . . . . . **$24.95**

## BONANZA

**Bench Rest Powder Measure**

Features high carbon precision cast body and charge arm. Working surfaces designed to automatically compensate for dimensional changes due to wear. Powder is metered from the charge arm to minimize charge variation and powder shearing. Throws charges of 2½ grains Bullseye to 95 grains 4320 without use of extra drums. Vernier scale located on charge arm permits minute changes in capacity. Small outlet in hopper serves as built-in baffle, and hopper cover can serve as primer turner. Two drop tubes for large and small capacity cases supplied with measure. Powder removal from hopper is done directly through charge arm into powder container. Mounts to bench or can be used with measure stand. Long drop tube also available. Weight: 3½ lbs. From Forster Products.

**Price:** . . . . . . . . . . . . . **$107.00**
**Price:** Measure stand . . . . . . . **$23.40**
**Price:** Long drop tube . . . . . . **$16.50**

**Bulls-Eye Pistol Powder Measure**

Machined steel body with hard brass fixed-charge rotors. Rotors drilled to measure Hercules Bullseye powder in set grain weights (2.5, 2.7, 3.0, 3.5, 4.0, 4.5, 5.0, 5.3, 5.5, 6.0, 6.5, 7.0, 7.5, 8.4). Blank rotors with pre-drilled pilot hole available for customer alteration. Comes with quick detachable bracket for use on bench or as hand-held charger. Rotor not included. Weight: 1½ lbs. From Forster Products.

**Price:** . . . . . . . . . . . . . **$27.70**
**Price:** Rotor . . . . . . . . . . . **$10.00**

## BRUNO

**Powder Measure**

Made on CNC equipment; features body of non-magnetic stainless steel with bearing and bronze inserts. Culver-type clicks. Precision machined to exacting tolerances. Powder measure comes complete with pill bottles, adapter and drop tube. From Bruno Shooters Supply.

**Price:** . . . . . . . . . . . . . **$279.99**

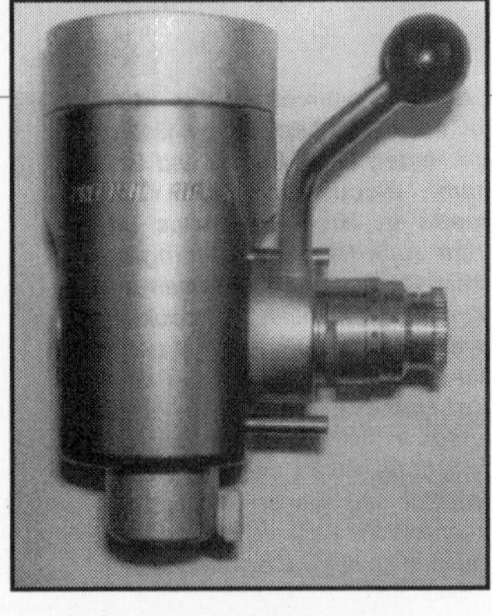

Bruno Powder Measure

Harrell's "Culver" Type Powder Measure

Harrell's Scheutzen Pistol Measure

## C-H/4-D

**#502 Micrometer Measure**

Aluminium cast non-sparking body; polished steel drum designed for right- or left-hand use; front or back micrometer positioning; up or down stroke powder charge drop. Powder hopper holds approximately ½-lb. powder; optional 10″ production hopper holds one pound. Micrometer adjusts up to 25 grains for more dense pistol powders and up to 100 grains for rifle. Base threaded 7/8-14 to fit any standard press or stand. Also available as pistol/rifle combo. From C-H Tool & Die/4-D Custom Die.

**Price:** . . . . . . . . . . . . . **$58.85**
**Price:** Combo, pistol/rifle . . . . . **$75.85**
**Price:** 10″ production hopper . . . . **$7.15**
**Price:** Micrometer . . . . . . . . **$17.55**

**Pushbutton Powder Measure**

Can be used with any single-station or turret press. Bells and expands case as it dispenses. Seventeen bushings available for over 215 powder/load combinations. Comes with or without hollow expander. Powder bushing not included. From C-H Tool & Die/4-D Custom Die.

**Price:** With expander . . . . . . **$43.45**
**Price:** Bushing . . . . . . . . . . **$3.30**

## HARRELL'S

**"Culver" Type Measure**

Precision hand-tooled measure made to exacting tolerances. From Harrell's Precision.

**Price:** . . . . . . . . . . . . . **$200.00**
**Price:** Bottles . . . . . . . . . . **$5.00**
**Price:** Extra drop tubes . . . . . . **$3.00**

**Schuetzen Pistol Measure**

Designed specifically for throwing small charges from 2 to 25 grains. Each click is .03-grain. From Harrell's Precision.

**Price:** . . . . . . . . . . . . . **$200.00**

### C-H/4-D AUTO CHAMP & 444-X PUSHBUTTON POWDER MEASURE BUSHING CHART

| Bushing | Bullseye | Red Dot | 700X | Unique | 2400 | 4227 | Herco | H-110 | 230 | 630 | 4756 | 296 | 7625 | 231 | HP38 |
|---|---|---|---|---|---|---|---|---|---|---|---|---|---|---|---|
| 1 | 2.4 | NR | 0.9 | NR | NR | NR | NR | NR | 2.1 | 4.2 | NR | NR | NR | 3.2 | 2.7 |
| 2 | 2.6 | NR | 1.0 | NR | NR | NR | NR | 4.0 | 2.6 | 4.5 | NR | NR | NR | 3.5 | 3.1 |
| 3 | 2.7 | 1.0 | 1.1 | NR | 4.0 | NR | NR | 4.5 | 2.9 | 4.6 | NR | NR | NR | 3.6 | 3.2 |
| 4 | 3.0 | 1.2 | 1.2 | NR | 4.4 | NR | NR | 5.1 | 3.1 | 5.0 | NR | NR | NR | 3.8 | NR |
| 5 | 3.5 | 1.5 | 1.5 | NR | 4.8 | NR | NR | 5.5 | 3.6 | 5.5 | 3.0 | NR | 3.2 | 4.1 | 3.4 |
| 6 | 3.8 | 1.8 | 2.4 | NR | 5.1 | NR | NR | 6.0 | 3.9 | 5.9 | 3.3 | NR | 3.7 | 4.4 | 4.0 |
| 7 | 5.0 | 3.0 | 3.5 | 4.0 | 6.6 | 6.6 | 4.2 | 7.8 | 5.1 | 7.8 | 4.5 | NR | 4.6 | 5.4 | NR |
| 8 | 5.9 | 4.2 | 4.9 | 5.5 | 8.6 | 8.5 | 5.4 | 10.2 | 6.5 | 10.2 | 5.9 | 10.0 | 6.3 | 7.0 | NR |
| 9 | 7.0 | 5.0 | 6.2 | 6.7 | 10.5 | 10.2 | 6.7 | 12.2 | 8.0 | 12.0 | 7.0 | 12.0 | 7.2 | 8.4 | NR |
| 10 | 8.2 | 6.2 | 7.0 | 7.8 | 12.5 | 12.3 | 7.8 | 14.2 | 9.7 | 14.2 | 8.1 | 14.0 | 8.7 | 10.0 | NR |
| 11 | 9.3 | 6.7 | 7.7 | 8.9 | 14.0 | 13.6 | 9.0 | 16.2 | 11.0 | 16.3 | 9.1 | 15.9 | 9.8 | 11.5 | NR |
| 12 | 10.8 | 7.9 | 9.0 | 10.3 | 16.7 | 15.6 | 10.0 | 18.7 | NR | 18.7 | 10.4 | 18.5 | 11.4 | 13.3 | NR |
| 13 | 11.5 | 8.5 | 10.0 | 11.0 | 17.5 | 17.0 | 11.0 | 20.0 | NR | 20.0 | 11.1 | 19.7 | 12.0 | NR | NR |
| 14 | 12.3 | 9.3 | 10.5 | 11.7 | 18.9 | 18.3 | 11.9 | NR | NR | 22.0 | 12.0 | 21.3 | 13.0 | NR | NR |
| 15 | NR | 10.0 | 11.8 | 12.7 | 21.5 | 20.7 | 13.5 | 24.5 | NR | 24.5 | 13.8 | 24.2 | 14.7 | NR | NR |
| 16 | NR | 10.7 | 12.5 | 14.0 | 22.5 | 22.1 | 14.2 | 26.1 | NR | 26.3 | 14.7 | 25.5 | 15.6 | NR | NR |
| 17 | NR | 12.9 | 15.0 | 16.7 | 27.2 | 26.3 | 16.6 | NR | NR | 31.0 | 17.3 | 30.3 | 18.5 | NR | NR |
| No Bushing | NR | 14.9 | 18.0 | 20.5 | 32.5 | 31.7 | 20.9 | NR | NR | 37.7 | 21.3 | 37.0 | 22.6 | NR | NR |

C-H/4-D #502 Micrometer Measure

## HART

**Drop Tubes for Lyman Measures**

Drop tubes 7/32" I.D. for Lyman 12", 3" and 5" measures. Will work with any caliber from 22 to 45. From Robert W. Hart & Son, Inc.

**Price:** For 12" . . . . . . . . . . . **$7.47**
**Price:** For 3" . . . . . . . . . . . **$6.83**
**Price:** For 5" . . . . . . . . . . . **$7.30**

**Pill Bottle Adaptor**

Adaptor for Redding or Lyman powder measures to allow use of Hodgdon powder bottle or Libby pill bottle as powder reservoir. From Robert W. Hart & Son, Inc.

**Price:** For 5" . . . . . . . . . . . **$19.95**

## HOLLYWOOD

**50-Caliber Powder Measure**

Identical to standard measure except for enlarged drum hole to throw 240-280 grains powder. Features 23" transparent cylinder; 2-1/8" adapter for 3-1/2" cylinder; one 50-caliber drop tube and cylinder cover. Threaded 7/8-14 for use in standard presses; spanner lock nut allows attachment to tool head. Comes with one 50-caliber drop tube. From Hollywood Engineering.

**Price:** . . . . . . . . . . . . . **$275.00**

**Standard Powder Measure**

Ductile iron body with ground, hardened steel drum. Adjustable from 2-1/2 grains Bullseye to 93 grains 4350. Disc baffle assures constant powder pressure on metering chamber. Hard-coated conical bearing surfaces for precise cutoff. Threaded 7/8-14 to fit most presses; large lock-spanner ring secures measure to press. Comes with one drop tube (22-270 or 7mm-45), cylinder cover and powder disk. From Hollywood Engineering.

**Price:** . . . . . . . . . . . . . **$125.00**
**Price:** Drop tube . . . . . . . . **$12.00**

## HORNADY

**Deluxe Powder Measure**

Micrometer adjustable measure for rifle or pistol powders. Comes complete with two powder-drop tubes (22-30 cal. and 30-45 cal.), large capacity hopper, bench stand and lock ring. Handle can be mounted for right- or left-hand operation. Standard 7/8-14 threads for mounting on bench stand or press. Weight: 5 lbs. From Hornady Mfg. Co.

**Price:** . . . . . . . . . . . . . **$69.50**
**Price:** 17-cal. drop tube . . . . . . **$5.10**
**Price:** Extra metering assembly . . **$15.75**

**Pistol Powder Measure**

Includes five standard, high-precision, interchangeable bushings, Nos. 7, 8, 9, 11 and 13 for wide load choices. Bushings fit into sliding charge bar. Threaded 7/8-14 for stand or press mounting. Comes complete with stand and lock ring. Weight: 3 lbs. From Hornady Mfg. Co.

**Price:** . . . . . . . . . . . . . **$40.30**
**Price:** Blank bushing . . . . . . . **$4.20**

Jones Micro Measure

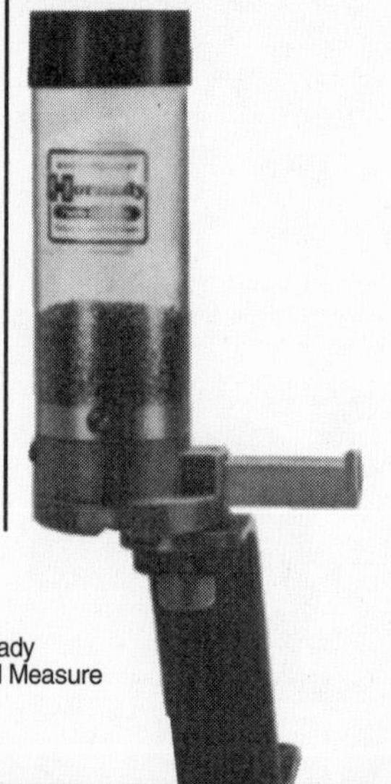



Hornady Pistol Measure

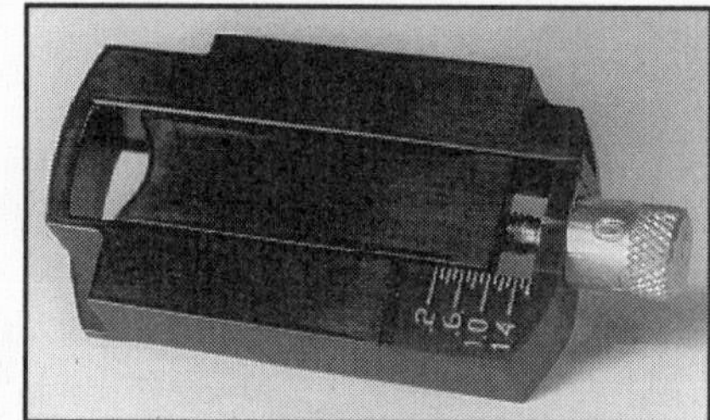



Lee Adjustable Charge Bar

### Hornady Pistol Powder Measure Bushing Chart

| Bushing | 700-X | 4227 | SR7625 | SR4756 | PB | Bullseye | 2400 | Red Dot | Unique | Herco | Blue Dot | HP38 | Trap 100 | HS5 | HS6 | HS7 | H110 | H4227 | R1 | R123 | 231 | 296 | 680 |
|---|---|---|---|---|---|---|---|---|---|---|---|---|---|---|---|---|---|---|---|---|---|---|---|
| 1 | 2.0 | NA | NA | NA | NA | 2.6 | NA | 1.7 | NA | NA | NA | 3.0 | 2.3 | 4.1 | 3.9 | 4.0 | 4.2 | 3.6 | 1.9 | NA | 3.0 | NA | NA |
| 2 | 2.1 | NA | NA | NA | NA | 2.8 | NA | 1.8 | NA | NA | NA | 3.2 | 2.5 | 4.5 | 4.2 | 4.4 | 4.5 | 3.9 | 2.0 | NA | 3.3 | NA | NA |
| 3 | 2.3 | NA | NA | NA | NA | 3.4 | NA | 2.4 | 3.4 | NA | NA | 4.0 | 3.1 | 5.6 | 5.2 | 5.5 | 5.6 | 4.9 | 2.6 | NA | 4.1 | NA | NA |
| 4 | 2.7 | NA | NA | NA | NA | 3.4 | NA | 2.4 | 3.4 | NA | NA | 4.3 | 3.4 | 6.1 | 5.8 | 6.0 | 6.1 | 5.3 | 2.9 | NA | 4.5 | NA | NA |
| 5 | 2.9 | NA | 3.1 | NA | 2.9 | 3.7 | NA | 2.6 | 3.6 | NA | NA | 4.3 | 3.4 | 6.1 | 5.8 | 6.0 | 6.1 | 5.3 | 2.9 | NA | 4.5 | NA | NA |
| 6 | 3.0 | NA | 3.5 | NA | 3.1 | 3.9 | NA | 2.7 | 3.9 | NA | NA | 4.5 | 3.6 | 6.4 | 6.0 | 6.2 | 6.4 | 5.5 | 3.1 | NA | 4.6 | NA | NA |
| 7 | 3.2 | NA | 3.6 | NA | 3.2 | 4.1 | NA | 2.8 | 4.3 | 3.6 | NA | 4.8 | 3.9 | 6.9 | 6.3 | 6.7 | 6.9 | 6.0 | 3.2 | NA | 4.8 | NA | NA |
| 8 | 3.5 | NA | 4.1 | NA | 3.3 | 4.4 | NA | 3.2 | 4.5 | 3.8 | NA | 5.0 | 4.0 | 7.4 | 7.0 | 7.3 | 7.4 | 6.5 | 3.7 | NA | 5.3 | NA | NA |
| 9 | 3.7 | NA | 4.2 | 3.7 | 3.4 | 4.5 | NA | 3.3 | 4.6 | 3.9 | NA | 5.2 | 4.2 | 7.7 | 7.4 | 7.6 | 7.7 | 6.7 | 3.8 | NA | 5.5 | NA | NA |
| 10 | 4.0 | 7.3 | 5.0 | 4.5 | 4.0 | 5.1 | NA | 3.6 | 5.3 | 4.3 | NA | 6.1 | 4.9 | 8.5 | 7.9 | 8.4 | 8.6 | 7.5 | 4.3 | NA | 6.3 | NA | NA |
| 11 | 4.3 | 7.5 | 5.1 | 4.6 | 4.6 | 5.2 | 7.3 | 3.7 | 5.4 | 4.5 | NA | 6.4 | 5.1 | 8.9 | 8.2 | 8.8 | 9.0 | 7.7 | 4.5 | NA | 6.4 | NA | 8.8 |
| 12 | 4.6 | 8.0 | 5.5 | 4.8 | 4.8 | NA | 7.9 | 3.9 | 5.8 | 4.8 | NA | 6.8 | 5.3 | 9.4 | 9.0 | 9.3 | 9.5 | 8.2 | 4.8 | NA | 6.9 | NA | 9.5 |
| 13 | 5.0 | 8.8 | 6.0 | 5.6 | 5.3 | NA | 8.7 | 4.4 | 6.5 | 5.3 | NA | 7.6 | 5.8 | 10.3 | 9.7 | 10.1 | 10.4 | 9.0 | 5.3 | NA | 7.6 | 10.3 | 10.5 |
| 14 | 5.5 | 9.4 | 6.4 | 6.0 | 5.8 | NA | 9.3 | 4.7 | 6.8 | 5.7 | NA | 8.1 | 6.4 | 11.1 | 10.5 | 11.0 | 11.1 | 9.6 | 5.7 | NA | 8.1 | 11.0 | 11.2 |
| 15 | 5.8 | 9.9 | 6.8 | 6.4 | 6.0 | NA | 9.8 | 4.9 | 7.2 | 5.9 | NA | 8.5 | 6.7 | 11.8 | 11.1 | 11.6 | 11.8 | 10.2 | 6.0 | NA | 8.5 | 11.6 | 11.9 |
| 16 | 6.1 | 10.3 | 7.1 | 6.7 | 6.4 | NA | 10.3 | 5.2 | 7.5 | 6.2 | 8.9 | 8.9 | 7.0 | 12.4 | 11.5 | 12.3 | 12.4 | 10.7 | NA | NA | 8.9 | 12.2 | 12.6 |
| 17 | 6.5 | 11.5 | 7.9 | 7.6 | 7.0 | NA | 11.4 | 5.8 | 8.4 | 6.8 | 9.7 | 9.8 | 7.7 | 13.7 | 12.8 | 13.5 | 13.7 | 11.8 | NA | NA | 9.9 | 13.6 | 13.8 |
| 18 | NA | 12.1 | 8.1 | 7.8 | 7.3 | NA | 12.0 | 6.1 | 8.7 | 7.3 | 10.1 | 10.2 | 8.0 | 14.1 | 13.3 | 13.9 | 14.0 | 12.2 | NA | 10.1 | NA | 14.0 | 14.3 |
| 19 | NA | 12.3 | 8.6 | 8.3 | 7.6 | NA | 12.7 | 6.3 | 9.2 | 7.7 | 10.8 | 10.6 | 8.4 | 15.0 | 13.9 | 14.6 | 14.9 | 12.9 | NA | 10.8 | NA | 14.7 | 15.1 |
| 20 | NA | 13.4 | 9.1 | 8.8 | 8.0 | NA | 13.4 | 6.7 | 9.7 | 8.1 | 11.4 | 11.4 | 8.8 | 15.7 | 14.9 | 15.6 | 15.6 | 13.6 | NA | 11.5 | NA | 15.6 | 16.0 |
| 21 | NA | 14.7 | 9.9 | 9.7 | 8.9 | NA | 14.7 | 7.4 | 10.6 | 8.7 | 12.5 | 12.6 | 9.7 | 17.6 | 16.2 | 17.1 | 17.5 | 15.1 | NA | 12.5 | NA | 17.1 | 17.5 |
| 22 | NA | 15.7 | 10.4 | 10.2 | 9.4 | NA | 15.5 | 7.7 | 11.4 | 9.5 | 13.2 | 13.2 | 10.4 | 18.3 | 17.0 | 17.7 | 17.9 | 15.9 | NA | 13.2 | NA | 17.9 | 18.3 |

## JONES

**Custom Products Micro Measure**

Tool steel body 100% machined assuring no rough surfaces. Features micrometer-adjustable brass drum with capacity of 16 to 114 grains and click value of approximately .1-grain; cutting edges designed to slice through most difficult of powders; bottle/adaptor assembly allows changing powders by changing bottles; bottom cutout and plug on reservoir makes it possible to return powder to reservoir without removing bottle from adaptor; baffle assures constant volume of powder on measure drum at all times. Can be mounted directly to bench or attached to powder measure stand. Optional 7/8-14 clamp adaptor or adaptor/baffle for Lyman 55 and other measures available. Comes complete with two 3″ drop tubes and one powder bottle. Weight: 5 lbs. From Neil Jones Custom Products.

**Price:** . . . . . . . . . . . . . **$279.00**
**Price:** Adaptor/baffle Lyman 55 . . **$20.00**
**Price:** Adaptor/baffle other measures **$20.00**
**Price:** Powder bottle . . . . . . . **$6.00**
**Price:** Padded cover . . . . . . . **$20.00**
**Price:** Drop tubes, 6″ . . . . . . . **$8.00**
**Price:** Drop tubes, 3″ . . . . . . . **$6.00**
**Price:** 7/8-14 clamp adap tor . . . **$5.00**

## LEE

**Adjustable Charge Bar**

Adjusts between .28 and 1.6cc. Zero backlash micrometer made of nylon with solid brass. From Lee Precision, Inc.

**Price:** . . . . . . . . . . . . . . **$9.98**

**Auto-Disk Powder Measure**

Fixed-capacity measure. Cast body with polycarbonate see-through hopper. Cartridge case actuates measure while case neck is being flared. Designed for use with Lee powder-through-expanding die. Six-cavity glass-reinforced plastic powder disks. Comes with all four disks for 24 charge weights. From Lee Precision, Inc.

**Price:** . . . . . . . . . . . . . **$27.98**

**Auto-Disk Pull Back Lever**

For Lee Pro-1000 and Load-Master to eliminate powder binding and reduce chance of missed or double charges. From Lee Precision, Inc.

**Price:** . . . . . . . . . . . . . . **$2.98**

**Deluxe Auto-Disk Measure**

Fixed-capacity measure. Chrome-plated casting with tough polycarbonate hopper and machined metering surfaces. Works best with ball powders. Designed for use with Lee powder-through-expanding die. Comes with all four disks for 24 charge weights. From Lee Precision, Inc.

**Price:** . . . . . . . . . . . . . **$35.98**

**Double Disk Kit**

Conversion unit designed for standard, deluxe and Safety measures. Allows two disk stacking for fine charge adjustments up or down to .1-grain with different combinations of disks. Complete listing of disk combinations, four extra disks screws and risers included. From Lee Precision, Inc.

**Price:** . . . . . . . . . . . . . **$14.98**

**Micro Disk**

For Auto-Disk powder measure. Designed to measure small charges below range of standard disks. Six cavities range from 1.1 to 2.5 grains of Bullseye. From Lee Precision, Inc.

**Price:** . . . . . . . . . . . . . . **$9.98**

## LEE

**Perfect Powder Measure**

Drum-type micro-adjustable measure adaptable to Lee Pro-1000 and Load-Master progressive presses. Features soft elastomer wiper to strike off metering chamber not cut the powder; a self-lubricating nylon cone-shaped drum adjusts to zero clearance; micrometer adjuster in cubic centimeters with O-ring lock; positive powder shutoff for hopper removal or stoppage of flow; tapered drop tube. Charges of from 2 grains to over 100 grains can be thrown. Optional Universal charging die makes measure case-actuated for automation. Adaptors fit most all cartridges. Steel measure stand included. From Lee Precision, Inc.

**Price:** . . . . . . . . . . . . . . **$29.98**

**Powder Measure Kit**

Contains fifteen graduated and proportioned powder dippers. Slide card lists number of grains of every powder type each measure will dispense. From Lee Precision, Inc.

**Price:** . . . . . . . . . . . . . . . **$8.98**

Lee Perfect Measure

Lee Micro Disk

## LEE

**Pro Auto-Disk**

New design with elastomer wiper and teflon-coated metal casting to prevent powder cutting and help eliminate powder leakage. Large capacity hopper with shut-off valve attaches with brass thumb nuts for disk change ease. The swivel adaptor allows die set transfer without rotation of the measure and ensures precise postioning with firm clamps. Comes with adjustable charge bar. From Lee Precision, Inc.

**Price:** . . . . . . . . . . . . . **$45.00**

**Pro Disk Update Kit**

To update the Lee Auto-Disk to Pro Auto-Disk. Includes oversize hopper and valve assembly with elastomer wiper, swivel adaptor, pullback lever, chain and attachments, solid knurled thumb nuts. From Lee Precision, Inc.

**Price:** . . . . . . . . . . . . . **$19.98**

**Safety Disk Powder Measure**

Fixed-capacity measure. Lever-operated with built-in powder baffle and see-through drop tube. Includes measure stand, four, six-cavity disks, and mounting screws. From Lee Precision, Inc.

**Price:** . . . . . . . . . . . . . **$27.98**

**Swivel Adaptor**

Screw attaches to die for transfer of Pro Disk measure between die sets with precise positioning. From Lee Precision, Inc.

**Price:** . . . . . . . . . . . . . . **$5.98**

Lee Swivel Adaptor

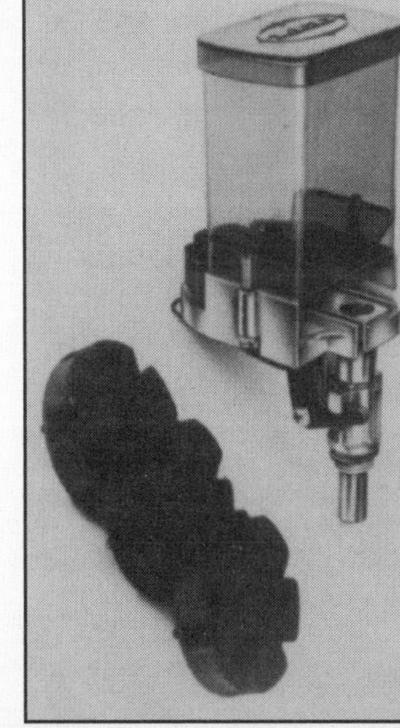

Lee Auto-Disk

## LYMAN

### AccuMeasure and Rotor Set

Small-capacity measure designed for pistol and small-caliber rifle cases. Features 15 interchangeable brass rotors for over 700 load combinations. Comes with three of the most popular rotors. Additional 12 available separately. From Lyman Products Corporation.

**Price:** . . . . . . . . . . . . . . **$35.00**
**Price:** 12 additional rotors . . . . **$46.00**
**Price:** Single rotor . . . . . . . . **$7.25**

### No. 55 Powder Measure

Features three-slide micrometer adjustable cavity with extra-fine adjustments of width and depth for consistent charges; 2400-grain capacity reservoir; attached knocker to assure complete charge; bench or press mountable. Includes 7/8-14 thread adapter for press or stand mounting. Optional 7,000-grain reservoir available. Weight: 2 lbs., 10 oz. From Lyman Products Corporation.

**Price:** . . . . . . . . . . . . . . **$71.50**
**Price:** 7,000-grain reservoir . . . . **$8.75**

### Powder Measure Stand

Bench mountable stand threaded 7/8-14 for any standard threaded powder measure. Weight: 3 lbs., 6 oz. From Lyman Products Corporation.

**Price:** . . . . . . . . . . . . . . **$17.95**

## RCBS

### Little Dandy Pistol Powder Measure

Designed for pistol shooters and small-caliber rifle shooters. Twenty-eight interchangeable, fixed-charge powder rotors available to load up to 400 combinations. No re-adjustment after rotor changeover. Can be used hand-held, bench-mounted or mounted to powder measure stand. From RCBS.

**Price:** . . . . . . . . . . . . . . **$27.50**
**Price:** Powder rotor . . . . . . . . **$8.00**
**Price:** Measure cover . . . . . . . **$7.13**

### Little Dandy Rotor Knob

High-strength aluminum, knurled outer edge knob attaches to Little Dandy rotor with a setscrew. Makes the handle easier to turn. From RCBS.

**Price:** . . . . . . . . . . . . . . **$2.75**

### Powder Measure Stand

Elevates any powder measure with standard 7/8-14 thread for positioning powder scale pan or case in a loading block under the drop tube. Bolts to loading bench or table. From RCBS.

**Price:** . . . . . . . . . . . . . . **$20.63**

## RCBS

### Uniflow Powder Measure

Features large capacity 5″ acrylic powder hopper, drop tubes for 22- to 45-caliber, precision-ground measuring cylinder surface and honed main casting. Adjustable cylinder for throwing charges from 0.5-grain Bullseye to 110 grains of 4350. Comes with stand plate for bolting to loading bench. 17-caliber drop tube optional. From RCBS.

**Price:** . . . . . . . . . . . . . . **$72.50**
**Price:** 17-cal. drop tube . . . . . . **$6.13**
**Price:** Measure cover . . . . . . . **$7.13**

### Uniflow Powder Baffle

Enhances charge uniformity and consistency with Uniflow powder measure. From RCBS.

**Price:** . . . . . . . . . . . . . . **$5.25**

### UPM Micrometer Adjustment Screw

Install on the RCBS Uniflow Powder Measure and record precise settings for powder charges. Dial in same number for that charge each time. To install, replace the Uniflow's standard metering screw. Available in large or small size. From RCBS.

**Price:** . . . . . . . . . . . . . . **$33.25**

## RCBS LITTLE DANDY ROTOR CHARGE TABLE

| Rotor # | 00 | 0 | 01 | 02 | 03 | 04 | 05 | 06 | 07 | 08 | 09 | 10 | 11 | 12 | 13 | 14 | 15 | 16 | 17 | 18 | 19 | 20 | 21 | 22 | 23 | 24 | 25 | 26 |
|---|---|---|---|---|---|---|---|---|---|---|---|---|---|---|---|---|---|---|---|---|---|---|---|---|---|---|---|---|
| Bullseye | 1.7 | 2.2 | 2.5 | 2.7 | 3.0 | 3.2 | 3.5 | 3.7 | 4.0 | 4.5 | 5.0 | 5.5 | 6.0 | 6.5 | 7.2 | 7.8 | 8.4 | 9.0 | 9.7 | NR | NR | NR | NR | NR | NR | NR | NR | NR |
| 231 | NR | NR | 2.7 | 3.0 | 3.3 | 3.6 | 3.9 | 4.2 | 4.5 | 5.0 | 5.6 | 6.2 | 6.8 | 7.2 | 7.9 | 8.6 | 9.3 | 10.0 | 10.6 | 11.3 | 12.1 | NR | NR | NR | NR | NR | NR | NR |
| HP38 | NR | NR | 2.8 | 3.0 | 3.4 | 3.6 | 4.0 | 4.2 | 4.5 | 5.1 | 5.5 | 6.2 | 6.8 | 7.5 | 7.9 | 8.8 | 9.4 | 10.3 | 10.9 | 11.7 | 12.3 | NR | NR | NR | NR | NR | NR | NR |
| Red Dot | NR | NR | 1.7 | 1.9 | 2.2 | 2.3 | 2.5 | 2.6 | 2.9 | 3.2 | 3.6 | 4.0 | 4.3 | 4.7 | 5.1 | 5.5 | 6.0 | 6.5 | 6.9 | 7.4 | 7.8 | 8.3 | 8.7 | 9.1 | NR | NR | NR | NR |
| 700-X | NR | NR | 2.0 | 2.2 | 2.4 | 2.6 | 2.8 | 3.0 | 3.2 | 3.6 | 4.0 | 4.4 | 4.8 | 5.1 | 5.7 | 6.2 | 6.8 | 7.3 | 7.7 | 8.2 | 8.7 | 9.2 | NR | NR | NR | NR | NR | NR |
| Green Dot | NR | NR | 1.9 | 2.1 | 2.3 | 2.5 | 2.8 | 3.0 | 3.1 | 3.5 | 3.9 | 4.4 | 4.8 | 5.1 | 5.5 | 6.1 | 6.6 | 7.0 | 7.5 | 8.0 | 8.8 | 8.9 | 9.6 | 10.0 | 10.5 | 10.7 | 11.4 | NR |
| SR4756 | NR | NR | NR | NR | NR | NR | NR | 3.5 | 3.7 | 4.2 | 4.7 | 5.1 | 5.6 | 6.2 | 6.8 | 7.3 | 7.9 | 8.5 | 9.1 | 9.7 | 10.3 | 10.9 | 11.4 | 12.0 | 12.4 | 13.4 | 13.9 | 14.5 |
| HS-5 | NR | NR | 4.2 | 4.5 | 5.0 | 5.3 | 5.9 | 6.2 | 6.6 | 7.4 | 8.2 | 9.0 | NR | NR | NR | NR | NR | NR | NR | NR | NR | NR | NR | NR | NR | NR | NR | NR |
| Unique | NR | NR | 2.3 | 2.5 | 2.8 | 3.0 | 3.3 | 3.5 | 3.7 | 4.2 | 4.7 | 5.2 | 5.7 | 6.0 | 6.6 | 7.2 | 7.8 | 8.4 | 9.0 | 9.5 | 10.1 | 10.7 | 11.3 | 11.8 | 12.4 | 13.1 | NR | NR |
| SR7625 | NR | NR | 2.5 | 2.7 | 3.0 | 3.2 | 3.5 | 3.8 | 4.0 | 4.5 | 5.0 | 5.5 | 6.0 | 6.5 | 7.2 | 7.7 | 8.3 | 9.0 | 9.6 | NR | NR | NR | NR | NR | NR | NR | NR | NR |
| HS-6 | NR | NR | NR | NR | NR | NR | 5.4 | 5.7 | 6.1 | 6.9 | 7.6 | 8.4 | 9.1 | 10.1 | 11.0 | 12.0 | 13.0 | 13.9 | 14.8 | 15.7 | 16.7 | 17.6 | NR | NR | NR | NR | NR | NR |
| HS-7 | NR | NR | NR | NR | NR | 4.9 | 5.4 | 5.7 | 6.1 | 6.8 | 7.5 | 8.3 | 9.1 | 10.1 | 11.0 | 11.9 | 12.9 | 13.9 | 14.8 | 15.8 | 16.8 | 17.7 | 18.6 | NR | NR | NR | NR | NR |
| Herco | NR | NR | NR | NR | NR | NR | 3.1 | 3.3 | 3.5 | 4.0 | 4.4 | 4.8 | 5.3 | 5.7 | 6.3 | 6.7 | 7.3 | 7.9 | 8.4 | 9.0 | 9.5 | 10.1 | 10.5 | 11.1 | 11.7 | 12.3 | 13.0 | 13.6 |
| Blue Dot | NR | NR | NR | NR | NR | NR | NR | NR | NR | NR | 5.9 | 6.5 | 7.1 | 7.7 | 8.4 | 9.1 | 9.8 | 10.6 | 11.3 | 12.0 | 12.8 | 13.5 | 14.2 | 14.9 | 15.7 | 16.6 | 17.5 | 18.3 |
| 630 | NR | NR | NR | NR | 5.0 | 5.3 | 5.8 | 6.1 | 6.5 | 7.3 | 8.1 | 8.9 | 9.7 | 10.8 | 11.7 | 12.7 | 13.7 | 14.8 | 15.8 | 16.9 | 17.9 | 18.8 | 19.8 | 20.8 | NR | NR | NR | NR |
| 2400 | NR | NR | NR | NR | NR | NR | NR | NR | NR | NR | 7.0 | 7.7 | 8.4 | 9.3 | 10.2 | 11.0 | 11.9 | 12.8 | 13.6 | 14.6 | 15.4 | 16.2 | 17.0 | 17.9 | 18.9 | 19.8 | 20.8 | 21.8 |
| H110 | NR | NR | NR | NR | NR | NR | NR | NR | NR | NR | NR | 8.9 | 9.7 | 10.7 | 11.7 | 12.6 | 13.6 | 14.6 | 15.6 | 16.6 | 17.6 | 18.5 | 19.5 | 20.5 | 21.5 | 22.5 | 23.7 | 24.8 |
| 296 | NR | NR | NR | NR | NR | NR | NR | NR | NR | NR | NR | 9.1 | 9.9 | 10.9 | 11.9 | 12.9 | 13.9 | 14.9 | 15.9 | 17.0 | 18.0 | 19.0 | 20.0 | 21.0 | 22.1 | 23.2 | 24.3 | 25.5 |
| SR4759 | NR | NR | NR | NR | NR | NR | NR | NR | NR | NR | NR | NR | NR | NR | NR | NR | NR | NR | 10.1 | 10.7 | 11.5 | 12.2 | 12.8 | 13.5 | 14.2 | 15.0 | 15.8 | 16.5 |
| IMR 4227 | NR | NR | NR | NR | NR | NR | NR | NR | NR | NR | NR | NR | NR | 9.1 | 9.9 | 10.8 | 11.6 | 12.6 | 13.3 | 14.3 | 15.1 | 16.0 | 16.8 | 17.6 | 18.6 | 19.5 | 20.5 | 21.5 |
| 680 | NR | NR | NR | NR | NR | NR | NR | NR | NR | NR | 8.2 | 9.1 | 9.9 | 10.9 | 11.9 | 12.9 | 13.9 | 14.9 | 15.9 | 16.9 | 17.9 | 18.9 | 19.9 | 20.9 | 21.9 | 23.1 | 24.2 | 25.3 |
| IMR 4198 | NR | NR | NR | NR | NR | NR | NR | NR | NR | NR | 6.5 | 7.2 | 7.9 | 8.5 | 9.4 | 10.2 | 11.0 | 12.0 | 12.7 | 13.5 | 14.4 | 15.2 | 16.1 | 16.8 | 17.8 | 18.7 | 19.6 | 20.4 |
| H322 | NR | NR | NR | NR | NR | NR | NR | NR | NR | NR | NR | NR | NR | NR | NR | NR | NR | 13.0 | 13.8 | 14.7 | 15.7 | 16.6 | 17.4 | 18.3 | 19.3 | 20.3 | 21.3 | 22.3 |
| Re-7 | NR | NR | NR | NR | NR | NR | NR | NR | NR | NR | NR | NR | NR | NR | 10.4 | 11.3 | 12.2 | 13.2 | 14.0 | 14.9 | 15.9 | 16.8 | 17.7 | 18.5 | 19.5 | 20.5 | 21.6 | 22.6 |
| AA-2 | NR | NR | 3.1 | 3.3 | 3.9 | 4.2 | 4.6 | 4.8 | 5.1 | 5.6 | 6.2 | 6.8 | 7.6 | 8.4 | 9.4 | 10.0 | 10.5 | 11.2 | 12.1 | 12.9 | 13.9 | 15.0 | 16.0 | 16.5 | 16.9 | 18.3 | 19.0 | 19.6 |
| AA-5 | NR | NR | 4.0 | 4.3 | 4.8 | 5.1 | 5.6 | 5.9 | 6.3 | 7.1 | 7.8 | 8.6 | 9.3 | 10.3 | 11.3 | 12.2 | 13.2 | 14.2 | 15.2 | 16.1 | 17.1 | 18.0 | 18.9 | 19.8 | 20.8 | 21.9 | 23.0 | 24.3 |
| AA-7 | NR | NR | 4.2 | 4.6 | 5.1 | 5.4 | 6.0 | 6.3 | 6.6 | 7.5 | 8.3 | 9.1 | 9.9 | 11.0 | 12.0 | 13.0 | 14.0 | 15.0 | 16.0 | 17.0 | 18.0 | 19.0 | 20.0 | 20.9 | 22.0 | 23.1 | 24.3 | 25.7 |
| AA-9 | NR | NR | 4.2 | 4.5 | 5.0 | 5.3 | 5.9 | 6.2 | 6.6 | 7.4 | 8.1 | 9.0 | 9.8 | 10.8 | 11.9 | 12.8 | 13.8 | 14.9 | 15.8 | 16.8 | 17.8 | 18.8 | 19.8 | 20.7 | 21.8 | 22.9 | 24.1 | 25.4 |
| Olin 473AA | NR | NR | 2.8 | 3.1 | 3.4 | 3.7 | 4.0 | 4.2 | 4.5 | 5.0 | 5.5 | 6.1 | 6.6 | 7.4 | 8.1 | 8.7 | 9.3 | 9.9 | 10.9 | 11.4 | 12.1 | 12.8 | 13.3 | 14.1 | 15.0 | 15.5 | 16.4 | 17.0 |
| Olin 452AA | NR | NR | 2.4 | 2.5 | 2.8 | 3.0 | 3.2 | 3.4 | 3.7 | 4.1 | 4.6 | 5.0 | 5.5 | 6.0 | 6.6 | 7.3 | 7.8 | 8.2 | 8.8 | 9.5 | 10.0 | 10.4 | 11.1 | 11.6 | 12.3 | 12.8 | 13.3 | 14.2 |
| Olin 540 | NR | NR | 3.9 | 4.3 | 4.7 | 5.0 | 5.6 | 5.9 | 6.2 | 7.0 | 7.7 | 8.5 | 9.2 | 10.2 | 11.1 | 12.1 | 13.0 | 14.0 | 14.9 | 15.9 | 16.8 | 17.8 | 18.9 | 19.6 | 20.7 | 21.7 | 22.7 | 23.9 |
| Olin 571 | NR | NR | 4.1 | 4.4 | 4.9 | 5.2 | 5.8 | 6.1 | 6.5 | 7.2 | 8.0 | 8.8 | 9.6 | 10.7 | 11.8 | 12.7 | 13.7 | 14.7 | 15.6 | 16.8 | 17.7 | 18.7 | 19.7 | 20.5 | 21.6 | 22.8 | 24.0 | 25.0 |

NR=No known recommended load. WARNING: The powder charge weights shown for individual rotors are to be used for general reference only. Lot to lot variations in powder density, temperature, humidity, operating techniques and manufacturing tolerances, all introduce variations in charge weights from the values listed. Each rotor-powder combination used must be checked on accurate scale to determine actual charge weight prior to loading ammunition. From RCBS.

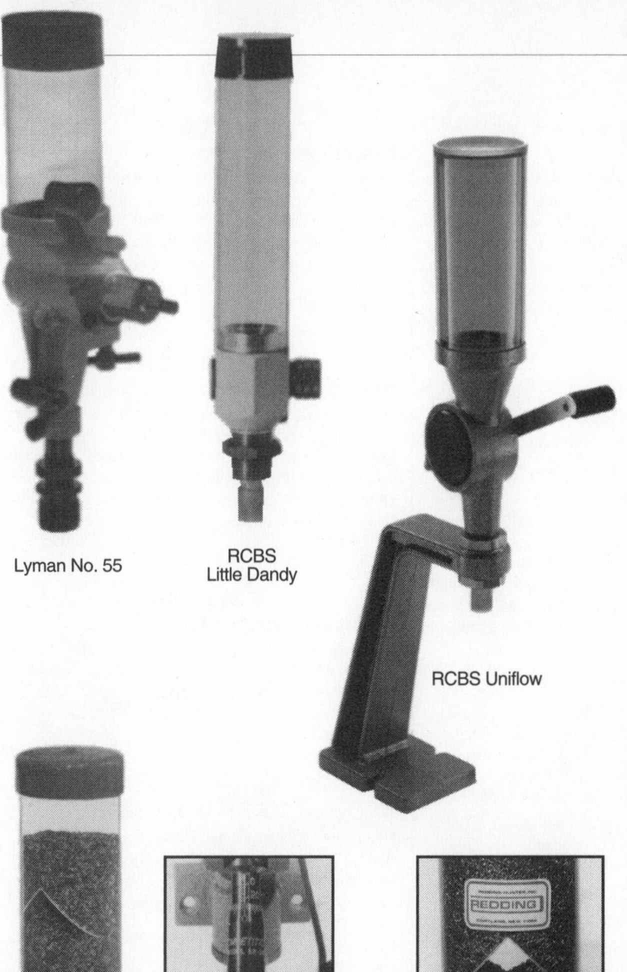

Lyman No. 55

RCBS
Little Dandy

RCBS Uniflow

RCBS Uniflow
Powder Baffle

BR-30 Zero Backlash
Micrometer

3R Powder Baffle

Redding Competition
Model BR-30

Redding Match-Grade
Model 3BR

Redding Model 3

Redding Reservoirs
on RS-6 Bench Stand

## REDDING

**Bench Stand**

For bench-top mounting all Redding powder measures or any other measure with $^{7}/_{8}$-14 threads. Stand is not threaded but fitted with lock ring for rotating measure to any desired position or for dumping of reservoir. From Redding Reloading Equipment.

**Price:** . . . . . . . . . . . . . **$27.00**

**Competition Model BR-30 Powder Measure**

Strictly a competition model with specialized drum and micrometer to limit overall charge range from low of 10 grains to maximum of about 50 grains. Has all same features of Redding Match-Grade model plus a reduction in metering cavity diameter and a change in the metering plunger shape to alleviate irregular powder settling and enhance charge uniformity. Unique rotating slightly heavier handle provides more uniform stroke. From Redding Reloading Equipment.

**Price:** . . . . . . . . . . . . . **$180.00**

**Master Model 3 Powder Measure**

Precision machined cast iron frame with hand-honed fit between frame and hard surfaced drum. Features micrometer metering chamber; cast mounting bracket for shelf or bench attachment; large capacity clear powder reservoir; see-through drop tube for all calibers 22 through 50; threaded to fit measure stand. Comes with Universal metering chamber or with both Universal and pistol chambers. From Redding Reloading Equipment.

**Price:** With Universal chamber . . **$120.00**
**Price:** Pistol chamber . . . . . . **$33.00**
**Price:** Measure with both chambers **$144.00**

**Match-Grade Model 3R Powder Measure**

Has all the features of Redding's Master Model 3 measure plus the match-grade conversion features. Match-grade features include micrometer metering chamber; zero backlash micrometer which takes up minute tolerances in screw thread so parts can't work loose and are self-adjusting; powder baffle positioned above metering chamber; positive lock system to allow micrometer setting changes without movement of micrometer body. Two metering chambers available. Universal chamber with charge range of approximately 5 to 100 grains; pistol metering chamber with range of 0 to 10 grains. Measure also offered with both chambers. From Redding Reloading Equipment.

**Price:** Measure with
Universal chamber . . . . . . **$150.00**
**Price:** Pistol chamber . . . . . . **$45.00**
**Price:** Measure with both chambers **$189.00**

**Powder Measure Reservoirs**

Replacement reservoirs available in three sizes with or without caps. Smallest is same size as supplied with any Redding measure. Intermediate is $7^{1}/_{2}''$ overall length with the largest being 10″. Fit any Redding powder measure using $2^{1}/_{8}''$ O.D. reservoir. From Redding Reloading Equipment.

**Price:** Original size, no cap . . . . . **$6.00**
**Price:** Original size, with cap . . . . **$7.50**
**Price:** Intermediate, no cap . . . . . **$9.00**
**Price:** Intermediate, with cap . . . **$10.50**
**Price:** Large, no cap . . . . . . . **$12.00**
**Price:** Large, with cap . . . . . . **$13.50**

**Supercharger Powder Measuring Kit No. 101**

Contains Redding Model RS-1 powder/bullet scale; Model No.3 powder measure; Model No. 5 trickler; and RS-6 bench stand. From Redding Reloading Equipment.

**Price:** . . . . . . . . . . . . . **$195.00**

## REDDING

**Supercharger Powder Measuring Kit No. 102**

Contains Redding Model No. 2 powder/bullet scale; Model No. 3BR powder measure; Model No. 5 powder trickler; and RS-6 bench stand. From Redding Reloading Equipment.

**Price:** . . . . . . . . . . . . . . **$219.00**

**Supercharger Powder Measuring Kit No. 102BR**

Contains Redding Model No. 2 powder/bullet scale; No. 3BR powder measure; Model No. 5 powder trickler; and RS-6 bench stand. From Redding Reloading Equipment.

**Price:** . . . . . . . . . . . . . . **$256.50**

## ROCK CRUSHER

**Maxi Measure**

Designed for loading very large caliber cases, 50 BMG on up. Made of machined steel and aircraft aluminum with solid brass drop tube. Design eliminates charge density variations by connecting hopper to charge reservoir which in turn is transferred to adjustable measuring chamber. Hopper is 1/2-gallon polypropylene bottle with capacity of 11 lbs. and capable of throwing charges of 700 grs. within .5-gr. Adjustable drop tube is solid brass with adjust range of 0 to 700 grains. Non-adjustable models available on special order. From The Old Western Scrounger.

**Price:** . . . . . . . . . . . . . . **$278.95**

SLAP Powder Buddy

## SINCLAIR

**Bottle Adaptors**

Designed for Redding, RCBS Uniflow and Lyman 55 measures to replace the powder hopper with commercial powder bottles and screw them directly onto measure. Requires drilling and tapping small hole in RCBS or Lyman measure casting to attach adaptor; Redding adaptor uses factory screws. From Sinclair International, Inc.

**Price:** . . . . . . . . . . . . . . **$18.50**

**Measure Bracket**

Bracket designed for attaching C-clamp type measures to corner of tool box for loading in the field. From Sinclair International, Inc.

**Price:** . . . . . . . . . . . . . . **$14.00**

**Powder Measure Stand**

Adjustable powder measure stand allows both height adjustments and bench thickness allowances. Solid stainless steel shaft with powder-coated mounting plates. Three-point of contact plates threaded 7/8-14 in standard models. Also available with custom threading. From Sinclair International, Inc.

**Price:** . . . . . . . . . . . . . . **$29.75**

**Powder Measure Tote Bag**

Vinyl bag with cotton lined interior for transporting powder measure to the field. From Sinclair International, Inc.

**Price:** . . . . . . . . . . . . . . **$9.50**

**Powder Bottles**

16-oz. bottles to use in conjunction with Sinclair bottle adaptors. Helpful when working from larger keg and must keep powder lots separate. Come either in solid bottom configuration or with removable plug. From Sinclair International, Inc.

**Price:** Solid bottom . . . . . . . . **$3.50**
**Price:** Removable plug . . . . . . **$4.95**

**Powder Drop Tubes**

Clear Plexiglass tubes for Redding, RCBS Uniflow and Lyman measures for better visibility and greater powder compression in high density cases. Available in two lengths, 4″ and 6″ for Lyman and RCBS; or 3″ or 5″ for Redding. Attachment adaptor required for Redding measure. From Sinclair International, Inc.

**Price:** . . . . . . . . . . . . . . **$9.00**

Maxi Measure

## SLAP

**Powder Buddy**

Accurate trip meter fitted to any powder measure or progressive/semi-progressive press to show a count from 1 to 99999 of each powder throw. Helps prevent double charging or no powder charge. All-metal construction. From SLAP Industries.

**Price:** . . . . . . . . . . . . . . **$29.95**

## VEGA TOOL

**Vega Schuetzen Meter**

A remanufacture of the now obsolete Belding & Mull measure with new improvements to include: measure threaded for stand mounting; subreservoir made of brass; operating lever redesigned for more positive and crisp feel. From Vega Tool Company.

**Price:** . . . . . . . . . . . . . . **$229.95**

## WELSH

**Precision Powder Measure**

Custom machined aluminum body with stainless steel liner and drum. Powder adjustment via Starrett micrometer. Dimensions: 3.25″x8″. Comes with or without powder bottle system. From Bud Welsh.

**Price:** . . . . . . . . . . . . . . **$232.00**

## CARL WERNER

**Powder Measure Bracket**

Swivel brackets attach permanently to metal tool box for mounting powder measure. Deluxe adapter for Redding measures also available. From Carl Werner.

**Price:** Standard . . . . . . . . **$22.00**
**Price:** Deluxe . . . . . . . . . **$30.00**

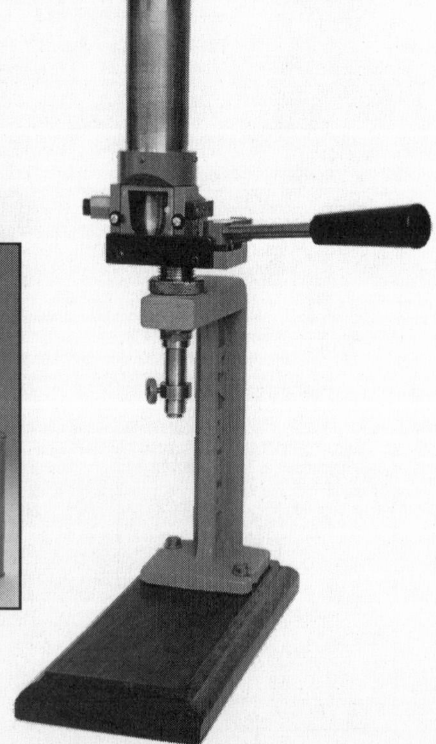

Vega Tool Schuetzen

## C-H/4-D

**Powder Funnel**

High-quality anti-static funnel with drop tube to fit 22- to 45-caliber cases. From C-H Tool & Die/4-D Custom Die.

**Price:** . . . . . . . . . . . . . . . . **$2.00**

## FORSTER

**"Blue Ribbon" Long Drop Tube Funnel**

For use with 4831 and other slow-burning powders where full capacity loads are needed. Long tube adds from 3 to 8 more grains of powder depending on case for a larger volume by weight. From Forster Products.

**Price:** . . . . . . . . . . . . . . **$14.30**

**"Blue Ribbon" Powder Funnel**

Made from Cycolac and designed with four mouth tabs to prevent rolling. One size for 22- to 45-caliber; another for 17-caliber. From Forster Products.

**Price:** Both sizes . . . . . . . . . . **$4.30**

**Large Powder/Shot Funnel**

Same funnel as used on Bonanza Bench Rest and Bulls-Eye powder measures. Made of tough plastic. From Forster Products.

**Price:** . . . . . . . . . . . . . . . . **$6.00**

## HORNADY

**Powder Funnel**

Tapered tube design to reduce powder spills; fits all cases inclusive of 45-caliber. Anti-static treated transparent plastic. Weight: 1/4-lb. From Hornady Mfg. Co.

**Price:** . . . . . . . . . . . . . . . . **$2.95**

**17 Caliber Powder Funnel Adaptor**

Aluminum adaptor for Hornady powder funnel seals around mouth of 17-caliber cases to help prevent powder leakage. From Hornady Mfg. Co.

**Price:** . . . . . . . . . . . . . . . . **$4.95**

## LEE

**Powder Funnel**

Large plastic funnel fits all cases from 22- to 45-caliber. Hole in flange permits mounting to Lee turret press, shelf or bench. From Lee Precision, Inc.

**Price:** . . . . . . . . . . . . . . . . **$2.49**

## LYMAN

**Powder Funnel**

Plastic funnel for cases from 22 Hornet through 45-70. From Lyman Products Corporation.

**Price:** . . . . . . . . . . . . . . . . **$3.00**

## MTM

**Powder Funnels**

Two see-through plastic models available. Universal model fits all calibers from 222 to 45. Adaptor 5-in-1 kit includes funnel and standard length adapters for 17 Remington, 222 Remington and 30 through 45 calibers. Long universal drop tube also available. From MTM Moulded Products Company.

**Price:** Universal . . . . . . . . . . **$2.83**
**Price:** Adaptor kit . . . . . . . . . **$4.09**

## PRECISION RELOADING

**Aluminum Funnels**

All aluminum one-piece construction funnels eliminate static cling of powder and buffer. Available in three sizes: 2 1/2-oz. with mouth OD of 2 5/8″ and spout OD 7/16″; 1/2-pint, with mouth OD 4″, spout OD 1/2″; and 3/4-pint, 5″ mouth OD, 5/8″ spout OD. From Precision Reloading, Inc.

**Price:** 2 1/2 oz. . . . . . . . . . . . **$1.89**
**Price:** 1/2-pint . . . . . . . . . . . **$2.49**
**Price:** 3/4-pint . . . . . . . . . . . **$3.49**

## RCBS

**Powder Funnel**

Specially-designed drop tube to avoid powder spills around case mouths, a non-stick, anti-static surface and square lip to prevent rolling. Available in one size for 22- to 45-caliber and another for 17. From RCBS.

**Price:** . . . . . . . . . . . . . . **$3.38**
**Price:** 17-cal. . . . . . . . . . . . **$4.63**

## REDDING

**Powder Funnel**

Lexan funnel fits all cartridge cases 22- to 45-caliber. Anti-static prevents powder sticking. From Redding Reloading Equipment.

**Price:** . . . . . . . . . . . . . . . . **$4.80**

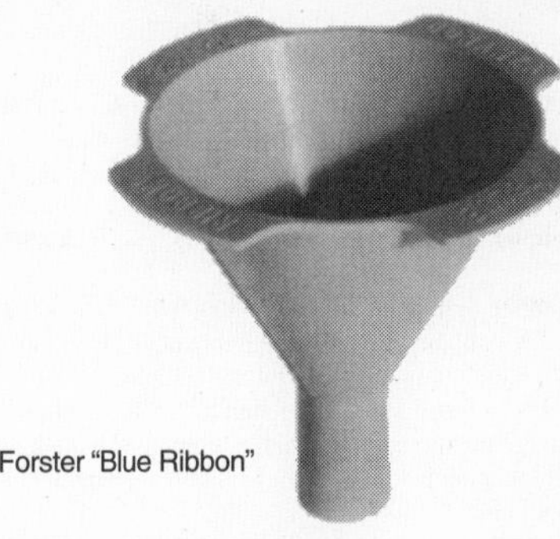

Forster "Blue Ribbon"

Lee Funnel

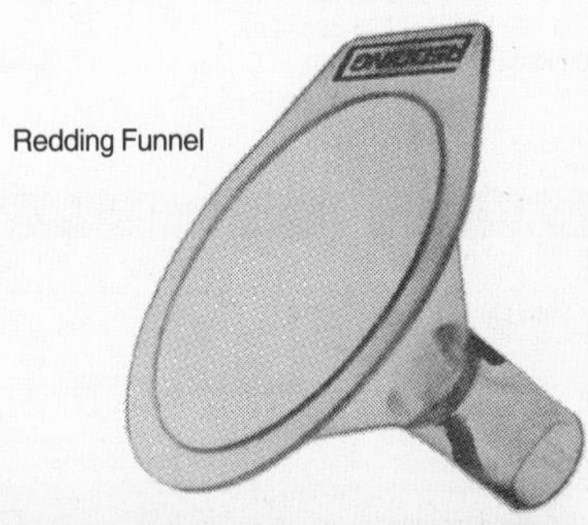

Redding Funnel

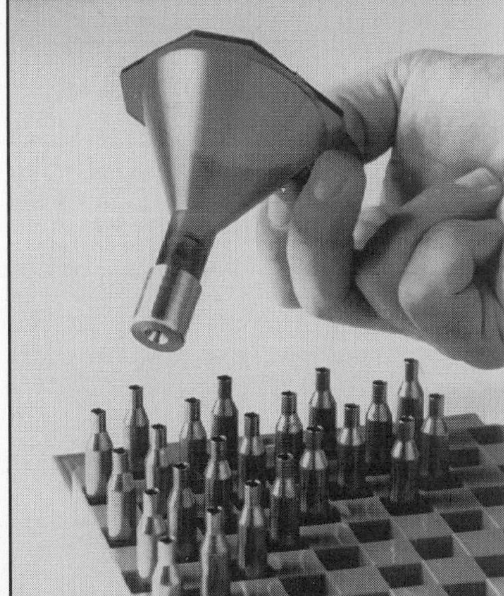

Hornady 17-Caliber Funnel Adaptor

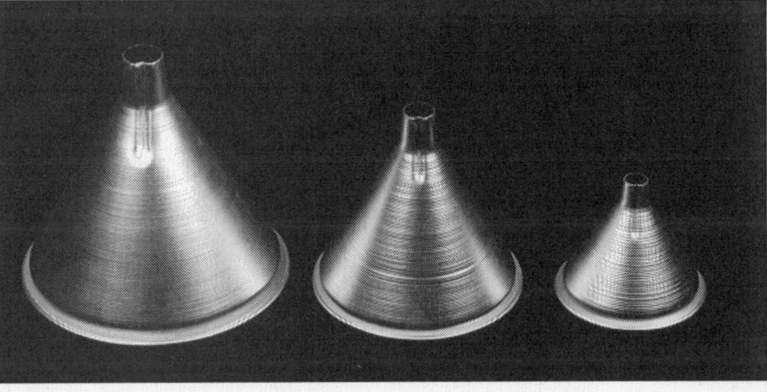

Precision Reloading Aluminum Funnels

## C-H/4-D

### 50 BMG Power Case Trimmer

Power trimmer with tungsten carbide cutter to trim and outside debur 50 BMG case necks. Comes complete with pilot and shellholder. From C-H Tool & Die/4-D Custom Die.

**Price:** . . . . . . . . . . . . . . **$239.95**

### Power Champ Case Trimmer

A self-contained power case trimmer that handles any case up to and including 50 BMG. Trims and deburrs outside of case neck in single operation. Tungsten carbide cutter. Comes with one shellholder and pilot. From C-H Tool & Die/4-D Custom Die.

**Price:** . . . . . . . . . . . . . . **$229.00**
**Price:** Pilot . . . . . . . . . . . **$7.00**
**Price:** Pilot, 50-cal. . . . . . . . . **$8.00**
**Price:** Pilot/shellholder, 50 BMG . **$225.00**

### Precision Case Trimmer

Hand-operated trimmer with clamping feature that ensures uniformity. Comes with one case holder. C-H and Wilson trimmer holders interchangeable. Custom holders available on request. From C-H Tool & Die/4-D Custom Die.

**Price:** . . . . . . . . . . . . . . **$31.85**
**Price:** Case holder . . . . . . . . **$5.50**
**Price:** Custom case holder . . . . **$11.00**
**Price:** Case holder clamp . . . . . **$2.50**
**Price:** Cutter assembly with handle . **$10.85**

### Trimmer Die

Fits any press with 7/8-14 threads. For checking case length or trimming to case length. From C-H Tool & Die/4-D Custom Die.

**Price:** . . . . . . . . . . . . . . **$14.00**

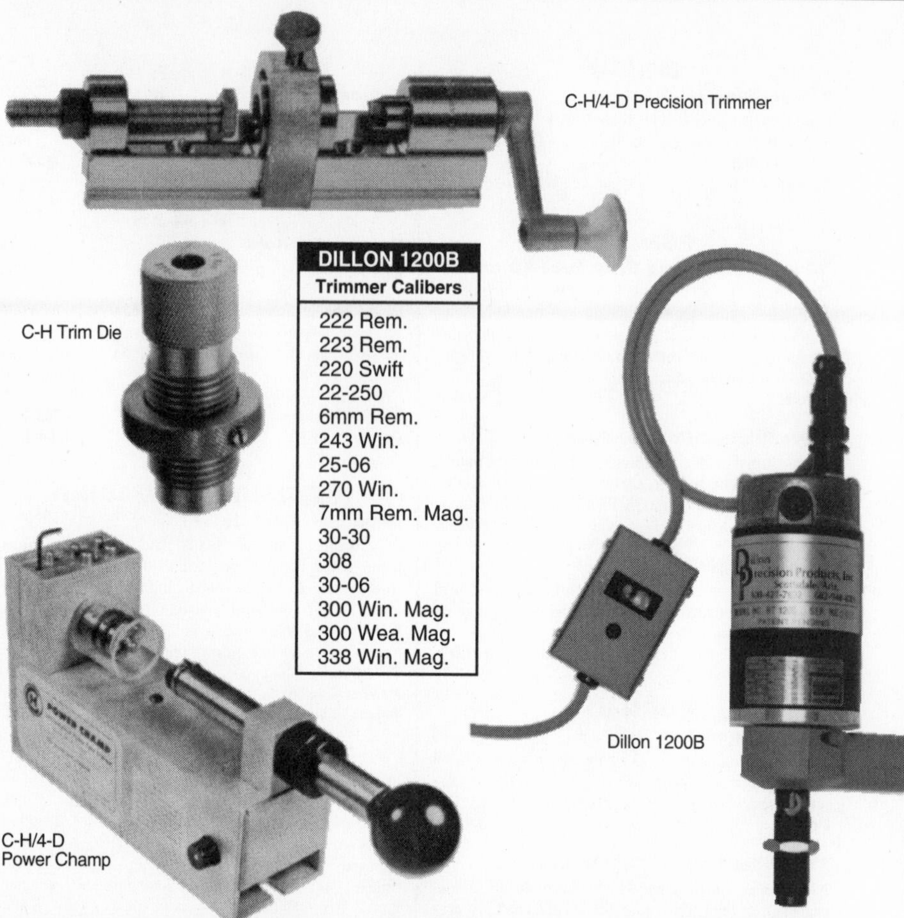

| DILLON 1200B |
|---|
| Trimmer Calibers |
| 222 Rem.<br>223 Rem.<br>220 Swift<br>22-250<br>6mm Rem.<br>243 Win.<br>25-06<br>270 Win.<br>7mm Rem. Mag.<br>30-30<br>308<br>30-06<br>300 Win. Mag.<br>300 Wea. Mag.<br>338 Win. Mag. |

C-H/4-D Precision Trimmer

C-H Trim Die

C-H/4-D Power Champ

Dillon 1200B

## C-H
### Precision Case Trimmer Shellholder Chart

**3011A**
22-06
228 Ackley Mag.
25-06
270 Win.
280 Rem.
30-06
333 OKH
338-06
35 Whelen
358-444
375 Whelen
375-444
400 Whelen
405 Win.
411-444
6mm-06
6.5-06
7mm Rem. Exp.
7mm-08
7x64 Brenneke
7x65R
8mm-06
8x60 JRS
9.5x56 M.S.
9.5x57
444

**3011B**
243 Rockchucker
244 Rem.
257 Roberts
5.6x57
5.6x57R
8x56 M.S.
6.5x58
7x57
7x57R
8x57
8x57R
9x56 M.S.
9x57 Mauser
9.3x74R

**3011C**
22 Cheetah
22-243 Middlestead
22-250 Improved
243 Win.
25-06 Improved
250 Donaldson
257 Ackley Imp. Roberts
260 AAR
270 Improved
280 Improved
30-06 Improved
300 Savage
308 Win.
338-06 Imp.
35 Whelen Imp.
35 Win.
375 Whelen Imp.
6mm Cheetah
6mm Rem. Imp.
6mm-06 Imp.
6.5-06 Imp.
7mm-06 Imp.
7mm-08
7x57 Imp.
7.65x53 Mauser
7.7x58 Japanese
8mm-06 Imp.
9.3x62
358 Win.

**3011D**
25 Rem.
30 Rem.
30-30 Rem.
32 Rem.
32 Win. Spl.
38-55 Win.
7-30 Waters

**3011E**
218 Bee
25-20 Win.

**3011F**
220 Swift
303 British
303 Savage

**3011G**
22-250
250 Sav. (250-3000)

**3011H**
22-3000
22 Lovell R2
25-20 SS
25-21 Stevens
25-25 Stevens

**3011I**
250 Ackley Mag.
257 Wea. Mag.
264 Win. Mag.
270 Ackley Short Mag.
270 Wea. Mag.
300 Ackley Short Mag.
300 Wea. Mag.
300 Win. Mag.
30 STW
30-338 Mag.
308 Norma Mag.
338 Win. Mag.
350 Rem. Mag.
358 Norma Mag.
357 Ackley Mag.
411 KDF
416 Rem Mag.
416 Taylor
450 Ackely Mag.
458 Win. Mag.
6.5 Rem. Mag.
7mm Ackley Short Mag.
7mm STW
7mm Rem. Mag.
7mm Wea. Mag.
8mm Rem. Mag.

**3011J**
219 Zipper
22 Savage Hi-Power
25-35 Win.

**3011K**
225 Win.
30 Herrett
357 Herrett
7-30 Waters

**3011L**
257 H&H Mag.
276 Dubiel
300 H&H Mag.
357 H&H Mag.
7x61 S&H

**3011M**
35 WSL
351 WSL
357 Mag.
357 Max.
38 Long Colt
38 Spl.

**3011N**
220 Rocket
6.5x52 Carcano
6.5x54 M.S.
7.35x52 Carcano

**3011O**
11.15x58R Spanish (43)
11.15x60RR Mauser (43)
30 Newton
35 Newton
6.5x68
6.5x68R
8x68
8x68R

**3011P**
7.63 Mauser (30)
7.65 Luger (30)
9mm Luger
9mm Mauser Pistol

**3011Q**
400-65
6.5x55

**3011R**
7.5x55 Swiss
7.62x54 Russian
8.2x53R

**3011S**
22-284
25-284
284 Win.
30-284
338-284
35-284
375-284
40-50 BN Sharps
40-70 BN Sharps
40-60 Win.
45-70
45-90
45-2.4
45-2.6
45 2 3/4
45 2 7/8
45-120
6mm-284

**3011T**
30-378 Wea.
338 Lapua
378 Wea.
416 Rigby
416 Wea.
460 Wea.
457 A&M Mag.
510 Wells
7mm-378 Wea.

**3011U**
17 Rem.
17-222
17-223
222 Rem.
222 Rem. Mag.
223 Rem.
5.6x50
5.6x50R

**3011V**
38 S&W
38 Super Auto
9mm Browning Long
9mm Largo
9mm Steyr

## DILLON

**1200B Case Trimmer**

Attach to any standard single-station or progressive press to use like a standard sizing die. As case is pushed into die a 1/4-hp electric motor driving a carbide cutter trims the case to length. Chips drawn off through vacuum manifold that clamps to outside of special size/trim die. Vacuum cleaner not included. Comes complete with one steel size/trim die. From Dillon Precision Products, Inc.

**Price:** . . . . . . . . . . . . . . **$139.95**
**Price:** Extra trim die . . . . . . . . **$24.95**

## FORSTER

**Case Trimmer**

Manual trimmer with hardened, ground cutter shaft. Shaft has four staggered teeth for chatterless cutting. Brown and Sharpe collet holds case without end movement. Stop collar features fine adjustment screws. Collet and pilot not included. Weight: 2 lbs. From Forster Products.

**Price:** . . . . . . . . . . . . . . **$55.20**
**Price:** Collet . . . . . . . . . . . **$9.60**
**Price:** Pilot . . . . . . . . . . . . **$3.50**

**Case Trimmer Kit**

Includes Forster manual case trimmer, three collets (#1, #2, #3) and six pilots (#22, 24, 25, 27, 28, 30). From Forster Products.

**Price:** . . . . . . . . . . . . . . **$83.90**

**Case Trimmer Power Adaptor**

Screws onto cutter shaft of Forster manual case trimmer in place of hand crank. Allows attachment of cordless screwdriver or small power drill. Collet and pilot not included. From Forster Products.

**Price:** . . . . . . . . . . . . . . **$15.00**
**Price:** Cutter shaft . . . . . . . **$14.70**
**Price:** Trimmer base . . . . . . . **$14.10**
**Price:** Collet . . . . . . . . . . . **$9.60**
**Price:** Pilot . . . . . . . . . . . . **$3.50**

**Power Case Trimmer**

Designed for use with drill press. Features line-up bar to align trimmer and drill press spindle; Brown and Sharpe-type collet; sturdy threaded lever for opening and closing collet; cutter shaft with 1/4″ shank of hardened steel with four staggered cutting edges. Pilot, collet not included. From Forster Products.

**Price:** . . . . . . . . . . . . . . **$56.30**
**Price:** Cutter shaft . . . . . . . **$14.70**
**Price:** Trimmer base . . . . . . . **$14.10**
**Price:** Collet . . . . . . . . . . . **$9.60**
**Price:** Pilot . . . . . . . . . . . . **$3.50**

## GRACEY

**Case Trimmer**

Power trimmer with two adjustable carbon steel cutters hardened to Rockwell 60-63. Ball burnished ballistic aluminum casting houses cutters and black oxide treated case holder. Trimmer mounted on wood base and features industrial electric motor externally grounded to steel frame. Motor 1/15 hp, 1550 rpm. Trims, deburs and chamfers in single operation. Indexes on resized case shoulder. 500 cases per hour. Case holder sizes: 223, 243, 270, 30-30, 308, 708. 30-06 and 300 Winchester. Comes with one case holder. Available with or without power source. From Match Prep.

**Price:** Non-powered trimmer . . . **$110.00**
**Price:** Powered trimmer . . . . . **$206.50**

Forster Trimmer

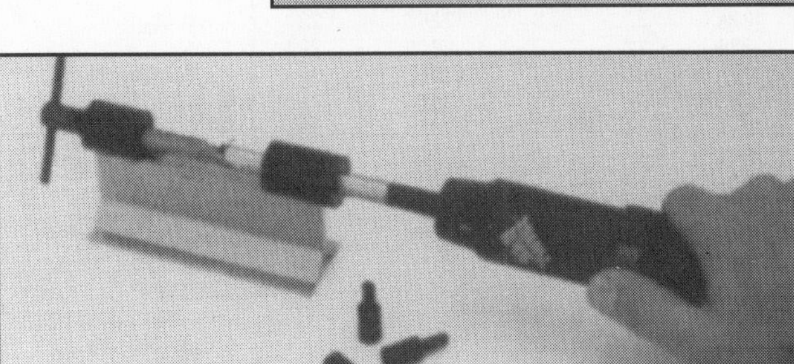

Forster Power Adaptor

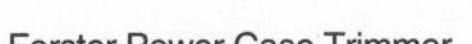

Forster Power Case Trimmer

Gracey Case Trimmer

# Section 1: Metallic Cartridges

**FORSTER** *Case Trimmers*

| Caliber | Bullet Dia. | Trim Pilot Mark | Collet Mark | Min. Neck Dia. | Neck Reamer Mark |
|---|---|---|---|---|---|
| 17 Remington | .171 | 17 | 1 | .1730 | 17 |
| 22 Hornet | .223 | 2 | 2,3 | .2255 | 223 |
| 22 K Hornet | .223 | 2 | 2,3 | .2255 | 223 |
| 222 Remington | .224 | 22 | 1 | .2265 | 224 |
| 222 Remington Mag. | .224 | 22 | 1 | .2265 | 224 |
| 22 Varmint | .224 | 22 | 1 | .2265 | 224 |
| 223 Remington | .224 | 22 | 1 | .2265 | 224 |
| 225 Winchester | .224 | 22 | 1 | .2265 | 224 |
| 5.6mmx50R | .224 | 22 | 1 | .2265 | 224 |
| 22-250 | .224 | 22 | 1 | .2265 | 224 |
| 220 Swift | .224 | 22 | 1 | .2265 | 224 |
| 221 Fireball | .224 | 22 | 1 | .2265 | 224 |
| 22 PPC | .224 | 22 | 1 | .2265 | 224 |
| 22 BR Remington | .224 | 22 | 1 | .2265 | 224 |
| 218 Bee & Mashburn | .224 | 22 | 2 | .2265 | 224 |
| 219 Zipper | .224 | 22 | 2 | .2265 | 224 |
| 219 Wasp | .224 | 22 | 2 | .2265 | 224 |
| 22 Savage | .224 | 22 | 2 | .2265 | 224 |
| 22-30-30 | .224 | 22 | 2 | .2265 | 224 |
| 228 Krag | .224 | 22 | 3 | .2265 | 224 |
| 22 Jet CF Magnum | .224 | 22 | 3 | .2265 | 224 |
| 224 Varmint Wea. | .224 | 22 | 3 | .2265 | 224 |
| 22 PPC | .224 | 22 | 3 | .2265 | 224 |
| 243 Winchester | .243 | 24 | 1 | .2455 | 243 |
| 6mm | .243 | 24 | 1 | .2455 | 243 |
| 6mm Mag. | .243 | 24 | 1 | .2455 | 243 |
| 6mm Belted Exp. | .243 | 24 | 1 | .2455 | 243 |
| 244 Rem. | .243 | 24 | 1 | .2455 | 243 |
| 6mm BR Rem. | .243 | 24 | 1 | .2455 | 243 |
| 6mm PPC | .243 | 24 | 3 | .2455 | 243 |
| 6mm Krag | .243 | 24 | 3 | .2455 | |
| 243®MDNM‾ | | | | | |
| 6mm Krag Long | .243 | 24 | 3 | .2455 | 243 |
| 257 | .257 | 25 | 1 | .2595 | 257 |
| 250 Savage | .257 | 25 | 1 | .2595 | 257 |
| 250 Ackley | .257 | 25 | 1 | .2595 | 257 |
| 250-3000 | .257 | 25 | 1 | .2595 | 257 |
| 25 Souper | .257 | 25 | 1 | .2595 | 257 |
| 25-06 | .257 | 25 | 1 | .2595 | 257 |
| 25-20 Repeater | .257 | 25 | 2 | .2595 | 257 |
| 25-35 | .257 | 25 | 2 | .2595 | 257 |
| 25 Remington | .257 | 25 | 2 | .2595 | 257 |
| 25 Krag Improved | .257 | 25 | 3 | .2595 | 257 |
| 256 Winchester | .257 | 25 | 3 | .2595 | 257 |
| 6.5x57 Mauser | .263 | 26 | 1 | .2655 | 263 |
| 6.5mm Winchester | .263 | 26 | 1 | .2655 | 263 |
| 6.5mm Jap.Mauser | .263 | 26 | 1 | .2655 | 263 |
| 6.5x55 Swede | .263 | 26 | 1 | .2655 | 263 |
| 6.5x55 SKAN | .263 | 26 | 1 | .2655 | 263 |
| 6.5x257 Japanese | .263 | 26 | 1 | .2655 | 263 |
| 256 Newton | .263 | 26 | 1 | .2655 | 263 |
| 260 AAR | .263 | 26 | 1 | .2655 | 263 |
| 264 Winchester Mag. | .263 | 26 | 1 | .2655 | 263 |
| 270 Winchester | .277 | 27 | 1 | .2795 | 277 |
| 270 Savage | .277 | 27 | 1 | .2795 | 277 |
| 270 Gibbs | .277 | 27 | 1 | .2795 | 277 |
| 270 Weatherby | .277 | 27 | 1 | .2795 | 277 |
| 270 Ackley | .277 | 27 | 1 | .2795 | 277 |
| 257 H&H | .277 | 27 | 1 | .2795 | 277 |
| 7mm Mauser | .284 | 28 | 1 | .2865 | 284 |
| 7x57 Mauser | .284 | 28 | 1 | .2865 | 284 |
| 7mm Weatherby | .284 | 28 | 1 | .2865 | 284 |
| 7mmx64 | .284 | 28 | 1 | .2865 | 284 |
| 276 | .284 | 28 | 1 | .2865 | 284 |
| 7mm-08 | .284 | 28 | 1 | .2865 | 284 |
| 7mm TCU | .284 | 28 | 1 | .2865 | 284 |
| 280 Remington | .284 | 28 | 1 | .2865 | 284 |
| 284 Winchester | .284 | 28 | 1 | .2865 | 284 |
| 7mm Rem. Mag. | .284 | 28 | 1 | .2865 | 284 |
| 7mm BR Rem. | .284 | 28 | 1 | .2865 | 284 |
| 30-06 | .308 | 30 | 1 | .3110 | 308 |
| 308 Winchester | .308 | 30 | 1 | .3110 | 308 |
| 300 Magnum | .308 | 30 | 1 | .3110 | 308 |
| 7.62 NATO | .308 | 30 | 1 | .3110 | 308 |
| 300 Savage | .308 | 30 | 1 | .3110 | 308 |

| Caliber | Bullet Dia. | Trim Pilot Mark | Collet Mark | Min. Neck Dia. | Neck Reamer Mark |
|---|---|---|---|---|---|
| 30-30 | .308 | 30 | 2 | .3110 | 308 |
| 30 Remington | .308 | 30 | 2 | .3110 | 308 |
| 30 WCF | .308 | 30 | 2 | .3110 | 308 |
| 303 Savage | .308 | 30 | 2 | .3110 | 308 |
| 7.5x55 Swiss | .308 | 30 | 2 | .3110 | 308 |
| 30-40 Krag | .308 | 30 | 3 | .3110 | 308 |
| 30 Carbine | .308 | 30 | 3 | .3110 | 308 |
| 30-40 Improved | .308 | 30 | 3 | .3110 | 308 |
| 7.62x39 | .308 | 30 | 3 | .3110 | 308 |
| 303 British | .311 | 31 | 1 | .3135 | 311 |
| 32 S&W Long | .311 | 31 | 1 | .3135 | 311 |
| 7.65 Mauser | .311 | 31 | 1 | .3135 | 311 |
| 7.7mm Japanese | .311 | 31 | 1 | .3135 | 311 |
| 32-20 | .311 | 31 | 2 | .3135 | 311 |
| 8x57 | .323 | 32 | 1 | .3255 | 323 |
| 8x57 JS | .323 | 32 | 1 | .3255 | 323 |
| 8x57 RS | .323 | 32 | 1 | .3255 | 323 |
| 8x60 | .323 | 32 | 1 | .3255 | 323 |
| 7.92x57 | .323 | 32 | 1 | .3255 | 323 |
| 8mm-06 | .323 | 32 | 1 | .3255 | 323 |
| 8mm Mauser | .323 | 32 | 1 | .3255 | 323 |
| 32 Winchester Spl. | .323 | 32 | 2 | .3255 | 323 |
| 32 Remington | .323 | 32 | 2 | .3255 | 323 |
| 32-40 | .323 | 32 | 2 | .3255 | 323 |
| 333 Winchester | .333 | 33 | 1 | | |
| 333 OKH | .333 | 33 | 1 | | |
| 333 Ackley | .333 | 33 | 1 | | |
| 33 Winchester | .338 | 3 | 4 | | |
| 338 Winchester | .338 | 3 | 1 | .3405 | 338 |
| 338 Winchester Mag. | .338 | 3 | 1 | .3405 | 338 |
| 338 Gibbs | .338 | 3 | 1 | .3405 | 338 |
| 340 Weatherby Mag. | .338 | 3 | 1 | .3405 | 338 |
| 348 Winchester | .348 | 34 | 4 | | |
| 35 Remington | .357, .358 | 35 | 1 | .3605 | 358 |
| 358 Winchester | .357, .358 | 35 | 1 | .3605 | 358 |
| 358 Norma Magnum | .357, .358 | 35 | 1 | .3605 | 358 |
| 38 Colt Super | .357, .358 | 35 | 2 | .3605 | 358 |
| 38 Special | .357, .358 | 35 | 3 | .3605 | 358 |
| 357 Magnum | .357, .358 | 35 | 3 | .3605 | 358 |
| 35 Winchester | .357, .358 | 35 | 3 | .3605 | 358 |
| 9mm Luger | .355, .356 | 351 | 2 | .3575 | 355 |
| 380 Auto | .356 | 351 | 1 | | |
| 9.3mmx74R | .365 | 368 | 1 | | |
| 9.3mmx62 | .365 | 368 | 1 | | |
| 375 Magnum | .375 | 375 | 1 | .3780 | 375 |
| 375-06 | .375 | 375 | 1 | .3780 | 375 |
| 375 Barnes | .375 | 375 | 1 | .3780 | 375 |
| 375 Weatherby | .375 | 375 | 1 | .3780 | 375 |
| 375 Ackley | .375 | 375 | 1 | .3780 | 375 |
| 375 H&H | .375 | 375 | 1 | .3780 | 375 |
| 38-50 | .375 | 375 | 4 | .3780 | 375 |
| 378 Weatherby | .375 | 375 | 4 | .3780 | 375 |
| 375 Winchester | .376 | 375 | 2 | .3780 | 375 |
| 41 Colt | .400 | 400 | 1 | | |
| 401 Winchester | .400 | 400 | 1 | | |
| 38-40 | .400 | 400 | 1 | | |
| 395-400 | .400 | 400 | 1 | | |
| 41 S&W | .400 | 400 | 1 | | |
| 10mm Auto Pistol | .400 | 400 | 3 | .4025 | 400 |
| 41 Rem. Mag. | .410 | 410 | 2 | .4125 | 410 |
| 416 Weatherby | .416 | 416 | 4 | | |
| 416 Rigby | .416 | 416 | 4 | | |
| 44 S&W Spl. | .429 | 432 | 1 | .4340 | 432 |
| 44 Rem. Mag. | .429 | 432 | 1 | .4340 | 432 |
| 44-40 | .429 | 432 | 1 | .4340 | 432 |
| 444 Marlin Magnum | .429 | 432 | 1 | .4340 | 432 |
| 45 ACP | .452 | 452 | 1 | .4545 | 452 |
| 45 Auto Rim | .452 | 452 | 1 | .4545 | 452 |
| 45 Winchester Mag. | .452 | 452 | 1 | .4545 | 452 |
| 45-90 | .454 | 452 | 4 | | |
| 45 Long Colt | .452, .454 | 455 | 1,2 | | |
| 45-70 | .457 | 458 | 4 | | |
| 450 Watts | .459 | 458 | 1 | .4605 | 458 |
| 458 Winchester | .459 | 458 | 1 | .4605 | 458 |
| 450 Ackley Magnum | .459 | 458 | 1 | .4605 | 458 |

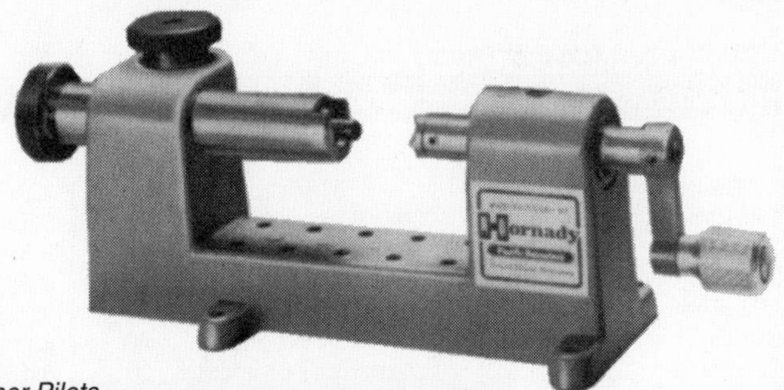
Hornady Trimmer

**HORNADY** *Case Trimmer Pilots*

| Caliber | Bullet Dia. | Pilot # | Caliber | Bullet Dia. | Pilot # |
|---|---|---|---|---|---|
| 22 | .224 | 1 | 8mm | .323 | 11 |
| | .228 | 2 | | .333 | 12 |
| 6mm | .243 | 3 | | .338 | 13 |
| 25 | .257 | 4 | | .348 | 14 |
| 6.5mm | .264 | 5 | 38 | .358 | 15 |
| 270 | .277 | 6 | | .375 | 16 |
| 7mm | .284 | 7 | 41 | .410 | 17 |
| | .300 | 8 | 44 | .429 | 18 |
| 30 | .308 | 9 | 45 | .452 | 19 |
| 303 | .312 | 10 | | .361 | 20 |
| | | | 40 | .400 | 21 |

| HORNADY<br>Trim Die Calibers | |
|---|---|
| 219 Zipper | 7x57/7mm Mauser |
| 17/222 | 7x61 Sharpe & Hart |
| 222 Rem. Mag. | 7mm Rem. Mag. |
| 223 Rem. | 7mm Wea. |
| 22/250 | 7mm Exp./280 |
| 220 Swift | 284 Win. |
| 243 Win. | 30/30 Win. |
| 6mm/284 | 303 British |
| 25-06 | 308 Win. |
| 25/35 Win. | 30-40 Krag |
| 25/284 | 308 Norma Mag. |
| 6.5-06 | 30-06 |
| 6.5 Rem. Mag. | 300 Win. Mag. |
| 6.5 Mann. | 30 Herrett |
| 6.5 Carcano | 32 Win. |
| 6.5 Japanese | 8mm-06 |
| 264 Win. Mag. | 35 Rem. |
| 270 Win. | 357 Herrett |
| 270 Wea. | |

Hornady Trim Die

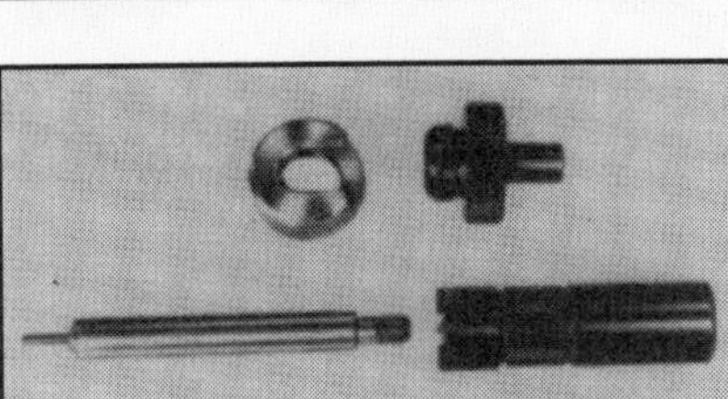
Lee Case Trimmer-2

Lyman Drill Press Trimmer

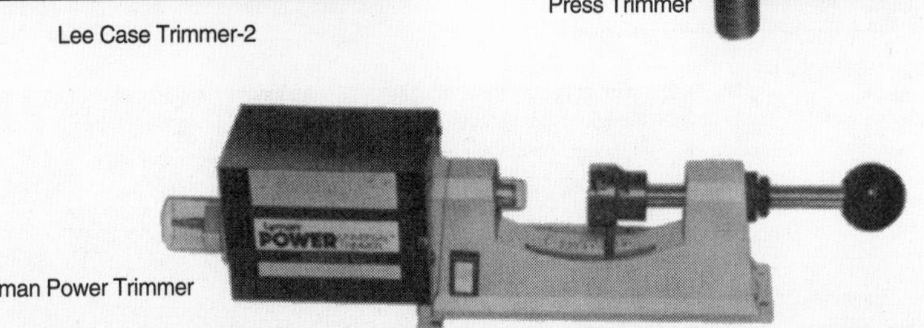

Lyman Power Trimmer

## HOLLYWOOD

**50 Caliber Case Trimmer**

Made of tool steel, this unit can be operated by hand, used in electric drill or drill press. Comes as complete set to trim, ream and chamfer cases. Includes trimmer, pocket reamer, chamfer tool and handle. From Hollywood Engineering.

**Price:** . . . . . . . . . . . . **$150.00**
**Price:** Trimmer . . . . . . . . . **$55.00**
**Price:** Primer pocket reamer . . . . **$55.00**
**Price:** Chamfer tool . . . . . . . **$55.00**
**Price:** Handle . . . . . . . . . . **$30.00**

## HORNADY

**Case Trimmer**

Uses standard removable shellholder heads. Adjusts to any case length. Mounts on bench or clamps in vise. Handle removable for electric drill attachment. Includes 10 pilots, Nos. 1, 3, 4, 6, 7, 9, 15, 17, 18, 19. Shellholder not included. From Hornady Mfg. Co.

**Price:** . . . . . . . . . . . . . **$49.95**
**Price:** Pilot . . . . . . . . . . . **$3.25**
**Price:** 17-cal. pilot . . . . . . . . **$8.95**
**Price:** Extra cutter . . . . . . . . **$7.95**

**Case Trimmer/Caliper Kit**

Includes Hornady case trimmer, 10 pilots and stainless steel dial caliper. Weight: 4¾ lbs. From Hornady Mfg. Co.

**Price:** . . . . . . . . . . . . . **$89.95**

**Trim Die**

Hardened steel trim die threaded 7/8-14 to fit any standard press. Available in most popular calibers. Weight: 1 lb. From Hornady Mfg. Co.

**Price:** . . . . . . . . . . . . . **$16.95**

## LEE

**Case Trimmer**

Four-piece tool kit includes lock stud and cutter for all calibers and caliber-specific shellholder plus case length gauge. For trimming cases manually or for use with electric drill. From Lee Precision, Inc.

**Price:** . . . . . . . . . . . . . . **$4.98**

## LYMAN

**Accu Trimmer**

Trims cases 17-caliber through 458 Winchester. Uses standard shellholders and standard Lyman cutter heads and pilots. Comes with nine pilots. From Lyman Products Corporation.

**Price:** . . . . . . . . . . . . . **$40.50**

**Case Trimmer Accessories**

Four accessories for Lyman case trimmers. Nine Pilot Multi-Pack for Lyman Universal trimmer or Accu trimmer. Calibers include: 22, 24, 27, 28/7mm, 30, 9mm, 35, 44 and 45 ACP; extra pilots; replacement cutter head; carbide cutter head. From Lyman Products Corporation.

**Price:** Multi-Pack . . . . . . . . **$10.75**
**Price:** Extra pilot . . . . . . . . **$3.40**
**Price:** Replacement cutter head . . . **$5.40**
**Price:** Carbide cutter head . . . . **$39.95**

**Drill Press Trimmer**

Universal chuck head eliminates need for collets. Extra cutter head included. Accepts standard Lyman pilots. From Lyman Products Corporation.

**Price:** . . . . . . . . . . . . . **$45.75**

## LYMAN

### Power Trimmer

Electric trimmer with 175 rpm motor in 110- or 220-volt. Features adjustable settings for overall trim length; replaceable cutter head; cartridge case lock/unlock. Includes nine pilots, two cutter heads and set of primer pocket brushes. High-speed drive with safety guard. Accessory carbide cutter available. Weight: 12 lbs. From Lyman Products Corporation.

**Price:** 110-volt . . . . . . . . . **$183.25**
**Price:** 220-volt . . . . . . . . . **$185.00**

### Universal Trimmer

Features coarse and fine adjustments; adjusting ring to dial and lock in approximate setting for repeatability. Comes separately or in Multi-Pack set with nine of most used pilots. From Lyman Products Corporation.

**Price:** Multi-Pack set . . . . . . **$64.95**

### Universal Trimmer Power Adapter

Converts the Universal case trimmer from hand mode to power. The Lyman Universal Chuckhead system can be used with any standard electric drill or power screwdriver to trim cases from 17- through 45-caliber. The chuck with cutter head fits only the Lyman trimmer. From Lyman Products Corporation.

**Price:** . . . . . . . . . . . . . . **$16.50**

### Universal Trimmer Power Pack Combo

Includes the Lyman Universal Hand Trimmer plus the power adapter and the trimmer multi-pack with nine pilots. From Lyman Products Corporation.

**Price:** . . . . . . . . . . . . . . **$74.95**

## NECO

### 50 BMG Case Trim Holder

Precision cartridge case holder designed specifically to rigidly hold empty resized 50 BMG cases on drill press table for trimming to correct overall length. Features stainless steel body, heat-treated 4140 interior and blued steel base. From NECO.

**Price:** . . . . . . . . . . . . . . **$123.50**

## PRECISION RELOADING

### Micro Case Trimmer Kit

Includes Wilson case trimmer plus shellholder; S-T Micrometer attachment head; Stalwart shellholder bracket clamp and trimmer base; locking micrometer head and ratchet with .0001″ division. The 1/2″ adjustable anvil stop sleeve is required for cases shorter than 1.720″. From Precision Reloading, Inc.

**Price:** . . . . . . . . . . . . . . **$112.50**
**Price:** Micrometer attachment . . . **$64.95**
**Price:** Stalwart base with shellholder clamp . . . . . . . **$27.95**
**Price:** Adjustable stop sleeve . . . **$14.00**
**Price:** 1 1/2″ stop sleeve for pistol cases **$16.00**

## RCBS

### Case Trimmer-2 Converter

Converts hand-turned trimmer into a power-driven tool. Works with any standard power drill. From RCBS.

**Price:** . . . . . . . . . . . . . . **$4.63**

### Three-Way Cutter

Available in 22 and 30 calibers for trimming cases to desired length, chamfer inside of the case necks and deburr the outside simultaneously. Fits all RCBS case trimmer tools. From RCBS.

**Price:** . . . . . **Contact manufacturer.**

### LYMAN *Case Trimmer Pilots*

| Cartridge | Pilot # | Cartridge | Pilot # | Cartridge | Pilot # |
|---|---|---|---|---|---|
| **— RIFLE —** | | | | | |
| 17 Rem. | 17 | 7mmx57R Mauser | 28 | 7.9x57 | 8mm |
| 22 Hornet | 22 | 280 Rem. | 28 | 9.3x62 | 36 |
| 222 Rem. | 22 | 7mm-08 Rem. | 28 | 9.3x64 | 36 |
| 222 Rem. Mag. | 22 | 7x30 Waters | 28 | 9.3x72R | 36 |
| 223 Rem. (5.56mm) | 22 | 7mm Wea. Mag. | 28 | 9.3x74R | 36 |
| 22-250 | 22 | 7mmx64 Brenneke | 28 | 8mmx57 Mauser | 8mm |
| 220 Swift | 22 | 7mmx65R Brenneke | 28 | 8x57JS | 8mm |
| 5.6mmx50R | 22 | 30 M1 Carbine | 30 | 8mm Rem. Mag. | 8mm |
| 243 Win. | 24 | 30-30 Win. | 30 | 338 Win. Mag. | 33 |
| 6mm Rem. | 24 | 30-06 | 30 | 35 Rem. | 35 |
| 25-06 Rem. | 25 | 307 Win. | 30 | 35 Whelen | 35 |
| 250 Savage | 25 | 308 Win. | 30 | 356 Win. | 35 |
| 257 Roberts | 25 | 300 Savage | 30 | 358 Win. | 35 |
| 25-20 Win. | 25 | 300 Wea. Mag. | 30 | 375 H&H | 37 |
| 6.5mmx57 Mauser | 26 | 300 Win. Mag. | 30 | 375 Win. | 37 |
| 6.5mmx57R Mauser | 26 | 7.62x39mm | 30 | 38-55 Win. | 37 |
| 6.5mmx55 Swed. Mau. | 26 | 7.62x54 Russian | 31 | 40-65 | 41 |
| 270 Win. | 27 | 7.62x63mm | 31 | 416 Rigby | 416 |
| 7mm TCU | 28 | 303 British | 31 | 44-40 Win. | 44A |
| 7mm Rem. Mag. | 28 | 7.65mm Arg. Mauser | 31 | 444 Marlin | 44 |
| 7mmx57 Mauser | 28 | 32-20 Win. | 31 | 45-70 Gov't. | 45 |
| | | 32 Win. Spl. | 32 | 50-70 Gov't. | |
| **— PISTOL —** | | | | | |
| 25 ACP | 25A | 38 S&W | 35 | 44 Mag. | 44 |
| 7mm TCU | 28 | 9mm Luger | 9mm | 44 Special | 44 |
| 30 Luger | 30 | 38 Special | 35 | 44-40 Win. | 44A |
| 30 Herrett | 30 | 357 Mag. | 35 | 45 ACP | 45A |
| 30 Mauser | 30 | 357 Rem. Max. | 35 | 45 Colt | 45A |
| 32 ACP | 30 | 9mm Makarov | 36 | 45 Win. Mag. | 45A |
| 32 S&W Long | 31 | 40 S&W | 39 | 45 Colt | 43A |
| 32 H&R Mag. | 31 | 10mm Auto | 39 | 475 Wildey Mag. | 47 |
| 38 Super Auto | 9mm | 41 Mag. | 41 | 50 AE | 50A |
| 380 Auto | 9mm | 41 Action Exp. | 41 | | |

RCBS Pro Power Case Trimmer

Lyman Universal Power Adaptor

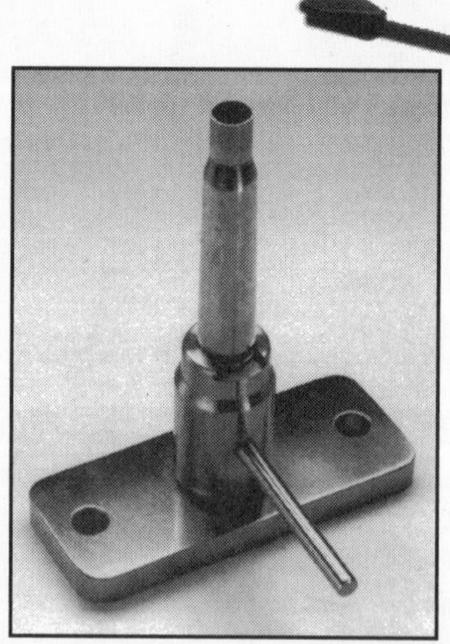

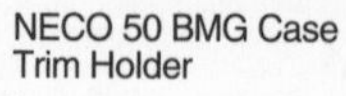

NECO 50 BMG Case Trim Holder

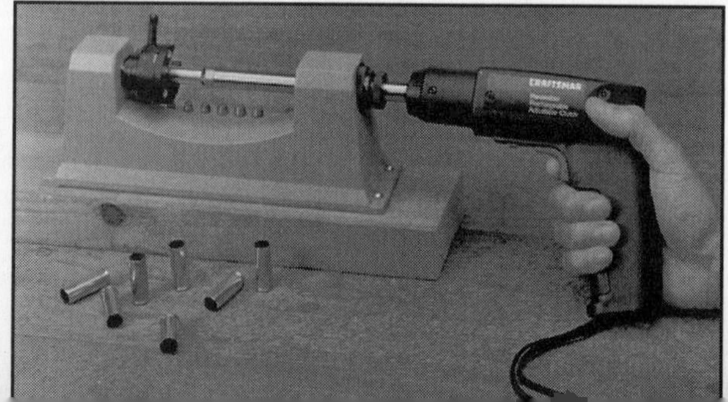

Lyman Universal Power Pack Combo

## RCBS Case Trimmer-2

| Caliber | Trim Collet | Trim Pilot | Trim Gauge | Max Length | Trim Length |
|---|---|---|---|---|---|
| 17 Rem. | 1 | 17 | 4 | 1.796 | 1.786 |
| 218 Bee | 2 | 22 | 2 | 1.345 | 1.335 |
| 22 Hornet | 2 | 22 | 2 | 1.403 | 1.393 |
| 22K-Hornet | 2 | 22 | 2 | 1.403 | 1.393 |
| 22 PPC | 3 | 22 | 4 | | |
| 22 Rem. Jet | 3 | 22 | 2 | 1.280 | 1.270 |
| 22 Sav. High-Power | 2 | 22 | 4 | | |
| 22-250 | 1 | 22 | 4 | 1.912 | 1.902 |
| 220 Swift | 1 | 22 | 4 | 2.205 | 2.195 |
| 221 Rem. Fire Ball | 1 | 22 | 2 | 1.400 | 1.390 |
| 222 Rem. | 1 | 22 | 3 | 1.700 | 1.690 |
| 222 Rem. Mag. | 1 | 22 | 4 | 1.850 | 1.840 |
| 223 Rem. | 1 | 22 | 3 | 1.760 | 1.750 |
| 224 Wea. Mag. | 3 | 22 | 5 | | |
| 225 Win. | 1 | 22 | 4 | 1.930 | 1.920 |
| 5.6mmx50 Rimmed | 2 | 22 | 4 | | |
| 240 Wea. Mag. | 1 | 24 | 5 | 2.500 | 2.490 |
| 243 Win. | 1 | 24 | 4 | 2.045 | 2.035 |
| 6mm PPC | 3 | 24 | 4 | | |
| 6mm Rem. | 1 | 24 | 4 | 2.233 | 2.223 |
| 25-06 | 1 | 25 | 5 | 2.494 | 2.484 |
| 25-20 Win. | 2 | 25 | 2 | | |
| 25-35 | 2 | 25 | 4 | | |
| 250 Sav. | 1 | 25 | 4 | 1.912 | 1.902 |
| 256 Win. Mag. | 3 | 25 | 1 | .281 | 1.271 |
| 257 Roberts | 1 | 25 | 4 | 2.233 | 2.223 |
| 257 Roberts Imp. | 1 | 25 | 4 | | |
| 257 Wea. Mag. | 1 | 25 | 5 | 2.545 | 2.535 |
| 264 Win. Mag. | 1 | 26 | 5 | 2.500 | 2.490 |
| 6.5 Rem. Mag. | 1 | 26 | 4 | | |
| 6.5mm T/CU | 1 | 26 | 3 | | |
| 6.5mm-06 | 1 | 26 | 5 | | |
| 6.5mmx50 Jap. Arisaka | 1 | 26 | 4 | | |
| 6.5mmx52 Carcano | 3 | 26 | 4 | | |
| 6.5mmx54 Man.-Schoen. | 1 | 26 | 4 | | |
| 6.5x55 Swedish Mauser | 1 | 26 | 4 | 2.165 | 2.155 |
| 6.5x57 | 1 | 26 | 4 | | |
| 270 Wea. Mag. | 1 | 27 | 5 | 2.545 | 2.535 |
| 270 Win. | 1 | 27 | 5 | 2.540 | 2.530 |
| 280 Rem. | 1 | 28 | 5 | 2.540 | 2.530 |
| 284 Win. | 1 | 28 | 4 | | |
| 7mm BR Rem. | 1 | 28 | 3 | 1.520 | 1.510 |
| 7mm Rem. Mag. | 1 | 28 | 5 | 2.500 | 2.490 |
| 7mm T/CU | 1 | 28 | 3 | | |
| 7mm Wea. Mag. | 1 | 28 | 5 | 2.545 | 2.535 |
| 7mm-08 Rem. | 1 | 28 | 4 | 2.035 | 2.025 |
| 7mmx57 Mauser | 1 | 28 | 4 | 2.235 | 2.225 |
| 7mmx64 Brenneke | 1 | 28 | 4 | | |
| 7mmx65 Rimmed | 1 | 28 | 5 | | |
| 7-30 Waters | 2 | 28 | 4 | | |
| 30 M-1 Carb. | 3 | 30 | 2 | 1.290 | 1.280 |
| 30 Herrett | 2 | 30 | 3 | 1.605 | 1.595 |
| 30 Luger | 2 | 30 | 1 | | |
| 30 Mauser | 2 | 30 | 1 | | |
| 30 Rem. | 2 | 30 | 4 | | |
| 30-06 Sprngfld. | 1 | 30 | 5 | 2.494 | 2.484 |
| 30-30 Win. | 2 | 30 | 4 | 2.039 | 2.029 |
| 30-338 Win. Mag. | 1 | 30 | 5 | | |
| 30-40 Krag | 3 | 30 | 4 | 2.314 | 2.304 |
| 300 H&H Mag. | 1 | 30 | 6 | 2.850 | 2.840 |
| 300 Sav. | 1 | 30 | 4 | 1.871 | 1.861 |
| 300 Wea. Mag. | 1 | 30 | 6 | 2.820 | 2.810 |
| 300 Win. Mag. | 1 | 30 | 5 | 2.620 | 2.610 |
| 303 British | 1 | 31 | 4 | 2.222 | 2.212 |
| 303 Savage | 2 | 30 | 4 | | |
| 307 Win. | 2 | 30 | 4 | | |
| 308 Norma Mag. | 1 | 30 | 5 | 2.560 | 2.550 |
| 308 Win. | 1 | 30 | 4 | 2.015 | 2.005 |
| 7.5mm Schmidt-Rubin | 2 | 30 | 4 | | |
| 7.62x39-308/311 | 3 | 30/31 | 3 | | |
| 7.62x54R Russ. | 4 | 30 | 4 | | |
| 7.65x53 Bel, Mau. | 1 | 31 | 4 | | |
| 7.7x58 Jap. Arisaka | 1 | 31 | 4 | | |
| 32 Auto | 1 | 31 | 1 | | |
| 32 H&R Mag. | 1 | 31 | 1 | | |
| 32 S&W Long | 1 | 31 | 1 | | |
| 32 Win. Spcl. | 2 | 32 | 4 | 2.040 | 2.030 |
| 32-20 Win. | 2 | 31 | 2 | | |
| 32-40 Win. | 2 | 32 | 4 | | |
| 8mm Rem. Mag. | 1 | 32 | 6 | 2.850 | 2.840 |
| 8mm-06 | 1 | 32 | 5 | | |
| 8mmx57 | 1 | 32 | 4 | 2.240 | 2.230 |
| 8mmx68S Mag. | 2 | 32 | 5 | | |
| 33 Win. | 4 | 33 | 4 | | |
| 338 Win. Mag. | 1 | 33 | 5 | 2.500 | 2.490 |
| 340 Wea. Mag. | 1 | 33 | 6 | 2.820 | 2.810 |
| 348 Win. | 4 | 34 | 4 | | |
| 35 Rem. | 1 | 35 | 4 | 1.920 | 1.910 |
| 35 Whelen | 1 | 35 | 5 | | |
| 350 Rem. Mag. | 1 | 35 | 4 | 2.170 | 2.160 |
| 356 Win. | 2 | 35 | 4 | | |
| 357 Herrett | 2 | 35 | 4 | 1.765 | 1.755 |
| 357 Mag. | 3 | 35 | 2 | 1.290 | 1.280 |
| 357 Rem. Mag. | 3 | 35 | 3 | | |
| 358 Norma Mag. | 1 | 35 | 5 | 2.508 | 2.498 |
| 358 Win. | 1 | 35 | 4 | 2.015 | 2.005 |
| 9mm Luger | 2 | 35 | 1 | .754 | .754 |
| 9mm Makarov | 2 | 35 | 1 | | |
| 9mmx21 | 2 | 35 | 1 | | |
| 9.3x62 Mauser | 1 | 36 | 5 | | |
| 9.3x72R | 2 | 36 | 6 | | |
| 9.3x74R | 1 | 36 | 6 | | |
| 375 H&H Mag. | 1 | 37 | 6 | 2.850 | 2.840 |
| 375 Win. | 2 | 37 | 4 | 2.020 | 2.010 |
| 378 Wea. Mag. | 4 | 37 | 6 | | |
| 38 Colt Super | 2 | 35 | 1 | | |
| 38 S&W | 3 | 35 | 1 | .775 | .770 |
| 38 Spcl. | 3 | 35 | 2 | 1.155 | 1.150 |
| 380 ACP | 1 | 35 | 1 | .680 | .680 |
| 38-40 Win. | 1 | 40 | 2 | | |
| 38-55 Win. & Ballard | 2 | 37 | 4 | 2.130 | 2.120 |
| 40 S&W | 3 | 40 | 1 | | |
| 10mm Auto | 3 | 40 | 1 | | |
| 41 AE | 2 | 41 | 1 | | |
| 41 Mag. | 2 | 41 | 2 | 1.290 | 1.285 |
| 416 Rem. Mag. | 1 | 416 | 6 | | |
| 416 Rigby | 4 | 416 | 6 | | |
| 44 Mag. | 2 | 44 | 2 | 1.285 | 1.280 |
| 44 Spcl. | 2 | 44 | 2 | 1.160 | 1.155 |
| 444 Marlin | 1 | 44 | 4 | 2.225 | 2.215 |
| 44-40 Win. | 1 | 44 | 2 | | |
| 45 ACP | 1 | 45 | 1 | .898 | .898 |
| 45 Auto Rim | 1 | 45 | 1 | .898 | .898 |
| 45 Colt | 1 | 45 | 2 | 1.275 | 1.270 |
| 45 Win. Mag. | 1 | 45 | 4 | | |
| 45-70 U.S. Gov't. | 4 | 45-R | 4 | 2.105 | 2.095 |
| 458 Win. Mag. | 1 | 45-R | 5 | 2.500 | 2.490 |
| 460 Wea. Mag. | 4 | 45 | 6 | | |
| 50 Action Express | SO | SO | NA | NA | |
| 50-70 Gov't. | SO | SO | NA | NA | |

SO = Special Order

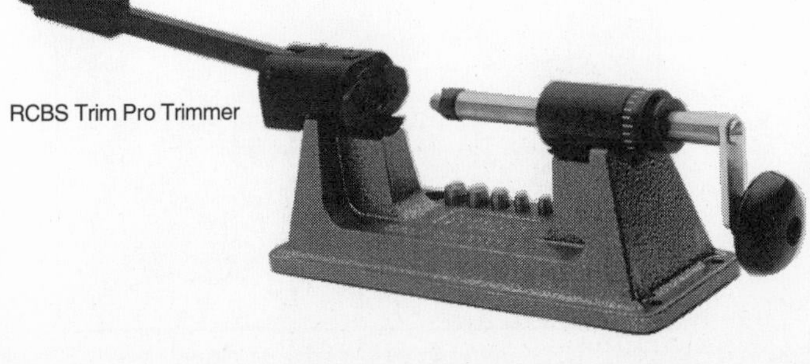

RCBS Trim Pro Trimmer

RCBS Trim Pro Case Trimmer Stand

## RCBS

### Trim Gauges

A metal collar with adjustable screw and lock nut for caliber changes on rotary case trimmers. Adjust the screw to desired length, lock it to size with nut and use over and over for that same trim length. Fits most 1/2″ diameter rotary shafts. Available in five lengths. From RCBS.

**Price:** . . . . . . . . . . . . . . . **$7.84**

### Trim Dies

Standard 7/8″-14 thread file trim die for checking and shortening cases. Available in all calibers with overall case length of 0.875″ or more. Cases measuring shorter than 1.70″ require an extension on shellholder. From RCBS.

**Price:** . . . . . . . . . . . . . . **$20.80**

### Trim Pro 3-Way Cutter

Three-blade cutter configuration attaches to Trim Pro trimmers for case length trimming, inside case chamfering and outside deburring in one step. From RCBS.

**Price:** . . . . . . . . . . . . . . **$40.25**

### Trim Pro Manual Case Trimmer

Die cast metal with hardened cutting blades. Spring-loaded lever shellholder handle replaces the draw collet system for ease of use and increased accuracy. Features flat plate shellholder to keep cases locked and aligned; micrometer fine adjustment bushing for exact trim accuracy to .001″. Works with standard RCBS pilots. From RCBS.

**Price:** . . . . . . . . . . . . . . **$67.38**
**Price:** Cover . . . . . . . . . . . . **$8.50**

### Trim Pro Case Trimmer Handle

To upgrade RCBS Case Trimmer-2 to the Trim Pro. From RCBS.

**Price:** . . . . . . . . . . . . . . **$30.38**

### Trim Pro Case Trimmer Kit

Includes Trim Pro case trimmer plus shellholders #2, #3, #4 and #10 and pilots for calibers 22, 24, 25, 27, 28, 30, 35, 40, 44 and 45. From RCBS.

**Price:** . . . . . . . . . . . . . . **$84.88**

RCBS Three Way Cutter

## RCBS

### Trim Pro Case Trimmer Stand

Designed for use with RCBS Trim Pro case trimmer to provide hand clearance and storage for flat plate shellholders and pilots. Mounts to accessory base plate or directly to bench. From RCBS.

**Price:** . . . . . . . . . . . . . **$14.25**

### Trim Pro Power Case Trimmer

Power box attachment for Trim Pro case trimmer. Low rpm for torque to handle large trimming jobs. Features positive locking handle and in-line power switch. Available as complete unit or power unit separately for use with RCBS Trimmer-2. Comes with shellholders #2, #3, #4 and #10 plus pilots for calibers 22, 24, 25, 27, 28, 30, 35, 40, 44 and 45. From RCBS.

**Price:** Complete unit . . . . . . **$205.75**
**Price:** Cover . . . . . . . . . . . **$8.50**

### Trim Pro Power Unit

To upgrade RCBS Case Trimmer-2 to Trim Pro Power Trimmer. From RCBS.

**Price:** . . . . . . . . . . . . . **$135.13**

## REDDING

### Model No. 1400 Case Trimmer

Unique design featuring stationary cutter for maximum rigidity and stiffness while case is turned. Features cast iron frame; universal collet to fit all popular rifle and pistol cases; adjustable cutter shaft to accommodate longest magnum cases; coarse and fine adjustments for case length to .001″ or less. Comes with Universal collet; six pilots, 22, 6mm, 25, 270, 7mm and 30; two neck cleaning brushes, 22- through 30-caliber; large and small primer pocket cleaners. From Redding Reloading Equipment.

**Price:** . . . . . . . . . . . . . **$93.00**

## SHERLINE

### Power Lathe

Steel bed, precision lathe for trimming large volumes of cases. Features 1/4-hp or 1/2-hp ball bearing motor. Blank collet for boring to caliber size. From Blue Ridge Machinery and Tools, Inc.

**Price:** 1/2-hp lathe . . . . . . . **$495.00**

## SINCLAIR

### Case Trimmer Mount for Wilson Trimmer

Accessory for standard Wilson case trimmer. From Sinclair International Inc.

**Price:** . . . . . . . . . . . . . **$15.60**

## SINCLAIR

### Clamp Mount Wilson/Sinclair Trimmer

Optional case holder clamping unit available for squaring case heads and trimming excessively long cases. From Sinclair International, Inc.

**Price:** Clamp mount . . . . . . . **$27.25**

### Power Screwdriver Cradle

Screwdriver cradle with power screwdriver adaptor for use with Wilson case trimmer. From Sinclair International Inc.

**Price:** 1/4-hp lathe . . . . . . . . **$13.25**

### Ultimate Trimmer Kit

Includes L.E. Wilson trimmer, micrometer attachment to replace standard Wilson adjustment screw, mounting bracket with crimp arm to hold down trimmer case holders. Starret 1″ travel micrometer head allows accurate setting of trimmer in increments of .001″. From Sinclair International Inc.

**Price:** . . . . . . . . . . . . . **$115.75**
**Price:** Micrometer attachment only . **$72.00**

## WHITETAIL DESIGN

### Cutter for Wilson Case Trimmer

Carbide cutter designed to fit the Wilson case trimmer. From Whitetail Design and Engineering Ltd.

**Price:** . . . . . . . . . . . . . **$30.00**

## WILSON

### Case Trimmer

Unique design supports case in chamber-type holder during trim operation to assure correct alignment. Cases trimmed squarely regardless of offset heads or varying neck diameters. Positive stop assures uniform length. Optional tooling allows case head squaring, inside neck reaming and removal of military primer crimp. From L.E. Wilson, Inc.

**Price:** Trimmer . . . . . . . . . . **$40.50**
**Price:** Rifle case holder . . . . . . **$6.50**
**Price:** Pistol case holder . . . . . **$9.00**
**Price:** "Q" pistol holder . . . . . **$14.00**
**Price:** Replacement cutter . . . . **$20.00**
**Price:** 17-cal. trimmer cutter . . . **$23.50**
**Price:** Replacement trimmer crank . . **$5.00**

**WILSON**
**Trimmer Case Holders**

| RIFLE | |
|---|---|
| 17 Mach IV | 7mm-08 |
| 17 Ackley Hornet | 7mm IHMSA |
| 17 Rem. | 7mm Wea. Mag. |
| 218 Bee | 30 Herrett |
| 219 Donaldson | 30 M1 Carbine |
| 219 Zipper | 30 Rem. |
| 22 Hornet | 30-06 |
| 22 PPC | 30-30 |
| 22 PPC SAKO | 30-338 |
| 22 Rem. BR | 30-40 |
| 22-250 | 300 H&H |
| 220 Swift | 300 Savage |
| 220 Wilson Arrow | 300 Wea. Mag. |
| 221 Rem. FB | 300 Win. Mag. |
| 222 Rem. | 308 Norma |
| 222 Rem. Mag. | 308 Win. |
| 223 Rem. | 7.62mm Russian |
| 224 Wea. Mag. | 7.62mmx39 |
| 225 Win. | 303 British |
| 240 Wea. Mag. | 7.65mm Belgian Mauser |
| 243 Win. | 32 Rem. |
| 6mm PPC | 32 Win. Special |
| 6mm PPC SAKO | 32-20 |
| 6mm Rem. | 32-40 |
| 6mmx47 | 8mmx57 Mauser |
| 6mm Int'l. | 8mm Rem. Mag. |
| 6mm Rem. BR | 8mm-06 |
| 25 Rem. | 338 Win. Mag. |
| 25-06 | 340 Wea. Mag. |
| 25-20 | 35 Rem. |
| 25-35 | 35 Whelen |
| 250 Savage | 35 Win. |
| 257 Roberts | 350 Rem. Mag. |
| 257 Wea. Mag. | 358 Norma Mag. |
| 264 Win. Mag. | 358 Win. |
| 6.5 Rem. Mag. | 375 H&H Mag. |
| 6.5x55 | 375 Wea. Mag. |
| 270 Wea. Mag. | 378 Wea. Mag. |
| 270 Win. | 38-40 |
| 280/7mm Express | 38-55 |
| 284 Win. | 44-40 |
| 7mm Rem. BR | 444 Marlin |
| 7mm Rem. Mag. | 45-70 Gov't. |
| 7mm TCU | 458 Win. Mag. |
| 7mmx57 Mauser | 460 Wea. Mag. |
| 7mmx61 S&H | |
| **PISTOL** | |
| 357 Magnum | 44 Magnum |
| 38 Special | 44 Special |
| 38 Super Auto | 45 Auto (ACP) |
| 9mm Luger | 45 Colt |
| 41 Magnum | |

Redding Model No. 1400

Wilson Trimmer with pistol case holder.

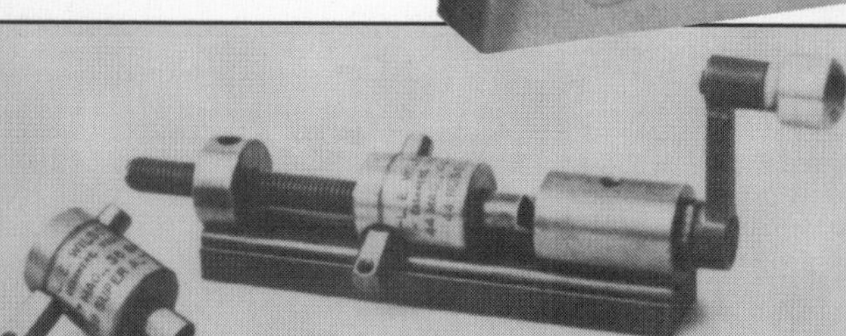

Whitetail Design Cutter

## BIRCHWOOD CASEY

**Brass Cleaner**

Liquid chemical concentrate for cleaning brass. 16-oz. bottle makes over 2 gal. of reusable cleaning solution. From Birchwood Laboratories, Inc.

**Price:** . . . . . . . . . . . . . . . **$6.95**

## MIKE DAVIS

**Brass Stripper**

Ammonia-free liquid brass cleaning concentrate. Comes in 12-oz. bottle. From Mike Davis Products.

**Price:** . . . . . . . . . . . . . . . **$5.00**

## DILLON

**Rapid Polish 290**

A cartridge case finish. Add to tumbler media. Contains no ammonia. Available in 8-oz. bottle. From Dillon Precision Products, Inc.

**Price:** . . . . . . . . . . . . . . . **$6.95**

## FLITZ

**FZ Liquid**

Non-toxic, non-abrasive liquid metal polish. Add to tumbler media. Available in three sizes of plastic bottles from 3.4-oz. to 23.6-oz. From Flitz International, Ltd.

**Price:** 3.4-oz. . . . . . . . . . . . **$5.35**
**Price:** 8.5-oz. . . . . . . . . . . . **$10.95**
**Price:** 23.6-oz. . . . . . . . . . . **$24.95**

## FORSTER

**Case Prep Cleaning Brush**

Cleans inside and outside of case necks. Fits chuck of any power drill. Available for 22, 270/7mm, 30 and 35 calibers. Five brushes in set. From Forster Products.

**Price:** . . . . . . . . . . . . . . **$21.30**

## G96

**Brass Case Cleaner**

Unique formula to clean and restore brass without etching or changing case dimension. Comes in 16-oz. plastic bottle. From G96 Products Co., Inc.

**Price:** . . . . . . . . . . . . . . . **$4.95**

## HART

**Accessory Tool Handle**

Anodized aluminum handle to hold case neck cleaning brushes threaded 8-32. From Robert Hart & Son, Inc.

**Price:** . . . . . . . . . . . . . . . **$3.95**

## HORNADY

**Case Neck Brushes**

Nine brush sizes for all popular calibers. 17, 22, 6mm, 25/6.5, 270, 7mm, 30, 338-35, 44-45 calibers. Case neck brush handle available. From Hornady Mfg. Co.

**Price:** . . . . . . . . . . . . . . . **$2.00**

**Universal Accessory Handle**

Steel, knurled handle fits all Hornady case neck brushes. From Hornady Mfg. Co.

**Price:** . . . . . . . . . . . . . . . **$2.95**

## IOSSO

**QuickBrite Case Cleaner**

Liquid immersion-type case cleaner. One quart cleans 2,000-5,000 cases. Reusable. Comes in quart, gallon containers or in kit form with strainer bag, pail, lid and quart of QuickBrite. From Iosso Products.

**Price:** Quart . . . . . . . . . . . **$8.25**
**Price:** Gallon . . . . . . . . . . **$25.85**
**Price:** Kit . . . . . . . . . . . . **$16.50**

**QuickBrite Case Polish**

Liquid additive for tumbling media. Available in quart or gallon containers. From Iosso Products.

**Price:** 8 oz. . . . . . . . . . . . **$10.30**
**Price:** Quart . . . . . . . . . . . **$36.17**
**Price:** Gallon . . . . . . . . . **$103.45**

## RCBS

**Case Neck Brushes**

Clean and lube inside case necks in one step. Three sizes of brushes: small for 22- to 25-caliber; medium for 270- to 30-caliber; and large for 35- to 45- caliber. From RCBS.

**Price:** . . . . . . . . . . . . . . . **$2.00**

## TSI

**400 Ammo Brass Cleaner**

A liquid brass cleaner that strips corrosion and oxidation inside and outside of cartridge cases. A drip process that requires no wire-brushing, tumbling or rubbing. Non-flammable, non-staining, non-etching. Is reusable, will last indefinitely. From American Gas & Chemical Company, Ltd.

**Price:** 16-oz. . . . . . . . . . . . **$5.40**
**Price:** 1-gal. . . . . . . . . . . . **$39.00**
**Price:** 55-gal. drum . . . . . . **$1,250.00**

Birchwood Casey Brass Cleaner

G96 Case Cleaner

IOSSO Quick Brite

Forster Polishing Roll

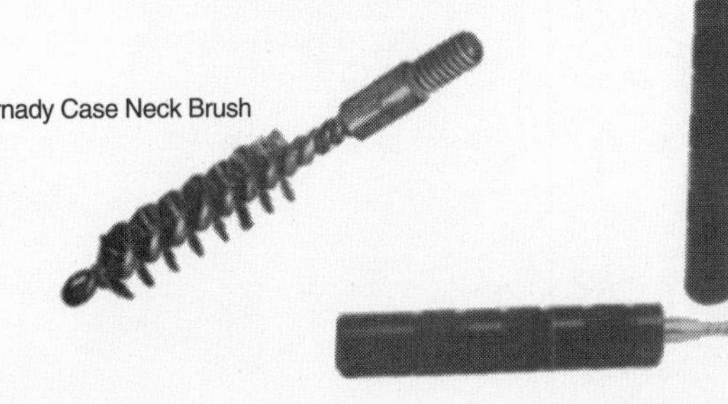

Hornady Case Neck Brush

Hart Accessory Tool Handle

METALLIC CASES/Cleaners & Polishers

## HAYDON

**Custom Case Kit**

Designed for cleaning, uniforming and deburring primer pockets. Tool ground to uniform pockets to .001″ short of max allowed. Includes debur tool, uniformer, adaptor neck brush and handle. From Russ Haydon.

**Price:** . . . . . . . . . . . . . . **$39.95**

## HORNADY

**Case Care Kit**

Includes Universal accessory handle, three case neck brushes (6mm, 338-35, and 44-45 caliber), case lube pad/load tray, chamfer/debur tool, large and small primer pocket cleaner heads and case-size lubricant. From Hornady Mfg. Co.

**Price:** . . . . . . . . . . . . . . **$23.95**

## LYMAN

**Case Care Kit**

Includes utility crank with adaptor for most Lyman accessories and standard thread; large and small primer pocket reamers and cleaners; inside/outside debur tool; case centering adaptor and ream/clean adaptor for Lyman Universal trimmer. Comes complete in plastic storage box. From Lyman Products Corporation.

**Price:** . . . . . . . . . . . . . . **$27.50**

**Case Preparation Kit**

Large and small primer pocket reamer for military brass; large and small primer pocket cleaner; two hardwood handles; three case neck brushes; case deburring tool. Comes in storage pouch and box. From Lyman Products Corporation.

**Price:** . . . . . . . . . . . . . . **$27.50**

**Power Deburring Kit**

High torque rechargeable power driver for all case prep functions. Set includes large and small primer pocket reamers and cleaners; case neck brushes; inside/outside deburring tools; hex adaptors; standard and Phillips driver bits. From Lyman Products Corporation.

**Price:** . . . . . . . . . . . . . . **$54.95**

## RCBS

**Trim Mate Case Prep Center**

Five gear driven rotating heads for chamfering, deburring, primer pocket cleaning, military crimp removal and flash hole deburring. Features 110-VAC high torque motor; two stationary positions for case neck brushes and cupped area for dry case lube. Includes large and small pocket brushes, inside chamfering and outside deburring tool, medium and small case neck brushes and dry case neck lube. From RCBS.

**Price:** 120 . . . . . . . . . . . **$109.13**
**Price:** 240 . . . . . . . . . . . **$122.00**
**Price:** Cover . . . . . . . . . . . **$6.88**

## REDDING

**Case Preparation Kit**

Contains accessory handle, large and small primer pocket cleaners and three case neck brushes to handle all cases from 22 through 45. From Redding Reloading Equipment.

**Price:** . . . . . . . . . . . . . . **$19.50**

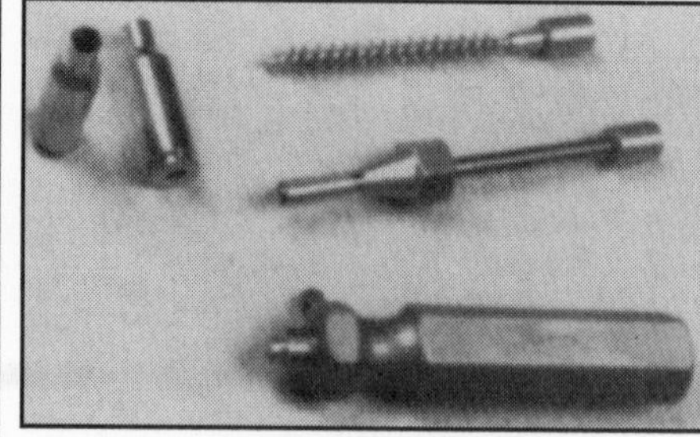

Haydon Custom Case Kit

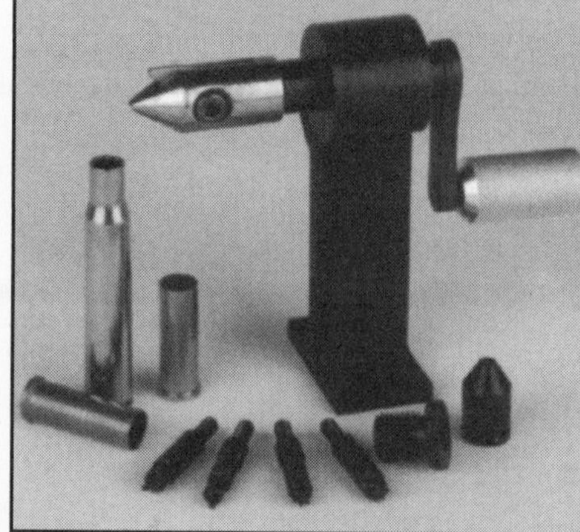

Lyman Case Care Kit

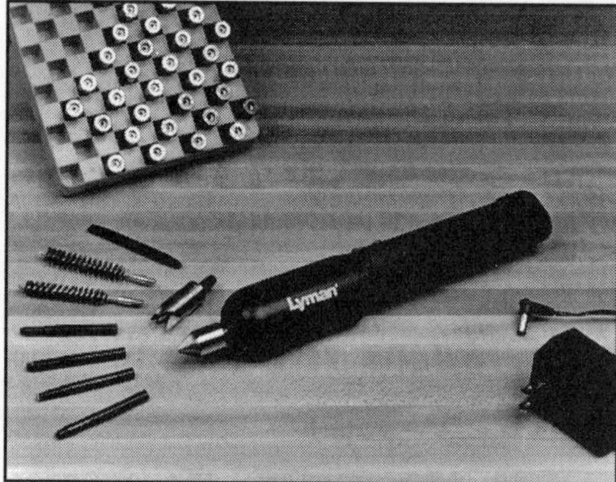


Lyman Power Deluxe Kit

Lyman Case Preparation Kit

RCBS Trim Mate

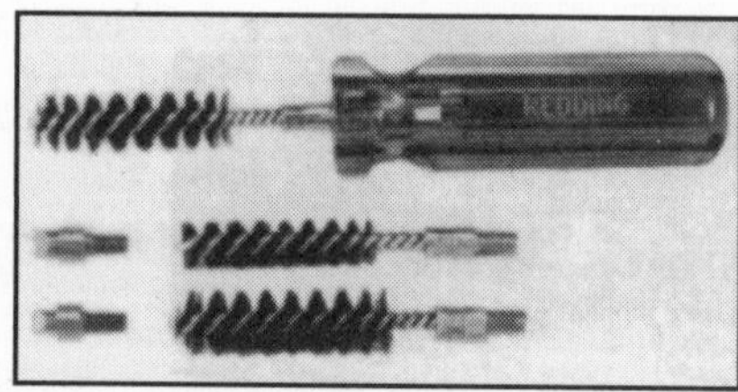


Redding Case Preparation Kit

## E. ARTHUR BROWN

**EbcoBright**

Liquid media additive to protect and polish brass. Does not contain ammonia. Comes in 4 oz. plastic bottle. From E. Arthur Brown Company.

**Price:** . . . . . . . . . . . . . . . . . **$3.50**

## BULL-X

**Tumbling Media**

Treated and untreated corn cob media available in 5- or 10-lb. quantities. From Bull-X, Inc.

**Price:** 5 lbs. treated . . . . . . . . . **$8.00**
**Price:** 5 lbs. untreated . . . . . . **$5.00**
**Price:** 10 lbs. treated . . . . . . **$15.00**
**Price:** 10 lbs. untreated . . . . . **$10.00**

## C-H/4-D

**Tumblers**

Two models available. The 60910 features 3-qt. capacity with 15-lb. max load, 10″ diameter bowl and runs on 120 VAC. The 60930 has 10-qt. capacity, 50-lb. max load, 15″ diameter bowl and runs on 120 VAC. Treated walnut shell media included. From C-H Tool & Die/4-D Die.

**Price:** 60910 . . . . . . . . . . **$119.00**
**Price:** 60930 . . . . . . . . . . **$395.00**

**Tumbling Media**

Treated or untreated fine grit walnut shell media. Comes in 5- or 10-lb. bags treated with polish or 50-lb. bag untreated. From C-H Tool & Die/4-D Custom Die.

**Price:** Treated, 5 lbs. . . . . . . . . **$5.50**
**Price:** Treated, 10 lbs. . . . . . . . **$9.50**
**Price:** Untreated, 50 lbs. . . . . . **$38.50**

**Tumbling Media Polish**

Dry powder additive for cleaning cases and removing tarnish. Does not give extremely high polish. One-ounce serves 6 lbs. of media. From C-H Tool & Die/4-D Custom Die.

**Price:** 2 oz. . . . . . . . . . . . . **$2.25**
**Price:** 1 lb. . . . . . . . . . . . . **$8.75**

## CORBIN

**Bullet Polisher Kit**

Vibratory polishing method that moves the media against cases or bullets versus rolling mixture and knocking components against each other. Includes mounting brackets, vibratory motor with enclosed eccentric weight for vibration, package of media, instructions and hardware. 115-volt operation. From Corbin Manufacturing & Supply, Inc.

**Price:** . . . . . . . . . . . . . **$49.50**

**Polishing Media**

Walnut shell media for vibratory polishing. Comes in 1-lb. bag. From Corbin Manufacturing & Supply, Inc.

**Price:** . . . . . . . . . . . . . . . **$2.00**

Corbin Bullet Polisher Kit

## MIKE DAVIS

**Corncob or Walnut Media**

Walnut shell media comes fine or medium ground in 5-lb. bags. Corncob available in 3-lb. bags and is fine ground. From Mike Davis Products.

**Price:** Walnut shell . . . . . . . . . **$2.75**
**Price:** Corncob . . . . . . . . . . **$3.00**

## DILLON

**Case Media Separators**

Large and small case/media separators. Both feature injection moulded rotating "squirrel-cage" hex-shaped basket with wall thickness of $\frac{3}{16}$″. Collection tubs of plastic with integral reliefs for the rotating handle. Large separator basket is 10″x14″ with capacity to hold 1600 38 Special cases. Plastic tub measures 18″x 22″. Small media separator basket measures $7\frac{3}{4}$″x $9\frac{3}{4}$″ with 13″x19″ tub. From Dillon Precision Products, Inc.

**Price:** Large separator . . . . . . **$44.95**
**Price:** Small separator . . . . . . **$29.95**

## DILLON

**CV500 Vibratory Case Cleaner**

Scaled-down version of the Dillon FL 2000B. Features 11-inch bowl with capacity for 360/30-06, 360/308, 600/44 Magnum, 720/223, 780/45 ACP, 780/357, 1000/38 Super or 1200/9mm; 115V AC electric motor with $\frac{1}{20}$-hp; rubber sealed lid and mounts; 5-lb. media capacity. From Dillon Precision Products, Inc.

**Price:** . . . . . . . . . . . . . **$79.95**

**FL 2000B Vibratory Case Cleaner**

Large $12\frac{1}{2}$-quart capacity allows polishing 1300 38/357 or 550 30-06 cases. Features $\frac{1}{20}$-hp internally cooled and protected motor; thick $\frac{7}{32}$″ injection moulded polypropylene bowl and base. From Dillon Precision Products, Inc.

**Price:** . . . . . . . . . . . . . **$129.95**

**Rapid Polish 290**

Ammonia-free liquid additive for tumbling media to shine cases and add protective coating. Comes in 8-oz. bottle. From Dillon Precision Products, Inc.

**Price:** . . . . . . . . . . . . . . . **$6.95**

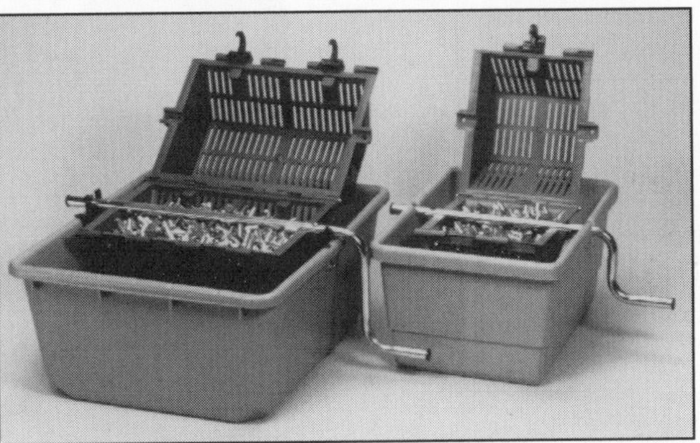

Dillon Case Media Separators

Dillon Rapid Polish

Dillon CV 500 and FL 2000B

## DILLON

**Walnut or Corncob Media**

Crushed walnut media available in 15-lb. bag; ground corn cob polishing media in 10-lb. bag. From Dillon Precision Products, Inc.

**Price:** Walnut . . . . . . . . . . **$15.95**
**Price:** Corncob . . . . . . . . . . **$8.00**

## ALLEN GODDARD

**Brass Polishing Media**

Ground walnut shell tumbler media for cleaning brass. Comes in 5-lb. quantities. From Allen Goddard.

**Price:** . . . . . . . . . . . . . . **$7.00**

## HORNADY

**M-2 Case Tumbler**

Vibratory case cleaner/polisher. Capacity for 500 38 Special cases. Available for 110- or 220-volt. Media not included. Weight: 6½ lbs. From Hornady Mfg. Co.

**Price:** 110-volt . . . . . . . . . **$79.95**
**Price:** 220-volt . . . . . . . . . **$90.95**

**Media Sifter**

Media sifter to separate brass from tumbler media. From Hornady Mfg. Co.

**Price:** . . . . . . . . . . . . . **$11.95**

**M-3 Case Tumbler**

Vibratory case cleaner/polisher with capacity for 1000 38 Special cases. Available in 110- or 220-volt. Media not included. From Hornady Mfg. Co.

**Price:** 110-volt . . . . . . . . . **$90.95**
**Price:** 120-volt . . . . . . . . . **$99.95**

**One Shot Tumbler Media**

Corncob media impregnated with cleaning solvent. Comes in ½-gallon plastic tub. From Hornady Mfg. Co.

**Price:** . . . . . . . . . . . . . . **$6.95**

## LORTONE

**Model 45C Case Tumbler**

Compact steel and aluminum frame tumbler with 10-sided solid rubber tumbling barrel. Continuous-duty overload-protected ball bearing motor enclosed in frame. Capacity for 180 38 Special or 75 30-06 cases. UL and CSA listed. Dimensions: 6¼"x10¼". Weight: 7 lbs. From Lortone, Inc.

**Price:** . . . . . . . . . . . . . **$74.50**

**Model QT-6, QT-12 and QT-66 Tumblers**

Heavy-duty, large-capacity tumblers feature 10-sided solid rubber barrel; welded steel frame; fully enclosed drive system and overload-protected ball bearing motor. Capacity of the QT-6 is 260 38 Special cases or 90 30-06 cases; QT-12 can hold 600 38 Specials or 200 30-06. The QT-66 features two barrels with total capacity for 520 38 Special cases or 180 30-06 cases. The two barrel design allows cleaning two different calibers of brass at same time. From Lortone, Inc.

**Price:** QT-6 . . . . . . . . . . **$110.00**
**Price:** QT-12 . . . . . . . . . **$128.00**
**Price:** QT-66 . . . . . . . . . **$142.50**

**Tumbler Media**

Black walnut shell treated with non-toxic industrial cleaning/polishing agents. Comes in 24-oz. plastic pouch. From Lortone, Inc.

**Price:** . . . . . . . . . . . . . . **$4.75**

Hornady M-3 and Media Sifter

Lortone Model 45C

Lyman Auto-Flo 2200

## LYMAN

**Auto-Flo Conversion System**

For converting Lyman 600, 1200, 2200 and 3200 tumblers to Auto-Flo. Includes bowl, lid, Auto-Flo drain base and media dump pan. From Lyman Products Corporation.

**Price:** 600/1200 . . . . . . . . . **$29.95**
**Price:** 2200 . . . . . . . . . . **$49.95**
**Price:** 3200 . . . . . . . . . . **$59.95**

**Auto-Flo Tumblers**

Available in Lyman 1200, 2200, 3200 and Mag models. Features automatic separation of media and cases via exit port in bowl for media removal after cleaning. Conversion kit also available to upgrade standard 600, 1200, 2200 or 3200 tumblers. Either 110- or 220-volt. From Lyman Products Corporation.

**Price:** 1200, 110-volt . . . . . **$109.95**
**Price:** 1200, 220-volt . . . . . **$115.00**
**Price:** 2200, 110-volt . . . . . **$125.00**
**Price:** 2200, 220-volt . . . . . **$134.00**
**Price:** 3200, 110-volt . . . . . **$175.00**
**Price:** 3200, 220-volt . . . . . **$195.00**

## LYMAN

**Case Separating Bags**

Allows separate cleaning of different calibers or batches of cases during tumbling. Come in packs of 12. From Lyman Products Corporation.

**Price:** . . . . . . . . . . . . . . **$4.25**

**Easy Pour Media**

Large plastic containers of treated corncob (6 lbs.), Tuf-Nut (7 lbs.) or untreated corncob with brass polish (6 lbs.) with flip-top lids. From Lyman Products Corporation.

**Price:** . . . . . . . . . . . . . **$14.95**

**Flash Hole Cleaner**

Designed to remove bits of media from flash holes and primer pockets. From Lyman Products Corporation.

**Price:** . . . . . . . . . . . . . . **$7.00**

**Super Mag Auto-Flo Tumbler**

For the high volume reloader. Features industrial strength motor, capacity of over 3 gallons to clean up to 2000 pistol cases. Auto Flo feature automatically separates media from cases with media draining into drain pan. Comes with media drain pan. Available in 110- or 220-volt. From Lyman Products Corporation.

**Price:** 110-volt . . . . . . . . **$229.95**
**Price:** 220-volt . . . . . . . . **$232.50**

Lyman Turbo Tumblers

**LYMAN** *Turbo Tumblers*

| Model * | Media Charge (lbs.) | # 38 Special Cases | Nominal Capacity | Bowl Size | Media Included | On/Off Switch | Weight (lbs.) | Price |
|---|---|---|---|---|---|---|---|---|
| Tubby | 3/4 | 100 | 2 pts. | NA | Y | Y | | $58.50 |
| 600 | 1 | 175 | 3 pts. | 8″ | Y | Y | 7 | 74.95 |
| 1200 | 2 | 350 | 1 gal. | 10″ | Y | Y | 10 | 99.95 |
| 2200 | 4 | 750 | 1.5 gal. | 12″ | N | N | 12 | 116.95 |
| 3200 | 5 | 1000 | 2.2 gal. | 13″ | N | N | 13 | 164.95 |
| Super Mag | 8.5 | 1800 | 3.25 gal. | 17″ | N | N | | 229.95 |

*For Auto-Flo models add 1 to 2 lbs. extra.

Lyman Super Mag

Lyman Turbo Sift Systems

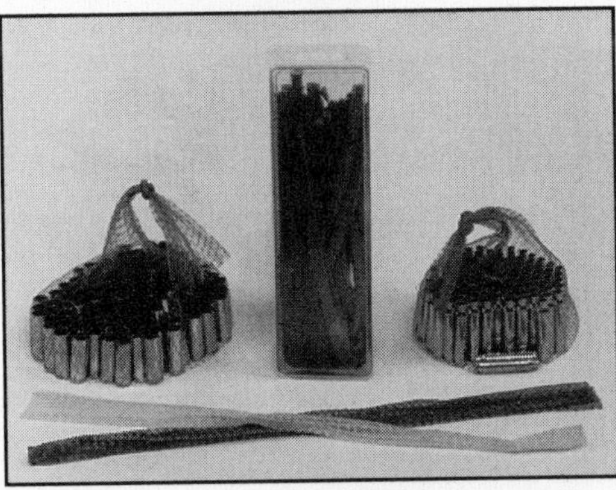

Lyman Case Separating Bags

Lyman Turbo Brite

## LYMAN

**Twin Tumbler**

Includes tumbler base for interchangeable use of both 1200 Pro Model or 600 Pop Top bowl system. Capacity of from 175 to 350 38 Special cases and 1 to 2 lbs. of media. 110-volt. From Lyman Products Corporation.

**Price:** 110-volt . . . . . . . . . . **$82.95**
**Price:** 220-volt . . . . . . . . . . **$92.50**

**Tubby Tumbler**

Small-capacity vibrating tumbler. Holds 100 38 Special pistol cases, 40-50 rifle cases. Features Vibra-Tab for adjustable tumbling speed; built-in handle for easy emptying; see-through lid. Available in 110- or 220-volt. From Lyman Products Corporation.

**Price:** 110-volt . . . . . . . . . . **$58.50**
**Price:** 220-volt . . . . . . . . . . **$64.00**

**Turbo Accessory Bowls**

To upgrade tumbler to use with liquid cleaners or double the capacity. 600 bowl for liquid use with 1200 tumbler. 1200 bowl for use with 600 doubles capacity. From Lyman Products Corporation.

**Price:** 1200 . . . . . . . . . . **$19.95**
**Price:** 600 . . . . . . . . . . **$14.95**

**Turbo Brite Polish**

Additive designed for untreated corncob media. Comes in 5-oz. or 20-oz. bottles. From Lyman Products Corporation.

**Price:** 5-oz. . . . . . . . . . . **$3.95**
**Price:** 20-oz. . . . . . . . . . . **$9.00**

**Turbo Charger Media Reactivator**

Restores heavily used corn cob media. Available in 4-oz. or 16-oz. bottles. From Lyman Products Corporation.

**Price:** 4-oz. . . . . . . . . . . **$3.75**
**Price:** 16-oz. . . . . . . . . . . **$9.00**

**Turbo Liquid Case Cleaner**

Non-etching solution for extremely fouled or corroded cases. Use manually or with tumbler. Comes in 16-oz. bottle. From Lyman Products Corporation.

**Price:** . . . . . . . . . . . . **$5.00**

**Turbo Media**

Specially treated corncob or Tufnut, rouge bearing crushed nut shell, media. Corncob available in 1-, 2- or 10-lb. quantities; Tuf-Nut in 3- and 12-lb. boxes. From Lyman Products Corporation.

**Price:** 2-lb. corncob/3-lb. Tuf-Nut . . **$6.50**
**Price:** 10-lb. corncob/12-lb. Tuf-Nut . **$16.50**

**Turbo Polishing Cloth**

Highly abrasive 160 square inch cloth for cleaning and burnishing all types of metal. Removes rust, tarnish and corrosion. From Lyman Products Corporation.

**Price:** . . . . . . . . . . . . **$3.50**

**Turbo Sift Systems**

Tub bucket, sifter and scoop for removing and separating cases from tumbler media. From Lyman Products Corporation.

**Price:** Sifter . . . . . . . . . . **$8.75**

**Turbo Tumblers**

Four basic models, 600, 1200, 2200 and 3200, with varying capacities. All feature high-speed agitation for 2-hour cleaning; top-load design for in-operation inspection; motor screen; on/off switches; ability to handle wet or dry media. From Lyman Products Corporation.

**Price:** . . . . . . . . . . . . **See chart.**

### M&D

**Vibrating Media**

Corn cob media for vibratory tumblers. Available in 50-lb. quantities. From M&D Munitions, Ltd.

**Price:** . . . . . . . . . . . . . . **$24.50**

### MIDWAY

**Brass Cleaning Media**

Ground corncob or walnut hull media available plain or treated with brass polish. From Midway Arms, Inc.

**Price:** Corncob, 15-lb. plain . . . . **$16.99**
**Price:** Corncob, 5-lb. treated . . . . **$13.99**
**Price:** Walnut, 18-lb. plain . . . . **$19.99**
**Price:** Walnut, 7-lb. treated . . . . **$15.99**

**Brass Polish**

Liquid media additive which contains no ammonia or petroleum distillates. Comes in 8-oz. or 32-oz. plastic bottle. From Midway Arms, Inc.

**Price:** 8-oz. . . . . . . . . . . . . **$4.99**
**Price:** 32-oz. . . . . . . . . . . . **$16.49**

**Brass Sifter and Plastic Bucket**

Designed specifically for brass and media separation. Sifter nests inside bucket top securely with large handles for removal. Bucket available in two sizes, 3½-gallon or 5-gallon. From Midway Arms, Inc.

**Price:** Sifter . . . . . . . . . . . **$12.99**
**Price:** 3½-gal. . . . . . . . . . . . **$7.99**
**Price:** 5-gal. . . . . . . . . . . . **$8.99**

**Clear Tumbler Lid**

Designed to fit Midway Model 1292, RCBS vibratory or Hornady M2 tumblers. Made of clear polycarbonate (Lexan) for case inspection during tumbler operation. From Midway Arms, Inc.

**Price:** . . . . . . . . . . . . . . **$5.99**

**Model 1292 Brass Tumbler**

Vibratory tumbler featuring all ball bearing motor with lightweight integrated rib bowl. Holds up to 500 38 Special cases or 185 30-06 Springfield cases. From Midway Arms, Inc.

**Price:** . . . . . . . . . . . . . . **$44.99**

**Rotary Brass Sifter**

Plastic manually-operated sifter designed for efficient seperation of media from brass. Comes with adapter to fit 3½-gal. bucket. From Midway Arms, Inc.

**Price:** . . . . . . . . . . . . . . **$19.99**

**Rotary Brass Sifter Kit**

Includes rotary sifter, bucket adapter, 3½-gal. bucket, 8 oz. brass polish and 7 lbs. corn cob media. From Midway Arms, Inc.

**Price:** . . . . . . . . . . . . . . **$34.99**

Midway Media

Midway Brass Polish

Midway Model 1292

Midway Brass Sifter

NECO Super Viking

### NATIONAL BULLET

**Tumbler Media**

Ground walnut shells for use in any standard tumbler to clean and polish brass cases. Comes in 5-lb. bag. From National Bullet Co.

**Price:** . . . . . . . . . . . . . . **$4.50**

**Media Recharger**

Recharging media for ground walnut shell tumbling media. Comes in 16-oz. plastic bottle. From National Bullet Co.

**Price:** . . . . . . . . . . . . . . **$2.00**

### NECO

**Super Viking Tumbler**

Heavy-duty 6-lb. capacity rotary tumbler with industrial grade fan-cooled motor. Geodesic design turns contents six times per revolution to prevent hang-up during cycle. From NECO.

**Price:** . . . . . . . . . . . . . **$339.50**

**Neco Coat**

Dry media to provide molybdenum disulfide friction lubricant to bullets followed by outer coating of carnauba wax. Comes in kit form and includes 4 oz. ultra fine moly, 3 oz. fine carnauba wax, 8 oz. corn cob grit, 4.5 lb. steel shot. From NECO.

**Price:** . . . . . . . . . . . . . **$137.35**

NECO Coat

RCBS Vibratory Case Cleaner

Raytech Screens

Tru-Square AR-6

## RANGE BRASS PRODUCTS

**Range Brass Cleaner**

Brass cleaning concentrate for pre-cleaning heavily tarnished range brass prior to tumbling. One quart cleans 1500-2000 severely tarnished 9mm Parabellum or 500-750 308 cases. Biodegradable and completely soluble in water. From Range Brass Products.

**Price:** 1-qt. concentrate . . . . . . **$12.00**

**Range Brass Neutralizer**

For brass that is to be stored after cleaning but prior to tumbling. The Range Brass Neutralizer is made of metallic carbonates and neutralizes the action of the brass cleaner concentrate. From Range Brass Products.

**Price:** 4-oz. neutralizer . . . . . . **$5.00**

**Range Brass Anti-Tarnish Strips**

For safe storage of cleaned brass to prevent tarnishing. Come in 2″x7″ strips and ten to a package. From Range Brass Products.

**Price:** . . . . . . . . . . . . . . . **$5.00**

## RAYTECH

**Separating Screens**

Separating tub and screen for separating media from cases. Screen diameter 14½″x 2½″ depth; 1 cubic foot tote container. Five screen sizes available from ¼″ openings to 1″. Made of high-impact polymer. From Raytech, Division of Lyman Products Corporation.

**Price:** Set of five . . . . . . . . **$135.00**
**Price:** Each . . . . . . . . . . . **$23.00**

## RCBS

**Case Cleaning Media**

Liquid or dry media. Liquid case cleaner concentrate for use in the Sidewinder tumbler comes in 8-oz. bottle and makes 4 gals. liquid cleaner. Formula 1 walnut shell dry media is ground to a 12/20 sieve size and coated with two cleaning oxides. It comes in 5-lb. box. Formula 2 corncob media combines ground corn cob with a chromium oxide polisher and cleaner. Available in 4-lb. box. From RCBS.

**Price:** Liquid media . . . . . . . **$4.38**
**Price:** Formula 1 . . . . . . . . **$11.50**
**Price:** Formula 2 . . . . . . . . **$12.75**

**Sidewinder Case Tumbler**

Liquid or dry media tumbler with capacity up to 300 38 Special or 150 30-06 cases. Features tilting drum for easy access; built-in timer for automatic shut-off from 5 minutes to 12 hours; self-aligning rear bearings; industrial-grade timing belt drive system; polyurethane drum; and two covers, one solid cap and one perforated cap that doubles as a media screen separator. Available in 120- or 240-volt models. 8-oz. bottle liquid case cleaner included. From RCBS.

**Price:** . . . . . . . . . . . . . . **$243.75**
**Price:** Drum Assembly . . . . . . **$45.70**

**Vibratory Case Cleaner**

Designed for dry-media cleaning and polishing of large quantities of cartridge cases. 3½-quart bowl holds up to 400 38 Special or 180 30-06 cases. Thermally protected ball-bearing motor operates on 120/240 VAC. From RCBS.

**Price:** 120 VAC . . . . . . . . **$119.38**
**Price:** 240 VAC . . . . . . . . **$147.00**
**Price:** Media sifter . . . . . . . . **$9.25**

## ROOSTER

**Brass Polish**

Ammonia-free liquid additive to tumbling media. Contains no petroleum distillates or hazardous ingredients. Cleans, polishes and provides protective finish. Comes in 8-oz., 32-oz., 1-, 5- or 55-gallon quantities. From Rooster Laboratories.

**Price:** 8-oz. . . . . . . . . . . . . **$4.50**
**Price:** 32-oz. . . . . . . . . . . . **$12.50**
**Price:** 1-gal. . . . . . . . . . . . **$30.00**
**Price:** 5-gal. . . . . . . . . . . **$135.00**
**Price:** 55-gal. . . . . . . . . . **$1,250.00**

## TOMBSTONE SMOKE N DEALS

**Corn Cob Tumbling Media**

For final polishing brass cases. Comes in 10-lb. or 50-lb. plastic bags. From Tombstone Smoke N Deals.

**Price:** 10 lbs. . . . . . . . . . . . **$6.95**
**Price:** 50 lbs. . . . . . . . . . . . **$35.00**

**Tumbler**

Vibratory tumbler featuring powerful self-cooling motor; 600-round (9mm) or 350-round (223) capacity bowl; lifetime warranty. Height, 22″; width, 11″; bowl depth, 4.5″. From Tombstone Smoke N Deals.

**Price:** . . . . . . . . . . . . . . **$49.95**

**Walnut Shell Media**

For deep cleaning brass cases. Comes in 15-lb. or 50-lb. plastic bags. From Tombstone Smoke N Deals.

**Price:** 15 lbs. . . . . . . . . . . . **$12.95**
**Price:** 50 lbs. . . . . . . . . . . . **$38.00**

**Brass Polish**

Specially formulated brass polish designed to polish and protect brass without ammonia. Removes dirt, lubricant and tarnish from brass. Comes in 8-oz. or 16-oz. plastic bottles. From Tombstone Smoke N Deals.

**Price:** 8-oz. . . . . . . . . . . . . **$4.49**
**Price:** 16-oz. . . . . . . . . . . . **$7.95**

## 3-D

**Brass Cleaning Media**

Maize cleaning media available in 4-lb. jugs or 24-lb. bulk containers. From 3-D Ammunition.

**Price:** . . . . . **Contact manufacturer.**

## TRU-SQUARE

**Brass Bags**

Bags to hold brass during tumbling operation. Come six bags to a pack. From Tru-Square Metal Products.

**Price:** . . . . . . . . . . . . . . **$2.10**

**Brass Polish Corncob Media**

Treated crushed corn cob for use in vibratory or rotary tumblers. Comes in 15-lb. bag. From Tru-Square Metal Products.

**Price:** . . . . . . . . . . . . . . **$49.09**

**Brass Polish Walnut Media**

Treated crushed black walnut shell media. Comes in 15-, 30- or 60-oz. containers. From Tru-Square Metal Products.

**Price:** 15-oz. . . . . . . . . . . . **$5.00**
**Price:** 30-oz. . . . . . . . . . . . **$9.75**
**Price:** 60-oz. . . . . . . . . . . **$19.55**

**Brass Media Booster**

Additive for walnut or corncob media. Available in 4-oz. bottle. From Tru-Square Metal Products.

**Price:** . . . . . . . . . . . . . . **$5.86**

## TRU-SQUARE

**Brass Pack**
Includes brass separator, 6 lbs. treated corncob media and 4-oz. bottle media booster. From Tru-Square Metal Products.
**Price:** . . . . . . . . . . . . . . **$35.47**

**Brass Separator**
Plastic 12″ diameter sifter to separate brass from media. From Tru-Square Metal Products.
**Price:** . . . . . . . . . . . . . . **$9.33**

**Liquid Brass Cleaner**
Designed for use in rotary tumblers to pre-clean cases. Comes in 8-oz. bottle. From Tru-Square Metal Products.
**Price:** . . . . . . . . . . . . . . **$5.37**

**Model AR-6 Rotary Tumbler**
Moulded rubber, water-tight barrel with 16-sided interior; 3-qt. capacity to hold 400 cases and weight capacity of 9 lbs.; heavy-gauge steel base; 115-volt, 1/75-hp, .67-amp thermally protected motor. Dimensions: 6″x11″x10½″. Weight: 7.5 lbs. From Tru-Square Metal Products.
**Price:** . . . . . . . . . . . . . **$130.07**

**Model AR-12 Rotary Tumbler**
Moulded rubber, water tight hexagonal barrel with 1-gal. capacity to hold 150-500 cases and weight capacity to 12 lbs; heavy-gauge steel base; 115-volt thermally protected motor. Dimensions: 11″x11″x11″. Weight: 10 lbs. From Tru-Square Metal Products.
**Price:** . . . . . . . . . . . . . **$147.78**

**Model B Rotary Tumbler**
Features water tight steel barrel with heavy rubber liner; 1¼-gal. barrel capacity to hold 200-600 cases with weight capacity of 15 lbs; heavy steel base; thermally protected 1/50-hp motor operating on 115-volt, draws .9 amps. Dimensions: 11″x11″x11″. Weight: 16 lbs. From Tru-Square Metal Products.
**Price:** . . . . . . . . . . . . . **$189.77**

**Model B Liner**
Polyethelene liner designed for moly-coating bullets in Model B rotary tumbler. From Tru-Square Metal Products.
**Price:** . . . . . **Contact manufacturer.**

**Model UV-10 Vibratory Tumbler**
Features removable heavy polyethylene bowl with lid; 3-qt. capacity to hold 125-400 cases and weight capacity to 10 lbs.; overload protected ball bearing motor operating on 115 volts; vibrating action at 3000 vpm. Comes with 3 lbs. media. Dimemsions: 10″x11″. Weight: 8 lbs. From Tru-Square Metal Products.
**Price:** . . . . . . . . . . . . . **$171.92**

**Model UV-18 Vibratory Tumbler**
Larger than Model UV-10 but with same features. Features 1½-gal. capacity to hold 200-700 cases and weight capacity to 18 lbs. Optional 6 lbs. media. Dimensions: 11½″x12½″. Weight: 11 lbs. From Tru-Square Metal Products.
**Price:** . . . . . . . . . . . . . **$211.24**
**Price:** With media . . . . . . . **$236.67**

**Model UV-45 Vibratory Tumbler**
Largest of Tru-Square offerings. Features 4¾-gal. capacity to hold 1000 30-06 cases and weight capacity to 57 lbs.; variable amplitude for desired finish during deburring. Optional with 15 lbs. media. Dimensions: 17″x18″. Weight: 26 lbs. From Tru-Square Metal Products.
**Price:** . . . . . . . . . . . . . **$576.18**
**Price:** With media . . . . . . . **$630.20**

Tru-Square Brass Polish

Vibrashine VS-10

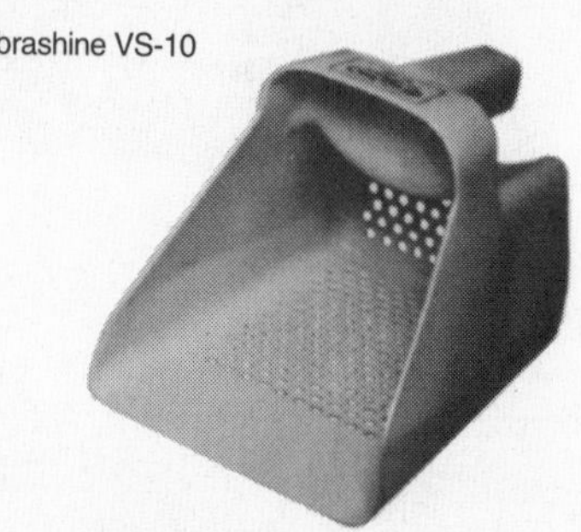
Wilcox Scoop

## TRU-SQUARE

**Brass Polish Media**
Reusable crushed corn cob media for use in vibratory or rotary tumblers available in 3- or 6-lb. quantities. From Tru-Square Metal Products.
**Price:** 3 lbs. . . . . . . . . . . . **$12.20**
**Price:** 6 lbs. . . . . . . . . . . . **$23.08**

## VIBRASHINE

**Brass Separator**
Plastic separator lid to fit VibraShine VS-20 and VS-30 tumblers and most other popular sizes of tumblers. From VibraShine, Inc.
**Price:** . . . . . . . . . . . . . . **$7.95**

**Treated Media**
Treated processed corncob media for use in vibratory tumblers. Comes in 6-lb. boxes. From VibraShine, Inc.
**Price:** . . . . . . . . . . . . . **$11.87**

**VS-10 Brass Polisher**
Dual vibrating motor design with no belts or bearings. 3-pint capacity to hold 50 30-06 or 100 45 cases. Features removable see-through bowl with snap-on lid, on/off switch, speed selection, heavy-duty power cord and housing constructed of one-piece injection moulded plastic. Comes with media. From VibraShine, Inc.
**Price:** . . . . . . . . . . . . . **$39.95**

**VS-15 Brass Polisher**
Heavy-duty tumbler designed specifically for impact moly-coating bullets with steel shot. Features capacity to coat 1000 6mm bullets in ½-hour; applies wax in one minute or less. Comes with three bowls for moly or wax application and for brass tumbling. From VibraShine, Inc.
**Price:** . . . . . **Contact manufacturer.**

## VIBRASHINE

**VS-20 Vibratory Tumbler**
Same features as VS-30 with 10″ diameter, 3-qt. capacity bowl. From VibraShine, Inc.
**Price:** . . . . . . . . . . . . . . **$64.95**

**VS-30 Vibratory Tumbler**
Designed for high-volume cleaning. Features 1½-gal. capacity heavy-duty bowl with removable lid; 1.4 amp thermally protected, fan-cooled, ball bearing motor; on-off switch. From VibraShine, Inc.
**Price:** . . . . . . . . . . . . . . **$84.95**

## VIBRA-TEK

**Brass Polishers**
Standard and magnum vibrating brass polishers. Capacity for 300 cases for standard model; magnum model holds 5 lbs. media. Features adjustable vibrating action; use with wet or dry media. Comes with polishing media. From Vibra-Tek Company.
**Price:** Standard with 2 lbs. media . . **$99.00**
**Price:** Magnum with 5 lbs. media . **$159.00**
**Price:** 2-oz. recharge liquid . . . . **$4.00**

**Polishing Media**
Fine-ground black walnut shell media impregnated with iron oxide. Available in 2- or 5-lb. quantities. From Vibra-Tek Company.
**Price:** 2 lbs. . . . . . . . . . . . . **$9.00**
**Price:** 5 lbs. . . . . . . . . . . . **$13.95**

## WILCOX

**All-Pro Scoops**
Two scoops for separating media and cases. Sifting Scoop perforated with 217 ¼″ diameter holes; Treasure Scoop has 54 ¾″ holes. From Wilcox.
**Price:** . . . . . . . . . . . . . . **$6.49**

## C-H

**50 BMG Flash Hole Deburring Tool**

Removes flash-hole burrs from inside 50 BMG primer pockets. Features adjustable stop collar and replaceable cutter. From C-H Tool & Die/4-D Custom Die.

**Price:** . . . . . . . . . . . . . . **$25.00**

**Deburring/Chamfering Tool**

Standard or magnum size tool for beveling inside and outside of case mouth. Standard tool fits 17- to 45-caliber; magnum tool for 45- to 60-caliber cases. From C-H Tool & Die/4-D Custom Die.

**Price:** Standard . . . . . . . . **$11.95**
**Price:** Magnum . . . . . . . . . . **$18.95**

**Standard Flash Hole Deburring Tool**

Removes flash-hole burrs from inside primer pockets. Features adjustable stop collar and replaceable cutter. From C-H Tool & Die/4-D Custom Die.

**Price:** . . . . . . . . . . . . . . **$15.00**

## FORSTER

**DBT Adapter**

Used with Forster deburring tool, this device converts Forster trimmer to deburring tool holder. Mounts on case trimmer cutter shaft and is used with case trimmer collet housing removed. From Forster Products.

**Price:** . . . . . . . . . . . . . . **$10.70**

**DBT Base**

Bench-mountable stand for Forster deburring tool with hand crank for speed of operation. May also be used with Forster power adapter which allows removal of hand crank and functions with cordless screwdriver. Weight: 10 oz. From Forster Products.

**Price:** . . . . . . . . . . . . . . **$23.50**
**Price:** Power adapter . . . . . . **$15.00**

**Inside/Outside Deburring Tool**

Deburring hand tool. Precision ground cutting edges allow smooth removal of irregularities and burrs at mouth of case. Handles all case sizes from 17- to 45-caliber. From Forster Products.

**Price:** . . . . . . . . . . . . . . **$16.40**

**Inside Neck Reamer**

Removes excess brass from case neck walls. Made from high grade, wear resistant tool steel and ground .002″ to .0025″ over maximum bullet diameter. Has staggered tooth design for chatterless cutting. For use with Forster case trimmer. Available in standard calibers (17, 223, 224, 243, 257, 263, 277, 284, 308, 311, 323, 338, 355, 358, 375, 400, 410, 432, 452, 458). Weight: 3 oz. From Forster Products.

**Price:** . . . . . . . . . . . . . . **$17.40**

**Outside Neck Turner Adapter Kit**

Adapter kit for RCBS Trimmer II case trimmer. Allows use of Forster outside/inside neck tools, primer pocket and case neck cleaning and chamfering tools plus Forster hollowpointer on RCBS trimmer. Weight: 1 lb. From Forster Products.

**Price:** . . . . . . . . . . . . . . **$48.00**

Forster DBT Adaptor

C-H Debur/Chamfer Tool

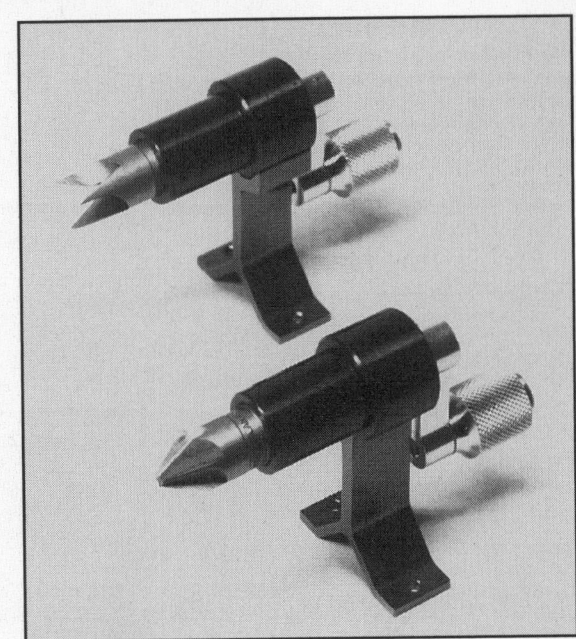

Forster DBT Base

Hanned Line Nexpander

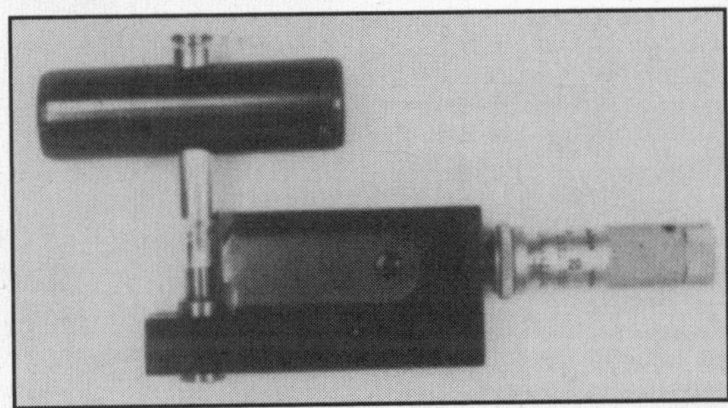

Hart Deluxe Neck Turner

## FORSTER

**Outside Neck Turner**

Turns any diameter case neck between .170 and .375 concentric to its true axis. For use with Forster case trimmer; replace short pilot with extra long, hardened and ground pilot of desired caliber. Pilot not included. Available in standard calibers (17, 224, 243, 257, 277, 263, 284, 308, 311, 323, 333, 338, 358, 375); custom calibers are additional cost. Long 6½″ base for neck turning 375 magnum or longer also available. Weight: 9 oz. From Forster Products.

**Price:** . . . . . . . . . . . . . . **$32.50**
**Price:** Pilot . . . . . . . . . . . . **$7.20**
**Price:** Long base . . . . . . . . . **$14.10**

## HANNED LINE

**Nexpander**

Double-ended stainless steel taper punch for putting a slight flare in case mouths to seat cast bullets without deformation. Will handle cases from 17 Remington to 50 BMG. From The Hanned Line.

**Price:** . . . . . . . . . . . . . . **$16.00**

## HART

**Deluxe Neck Turning Tool**

Features micrometer dial adjustment for precision cutting. Includes one mandrel, one expansion plug and handle. From Robert Hart & Sons, Inc.

**Price:** . . . . . . . . . . . . . . **$115.95**
**Price:** Extra mandrel and plug . . . **$16.95**
**Price:** Extra handle . . . . . . . . **$7.95**

**Standard Neck Turning Tool**

Designed to turn the outside of case neck to desired wall thickness and depth; will hold a wall thickness of .0003″. Mandrel has end stop to assure consistency. Requires handle, mandrel and expansion plug for each caliber from 22 through 30. High speed steel cutter with hardened mandrels. From Robert Hart & Son, Inc.

**Price:** . . . . . . . . . . . . . . **$79.95**
**Price:** Handle . . . . . . . . . . . **$7.95**
**Price:** Mandrel and expansion plug . **$16.95**
**Price:** Replacement cutter . . . . **$21.00**

## HOEHNS

**Carbide Neck Turning Mandrel**

Will fit all major manufacturers' neck turners. Available for 17-, 22-, 6mm, 25-, 7mm and 30-calibers. Available with long shank for use with power screwdriver or power drill. From Hoehns Shooting Supply.

**Price:** . . . . . . . . . . . . . . **$30.00**
**Price:** Long shank . . . . . . . **$35.00**

## HORNADY

**Chamfer/Debur Tool**

Dual-function knurled steel tool to smooth and debur inside and outside of case mouths. From Hornady Mfg. Co.

**Price:** . . . . . . . . . . . . . . **$10.50**

## K&M

**Expandiron**

Adapter threaded 7/8-14 to fit standard presses with mandrels sized for correct use with K&M Case Neck Turning Tool. Smooths out and slightly expands case neck so brass will spring back to correct size for neck turning. Mandrels available in 17-, 22-, 6mm, 25-, 6.5mm, 270-, 7mm and 30-calibers. Mandrels screw-adjustable to prevent case mouth from hitting mandrel shoulder. From K&M Services.

**Price:** Adapter with one mandrel . . **$15.00**
**Price:** Additional mandrels . . . . . **$9.00**

**Micro-Adjustable Case Neck Turning Tool**

Adjustable outside neck turning tool. Removes desired amount of brass from thick side of case to equal thin side or can be adjusted to cut down case wall thickness to desired dimension. Tolerance to .0001″ possible via compound thread equal to 440 turns to the inch. Index marks provided to assist adjustment. Tool is special ground with angles unique to cutting brass. Case holder uses Lee Auto Prime shellholder for various calibers. Power adaptor available for use with low speed drill or cordless screwdriver. Mandrels available in 17-, 22-, 6mm, 25-, 6.5mm, 270-, 7mm and 30-calibers. Comes complete for one caliber with pilot and case holder or without case holder. From K&M Services.

**Price:** Complete tool . . . . . . . **$60.00**
**Price:** Without case holder . . . . **$48.00**
**Price:** Power adaptor . . . . . . **$20.00**
**Price:** Pilots . . . . . . . . . . **$9.00**

**Controlled Depth Tapered Case Mouth Reamer**

Six-fluted reamer features 4° per side taper with adjustable depth stop. For all cases 22- through 30-caliber. Provides consistent chamfer case to case. From K&M Services.

**Price:** . . . . . . . . . . . . . . **$18.00**

## LEE

**Chamfer Tool**

Chamfer tool with knurled base to chamfer and debur inside and outside of case neck. Also used to remove crimp from primer pockets of military brass. From Lee Precision, Inc.

**Price:** . . . . . . . . . . . . . . **$2.98**

## LYMAN

**Chamfer/Debur Accessory Tool**

For use with Lyman case trimmers and Utility crank. Chamfers and deburs trimmed cases simultaneously. Adjusts to fit case mouths from 17- to 45-caliber. From Lyman Products Corporation.

**Price:** . . . . . . . . . . . . . . **$10.75**

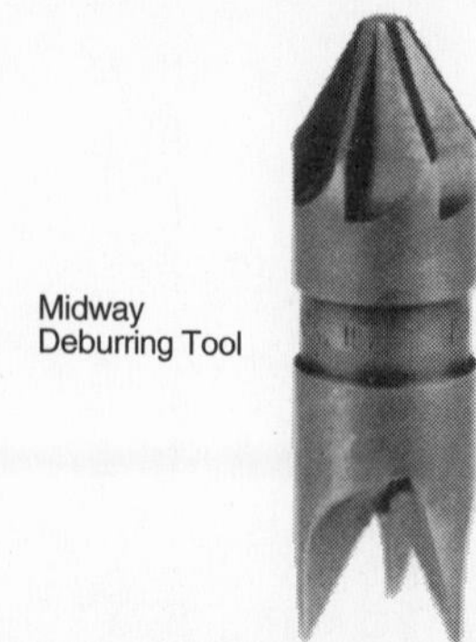

Midway Deburring Tool

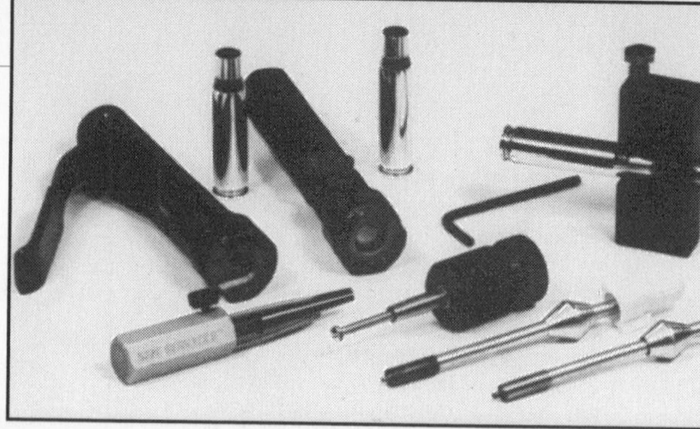
K&M Tools

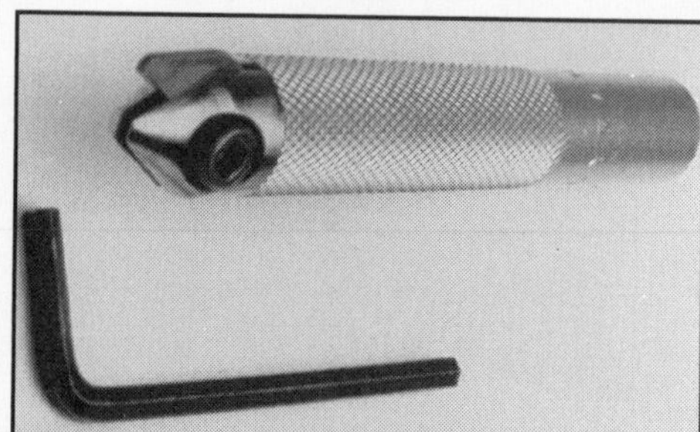
Lyman Inside/Outside Debur Tool

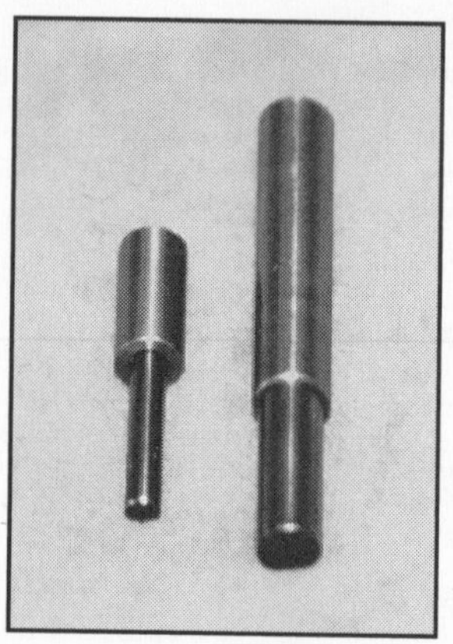
Hoehns Neck Mandrel

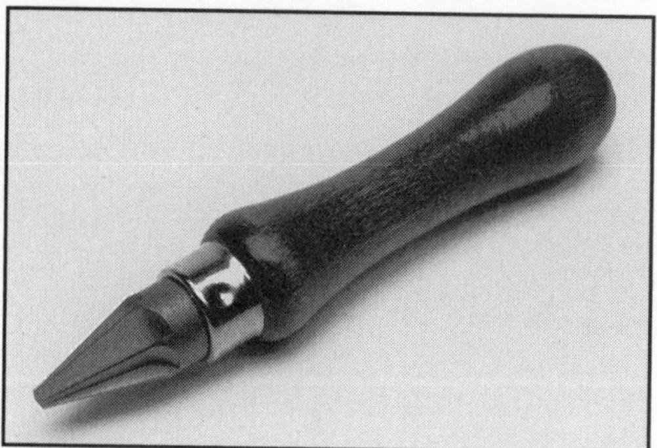
Lyman VLD Chamfer/Reamer

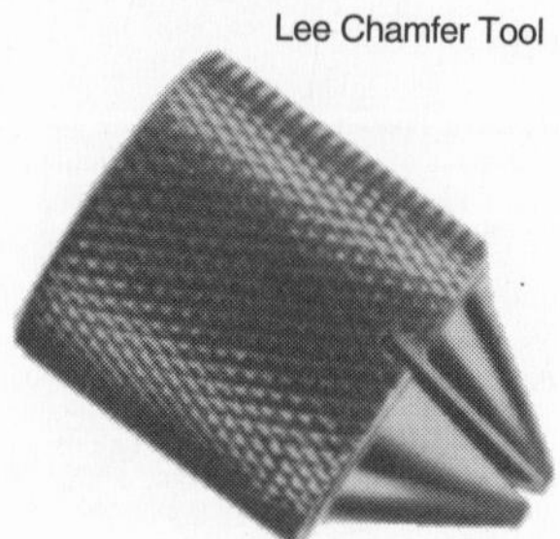
Lee Chamfer Tool

## LYMAN

**Outside Neck Turner Accessory Tool**

Designed for use with Lyman's Universal trimmer and Accu trimmer to maintain correct neck wall thickness and outside neck diameter. Features cutter adjustable for length of cut and rate of feed. Cutter blade adjusted to any diameter from .195″ to .405″. Comes with two extra cutting blades. Mandrels from 22 to 375. Available also with six mandrel Multi-Pack (22-, 243-, 25-, 270-, 7mm and 30-calibers). From Lyman Products Corporation.

**Price:** With Multi-Pack . . . . . . **$27.95**
**Price:** Multi-Pack . . . . . . . . **$10.00**
**Price:** Replacement cutters (2) with wrench . . . . . . . . . . **$5.75**
**Price:** Extra mandrel . . . . . . . **$4.00**

**Deburring Tool**

Bevels and removes burrs from inside and outside of case mouth. Precision machined and hardened with wood handle; fits all cases 17- to 45-caliber. From Lyman Products Corporation.

**Price:** . . . . . . . . . . . . . . **$12.95**

## LYMAN

**Universal Inside/Outside Debur Tool**

All steel tool with anodized aluminum handle machine-knurled for gripping. Features cutting blade which adapts with hex wrench adjustment to any pistol or rifle case. Deburs inside and outside of case in one step. From Lyman Products Corporation.

**Price:** . . . . . . . . . . . . . . **$13.50**

**VLD Chamfer/Reamer**

Designed to chamfer cases holding VLD match bullets. Features 22° cutting angle to eliminate long boattail bullets being cut by the case mouth during bullet seating. From Lyman Products Corporation.

**Price:** Per pound . . . . . . . . **$8.25**

Marquart Case Neck Turner

NECO 50 BMG Case Holder

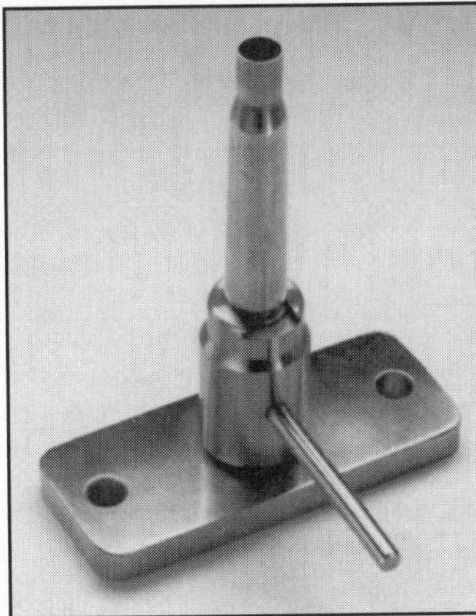

Sinclair Phase I & II

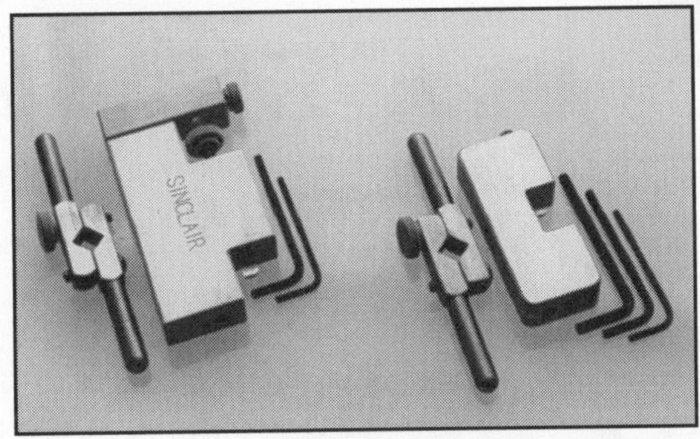

RCBS Deburring Tool

## MARQUART

**Precision Case Neck Turner**

Uniformly turns case necks within .0001″. "On center" design used for ease of operation. Adjustable cutter with screw threaded 40 threads per inch for .025″ increment advancements with each turn. Pilot can be adjusted in frame to govern length of cut. From Marquart Precision Company.

**Price:** Complete tool . . . . . . . . **$48.00**
**Price:** Holders 222 Rem. to 378 Wea. . **$8.00**
**Price:** Pilots 17- to 30-caliber . . . . **$8.00**

## MIDWAY

**Deburring Tool**

Precision machined cutting edges debur and chamfer 17- to 45-caliber cases. Recessed midsection offers positive gripping. From Midway Arms, Inc.

**Price:** . . . . . . . . . . . . . . **$9.99**

**Deburring Tool Adapter**

Chucks into any 1/4″ power drill and accepts any Midway, RCBS or Wilson chamfer/debur tool. From Midway Arms, Inc.

**Price:** . . . . . . . . . . . . . . **$10.99**

## NECO

**50 BMG Case Holder**

Precision-made stainless steel cartridge case holder designed to accept empty, resized 50 BMG cartridge cases on drill press table for trimming to overall length. Interior center section heat-treated 4140; base of blued steel. Designed for use with a piloted shank counter-boring cutter. From NECO.

**Price:** . . . . . . . . . . . . . **$123.50**

## RCBS

**Case Neck Turning Accessories**

Two tools for removal of excessive neck thickness, high spots and case neck out-of-roundness. Guides cutter over sized cartridge case neck and is supported by the pilot. Auto Feed Attachment (Case Trimmer-2 and Trim Pro) advances tool over case neck with each turn of the handle. Pilot/neck reamers available in 17-, 223-, 6mm/243, 25-, 6.5mm, 270-, 7mm, 30-, 8mm, 338- and 35-calibers. From RCBS.

**Price:** With Auto Feed . . . . . . **$53.63**
**Price:** Case Neck Turner . . . . . **$26.00**
**Price:** Auto Feed . . . . . . . . **$34.75**
**Price:** Pilot/Neck Reamers . . . . . **$6.58**

## RCBS

**Deburring Tool**

Case prep tool for beveling inside neck lip and removing interior and exterior case mouth burrs. Features hardened cutting flutes and knurled surface for hand or lathe use. For all cases from 17- to 45-caliber. From RCBS.

**Price:** . . . . . . . . . . . . . **$13.00**

## REDDING

**Deburring Tool**

Hardened precision ground flutes for chatter-free cutting. Accepts all cases from 17- to 45-caliber. From Redding Reloading Equipment.

**Price:** . . . . . . . . . . . . . **$19.50**

## ROCK CRUSHER

**Debur/Chamfer Tool**

For use on 50 BMG cartridges to debur and chamfer case neck. From The Old Western Scrounger.

**Price:** . . . . . . . . . . . . . **$20.95**

## SINCLAIR

**Caseholders and Drivers**

Stainless steel caseholder and hex-shaft driver for use with power screwdriver or drill for case spinning while neck-turning and case mouth deburring. From Sinclair International, Inc.

**Price:** Driver . . . . . . . . . . **$9.25**
**Price:** Caseholder . . . . . . . . **$11.50**
**Price:** Set of three . . . . . . . . **$37.95**

**Case Mouth Deburring Tool Holder**

Stainless steel debur tool holder for use with power screwdriver or drill. Works with Wilson and RCBS case mouth debur tools. From Sinclair International, Inc.

**Price:** . . . . . . . . . . . . . **$10.70**

**Phase II Neck Turning Tool**

Hand-held tool constructed of anodized aluminum and using stainless steel double-ended mandrels for 22/6mm, 25/270-, 7mm/30- and 6.5mm/338- or single mandrels for 17-, 8mm and 35-calibers to remove excess neck thickness, high spots and case neck uniformity. Can be used with optional .001″ dial indicator for setting desired cutting depth. Comes with universal case holder, instructions and Allen wrenches. Mandrels sold separately by caliber. From Sinclair International, Inc.

**Price:** . . . . . . . . . . . . . **$59.50**
**Price:** Mitutoyo .0001″ dial indicator . . . . . . . **$114.00**
**Price:** .0001″ dial indicator . . . . **$26.00**
**Price:** Extra handle . . . . . . . **$17.50**
**Price:** Dual mandrel . . . . . . . **$9.75**
**Price:** Single mandrel . . . . . . . **$8.50**
**Price:** Replacement cutter . . . . . **$9.50**
**Price:** Cutter ground to 40° . . . . **$11.50**

**Phase I Neck Turning Tool**

Forerunner of the Phase II tool brought back in 1994 due to consumer demand. The same tool as the Phase II but can not be modified to accept dial indicator. Comes with universal case holder and instructions. From Sinclair International, Inc.

**Price:** . . . . . . . . . . . . . **$49.75**
**Price:** Extra handle . . . . . . . **$17.50**
**Price:** Dual mandrel . . . . . . . **$9.75**
**Price:** Single mandrel . . . . . . . **$8.50**
**Price:** Replacement cutter . . . . . **$9.50**
**Price:** Cutter ground to 40° . . . . **$11.50**

## SINCLAIR

**Expander Body**

Stainless steel accessory for Phase I and Phase II neck turning tools to reduce turning effort and speed up operation. Designed similar to regular sizing die and made to accept same mandrels used with neck turning tools. From Sinclair International, Inc.

**Price:** . . . . . . . . . . . . . . **$16.00**
**Price:** Dual mandrel . . . . . . . . **$9.75**
**Price:** Single mandrel . . . . . . . . **$8.50**

**Stalwart Base and Clamp Mount for Wilson Neck Turner**

A base and clamp mount for the Wilson Outside Neck Turning tool. From Sinclair International, Inc.

**Price:** Sinclair standard mount . . . **$15.60**
**Price:** Sinclair clamp mount . . . . **$27.25**

## SYNCHRONIZED

**Burr Catt**

Attaches to cordless electric screwdriver and accepts any chamfer-debur tool. From Synchronized Shooting Systems.

**Price:** . . . . . . . . . . . . . . **$10.00**

## WHITETAIL DESIGN

**Mandrel for K&M Neck Turner**

Carbide mandrel available in 17-, 22-, 6mm, 25-, 7mm and 30-calibers. From Whitetail Design and Engineering Ltd.

**Price:** . . . . . . . . . . . . . . **$30.00**

## WILSON

**Deburring Tool**

Knurled tool for deburring outside of case mouth and chamfering the inside. Handles cases from 17- through 45-caliber. From L.E. Wilson, Inc.

**Price:** . . . . . . . . . . . . . . **$11.50**

**Inside Neck Reamer**

To remove excess neck material to guarantee clearance between case and chamber. Reamers replace the Wilson trimmer cutter when in operation. From L.E. Wilson, Inc.

**Price:** . . . . . . . . . . . . . . **$26.50**

**Outside Neck Turning Tool**

Similar to Wilson trimmer with chamber-type case holder enclosing case. Case holders will not interchange with trimmer case holders; tool also requires neck pilots. Pilots available only in 22-, 6mm, 25-, 6.5mm, 270-, 7mm and 30-calibers. Optional power adapter for attaching drill motor. Can be converted to case trimmer with optional trimmer cutter and case holders. Wilson case neck reamer and primer pocket reamer work in this tool. Grip tool in vise or mount on Stalwart standard or clamp mount. Pilots and case holders separate. From L.E. Wilson, Inc.

**Price:** . . . . . . . . . . . . . . **$107.25**
**Price:** Pilot . . . . . . . . . . . **$10.25**
**Price:** Case holder . . . . . . . **$10.50**
**Price:** Power adapter . . . . . . . **$9.50**

Synchronized Burr Catt

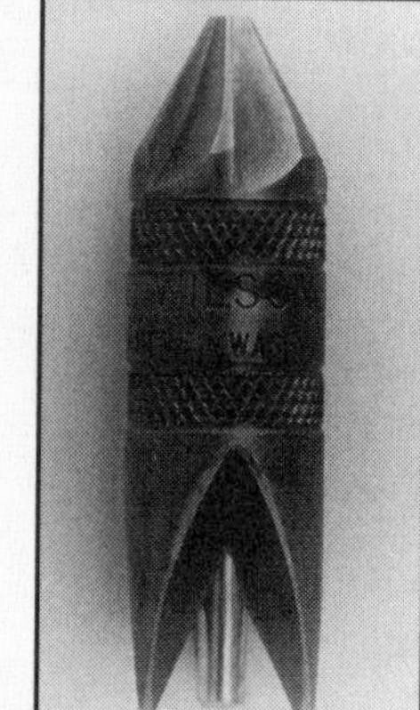

Wilson Debur Tool

**WILSON** *Neck Turner Pilots & Holders*

| Caliber | Pilot | —Holder— Fired | New |
|---|---|---|---|
| 219 Donaldson | Y | Y | Y |
| 22 PPC | Y | Y | Y |
| 22 PPC SAKO | Y | Y | Y |
| 22 Rem. BR | Y | Y | Y |
| 22-250 | Y | Y | Y |
| 220 Swift | Y | Y | Y |
| 220 Wilson Arrow | Y | Y | Y |
| 222 Rem. | Y | Y | Y |
| 222 Rem. Mag. | Y | Y | Y |
| 223 Rem. | Y | Y | Y |
| 243 Win. | Y | Y | Y |
| 6mm PPC | Y | Y | Y |
| 6mm PPC SAKO | Y | Y | Y |
| 6mm Rem. | Y | Y | Y |
| 6mmx47 | Y | Y | Y |
| 6mm Int'l. | Y | N | N |
| 6mm Rem. BR | Y | Y | Y |
| 25-06 | Y | Y | Y |
| 250 Savage | Y | Y | Y |
| 257 Roberts | Y | Y | Y |
| 264 Win. Mag. | Y | Y | Y |
| 6.5mmx55 | Y | Y | Y |
| 270 Win. | Y | Y | Y |
| 280/7mm Exp. | Y | Y | Y |
| 7mm Rem. BR | Y | Y | Y |
| 7mm Rem. Mag. | Y | Y | Y |
| 7mmx57 Mauser | Y | Y | Y |
| 7mm-08 | Y | Y | Y |
| 30-06 | Y | Y | Y |
| 30-30 | Y | Y | Y |
| 30-338 | Y | Y | Y |
| 300 Win. Mag. | Y | Y | Y |
| 308 Win. | Y | Y | Y |

Wilson Neck Turner

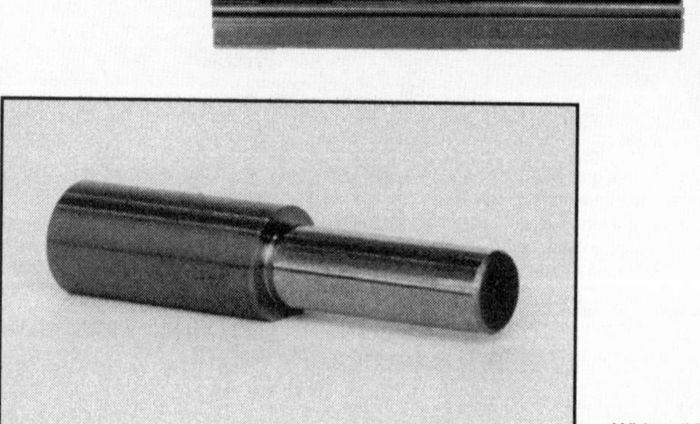

Whitetail Design Mandrel

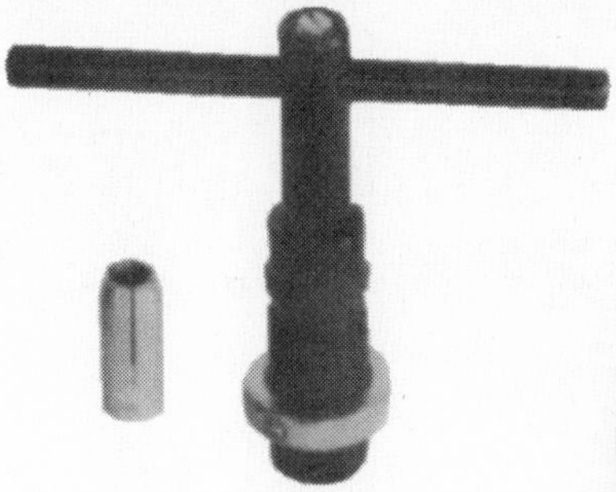

C-H/4-D Puller

Forster Collet-Type Puller

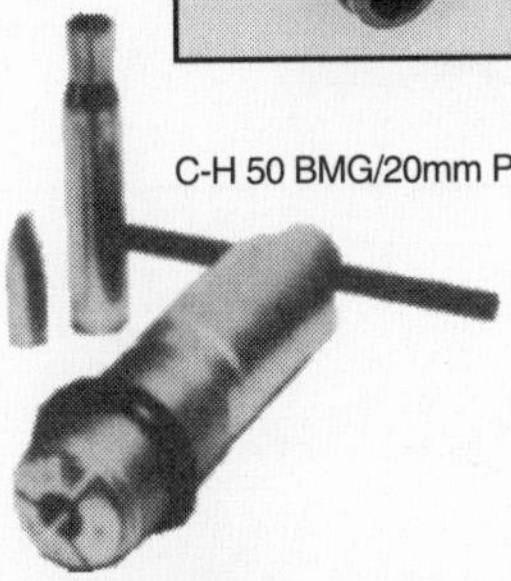

C-H 50 BMG/20mm Puller

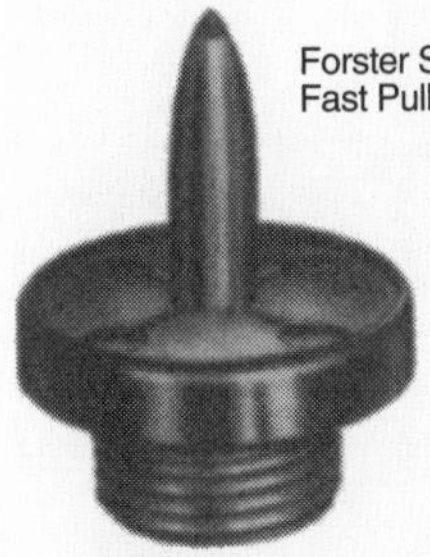

Forster Super Fast Puller

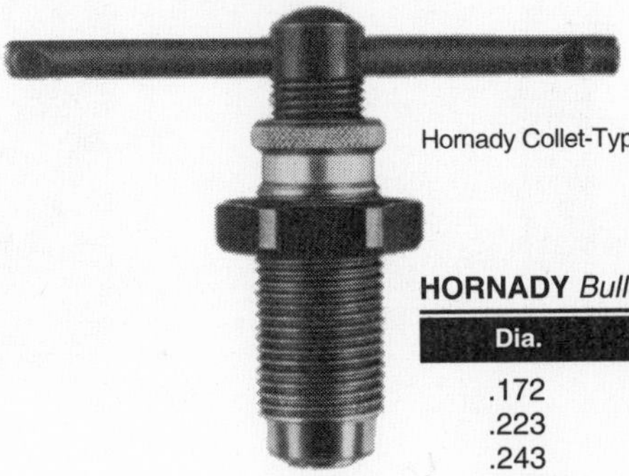

Hornady Collet-Type Puller

**HORNADY** *Bullet Puller Collets*

| Dia. | Collet |
|---|---|
| .172 | 1 |
| .223 | 2 |
| .243 | 3 |
| .260 | 4 |
| .277 | 5 |
| .284 | 6 |
| .308 | 7 |
| .322 | 8 |
| .358 | 9 |
| .375 | 10 |
| .410 | 11 |
| .430 | 12 |
| .454 | 13 |

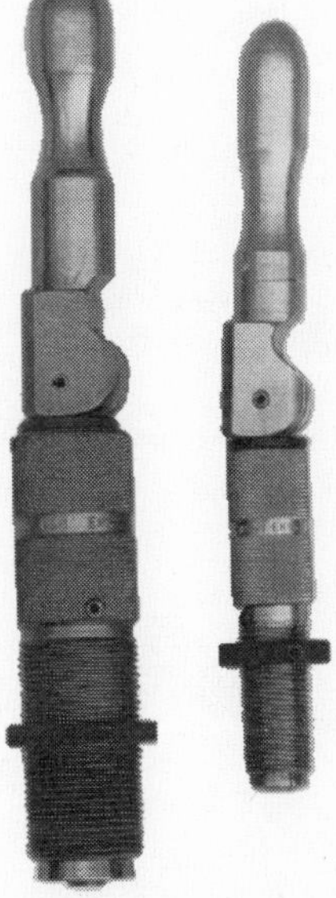

Hollywood Puller

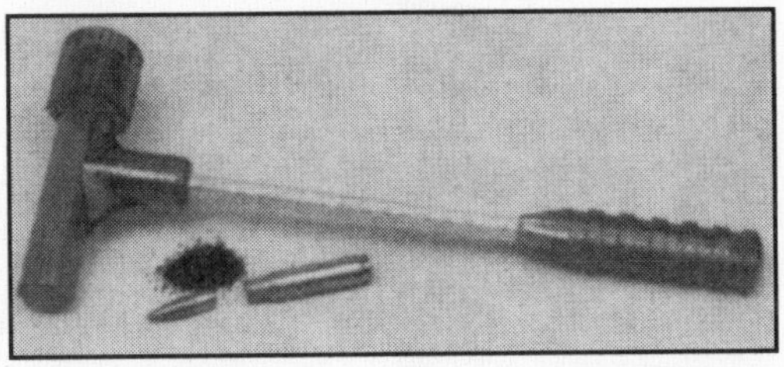

Dillon Bullet Puller

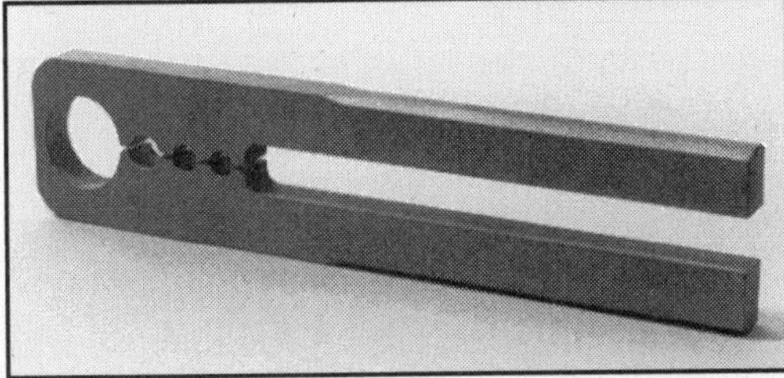

Haydon Bullet Puller

## C-H

### 50 BMG & 20mm Lahti Bullet Puller

Breaks down questionable military 50 BMG or 20mm Lahti ammo. Long shank collet fits bullet properly. Ball thrust bearing and spring ejector for ease of operation. Thread size $1^1/_2$x12. Collets for other large calibers available. From C-H Tool & Die/4-D Custom Die.

**Price:** . . . . . . . . . . . . . **$99.95**
**Price:** Collets . . . . . . . . . . **$21.95**

## C-H/4-D

### Bullet Puller

Positive die-locking action bullet puller for calibers 224 to 45. Comes with or without collet. From C-H Tool & Die/4-D Custom Die.

**Price:** Without collet . . . . . . . **$13.20**
**Price:** With collet . . . . . . . . **$19.80**
**Price:** Extra collet . . . . . . . . **$6.60**

### Kinetic Bullet Puller

For all popular rifle, pistol, rim or rimless centerfire cartridges. Features three jaw chuck to grip and hold case without damage to extractor groove or case rim. From C-H Tool & Die/4-D Custom Die.

**Price:** . . . . . . . . . . . . . **$19.95**

## DAVIDSON

### Plier-Style Bullet Puller

Designed for soft seated bullets not crimped or seated too tightly. Made from anodized aircraft quality aluminum and available in two models, one for 22-, 6mm and 30-caliber; the other for 25-, 7mm and 30-caliber. From Sinclair International, Inc.

**Price:** . . . . . . . . . . . . . **$18.25**

## DILLON

### Kinetic Bullet Puller

Tough plastic head with three-jaw chuck for separating bullet, case and powder. From Dillon Precision Products, Inc.

**Price:** . . . . . . . . . . . . . **$14.99**

## FORSTER

### Collet-Type Bullet Puller

Threaded $^7/_8$-14, this unit will fit any standard reloading press. Hardened steel collet designed to tighten grip on the bullet as pulling pressure is increased. Collets available for following sizes: 17, 224, 243, 257, 264, 277, 284, 308, 311, 323, 333, 338, 348, 357, 358, 375, 410, 432, 452 and 458. Collet not included. Weight: 8 oz. From Forster Products.

**Price:** . . . . . . . . . . . . . **$15.90**
**Price:** Collet . . . . . . . . . . **$9.10**

### Super Fast Bullet Puller

Designed for use on the Co-Ax, this puller is threaded $^7/_8$-14 for use on any conventional reloading press. Pulls all jacketed bullets including G.I. armor piercing bullets. Hardened flexible jaw closes on bullet automatically and extracts it from case without bullet damage. Available for the following diameters: .224, .243, .257, .264, .277, .284, .308. From Forster Products.

**Price:** . . . . . . . . . . . . . **$17.90**

## HAYDON

### Bullet Puller

Tong-type puller for 22-, 6mm and 30-caliber bullets. From Russ Haydon's Shooters' Supply.

**Price:** . . . . . . . . . . . . . **$15.75**

## HOLLYWOOD

**Bullet Puller**

Standard collet design pulls bullets from pistol and rifle cases up to 20mm. Comes threaded either standard 7/8" or large 1½" to fit most presses. From Hollywood Engineering.

**Price:** 7/8" . . . . . . . . . . . **$100.00**
**Price:** 1½" . . . . . . . . . . . **$150.00**
**Price:** Collet, 7/8" . . . . . . . . **$40.00**
**Price:** Collet, 1½" . . . . . . . . . **$75.00**

## HORNADY

**Collet-Type Bullet Puller**

Threaded, heavy-duty puller designed for use on any standard press. Hardened steel handle. Collet not included. Weight: 1 lb. From Hornady Mfg. Co.

**Price:** . . . . . . . . . . . . . . **$14.95**
**Price:** Collet . . . . . . . . . . . **$6.50**

**Kinetic Bullet Puller**

For use on rifle or pistol cartridges up to 45-caliber. From Hornady Mfg. Co.

**Price:** . . . . . . . . . . . . . . **$23.95**

## LYMAN

**Inertia Bullet Puller**

Three-jaw chuck fits all cartridges from 22 to 45. Made of tough polycarbonate over aluminum handle. From Lyman Products Corporation.

**Price:** . . . . . . . . . . . . . . **$24.50**

## MIDWAY

**Impact Bullet Puller**

Inertia-type puller with three collets to fit most centerfire calibers. From Midway Arms, Inc.

**Price:** . . . . . . . . . . . . . . **$12.99**

## PONSNESS/WARREN

**Bullet Puller**

Tapered die body threaded 7/8-14 and bullet puller collets remove bullets safely. Only one die body needed; collets available in 224, 243, 257, 264, 270, 284, 308, 311, 323, 338, 358, 375 and 429. From Ponsness/Warren.

**Price:** Die body . . . . . . . . . **$14.95**
**Price:** Collet . . . . . . . . . . . **$12.95**

## RCBS

**Pow'r Pull Bullet Puller**

New design offers one-piece construction for strength. Features a 3-jaw chuck to grip the case without damage to rim. Bullet chamber includes soft cushion to protect bullet points. Made of unbreakable plastic. Works with most centerfire cartridges from 22- to 45-caliber. Not for use with rimfire cartridges. From RCBS.

**Price:** . . . . . . . . . . . . . . **$24.25**

**Standard Bullet Puller**

Usable in all presses with 7/8"-14 thread. Pulls most lengths or shapes of bullet without damaging or distorting lead. Interchangeable collets lock onto bullet as the case is pulled away. Collets available in 17- to 45-caliber. Collet not included. From RCBS.

**Price:** . . . . . . . . . . . . . . **$13.98**
**Price:** Collet . . . . . . . . . . . **$8.20**

## ROCK CRUSHER

**Bullet Puller**

Designed for use on very large calibers: 50 BMG, 55 Boyes rifle, 12.7mm Russian, 14.5mm, 20mm Lahti, 20mm Solothurn, 23mm Soviet. State caliber when ordering. From The Old Western Scrounger.

**Price:** 50 BMG, 20mm . . . . . **$110.25**
**Price:** 14.5mm . . . . . . . . . . **$136.50**

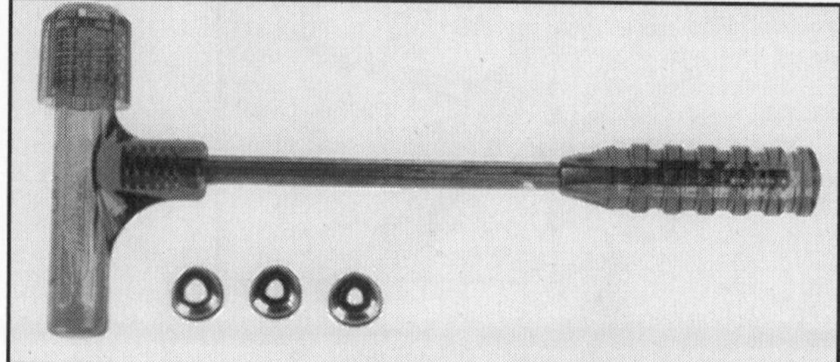

Midway Impact Puller

RCBS Standard Puller

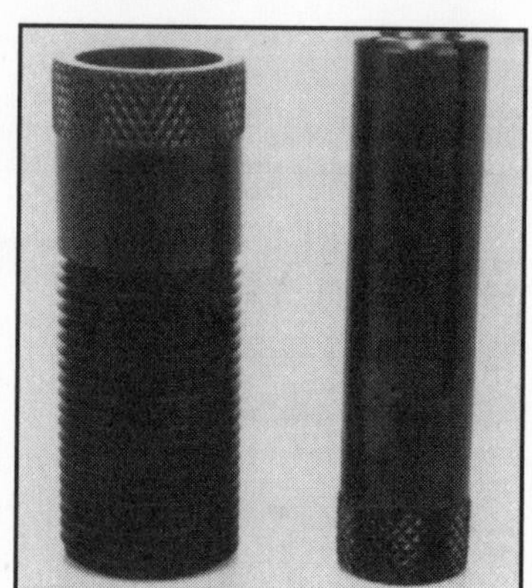

Ponsness/Warren Puller

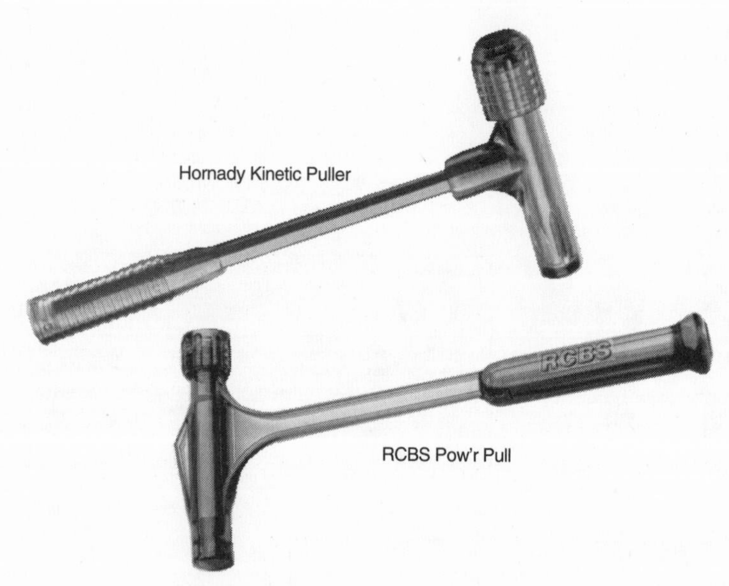


Hornady Kinetic Puller

RCBS Pow'r Pull

## ACCURACY DEN

**Electronic Thickness Tester**

Electronic case wall or bullet thickness tester for precise measurements. Motor-driven readout cuts testing time to 7 seconds. Will look inside a finished bullet ignoring the lead core and reading only jacket construction. Deviation needle 10 to 20 times more sensitive than comparable mechanical units. Uses standard 115 VAC 50/60 cycles. Remote battery operation possible upon request. VHS instructional video available. From The Accuracy Den.

**Price:** . . . . . . . . . . . . . **$595.00**

## BALD EAGLE

**Rimfire Cartridge Gauge**

Measures consistency of rim thickness of 22 rimfire cases. From Bald Eagle Precision Machine Company.

**Price:** . . . . . . . . . . . . . **$85.00**

## BLUE RIDGE

**Dial Caliper**

With continuous dial reads 1-100. Dial hand makes one complete revolution every one hundred thousandths. One revolution of dial hand equals smallest graduation on main beam. From Blue Ridge Machinery and Tools, Inc.

**Price:** 6″ capacity . . . . . . . . **$42.00**
**Price:** 8″ capacity . . . . . . . . **$72.00**

## E. ARTHUR BROWN

**Dial Caliper**

Satin stainless steel 6″ precision calipers with hardened ground measuring surfaces. Continuous dial reads 0-100 thousandths in .001″ increments. Maximum measurable length is 6″. From E. Arthur Brown Company.

**Price:** . . . . . . . . . . . . . **$25.00**

**22 Rimfire Gauge**

Measures 22 rim thickness for uniform headspacing and accuracy. From E. Arthur Brown Company.

**Price:** . . . . . . . . . . . . . **$43.95**

## C-H/4-D

**Dial Caliper**

Hardened stainless steel single revolution caliper. Features no-glare dial with adjustable bezel; free-wheeling friction roller for accurate repetitive readings; 6″ capacity, .001″ graduations; four-way measuring for inside, outside, depth and step readings. Specifications: 0-6″ dial reading; graduations in .001″ increments, .100″ per revolution; resolution, .001″; accuracy, .001″. From C-H Tool & Die/4-D Custom Die.

**Price:** . . . . . . . . . . . . . **$39.95**

## CCG

**Concentricity Gauge**

Inspects concentricity of fired and sized cases or loaded rounds. Adjustable indicator rod for taking readings along any point on case body. Design allows bullet seating depth measurements. From CCG Enterprises.

**Price:** . . . . . . . . . . . . . **$95.00**

**CLYMER** *Headspace Gauge Interchangeability*

| Gauge | Calibers Used With |
|---|---|
| 22 LR | 22 Short, 22 Long, 22 Bentz, 22 LR Match |
| 22 Hornet | Hornet-based wildcats |
| 25-50 | 32-20, 218 Bee, 218 Mashburn Bee |
| 30-30 WCF | 219 Zipper, 219 Zipper Imp., 219 Donaldson Wasp, 25-35 WCF, 7-30 Waters, 7mm Int. R, 30-30 based wildcats, 30 Herrett, 303 Savage, 307 Winchester, 32-40, 32 Winchester Special, 356 Winchester, 357 Herrett, 375 Winchester, 38-55 WCF |
| 30-40 Krag | 303 British |
| 32 H&R Magnum | 32 S&W Long |
| 357 Magnum | 256 Winchester Magnum, 357 Max., 38 S&W Special |
| 44-40 WCF | 38-40 |
| 44 Rem. Mag. | 44 Special |
| 45-70 Gov't. | 33 Winchester, 348 Winchester |
| Belted Gauges | .535" base belted calibers |
| 378 Weatherby | 30/378 Weatherby, 416 Weatherby, 460 Weatherby, 378 or 460-based wildcats. |
| 223 Remington | 6x45 |
| 222 Remington Mag. | 6x47 |
| PPC Gauges | 22 PPC, 6mm PPC |
| BR Rem. Gauges | 22 Remington BR, 6mm Remington BR, 7mm Remington BR |
| TCU Gauges | 6mm TCU, 257 TCU, 6.5 TCU, 7mm TCU |
| 7x57 | 257 Roberts, 6.5x257 Roberts |
| 284 Winchester | 22/284, 6mm/284, 25/284, 6.5/284, 270/284, 30/284, 35/284 |
| 308 Winchester | 243 Winchester, 7mm-08, 358 Winchester |
| 30-06 | 25-06, 6.5-06, 270 Winchester, 8mm-06, 338-06, 35 Whelen |
| 32 Remington | 32 Remington |

C-H/4-D Dial Caliper

## CLYMER

**Headspace Gauges**

"Go" and "No-Go" headspace gauges for rifle and pistol cartridges or shotshell gauges. Rimmed or belted gauges check headspace from a flange that duplicates the minimum or maximum space allowed in a chamber to secure cartridge rim or belt. Rimless pistol gauges for cartridges that headspace off the case mouth. Rimless gauges for shouldered calibers gauge headspace from the breech face to datum diameter on the shoulder. Precision ground within SAAMI or CIP specs. Standard or special-order gauges available. From Clymer Manufacturing Co., Inc.

**Price:** Pistol and rifle . . . . . . **$20.00**
**Price:** Rimless shouldered . . . . **$23.00**
**Price:** Shotgun . . . . . . . . . **$25.00**
**Price:** 50-cal. U.S. Ordnance . . . . **$50.00**
**Price:** Special order . . . . . . . **$45.00**

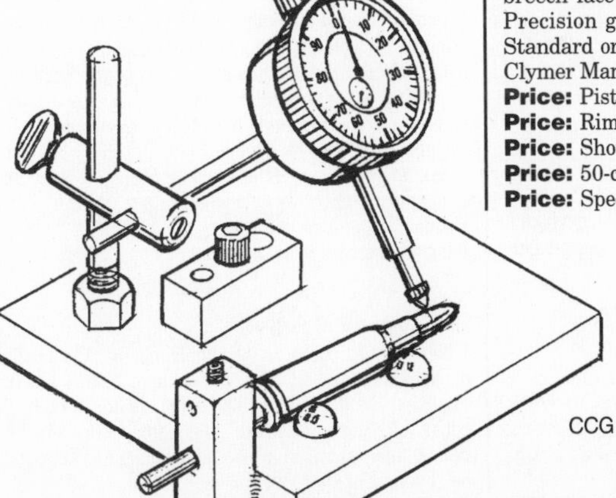

CCG Concentricity Gauge

## DAVIDSON

**Seating Depth Checker**

Attachment for dial calipers to check seating depth of loaded rounds or ogive to base length of bullet. Nose piece has 6″ included angle hole machined .001″ smaller than the caliber to represent barrel groove diameter. Available in .224, .243, .257, .277, .284, .308, .338, .35, .375 and .458 diameters. Base piece with three steps machined to accept three different case head diameters. Made of steel with mounting slot width of .140. From Sinclair International, Inc.

**Price:** . . . . . . . . . . . . . . **$10.75**
**Price:** Nose piece . . . . . . . . . **$10.75**
**Price:** Base piece . . . . . . . . . **$10.75**

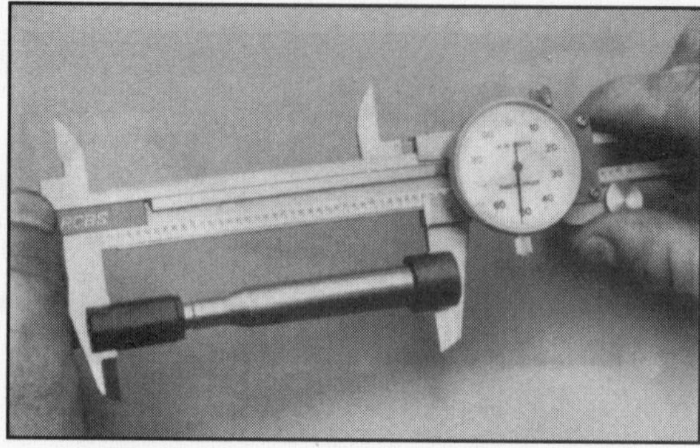

Davidson Seating Depth Checker

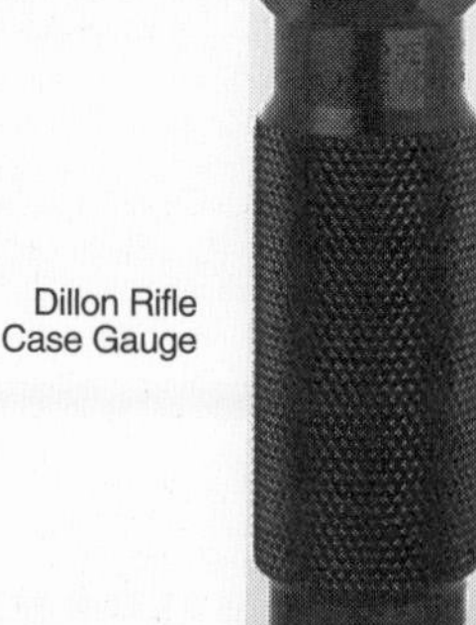

Dillon Rifle Case Gauge

## DILLON

**Pistol Case Gauges**

Stainless steel case gauges for 380 ACP, 9mm, 38 Super, 38 Special, 357 Magnum, 40 S&W, 10mm, 44 Magnum, 45 ACP and 45 Colt. From Dillon Precision Products, Inc.

**Price:** . . . . . . . . . . . . . . . . **$7.95**

**Rifle Case Gauges**

Measures distance from the case head to middle of shoulder. Allows size die adjustment to ensure proper headspace. Also shows maximum case length and trim-to-case length. For 223, 308 and 30-06. From Dillon Precision Products, Inc.

**Price:** . . . . . . . . . . . . . . **$15.95**

**Dial Caliper**

Hardened stainless steel caliper with satin chrome finish. Measuring faces hardened, ground and lapped. Features include: .100 per revolution; covered track for longer life; large adjustable dial; complete with fitted case. From Dillon Precision Products, Inc.

**Price:** . . . . . . . . . . . . . . **$29.95**

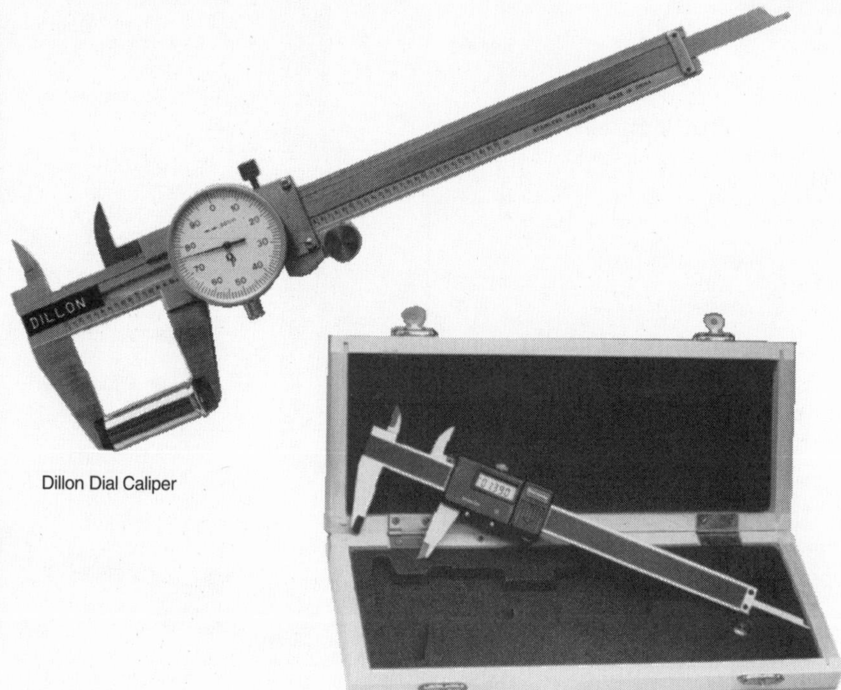


Dillon Dial Caliper

Hornady Digital Caliper

## DONALD EAGAN

**MX3 Seating Depth and Taper Sizing Gauge**

Made of steel and tapered on inside diameter to same taper as MX3 .30-cal. bullets. Will also work with conventional bullets. Gauge is 1/2″ in diameter and 1″ long. From Donald Eagan.

**Price:** . . . . . . . . . . . . . . . **$6.00**

**MX3 Flash Hole Gauge**

Designed to check cases for off-center flash holes. Gauge will reject cases with runout over .006″ of the flash hole with the outside diameter of the case. Flash hole centered within .003″ assuring match quality cases. From Donald Eagan.

**Price:** . . . . . . . . . . . . . . . **$9.00**

## FORGREEN

**Headspace Gauge**

Headspace gauges for rimmed/rimless or 50-caliber and over. From Forgreen Tool Mfg.

**Price:** Rimmed or rimless . . . . . **$25.00**
**Price:** 50-cal. or over . . . . . . . **$35.00**

## FORSTER/BONANZA

**Co-Ax Indicator**

Measures degree of concentricity between case and bullet to within .0005″. Designed to work with any 2″ face dial indicator with back mounting lug. Indicator not included. From Forster Products.

**Price:** . . . . . . . . . . . . . . **$53.20**
**Price:** Indicator dial . . . . . . . **$60.40**

## FORSTER

**Combo Case Length/Headspace Gauge**

Visually check case length and headspace. Proper head to shoulder length is evident when cartridge is placed into the gauge and the rim is even with or lower than maximum step but not below minimum step of gauge. Overall case length is evident when mouth or neck of case is between max and minimum step of neck end of gauge. Weight: 7 oz. From Forster Products.

**Price:** . . . . . . . . . . . . . **$22.90**

**Headspace Gauges**

Chamber gauges in three lengths, Go (minimum chamber size), No-Go and Field (maximum allowable chamber size). Made to .0003″ total tolerance. Available for rimmed or rimless cases and in most popular calibers. Weight: 3 oz. From Forster Products.

**Price:** . . . . . . . . . . . . **$18.60**
**Price:** 30 Carbine . . . . . . . . . **$25.60**

## HORNADY

**Dial Caliper**

Stainless steel caliper measures to .001″. Measures case length, bullet length, inside and outside diameters, primer pocket depth and overall cartridge length. Comes with carrying case. Available in metric. From Hornady Mfg. Co.

**Price:** . . . . . . . . . . . . . **$49.95**

**Digital Caliper**

LCD display digital caliper reads in either inches or metric; measures inside and outside diameters, lengths, and primer pocket and case depths. Comes in padded wooden storage case with battery plus a spare. From Hornady Mfg. Co.

**Price:** . . . . . . . . . . . . . **$109.95**

**Micrometer**

Accurate to .001″ for bullet and case diameter measurements. Includes wrench to adjust zero and carrying case. From Hornady Mfg. Co.

**Price:** . . . . . . . . . . . . . . **$29.95**

**FORSTER** *Rimmed & Belted Caliber Headspace Gauges*

| Caliber | Go | No Go | Field |
|---|---|---|---|
| 219 Wasp | .063 | .067 | .070 |
| 219 Zipper | .063 | .067 | .070 |
| 22 Savage High Power | .063 | .067 | .070 |
| 25-35 | .063 | .067 | .070 |
| 30-30 | .063 | .067 | .070 |
| 32 Winchester Spl. | .063 | .067 | .070 |
| 32-40 | .063 | .067 | .070 |
| 38-55 | .063 | .067 | .070 |
| 22 Rimfire | .043 | .046 | .049 |
| 300 Magnum | .220 | .223 | .226 |
| All belted magnums | .220 | .223 | .226 |
| 303 British | .064 | .067 | .070 |
| 30-40 Krag | .064 | .067 | .070 |
| 30 Carbine | 1.290 | 1.296 | 1.299 |

**FORSTER** *Rimless Caliber Headspace Gauges*

| Caliber | Go | No-Go | Field |
|---|---|---|---|
| 22-250 | 1.574 | 1.579 | 1.583 |
| 220 Swift | 1.806 | 1.810 | 1.814 |
| 222 Remington | 1.294 | 1.297 | 1.300 |
| 222 Remington Magnum | 1.493 | 1.496 | 1.499 |
| 223 Remington | 1.464 | 1.467 | 1.470 |
| 243 Winchester | 1.630 | 1.634 | 1.638 |
| 308 Winchester | 1.630 | 1.634 | 1.638 |
| 358 Winchester | 1.630 | 1.634 | 1.638 |
| 7mm-08 Remington | 1.630 | 1.634 | 1.638 |
| 7.62mm NATO | 1.630 | 1.634 | 1.638 |
| 244 Remington | 1.777 | 1.781 | 1.785 |
| 250 Savage | 1.579 | 1.583 | 1.587 |
| 6.5mm SKAN | 1.831 | 1.835 | NA |
| 6.5mmx55 Swede | 1.779 | 1.785 | 1.789 |
| 257 Roberts | 1.794 | 1.800 | 1.804 |
| 7mm Mauser | 1.794 | 1.800 | 1.804 |
| 280 Remington | 2.100 | 2.104 | 2.108 |
| 284 Winchester | 1.810 | 1.815 | 1.817 |
| 30-06 Remington | 2.049 | 2.055 | 2.058 |
| 270 Winchester | 2.049 | 2.055 | 2.058 |
| 25-06 Remington | 2.049 | 2.055 | 2.058 |
| 8mmx57 Mauser | 1.874 | 1.880 | 1.884 |

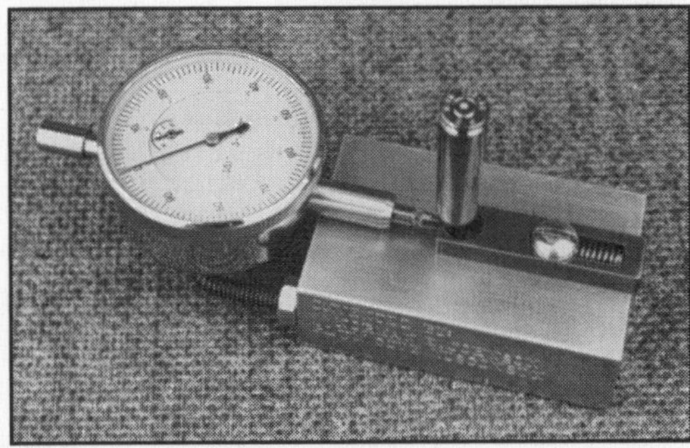

Johnson Case Neck Gauge

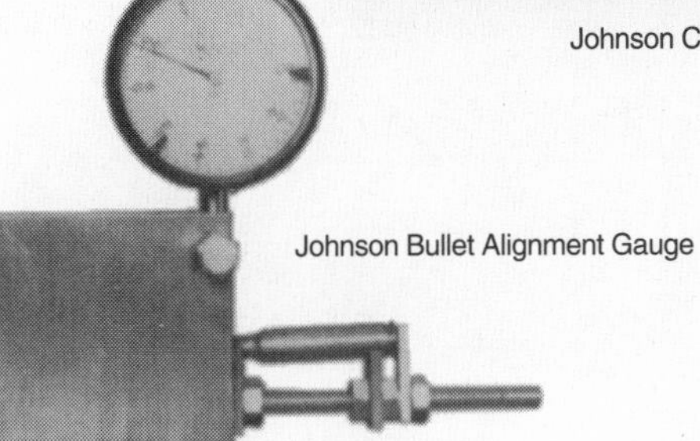

Johnson Bullet Alignment Gauge

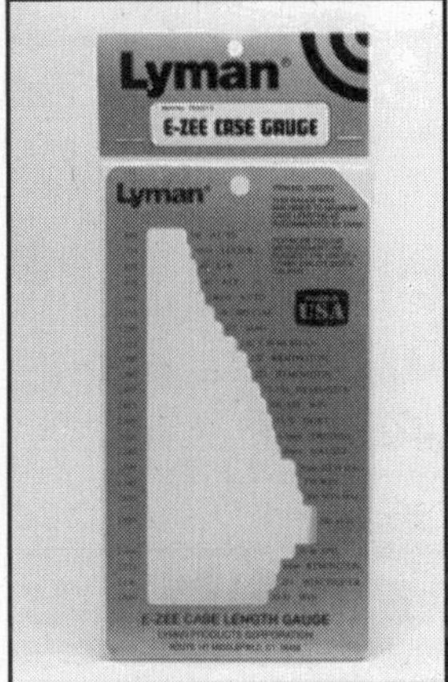


Lyman E-Z Case Trim Gauge

| FORSTER Combo Case Length/Headspace Gauge Calibers |
|---|
| 222 Rem. |
| 222 Rem. Mag. |
| 223 Rem. |
| 22-250 |
| 243 Win. |
| 244 Rem. |
| 257 Roberts |
| 270 Win. |
| 7x57 Mauser |
| 7mm-08 |
| 280 Rem. |
| 308 Win. |
| 30-06 |
| 25-06 |
| 8x57 Mauser |
| 38 S&W Spl. |
| 357 Mag. |
| 45 ACP |
| 44 Mag. |
| 9mm |

## JOHNSON

**Bullet Alignment Gauge**

Concentricity gauge for loaded rounds. Includes dial indicator. From Plum City Ballistic Range.

**Price:** . . . . . . . . . . . . . . **$59.00**

**Case Neck Gauge**

Features spring-loaded stabilizing block to press case neck tightly against polished spindle. Measures variation in case wall thickness to .001″ or less. Includes dial indicator. From Plum City Ballistic Range.

**Price:** . . . . . . . . . . . . . . **$64.00**

## K&M

**Ball Micrometer**

Mitutoyo micrometer with modified spindle that has diamond ground 60° angle, leaving 1/8″ flat for measuring to within 1/16″ of case shoulder. Micrometer features carbide spindle face, large diameter satin-chrome-finished sleeves and thimble, ratchet stop, spindle lock and readings to .0001″. Intended for checking concentricity of case necks and jackets, it can be used to check any wall thickness not over one inch with bore not under .190″. From K&M Services.

**Price:** . . . . . . . . . . . . . . **$99.95**

## LYMAN

**E-Z Case Trim Gauge**

Precision made of high strength steel. For measuring case length of both fired and resized cartridge cases. 50 popular rifle and pistol cases represented. From Lyman Products Corporation.

**Price:** . . . . . . . . . . . . . . **$12.95**

**Dial Caliper**

High strength plastic frame. Includes storage case and case length trim guide. From Lyman Products Corporation.

**Price:** . . . . . . . . . . . . . . **$29.95**

**Digital Dial Caliper**

Electronic 6″ caliper with direct digital readout for both inches or millimeters. Powered by standard calculator battery. Features automatic shutoff and push button zeroing to select a zero dimension and sort parts by plus or minus variation. Performs inside, outside and depth measurements. Comes in padded wooden storage box. From Lyman Products Corporation.

**Price:** . . . . . . . . . . . . . . **$84.95**

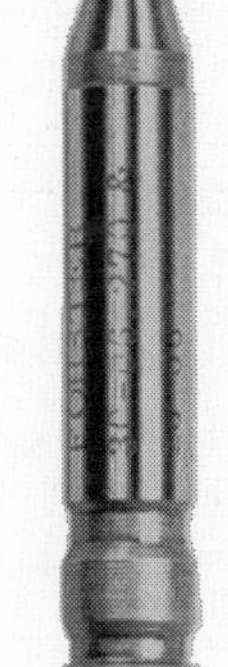

Forster Rimless Gauges

Forster Combo Gauge

## LYMAN

**Digital and Vernier Micrometers**

Precision micrometers to measure bullet and cartridge diameters featuring spindle locks, friction thimbles and ability to read to .0001″ (digital reads to .001″ and by Vernier scale to .001″). Comes in padded wooden storage box. From Lyman Products Corporation.

**Price:** 1″ Vernier . . . . . . . . **$19.95**
**Price:** 1″ Digital . . . . . . . . **$39.95**

**Electronic Micrometer**

Battery-operated electronic micrometer with LCD display reads to .001″. Converts from inches to millimeters. Zero reset allows parts sorting by plus or minus variations. Features spindle lock and friction thimble. Comes in padded wooden storage box. From Lyman Products Corporation.

**Price:** 1″ Digital . . . . . . . . **$89.95**

**Partner Pak Caliper Set**

Includes Lyman plastic dial caliper and plastic folding rule. From Lyman Products Corporation.

**Price:** . . . . . . . . . . . . . **$31.50**

**Pistol Maximum Cartridge Gauges**

Seven pistol gauges, 9mm, 38 Special, 357 Magnum, 10mm, 40 S&W, 44 Magnum, 45 ACP, to check all critical dimensions to ensure proper functioning. Checks case length, diameter and overall cartridge length. Other calibers available: 38 Special, 357 Magnum, 44 Magnum. From Lyman Products Corporation.

**Price:** . . . . . . . . . . . . . **$12.50**

**Rifle Case Length/Headspace Gauges**

Set of four gauges, 223, 243, 308 and 30-06, to check maximum and minimum allowable headspace and identify cases exceeding maximum allowable case length. Other available calibers include: 22-250, 6.5x55 Swedish, 270 Winchester, 7.62x39. From Lyman Products Corporation.

**Price:** . . . . . . . . . . . . . **$17.50**

**Stainless Steel Caliper**

Delivers .001″ accuracy. Comes with storage case. From Lyman Products Corporation.

**Price:** . . . . . . . . . . . . . **$33.25**

## MARMIK

**50 BMG Case Length/Headspace Gauge**

One-piece, non-adjustable 12L14 steel, 1.372″ O.D. headspace/OAL gauge made to military standards. From MarMik, Inc.

**Price:** . . . . . . . . . . . . . **$22.00**

**50 BMG Case Length/Headspace/Profile Gauge**

One-piece, non-adjustable 12L14 steel case length/headspace/profile gauge made to military standards. Used to measure fired cases for full-length resizing die adjustment. From MarMik, Inc.

**Price:** . . . . . . . . . . . . . **$40.00**

## McKILLEN & HEYER

**Case Length Gauge**

Multiple case length gauge to check overall length. Maximum tolerance of .002″ less than maximum for each caliber. Chrome-plated steel gauge. From McKillen & Heyer, Inc.

**Price:** . . . . . . . . . . . . . **$14.95**

Lyman Micrometer

Lyman Electronic Micrometer

Lyman Pistol/Rifle Headspace Case Length Gauges

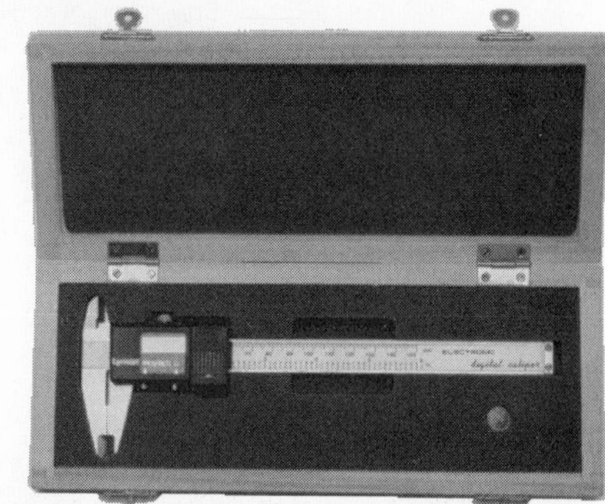

Lyman Digital Dial Calipers

Lyman Dial Calipers

MarMik 50 BMG Gauges

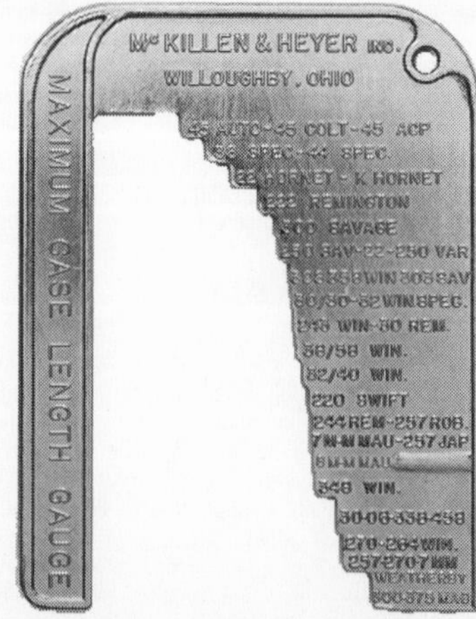


McKillen & Heyer Case Length Gauge

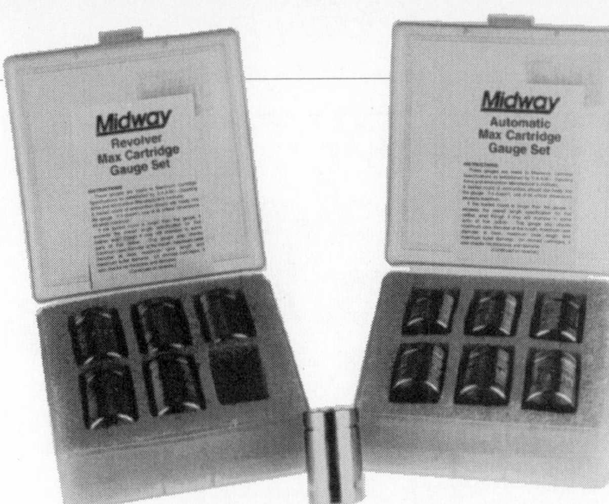


Midway Max Cartridge Gauge

**MITUTOYO** *Dial Calipers*

| Model | Range/ins. | Range* | Price |
|---|---|---|---|
| 629 | 4 | .200 | $74.00 |
| 626 | 6 | .200 | 88.00 |
| 637 | 6 | .100 | 100.00 |
| 627 | 8 | .200 | 128.00 |
| 644 | 8 | .100 | 138.00 |
| 628 | 12 | .200 | 192.00 |
| 645 | 12 | .100 | 208.00 |
| 611 | 6 | .100 | 113.00 |

*Per Revolution

**MITUTOYO** *Vermier Calipers*

| Model | Range/ins. | Range* | Price |
|---|---|---|---|
| 101 | 150mm | .06 | $72.50 |
| 105 | 6 | .001 | 72.50 |
| 116 | 8 | .001 | 86.50 |
| 118 | 8 | .02mm | 86.50 |
| 312 | 6 | .02mm | 72.50 |
| 314 | 6 | .001 | 86.50 |

Mitutoyo Micrometer

**MITUTOYO** *Outside Micrometers*

| Range (ins.) | Graduation | Type | Price/Ins. | Price/Metric |
|---|---|---|---|---|
| | | —STAINLESS— | | |
| 0-1/2 | .0001 | Rachet | $109.00 | |
| 0-1 | .0001 | Ratchet | 89.50 | $90.50 |
| 0-1 | .0001 | Friction | 89.50 | 89.50 |
| 1-2 | .0001 | Ratchet | 109.00 | 112.00 |
| 1-2 | .0001 | Friction | 109.00 | 109.00 |
| 2-3 | .0001 | Ratchet | 119.00 | |
| 3-4 | .0001 | Ratchet | 131.00 | |
| | | —CAST— | | |
| 0-1 | .0001 | Ratchet | 80.00 | |
| 1-2 | .0001 | Ratchet | 93.60 | |
| 2-3 | .0001 | Ratchet | 105.00 | |
| 3-4 | .0001 | Ratchet | 119.00 | |
| 4-5 | .0001 | Ratchet | 130.00 | |
| 5-6 | .0001 | Ratchet | 144.00 | |

## MCS

**Case Length and Headspace Gauge**

Designed for use with rimless cases to measure both case length and headspace. Each graduation of the micrometer thimble is .001″ with 50 graduations in one revolution. Available for 222, 223, 243, 308, 30-06, 7mm-08, 30-338 and 300 Win. Mag. From MCS Inc.

**Price:** 222, 223, 243, 308, 30-06, 7mm-08 . . . . . . . . . . . **$35.00**
**Price:** 30-338, 300 Win. Mag. . . . **$38.00**
**Price:** Other calibers . . . . . **Add $16.00**

## MIDWAY

**Cartridge Headspace Gauges**

Rifle gauges to check maximum case length and length from base to shoulder. All popular calibers from 17 to 375 H&H Magnum. From Midway Arms, Inc.

**Price:** Each . . . . . . . . . . . **$19.99**
**Price:** 7mm Wby. Mag., 7mm Rem. Mag., 200 Win. Mag., 300 Wby. Mag., 338 Win. Mag., 375 H&H Mag. . . . . . . . . **$26.99**

## MIDWAY

**Case Length Gauges**

Stainless steel case length gauges to check overall length. Four sizes cover 139 calibers: #1 (17- to 25-caliber); #2 (6.5mm to 30-caliber); #3 (31- to 50-caliber); #4 (pistol). From Midway Arms, Inc.

**Price:** Each . . . . . . . . . . . **$9.99**
**Price:** Set of 4 . . . . . . . . . **$24.99**

**Dial Calipers**

Stainless steel caliper to measure case length, bullet diameter, overall case length up to 6″. Accurate to .001″. From Midway Arms, Inc.

**Price:** . . . . . . . . . . . . . **$24.99**

**Digital Micrometer**

Precision 1″ digital micrometer gives measurements to .0001″. From Midway Arms, Inc.

**Price:** . . . . . . . . . . . . . **$39.99**

**Electronic Dial Caliper**

Stainless steel caliper featuring electronic LCD readout display to .0005″; conversion from English to metric; zero reset; protective case. Battery included. From Midway Arms, Inc.

**Price:** . . . . . . . . . . . . . **$69.99**

## MIDWAY

**Electronic Digital Micrometer**

Precision 1″ electronic micrometer featuring LCD readout display to .0001″; auto shut-off to extend battery life; conversion from inches to millimeters. Comes in protective case with battery. From Midway Arms, Inc.

**Price:** . . . . . . . . . . . . . **$79.99**

**Max Cartridge Gauges**

Automatic pistol and revolver gauges to check mouth diameter, base diameter, rim thickness and diameter, case and cartridge length and bullet diameter. Sold separately or in sets of six for automatics (380 ACP, 9mm Luger, 38 Super, 40 S&W, 10mm, 45 ACP) or revolvers (38 Special, 357 Magnum, 41 Magnum, 44 Special, 44 Magnum, 45 Long Colt). From Midway Arms, Inc.

**Price:** Set of 6 . . . . . . . . . **$24.99**
**Price:** Each . . . . . . . . . . . **$6.99**

## MITUTOYO

**Dial Calipers**

Feature rigid main beams 3.4mm thick; measuring range from 4″ to 12″; extra large dial face; made of hardened stainless steel; measures inside, outside depth and step measurements; supplied with fitted carrying case. From Blue Ridge Machinery and Tools, Inc.

**Price:** . . . . . . . . . . . **See chart.**

**Digimatic Caliper**

Digital readout caliper with optional SPC output for Mitutoyo Digimatic Processor. Standard measuring jaws with measuring range of 0 to 6″ or 0 to 150mm. From Blue Ridge Machinery and Tools, Inc.

**Price:** . . . . . . . . . . . . . **$133.00**

**Outside Micrometers**

Ratchet stop or friction thimble-type micrometers. Two styles available: tubular stainless steel frame with satin-chrome finish; or cast solid frame. Both come with carbide tipped anvil and spindle. Graduations in .0001″; measure ranges from 0 to 1/2″ to 5″ to 6″ or 0-25mm and 25mm-50mm. Larger sizes available. From Blue Ridge Machinery and Tools, Inc.

**Price:** . . . . . . . . . . . . **See chart.**

## MITUTOYO

**DP-1HS Portable Digimatic Processor**

A data processor to connect directly to dial caliper or micrometer via SPC connecting cables. Offers three separate analysis modes selected via DIP switches on side panel. Connecting cables available to fit most calipers and micrometers. From Blue Ridge Machinery and Tools, Inc.

**Price:** . . . . . . . . . . . . . . **$322.00**
**Price:** Cables, caliper . . . . . . **$25.00**
**Price:** Cables, micrometer . . . . . **$32.00**

**Precision Vernier Calipers**

Satin-chrome finish with raised sliding surfaces to prevent defacement and wear. All measuring surfaces ground and lapped. Jaws designed for outside, inside and step measurements. From Blue Ridge Machinery and Tools, Inc.

**Price:** . . . . . . . . . . . . . **See chart.**

**"Quick Set" Test Indicator**

To check case concentricity or runout. Measures anywhere within 240°. Horizontal or vertical type dial indicator comes with jewelled bearings. From Blue Ridge Machinery and Tools, Inc.

**Price:** Horizontal . . . . . . . . . **$93.60**
**Price:** Vertical . . . . . . . . . **$120.00**

## NECO

**Concentricity, Wall Thickness and Runout Gauge**

Precision made of hard anodized aluminum and stainless steel. To measure variation in the cartridge case and loaded round. Comes complete with GEM Model 222 all angle dial indicator, two removable guides for bullet tips, two "step cones" for empty cases, a "chord anvil" for case wall measurements and instruction manual. Measures calibers from 22 through 45-70. From NECO.

**Price:** With Gem 222 . . . . . . **$137.17**
**Price:** Without Gem 222 . . . . . **$85.00**

**50-Caliber Concentricity Gauge**

Comes with runout gauge base unit, GEM dial indicator, bullet holder 30- through 50-caliber and bullet holder 8mm through 22-caliber, two step cones for calibers 22 through 44, cord anvil rod, four plastic capped thumb screws and NECO *Concentricity Wall Thickness and Runout Gauge Manual.* From NECO.

**Price:** With Gem . . . . . . . . **$167.50**
**Price:** Without Gem . . . . . . . **$95.00**

## BOB PEASE

**Depth Checker**

Device fits on 4″ or 6″ calipers to gauge point at which bullet touches lands and transfer reading to another bullet ogive. Can also be used to check bullet uniformity. Made in .224, .243, .284 and .308 in 1″ length for easy calculations. Nickel-plated. Odd calibers available on special order. From Bob Pease Accuracy.

**Price:** . . . . . . . . . . . . . **$10.00**

## PRECISION RELOADING

**Trim Length Masters**

Designed for Wilson case trimmer to eliminate setting trimmer up for proper trim length. Master gauges measure .010″ less than maximum case length and are available for all calibers. Two sleeve sizes: 1″ small caliber; 1 3/4″ mild/magnum calibers. All Masters fit in either sleeve. From Precision Reloading, Inc.

**Price:** 1 3/4″ sleeve . . . . . . . . **$9.95**
**Price:** 1″ sleeve . . . . . . . . . **$8.95**

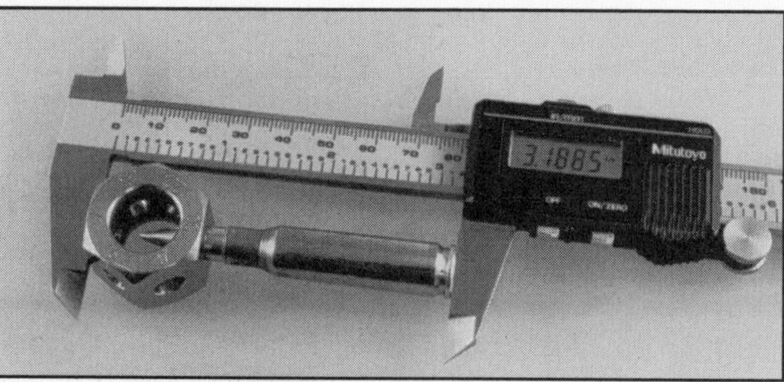

Sinclair Bullet Comparator

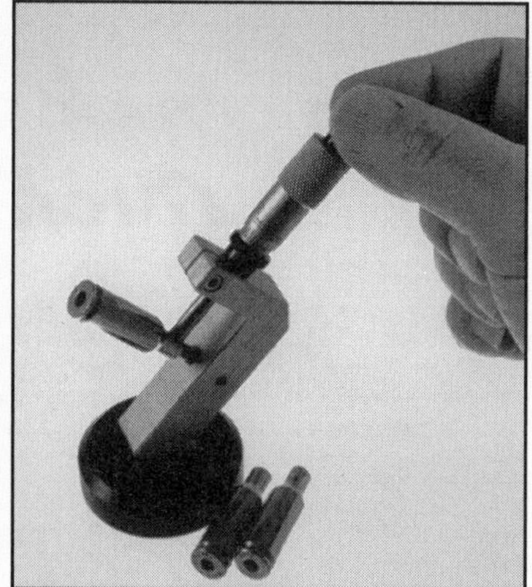

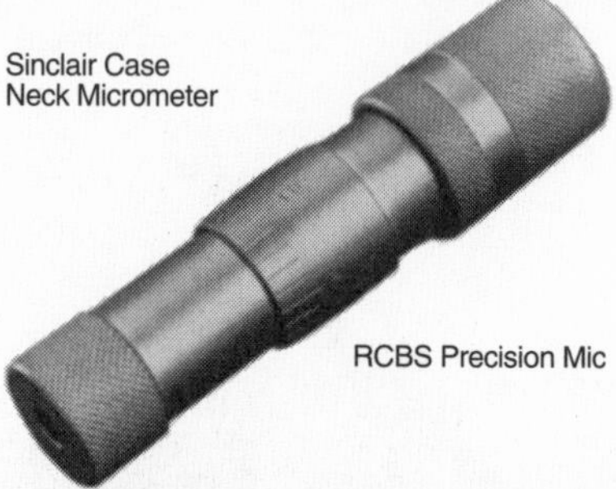

Sinclair Case Neck Micrometer

RCBS Precision Mic

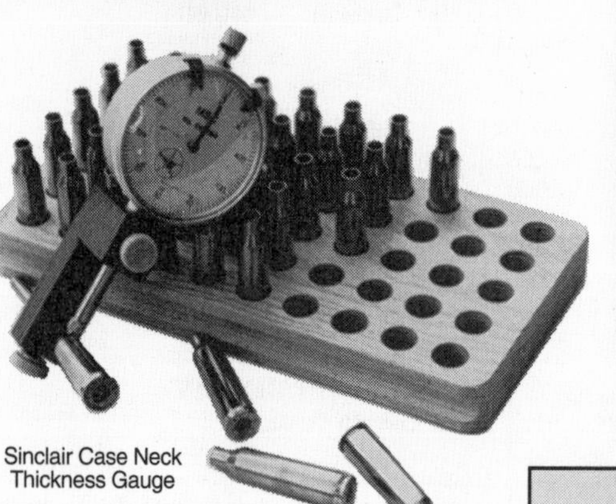

Sinclair Case Neck Thickness Gauge

Sinclair Concentricity Gauge

## RCBS

**Caliper/Case Length Gauge**

Features easy-to-read dial; 6″ capacity; measurement of four dimensions: outer, inner, depth and step. Dial has .001″ gradations for case and bullet measurement. Included are a chart with maximum and trim lengths for all popular calibers and a case with instructions. Stainless steel or plastic versions available. From RCBS.

**Price:** Stainless steel . . . . . . **$58.88**
**Price:** Plastic . . . . . . . . . **$37.50**

**Case Master Gauging Tool**

Precision dial indicator for measuring case neck concentricity, case neck thickness, case length and bullet run-out. Also detects case head separation. From RCBS.

**Price:** . . . . . . . . . . . . **$68.38**

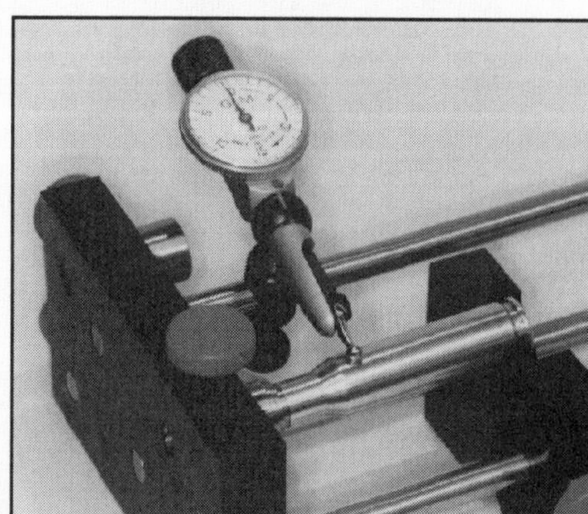

NECO Gauge

## SINCLAIR

**Bullet Comparator**

Stainless steel six-sided tool designed to assist in adjusting bullet seater to correct depth from bullet to bullet. Comparator available for 224, 243/6mm, 257, 277, 284/7mm and 308. Use with standard dial calipers. From Sinclair International, Inc.

**Price:** . . . . . . . . . . . . . **$14.25**

**Case Neck Micrometer**

Measures exact thickness of cartridge case neck to .0001″. Starrett micrometer head installed on steel base for hands-free operation to rotate cases and use micrometer thimble. Adjustable micrometer and offset anvil plus ratchet control allow measurements up to shoulder and neck junction and dead zero the tool for individual sensitivity. From Sinclair International, Inc.

**Price:** . . . . . . . . . . . . . **$96.25**

**Case Neck Thickness/Variance Gauge**

Pre-sort cases by neck wall thickness. Designed to be used with standard .001″ by 1″ travel dial indicator. Pilots for calibers 22- through 45-caliber available. One pilot stop comes with tool. From Sinclair International, Inc.

**Price:** . . . . . . . . . . . . . **$20.90**
**Price:** Dial indicator . . . . . . . **$26.00**

**Concentricity Gauge**

Designed with stainless steel V-block to support case. Inspects concentricity of fired and sized cases or loaded rounds up to 460 Weatherby. Features adjustable indicator tower for taking readings any point along case body. Fixture accepts only .001″ dial indicators with .375″ mounting post and minimum stem/post length of 2.25″. Dial indicator sold separately. From Sinclair International, Inc.

**Price:** . . . . . . . . . . . . . **$37.00**
**Price:** Dial indicator . . . . . . . **$26.00**

**Gauge Package**

Includes Neck Wall Thickness gauge, Concentricity gauge, pilot stop for one caliber of choice and dial indicator. From Sinclair International, Inc.

**Price:** . . . . . . . . . . . . . **$73.90**

**Seating Depth Tool**

Seating depth tool of stainless steel to find distance from case head to rifle lands for individual bullets. Comes with nylon bolt guide to fit most actions, universal measuring rod and two stops of equal length. Stops allow accurate measurements with pair of calipers. For all calibers from 22 on up. Comes with one guide. From Sinclair International, Inc.

**Price:** . . . . . . . . . . . . . **$17.25**
**Price:** Extra guides . . . . . . . . **$5.50**

## STONEY POINT

**Cartridge Headspace Gauge**

Allows precise measurement of headspace dimensions using a caliper, eliminating the need for special "mics" for each cartridge loaded. Measures from the case head to datum line on case shoulder allowing proper shoulder set back for a precise fit in the chamber. Minimizes case stretching, reduces work hardening, extends case life and improves accuracy. Headspace body is the same as used in the Stoney Point Comparator and comes with five-peice bushing set to use with most bottleneck cases, from 17 Remington through the belted magnums. From Stoney Point Products, Inc.

**Price:** . . . . . . . . . . . . . **$29.95**
**Price:** 5-peice bushing set . . . . . **$19.95**

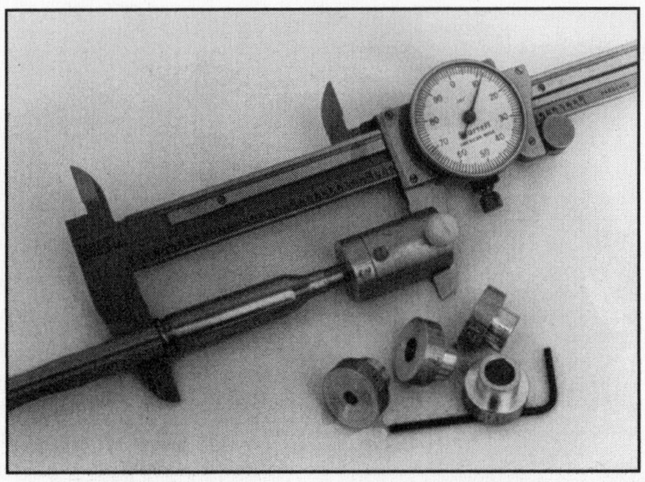

Stoney Point Bullet Comparator

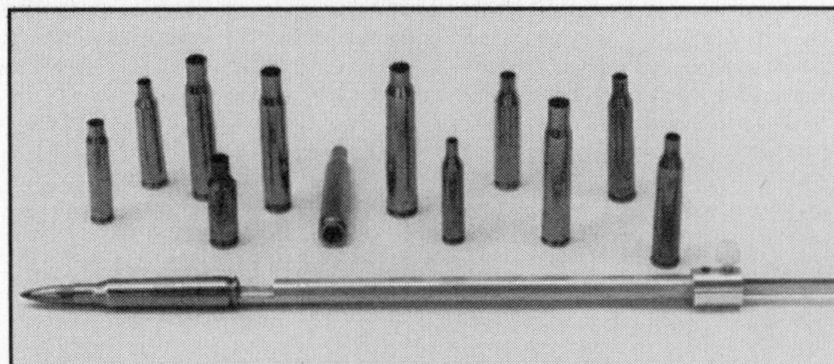

Stoney Point OAL Gauge

## STONEY POINT

**Chamber-All Bullet Comparator**

Precision machined from tempered alloy aluminum. Measures overall cartridge length from the ogive. Special body design allows proper alignment of caliper in either offset with Stoney OAL gauge or centerline with conventional caliper measurement. Attaches to caliper with thumbscrew. Twelve bullet inserts available: 17, 22, 6mm/24, 25, 6.5mm, 270, 7mm, 30, 33, 35, 37 and 45. From Stoney Point Products, Inc.

**Price:** . . . . . . . . . . . . . **$11.75**
**Price:** Bullet inserts . . . . . . . **$3.00**

**Chamber-All OAL Gauge**

Designed to accurately determine maximum overall cartridge length, thus establishing proper bullet free run and bullet seating depth dimensions. Gauge, made of anodized tempered alloy aluminum machined to close tolerances, employs modified cases of desired caliber machined to thread onto gauge. Case necks expanded slightly to allow bullets to pass through. From Stoney Point Products, Inc.

**Price:** . . . . . . . . . . . . . **$32.75**
**Price:** Modified case . . . . . . . **$4.25**

**Chamber-All Bullet Comparator Set**

Includes Chamber-All Bullet Comparator and six popular inserts in plastic storage box. Insert calibers: 22, 6mm/24, 25, 270, 7mm and 30. From Stoney Point Products, Inc.

**Price:** . . . . . . . . . . . . . **$26.75**

**Hornet Adaptor**

Threads to Chamber-All OAL Gauge to allow use of Hornet-size modified cases. Measures precise overall length from case base to lands. Comes with one Hornet modified case. From Stoney Point Products, Inc.

**Price:** . . . . . . . . . . . . . **$13.99**

## TOMBSTONE SMOKE N DEALS

**Dial Calipers**

Hardened stainless steel dial calipers with dial graduations of .001″ to measure bullet diameter, case length, inside and outside case diameter, depth and overall cartridge length. Measures up to six inches. Comes with carry case. From Tombstone Smoke N Deals.

**Price:** . . . . . . . . . . . . . **$24.95**

## VARNER'S

**Bullet Seating Gauge**

"Lands finder" gauge measuring system to determine correct bullet seating depth. Comes with gauge rod, sleeve spacer, spacer block and case of desired caliber. From Varner's.

**Price:** . . . . . . . . . . . . . **$19.50**
**Price:** Additional case calibers . . . **$4.00**

## WILSON

**Cartridge Case Gauges**

Available in two configurations, regular and adjustable. The regular gauge checks overall length, cone to head length and is available in most popular rimless calibers. Adjustable gauge available for belted magnums and can be used with different rifles of same caliber. From L.E. Wilson, Inc.

**Price:** Regular . . . . . . . . . **$21.50**
**Price:** Adjustable . . . . . . . . **$30.00**
**Price:** Length only . . . . . . . **$12.00**
**Price:** Pistol max. gauges . . . . . **$13.50**

**Pistol Case Gauges**

For checking mouth diameter, base diameter, rim thickness and diameter, case and cartridge length, and bullet diameter. Available for 357 Mag., 38 Special, 38 Super Auto, 380 Auto, 9mm Luger, 40 S&W, 20mm Auto, 41 Magnum, 44 Magnum, 44 Russian, 44 Special, 45 ACP and 45 Colt. From Sinclair International, Inc.

**Price:** . . . . . . . . . . . . . **$9.10**

## E. ARTHUR BROWN

**Spray-Dry**

Non-stick, dry lubricant in a liquid suspension for lubricating cases and dies. Spray it on and the liquid evaporates; the lube remains. Comes in 4-oz. pump plastic bottle. From E. Arthur Brown Company.

**Price:** . . . . . . . . . . . . . . . **$3.50**

## C-H/4-D

**Case Die Lube**

Oil-base liquid die lube also available in water-soluble (#42200) or dry (#42300) formulas. Come in 2-ounce bottle. From C-H Tool & Die/4-D Custom Die.

**Price:** . . . . . . . . . . . . . . . **$1.99**

## CHEM-PAK

**Size-All**

Formula includes tungsten disulfide and molybdenum disulfide, industrial performance wear reducing lubricants and other extreme pressure lubricity agents. Conditions die and expander ball for smoother operation. Spray lube wipes off with dry or damp cloth. Comes in 8-oz. aerosol cans. From Chem-Pak, Inc.

**Price:** . . . . . . . . . . . . . . . **$5.95**

## DILLON

**D.C.L. Case Lube**

Non-aerosol cartridge case lube spray. Environmentally safe. Available in 8-oz. spray bottle. From Dillon Precision Products, Inc.

**Price:** . . . . . . . . . . . . . . . **$6.95**

## ELKHORN

**Case Sizing Lube**

Wax-based lube for case resizing. Comes in 2-oz. tin. From Elkhorn Bullets.

**Price:** . . . . . . . . . . . . . . . **$5.00**

## E-Z WAY SYSTEMS

**Imperial Sizing Die**

High lubricity sizing die wax developed in the 1970s by Robert Le Clear of Imperial Industries. Comes in 1-oz. and 2-oz. tins. From E-Z Way Systems.

**Price:** 1-oz. . . . . . . . . . . . . **$3.75**
**Price:** 2-oz. . . . . . . . . . . . . **$6.00**

**Imperial Dry Neck Lube**

Graphite-based dry lube designed to reduce chatter and drag of the case neck in the sizing die. Prevents contamination of the powder and wax buildup on shoulder sizing area of the die. Comes in 1-oz. tin. From E-Z Way Systems.

**Price:** . . . . . . . . . . . . . . . **$2.50**

## INTEC

**Ultra Lube One**

Aerosol case resizing lubricant designed to eliminate case dents and reduce resizing force. From Intec International, Inc.

**Price:** . . . . . **Contact manufacturer.**

## FORSTER

**Case Graphiter**

Powder graphite lube dispenser constructed of sturdy plastic with three brushes to accommodate all calibers from 22 to 35. Base is drilled for bench mounting. Comes with cover to prevent graphite contamination. From Forster Products.

**Price:** . . . . . . . . . . . . . . **$11.00**

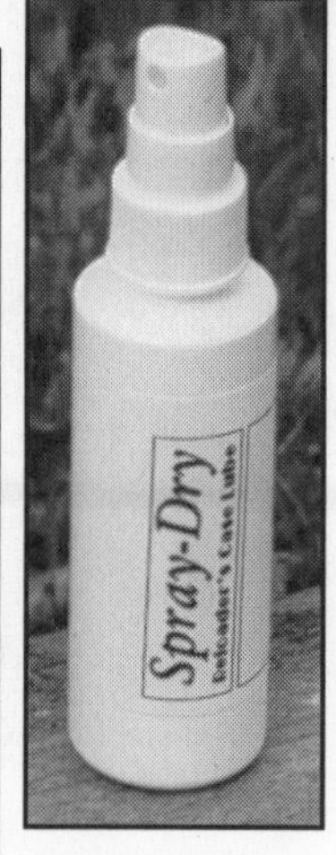


E. Arthur Brown Spray-Dry

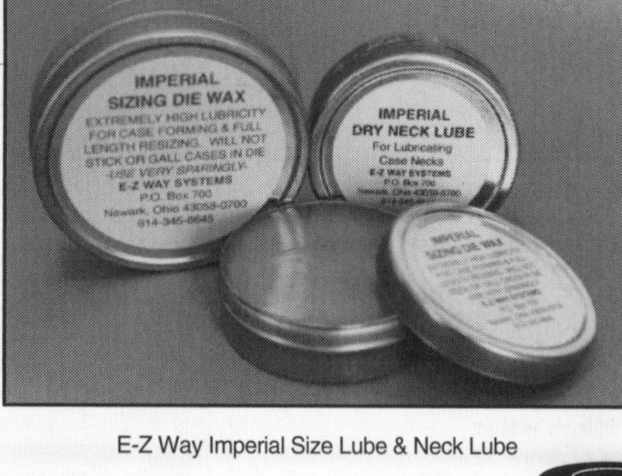


E-Z Way Imperial Size Lube & Neck Lube

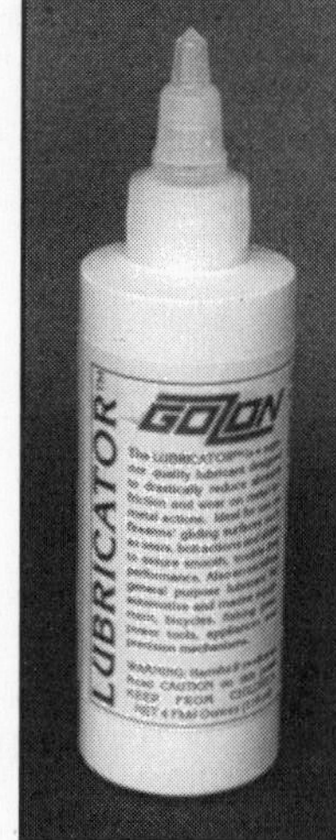


Gozon

Chem-Pak Size-All

## FORSTER

**Sportlube**

Water soluble, 100% animal base lubricant for full-length case sizing operations. Available in 3-oz. and 16-oz. sizes. From Forster Products.

**Price:** 3-oz. . . . . . . . . . . . . **$4.30**
**Price:** 16-oz. . . . . . . . . . . . **$10.00**

## FORSTER/BONANZA

**Blue Ribbon Lubricant**

High pressure lubricant for full-length case resizing. Available in 2-oz. bottle or case of 12. From Forster Products.

**Price:** 2-oz. . . . . . . . . . . . . **$4.10**
**Price:** Case . . . . . . . . . . . **$35.30**

## GOZON

**Lubricator**

High pressure lubricant designed for use on metal-to-metal actions. Comes in 4-oz. squeeze bottle. From Gozon Corporation.

**Price:** . . . . . . . . . . . . . . . **$4.95**

## HORNADY

**Case Lube Pad/Load Tray**

Lid of Hornady case lube pad is load tray. Used with Hornady case-size lube, a roll-type lube applicator. From Hornady Mfg. Co.

**Price:** . . . . . . . . . . . . . . . **$6.75**

**Case-Sizing Lube**

Liquid lube for use with Hornady pad to lube cases prior to sizing. From Hornady Mfg. Co.

**Price:** . . . . . . . . . . . . . . . **$3.45**

## HORNADY

**One Shot Case Lube**

Aerosol lube with DynaGlide applies thin non-tacky layer of wax to cases. A non-petroleum product that will not contaminate powder or primers. Weight: 2 lbs. From Hornady Mfg. Co.

**Price:** . . . . . . . . . . . . . . . **$7.95**

**Unique Case Lube**

Semi-solid-type lube. Comes in plastic tub. Weight: 1/2-lb. From Hornady Mfg. Co.

**Price:** . . . . . . . . . . . . . . . **$3.45**

## LEE

**Sizing Lube**

Automotive deep draw lubricant. Can be thinned with water, is non-sticky and non-allergenic. Comes in 2-oz. squeeze tube. From Lee Precision, Inc.

**Price:** . . . . . . . . . . . . . . . **$1.98**

## LYMAN

**Case Lube Kit**

Complete kit includes cloth lubricating pad, 2 oz. Lyman case lube, three interchangeable neck brushes and wooden handle in plastic case. From Lyman Products Corporation.

**Price:** . . . . . . . . . . . . . . **$14.95**
**Price:** Case lube . . . . . . . . **$3.25**
**Price:** Lube pad . . . . . . . . . **$6.95**

**Case Neck Dipper**

Dry lube to reduce friction from sizing die expander button on interior of bottleneck cases. Includes three brushes and 2 oz. dry mica for all cases from 17- to 45-caliber. From Lyman Products Corporation.

**Price:** . . . . . . . . . . . . . . . **$8.50**
**Price:** Mica refill (1 oz.) . . . . . . **$2.50**

**Qwik Spray Case Lube**

Petroleum based lube in aerosol can with spray trigger gun. From Lyman Products Corporation.

**Price:** Spray lube . . . . . . . . **$6.25**

Hornady One Shot

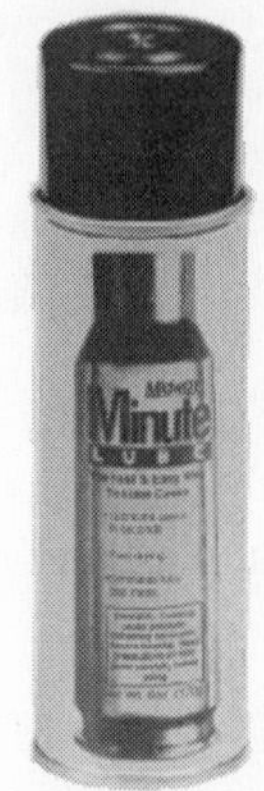

Midway Minute Lube

Lyman Case Lube

Dillon D.C.L. Lube

RCBS Case Slick

## MIDWAY

**Case Neck Lubricator**

Designed for use with liquid or dry lube. Includes six nylon brushes for use with most rifle calibers, two mounting screws and Midway Mica lube. From Midway Arms, Inc.

**Price:** . . . . . . . . . . . . . . **$7.99**

**Mica**

Dry lubricant for neck sizing without powder contamination. Available in 4-oz., 1-lb. or 10-lb. quantities. From Midway Arms, Inc.

**Price:** 4-oz. . . . . . . . . . . . **$4.99**
**Price:** 1-lb. . . . . . . . . . . . **$12.99**
**Price:** 10 lbs. . . . . . . . . . . **$42.99**

**Minute Lube**

Spray-on sizing lubricant that contains no chlorocarbons. Comes in 6-oz. can. From Midway Arms, Inc.

**Price:** . . . . . . . . . . . . . . **$5.99**

**Spray'n Size Case Lube**

Non-aerosol spray case sizing lube. Comes in 8-oz. pump bottle. From Midway Arms, Inc.

**Price:** . . . . . . . . . . . . . . **$6.99**

## NECO

**Neck Luber**

Molybdenum disulfide lube-coated stainless steel balls designed to lubricate the inside and outside of case necks for neck turning or resizing. From NECO.

**Price:** . . . . . . . . . . . . . . **$34.65**

## PONSNESS/WARREN

**STOS Lubricant**

Moisture resistant non-petroleum lubricant for case sizing. Comes in 2-oz. jar. From Ponsness/Warren.

**Price:** . . . . . . . . . . . . . . **$5.20**

## RCBS

**Case Lube 2**

Water soluble non-toxic lube applied to cases using case lube pad or fingers. Available in 2-oz. bottle. From RCBS.

**Price:** 2-oz. . . . . . . . . . . . **$2.63**

**Case Lube Pad**

For lubing cases or bullet jackets before sizing or forming. From RCBS.

**Price:** . . . . . . . . . . . . . . **$7.13**

**Case Slick Spray Lube**

Aerosol spray for lubing cases for resizing or case forming. Reduces the force needed to resize cases and helps prevent possibility of denting the shoulder. Comes in 4.5-oz. can. From RCBS.

**Price:** . . . . . . . . . . . . . . **$4.75**

**Case Lube Kit**

Includes case lube pad, 2-oz. bottle of Case Lube 2, accessory handle with case neck brushes for 22- through 30-caliber. From RCBS.

**Price:** . . . . . . . . . . . . . . **$15.38**

## REDDING

**Case Lube Kit**

Case lube pad with non-skid feet and 2-oz. bottle of Redding case lubricant. From Redding Reloading Equipment.

**Price:** Kit . . . . . . . . . . . **$13.50**
**Price:** Pad only . . . . . . . . . **$10.50**

**Case Lube Kit (Tong Type)**

Tongs conform to body walls of any cartridge case from 22 Hornet up to 458 Magnum for lubing. Includes 2-oz. bottle Redding case lubricant. From Redding Reloading Equipment.

**Price:** . . . . . . . . . . . . . . **$12.00**

**Original Formula Lube**

Formulated for tough resizing and forming operations. Comes in 2-oz. squeeze bottle. From Redding Reloading Equipment.

**Price:** . . . . . . . . . . . . . . **$4.20**

**Water Soluble Case Lube**

Water soluble case lubricant ideal for neck sizing and use with straight-wall pistol cases. Comes in 2-oz. squeeze bottle. From Redding Reloading Equipment.

**Price:** . . . . . . . . . . . . . . **$4.20**

## ROOSTER

**Case-Forming Lubricants**

Three lubes for resizing and reforming of cases. CFL-56 designed for radical reforming; slightly softer gel with brass protectant built in. CSL-71 is lighter in body and good for cold weather application; good for resizing and moderate reforming operations. CL-WR-14 liquid lube developed for routine resizing of cases. Available in 2-oz. or 4-oz. jar. From Rooster Laboratories.

**Price:** CFL-56/CSL-71, 2-oz. . . . . **$5.00**
**Price:** CFL-56/CSL-71, 4-oz. . . . . **$9.00**
**Price:** CL-WR-14, 2-oz. . . . . . . **$4.50**
**Price:** CL-WR-14, 4-oz. . . . . . . **$8.00**

## STALWART

**Case Lube Rack**

Machined from 6061-T6 aluminum bar stock and anodized with dichromate seal. Designed to facilitate application of aerosol lubricants to cases. Available for most popular rifle cases. From Stalwart Corp.

**Price:** . . . . . . . . . . . . . . **$18.95**

## TOMBSTONE SMOKE N DEALS

**Case Lube**

Non-aerosol sizing lubricant spray. Comes in 8-oz. spray plastic bottle. From Tombstone Smoke N Deals.

**Price:** . . . . . . . . . . . . . . **$4.49**

## VIBRASHINE

**Case Neck Dipper**

Cleans and lubes interior of bottleneck cases. Includes plastic housing with removable cover, three brush sizes and mica lubricant. From VibraShine, Inc.

**Price:** . . . . . . . . . . . . . . **$7.95**

## YOUNG COUNTRY

**Case Plus Lube**

Non-toxic environmentally safe cartridge case lube. Comes in 4-oz. or 1-lb. jar. From Young Country.

**Price:** 4 oz. . . . . . . . . . . . **$8.00**
**Price:** 1-lb. . . . . . . . . . . . **$25.00**

## BRUNO SHOOTER'S SUPPLY

**Delrin Loading Block**

White delrin loading block holds 20 cartridges of specified caliber, 308, PPC, 222. From Bruno Shooter's Supply.

**Price:** . . . . . . . . . . . . . . **$12.95**

**Loading Block**

Lucite loading block holds 20 cartridges of specified caliber, 308, PPC or 222. From Bruno Shooter's Supply.

**Price:** . . . . . . . . . . . . . . **$13.95**

## C-H/4-D

**Cartridge Rack**

Holds 60 cartridges of varying calibers. Too deep for 38 Special, not large enough for 45-70 or 348 but holds all other sizes up to 375 H&H. Size: 8 1/8x3 7/8x1 1/8. Comes in black or white. From C-H Tool & Die/4-D Custom Die.

**Price:** . . . . . . . . . . . . . . **$1.99**

## FLAMBEAU

**Loading Blocks**

Two durable plastic loading blocks to hold either 50 or 60 cases. Can accommodate most popular calibers. From Flambeau Products Corporation.

**Price:** 50 . . . . . . . . . . . . . **$4.55**
**Price:** 60 . . . . . . . . . . . . . **$2.45**

## HORNADY

**Universal Reloading Block**

Holds 50 cases from calibers 32 ACP through 458 Magnum. Made of high-impact plastic. Weight: 1 lb. From Hornady Mfg. Co.

**Price:** . . . . . . . . . . . . . . **$3.95**

## LYMAN

**Loading Block**

Twin heavy-duty plastic loading block holds 50 rifle or pistol cases 22- through 45-caliber. From Lyman Products Corporation.

**Price:** . . . . . . . . . . . . . . **$4.60**

## MIDWAY

**Loading Blocks**

Manufactured of fine-grain hardwood. Come in 12 sizes, each fitted for a single caliber or family of calibers ranging from 25 ACP through 460 Weatherby Magnum. All trays hold 50 rounds. From Midway Arms, Inc.

**Price:** . . . . . . . . . . . . . . **$3.99**

## MTM

**Loading Trays**

Hard plastic trays in two models, Universal and Compact. Universal holds rifle cartridges 17- through 45-caliber; 9mm, 38 and 45 pistol cartridges. Compact tray holds all calibers of rifle and pistol. From MTM Moulded Products Company.

**Price:** . . . . . **Contact manufacturer.**

## PRECISION/STALWART

**Benchrest Soft-Top Cartridge Blocks**

Deep drilled blocks that hold 15 rounds with soft nylon cover and velcro strap to secure rounds. Available for 17 Rem. through 6x47, 7mm BR through 308 and all PPC cartridges. From Precision Reloading, Inc.

**Price:** . . . . . . . . . . . . . . **$10.50**

Midway Blocks

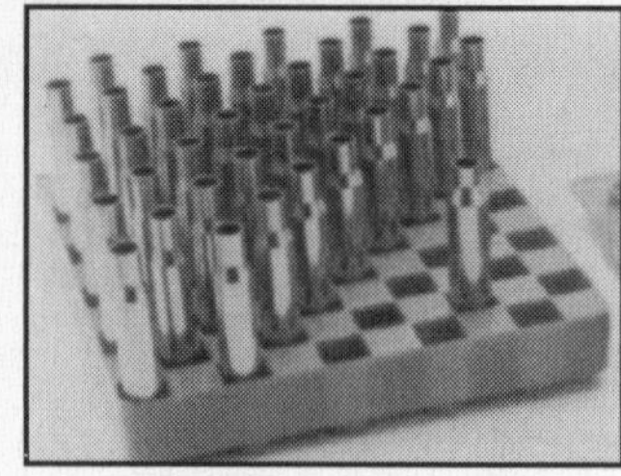

MTM Loading Tray

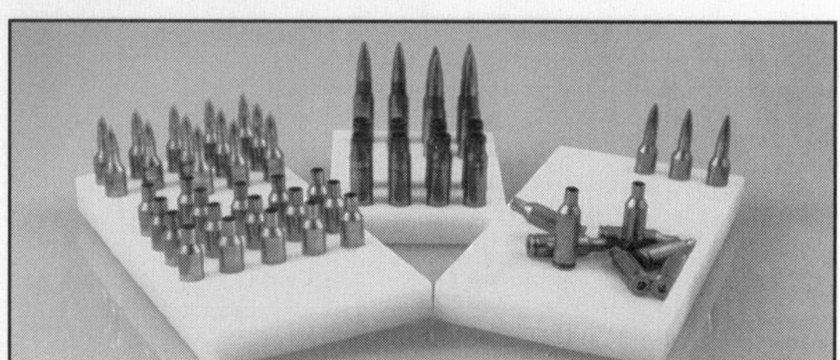

Sinclair Loading Blocks

Stalwart Loading Blocks

Hornady Universal Block

## RCBS

**Case Loading Blocks**

Heavy plastic blocks hold up to 40 pistol/rifle cases. Features two hole sizes with inside steps to accept most popular calibers. From RCBS.

**Price:** . . . . . . . . . . . . . . **$4.88**

## REDDING

**Combo Die Box/Loading Block**

Hard plastic box. Top has provision for 20 cartridges with base size up to 30-06; 20 magnum base size cartridges. From Redding Reloading Equipment.

**Price:** . . . . . . . . . . . . . . **$4.80**

## SINCLAIR

**Polyethylene Loading Blocks**

Machined from solid white polyethylene in 50-, 25-round size or benchrest 25-round size with cavity for empties. Dishwasher safe. From Sinclair International Inc.

**Price:** 50-round . . . . . . . . . **$6.10**
**Price:** 25-round . . . . . . . . . **$4.10**
**Price:** Benchrest . . . . . . . . . **$7.95**

## STALWART

**Loading Blocks**

Wooden 25- and 50-hole loading blocks for rifle, handgun calibers and shotshell gauges from 25 ACP through 570 Nitro and 10-, 12-, 20- and 410-gauges. The 20-ga. block also suitable for 50 BMG. Shotshell blocks stackable for storage.

**Price:** . . . . . . . . . . . . . . **$6.25**
**Price:** 25-hole shotshell . . . . . **$8.50**
**Price:** 50-hole shotshell . . . . . **$13.25**
**Price:** 50-hole 410 shotshell . . . . **$9.45**

## C-H/4-D

**Hand/Power Primer Pocket Kit**

Electric screwdriver kit for cleaning or reaming primer pockets. Includes both large and small primer pocket brushes, large and small primer pocket reamers, 1/4" hex adapter which fits most battery/electric screwdrivers and a plastic handle for manual operation. All parts have 8-32 threads. From C-H Tool & Die/4-D Custom Die.

**Price:** . . . . . . . . . . . . . **$12.95**
**Price:** Handle . . . . . . . . . . . **$2.50**
**Price:** Adapter . . . . . . . . . . **$2.95**
**Price:** Brush, large or small . . . . **$1.95**
**Price:** Reamer, large or small . . . . **$2.95**

## FORSTER

**Co-Ax Primer Seater**

Features automatic 40-primer feed with built-in primer flipper and loading tray. Primer tube has open slot for safely stacking primers sideways. Tool's jaws accommodate most modern Boxer-primed rifle and pistol cartridges with rim thickness of .050" to .072". Comes with small and large primer tubes. Weight: 3 lbs. From Forster Products.

**Price:** . . . . . . . . . . . . . . **$66.00**

## HORNADY

**Hand-Held Priming Tool**

Featuring plier-type handle designed to eliminate thumb fatigue; solid steel construction with ribbed and covered primer tray; uses standard shellholders. From Hornady Mfg. Co.

**Price:** . . . . . **Contact manufacturer.**

## JONES

**Decapping Tool**

For decapping cases as a separate operation to prevent die contamination. Reversible shellholder head takes either .378" or .473" case heads. Decapping mandrels screw off. Mandrels available for 222, 6mm, 7mm and 30-calibers; other calibers available on request. Comes complete for one caliber. Weight: 1 lb. From Neil Jones Custom Products.

**Price:** . . . . . . . . . . . . . **$40.00**
**Price:** Extra mandrels . . . . . . **$10.00**
**Price:** Non-standard mandrels . . . **$12.00**
**Price:** Shellholder . . . . . . . . **$12.00**

## LEE

**Auto Prime**

Hand tool with auto feed system and unbreakable steel connecting rod. Large or small primer tray affixed to hand tool with shellholder. Built-in primer flipper turns primers right side up. From Lee Precision, Inc.

**Price:** . . . . . . . . . . . . . **$18.98**
**Price:** Connecting rod . . . . . . . **$2.50**

**Improved Priming Tool**

Same tool as Auto Prime except without automatic feed tray. Plastic tab releases shellholder upon depression. From Lee Precision, Inc.

**Price:** . . . . . . . . . . . . . **$13.98**

## K&M

**Primer Tool/Gauge**

Dial indicator attached to K&M priming tool eliminates variables in primer seating and allows primers to be seated to exact same depth. Both large and small primer stations and shellholder for specified caliber are included. From K&M Services.

**Price:** . . . . . . . . . . . . . **$97.50**

## K&M

**Priming Tool Deluxe**

In-line primer seater with controlled feel. Primer shroud spring-loaded to push upward squarely on shellholder. Shellholder position adjustable up or down to feel primer seat. Comes complete with shellholder of choice. From K&M Services.

**Price:** . . . . . . . . . . . . . **$39.95**

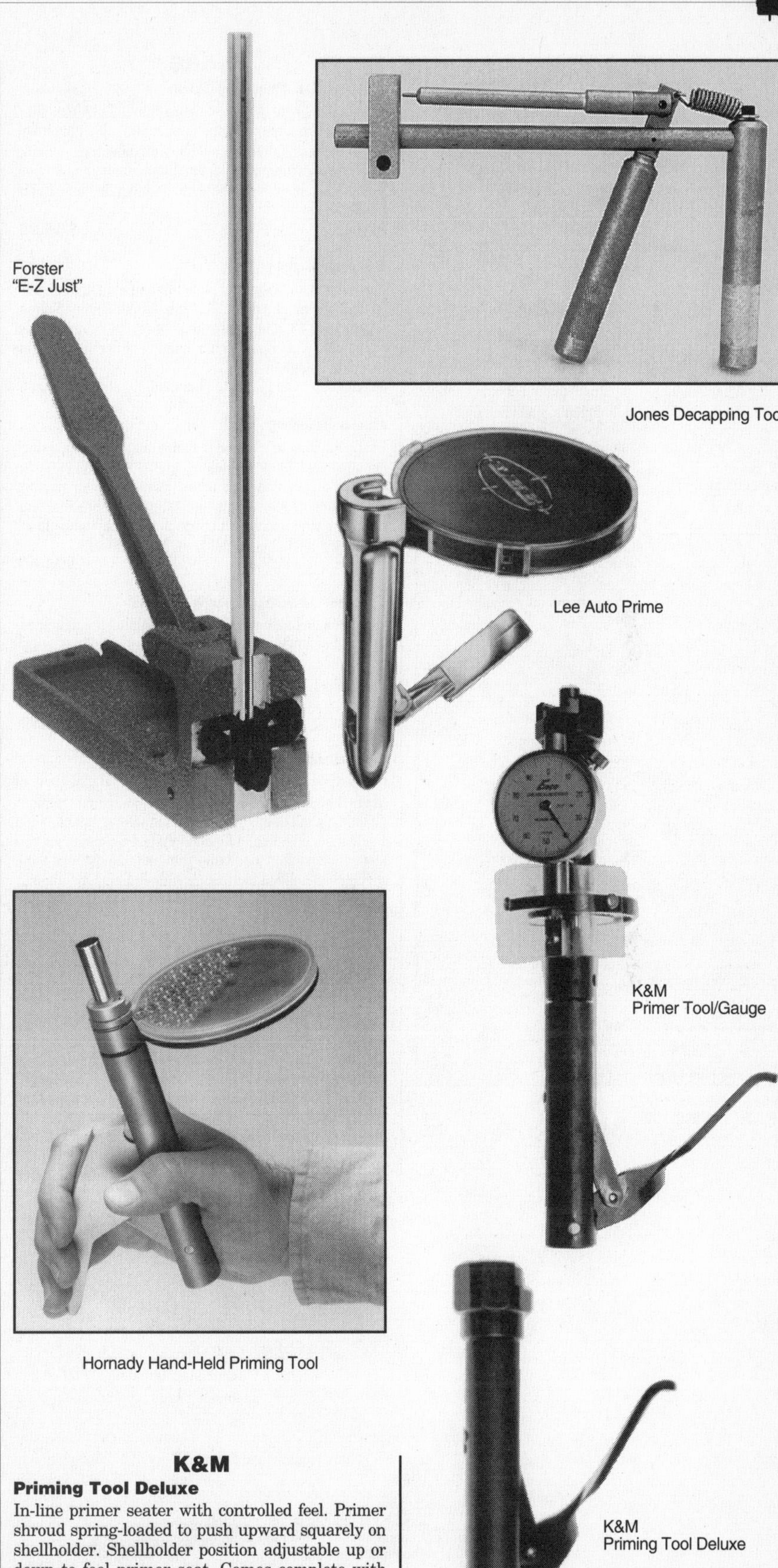

Forster "E-Z Just"

Jones Decapping Tool

Lee Auto Prime

K&M Primer Tool/Gauge

Hornady Hand-Held Priming Tool

K&M Priming Tool Deluxe

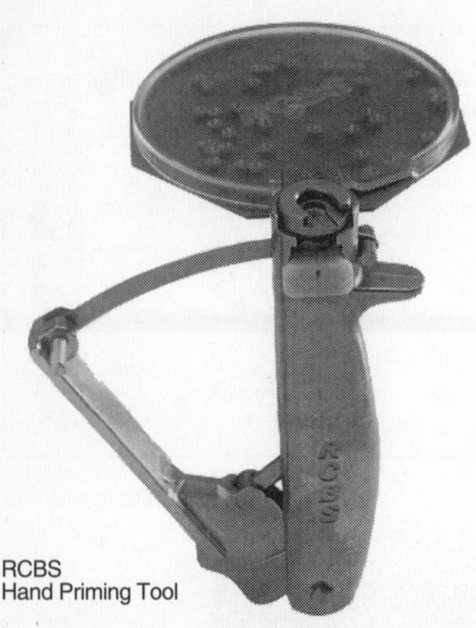
RCBS
Hand Priming Tool

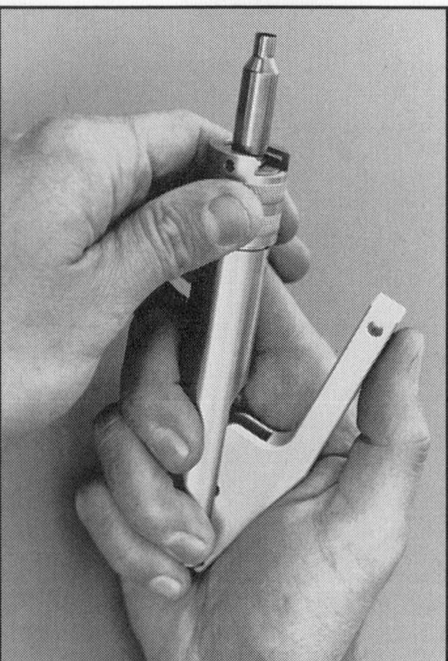
Sinclair Priming Tool

## RCBS

**Automatic Priming Tool**

One-hand, one-step priming tool. Primers feed through an auto prime feed tube. Single-stage lever system gives sensitive and positive seating feel. Two primer rod assemblies and primer feed tubes included. Shellholder not included. From RCBS.

**Price:** . . . . . . . . . . . . . **$64.38**

**Berdan Decapping Tool**

Handles wide range of Berdan-primed cases such as the 8mm Rimless, 6.5mm Mannlicher-Schoenauer and 11.7mm Rimmed. Made of heat-treated steel alloy. Comes with case holder and Allen wrench. From RCBS.

**Price:** . . . . . . . . . . . . . **$41.13**

**Hand Priming Tool**

Made of cast metal with unique patented safety mechanism to separate seating operation from primer supply to eliminate possibility of primer detonation. Primer tray installation, removal and filling require no hand contact with primers. Uses standard RCBS shellholders. From RCBS.

**Price:** . . . . . . . . . . . . . **$25.50**

**Primer Seating Depth Gauge**

To check primer seating depth without a micrometer. One end of gauge "rocks" on a primer-high case head; opposite end rests flat on primer-low case head. Made of hardened ground steel. From RCBS.

**Price:** . . . . . . . . . . . . . . **$5.88**

**Standard Priming Tool**

Cam-operated for sensitivity and detection of oversized or undersized pockets. Will accept most popular shellholders. Tool attaches to bench with C-clamp or bolts. Comes with two primer rod assemblies for all American-made Boxer-type primers. Shellholder not included. From RCBS.

**Price:** . . . . . . . . . . . . . **$40.50**

## SINCLAIR

**Priming Tool**

Precision machined hand tool with stainless steel body and anodized aluminum handle. Manually "locks" case head flush and at right angle with priming punch to ensure alignment and eliminate influence of case rim on primer seating. Designed for use with Lee Auto-Prime shellholders. Comes complete with instructions and push rods for both large and small primers. From Sinclair International, Inc.

**Price:** . . . . . . . . . . . . . **$87.00**

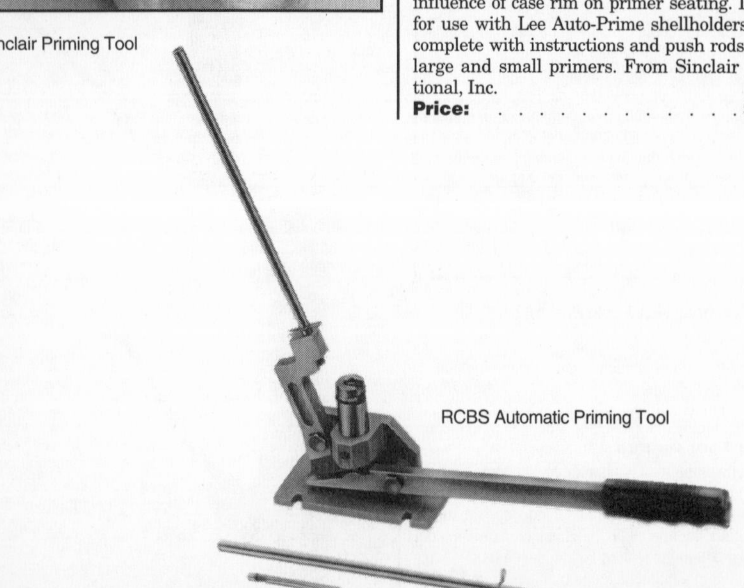
RCBS Automatic Priming Tool

## C-H/4-D

**50 BMG Priming Accessories**

Swage punch, priming post and shellholder. Swage punch used with priming tool removes crimp from military primer pockets. Priming post and shellholder can be used with any Hollywood press. With the addition of the shellholder die, these accessories can be used on any press with 7/8″ top threads. Sold separately or as complete set. From C-H Tool & Die/4-D Custom Die.

**Price:** Priming assembly . . . . . **$35.00**
**Price:** Swage assembly . . . . . . **$35.00**
**Price:** Complete set . . . . . . . **$45.00**

**Automatic Primer Feed**

Fits all C-H/4-D "H"-type presses. Available in large, small or conversion for large to small and vise versa. From C-H Tool & Die/4-D Custom Die.

**Price:** Large or small . . . . . . **$32.95**
**Price:** Both large and small . . . . **$43.95**
**Price:** Conversion . . . . . . . . **$13.75**

**Magnum H Press Primer Arm**

Replacement for original Magnum H-Press primer arm. Will work with all current snap-in shellholders and comes with both large and small primer punches. Replacement parts are available. From C-H Tool & Die/4-D Custom Die.

**Price:** . . . . . . . . . . . . . **$13.20**

**Primer Pocket Swage**

Removes crimp from any military case. No stripper washers needed; hardened swage punches; use with any reloading press and standard shellholder; large and small primer swage punches furnished. From C-H Tool & Die/4-D Custom Die.

**Price:** . . . . . . . . . . . . . **$18.65**
**Price:** Shellholder . . . . . . . . **$6.05**

**Priming Tool**

All steel priming tool that fits any reloading press with standard snap-in shellholder and 7/8-14 dies. Complete with large and small priming punches and cups. From C-H Tool & Die/4-D Custom Die.

**Price:** . . . . . . . . . . . . . **$16.45**

**Swage/Prime Combo**

Primer pocket swage complete plus priming tool punch body, base and both large and small punches and cups. From C-H Tool & Die/4-D Custom Die.

**Price:** . . . . . . . . . . . . . **$26.35**

**Universal Priming Arm**

Fits most "C"-type presses. Seats all sizes of primers. Complete with both large and small posts and cups. From C-H Tool & Die/4-D Custom Die.

**Price:** . . . . . . . . . . . . . **$7.65**

## DILLON

**RL 1050 and XL 650 Priming System**

For switching to large or small primer feed. From Dillon Precision Products, Inc.

**Price:** RL 1050 . . . . . . . . . **$29.95**
**Price:** XL 650 . . . . . . . . . . **$59.95**

## HUNTINGTON

**Berdan Primer Seater**

RCBS ram prime unit adapted to take the RCBS Berdan primer assembly to seat Berdan primers using reloading press. Unit fits in the top of press and primer assembly in a holder in the shellholder slot of press ram. Three size assemblies available to accommodate three Berdan primer sizes. From Huntington Die Specialties.

**Price:** Primer seater . . . . . . . **$19.98**
**Price:** Seater assembly, .217, .240, .255 . . **$11.10**
**Price:** Shellholder head drilled to fit . **$17.50**

## LEE

**Auto-Prime II**

Uses standard shellholders and will fit any brand loading press with vertical ram. Primes on upstroke. Includes primer feeders and punches for both large and small primers. Primer trap detaches for filling. Primers positioned correctly by shaking tray. From Lee Precision, Inc.

**Price:** . . . . . . . . . . . . . **$18.98**

**Ram Prime**

Primes on the press up-stroke. Includes punches for both large and small primers. Fits all brands of presses. From Lee Precision, Inc.

**Price:** . . . . . . . . . . . . . **$11.98**

## RCBS

**Auto Primer Feed Combo**

Feeds primers one at a time into primer plug and sleeve. Comes with 100-count primer tube, large or small. Fits most RCBS and C-type presses. Does not fit RS-2, 3, or 5, or Partner press. From RCBS.

**Price:** Combo . . . . . . . . . **$20.50**
**Price:** Feed tube, large or small . . . **$8.50**

**Primer Catcher**

Attaches without screws to Reloader Special, Jr. and Rock Chucker presses. From RCBS.

**Price:** . . . . . . . . . . . . . **$6.13**

**Primer Pocket Swager Combo**

Removes primer-pocket crimp from military cases. Creates primer pocket correct in dimension for Boxer-type primers. Comes with swager heads for large and small pockets; fits nearly all 7/8″-14 presses with removable shellholders. From RCBS.

**Price:** . . . . . . . . . . . . . **$23.88**

**Primer Tray-2**

Designed to position primers anvil side up for insertion into primer arm sleeve or anvil down for loading automatic primer feed tubes. Holds 100 primers. From RCBS.

**Price:** . . . . . . . . . . . . . **$3.75**

## RCBS

**Ram Priming Unit**

Works with any press with 7/8″-14 thread and removable shellholder. Seats the primer at the top of the press stroke. Also allows pre-setting of positive stop for reload speed. Includes primer rod assemblies for all rifle and pistol Boxer-type primers. From RCBS.

**Price:** . . . . . . . . . . . . . **$15.88**

**Universal Decapping Die**

Removes primers from uncleaned, unlubricated cases prior to tumbling. Handles calibers 22 through 45. Includes die body, decapping assembly with lock nut, die lock ring and plastic storage box. From RCBS.

**Price:** . . . . . . . . . . . . . **$11.13**

**Universal Primer Arm**

Accessory for Reloader Special, Jr. and Rock Chucker presses. Flat return spring prevents jamming. Plugs and sleeves included. Does not fit RS-2, 3, or 5, or Partner press. From RCBS.

**Price:** Primer arm . . . . . . . . **$10.25**
**Price:** Plugs and sleeves . . . . . . **$2.88**

## REDDING

**Automatic Primer Feeder**

Designed for Model 7 and Model 25 presses to eliminate handling of primers during sizing. Comes complete with individualized tubes for large and small primers. Capacity for approximately 75 primers. From Redding Reloading Equipment.

**Price:** Model 7 press . . . . . . . **$18.90**
**Price:** Model 25 press . . . . . . **$21.90**

## ROCK CRUSHER

**Priming Tool**

Designed for use with the Rock Crusher press for priming 50 BMG or 20mm Lahati cartridges. From The Old Western Scrounger.

**Price:** . . . . . . . . . . . . . **$65.10**

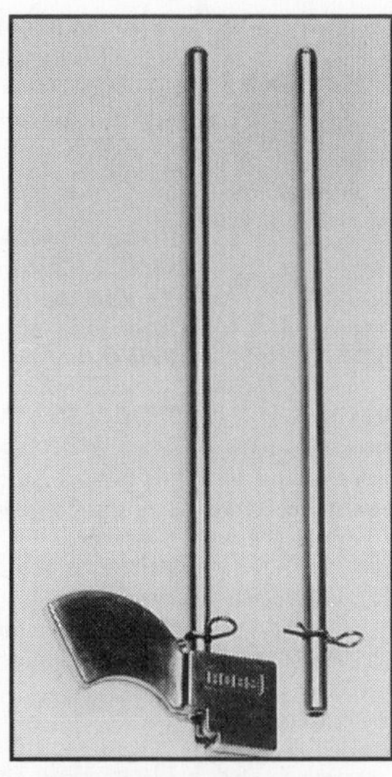

RCBS Automatic Primer Feed

PRIMING TOOLS/Primer Pocket Tools

## E. ARTHUR BROWN

**Primer Pocket Reamer**

Reams rifle and pistol primer pockets square and to correct depth. From E. Arthur Brown Company.

**Price:** . . . . . . . . . . . . . **$22.50**

**Flash Hole Uniformer**

Deburr and bevel flash holes to consistent depth. Comes in standard or deluxe configurations.

**Price:** Standard . . . . . . . . . **$8.95**
**Price:** Deluxe . . . . . . . . . **$13.95**

## C-H/4-D

**50 BMG Flash Hole Deburer**

Features adjustable stop collar and double end cutter. From C-H Tool & Die/4-D Custom Die.

**Price:** . . . . . . . . . . . . . **$26.50**

**Flash Hole Debur Tool**

Features adjustable stop collar; double end cutter; for 17- to 45-caliber. From C-H Tool & Die/4-D Custom Die.

**Price:** . . . . . . . . . . . . . **$16.50**

**Hand/Power Primer Pocket Tool**

Six-piece kit for manually cleaning and reaming primer pockets, or with 1/4" hex adapter converting to electric screwdriver or drill. Includes plastic handle, adapter, large and small brushes, and large and small reamers. From C-H Tool & Die/4-D Custom Die.

**Price:** . . . . . . . . . . . . . **$14.25**

## DEWEY

**"Baby Crocogator"**

Cleans both large and small primer pockets. Tool ends are radiused to conform to pocket contours. Small diamond-shaped teeth assure proper cleaning. Made from hardened steel. From J. Dewey Mfg. Co., Inc.

**Price:** . . . . . . . . . . . . . **$3.25**

## DILLON

**Super Swage 600**

Swages primer pockets of military brass. Case is supported from inside to prevent tearing of the rim. Tool steel hardened swage rod, changeable from large to small primers, rolls crimp away. No reaming necessary. Compound cam leverage system assures alignment. From Dillon Precision Products, Inc.

**Price:** . . . . . . . . . . . . . **$69.95**

## FORSTER

**Primer Pocket Chamfering Tool**

To remove crimp from military brass. Tool fits both small and large primer pockets and can be used on any Forster case trimmer with primer pocket center. Weight: 4 oz. From Forster Products.

**Price:** . . . . . . . . . . . . . **$15.40**
**Price:** Primer pocket center . . . . **$7.20**

**Primer Pocket Cleaner**

Scraper-type tool that mounts in the cutter shaft of the Forster case trimmer in place of the pilot; the hardened case mouth center mounts in the trimmer collet. Same center cleans both large (.210) and small (.175) primer pockets. Weight: 3 oz. From Forster Products.

**Price:** . . . . . . . . . . . . . **$7.20**

Forster Primer Pocket Chamfering Tool

Hornady Cleaner Head

Dillon Super Swage 600

Dewey Baby Crocogator

Hart Flash Hole Deburrer

Hart Primer Pocket Cleaner

## GRACEY

**Primer Pocket Cleaner**

Power primer pocket cleaner with Dayton 1/30 hp, 1.05 amp, 1550 rpm motor operating copper brush that cleans without increasing pocket diameter. Brush construction features copper elements set in steel cup retained by a resin of tremendous strength. Brush elements are offset .007" from center for scrubbing action. A coil spring vibrates freely along length of copper cleaner to prevent the copper elements from spreading. From Match Prep.

**Price:** . . . . . . . . . . . . . **$64.50**

## HART

**Internal Flash Hole Debur Tool**

Hand-held stainless steel tool with steel cutter for removing burrs around primer flash hole. Available in two sizes: standard for U.S. cases and small for PPC cases. From Robert Hart & Son, Inc.

**Price:** . . . . . . . . . . . . . **$14.95**

**Primer Pocket Cleaner**

Cleans both large and small primer pockets. Knurled body for easy gripping. From Robert Hart & Son, Inc.

**Price:** . . . . . . . . . . . . . **$8.25**

**Primer Depth Reamer**

Made of tool steel or carbide with adjustable cutter to assure uniform primer pocket depth. Comes in either large or small size. From Robert Hart & Son, Inc.

**Price:** Steel reamer . . . . . . . **$15.95**
**Price:** Steel replacement cutter . . . **$7.95**
**Price:** Carbide reamer . . . . . . **$23.95**
**Price:** Carbide replacement cutter . **$11.95**

## HAYDON

**Flash Hole Deburring Tool**

Deburs inside of primer flash hole with cutter and steel body. From Russ Haydon's Shooter's Supply.

**Price:** . . . . . . . . . . . . . **$15.50**
**Price:** Handle . . . . . . . . . . **$7.50**

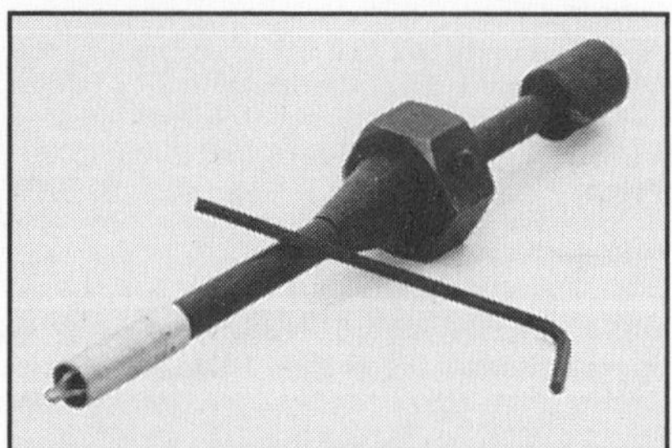

Haydon Flash Hole Deburring Tool

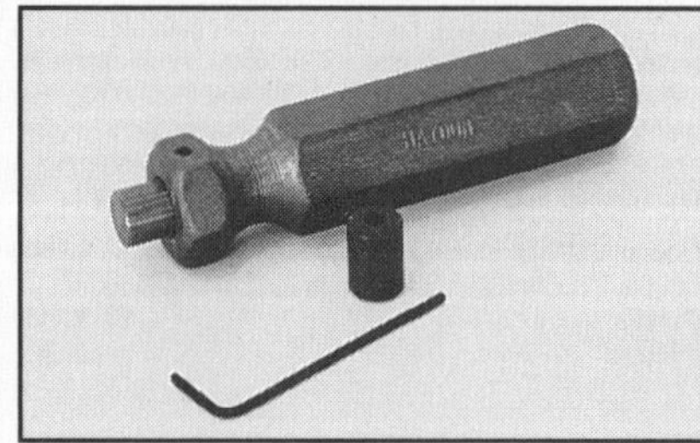

Haydon Primer Pocket Uniformer

## HAYDON

**Primer Pocket Uniformer**

Carbide uniformer for pistol or rifle cases. Comes with or without handle. From Russ Haydon's Shooter's Supply.

**Price:** . . . . . . . . . . . . . **$18.00**
**Price:** With handle . . . . . . . **$24.95**
**Price:** Brush adaptor . . . . . . . **$2.00**

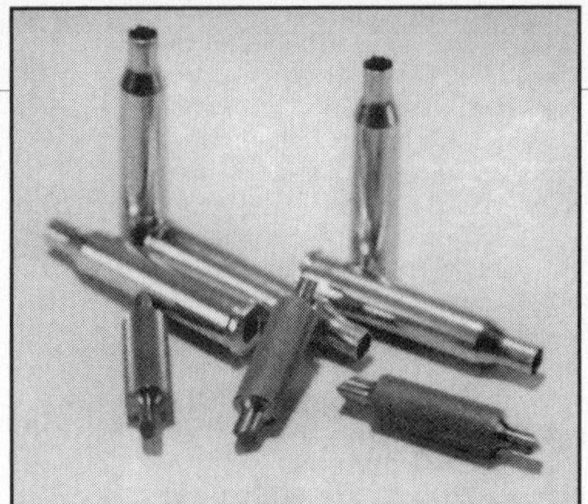

Hollands Primer Pocket Cleaner

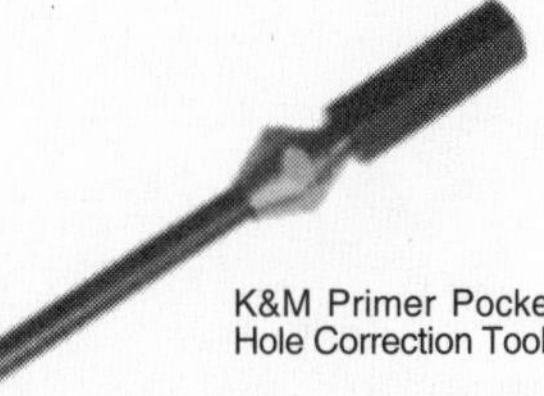

K&M Primer Pocket Hole Correction Tool

Lyman Primer Pocket Cleaning

Lee Cleaner

Lee Decapper

## HOLLANDS

**Primer Pocket Cleaner**

For both large and small primer pockets. Features stippled surface for sure grip. From Hollands Gunsmithing, Inc.

**Price:** . . . . . . . . . . . . . . **$14.95**

## HORNADY

**Primer Pocket Cleaners**

Metal cleaner heads to remove fouling from large or small primer pockets. Use in conjunction with Universal accessory handle. From Hornady Mfg. Co.

**Price:** . . . . . . . . . . . . . . **$5.55**
**Price:** Handle . . . . . . . . . . **$2.95**

**Primer Pocket Reamer**

Cuts away crimp from military brass. Available for large or small primer pockets. Comes separately or with accessory handle. From Hornady Mfg. Co.

**Price:** . . . . . . . . . . . . . . **$5.95**
**Price:** Complete with handle . . . . **$7.65**

## JONES

**Primer Pocket Uniforming Fixture**

Holds cases square to cutter for uniform cutting. Uses Whitetail or Sinclair cutters. Comes with one shellholder. From Neil Jones Custom Products.

**Price:** . . . . . . . . . . . . . . **$65.00**
**Price:** Cutters . . . . . . . . . . **$18.00**
**Price:** Handle . . . . . . . . . . **$8.00**

## K&M

**Flash Hole Uniformer**

Patented tool for benchresters to precisely ream, debur and chamfer the inside of flashhole. Features a pre-set depth stop surrounding steel cutter which is referenced to inside-bottom of case not case mouth. Reversible sliding centering cone supplied to keep case aligned and centered during uniforming operation. Accepts all pistol and rifle brass from 22- through 458-caliber. Standard uniformer .080″; PPC/BR .0625″. Available in "Master" or "Pro" models. From K&M Services.

**Price:** Master . . . . . . . . . . **$9.50**
**Price:** Pro . . . . . . . . . . . . **$14.50**
**Price:** Replacement cutter . . . . . **$5.00**

## K&M

**Primer Pocket Correction Tool**

Features tungsten carbide cutter set to optimum depth, .131″ for large rifle; .122″ for small rifle and small/large pistol. 1/4″ hex drive allows use with power screwdriver or drill. Hex shape handle body available. From K&M Services.

**Price:** . . . . . . . . . . . . . . **$17.00**
**Price:** Handle . . . . . . . . . . **$4.00**

## LEE

**Primer Pocket Cleaner**

Double ended design cleans both large and small primer pockets. From Lee Precision, Inc.

**Price:** . . . . . . . . . . . . . . **$1.98**

**Decapper and Base**

Removes crimped-in primers from military cases. From Lee Precision, Inc.

**Price:** . . . . . . . . . . . . . . **$3.98**

## LYMAN

**Flash Hole Uniformer**

Removes internal flash hole burrs. Features tool steel cutter with adjustable stop collar for use with any size case. Comes with wood handle. From Lyman Products Corporation.

**Price:** . . . . . . . . . . . . . . **$10.25**

**Primer Pocket Cleaner**

Cleans fouling from primer pocket bottoms. Wooden handle included. Available in large or small sizes. From Lyman Products Corporation.

**Price:** . . . . . . . . . . . . . . **$8.50**

**Primer Pocket Reamer**

Removes military crimps and rough metal edges from primer pocket. Comes with wooden handle. Available in large or small sizes. From Lyman Products Corporation.

**Price:** . . . . . . . . . . . . . . **$8.50**

**Primer Pocket Uniformer**

Assures uniform primer depth with pre-set stop collar set to SAAMI specs. Available in large and small sizes. From Lyman Products Corporation.

**Price:** . . . . . . . . . . . . . . **$16.25**

Jones Uniforming Fixture

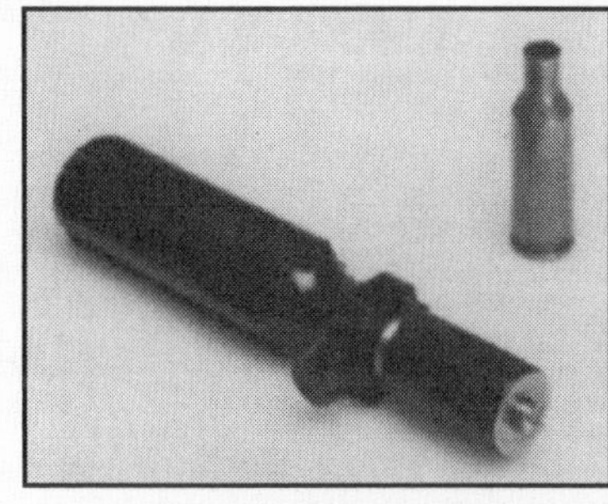

K&M Flash Hole Uniformers

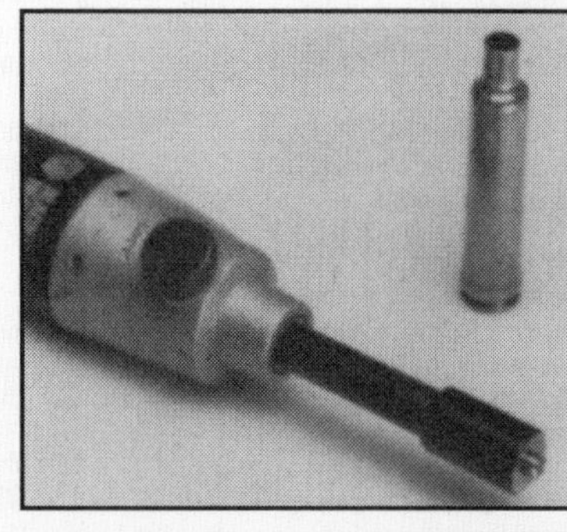

## MARMIK

**50 BMG Deprimer/Case Mouth Rounder**

Steel punch .500″ diameter with tapered entrance and 1/8″ hardened steel depriming pin. Will automatically bring out-or-round case mouths back to shape for resizing. From MarMik, Inc.

**Price:** . . . . . . . . . . . . . . **$4.00**

## MIDWAY

**Primer Pocket Uniformer**

Squares bottom of primer pocket with respect to case head and ensures uniform and consistent primer depth. Carbide cutters for both small and large primer flash holes. Octagonal body for positive grip. From Midway Arms, Inc.

**Price:** . . . . . . . . . . . . . **$27.99**

**Flash Hole Deburring Tool**

For 22- through 45-caliber cases to remove flash hole burrs inside of case. From Midway Arms, Inc.

**Price:** . . . . . . . . . . . . . **$14.49**

## MWG

**Case Saver**

Primer pocket swager to form a seating seal in the primer pocket of a worn case. Includes support stand and punch with guide pin. Two sizes: large for 30-cal. and above; small for 22-cal. to 7mm. Fro MWG Company.

**Price:** . . . . . . . . . . . . . **$33.85**

## PEM'S

**Pedestal Crank**

Use with PEM primer pocket cleaner brush for faster operation. Drilled and tapped for bench mounting. From PEM'S Mfg. Co.

**Price:** . . . . . . . . . . . . . . **$7.50**

**Primer Pocket Cleaner**

Fine steel wire brush with metal sleeve. Specify large or small primer pocket. Manual tool or can be used in any motor or hand-driven chuck. From PEM'S Mfg. Co.

**Price:** . . . . . . . . . . . . . . **$1.50**

## RCBS

**Flash Hole Deburring Tool**

Removes flash-hole burrs from inside. Features self-locating pilot stop collar to prevent removal of too much brass. Threaded shaft can be chucked into an electric drill. Pilot not included. From RCBS.

**Price:** . . . . . . . . . . . . . . **$9.75**
**Price:** Pilot . . . . . . . . . . . **$2.63**

**Primer Pocket Brush Combo**

Removes residue from primer pockets. Brushes have stainless bristles and interchangeable mounts for large and small primer pockets. Comes as combo with accessory handle or as separate components. From RCBS.

**Price:** Combo . . . . . . . . . **$11.88**
**Price:** Brush only, large or small . . **$5.25**
**Price:** Accessory handle . . . . . . **$3.50**

## SINCLAIR

**Decap Punches and Bases**

Removes crimped-in primers on military brass. Case-hardened base collects spent primers. Punches and bases ordered separately by cartridge. From Sinclair International, Inc.

**Price:** Base . . . . . . . . . . . **$2.50**
**Price:** Punch . . . . . . . . . . **$4.95**

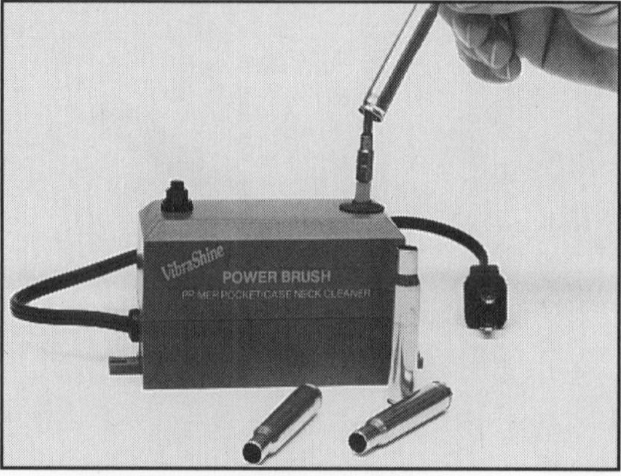


VibraShine Power Brush

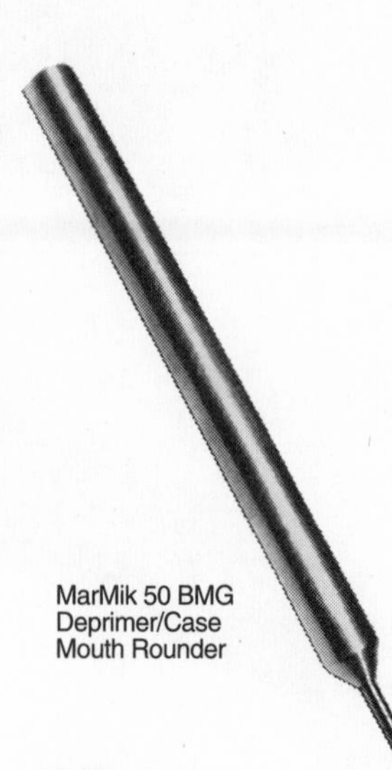

MarMik 50 BMG Deprimer/Case Mouth Rounder

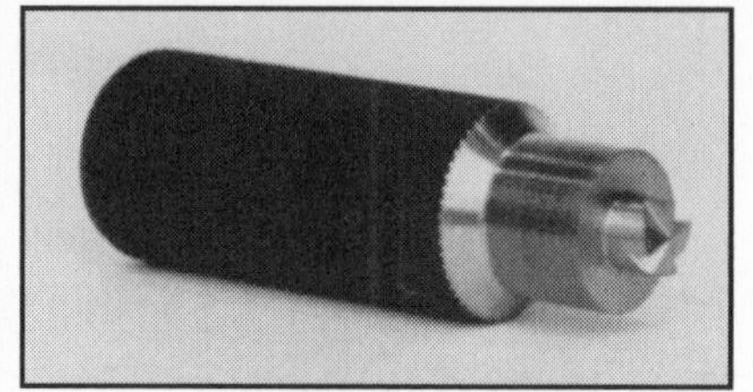

Whitetail Match Prep Tool

## SINCLAIR

**Deluxe Flash Hole Debur Tool**

Cutting depth controlled by hexagon stop tapered to center the cutting shaft during deburring operation. Will work on rifle and pistol cases from 22- through 45-caliber. 17-cal. and 50 BMG debur/uniformer tool also available. From Sinclair International, Inc.

**Price:** . . . . . . . . . . . . . **$15.75**
**Price:** 17-cal. . . . . . . . . . . **$20.25**
**Price:** 50 BMG . . . . . . . . . **$39.50**

**PPC Flash Hole Debur Tool**

To accommodate the different internal case head designs of imported Russian 220 and new PPC cases with .060″ flash holes, this flash hole tool has no preset cutting depth. From Sinclair International, Inc.

**Price:** . . . . . . . . . . . . . **$15.75**

**8000 Series Primer Pocket Uniformer**

Precision ground from solid carbide in large rifle, large pistol and small rifle/pistol. Use in drill or drill press (3/8″ chuck) for uniforming primer pockets to correct depth or mount in handle for use as hand tool. Handle is anti-fatigue style with stainless steel insert for holding cutter. From Sinclair International, Inc.

**Price:** . . . . . . . . . . . . . **$18.75**
**Price:** With handle . . . . . . . **$26.70**
**Price:** Adaptor for power screwdriver . **$9.75**
**Price:** DBT base adaptor . . . . . . **$4.50**

**Phase II Uniformers**

Portable hand tool or power bench tool with solid carbide cutter set into hardened stop collar. Cutter and stop collar mount into anti-fatigue handle for hand use or chuck into drill or drill press of less than 1100 rpm for power use. From Sinclair International, Inc.

**Price:** . . . . . . . . . . . . . **$22.95**

## SINCLAIR

**Power Uniformer**

Same carbide cutter and hardened stop collar as Phase II uniformer but without handle. Height-adjustable cradle to support the power screwdriver offered as optional accessory. Use in drill or drill press of less than 1100 rpm. From Sinclair International, Inc.

**Price:** . . . . . . . . . . . . . **$16.50**
**Price:** Uniformer cradle . . . . . **$13.25**

## VIBRASHINE

**Power Brush**

Vibratory action cleans fouling from primer pockets or with case neck brush becomes case neck cleaner. Push-button on/off switch. 120-volt AC. From VibraShine, Inc.

**Price:** . . . . . . . . . . . . . **$29.95**

## WHITETAIL DESIGN

**Match Prep Deluxe**

Primer pocket uniformer with anodized aluminum handle and tungsten carbide tipped cutter. Wrench loosens handle to accept cutter; reverse cutter in handle for protection and storage. Available for large rifle, large pistol and small pistol/rifle. From Whitetail Design and Engineering Ltd.

**Price:** . . . . . . . . . . . . . **$25.50**
**Price:** Extra cutters . . . . . . . **$18.00**
**Price:** Extra handle . . . . . . . . **$7.50**

**Match Prep Tool**

Tungsten carbide tipped primer pocket uniformer in three sizes, small rifle and pistol, large rifle and large pistol. Knurled body for gripping. From Whitetail Design and Engineering Ltd.

**Price:** . . . . . . . . . . . . . **$22.50**

## WILSON

**Primer Pocket Reamer**

Removes crimp on military brass. Specify large or small primer pocket. From L.E. Wilson, Inc.

**Price:** . . . . . . . . . . . . . **$22.00**

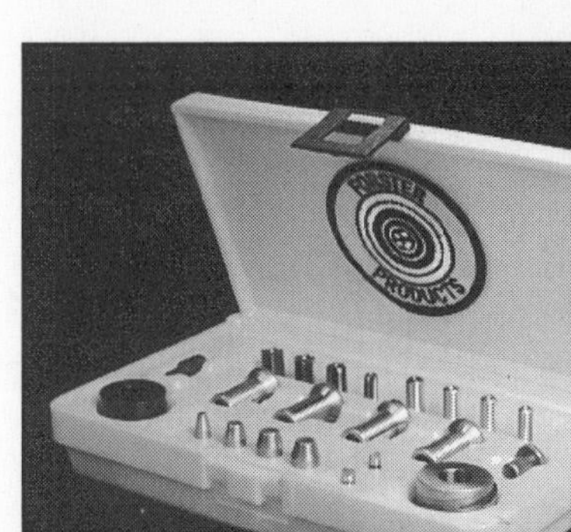


George & Roy's Primer Sealant

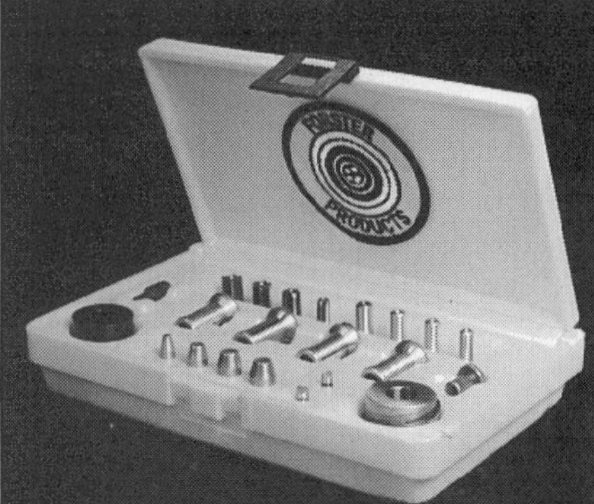


Forster Case Trimmer Accessory Case

Hornady Shooter's Journal

Guardsman Dri-slide

Hornady Primer Turner

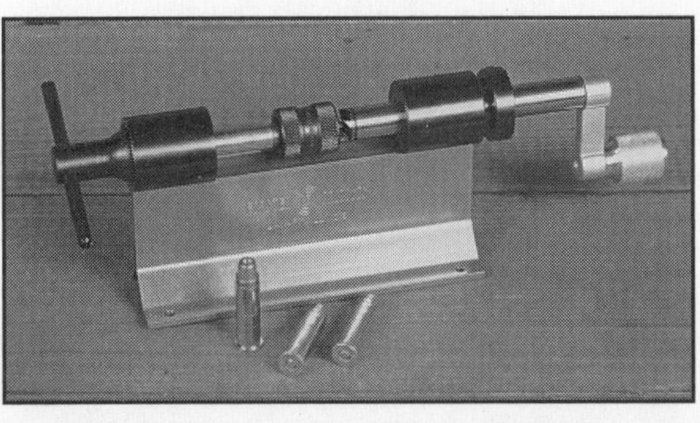

Forster Hollow Pointer

## C-H/4-D

**Cannelure Tool**

Solid steel tool for rolling in grooves on bullets prior to crimping or case cannelure on straight-wall cases. Adjustable for depth and height. For bullets from 17- to 45-caliber. Hardened cutting wheel; precision machined. From C-H Tool & Die/4-D Custom Die.

**Price:** . . . . . . . . . . . . . . **$45.00**

## DILLON

**Primer Flip Tray**

Heavy tray large enough for new NATO primer package. From Dillon Precision Products, Inc.

**Price:** . . . . . . . . . . . . . . **$10.95**

**Primer Pickup Tubes**

Used to transfer large or small primers from flip tray into 100-primer capacity Dillon auto prime tube. From Dillon Precision Products, Inc.

**Price:** . . . . . . . . . . . . . . **$3.75**

## DONALD EAGAN

**Bullet Base Chamfering Tool**

Designed to bevel bullet base to facilitate full seating of gas checks. Uses scraping action to minimize metal loss. For 22 through 45 calibers. From Donald Eagan.

**Price:** . . . . . . . . . . . . . . **$6.00**

## FORSTER

**Hollow Pointer**

Use with Forster case trimmers for hollowpointing softpoint jacketed rounds. Available in either 1/8″ or 1/16″ drill sizes for pistol and rifle cartridges, respectively. Weight: 4 oz. From Forster Products.

**Price:** . . . . . . . . . . . . . . **$14.80**

## GUARDSMAN

**DriSlide**

Molybdenum disulfide dry film lubricant. Withstands pressures up to 100,000 psi and allows use in extreme hot or cold temperatures. Comes in a 4-oz. can. Available from Buckeye Sports Supply.

**Price:** . . . . . . . . . . . . . . **$5.00**

## GEORGE & ROY'S

**Primer Sealant**

Seals and weatherproofs primers of handloads. Is removeable with all normal brass cleaning methods. Dries in less than 3 minutes. One bottle seals a minimum of 1,000 rounds. Comes in 1/2-fluid oz. bottle. From George & Roy's.

**Price:** . . . . . . . . . . . . . . **$10.00**

## HART

**Base for Wilson Neck Die**

Base brings height of Wilson neck die to that of Wilson bullet seater, preventing necessity of arbor press height adjustments. From Robert W. Hart & Son, Inc.

**Price:** . . . . . . . . . . . . . . **$16.50**

## HORNADY

**Shooting Journal**

Packaged in weatherproof binder. Contains three styles of sight-in targets with fill-in-the-blank load information, preprinted load analysis tables arranged according to firearm and Post-It-Note notepad for recording velocity and trajectory. From Hornady Mfg. Co.

**Price:** . . . . . . . . . . . . . . **$21.95**

## HORNADY

**Primer Turning Tray**

Made of sturdy plastic with transparent cover. Weight: 4 oz. From Hornady Mfg. Co.

**Price:** . . . . . . . . . . . . . . . **$3.95**

## LYMAN

**Primer Tray**

Durable plastic tray flips primers anvil-side up for loading. From Lyman Products Corporation.

**Price:** . . . . . . . . . . . . . . . **$3.50**

**Reloading Data Log**

A $8^1/_2$″x11″ 50-page journal with four large load sections per page to record load data information. Bound in pad and three-hole punched for insertion into binder. From Lyman Products Corporation.

**Price:** . . . . . . . . . . . . . . . **$4.50**

## MA SYSTEMS

**Easy Collater Tray**

Orients cases or bullets in slotted tray to slide easily into feed tubes. Tray accepts 100 rounds. Dimensions: $8^1/_2$″x9″. Weight: 12 lbs. From MA Systems.

**Price:** . . . . . . . . . . . . . **$14.95**

## MIDWAY

**Rust Inhibitor Chips**

Impregnated 1″x1″ rust inhibitor chips to protect moulds. Each chip protects up to 20 cubic inches of aluminum or steel. Come in packages of 50 or 200. From Midway Arms, Inc.

**Price:** 50 . . . . . . . . . . . . . **$5.99**
**Price:** 200 . . . . . . . . . . . . **$16.99**

**Shooter's Notebook Kit**

Notebook kit includes firearms data sheets to record reloading and shooting information plus 100 reloader labels for ammo boxes and five different types of Midway targets, 100 1″ shooting spots, 50 2″. From Midway Arms, Inc.

**Price:** Kit . . . . . . . . . . . **$19.99**
**Price:** Notebook only . . . . . . . **$15.99**

## MTM

**Handloaders Log**

Space provided for 1000 entries: Date, Range Group Size or Score, Components and Conditions. Reinforced, heavy-duty vinyl three-ring binder. Extra pages available in packs of 50. From MTM Moulded Products Company.

**Price:** . . . . . . . . . . . . . **$14.99**

**Primer Flipper Tray**

Plastic see-through tray to align primers anvil-side up. From MTM Moulded Products Company.

**Price:** . . . . . . . . . . . . . . . **$2.26**

## NECO

**P-Wads and Wad Insertion Tool**

Precision, hand cut plastic P-Wads for plain base cast bullets to act as gas seal for prevention of gas cutting. Precision stainless steel and tool steel insertion tool designed to seat the P-Wad squarely and uniformly in case mouth. P-Wads come 100 to a bag. From NECO.

**Price:** . . . . . . . . . . . . . **$39.75**
**Price:** P-Wads (22-29) . . . . . . . **$3.75**
**Price:** P-Wads (40-44) . . . . . . . **$5.50**

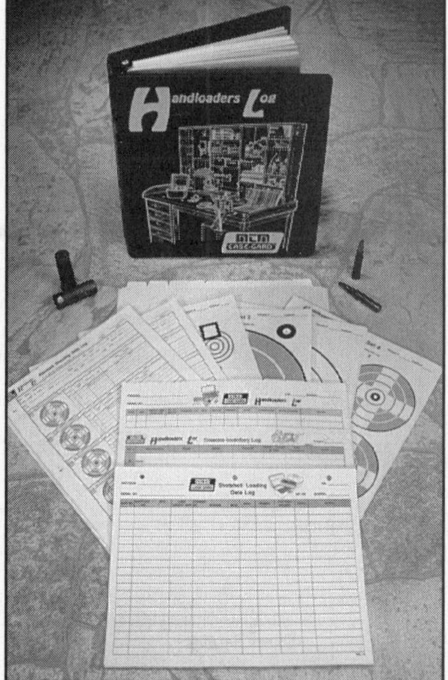


MTM Handloader's Log

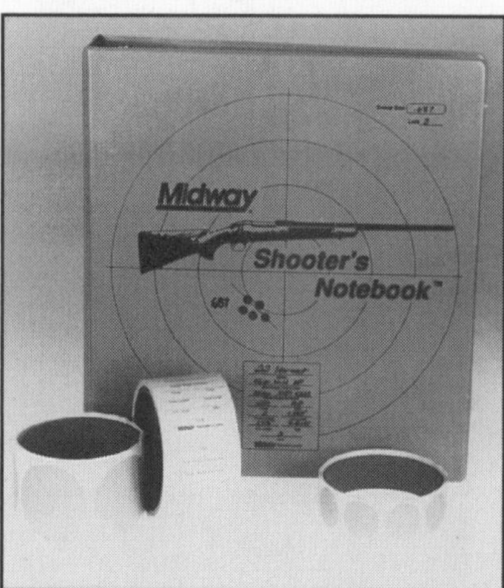


Midway Shooter's Notebook Kit

NECO P-Wads and Insertion Tool

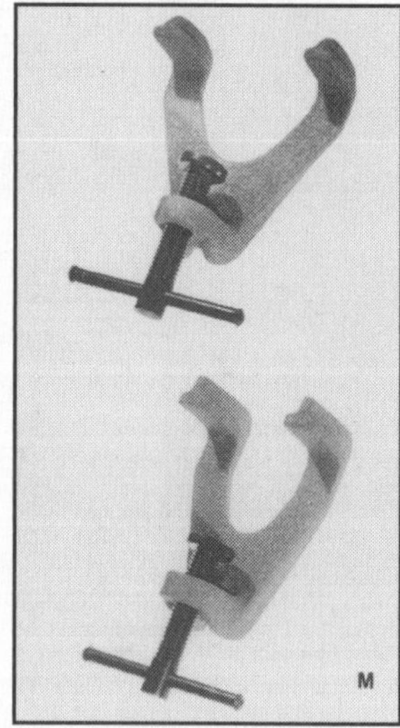

Redding Double "C" Clamp

## POWLEY

**Computers**

Two computers for handloaders. Powley Computer for Handloaders prescribes powder and calculates velocity; Powley psi Calculator gives chamber pressures. Includes up-to-date table on how to adapt recently introduced powders to calculators. From Hutton Rifle Ranch.

**Price:** Each . . . . . . . . . . . **$10.00**
**Price:** Both . . . . . . . . . . . **$20.00**

## RCBS

**Hex Key Set**

Eight black-oxide heat-treated hex keys in fold-up unit. Fit most Allen screws on RCBS equipment. Case is made of chrome-plated steel. Key sizes: .050, $^1/_{16}$″, $^5/_{64}$″, $^3/_{32}$″, $^7/_{64}$″, $^1/_8$″, $^9/_{64}$″ and $^5/_{32}$″. From RCBS.

**Price:** . . . . . . . . . . . . . . **$5.75**

## RCBS

**Primer Tray-2**

Sturdy plastic tray with 100-primer capacity. Positions primers anvil side up or down. From RCBS.

**Price:** . . . . . . . . . . . . . . **$3.75**

## REDDING

**Double "C" Clamp**

Designed for clamping the Redding powder measure stand and case trimmer to benchtop. Will accommodate bench thickness of up to $2^1/_4$″. From Redding Reloading Equipment.

**Price:** . . . . . . . . . . . . . **$19.50**

Sinclair Reloading Logbook

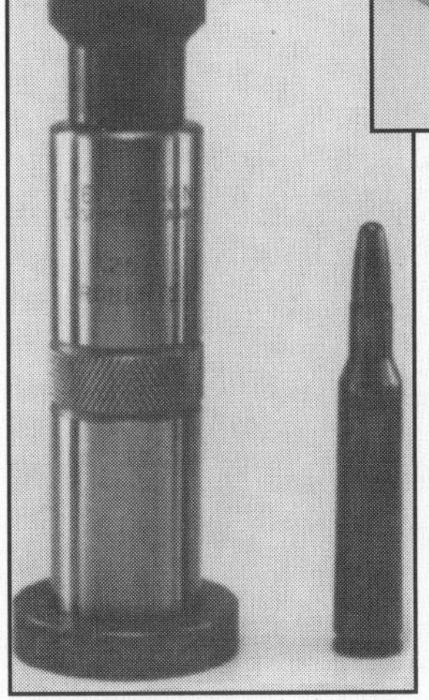

Wilson Chamber Type Bullet Seater

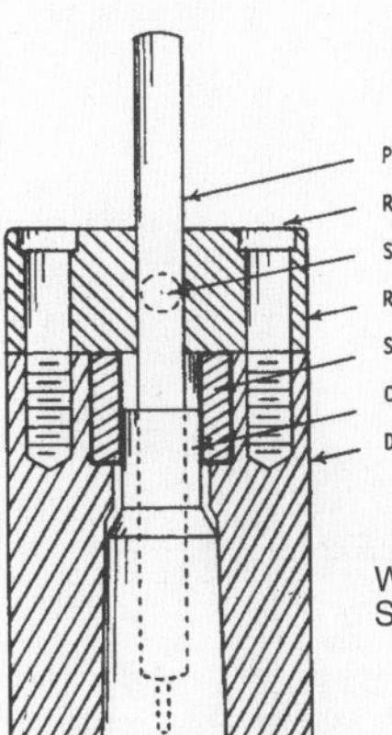


Wilson Neck Sizing Die

TSI 301 Lubricant

**WILSON**
**Neck Sizer Rifle Calibers**

| | |
|---|---|
| 17 Ackley Hornet | 6mm Rem. BR |
| 17 Mach IV | 25-06 |
| 17 Remington | 250 Savage |
| 218 Bee | 257 Roberts |
| 219 Donaldson | 264 Win. Mag. |
| 22 Hornet | 6.5x55 |
| 22 PPC | 270 Win. |
| 22 PPC SAKO | 280/7mm Exp. |
| 22 Remington BR | 284 Win. |
| 22-250 | 7mm Rem. BR |
| 220 Swift | 7mm Rem. Mag. |
| 22 Remington FB | 7mm TCU |
| 222 Remington | 7mmx57 Mauser |
| 222 Rem. Mag. | 7mm-08 |
| 223 Remington | 7mm IHMSA |
| 243 Winchester | 30 IHMSA |
| 6mm PPC | 30-06 |
| 6mm PPC SAKO | 30-30 |
| 6mm Remington | 30-338 |
| 6mmx47 | 300 Win. Mag. |
| | 308 Win. |

**WILSON**
**Bullet Seater Calibers**

| | |
|---|---|
| 17 Ackley Hornet | 25-06 |
| 17 Mach IV | 250 Savage |
| 17 Rem. | 257 Roberts |
| 218 Bee | 6.5x55 |
| 219 Donaldson | 270 Win. |
| 22 Hornet | 280/7mm Express |
| 22 PPC | 284 Win. |
| 22 PPC SAKO | 7mm Rem. BR |
| 22 Rem. BR | 7mm Rem. Mag. |
| 22-250 | 7mm TCU |
| 220 Swift | 7mmx57 Mauser |
| 221 Rem. FB | 7mm-08 |
| 222 Rem. | 7mm IHMSA |
| 222 Rem. Mag. | 30 IHMSA |
| 223 Rem. | 30-06 |
| 225 Win. | 30-30 |
| 243 Win. | 30-338 |
| 6mm PPC | 300 H&H |
| 6mm PPC SAKO | 300 Win. Mag. |
| 6mm Rem. | 308 Win. |
| 6mmx47 | 338 Win. Mag. |
| 6mm Rem. BR | |

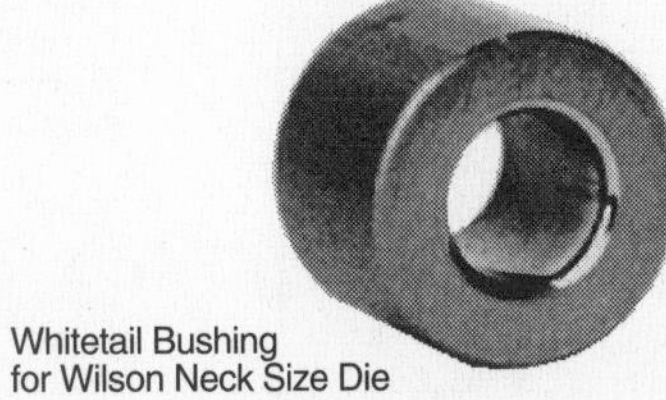

Whitetail Bushing for Wilson Neck Size Die

## RIG

### RIG 2 and RIG 3

Aerosol degreaser (RIG 3) and lubricant (RIG 2) for removing sizing and bullet lube from dies and protecting them from rust during storage. Available in 8-oz. spray can or 1-gal. container. From RIG Products.

**Price:** 8-oz. . . . . . . . . . . . . **$3.00**
**Price:** 1-gal. . . . . . . . . . . . **$28.33**

### Universal Grease

Semi-solid preservative for storage of dies. Comes in 1-oz., 3³/₄-oz., 15-oz. and 1-gallon jars. From RIG Products.

**Price:** 1-oz. . . . . . . . . . . . **$2.58**
**Price:** 3³/₄-oz. . . . . . . . . . . **$4.72**
**Price:** 15-oz. . . . . . . . . . . . **$8.84**
**Price:** 1-gal. . . . . . . . . . . . **$53.06**

## SINCLAIR

### Data Log Book

Data log book for recording date, temperature, wind, conditions, case, primer, powder, charge/setting, bullet, weight, style, OAL, number of shots, group size and observations. Spiral bound with 50 pages per book with room for 300 loads. From Sinclair International, Inc.

**Price:** 5¹/₂x8¹/₂ . . . . . . . . . **$3.95**
**Price:** 8¹/₂x11 . . . . . . . . . . **$4.50**

### Micrometer Kit for Wilson Seaters

Converts Wilson seater to micrometer seater. Consists of a stainless steel head assembly utilizing the seating plug of Wilson seater. Graduated in increments of .005″ but .001″ adjustments possible. From Sinclair International, Inc.

**Price:** . . . . . . . . . . . . . **$29.75**

## TSI

### 301 Lubricant

A synthetic lubricant/degreaser to clean, protect and lube metal reloading tools. Removes both sizing and bullet lube. Spraying dies prior to storage protects against rust and corrosion. From American Gas & Chemical Co. Ltd.

**Price:** 6 oz. aerosol . . . . . . . . **$8.25**
**Price:** 11 oz. aerosol . . . . . . . **$11.25**
**Price:** 21 oz. pump . . . . . . . . **$18.00**

## WILSON

### Chamber Type Bullet Seater

Positively controls both bullet and case alignment during seating operation. Case pushed firmly into die and bullet pushed straight into case by precision fitting plunger sliding in alignment. Available in most popular calibers. From L.E. Wilson, Inc.

**Price:** . . . . . . . . . . . . . **$50.00**
**Price:** Extra cap and stems . . . . **$19.00**

### Neck Sizing Die

Precision hand die used with either small mallet or arbor press to control and/or change incrementally cartridge case neck reduction through a series of interchangeable bushings. Bushings available in increments of .001″, from .236 through .343. All neck dies size neck to ³/₁₆″ from mouth end. Available with or without one bushing. From L.E. Wilson, Inc.

**Price:** With bushing . . . . . . . **$62.50**
**Price:** Without bushing . . . . . . **$50.00**
**Price:** Bushing . . . . . . . . . . **$12.50**

### AMMO LOAD Mark III

**Calibers:** 38 Special, 357 Magnum, 45 ACP, 45 Win. Mag., 454 Casull, 9mm (standard); 38 S&W, 380 Auto, 44 Magnum, 44 S&W (special order); 25 Auto, 30 Carbine, 32 Auto, 32 S&W Long, 32 S&W Short, 38 Auto, 41 Magnum, 45 Long Colt, 10mm, 40 S&W (custom order)
**Rounds Per Hour:** 3,600-5,000
**Dimensions:** 25″ x 31½″ x 29¾″
**Weight:** 315 lbs.
**Features:** Foot-switch activated ½-hp motor on 110-volt (standard) or 220-volt; automatic case feeder with 500 case capacity; primer magazine; 32-oz. capacity powder flask with removable filter screen; bullet feed tubes with capacity for forty 38- or 45-caliber wadcutters; transparent front guard and slide assembly for automatic case positioning. Safety features include: shut-off switch insulators to keep foreign particles from entering switch; primer filler tube retaining clip to prevent primers coming out top of tube; adjustable bullet knockout to punch out stuck round at top of stroke; powder check rod to eliminate powder spillage at powder check station; powder disk cover to restrict foreign particles entering powder disk; removable flask screen to filter the powder before it is dropped; taller transparent front guard. From Ammo Load, Inc.
**Price:** . . . . . . . . . . . . . . . . . . . . . **$11,606.00**
**Price:** Powder Flask Shut-Off . . . . . . . . . . **$73.00**
**Price:** Carbide Final Die . . . . . . . . . . . . . **$81.00**
**Price:** Variable Speed Motor (D.C.) . . . . . . . . **$662.00**
**Price:** Special Order Calibers (38 S&W, 380 Auto, 44 Mag., 44 S&W) . . . . . . . . . . . . . . **$624.00**
**Price:** Custom Order Calibers . . . . . . . . **Price Varies**
**Price:** 9mm Double Sizing Set-Up . . . . . . . . . **$461.00**
**Price:** 220/240v.-50/60 Cycle Transformer . . . . . . **$885.00**
**Price:** Electronic Brake . . . . . . . . . . . . **$350.00**
**Price:** Conversion Kit (38 Spl., 357 Mag., 45 ACP, 9mm) . . . . . . . . . . . . . . . . . . **$2,835.00**
**Price:** Conversion Kit (38 S&W, 380 Auto, 44 Mag., 44 S&W) . . . . . . . . . . . . . . . . . **$2,982.00**

### AMMO LOAD Mark IV

**Calibers:** 38 Special, 357 Magnum, 45 ACP, 9mm (standard); 38 S&W, 380 Auto, 44 Magnum, 44 S&W (special order); 25 Auto, 30 Carbine, 32 Auto, 32 S&W Long, 32 S&W Short, 38 Auto, 41 Magnum, 45 Long Colt, 10mm, 40 S&W (custom order)
**Rounds Per Hour:** 3,600-5,000
**Dimensions:** 25″ x 34¾″ x 29¾″
**Weight:** 323 lbs.
**Features:** Comes with all the features of the Mark III plus: a carbide final sizing die; variable-speed DC motor with control box; three auto shut-off switches for low feed at case feed, primer feed and bullet feed; a light panel for low feed signaling; and powder flask shut-off assembly. Safety features include: shut-off switch insulators to keep foreign particles from entering switch; primer filler tube retaining clip to prevent primers coming out top of tube; adjustable bullet knockout to punch out stuck round at top of stroke; powder check rod to eliminate powder spillage at powder check station; powder disk cover to restrict foreign particles entering powder disk; removable flask screen to filter the powder prior to charging; taller transparent front guard. From Ammo Load, Inc.
**Price:** . . . . . . . . . . . . . . . . . . . . **$13,139.00**
**Price:** Special Order Calibers (38 S&W, 380 Auto, 44 Mag, 44 S&W) . . . . . . . . . . . . . . **$624.00**
**Price:** Custom Order Calibers . . . . . . . . **Price Varies**
**Price:** 9mm Double Sizing Set-Up . . . . . . . . . **$461.00**
**Price:** 220/240v.-50/60 Cyle Transformer . . . . . . **$885.00**
**Price:** Electronic Brake . . . . . . . . . . . . **$350.00**
**Price:** Conversion Kit (38 Spl., 357 Mag., 45 ACP, 9mm) . . . . . . . . . . . . . . . . . . **$2,835.00**
**Price:** Conversion Kit (38 S&W, 380 Auto, 44 Mag., 44 S&W) . . . . . . . . . . . . . . . . . **$2,982.00**

### AMMO LOAD Primer Tube Filler

For use on the Ammo Load Mark III or Mark IV. Features a vibratory bowl to orient the primers and fill the primer tube. The capacity is approximately 5,000 primers per hour. Primer tubes hold 125 primers each. Handles either small or large primers with minor equipment adjustment. Dimensions: 6″ x 7¼″ x 17¼″. Weight: 28 lbs. From Ammo Load, Inc.
**Price:** . . . . . . . . . . . . . . . . . . . . **$959.00**

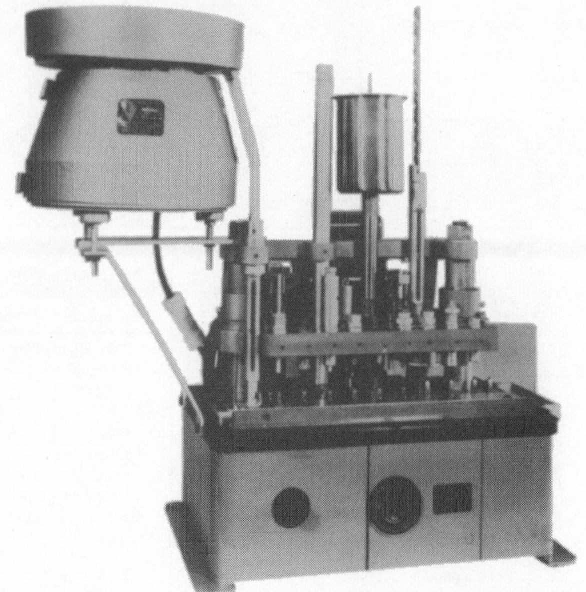

Ammo Load Mark II

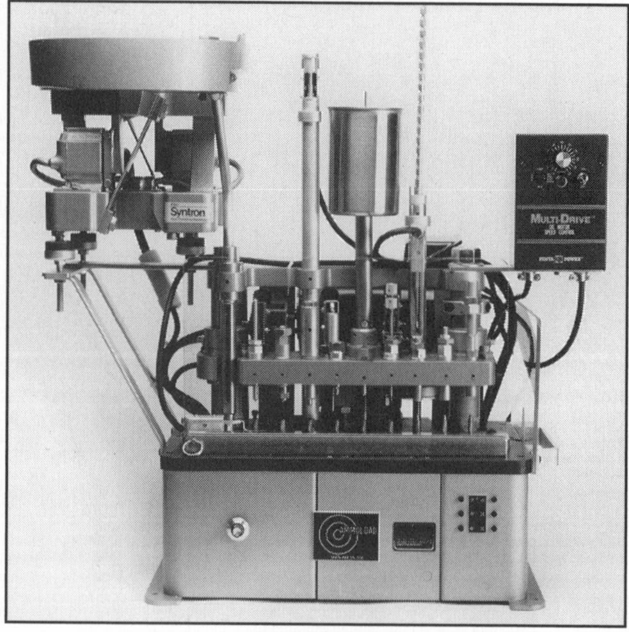


Ammo Load Mark IV

### BALLISTI-CAST Mark I Handcaster

**Frame:** Welded tubular steel.
**Calibers:** #4 buckshot to 54 Maxi
**Moulds:** Four 2-cavity.
**Avg. Bullets Per Hour:** Operator controlled manual lever.
**Dimensions:** 41″ x 19″ x 26″
**Weight:** 240 lbs.
**Features:** Positive indexing carrier system; quick mould adjustment and replacement; cam-oriented mould closure and spring-loaded opening; timed lead control; 2600-watt, 200-volt, 20-amp thermostatically controlled 100-lb. capacity furnace. Available with Hensley & Gibbs or SAECO moulds. From Ballisti-Cast, Inc.
**Price:** Hensley & Gibbs moulds . . . . . . . . . **$3,455.00**
**Price:** Saeco moulds . . . . . . . . . . . . . . **$3,290.00**

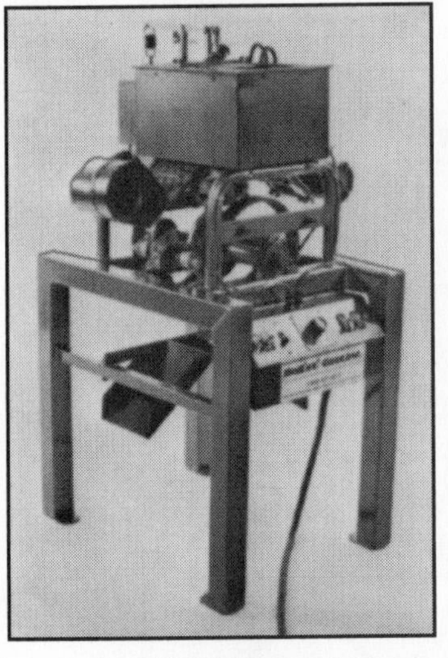

Ballisti-Cast Mark I

Ballisti-Cast Mark II

Ammo Load
Primer Tube Filler

Ben's Machines Lazy Luber No. 1

### BALLISTI-CAST Mark II Automatic Caster

**Frame:** Welded tubular steel.
**Calibers:** #4 buckshot to 54 Maxi
**Moulds:** Four 2-cavity.
**Avg. Bullets Per Hour:** 2400+
**Dimensions:** 41″ x 19″ x 26″
**Weight:** 265 lbs.
**Features:** Gear-driven motor; two heavy-duty air blowers; dust-sealed control panel, indicator working lights, electronic counter; timed lead control; positive indexing carrier system; quick mould adjustment and replacement; cam-oriented mould closure and spring-loaded opening; 2600-watt, 200-volt, 20-amp thermostatically controlled 100-lb. capacity furnace. Available with Hensley & Gibbs or SAECO moulds. From Ballisti-Cast, Inc.
**Price:** Hensley & Gibbs moulds . . . . . . . . . **$5,270.00**
**Price:** Saeco moulds . . . . . . . . . . . . . . . . . **$5,115.00**
**Price:** Variable speed motor . . . . . . . . . . . **$325.00**

### BALLISTI-CAST Mark IV Mini Caster

**Frame:** Aluminum
**Moulds:** 2-cavity
**Avg. Bullets Per Hour:** Operator controlled
**Dimensions:** 23″ x 16″ x 16″
**Weight:** 65 lbs.
**Features:** Manually operated lever control; 110-volt, 20-amp electric blower; positive indexing carrier system; quick mould replacement; cam-oriented mould closure and spring-loaded opening; 750-watt, thermostatically controlled 45-lb. capacity furnace. Available with Lyman, RCBS, Saeco or Hensley & Gibbs 2-cavity moulds. From Ballisti-Cast, Inc.
**Price:** . . . . . . . . . . . . . . . . . . . . . . . **$1,295.00**

### BALLISTI-CAST Mark V Lube-Sizer and Collator

Lubes and sizes 3500+ bullets per hour using Star and Mercer dies. Lube tube preheater for very hard lubes; auto digital heat controller on base plate; empty lube cylinder auto shutoff; variable-speed motor. Bullet collator feeds 9mm through 45 Long Colt bullets base up or down; does not collate full wadcutters; electric stop-start feed control. From Ballisti-Cast, Inc.
**Price:** . . . . . . . . . . . . . . . . . . . . . . . **$3,450.00**

### BEN'S MACHINES Brass Processor

Automated processor checks primer pockets; deprines; swages military primer pockets; resizes full-length, straight-walled 30-06, 308 and 7.62x39 cases at a rate of 1500 per hour. Comes with large and small feed tubes and one die. From Ben's Machines.
**Price:** . . . . . . . . . . . . . . . . . . . . . . . **$3,500.00**
**Price:** M-A Systems case sorter . . . . . . . . **$595.00**

### BEN'S MACHINES Lazy Luber No. 1

Electric/mechanical conversion for a Star lube-sizer available as a complete unit or in component form. Maximum output capacity of 2,400 bullets per hour with realistic capability of 1,750-2,000. Combines conversion table with MA Systems bullet collator and Ben's lube heater and auto feed. From Ben's Machines.
**Price:** Complete unit . . . . . . . . . . . . . . **$1,510.00**
**Price:** Conversion table . . . . . . . . . . . . **$525.00**
**Price:** Heater (120/240 volt) . . . . . . . . . **$70.00**
**Price:** Auto-feeder (one bar included) . . . . . . . **$75.00**
**Price:** Additional feed bar . . . . . . . . . . . **$17.50**
**Price:** MA Systems collator . . . . . . . . . . **$625.00**
**Price:** Star dies (any caliber) . . . . . . . . . **$26.00**

Ballisti-Cast
Mark V Lube-Sizer
and Collator

**BEN'S MACHINES Lazy Luber No. 2**

Same as above except air-powered version. Mountable unit includes valves, pistons and adapters. Air compressor used must deliver 90 lbs. constant pressure. Available as complete unit or in component form. From Ben's Machines.

**Price:** Complete unit . . . . . . . . . . . . . . **$1,710.00**
**Price:** Air-powered conversion . . . . . . . . . . . **$720.00**
**Price:** Heater (120/240 volt) . . . . . . . . . . . . . **$70.00**
**Price:** Auto-feeder (one bar included) . . . . . . . . . **$75.00**
**Price:** Additional feed bar . . . . . . . . . . . . . . . **$17.50**
**Price:** MA Systems collator . . . . . . . . . . . . . **$625.00**
**Price:** Star dies (any caliber) . . . . . . . . . . . . . **$26.00**

**BEN'S MACHINES Sorter Lazy**

Automated case sorter by diameter for 22-25 ACP, 380-9mm, 45 ACP, 32 ACP, 38-357-10mm, 44 Spl.-44 Mag. Depending on size of brass, sorts 7,000-10,000 per hour. Will also sort bullets or loaded ammo. From Ben's Machines.

**Price:** . . . . . . . . . . . . . . . . . . . . . . . . **$1,500.00**

**BEN'S MACHINES Sorter Lazy Two**

Sorts by case length 380-9mm-38 Super, 40 S&W-10mm-38 Spl.-357 Mag. Cycle rate is approximately 3,000 per hour; production rate, 2,500 per hour. Special feed and rails available for 44 Spl.-44 Mag. Brass collator not included. From Ben's Machines.

**Price:** . . . . . . . . . . . . . . . . . . . . . . . . **$1,500.00**
**Price:** MA Systems collator . . . . . . . . . . . . . **$625.00**

**CAMDEX 2100 Series Loader**

**Calibers:** Any NATO or commercial handgun caliber.
**Avg. Rounds Per Hour:** 4400
**Dimensions:** 32″ x 28″ x 36″
**Weight:** 200 lbs.
**Features:** Comes in three configurations: **Basic Loader** includes case feed, primer pocket, primer feed, primer slide and powder probe monitoring system. Case probe checks for case feeding, foreign particles and live rounds; primer pocket probe mechanically checks the primer pocket for ringers; the primer feed monitors primer feed mechanism; primer slide probe ensures that a jam has not occurred; and powder probe checks for both high and low powder charges. Basic loader also features primer follower rod and weight to maintain primer feed and supply; automatic case feeder with eight-station bullet turret and carbide final size die. **Auto & Continuous Loader** has same features as above plus auto primer feed with air/vacuum system for assisting and monitoring the feed. **2100 Series** has all the features of the A&C loader plus a 14″ variable-speed auto bullet feeder as standard equipment. All three come with brass powder canister that holds over one pound of powder; die set screws for rapid removal or adjustment; adjustable-speed 3/4-hp motor. Conversion units for 9mm, 45 ACP available. From Camdex, Inc.

**Price:** Basic Loader . . . . . . . . . . . . . . **$12,900.00**
**Price:** Automatic & Continuous Loader . . . . . **$14,175.00**
**Price:** 2100 Series . . . . . . . . . . . . . . . **$15,800.00**
**Price:** Auto primer tube filler . . . . . . . . . . . **$820.00**
**Price:** Inspection table . . . . . . . . . . . . . **$1,750.00**
**Price:** Conversion units . . . . . . . . . . . . . **$3,150.00**
**Price:** Final size die . . . . . . . . . . . . . . . . **$150.00**

Camdex 2100 Series Loader

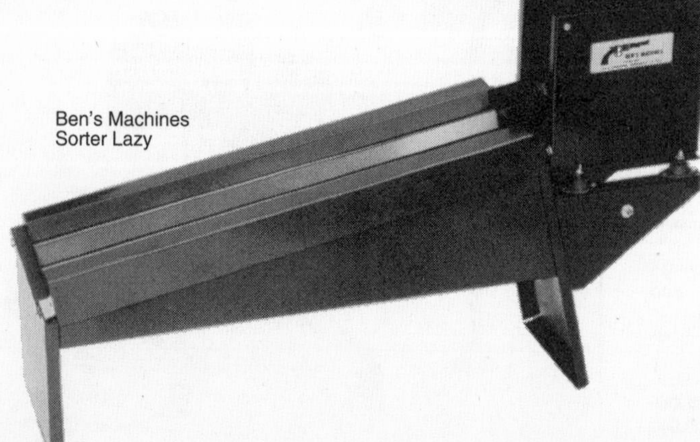

Ben's Machines Sorter Lazy

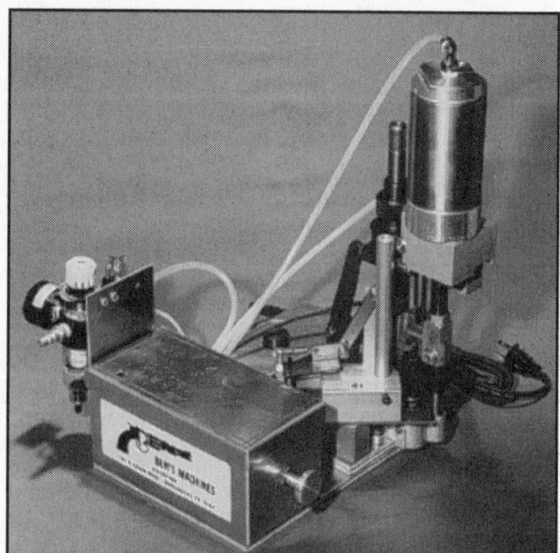


Ben's Machines Lazy Luber No. 2



Commercial Loading Equipment & Accessories

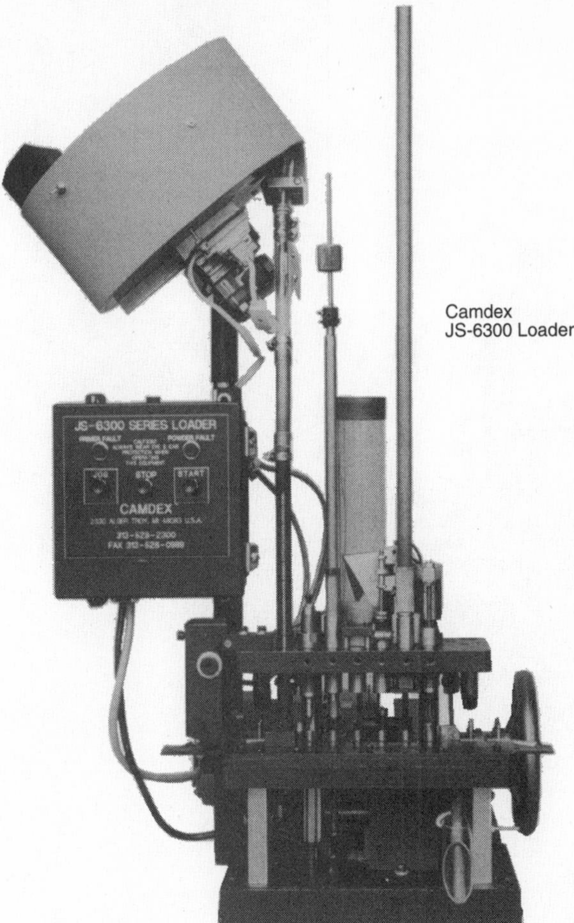

Camdex JS-6300 Loader

Camdex Case Processor

### CAMDEX JS-6300 Loader

**Calibers:** Any centerfire pistol caliber.
**Avg. Rounds Per Hour:** 1800 (auto version)
**Dimensions:** 20″ x 28″ x 24″
**Weight:** 110 lbs.
**Features:** Hand or auto operation. Cases are tube fed and auto-indexed to each station; size and depriming done by standard $^7/_8$-14 die threaded into upper platen; priming movement by cable operated spring-loaded slide; primer pickup and seating locations adjustable; powder drop station cam activated and synchronized with platen movement; powder slide uses replaceable bushings; fully adjustable case bell function; tube fed bullet slide. The auto model includes same features as above plus control panel and micro switches to monitor powder charge, primer level and primer jamming. Comes with $^1/_4$-hp motor. Optional equipment: auto case feeder; eight-station bullet turret or auto bullet feeder; auto low case level shutoff; final carbide sizing die; caliber conversion units. From Camdex, Inc.

**Price:** Hand-operated loader . . . . . . . . . . **$2,600.00**
**Price:** Automatic model . . . . . . . . . . **$5,000.00**
**Price:** Caliber conversion kit . . . . . . . . . . **$1,150.00**
**Price:** 8-station bullet turret . . . . . . . . . . **$115.00**
**Price:** Final carbide size die . . . . . . . . . . **$150.00**
**Price:** Extra primer feed tubes . . . . . . . . . . **$8.00**
**Price:** Extra cartridge tubes . . . . . . . . . . **$7.95**
**Price:** Extra bullet tubes . . . . . . . . . . **$7.50**
**Price:** Case feeder . . . . . . . . . . **$510.00**
**Price:** 220/50 HZ electrical . . . . . . . . . . **$360.00**

### CAMDEX Case Processor

Transforms 9mm cases into "like new" condition. Automatically ejects Berdan primed cases, split and cracked cases, and 380 cases. All cases fully resized including base of rimless cases to assure accurate uniform chambering. Military crimp is removed by swaging operation on the primer pocket. Features friction disc clutch, 3750 cycles per hour, two tungsten carbide sizing dies; MA Systems auto case feeder; one tungsten carbide base size exit die; $^1/_3$-hp compressor/vacuum pump; $^1/_2$-hp electric motor. Available in all handgun calibers. Can also be purchased with additional caliber conversions for processing more than one caliber. From Camdex, Inc.

**Price:** . . . . . . . . . . **$10,450.00**
**Price:** Conversion kit . . . . . . . . . . **$1,700.00**

### CAMDEX Lube Sizer

Lubes at the rate of 4400 per hour. Vertical feed and horizontal dispensing for bulk or tube packaging. Bullet lube heated by cartridge-type element in aluminum block and lube pressure held constant by ratchet and spring assembly inside reservoir. Powered by $^1/_3$-hp motor. Comes with cartridge heater, foot pedal and forward/reverse switch. From Camdex, Inc.

**Price:** . . . . . . . . . . **$4,850.00**
**Price:** 45 ACP conversion . . . . . . . . . . **$775.00**
**Price:** 220/50 HZ electrical . . . . . . . . . . **$630.00**

### CAMDEX Packer

Ammunition packaging machine for the commercial reloader. Capable of boxing over 16,000 rounds per hour. Integral feed hopper holds over 8,000 rounds of 9mm. Operates on 120-volt AC power and draws 4 amps. Available in all popular handgun calibers. Conversion from one caliber to another requires $^1/_2$-hour. Dimensions: 33″x15″x22$^1/_2$″. Weight: 115 lbs. From Camdex, Inc.

**Price:** . . . . . . . . . . **$4,500.00**
**Price:** Conversion kit . . . . . . . . . . **$850.00**

### CASE-PRO 100

Brass processor to roll size 500-1500 cases per hour to SAMMI specs; clean and true extractor groove; tighten primer pocket; uniform the chamfer at base of rim; case feed tube adapts to Dillon 650 or 1050 case feeder. Available for 45 ACP, 38 Super, 40/10mm, 9x25 Dillon, 9x19, 9x21 and 9x23. From Image Ind., Inc.

**Price:** . . . . . . . . . . **$465.00**
**Price:** Additional die set . . . . . . . . . . **$175.00**

**CASE SORTING SYSTEMS GNQL8-3600-A Pistol Brass Sorter**

Designed to sort 40-cal., 10mm, 38 Spl. and 357 Mag. one from the other. Sorts up to 4,000 cases per hour. Optional floor stand and four-tube kit with clamps available. From Case Sorting Systems.
**Price:** . . . . . . . . . . . . . . . . . . . . **$1,495.00**
**Price:** Floor stand . . . . . . . . . . . . . . . **$50.00**
**Price:** Four-tube kit with clamps . . . . . . . . . . **$55.00**

**C-H/4-D Tumbler**

Commercial size 10-qt. capacity tumbler for high volume reloaders. 50-lb. max. load with 15″ diameter bowl. Runs on 120v AC. Comes with treated walnut shell media. From C-H Tool & Die/4-D Custom Die.
**Price:** . . . . . . . . . . . . . . . . . . . . **$395.00**

**CORBIN CHP-1 Hydro-Press**

**Die Thread:** 1½-12
**Ram Stroke:** 6″
**Weight:** 350 lbs.
**Features:** Ability to manufacture lead wire, jackets, gas checks, base guards and bullets from 224 to 22mm and reload calibers up to 20mm. Swages hardest lead alloys in calibers from 224 to 512, bullet weights to 1000 grains and lengths to 2.5 inches. Makes lead wire from .120 to .500-inch diameter; draws heavy copper or brass partitioned tubing jackets of .030- to .065-inch walls; and shotgun slugs up to 10-gauge. Uses forced air cooling and 5-gallon hydraulic reservoir to service industrial-grade vertical-drive cylinder. Die pressures exceeding 200,000 psi. Electronic transducers monitor pressure and control ram force. Logic circuits establish stroke length, dwell time and pressure. Color-coded control panel; heavy-duty key-lock safety switch; dual-hand control interlock. Press comes standard with 115-120 volt 60 Hz power; 220-240 volt 50-60 Hz conversion optional. From Corbin Manufacturing & Supply, Inc.
**Price:** . . . . . . . . . . . . . . . . . . . . **$5,950.00**
**Price:** 240-volt conversion . . . . . . . . . . . . **$250.00**
**Price:** JMK-1H Jacket Making Kit . . . . . . . . **$1,950.00**
**Price:** JMK-2-H Jacket Making Kit . . . . . . . **$4,950.00**
**Price:** CSU-1 Strip Uncoiler . . . . . . . . . . **$1,450.00**

**CORBIN CSU-1 Strip Uncoiler**

For use with Hydro-Press to feed copper jacket strips from coil into jacket draw machinery. Electronically controlled feeding and tension sensing. Can be used to feed strip and coil strip after punching. From Corbin Manufacturing & Supply, Inc.
**Price:** . . . . . . . . . . . . . . . . . . . . **$1,950.00**

**CORBIN Hydro-Mite Swaging Press**

**Frame:** Steel
**Frame Type:** H-frame
**Die Thread:** 7/8-14
**Ram Stroke:** 2″ swaging; 4″ drawing or jacket making.
**Weight:** 22 lbs.
**Features:** Comes on bench stand with separate electric remote control hydraulic pressure system for long production runs, professional pyrotechnic and explosives work. Four precision roller bearings mounted in heavy-duty steel links, bearing on hardened tool steel pins; oil-impregnated bronze bearings surrounding ram; ordnance steel alloy supports ram; machined frame; electrostatic powder-coated, baked-on finish. Hand-built, hand-assembled press. Swages bullets from 14- to 458-caliber. Maximum bullet length, 1.25″ in the M dies; 1.35″ in S dies; maximum pressure, over 200,000 psi. Comes with floating punch holder for use with external punches of Corbin swage dies. Made for use with Corbin M or S type dies. From Corbin Manufacturing & Supply, Inc.
**Price:** 120v AC . . . . . . . . . . . . . . . . **$2,250.00**

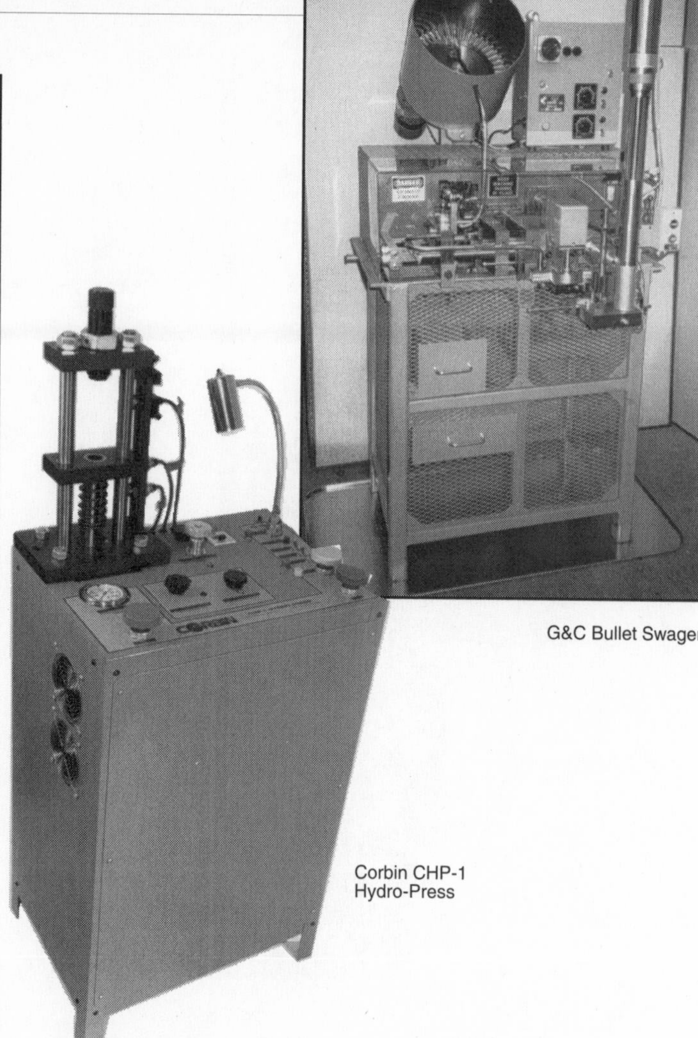

G&C Bullet Swager

Corbin CHP-1 Hydro-Press

**CORBIN Mega-Mite Hydraulic Swaging Press**

**Frame:** Steel
**Frame Type:** H-frame
**Die Thread:** 1½-12
**Ram Stroke:** 3″
**Weight:** 250 lbs.
**Features:** Features pressure gauge, panel-mounted direction controls, adjustable ram thrust, self-contained floor stand. Roller bearing linkage; hardened tool steel pivots; precision bronze bushings on polished steel guide rods. Dual-stroke operation allows changing from 5.5-inch to 3-inch stroke for reloading up to 50 BMG cases or heavy swaging. Can swage hard lead bullets up to .475 diameter and soft lead to .600. Maximum pressure, 180,000 psi; maximum bullet length, 1½″; maximum jacket wall, 0.50″ copper. Made for use with Corbin H dies. Comes with thick steel floor stand with 4-inch diameter iron tube and punch holder. Height with floor stand is 66″. From Corbin Manufacturing & Supply, Inc.
**Price:** . . . . . . . . . . . . . . . . . . . . **$3,450.00**

**CORBIN Power Cannelure Machine**

High-production machine cannelures 100 lead or jacketed bullets per minute. Cabinet is 10″ high with 6″ x 8″ top work space. Includes one cannelure wheel for all calibers and guide plate for one caliber. Caliber plates available from 22 to 512. From Corbin Manufacturing & Supply, Inc.
**Price:** . . . . . . . . . . . . . . . . . . . . **$469.00**
**Price:** Custom cannelure wheel . . . . . . . . . . **$75.00**
**Price:** Position spacer, .025″ or .048″ . . . . . . . **$10.00**
**Price:** Spare back plate . . . . . . . . . . . . . **$40.00**
**Price:** Lead knurling back plate . . . . . . . . . **$75.00**

### G&C Commercial Automatic Bullet Swager

Commercial swager produces 7,200 bullets per hour, sized, lubed and tubed in correct direction for loader. A 3-hp, 220 single- or three-phase motor powers single-die swager. Hardened single die ensures bullets are identical. Includes die set-up for one caliber and bullet shape. From G&C Bullet Company, Inc.

**Price:** . . . . . . . . . . . . . . . . . . . . **$45,000**

### G&C Swage Core Caster

Variable-speed single or double caster to produce up to 7,200 cores per hour with double caster. Completely automatic with 1-hp single- or three-phase motor. Melting pot electrically, gas or propane fired. From G&C Bullet Company, Inc.

**Price:** Single caster . . . . . . . . . . . . . . . . **$5,520.00**
**Price:** Double caster . . . . . . . . . . . . . . . . **$8,500.00**

### LORTONE Model R-20 and R-40 Case Tumblers

Commercial-size tumblers engineered to industrial standards. The R-40 tumbler has capacity for 2,400 38 Special cases or 800 30-06 cases. Constructed of heavy-gauge welded steel with hexagonal three-point closure steel barrels. Features neoprene rubber liner and gasket; dual rubber-covered drive shafts; heavy-duty bronze bearings and ball-bearing barrel guides. Requires 1/3-hp electric motor. A total of six Model R-40 machines can be coupled and driven by a single 1/3-hp motor. Lortone R-20 is smaller version with capacity for 1,200 38 Special cases and 400 30-06 cases. Dimensions: R-40, 19″ x 16″; R-20, 14″ x 16″. Weights: R-40, 51 lbs.; R-20, 39 lbs. From Lortone, Inc.

**Price:** R-20 . . . . . . . . . . . . . . . . . . **$355.00**
**Price:** R-40 . . . . . . . . . . . . . . . . . . **$425.00**
**Price:** Optional 1/3-hp motor with switch and cord . . **$125.00**

### MA SYSTEMS Auto Bullet Collater-14

Designed for high-speed reloading. Feeds round-nose, semi-round-nose or pointed 9mm through 45 Long Colt bullets base down or base up at rates averaging 6,000 bullets per hour. Features 14-lb. capacity; vari-speed, 3 to 7 rpm, rate control for collating or feeding; electric stop/start feed control; adjustable 5/8″ O.D. feed tube for varying bullet sizes; standard collating plate to feed 9mm (.550″) through 45 (.950″); optional plates available for bullets 1.312″ to .400″. Adapts easily to any machine accepting tubed bullets. Does not collate full wadcutters. Comes complete with feed tube, flex bends, electric control, mounting column and plastic piping. Also available for 380 Auto and hollow base wadcutter 38-caliber. Weight: 22 lbs. From MA Systems.

**Price:** . . . . . . . . . . . . . . . . . . . . **$1,150.00**
**Price:** 38-cal. hollow base . . . . . . . . . . **$1,395.00**
**Price:** 380 Auto . . . . . . . . . . . . . . . **$1,250.00**
**Price:** Adapt kit for Camdex or Ammo Load . . . . . **$36.00**

### MA SYSTEMS Conversion Kits

Converts MA Auto Bullet Collator-14 to 380 Auto collator or 380 collator to ABC-14. Weight: 4 lbs. From MA Systems.

**Price:** ABC-14 to 380 . . . . . . . . . . . . . **$350.00**
**Price:** 380 to ABC-14 . . . . . . . . . . . . . **$295.85**

### MA SYSTEMS Easy Bullet Collater-12

Collates 9mm (.600″) through 45 Long Colt (1.000″) bullets at rate of 1,800 to 3,600 per hour depending on bullet size. Special collating plates available for 380 Auto and rifle calibers. Collating bowl holds 7 lbs. Features electric stop/start feed; unique column design to rotate bowl away from machine or remove in five seconds. Adapts easily to any press accepting tubed bullets and feeds base up or down. Comes complete with feed tubes, electric control, mounting column and plastic piping. Weight: 12 lbs. From MA Systems.

**Price:** . . . . . . . . . . . . . . . . . . . . **$625.00**

### MA SYSTEMS Easy Case Collater-12

Automatically feeds all pistol cartridge cases from 380 Auto to 45 Long Colt base down at a rate of 2,000 or 4,000 per hour depending upon caliber. Collater bowl holds 575 9mm or 360 44 Magnum cases. Unique mounting column allows bowl to rotate away or be removed in five seconds. Will fit Star, Dillon RL-1000, C-H/4-D Die Inline and RCBS Green Machine or adapt to any press utilizing tubed cases. Feed case tube 5/8″ O.D. From MA Systems.

**Price:** For hand-operated presses . . . . . . . . . **$395.00**
**Price:** For auto presses . . . . . . . . . . . . . **$595.00**

### MA SYSTEMS Easy Collater Tray

For cases or bullets. Orients either in slotted tray to slide easily into feed tubes. Tray accepts 100 rounds. Dimensions: 8½″ x 9″. Weight: 12 lbs. From MA Systems.

**Price:** . . . . . . . . . . . . . . . . . . . . **$14.95**

### MA SYSTEMS Roto-Ease for Star Press

Designed for the Star press to automatically advance shellplate increasing reload rate from 400 to 800 rounds per hour. Operates with all calibers. Cam operation controls acceleration and deceleration of shellplate. Operating hook pulls in plane with shellplate and mounts to right rear of press. No press modification required. Weight: 2 lbs. From MA Systems.

**Price:** . . . . . . . . . . . . . . . . . . . . **$195.50**

### MA SYSTEMS Rotary Separator-14

Separates 7,000 10mm, 40 S&W, 38 Special and 357 Magnum cases per hour automatically. Features ABS plastic bowl; 13″ column and mounting flange; 3″ square tube for dispensing sorted cases. From MA Systems, Inc.

**Price:** . . . . . . . . . . . . . . . . . . . . **$1175.00**

### MA SYSTEMS Rotary Separator-12

Separates 6,000 380 from 9mm cases per hour. Cases automatically fed base down. Features ABS plastic bowl; 6 rpm motor; 13″ column and mounting flange. From MA Systems, Inc.

**Price:** . . . . . . . . . . . . . . . . . . . . **$595.00**

### MA SYSTEMS Easy Loader

Mounts to Star, Dillon RL 1000 and C-H/4-D Die Inline to feed bullets base down at rate of 2,500 per hour. Operates automatically in sequence with press from regulated 50-60 psi air source. Accepts all flat-based bullets, some hollow-base, round-nose, wadcutters and semi-wadcutters. Comes complete for 9mm through 45-caliber with two sizes of bullet supply tubes, four feed tubes and two sets of bullet grippers. 223 and 380 Auto require special grippers; 223-caliber requires special feed tubes. Weight: 4 lbs. From MA Systems, Inc.

**Price:** Star . . . . . . . . . . . . . . . . . . **$450.00**
**Price:** Dillon . . . . . . . . . . . . . . . . . **$495.00**

### MAGMA Cast Master

Melting furnace with 90-lb. capacity. Features bottom pour with trip lever on right side; four lugs tapped 1/2-13 for mounting to bench or setting caster to preferred height; stainless valve components; removable orifice plate on bottom to increase or decrease metal flow. Comes complete with three-wire cord and one orifice plate installed. Weight: 40 lbs. From Magma Engineering Company.

**Price:** . . . . . . . . . . . . . . . . . . . . **$375.00**

Magma Cast Master

### MAGMA Bullet Master Mk VI

High-production bullet casting machine produces 3,600 bullets per hour. Features modular electrical system to ensure proper connections and easy removal; solid-state controllers with LED readouts; temperature control to +/- 7°; stainless steel springs and valves; divided pot for optimum bullet quality; float transfer device for constant lead head pressure; automatically separates bullets and sprues. Moulds available from 32- to 45-caliber. Weight: 225 lbs. From Magma Engineering Company.

**Price:** Vari-Speed . . . . . . . . . . . . . . . . **$5,390.00**
**Price:** Fixed speed . . . . . . . . . . . . . . . **$5,235.00**
**Price:** Magma mould . . . . . . . . . . . . . . **$65.00**
**Price:** Set of eight moulds . . . . . . . . . . . **$520.00**
**Price:** Lyman mould . . . . . . . . . . . . . . **$71.50**
**Price:** Saeco mould . . . . . . . . . . . . . . **$77.00**
**Price:** RCBS mould . . . . . . . . . . . . . . **$79.00**
**Price:** H&G mould . . . . . . . . . . . . . . . **$125.00**

### MAGMA Case Sizer

Swaging case sizer with tungsten carbide die to resize to SAAMI specifications. Automatically sizes and deprimes, separating primers and cases. Will resize over 5,100 cases per hour. Optional equipment includes case feeder to orient case in proper direction and LED proximity detector counter. Available for 380 ACP, 9mm, 9x21, 40 S&W, 10mm and 45 ACP. Comes with one die. From Magma Engineering Company.

**Price:** . . . . . . . . . . . . . . . . . . . . **$2,850.00**
**Price:** Sizing dies . . . . . . . . . . . . . . . **$165.00**
**Price:** Case sizer with collator . . . . . . . . . **$2850.00**
**Price:** Case counter . . . . . . . . . . . . . . **$351.00**

### MAGMA Lube Master

Sizes and lubes 4,300 bullets per hour. All working parts are hardened steel; parts engaged in sliding contact are ground to precise tolerances. Base block contains cartridge heating element controlled to +/- 5°. Uses Star die. Comes complete for one caliber. Additional sizing dies available in most calibers. Conversion sets for 380- and 32-caliber contain guide bushing and drop tube. Bullet collator and counter optional. 120 or 240 volts. Weight: 125 lbs. From Magma Engineering Company.

**Price:** . . . . . . . . . . . . . . . . . . . . **$3,635.00**
**Price:** MA Systems collator . . . . . . . . . . . **$1,310.00**
**Price:** Conversion set . . . . . . . . . . . . . **$152.50**
**Price:** Digital heat controller . . . . . . . . . . **$378.00**
**Price:** Counter . . . . . . . . . . . . . . . . . **$351.00**
**Price:** Star size die . . . . . . . . . . . . . . . **$27.50**
**Price:** Mercer/Stillwell size die . . . . . . . . . **$32.00**
**Price:** Lube Master lube, per pound . . . . . . . **$5.90**

### MAGMA Master Caster

Produces 800 to 1,000 bullets per hour. Features melting pot, two-cavity mould; automatic sprue cutoff; automatic bullet/sprue sorting; automatic bullet ejection; automatic sprue cutter and mould alignment; single hand operation. SAECO, Lyman, RCBS and H&G moulds can be converted for use on Master Caster at additional charge. 120 or 240 volts, 1350 watts. Weight: 55 lbs. From Magma Engineering Company.

**Price:** . . . . . . . . . . . . . . . . . . . . **$595.00**

### RAYTECH Model 40 and Model 75 Commercial Case Tumblers

Commercial-size tumblers with industrial motor-drive systems to handle heavy loads. Capacity of Model 40 is 2,800 38 Special cases; Model 75 can handle 4,500 38 Special cases. Bowls made of cross-linked polyethylene in 3/8″ or 1/2″ thicknesses. Features amplitude adjustment, inlet and outlet ports for compound rinsing systems. Both models also offered with Tumble Dump (TD) feature which allows bowl to be disengaged and tipped on hinge point for unloading. For dry or wet media. From Raytech, Division of Lyman Products Company.

**Price:** Model 40 . . . . . . . . . . . . . . . . **$885.00**
**Price:** Model 40 TD . . . . . . . . . . . . . . **$1,170.00**
**Price:** Model 75 . . . . . . . . . . . . . . . . **$1,069.00**
**Price:** Model 75 TD . . . . . . . . . . . . . . **$1,348.00**
**Price:** Replacement bowl, M40 . . . . . . . . . **$170.00**
**Price:** Replacement bowl, M75 . . . . . . . . . **$200.00**

Magma Bullet Master Mk VI

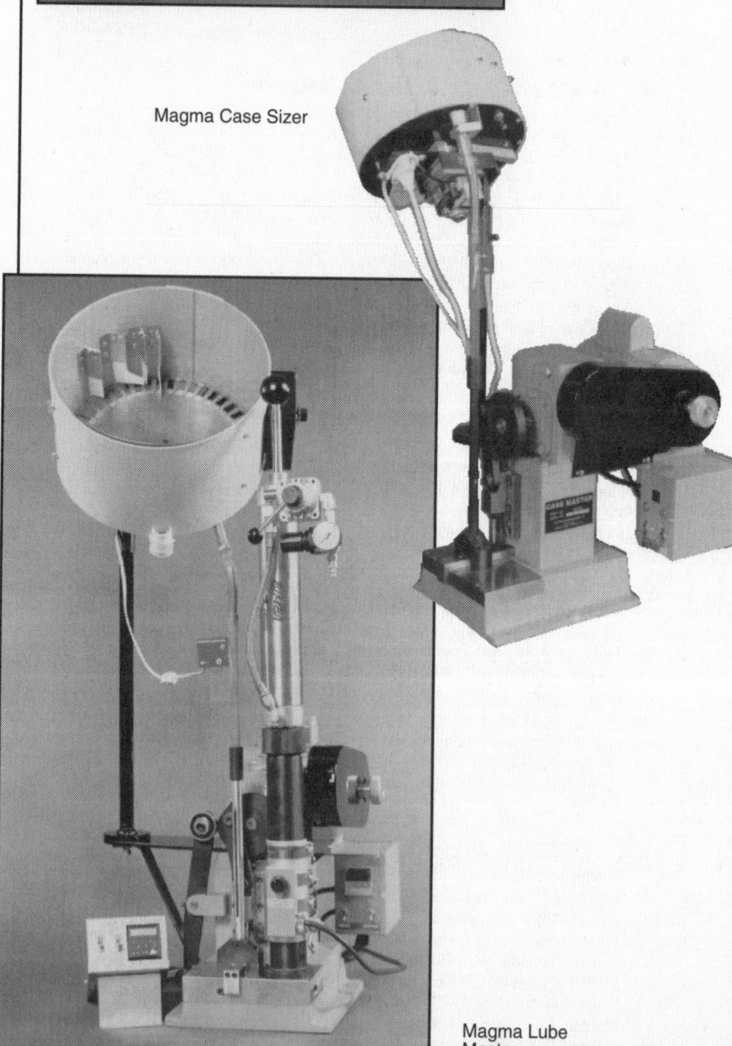


Magma Case Sizer

Magma Lube Master

Magma Master Caster

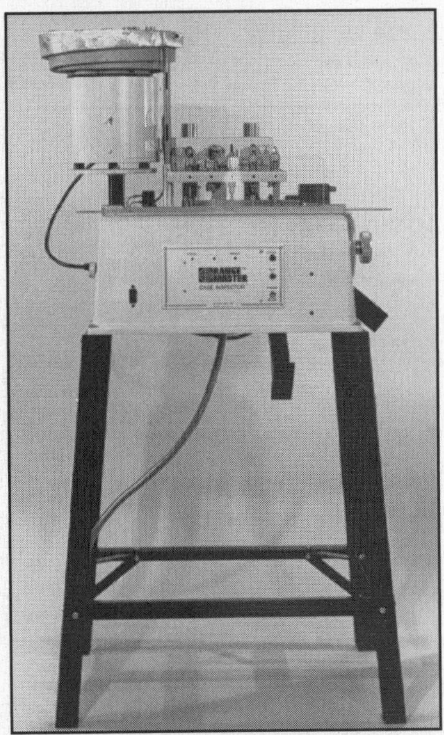
Scharch Case Inspector Auto Reamer

**RAYTECH MS-75 Media Separator**

Variable-speed commercial separator with capacity for 4,500 38 Special cases. Automatically separates cases from wet or dry media in two minutes, sending media and cases out two frontal chutes into two 70-lb. capacity tote boxes. A variety of optional quick-change screens available. From Raytech, Division of Lyman Products Company.

**Price:** . . . . . . . . . . . . . . . . . . . . **$1,350.00**
**Price:** Screens, 9/64″ round to 2″ round . . . **$105.00-$158.00**

**RAYTECH Media**

Four types of brass finishing media for use in vibratory tumblers. Dri Shine I is rouge-treated shell; Dri Shine II, untreated shell; Dri Shine III, treated corn cob; Dri Shine IV, untreated corncob. Come in 30- or 50-gal. drums. From Raytech, Division of Lyman Products Company.

**Price:** Dri Shine I, 30-gal. . . . . . . . . . . . . . . **$99.00**
**Price:** Dri Shine I, 50-gal. . . . . . . . . . . . . . **$168.00**
**Price:** Dri Shine II, 30-gal. . . . . . . . . . . . . . **$74.00**
**Price:** Dri Shine II, 50-gal. . . . . . . . . . . . . **$111.00**
**Price:** Dri Shine III, 30-gal. . . . . . . . . . . . . **$98.00**
**Price:** Dri Shine III, 50-gal. . . . . . . . . . . . **$155.00**
**Price:** Dri Shine IV, 30-gal. . . . . . . . . . . . . **$61.00**
**Price:** Dri Shine IV, 50-gal. . . . . . . . . . . . . **$97.00**

**R.E.I. Hy-Drive System for Dillon RL 1050**

Hydraulic 110-volt power unit and variable-speed rotary actuator designed for attachment to the Dillon RL 1050 press. Reloads 1,800 rounds per hour with maximum cycle time 2,100 per hour. Features sealed hydraulics to reduce leaking; adaptable continuous operation for brass processing (adaptable to MA Systems and Howell CNC bullet feeders); no cutting or drilling to fit to press; enclosed pump, motor, valve and rotary actuator; full hydraulic operation; stop and reverse in loading cycle; optional photo-electric switch for deactivation for manual insertion of bullet. From R.E.I.

**Price:** . . . . . . . . . . . . . . . . . . . . **$2,795.00**

**SCHARCH Ammunition Boxing Machine**

Designed to place rimmed or rimless ammunition directly into Styrofoam or Federal style plastic trays. Will package up to 30,000 rounds per hour. Allows for visual and gauge block inspection. Mounted on solid maple top work bench. 110-volt operation. From Scharch Mfg., Inc.

**Price:** Rimless calibers . . . . . . . . . . . . . **$3,895.00**
**Price:** Caliber conversion rimless . . . . . . . . . **$800.00**
**Price:** Rimmed calibers . . . . . . . . . . . . . **$4,595.00**
**Price:** Caliber conversion rimmed . . . . . . . . **$1,200.00**

**SCHARCH Case Inspector/Auto Reamer**

Same as Range Master Case Inspector but only reams primer pocket and cuts correct radius at pocket opening. From Scharch Mfg., Inc.

**Price:** Pistol . . . . . . . . . . . . . . . . . **$11,650.00**
**Price:** Rifle . . . . . . . . . . . . . . . . . **$12,950.00**
**Price:** Rifle to pistol conversion . . . . . . . . . **$225.00**
**Price:** Pistol to rifle conversion . . . . . . . . . **$395.00**

**SCHARCH Range Master Case Inspector**

High-production case inspector for 38/357, 9mm/380 or 45 ACP brass. Processes 5100 cases per hour. Features inspection for bent cases, loaded or foreign objects; pressure check for mouth or sidewall splits; deprimes; inspection of primer pocket for ringers or military crimp; electronic counter for good cases only; electronic memory for rejection of bad cases; chute for good cases, trap for bad cases; primer tube for spent primers; eye shield for operator protection; case feed tube with auto shut-off. Operates on 120v AC 60 Hz. Dimensions: 31″ x 23″ x 35″. Weight: 340 lbs. From Scharch Mfg., Inc.

**Price:** 38/357 . . . . . . . . . . . . . . . . . **$6,995.00**
**Price:** Other calibers . . . . . . . . . . . . . . **$7,200.00**
**Price:** Caliber conversions . . . . . . . . . . . **$1,475.00**

**SCHARCH Roller Mics**

Fully-automated 2- or 4-track pistol brass seperator featuring adjustable track speed rate; double-feed variable speed case feeder; separates 10,000 (2-track) or 20,000 (4-track) cases per hour; plexiglass safety guard; heavy-duty industrial bearings. For 380 Auot, 223, 9mm, 38 Spl., 357 Mag., 40 S&W, 10mm, 45 ACP, 44 Mag., 45 Colt. From Scharch Mfg. Co.

**Price:** 2-track . . . . . . . . . . . . . . . . . **$3,295.00**
**Price:** 4-track . . . . . . . . . . . . . . . . . **$5,195.00**

**SCHARCH Roller Sizer**

Sizes fired cases to proper diameter at rate of 6000 per hour. Comes complete with case feeder and sturdy steel frame stand. Available in all popular handgun sizes plus 223. Operates on 110 volts. Weight: 180 lbs. From Scharch Mfg., Inc.

**Price:** . . . . . . . . . . . . . . . . . . . . **$3,395.00**
**Price:** Caliber conversion . . . . . . . . . . . . **$425.00**

# Section 1: Metallic Cartridges



## ACCURATE BULLET CO.

**Blackpowder Bullets**

Hand cast, competition quality bullets for metallic blackpowder silhouette shooters. Bullets are weighed and packaged accordingly. From Accurate Bullet Co.

**Price:** . . . . . . **Contact manufacturer.**

## ACTION BULLETS

**Cowboy Action Shooting Bullets**

Hard cast bullets in 38-40 (180-gr.), 44 Mag. (220-gr.), 44-40 (200-gr.) and 45 Colt (250-gr.) sized to exact diameter required and pressure lubed with high temperature, non-sticky hard bullet lube. Come 500 or 1000 to a box. From Action Bullets, Inc.

**Price:** 38-40 (500) . . . . . . . . **$21.50**
**Price:** 38-40 (1000) . . . . . . . . **$41.00**
**Price:** 44 Mag., 44-40 (500) . . . . **$22.00**
**Price:** 44 Mag., 44-40 (1000) . . . . **$42.00**
**Price:** 45 Colt (500) . . . . . . . . **$23.50**
**Price:** 45 Colt (1000) . . . . . . . . **$45.00**

## AMERICAN BULLET CO.

**Competition Bullets**

Hard virgin alloy competition-quality bullets cast from single cavity moulds by hand, individually inspected and weighed. Available with or without sizing and lubing. From American Bullet Co.

**Price:** . . . . . . . . . . . . . **See chart.**

**Wax Wad Sheets**

Paraffin or pure beeswax sheets 5½"x2⅞"x.065". From American Bullet Co.

**Price:** Paraffin, each . . . . . . . . . **$.50**
**Price:** Beeswax, each . . . . . . . . **$1.00**

**Wad Punch**

Fred Cornell wad punch to fit any standard ⅞-14 reloading press. From American Bullet Co.

**Price:** . . . . . . . . . . . . . . . **$49.95**

**AMERICAN BULLET CO.** ***Competition Bullets***

| Caliber | Mould | Dia. | Wgt. Grs. | Type | Grooves |
|---|---|---|---|---|---|
| 25 | Rapine | .257 | 75 | | NA |
| 30 | Jones | .313 | 150 | FT | 4 |
| 32 | Rapine | .325 | 195 | RNFT | 6 |
| 38 | Rapine | .378 | 250 | FT | 4 |
| | Rapine | .380 | 250 | FT | 4 |
| 40 | Rapine | .408 | 336 | LT | 3 |
| | Rapine | .413 | 300 | LT | 3 |
| | Jones | .410 | 410 | Creedmore | 4 |
| | Jones | .410 | 450 | S | 4 |
| | Snover | .410 | 400 | Creedmore | 4 |
| | Saeco | .410 | 410 | SS | 5 |
| | Brooks | .410 | | Wind-Buster | 5 |
| 45 | Rapine | .449 | 420 | PP | |
| | Rapine | .449 | 500 | PP | |
| | RCBS | .451 | 550 | TPPHB | |
| | Lyman | .458 | 385 | RN | 3 |
| | Rapine | .460 | 405 | FN | 5 |
| | Lyman | .458 | 490 | S | 3 |
| | Saeco | .459 | 490 | SS | 5 |
| | Jones | .459 | 500 | Creedmore | 4 |
| | Rapine | .459 | 500 | RN | |
| | Rapine | .460 | 510 | FN | 7 |
| | Hoch | .459 | 500 | SS | |
| | RCBS | .459 | 510 | SS | |
| | Lyman | .458 | 510 | Roller | |
| | Jones | .459 | 520 | RN | 4 |
| | Lyman | .458 | 525 | Postell | 4 |
| | Hoch | .459 | 525 | SS | |
| | Saeco | .459 | 530 | SS | 5 |
| | Jones | .457-.460 | 540 | Creedmore | 4 |
| | Hoch | .459 | 555 | SS | |
| | Brooks | .459 | | Wind-Buster | |
| 50 | RCBS | .516 | 450 | FN | 4 |
| | Saeco | .512 | 425 | FN | 4 |
| 54 | Rapine | .544 | 475 | PNRT | |
| | Rapine | .548 | 415 | RNFTHB | |

FT = Flat Tip; RN = Round-Nose; S = Spitzer; LT = Large Tapered; SS = Semi-Spitzer; PP = Paper Patch; TPPHB = Tapered Paper Patch Hollow Base; FN = Flat Nose; PNRT = Pointed Nose Ring Tail.

**ACTION BULLETS** ***Round & Maxi Balls***

| Caliber | Dia. | Price/Per |
|---|---|---|
| 36 | .350 | $4.00/100 |
| | .375 | 4.30/100 |
| 44 | .433 | 5.20/100 |
| 45 | .440 | 5.20/100 |
| | .445 | 5.50/100 |
| 44 | .451 | 5.75/100 |
| | .454 | 5.75/100 |
| 45 | .457 | 5.75/100 |
| 50 | .490 | 6.10/100 |
| | .495 | 6.10/100 |
| 54 | .530 | 3.50/50 |
| | .535 | 3.75/50 |
| 56 | .562 | 4.00/50 |
| 58 | .570 | 4.50/50 |
| 69 | .690 | 2.75/25 |
| 45 | 200-gr. Maxi | 4.25/25 |
| 50 | 350-gr. Maxi | 4.50/25 |
| 54 | 400-gr. Maxi | 4.75/25 |
| | 415-gr. Maxi | 4.90/25 |

Andela Single-Cavity Mould

**A-SQUARE** ***Unprimed Brass***

| Caliber | Packaging | Price |
|---|---|---|
| 45 Basic | B | $43.00 |
| 405 Basic | B | 44.00 |
| 43 Spanish | B | 44.00 |
| 11mm Beaumont | B | 44.00 |
| 11mm Mauser | B | 44.00 |
| 50 Basic | B | 44.00 |

B = Plastic box of 20 rounds.

Arco Blackpowder

### ANDELA *Bullet Moulds*

| Caliber | Mould #/Dia. | Style | Type | Wgt. Grs. | Comments |
|---|---|---|---|---|---|
| 22 | .224A | A | | 55 | |
| | .224B | B | | 60 | |
| | .228B | B | | 65 | |
| 25 | .256B | B | | 90 | Copy of factory 25-25. |
| | .257B | B | | 95 | Similar to original factory 25-20ss. |
| | .260-.250E | E | | 100 | Popular Pope style. |
| | .264-.254 | | | | 2-groove GC |
| 28 | .285B | B | | 130 | 28-30 bullet |
| | .287A | A | | 175 | Lyman 287221 |
| | .287-.276C | C | | 130 | Pope-style 20-30 |
| | .288B | B | | 135 | |
| | .288K | K | RN | 125 | |
| 30 | .308L | L | P | | Similar to Lyman 311334 |
| | .308L | L | | | |
| | .309B | B | | 155 | |
| | .309B | B | | 170 | |
| | .309L | L | P | | |
| | .309-.300E | E | Tapered | | Thick Band |
| | .309-.300L | L | | 160 | Base band bullet. |
| | .309L | L | PBT | | |
| | .310-.302L | L | | | Two diameter bullet. |
| | .310-.304L | L | | | |
| | .310-.308 | | | | Former NEI 43A |
| | .311A | A | | 165 | Lyman 31157 |
| | .311B | B | | 170 | Similar to German Schuetzen. |
| | .311L | L | | | Lyman 311414 |
| | .311-.310L | L | | | Former NEI 52A. |
| | .312-.304D | D | FN | 180 | GC, 4 groove |
| | .315B | B | | 180 | Similar to German Schuetzen. |
| | .316-.301D | D | FN | 190 | GC, 1 groove. |
| 32 | .319-.314B | B | | 180 | Base band bullet. |
| | .319-.314F | F | | 185 | |
| | .319-.314F | F | | 185 | |
| | .321 | | | | Heeled bullet, .339 band |
| | .321B | B | | 190 | |
| | .322K | K | RN | 185 | |
| | .322L | L | SPBT | | |
| | .322L | L | P | 180 | |
| | .322-.314 | | | | Copy heeled German Schuetzen. |
| | .322-.314E | E | SPBT | | |
| | .323B | B | | 190 | |
| | .323L | L | | 180 | |
| | .323-.313D | D | | 195 | Two diameter bullet. |
| | .323-.313E | E | | 190 | Pope-style tapered. |
| | .323-.321L | P | | | Tapered |
| | .323-.317L | L | P | | Tapered |
| | .324B | B | | 190 | |
| | .324-.314E | E | | | Pope-style Paul Clark. |
| | .325B | B | | 190 | |
| | .325-.322D | D | | 190 | Pope-style two diameter. |
| | .326-.317C | C | | 175 | Pope-style two diameter. |
| 33 | .330-.320E | E | | 170 | Tapered |
| | .331B | B | | 195 | |
| | .335B | B | | 215 | |
| | .335-.327E | E | | | Pope-style two diameter. |
| | .338A | A | | 220 | Pope-style cylindrical. |
| | .338B | B | | 220 | |
| | .338L | L | P | 220 | |
| | .338-.329D | D | | 220 | Two diameter. |
| | .338-.332C | C | | 225 | Pope-style |
| | .339-.330D | D | | 220 | Two diameter. |
| | .339-.330E | E | | 220 | Pope-style tapered. |
| | .339-.331C | C | | 220 | Two diameter. |
| | .343-.330C | C | | 220 | Copy original Pope bullet. |
| 35 | .350A | A | | 220 | Pope-style. |
| | .354B | B | | 260 | Cylindrical. |
| | .357 | | WC | | Pistol bullet. |
| | .358-70J | J | | | Copy Lyman bullet. |

con't. page 308

## ANDELA

**Bullet Moulds**

Single-cavity moulds in 14 basic bullet styles. Cherries cut from 11L17 steel. Mould number designates as-cast bullet diameter (cylindrical bullets); large rear band, small front band (two-diameter bullets); or rear band diameter tapering to smaller front band diameter (tapered bullets). Andela will also design bullet mould to specifications.

**Style A**: Cylindrical: Similar to originial blackpowder factory bullets; front band same as base band; rounded lube grooves.

**Style B:** Cylindrical: Same as A without front wiper band. Rounded lube grooves.

**Style C:** Two Diameter: Rear bands slightly larger than bore diameter; front band is groove diameter.

**Style D:** Two Diameter: Same as C, except without front wiper band; rounded lube grooves.

**Style E:** Tapered: Front band near groove diameter, tapering to slightly larger than groove diameter.

**Style F:** Hudson Bullet: Two diameter; front bands near base diameter; two rear bands slightly larger.

**Style G:** Two Diameter: Same as D, except with beveled band.

**Style H, I:** Cylindrical: Shorter nose and larger lube grooves than A. For 40-cal. and larger.

**Style J:** Lightweight bullet.

**Style K:** Round Nose: Similar to French designs in Lyman catalog.

**Style L:** Pointed bullet.

**Style M, N:** Paper patch bullet.

From Andela Tool & Machine, Inc.

**Price:** . . . . . . **Contact manufacturer**

## ARCO

**Black Mag**

Moisture resistant, non-corrosive, non-toxic blackpowder. Comes in 1-lb. plastic canister. From Arco Powder.

**Price:** 1 lb. . . . . . . . . . . . **$17.95**

## BARNES

**Expander-M2 Muzzleloader Bullets**

Non-lead projectile .451″ 250- and 300-grain and .500″ 275- and 325-grain 54-caliber bullets designed specifically for muzzleloaders. From Barnes Bullets, Inc.

**Price:** 50-cal. . . . . . . . . . . . **$12.99**
**Price:** 54-cal. . . . . . . . . . . . **$14.99**

Barnes Expander-M2 Muzzleloader Bullets

### ANDELA *Bullet Moulds*

| Caliber | Mould #/Dia. | Style | Type | Wgt. Grs. | Comments |
|---|---|---|---|---|---|
| 35 | .358A | | | | Pistol bullet. |
| | .358K | K | RN | 180 | Pistol bullet. |
| | .358L | L | SWC | | Pistol bullet. |
| | .360 | | WC | | Pistol bullet. |
| | .360B | B | | 360 | Cylindrical. |
| | .360-.351D | D | | 260 | Cylindrical. |
| | .360-.352 | | BT | | Base band bullet. |
| | .363-.354D | D | | 280 | Two diameter. |
| | .364B | B | | 200 | Two diameter. |
| 38 | .372-.368D | D | | | Two diameter. |
| | .375B | B | | 330 | Copy of Lyman 375166. |
| | .376B | B | | 280 | |
| | .377B | B | | 220 | Cylindrical. |
| | .377-.367D | D | | 280 | |
| | .378L | L | PBT | | |
| | .378-.372D | D | | 320 | Tapered. |
| | .378-.373F | F | | 290 | 38-55 Schuetzen. |
| | .379-.366C | C | BT | | Two diameter. |
| | .380A | A | | 280 | Pope-style cylindrical. |
| | .380B | B | | 280 | |
| | .380L | L | P | | Three-groove. |
| | .380-.372E | E | | 285 | Pope-style. |
| | .380-.375C | C | | | Pope-style two diameter. |
| | .381L | L | P | | Schuetzen. |
| | .382B | B | | 285 | |
| | .383A | A | | 310 | Pope-style. |
| | .383B | B | | 320 | |
| | .383-.377F | | | | |
| | .387K | K | RN | | |
| 40 | .402A | A | | 325 | Cylindrical. |
| | .403L | L | PBT | | |
| | .404-.398C | C | | 325 | Pope-style. |
| | .405A | A | | 300 | Pope-style cylindrical. |
| | .410-.400D | D | | 330 | Two diameter. |
| | .413B | B | | 330 | |
| | .413-.406D | D | | 330 | Two diameter. |
| | .415-.407L | L | P | 325 | Two diameter. |
| | .417B | B | | 330 | |
| 44 | .429A | A | | 380 | GC |
| | .431-.425F | F | | 275 | Two-groove. |
| | .437K | K | | | 43 Spanish bullet. |
| | .440N | N | | 495 | Paper patch. |
| | .440-.413D | D | | 350 | Similar to Lyman 441267. |
| | .445A | A | | 380 | For 44-77, 44-90 Pope-style. |
| | .445B | B | | 380 | Cylindrical. |
| | .448A | A | | 380 | Cylindrical. |
| 45 | .450B | B | | 450 | For slug gun. |
| | .455B | B | | 470 | |
| | .455B | B | | 500 | Cylindrical. |
| | .457A | A | | 300 | Copy Lyman 457191. |
| | .457A | A | | | Similar to Lyman 457122 w/o HP. |
| | .457B | B | | 300 | Pistol bullet. |
| | .457-.451D | D | | 425 | Two dia. similar to Lyman 451114. |
| | .457K | K | | 450 | Heeled bullet. |
| | .458A | A | | 470 | |
| | .458B | B | SPBT | 450 | |
| | .458-.451C | C | | 425 | Two dia. similar to Lyman 45111K. |
| | .459K | K | RN | 500 | Cylindrical. |
| | .464A | A | | | Woodworth Pope style. |
| | .471A | A | | 550 | |
| | .472L | L | P | 620 | |
| | .480A | A | | | Pope-style cylindrical. |
| 50 | .505-.500C | C | | 470 | 50-70. |
| | .510B | B | | 600 | |
| | .520 | | | 350 | Three-groove. |
| | .525B | B | | 340 | For 52 Maynard. |
| Slugs | .500 | | | | One-oz. for recycled 12-ga. sabots. |
| | .720 | | SWC | 800 | Two-groove. For 12-ga. rifled barrels. |
| | .500 | | | | 12-ga. sabot slug-Reno bullet. |

### BERTRAM *Obsolete Rifle/Pistol Cases*

| Case | Price/20 |
|---|---|
| —RIFLE— | |
| 38-56 WCF | 33.98 |
| 38-72 WCF Basic | 31.98 |
| 40-65 WCF | 33.98 |
| 40-70 Sharps | 31.98 |
| 40-72 WCF | 31.98 |
| 40-82 WCF | 33.98 |
| 405 Basic 3¼″ | 31.98 |
| 40-90 3¼″ | 31.98 |
| 425 Westley Richards | 68.98 |
| 43 Spanish | 31.98 |
| 11mm 43 Mauser | 33.98 |
| 45-90 WCF | 31.98 |
| 45 Basic 2.6″ | 31.98 |
| 45 Basic 3¼″ | 58.98 |
| 50 Sharps Basic | 56.98 |
| 50-70 Gov't. | 38.98 |
| 50-110 WCF | 58.98 |
| 577-450 MH | 109.98 |
| —PISTOL— | |
| 41 Long Colt | 17.98 |
| 11.75mm Montenegrin | 19.98 |

From Huntington Die Specialties.

Bertram Unprimed Brass

## BERRY'S MFG.

**Cowboy Action Bullets**

Cast bullets in 38-, 44-, 44-40 and 45 LC caliber. From Berry's Mfg.

**Price:** . . . . . **Contact manufacturer.**

## BIG BORE

**Black Belt Bullets**

Underbore .0001″ lead bullets seated on an overbore rubber power check disk. Available in 45-, 50- and 54-caliber in 295-, 348-, 405-, 444- and 520-grain weights. Come in boxes of 20. From Big Bore Express, Ltd.

**Price:** . . . . . . . . . . . . . **$9.95**

**Copper Magnum Black Belt Bullets**

Copper jacketed pure lead 45-, 50- and 54-caliber underbore hollowpoint or flat point bullets seated on an overbore power check disk. Available in 295-, 348-, 405-, 444- and 520-grain weights. Come in boxes of 20. From Big Bore Express, Ltd.

**Price:** . . . . . . . . . . . . . **$15.95**

**Ultra-Score Lube**

All natural bullet and patch lube. Comes in plastic jars. From Big Bore Express, Ltd.

**Price:** . . . . . . . . . . . . . **$5.95**

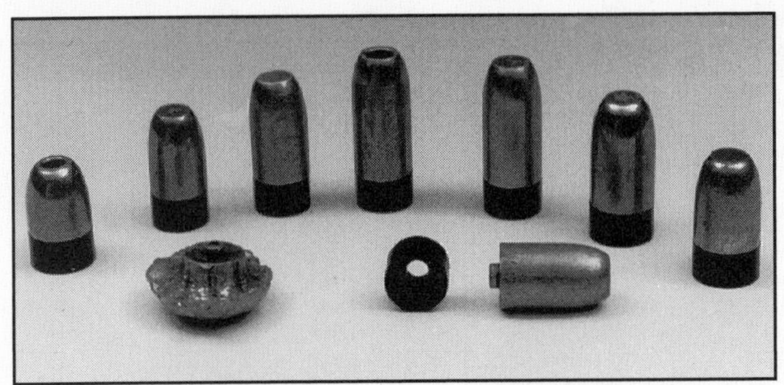

Big Bore Black Belt Bullets

**BUFFALO ARMS** ***Reformed Brass***

| Caliber | Price/100 |
|---|---|
| 25 Rem. | $24.00 |
| 310 Cadet | 27.00 |
| 32 Win. SL | 30.00 |
| 32-40 Win. | 35.00 |
| 32-40 Rem. | 48.00 |
| 33 Win. | 50.00 |
| 35 Win. | 72.00 |
| 38 LC .88″ | 17.00 |
| 38 LC 1.03″ | 17.00 |
| 38-56 Win. | 50.00 |
| 38-70 Win. | 77.00 |
| 38-72 Win. | 77.00 |
| 401 Win. SL | 48.00 |
| 40-50 Sharps BN 45 | 46.00 |
| 40-60 Win. | 48.00 |
| 40-60 Maynard | 48.00 |
| 40-65 (45-70 Rem.) | 47.00 |
| 40-65 (45-70 Win.) | 48.00 |
| 405 Win. | 72.00 |
| 40-70 SS 2 1/2″ | 72.00 |
| 40-70 SBN 2 1/4″ | 77.00 |
| 40-70 Win. | 77.00 |
| 40-72 Win. | 77.00 |
| 40-82 Win. | 77.00 |
| 40-90 Sharps BN | 97.00 |
| 41 LC | 40.00 |
| 43 Dutch Beaumont | 53.00/20 |
| 43 Egyptian | 53.00/20 |
| 43 Spanish | 97.00 |
| 44 Colt | 36.00 |
| 44 Russian | 20.00 |
| 44 American | 20.00 |
| 44-70 Maynard | 77.00 |
| 44-77 SBN | 97.00 |
| 44-90 SBN | 97.00 |
| 44-90x2.4 Rem. | 77.00 |
| 44-100x2.6 Rem. | 97.00 |
| 45 S&W Schofield | 22.00 |
| 45-75 Win. | 80.00 |
| 45-90x2.4SS | 77.00 |
| 45-100x2.6 Sharps | 97.00 |
| 455 Colt | 34.00 |
| 455 Webley | 34.00 |
| 455/476 Revolver | 34.00 |
| 476 Revolver | 34.00 |
| 476 Enfield MkII | 34.00 |
| 476 Eley | 34.00 |
| 50-95 Win. | 53.00 |
| 50-110 Win. | 97.00 |
| 6mm Lee Navy | 48.00 |
| 7.65 French | 22.00 |
| 8x56R Hungarian | 77.00 |
| 8x52R | 72.00 |
| 9mm Steyr | 24.00 |
| 9.3x72R | 50.00 |

**BOB FOWLER**
***Blackpowder Bullets***

| Caliber | Price/100 |
|---|---|
| —PISTOL— | |
| 44-45 | $4.50 |
| 45 | 4.50 |
| 50 | 4.50 |
| 54 | 5.50 |
| —RIFLE— | |
| 45 | 9.00 |
| 50 | 9.00 |
| 54 | 10.00 |
| 69 Round ball | 16.00 |
| 69 Minie | 18.00 |

**BUFFALO BULLET**
***Muzzle-Loading Bullets***

| Caliber | Wgt. Grs. | Type | Price/Per |
|---|---|---|---|
| 36 Buffalo | 125 | HPFB | $9.90/50 |
| 45 Buffalo | 285 | HPHB | 7.90/20 |
| | 325 | HPFB | 7.95/20 |
| 50 Buffalo | 350 | HPHB | 8.10/20 |
| | 385 | HPHB | 8.25/20 |
| | 410 | HPFB | 8.35/20 |
| | 490 | HPFB | 8.45/16 |
| 54 Buffalo | 390 | HPFB | 8.35/20 |
| | 425 | HPHB | 9.10/20 |
| | 435 | RNHB | 9.45/20 |
| | 460 | RNFB | 9.85/20 |
| | 510 | HPFB | 8.85/16 |
| 58 | 525 | HPHB | 10.10/16 |
| 36 Pistol | 124 | RNSB | 9.95/50 |
| 44 Pistol | 180 | RNSB | 10.50/50 |
| 45 Pistol | 190 | RNSB | 10.70/50 |
| 45 Sabot | 145 | HP | 12.85/40 |
| | 162 | HP | 12.95/40 |
| 50 Sabot | 225 | HP | 13.10/40 |
| | 252 | HP | 13.55/40 |
| | 302 | HP | 13.85/40 |
| | 375 | SHP | 14.25/36 |
| | 435 | SHP | 14.95/36 |
| | 435 | SHP | NA |
| | 450 | SHP | NA |
| 54 Sabot | 225 | HP | 13.10/40 |
| | 252 | HP | 13.55/40 |
| | 302 | HP | 13.85/40 |
| | 435 | SHP | NA |
| | 435 | SFP | NA |
| 50 CP Sabot | 240 | HP | 13.95/36 |
| 54 CP Sabot | 240 | HP | 13.95/32 |

## BLACK CANYON

**Blackpowder**

Non-corrosive, non-fouling blackpowder. Direct replacement for blackpowder on a weight for weight basis. From Legend Products Corporation.

**Price:** . . . . . **Contact manufacturer.**

## BLACK POWDER PRODUCTS

Unsized, unlubed cast pistol and rifle bullets. Pistol bullets come in packages of 500 in calibers 32 ACP, 380 ACP, 9x18, 9mm, 38/357, 40 S&W, 10mm, 41 Magnum, 44 Magnum, 45 ACP and 45 Long Colt and in a variety of grain weights and nose configurations. Rifle bullets are available in packages of 100 in 7.62x39, 7x57, 30-30, 30-06, 375 Winchester, 45-70 and 50-70. From Black Powder Products.

**Price:** . . . . . . . . . . . . **See chart.**

## BUCKSKIN BULLET

**Bullet Lube**

All-natural blackpowder bullet lube formulated with higher melting point but designed for performance in cold weather. Comes in 4-oz. tin. From Buckskin Bullet Co.

**Price:** . . . . . . . . . . . . . . **$6.95**

**Hunting Bullets**

Custom-made premium hunting bullets in 45- and 50-caliber from 200-450 grains (45) and 260-650 grains (50). 45-caliber bullets come 10 to a box; 50-caliber bullets come 12 to a box. From Buckskin Bullet Co.

**Price:** . . . . . . . . . . . . . . **$7.99**

## BUFFALO ARMS

**Brass**

Drawn brass cases for obsolete calibers. Brass is made by redrawing, annealing, sizing and trimming readily available cases. Available in boxes of 100. From Buffalo Arms.

**Price:** . . . . . . . . . . . . **See chart.**

**Over Powder Wads**

Dry lubricated 100% felt overpowder wads for 31-32, 36-38, 40-41, 44-45, 50 or 54 calibers. Come 100 to a bag. From Buffalo Arms.

**Price:** 31-32, 36-38, 40-41 cals. . . . **$4.60**
**Price:** 44-45, 50, 54-cals. . . . . . . **$4.70**

**Sabots**

Designed for use with either copper jacketed or lead bullets. Come 50 to a bag. From Buffalo Arms.

**Price:** . . . . . . . . . . . . . . **$5.95**

## BUFFALO BULLET

**Muzzle-Loading Bullets**

Patented, swaged muzzle-loading bullets for rifle or pistol. Buffalo bullets swaged to exact weight tolerances in 45- and 50-caliber. Saboted bullets made of lead with truncated cone, hollowpoint and boattail base in 45-, 50- and 54-caliber. Conical round-nose revolver bullet in 36-, 44- and 45-calibers and heavyweight maximum range bullets for fast-twist rifling with hollowpoint and falt base in 54- and 58-caliber. From Buffalo Bullet Co., Inc.

**Price:** . . . . . . . . . . . . **See chart.**

## BUTLER CREEK

**Bullet Lube**

Lube designed for both blackpowder and smokeless powder shooting with cast lead bullets. Contains no petroleum products. Available in hollow sticks. From Butler Creek Corporation.

**Price:** Each . . . . . . . . . . . . . **$3.95**

## C-H/4-D

**Custom Reloading Dies**

Die sets, forming dies, trim dies, etc. can be supplied for all listed calibers. For calibers not listed, dies can be made to order for an additional tooling charge. Die groups F through H are standard 7/8-14 thread; groups J and K are 1-14 thread. All dies are for use with shellholders or shellplates having industry standard dimension of 0.125″ from case head to top of shellholder. From C-H Tool & Die/4-D Custom Die.

**Price:** . . . . . . . . . . . . . **See chart.**

**Universal Decapping Die**

Comes in two sizes—large and small. Small die decaps calibers 22 Hornet through 6mm-06. Larger die accommodates all calibers from 25-20 to 50-110 Winchester and with 1/4″ diameter decap rod and .070″ decap rod will decap military 308 and 30-06 cases with crimped-in primers. From C-H Tool & Die/4-D Custom Die.

**Price:** . . . . . . . . . . . . . **$17.95**

## COLORADO SHOOTER'S SUPPLY

**Hoch Pistol Bullet Moulds**

Custom and standard base-pour, lathe-bored 2-, 3- and 4-cavity moulds. Standard design moulds fitted with 3/16″ sprue plate and 1/4″ dowel pins. Driving bands and grease grooves can be added or lengthened to increase weight of any design. Any gas-check design can be made plain base and vice versa. Custom pistol moulds made to customer design and specifications. Maximum bullet length: .950″; Maximum bullet diameter: .510″; Minimum bullet diameter: 38-cal. (.350″). Mould handles available. From Colorado Shooter's Supply.

**Price:** Standard, 2-cavity . . . . . **$65.00**
**Price:** Standard, 3-cavity . . . . . **$80.00**
**Price:** Standard, 4-cavity . . . . . **$95.00**
**Price:** Handles . . . . . . . . . . **$18.00**
**Price:** Custom, 2-cavity . . . . . . **$90.00**
**Price:** Custom, 3-cavity . . . . . **$110.00**
**Price:** Custom, 4-cavity . . . . . **$130.00**
**Price:** Handles . . . . . . . . . . **$18.00**

**Hoch Rifle and Pistol Bullet Moulds**

Custom-made 1-, 2-, 3- and 4-cavity bullet moulds. Lathe-bored from fine-grain cast iron (meehanite) in nose-pour only design. Machining tolerances 0 to +.001″. Hoch handles and push-type breech seat bullet starters available. From Colorado Shooter's Supply.

**Price:** Single, 22- to 51-cal. . . . . **$70.00**
**Price:** Single, 52- to 75-cal. . . . . **$80.00**
**Price:** Single, adjustable . . . . . **$125.00**
**Price:** Single, hollow-base . . . . **$125.00**
**Price:** 2-cavity, 22- to 50-cal. . . . **$120.00**
**Price:** 3-cavity, 22- to 50-cal. . . . **$170.00**
**Price:** 4-cavity, 25- to 45-cal. . . . **$220.00**
**Price:** Hoch handles . . . . . . . . **$18.00**
**Price:** Bullet starter . . . . . . . **$45.00**

## CURTIS CAST BULLETS

**Bullets**

Cast bullets of 25:1 ratio lead-to-tin and lubed with a soft lubricant designed to reduce fouling and improve accuracy. From Curtis Gun Shop.

**Price:** . . . . . . . . . . . . . **See chart.**

**C-H 4-D *Custom Blackpowder Cartridge Die Sets***

| Caliber | Die Group | Caliber | Die Group |
|---|---|---|---|
| 35-40 Maynard 1882 | F | 44 Extra Long Wesson | F |
| 38 Extra Long Ballard | F | 44 Henry Center Fire | F |
| 38 Long Center Fire | F | 44 S&W American | F |
| 38 Long Colt | F | 44 S&W Russian | F |
| 38 Short Colt | F | 44 Webley | F |
| 38-35 Stevens | F | 44-100 Ballard | H |
| 38-40 Rem.-Hepburn | G | 44-100 Wesson | H |
| 38-45 Stevens | F | 44-70 Maynard 1882 | G |
| 38-50 Ballard | G | 44-75 Ballard | F |
| 38-50 Maynard | G | 44-77 Sharps | H |
| 38-50 Remington | G | 44-85 Wesson | H |
| 38-50 Win. | G | 44-90 (44-100) Rem. St. | H |
| 38-70 Win. | G | 44-90 Sharps Necked(44-100) | |
| 38-72 Win. | G | 44-90 Shiloh (Necked) | H |
| 38-90 Win. | G | 45 Boxer-Henry Long 1869 | H |
| 38-90 Win. | H | 45 New South Wales | H |
| 380 Long Rifle | F | 45 S&W Schofield Revolver | F |
| 380 Revolver | F | 45 Sharps 2 3/4″ | H |
| 40-110 Win. Exp. | H | 45 Sharps 2.1″ | F |
| 40-40 Maynard 1882 | F | 45 Webley Revlover | F |
| 40-50 Sharps Necked | G | 45 Win. Mag. | F |
| 40-50 Sharps St. | G | 45-100 2.6″ | G |
| 40-60 Marlin | F | 45-100 Ballard | H |
| 40-60 Maynard 1882 | F | 45-110 2 7/8″ | H |
| 40-60 Win. | F | 45-120 Sharps 3 1/4″ | H |
| 40-63 Ballard | G | 45-125 Win. Exp. | H |
| 40-65 Ballard | G | 45-60 Win. | F |
| 40-65 Win. | F | 45-75 Win. | G |
| 40-70 Ballard | G | 45-80 Sharpshooter | F |
| 40-70 Maynard 1882 | F | 45-90 Win. & Sharps 2.4″ | F |
| 40-70 Rem. (Necked) | G | 450 Black Powder Exp. | H |
| 40-70 Sharps Necked 2 1/4″ | G | 50-110 Win. 2.4″ | H |
| 40-70 Sharps St. (Orig.) | G | 50-140 Sharps 3 1/4″ | H |
| 40-70 Sharps St. (Shiloh) | G | 50-140 Win. | H |
| 40-70 Shiloh Necked 2.1″ | G | 50-50 Maynard 1882 | G |
| 40-70 Win. | G | 50-90 Sharps 2 1/2″ | H |
| 40-72 Win. | G | 50-95 Win. | G |
| 40-82 Win. | G | 500-450 #2 Musket | H |
| 40-85 Ballard (40-90 Ballard) | H | 52-70 Sharps | G |
| 40-90 Sharps Necked | H | 55-100 Maynard 1882 | G |
| 40-90 Sharps St. | H | 56-46 Spencer | G |
| 400 Black Powder Exp. | H | 56-50 Spencer | G |
| 41 Long Colt | F | 56-56 Spencer | G |
| 41 Short Colt | F | 577 Snider | K |
| 44 Ballard Long | F | 58 Berdan | K |
| 44 Bulldog | F | 58 Berdan Musket | K |
| 44 Colt | F | 58 Gatling 1875 | K |
| 44 Evans Long | F | 58 Rem. Carbine | K |
| 44 Evans Short | F | 58 Roberts Conversion | K |
| 44 Extra Long Ballard | F | | |

**C-H/4-D *Custom Die Prices***

| Dies | Group F | G | H | J,K |
|---|---|---|---|---|
| Die Set | $55.00 | $76.00 | $109.00 | $139.00 |
| Neck Size Die | 36.00 | 50.00 | 70.00 | 90.00 |
| Full-Length Size Die | 36.00 | 50.00 | 70.00 | 90.00 |
| Seating Die | 27.00 | 37.00 | 50.00 | 65.00 |
| File Trim Die | 27.00 | 37.00 | 50.00 | 65.00 |
| Case Form Die | 27.00 | 37.00 | 50.00 | 65.00 |
| Taper Crimp Die* | 20.00 | 27.00 | 38.00 | 48.00 |
| Taper Crimp Die** | 35.00 | 45.00 | 60.00 | 80.00 |
| Reamer Die/Reamer | 70.00 | 80.00 | 90.00 | 100.00 |

*Straight Wall; **Bottleneck/Straight Taper

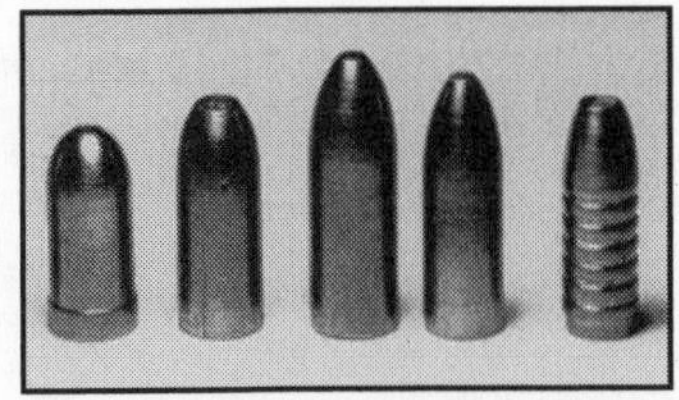

Colorado Shooter's Supply Bullets

Colorado Shooter's Supply Mould

### COLORADO SHOOTER'S SUPPLY
***Standard Pistol Moulds***

| Caliber | Wgt. Grs. | Type |
|---|---|---|
| 355 | 120 | SWC |
| | 125 | RN |
| 358 | 160 | SWC |
| | 150 | SWC |
| | 158 | Speed Loader |
| | 165 | SWC GC |
| | 148 | WC |
| 410 | 210 | Speed Loader |
| | 225 | TC Silhouette |
| | 220 | SWC |
| 431 | 250 | TC Silhouette |
| | 255 | RNFN |
| | 250 | SWC GC |
| | 250 | SWC |
| | 235 | Speed Loader |
| | 225 | WC |
| 454 | 255 | RNFN |
| | 255 | SWC |
| 452 | 200 | SWC |
| | 230 | T/C |
| | 230 | RNFN |

SWC = Semi-Wadcutter; RN = Round Nose; GC = Gas Check; FN = Flat Nose; WC = Wadcutter.

### CURTIS CAST BULLETS *Bullets*

| Bullet Dia. | Wgt. Grs. | Type | Price/Per |
|---|---|---|---|
| | —PISTOL— | | |
| .401 | 175 | FPBB | $42.50/1000 |
| .429 | 200 | FPBB | 46.00/1000 |
| .454 | 255 | FPBB | 50.00/1000 |
| | —RIFLE— | | |
| .410 | 410 | FP | $36.00/300 |
| .459 | 405 | FP | 30.00/250 |
| | 405 | FP | 30.00/250 |
| | 415 | SP | 30.00/250 |
| | 500 | FP | 37.50/250 |

FP = Flat Point; SP = Spire Point

### DKT, INC. *New Formed Brass*

| Caliber | Price/20 |
|---|---|
| 28-30-120 | $51.00 |
| 32-40 Remington | 26.25 |
| 32-40 WCF | 26.25 |
| 38/56 WCF | 30.00 |
| 38/70 WCF | 48.75 |
| 38/72 | 37.00 |
| 40-60 Marlin | 30.00 |
| 40-60 WCF | 30.00 |
| 40-65 WCF | 30.00 |
| 40-70 Sharps BN | 48.75 |
| 40-70 Sharps Straight | 52.00 |
| 40-70 WCF | 38.00 |
| 40-72 WCF | 37.00 |
| 40-82 WCF | 38.00 |
| 40-90 Sharps BN | 52.50 |
| 44 Evans Long | 30.00 |
| 44 Evans Short | 30.00 |
| 45/75 WCF | 60.00 |
| 45/120 3¼″ Sharps | 75.00 |
| 45/90 WCF | 45.00 |
| 45/110 2⅞″ Sharps | 75.00 |
| 45/120 3¼″ Sharps | 75.00 |
| 50 Carbine | 55.00 |
| 50-70 Sharps | 44.00 |
| 50-70 Springfield/Sharps | 44.00 |
| 50-90 Sharps | 75.00 |
| 50-95 WCF | 60.00 |
| 50-110 WCF | 45.00 |
| 50-140 3¼″ | 50.00 |

C-H/4-D 577/450 Dies

## CVA

**Elite Pure Lead Bullets with Sabots**
Boattail, hollowpoint 225-grain 50- and 54-caliber bullets. Come in packages of 12. From CVA.
**Price:** . . . . . . . . . . . . . . **$6.75**

**Elite Sabots**
Plastic sabots for 44 (.429) and 45 (.451) calibers. From CVA.
**Price:** . . . . . . . . . . . . . . **$6.25**

**Deerslayer Bullets**
Pre-lubed, pure lead, flat nose 50- (300-gr.) and 54-caliber (375-gr.) bullets. Come in packs of 12 or 20. From CVA.
**Price:** 50-cal. (12) . . . . . . . . **$6.50**
**Price:** 50-cal. (20) . . . . . . . . **$9.25**
**Price:** 54-cal. (12) . . . . . . . . **$6.75**
**Price:** 54-cal. (12) . . . . . . . . **$9.75**

**Sabot Big Game Bullet**
Lead 50- and 54-caliber 300-grain saboted big game bullets. Come in packages of 12. From CVA.
**Price:** . . . . . . . . . . . . . . **$6.75**

**Shooting Patches**
Tight woven ticking patches .015″ thick for 32-36, 40-49 and 50-58 calibers. Come in bags of 100. From CVA.
**Price:** . . . . . . . . . . . . . . **$3.50**

**Slick Load Lube**
All natural bullet and patch lube comes in 2-oz. or 5-oz. squeeze tube. From CVA.
**Price:** 2-oz. . . . . . . . . . . . **$4.50**
**Price:** 5-oz. . . . . . . . . . . . **$6.25**

**Slick Load Patches**
Pre-lubricated 100% cotton .015″ thick 40-49 and 50-58 caliber patches. Come in bags of 100. From CVA.
**Price:** . . . . . . . . . . . . . . **$5.25**

## DROPKICK

**Lube**
Beeswax-based lube developed for blackpowder cartridge shooting. Available in hollow sticks. From Dropkick.
**Price:** Each . . . . . . . . . . . **$3.00**

**Wax Wads**
Wax wads in standard or premium beeswax for blackpowder cast bullet rifle or pistol loads. Wax sheets come 20 to a pack. From Dropkick.
**Price:** Standard . . . . . . . . . **$10.00**
**Price:** Premium . . . . . . . . . **$20.00**

**Ballistics Program**
IBM PC compatible running DOS 3.0. Requires 256K free memory and one disc drive. Calculates 40 separate functions for blackpowder silhouette, including remaining velocity, energy, momentum, drop, windage, maximum ordinate, time of flight and lead. Generates windage diagrams and computes terminal performance using six different scales. From Dropkick.
**Price:** . . . . . . . . . . . . . **$55.00**

**Casting Flux**
Effective all natural casting flux to blend alloy and remove dross from casting pot. Comes in 3.5-oz. tube. From Dropkick.
**Price:** Premium . . . . . . . . . **$4.00**

## DENNIS FEKEN

**Wad Punch**

Made of high-quality stainless steel in .410- and .458-inch diameters. Meant to be used in drill press or arbor press, but can be used with rawhide mallet. From Dennis Feken.

**Price:** Premium . . . . . . . . . **$34.95**

## GOEX

**Black Powder**

U.S.-made blackpowder for sporting use in grades Fg, FFg, FFFg and FFFFg and Cartridge. Sold in 1-lb. cans. From Goex, Inc.

**Price:** . . . . . **Contact manufacturer.**

## GOODWIN

**Reloading/Case Form Dies**

Precision-machined steel reloading and case forming dies made in England by James Goodwin for unusual and hard-to-find calibers. Reloading dies threaded 7/8-14. Special shellholders available. From Jack First, Inc.

**Price:** Die set . . . . . . . . . . **$110.00**
**Price:** Shellholder . . . . . . . . **$12.00**

## HARVESTER

**45-Caliber Cast Bullets with Sabots**

Hard cast, flat-nosed .451 diameter bullets in 300- or 400-grain weights with 50-caliber or 54-caliber sabots. Come in packages of 10 each bullets and sabots. From C&D Special Products.

**Price:** . . . . . . . . . . . . . . **$7.99**

## HODGDON

**Pyrodex**

Blackpowder substitute sold in RS (muzzleloaders), P (pistol) and CTG (cartridge) and Select (premium) granulations. Sold in 1-lb. cans. From Hodgdon Powder Company, Inc.

**Price:** RS, P, CTG . **Contact manufacturer.**

**Pyrodex Pellets**

Compact cylindrical propellant pellet 3/4" in length with ignition pad on one end and hollow center for even burning. Sold in boxes of 50. From Hodgdon Powder Company, Inc.

**Price:** . . . . . **Contact manufacturer.**

## HOLLYWOOD

**Carbide Die Sets**

Hollywood offers carbide decap rods, taper crimp dies and neck sizer dies. They also offer full-length carbide sizer dies, full-length bottleneck sizer dies, full-length carbide sets and full-length bottleneck carbide sets for Hollywood, RCBS, Dillon and Star presses. From Hollywood Engineering.

**Price:** . . . . . . . . . . . . . **See chart.**

**Standard Pistol/Rifle Die Sets**

Two- and 3-die sets. Dies made of steel and threaded 7/8-14. From Hollywood Engineering.

**Price:** . . . . . . . . . . . . . **$45.00**

## HORNADY

**Bullets/Saboted XTP**

Self-lubricating, saboted XTP pistol bullets in 45-caliber (158-, 180-grain); 50-caliber (180-, 240-, 300-grain); 54-caliber (180-, 240-, 265-, 300-grain); 58-caliber (250-, 300-grain). 45-, 50- and 54-caliber bullets come in packages of 50; 58-caliber in packages of 40. All come in weather resistant plastic boxes. From Hornady Mfg. Co.

**Price:** . . . . . . . . . . . . . **$5.35**

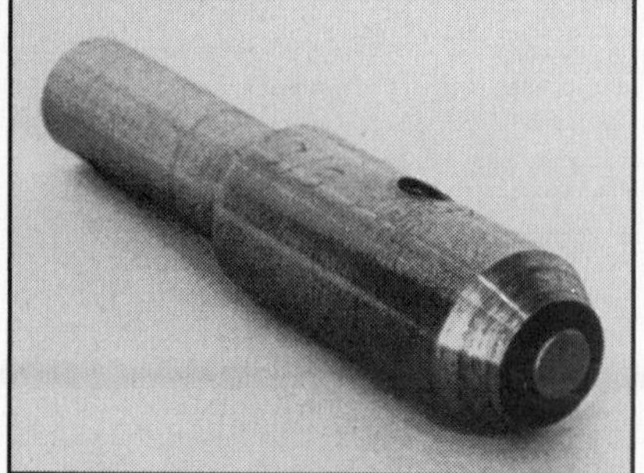

Dennis Feken Wad Punch

Goex Blackpowder

**GOODWIN *Blackpowder Cartridge Die Sets***

| Die | Die | Die |
|---|---|---|
| 240 Flanged | 400-360 | 45-75 Win. |
| 242 Vickers | 360-2 1/2" NE* | 45-90 Win. |
| 6mm Lee Navy | 360 #2 NE* | 450 3 1/4" NE |
| 244 Holland | 369 Purdey* | 500-450 3 1/4" |
| 255 Rook | 9.3x62 Mauser | 500-450 #2 |
| 6.5x68 | 9.3x64 | 577-450 Martini Henry* |
| 26 BSA | 9.3x72R | 455 Colt |
| 280 Ross* | 9.3x74R | 455 Webley* |
| 30 Newton | 375-2 1/2" NE | 455 Webley Auto |
| 300 Sherwood | 375 Flanged* | 461 #1 Gibbs |
| 7.62 Nagant Rev. | 9.5x56 | 461 #2 Gibbs |
| 351 Win. SL | 38-56 | 500-465 NE |
| 375-303 | 38-72 | 470 3 1/4" |
| 310 Cadet | 40-60 Win. | 475 NE |
| 318 Richards | 40-82 Win. | 475 #2 |
| 7.65 French Long* | 400 Purdey | 476 NE |
| 8mm Lebel Rev. | 400-375 | 50-70 |
| 8mm Lebel Rifle* | 450-400 3"* | 50-95 Win. |
| 8x50R | 450-400 3 1/4" NE* | 50-110 Win. |
| 8x57S | 401 Win. SL | 50-140 Win. |
| 8x60R Port. | 10.75x68 Mauser | 500 Jeffrey |
| 8x68S | 10.75x73 Jeffrey* | 500 3" NE |
| 8.15x46.5R | 405 Win. | 577-500 Magnum |
| 32 Win. Spl. | 416 Rigby | 505 Gibbs |
| 33 Win.* | 425 Westley Richards | 577 Snider* |
| 333 Jeffre | 11 Gras | 577 2 3/4" |
| 9x56 | 43 Egyptian | 577 3" NE |
| 35 Win. | 11 Mauser* | |
| 400-350 | 45-60 Win. | |

*Shellholder available.

Hodgdon Pyrodex

| HOLLYWOOD STANDARD Pistol/Rifle Dies |
|---|
| **3-DIE SETS** |
| 32-20 Rev. |
| 38 Long Colt |
| 38-40 Rev. |
| 41 Short Colt |
| 41 Long Colt |
| 44 American |
| 44 Russian |
| 44 Webley |
| 44-40 Rev. Old |
| 44-40 Rev. New |
| **2-DIE SETS** |
| 32-20 Win. |
| 32-40 |
| 38 WCF |
| 38-55 |
| 38-56 |
| 44 WCF |
| 45-70 |
| 45-90 |
| 50-110 |
| 11mm (43 Mauser) |

**HORNADY *Custom Grade New Dimension Die Prices***

| DIE SERIES | 2-DIE RIFLE | 3-DIE RIFLE | CUSTOM PISTOL |
|---|---|---|---|
| **Series I Set** | $25.95 | $27.95 | |
| Full-Length Die | 17.35 | 22.10 | |
| Seat Die | 13.70 | 13.70 | |
| Expander | 6.35 | 7.40 | |
| **Series II Set** | | | 37.00 |
| Full-Length Die | | | 22.10 |
| Seat Die | | | 16.85 |
| Expander | 6.35 | | 7.40 |
| **Series III Set** | 31.50 | | |
| Full-Length Die | 24.25 | | |
| Seat Die | 13.71 | | |
| Expander | 6.35 | | |

**HORNADY *Rifle/Pistol Dies***

| Cartridge | Die Group | Shellholder |
|---|---|---|
| 32/20 Win. | III | 7 |
| 32/40 Win. | IV | 2 |
| 38/40 Win. | IV | 9 |
| 44/40 Win. | IV | 9 |
| 45 Long Colt | II | 32 |
| 45/70 Gov't | I | 14 |

**HORNADY *Round Balls***

| Dia. | Price/100 |
|---|---|
| .310 | $5.77 |
| .315 | 5.77 |
| .350 | 5.77 |
| .375 | 5.81 |
| 395 | 6.44 |
| .433 | 6.88 |
| .440 | 6.88 |
| .445 | 7.60 |
| .451 | 7.85 |
| .454 | 7.65 |
| .457 | 7.75 |
| .490 | 8.57 |
| .495 | 8.57 |
| .520 | 9.80 |
| .530 | 9.80 |
| .535 | 10.05 |
| .570 | 6.01* |

*Price for 50.

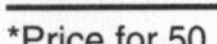

Hornady XTP, Great Plains bullets and round balls

## HORNADY

### Custom Grade New Dimension Series I, II, III, IV Dies

Made of high-quality hand-inspected steel. Dies are lathed to industry-established dimensional tolerances for maximum cartridge size; inside surface hand polished and protective coating applied. Other features include: eliptical expander to reduce friction, case neck stretch and eliminate need for tapered expander; hardened steel decap pin; no-lube Titanium Nitride pistol size die; floating seating stems; and wrench flats. In-line bullet seater has floating alignment sleeve and built-in crimper. Available in most standard rifle/pistol calibers (Series I, II, III). Custom dies (Series IV) also offered on special order. From Hornady Mfg. Co.

**Price:** . . . . . . . . . . . . **See chart.**

### Great Plains Bullets

Cold-swaged blackpowder rifle bullets with short ogive, smaller than bore base diameter, three-diameter bearing surface, hollow base. Available in 45-caliber (285-, 325-grain); 50-caliber (385-, 410-, 460-grain); 54-caliber (390-, 425-, 460-grain); 58-caliber (525-grain). 45- and 50-caliber come in packs of 20; 54- and 58-caliber in packs of 15. From Hornady Mfg. Co.

**Price:** 45-cal. (285-gr.) . . . . . . . **$6.79**
**Price:** 45-cal. (325-gr.) . . . . . . . **$7.13**
**Price:** 50-cal. (325-gr.) . . . . . . . **$7.40**
**Price:** 50-cal. (410-gr.) . . . . . . . **$7.60**
**Price:** 50-cal. (460-gr.) . . . . . . . **$7.90**
**Price:** 54-cal. (390-gr.) . . . . . . . **$6.24**
**Price:** 54-cal. (425-gr.) . . . . . . . **$6.44**
**Price:** 54-cal. (460-gr.) . . . . . . . **$7.20**
**Price:** 58-cal. (525-gr.) . . . . . . . **$8.61**

### Round Balls

Cold-swaged pure lead round balls. Available in .310 to .570 diameter. Come in 25-ball blister packs or boxes of 100. From Hornady Mfg. Co.

**Price:** . . . . . . . . . . . . **See chart.**

## HUNTINGTON

### Brass

Drawn brass available in basic case style or ready to load. All cases headstamped with HDS and caliber. Available calibers, 40-70 Sharps Straight, 405 WCF Basic, 44 Sharps Basic, 45 Basic, 50-70 Government and 50-90 Sharps. Come 20 per box. From Huntington Die Specialties.

**Price:** 40-70, 44 Sharps Basic . . . **$51.98**
**Price:** 495 WCF Basic, 45 Basic . . **$46.98**
**Price:** 50-70 Gov't, 50-90 Sharps . . **$47.98**

Hornady Frontier Cowboy Ammunition

Hodgdon Pyrodex Bullets

## PAUL JONES

**Bullet Moulds**

Solid cast iron single-cavity lathe-bored or cherry-cut moulds for Schuetzen and blackpowder cartridge rifle silhouette competition. Mould blocks have three alignment pins and faces ground flat to .0003″. Available calibers: 32, 33, 38, 40, 44 and 45. Fit Saeco handles. From Paul Jones.

**Price:** . . . . . . . . . . . . . **$90.00**

## KNIGHT

**High Pressure Sabot Bullets**

Designed to be used with Pyrodex pellets. Jacketed 50-caliber bullets in 250-, 160-, 300- and 310-grain weights with high impact plastic sabot. From Knight.

**Price:** . . . . . **Contact manufacturer.**

**Jacketed Saboted Bullets**

Hollowpoint, flat-nose jacketed 240-, 260-, 300-, 325-grain bullets in 50- and 54-caliber with plastic sabots. Com 10 or 20 per pack. From Knight.

**Price:** . . . . . **Contact manufacturer.**

**Lead Saboted Bullets**

Hollowpoint lead 260- and 310-grain bullets in 50- and 54-caliber with plastic sabots. Come 10 or 20 per pack. From Knight.

**Price:** . . . . . **Contact manufacturer.**

**Red Hot Bullets**

All copper 50- and 54-caliber bullets available in 250-, 300- and 325-grain weights for small to dangerous game. Come 10 per pack. From Knight.

**Price:** . . . . . **Contact manufacturer.**

## DOUG KNOELL

**Decapping Tool**

Tool made of steel and designed to handle any blackpowder cartridge. Has a primer pocket cleaner on one leg. From Doug Knoell.

**Price:** . . . . . . . . . . . . . **$40.00**

## LEE

**Bullet Moulds**

Aluminum 1- and 2-cavity mould blocks lathe-bored to roundness of .001″ or less. Most bullets from Lee moulds can be used as cast without sizing. Lee single-cavity, double-cavity, hollowpoint and hollow base single-cavity moulds come with sprue plate and wood handles. Hollowpoint and hollow base moulds have self-centering automatic core pins. From Lee Precision, Inc.

**Price:** 1-cavity . . . . . . . . . **$19.98**
**Price:** 2-cavity . . . . . . . . . **$23.98**
**Price:** Hollowpoint/hollow base . . . **$24.98**
**Price:** Shotgun slug mould . . . . **$25.98**

**Mould Handles**

Precision steel mould handles fit all Lee moulds as well as most other brands of one- and two-cavity moulds. From Lee Precision, Inc.

**Price:** . . . . . . . . . . . . . **$14.98**

**Steel Pistol Dies**

Set includes sizer/decapper, powder-through-expander and bullet seater. Each die has enlarged mouth to align with cases, even damaged cases. Steel dies have same features as carbide except case must be lubricated. Come with free shellholder. From Lee Precision, Inc.

**Price:** Carbide . . . . . . . . . **$36.98**
**Price:** Steel . . . . . . . . . . **$27.98**

Knight Jacketed Saboted Bullets

Knight Lead Saboted Bullets

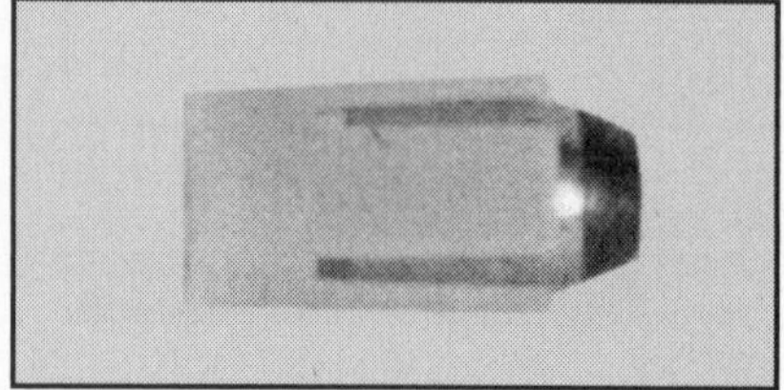

Knight High Pressure Sabot Bullets

**LEE *Rifle Bullet Moulds***

| Dia. | Wgt. Grs. | Type | Mould |
|---|---|---|---|
| **45-70 CALIBER** | | | |
| .457 | 340 | F | 1-cavity |
| .457 | 405 | F | 1-cavity* |
| .457 | 450 | F | 1-cavity |
| .457 | 500 | F | 1-cavity |

F = Flat. *Hollow Point

**LEE *Rifle/Pistol Dies***

| Caliber | RGB Series | PaceSetter 3-Die | PaceSetter Ltd. | Limited Production | Collet Necksize | Factory Crimp | Taper Crimp |
|---|---|---|---|---|---|---|---|
| **RIFLE** | | | | | | | |
| 32-20 | NA | NA | NA | A* | NA | A | NA |
| 32-40 | NA | NA | NA | A | NA | NA | NA |
| 38-40 | NA | NA | NA | A* | NA | A | NA |
| 38-55 | NA | NA | NA | A* | NA | A | NA |
| 38-56 | NA | NA | NA | A | NA | NA | NA |
| 43 Mauser | NA | NA | NA | A | NA | NA | NA |
| 43 Spanish | NA | NA | NA | A | NA | NA | NA |
| 44-40 | NA | NA | NA | A* | NA | A | NA |
| 45-70 Gov't. | NA | NA | NA | A* | NA | A | NA |
| **PISTOL** | | | | | | | |
| 32-20 | NA | A | NA | NA | A* | NA | A** |
| 38-40 | NA | A | NA | NA | A* | NA | A** |
| 44-40 | NA | A | NA | NA | A* | NA | A** |
| 45 Colt | A | NA | NA | A | A | A | A |

A:Available; NA:Not available. *Special Order. **Custom die $30.00.

**LIBERTY *Cases***

| Caliber | Qty. | Price |
|---|---|---|
| 40-65 | 20 | $36.00 |
| 40-72 | 20 | 36.00 |
| 40-82 | 20 | 36.00 |
| 40-90 Basic 3 1/4″ | 20 | 36.00 |
| 405 Basic 3 1/4″ | 20 | 36.00 |
| 43 Mauser | 20 | 36.00 |
| 45-70 Nickel | 20 | 9.00 |
| 45-70 Brass | 20 | 8.00 |
| 45-90 | 20 | 36.00 |
| 45 Basic 3 1/4″ | 20 | 56.00 |
| 50 Basic 3 1/4″ | 20 | 56.00 |

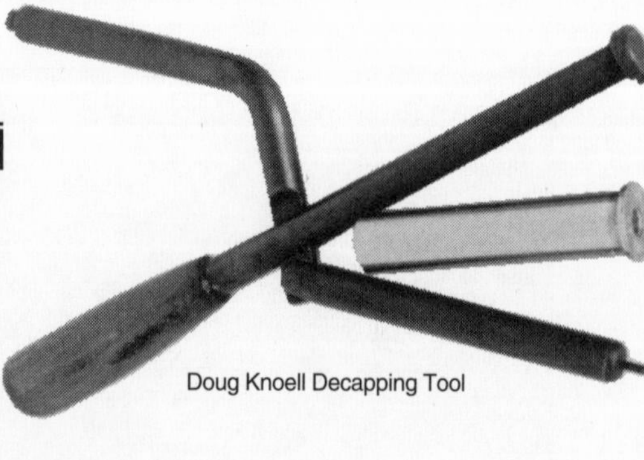

Doug Knoell Decapping Tool

**LIBERTY SHOOTING SUPPLIES *Cast Bullets***

| Caliber | Dia. (ins.) | Wgt. Grs. | Type | Price/100 | Price/250 |
|---|---|---|---|---|---|
| **PISTOL** | | | | | |
| 38-40 | .401 | 165 | FP | $6.00 | $27.00 |
| | .401 | 195 | SWC | 6.50 | 29.25 |
| | .401 | 220 | FP | 7.00 | 31.50 |
| 44-40 | .427 | 200 | FP | 6.50 | 29.25 |
| | .427 | 205 | FP | 6.50 | 29.25 |
| 45 Colt | .454 | 240 | FP | 7.50 | 33.75 |
| | .454 | 310 | BBSWC | 6.50 | 29.25 |
| **RIFLE** | | | | | |
| 38-55 | .379 | 250 | GCFP | 6.00 | 27.00 |
| | .379 | 255 | RNDD | | 33.75 |
| | .379 | 290 | FP | 6.50 | 29.25 |
| 43 Spanish | .439 | 370 | FP | 8.50 | 38.25 |
| 43 Mauser | .446 | 390 | FP | 8.50 | 38.25 |
| 45-70 | .458 | 285 | FP | 6.00 | 27.00 |
| | .458 | 300 | RN | 6.50 | 29.25 |
| | .458 | 300 | GCFP | 6.00 | 27.00 |
| | .458 | 360 | RN | 6.50 | 29.25 |
| | .458 | 370 | SP | 7.00 | 31.50 |
| | .458 | 405 | FP | 7.50 | 33.75 |
| | .458 | 425 | BTSP | 8.00 | 36.00 |
| | .452 | 435 | FPPP | 9.00 | 40.50 |
| | .458 | 446 | GCFP | 9.00 | 40.50 |
| | .458 | 455 | SP | 10.00 | 45.00 |
| | .452-.458 | 465 | TP | 10.00 | 45.00 |
| | .458 | 490 | GCFP | 11.00 | 49.50 |
| | .458 | 500 | RN | 11.00 | 49.50 |
| | .451 | 500 | RNPP | 11.00 | 49.50 |
| | .458 | 530 | GCFP | 12.00 | 54.00 |
| | .452-.458 | 580 | TP | 13.00 | 58.50 |

FP = Flat point; SWC = Semi-Wadcutter; BB = Bevel Base; GC = Gas Check; RN = Round Nose; BT = Boattail.

Liberty Cast Bullet

Lyman Black Powder Gold Lube

**LYMAN *Rifle/Pistol Dies***

| Cartridge | Die Group | Shellholder |
|---|---|---|
| 32-20 Win. | AA-3 | 10 |
| 38-55 Win. | AA-3 | 6 |
| 44-40 Win. | AA-3 | 14B |
| 40-65 | AA-3 | 17 |
| 45-70 Gov't | AA-3 | 17 |
| 50-70 Gov't | AA-3 | 22 |
| 45 Colt | C-4, C-3, S-3 | 11 |

## LEE

### Limited Production Rifle Dies

Limited Production 2-die set includes full-length sizer, bullet seater/roll crimper, shellholder, powder dipper and load data for single cartridge in transparent storage container. This set does not include a factory crimp die. See chart for available calibers. From Lee Precision, Inc.

**Price:** . . . . . . . . . . . . . . **$29.98**

## LIBERTY

### Cast Bullets and Brass Cases

Hand cast bullets with Brinell hardness of 19-20. Bullets come lubed with Rooster Red or SPG lube (extra). Come in boxes of 100 or 500. Brass cases come in boxes of 20 or 50. From Liberty Shooting Supplies.

**Price:** . . . . . . . . . . . . **See chart.**

## LYMAN

### AA Rifle 3-Die Set

For reloading straight-wall cases. Full-length sizing die with decapping stem, AA two-step neck expanding (M) die and bullet seating die. Also good for loading cast bullets. From Lyman Products Corporation.

**Price:** . . . . . . . . . . . . . . **$32.00**

### Black Powder Gold Lube

Formulated specifically for blackpowder use. High melting temperature makes it suitable for long-range shooting. Fits all popular lube sizers. Comes in tubes. From Lyman Products Corporation.

**Price:** . . . . . . . . . . . . . . . **$3.50**

### Carbide Pistol 3-Die Set

Tungsten carbide full-length resizing and decapping die, two-step neck expanding die, and bullet seating chamber and screw. Comes with extra seating screws for loading all popular bullet designs for given caliber. Two-step expander prevents cast bullet distortion and assures precise case neck tension. Loads both magnum and special length cases. Resizing ring eliminates need for case lubing. From Lyman Products Corporation.

**Price:** . . . . . . . . . . . . . **$38.95**

### Ideal Moulds

Machined from high-grade steel, blocks are hand fit for precision alignment. Pistol bullet moulds come in 2- or 4-cavity blocks. Rifle moulds available in 2-cavity only except where bullet size necessitates single cavity. From Lyman Products Corporation.

**Price:** Pistol, 2-cavity . . . . . . **$49.95**
**Price:** Pistol, 4-cavity . . . . . . **$76.50**
**Price:** Rifle . . . . . . . . . . **$49.95**

### LRHP High-Performance Bullets

Designed for long-range target and blackpowder silhouette shooting. Available in 45-caliber Schmittzer and Postell designs and 40-caliber Schmittzer and Snover designs. Come pre-lubed in packs of 20 or 50. From Lyman Products Corporation.

**Price:** 20 . . . . . . . . . . . . **$7.75**
**Price:** 50 . . . . . . . . . . . **$13.75**

### Mould Box

Made of tough plastic with snap-lock cover. Impervious to moisture, bore cleaner or oil. Fits single- and double-cavity moulds only. From Lyman Products Corporation.

**Price:** Each . . . . . . . . . . . . **$2.00**
**Price:** 10 . . . . . . . . . . . . **$15.00**

## LYMAN

**Mould Handles**

*Lyman no longer manufactures small single-cavity mould blocks. All current Lyman single- and double-cavity moulds are now made using standard large mould blocks and require large mould handles.* Solid metal frame with hardwood handles designed to provide uniform grip. Three sizes available: small, for older single-cavity moulds; large, for current manufacture large block single-cavity and double-cavity moulds; and four-cavity for Lyman four-cavity moulds. From Lyman Products Corporation.

**Price:** 1- and 2-cavity . . . . . . **$24.00**
**Price:** 4-cavity . . . . . . . . . **$28.00**

**Mould Rebuild Kit**

Includes sprue cutter, washer, all screws for mould block and handle. From Lyman Products Corporation.

**Price:** 1- and 2-cavity . . . . . . . **$5.00**
**Price:** 4-cavity . . . . . . . . . . **$6.50**

**Shocker Black Powder Bullets**

Designed for big game hunting. Semi-pointed 50- and 54-caliber cast conicals in 420-grain and 445-grain weights respectively. Come pre-lubed in packs of 20. From Lyman Products Corporation.

**Price:** 50-cal. . . . . . . . . . . **$6.25**
**Price:** 54-cal. . . . . . . . . . . **$6.50**

**Shocker Saboted Shotgun Slugs**

Saboted 12- and 20-gauge shotgun slugs designed to fit into standard shotgun wads and be fold crimped. Wasp-waist design controls expansion and energy transfer. 12-ga. 525-grain come in 12 pack; 20-ga. 350-grain come in packs of 15. From Lyman Products Corporation.

**Price:** 12-ga. . . . . . . . . . . **$5.95**
**Price:** 20-ga. . . . . . . . . . . **$6.50**
**Price:** . . . . . . . . . . . . . **$3.50**

**Shotgun Slug Moulds**

Available for 12- or 20-gauge slugs. Mould casts hollow-base slugs which require no rifling. Single-cavity only and cut into the larger double-cavity block. Require double cavity handles. From Lyman Products Corporation.

**Price:** . . . . . . . . . . . . . **$48.75**

**Silver Star Bullet Moulds**

Four moulds in 38/357, 44-40, 44 Spl./44 Mag. and 45 Long Colt for modern cowboy action shooters. Bullet nose aligns in cylinder throat to ensure accuracy; crimp groove helps maintain proper overall length. From Lyman Products Corporation.

**Price:** 2-cavity . . . . . . . . . **$49.95**
**Price:** 4-cavity . . . . . . . . . **$76.50**

**Standard Pistol 3-Die Set**

Includes same features as carbide 3-die set except resizing die is steel. From Lyman Products Corporation.

**Price:** . . . . . . . . . . . . . **$28.50**

**Super Moly Bullet Lube**

All purpose, high temperature bullet lube with molybdenum disulfide. Comes in tubular form and fits all popular lube sizers. From Lyman Products Corporation.

**Two-Step Expanding (M) Die**

Designed for cast and jacketed bullet loads. Prevents case stretching to extend case life. Expands inside of case neck to just under bullet diameter then expands case mouth to bullet diameter or slightly over. From Lyman Products Corporation.

**Price:** . . . . . . . . . . . . . **$11.75**

LYMAN *Bullet Moulds*

| Bullet # | Caliber | Dia. | Wgt. Grs. | Top Punch # | Gas Check | # Cavity Mould |
|---|---|---|---|---|---|---|
| | | | —PISTOL— | | | |
| 358665 | 38/357 | .358 | 158 | 495 | | 2 |
| 429667 | 44 Spl./44 Mag. | | 240 | 649 | | 2 |
| 427666 | 44-40 | .427 | 200 | 649 | | 2 |
| 427098 | | .427 | 205 | 43 | | 2 |
| 454190 | 45 Colt | .454 | 250 | 190 | | 2 |
| 452424 | | .452 | 255 | 424 | | 2 |
| 452664 | 45 Long Colt | .452 | 250 | 649 | | 2 |
| | | | —RIFLE— | | | |
| 375248 | 38-55 | .375 | 249 | 449 | | 2 |
| 410655 | 40 | .410 | 400 | 449 | | 2 |
| 410660 | Scheutzen | .410 | 385 | 658 | | 2 |
| 457122 | 45 HP | .457 | 330 | 191 | | 2 |
| 457124 | | .457 | 385 | 374 | | 2 |
| 457643 | | .457 | 400 | 191 | | 2 |
| 457193 | | .457 | 405 | 191 | | 2 |
| 457406 | | .457 | 475 | 374 | GC | 2 |
| 457658 | 45-70 Schmittzer | .457 | 480 | 658 | | 2 |
| 515141 | 50 | .515 | 425 | 141 | | 2 |

Lyman Silver Star Bullets

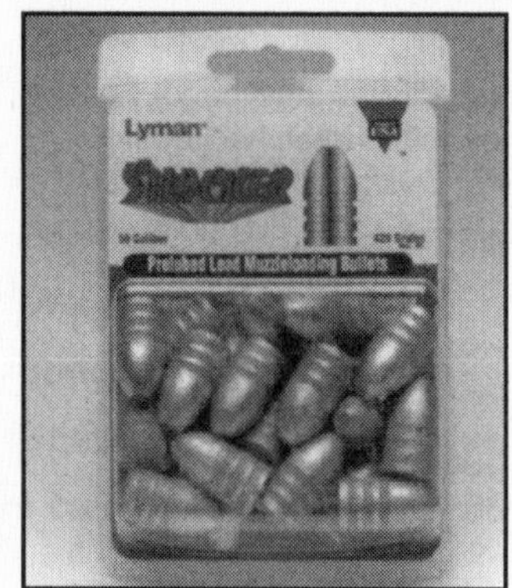


Lyman Shocker Bullets

## LYMAN

**Universal Decapping Die**

For all calibers 22 through 45. Solid one-piece construction of hardened tool steel. Works well for military crimped primers. From Lyman Products Corporation.

**Price:** . . . . . . . . . . . . . **$10.75**

## MICHAELS OF OREGON

**Hot Shot Lubed Patches**

Made of .010" or .015" thick 100% cotton and lubed with Hot Shot Lube for 40- to 59-caliber. Come in packages of 100. From Michaels of Oregon.

**Price:** . . . . . . . . . . . . . **$5.25**

**Hot Shot Patch & Bullet Lube**

All-natural, biodegradable blackpowder patch and bullet lube. Comes in 4-oz. jar. From Michaels of Oregon.

**Price:** . . . . . . . . . . . . . **$6.95**

**Hot Shot Wads**

Woven wool pre-cut and pre-lubed 44-, 45- and 50-caliber wads. Come 50 per bag. From Michaels of Oregon.

**Price:** 44, 45 cals. . . . . . . . . **$3.99**
**Price:** 50 cal. . . . . . . . . . . **$4.99**

## MI-TE BULLETS

**Cast Bullets**

Hard cast 45-caliber 525-grain semi-spitzer bullet for blackpowder cartridge made of Acculoy with BHN of 16 or heat-treated to BHN 25. Come in boxes of 50. From Mi-Te Bullets.

**Price:** . . . . . . . . . . . . . **$10.00**

## MONTANA ARMORY

**Blackpowder Lubricant**

Semi-solid blackpowder lubricant designed to help keep fouling down in rifle barrel. Come in five stick packs. From Huntington Die Specialties.

**Price:** . . . . . . . . . . . . . **$15.00**

**Lube Ribbon Extruder**

Designed for use with standard reloading press. Extrudes 1/8" thick by 1" wide ribbon of lube with option of cutting 1/8" cookie of lube to seat under bullet to keep blackpowder fouling soft. From Huntington Die Specialties.

**Price:** . . . . . . . . . . . . . **$49.95**

## MONTANA PRECISION SWAGING

**Bullets**

Cast rifle and pistol bullets and swaged paper patch bullets. Cast bullets come lubed and sized. From Montana Precision Swaging.

**Price:** . . . . . . . . . . . . **See chart.**

**Blackpowder Compression Die**

Available in 30-, 32-, 38-, 40-, 44-, 45- and 50-caliber. Comes with one stem for single rifle caliber or 10- to 20-gauge shotgun. Additional stems extra. From Montana Precision Swaging.

**Price:** Rifle . . . . . . . . . . **$40.00**
**Price:** Shotgun . . . . . . . . . **$42.00**
**Price:** Interchangeable stem, rifle . . **$6.00**
**Price:** Interchangeable stem, shotgun . **$8.00**

Lyman Super Moly Lube

Mt. Baldy Bullets

Mountain State Tru-Charger

**MONTANA PRECISION SWAGING *Bullets***

| Caliber | Dia. (ins.) | Wgt. Grs. | Price/100 |
|---|---|---|---|
| **Paper Patch Straight Sided Unpatched** | | | |
| 38 | .365 | 250, 300 | $21.50 |
| 40 | .395 | 330, 370, 400 | 23.30 |
| | .399 | 330, 370, 400 | 23.30 |
| 43 Span. | .439 | 350, 400, 500 | 23.30 |
| 44 | .440 | 380, 400, 500 | 25.00 |
| 45 | .450 | 400, 475, 500, 510, 540 | 25.50 |
| 50 | .505 | 450, 500, 550 | 26.00 |
| 58 | .577 | 450, 500, 550 | 26.00 |
| **Paper Patch Tapered Unpatched** | | | |
| 40 | .402 | 330,350,370,420 | 27.50 |
| 45 | .450 | 450, 510, 540 | 30.00 |
| 50 | .500 | 450, 550 | 31.00 |
| **Jacketed Bullets** | | | |
| 40 | .408 | 260 | 18.75 |
| 40 | .408 | 300, 330, 350, 370, 400 | 18.25/50 |
| 405 | .412 | 300 | 17.25/50 |
| 45 | .458 | 300, 350, 405 | 17.25/50 |
| **Grease Groove Rifle Bullets** | | | |
| 32-40 | .323 | 200 | 18.00 |
| 38-40 | .400 | 184 | 15.50 |
| 38 | .376 | 255 | 18.00 |
| | .379 | 255 | 18.00 |
| | .381 | 265 | 18.00 |
| 40 | .408 | 300 | 18.00 |
| | .408 | 350 | 19.70 |
| | .408 | 370 | 19.70 |
| | .408 | 400 | 19.70 |
| | .408 | 410 | 19.70 |
| 43 | .440 | 370 | 19.70 |
| 44 | .446 | 370 | 19.70 |
| 45 | .458 | 300 | 18.00 |
| 45 HB | .458 | 405 | 21.50 |
| 45 | .458 | 480 | 19.70 |
| | .458 | 465 | 21.80 |
| | .458 | 480 | 19.70 |
| | .458 | 500 | 20.30 |
| | .458 | 525 | 20.30 |
| | .458 | 550 | |
| **Grease Groove Handgun** | | | |
| 32 | .311 | 93 | 7.25 |
| 44 | .428 | 214 | 8.25 |
| 44-40 | .429 | 214 | 9.00 |
| 45 | .452 | 255 | 9.00 |
| | .452 | 300 | 11.10 |
| | .454 | 250 | 9.25 |

**MT. BALDY *Bullets***

| Dia. (ins.) | Wgt. Grs. | Price/100 |
|---|---|---|
| .320 | 160 | $8.00 |
| .387HB | 205 | 9.00 |
| .301 | 172 | 7.50 |
| .401 | 190 | 7.50 |
| .406 | 275 | 9.00 |
| .409 | 260 | 11.00 |
| .409 | 300 | 11.00 |
| .409 | 370 | 11.00 |
| .409 | 400 | 11.00 |
| .409 | 410 | 11.00 |
| .410 | 210 | 7.00 |
| .428 | 210 | 7.00 |
| .439 | 370 | 11.00 |
| .446 | 370 | 11.00 |
| .452 | 250 | 8.00 |
| .454HB | 250 | 14.00 |
| .454 | 250 | 8.00 |
| .459 | 405 | 11.00 |
| .459HB | 405 | 16.00 |
| .459 | 500 | 11.00 |
| .459 | 500 | 12.00 |
| .459 | 535 | 12.00 |
| .459 | 535 | 12.00 |
| .512 | 450 | 12.00 |
| .515 | 450 | 12.00 |

HB = Hollow Base

## MT. BALDY

**Bullets**

Cast bullets in a wide variety of blackpowder cartridge rifle and handgun calibers (see chart). Will come lubed with modern hard lube or SPG Lube upon request. From Mt. Baldy Bullet Company.

**Price:** . . . . . **Contact manufacturer.**

## MOUTAIN STATE MUZZLELOADING

**Dry Patches**

Pre-cut 100% cotton patches .010″, .015″ and .020″ thick for 30- to 69-caliber. Come 100 per bag. From Mountain State Muzzleloading.

**Price:** . . . . . . . . . . . . . . **$2.85**

**E-Z Mould Handle**

Designed to fit the sprue cutter of most popular single and double-cavity bullet moulds for ease of sprue cutting. From Moutain State Muzzleloading.

**Price:** . . . . . . . . . . . . . **$11.95**

**Pre-Lubed Pre-Cut Patches**

Pre-lubed, pre-cut 100% cotton patches .010″, .015″ and .020″ thick for 30- to 69-caliber. Come 100 per bag. From Mountain State Muzzleloading.

**Price:** . . . . . . . . . . . . . . **$4.40**

**Tru-Charger**

Blackpowder cartridge adjustable powder measure featuring a main body with shutoff valve; and adjustable sliding gauge with cut-off valve; powder hopper. From Mountain State Muzzleloading.

**Price:** . . . . . . . . . . . . . **$49.95**

## N.D.F.S

**Die Service for Obsolete Cartridges**

This English company manufactures custom three-die sets with standard threading for obsolete blackpowder cartridges. See chart for partial listing of available die sets. From N.D.F.S.

**Price:** . . . . . **Contact manufacturer.**

## NECO

**P-Wads and Insertion Tool**

Precision hand-cut plastic P-wads for plain base cast bullets to act as gas seal for prevention of gas cutting. Precision stainless steel and tool steel insertion tool designed to seat the P-Wad squarely and uniformly in case mouth. P-Wads come 100 to a bag. From NECO.

**Price:** Insertion Tool . . . . . . . . **$39.75**
**Price:** P-Wads (22-39 cal.) . . . . . **$3.75**
**Price:** P-Wads (40-44 cal.) . . . . . **$5.50**
**Price:** P-Wads (45-49 cal.) . . . . . **$5.90**
**Price:** P-Wads (50-54 cal.) . . . . . **$6.25**

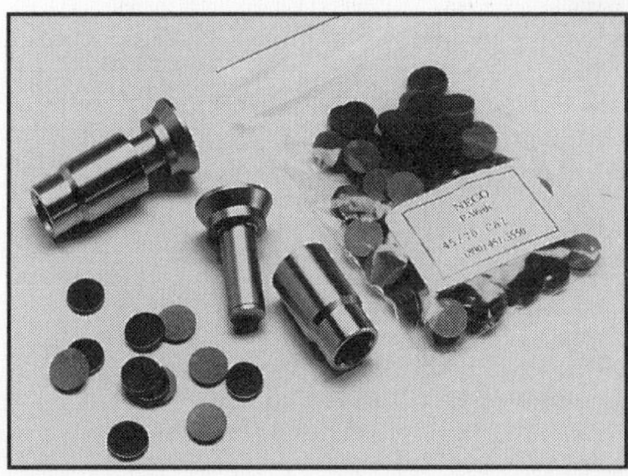

NECO P-Wads and Insertion Tool

## OCTOBER COUNTRY

**Brass Pedersoli Moulds**

Remington and Colt two-cavity all-brass moulds to cast 36- and 44-caliber round balls and conical bullets. Walker single-cavity brass mould with wooden handles to cast conical (ogival) bullet. From October Country.

**Price:** Remington/Colt . . . . . . **$22.25**
**Price:** Walker . . . . . . . . . **$32.95**

**Drop Tube**

Solid brass 30″ or 40″ drop tube with brass funnel for loading blackpowder cases. Comes with or without poplar stand. From October Country.

**Price:** 30″ with stand . . . . . . **$39.95**
**Price:** 30″ without stand . . . . . **$19.95**
**Price:** 40″ without stand . . . . . **$22.95**

**Lube Cutter**

Hollow cutter to fit over 40-, 45-, 50-, 54- and 58-caliber bullets. From October Country.

**Price:** . . . . . . . . . . . . **$19.95**

**Ol' Thunder Patch Lube**

Water soluble non-caustic patch lube available in pint or quart bottles. From October Country.

**Price:** Pint . . . . . . . . . . . **$3.75**
**Price:** Quart . . . . . . . . . . **$5.95**

## OLD WEST

**Bullet Moulds**

Custom lathe or cherry cut single-, double- or triple-cavity moulds for obsolete rifles and handguns in calibers from 375- to 54-caliber. Nose-pour or base-pour styles available. Cherry cut moulds are base-pour and made of brass. Lathe-bored nose-pour moulds have minimum bullet length, .950″; maximum length, 1.4″. Lathe-bored base-pour moulds, any length up to 1.4″. Max number driving bands is six; minimum diameter meplat .1″. Sprue plate of 1/8″ thick steel, but 3/16″ thick plates available. Single- and double-cavity moulds fit RCBS or Lyman handles; for three-cavity only RCBS handles. Economy moulds with each cavity a different caliber or bullet weight also offered. From Old West Bullet Moulds.

**Price:** Cherry cut single, 25 to 50 cal. **$55.00**
**Price:** Lathed bored single, nose pour **$72.00**
**Price:** Lathed bored single, base pour **$65.00**
**Price:** Cherry cut 2-cavity 25 to 45 cal. **$68.00**
**Price:** Cherry cut 2-cavity economy, 25 to 45 cal. . . . . . . . . **$76.00**
**Price:** Hollow base single cavity . . **$103.00**
**7Price:** Adjustable 22 to 54 cal. . . . **$150.00**

## OREGON TRAIL

**Laser-Cast Bullets**

Match-grade cast silver alloy bullets providing reliable accuracy, less distortion and fewer heavy deposits. From Oregon Trail Bullet Company.

**Price:** . . . . . . . . . . . . **See chart.**

## OX-YOKE

**Dry Shooting Patches**

Pre-cut dry patches .005″, .010″, .015″ and .020″ thick in four sizes: 7/8″ (30-39 cals.); 1 1/8″ (40-49 cals.); 15/16″ (50-59 cals.); 1 1/2″ (60-70 cals.). Come in bags of 100. From Ox-Yoke Originals, Inc.

**Price:** . . . . . . . . . . . . **$3.63**

**Liquid Wonder Competition Lube**

Round ball patch lube in 8-oz. squeeze bottle. From Ox-Yoke Originals, Inc.

### OREGON TRAIL *Cast Bullets*

| Caliber | Wgt. Grs. | Type | Price/500 |
|---|---|---|---|
| 30 | 115 | RNBB | $16.00 |
| 32-20 | 115 | FPBB | 15.00 |
| 9mm | 115 | RNBB | 16.00 |
| | 122 | FPBB | 16.50 |
| | 124 | RNBB | 16.50 |
| | 135 | RNBB | 16.50 |
| | 147 | FPBB | 16.50 |
| 38 | 125 | FPBB | 16.50 |
| | 145 | RNBB | 17.50 |
| | 148 | WCDBB, SGG | 19.00 |
| | 158 | RNBB, RNFP | 17.50 |
| | 158 | SWCBB | 17.50 |
| | 180 | FPBB | 19.50 |
| 38-40 | 180 | RNFPBB | 19.50 |
| 10MM | 155 | RNSWCBB | 17.50 |
| | 170 | SWCBB | 17.50 |
| | 180 | FPBB | 19.50 |
| | 200 | TCBB | 20.50 |
| 41 | 215 | SWCBB | 20.50 |
| 44-40 | 200 | RNFPBB | 20.50 |
| 44 | 200 | RNFPBB | 20.50 |
| | 240 | SWCBB | 24.00 |
| | 300 | TCBB | 28.00 |
| 45 | 180 | SWCBB | 19.50 |
| | 200 | SWCBB | 20.50 |
| | 225 | FPBB | 24.00 |
| | 230 | RNBB | 24.00 |
| | 250 | RNFPBB | 25.00 |
| | 300 | FPBB | 28.00 |
| 45-70 | 350 | FPBB | 38.00 |
| | 405 | FPBB | 46.00 |

FP = Flat Point; BB = Bevel Base; RN = Round Nose; WC = Wadcutter; SWC = Semi-Wadcutter; DBB = Double Bevel Base.

Oregon Trail Laser-Cast Bullet

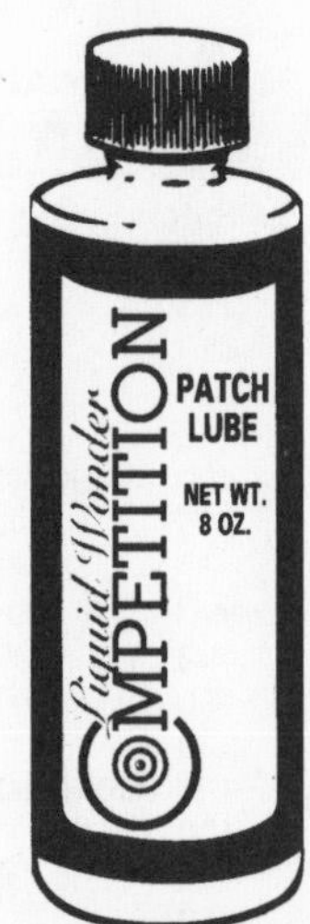


Ox-Yoke Liquid Wonder Competition Lube

### OLD WESTERN SCROUNGER *Bullets*

| Diameter | Wgt. Grs. | Type | Price/100 |
|---|---|---|---|
| .320 | 160 | FN | 14.90 |
| .401 | 172 | FN | 13.15 |
| | 190 | FN | 13.15 |
| .375 | 250 | FN | 12.35 |
| .376 | 250 | FNGC | 14.00 |
| .387 | 200 | HB | 16.50 |
| .410 | 205 | HE | 16.50 |
| .428 | 210 | FN | 13.30 |
| .430 | 195 | FN | 13.65 |
| | 240 | SWCBB | 13.65 |
| | 240 | SWCGC | 14.40 |
| | 300 | FNGC | 18.25 |
| .452 | 250 | RN | 14.65 |
| | 325 | FNGC | 19.50 |
| | 340 | FNGC | 21.20 |

BB = Bevel Base; RN = Round Nose; TC = Truncated Cone; GC = Gas Check; SWC = Semi-Wadcutter; SP = Spitzer; FP = Flat Point; BT = Boattail.

### OLD WEST *Bullet Moulds*

| Caliber | Cast Size | Wgt. Grs. | Type | OAL |
|---|---|---|---|---|
| 32-20 | .313 | 100 | PB | .545 |
| | .313 | 118 | GC | .645 |
| 32-40 | .323 | 172 | PB | .865 |
| | .323 | 189 | GC | .950 |
| 38-55 | .381 | 255 | PB | .925 |
| | .381 | 286 | GC | 1.025 |
| 40/41 | .405 | 160 | | .530 |
| | .411 | 210 | PB | .680 |
| | .413 | 240 | PB | .760 |
| | .411 | 260 | GC | .760 |
| | .413 | 280 | PB | .860 |
| 44 | .431 | 320 | GC | .910 |
| | .215 | .420 | PB | .670 |
| | .220 | .431 | PB | .820 |
| | .270 | .810 | PB | .810 |
| | .280 | .431 | PB | .820 |
| 45 | .459 | 255 | PB | .650 |
| | .454 | 310 | PB | .770 |
| | .454 | 390 | PB | .970 |
| | .454 | 490 | PB | 1.200 |
| 50 | .515 | 385 | PB | .830 |
| | .515 | 470 | PB | 1.070 |
| | .515 | 525 | PB | 1.180 |

PB = Plain Base; GC = Gas Check.

**RAPINE *Bullet Moulds***

| Bullet | Caliber | Dia. | Wgt. Grs. | Bullet | Caliber | Dia. | Wgt. Grs. |
|---|---|---|---|---|---|---|---|
| 31 | 36 Maynard | .366 | 158 | 67 | 45-70 | .457 | 150 |
| 32 | 38-55 | .375 | 250 | | | .460 | 150 |
| | | .375 | 265 | 68 | | .460 | 210 |
| | | .380 | 265 | 69 | | .457 | 250 |
| 33 | 36 | .380 | 125 | | | .460 | 250 |
| 34 | 36 Conv. | .380 | 100 | 70 | | .457 | 280 |
| 35 | 41 LC | .386 | 185 | | | .457 | 311 |
| 36 | 40 Dixie | .400 | 250 | | | .460 | 280 |
| 37 | 38-40 | .401 | 180 | | | .460 | 311 |
| 38 | Paper Patch | .400 | 360 | 71 | | .460 | 350 |
| 39 | 40-60 | .403 | 185 | | | .460 | 405 |
| | | .403 | 225 | | | .460 | 450 |
| | | .403 | 250 | | | .460 | 510 |
| | | .403 | 290 | 72 | | .457 | 350 |
| 40 | 40-65 | .406 | 185 | | | .457 | 405 |
| | | .496 | 225 | | | .457 | 450 |
| | | .406 | 250 | | | .457 | 510 |
| | | .406 | 290 | 73 | 45-70 1881 | .460 | 500 |
| 41 | 40-70 | .406 | 330 | 74 | | .457 | 500 |
| 51 | 44-40 | .427 | 210 | 75 | 45-70 Gov't. Issue | .457 | 406 |
| | | .429 | 210 | | | .460 | 406 |
| 54 | 43 Spanish | .439 | 385 | 76 | Paper Patch | .500 | 500 |
| | | .446 | 385 | 77 | 50-70 Gov't.&May. | .515 | 320 |
| 55 | 11mm Mauser | .446 | 355 | | | .515 | 385 |
| 56 | 44 Colt Conv. | .451 | 210 | | | .515 | 450 |
| 57 | Paper Patch | .451 | 420 | 78 | Smith May. | .520 | 300 |
| | | .451 | 501 | | | .520 | 350 |
| 58 | | .451 | 365 | 79 | Orig. Smith | .520 | 370 |
| | | .451 | 430 | 80 | Orig. Mayn. | .515 | 357 |
| | | .451 | 500 | 81 | Smith | .515 | 365 |
| 64 | 45 LC | .454 | 250 | 82 | Spencer 56/50 | .520 | 375 |
| 65 | 45 | .454 | 252 | 83 | Spencer 56/56 | .535 | 370 |
| 66 | | .454 | 220 | 84 | | .546 | 375 |
| | | .454 | 290 | | | | |

RCBS Mould Blocks

tro-Explo Elephant Blackpowder

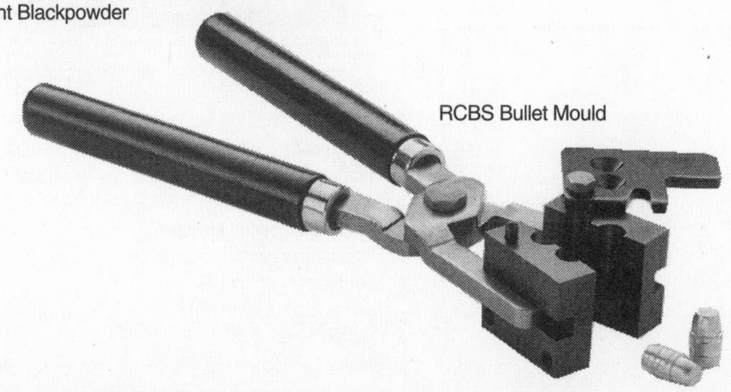

RCBS Bullet Mould

## OX-YOKE

**Oiled Shooting Patches**

Pre-oiled patches .005″, .010″, .015″ and .020″ thick in four sizes: 7/8″ (30-39 cals.); 1 1/8″ (40-49 cals.); 1 5/16″ (50-59 cals.); 1 1/2″ (60-70 cals.). Come in bags of 100. From Ox-Yoke Originals, Inc.

**Price:** . . . . . . . . . . . . . . **$4.07**

**Precision Pillow Ticking Patches**

Pre-cut, unlubed patches .016″ or .018″ thick in four sizes: 7/8″ (30-39 cals.); 1 1/8″ (40-49 cals.); 1 5/16″ (50-59 cals.); 1 1/2″ (60-70 cals.). Come in bags of 100. From Ox-Yoke Originals, Inc.

**Price:** . . . . . . . . . . . . . . **$3.84**

**Wonder Lube**

Micronized muzzle-loading patch and bullet lube made of natural products. Comes in 4-oz. and 12-oz. jars. From Ox-Yoke Originals, Inc.

**Price:** 4-oz. . . . . . . . . . . . . **$7.38**
**Price:** 12-oz. . . . . . . . . . . . **$14.76**

**Wonder Patches**

Made of 100% cotton fabric in four thicknesses (.005, .010, .015, .020) and lubed with Wonder Lube. Four pre-cut sizes available: 7/8″ (30-39 cals.); 1 1/8″ (40-49 cals.); 1 5/16″ (50-59 cals.); 1 1/2″ (60-70 cals.). Come in bags of 100. From Ox-Yoke Originals, Inc.

**Price:** . . . . . . . . . . . . . . **$6.13**

**Wonder Ticking 1000 Plus**

Lubed and pre-cut pillow ticking patches in .016″ or .018″ thick in four sizes: 7/8″ (30-39 cals.); 1 1/8″ (40-49 cals.); 1 5/16″ (50-59 cals.); 1 1/2″ (60-70 cals.). Come in bags of 100. From Ox-Yoke Originals, Inc.

**Price:** . . . . . . . . . . . . . . **$6.51**

**Wonder Wads**

Unlubed 100% woven wool fabric wads for 31, 36, 40, 40-70, 50, 54, 56, 58 calibers and 10, 12, 20 and 28 gauges. Come 100 to a bag. From Ox-Yoke Originals, Inc.

**Price:** 31, 36, 44-45 cals. . . . . . . **$6.25**
**Price:** 50, 54, 58 cals. . . . . . . . **$8.54**
**Price:** 10 ga. . . . . . . . . . . . **$11.75**
**Price:** 12, 20 ga. . . . . . . . . . **$9.85**
**Price:** 28 ga. . . . . . . . . . . . **$8.54**

## PETRO-EXPLO

**Elephant Black Powder**

Manufactured in Brazil since 1866 and now available to U.S. reloaders. Available in granulations Fg, FFg, FFFg, FFFFg and FFFFFg. Sold in 1-lb. cans. From Petro-Explo, Inc.

**Price:** . . . . . **Contact manufacturer.**

## RAPINE

**Bullet Moulds**

Single- and double-cavity moulds machined from high-strength aluminum alloy to precise caliber with highly polished finish. Come with long wooden handles placed close together to reduce fatigue. From Rapine Bullet Mould Mfg. Co.

**Price:** Plain base . . . . . . . . **$59.75**
**Price:** Hollow base . . . . . . . **$62.50**

## RCBS

**Bullet Moulds**

Hand-machined from blocks of precision-cast, malleable iron. Hardened pins ensure permanent alignment. The sprue cutter is solid carbon steel, locked in place with Allen set-screw. Bullet roundness tolerance to .001″. 200 different moulds available. From RCBS.

**Price:** Pistol or round ball . . . . . **$50.00**
**Price:** Rifle or silhouette . . . . . **$51.88**

## RCBS

**Mould Handles**

Solid steel frames with extra long wood handles. One size fits all RCBS moulds. From RCBS.

**Price:** . . . . . . . . . . . . . **$26.38**

**Carbide Rifle/Pistol Dies**

RCBS **Group B** and **Group C** three-die sets include: carbide sizer die with decapping assembly, expander die, and seater die. Tungsten carbide inner ring resizes without the need for case lubing. From RCBS.

**Price:** . . . . . . . . . . . . **See chart.**

**Neck Expander Die**

For use when reloading cast bullets. Die expands case neck and slightly flares case mouth to prevent lead shearing. From RCBS.

**Price:** . . . . . . . . . . . . . **$19.63**
**Price:** Die body . . . . . . . . . **$14.88**
**Price:** Plug . . . . . . . . . . . **$7.13**
**Price:** Plug rod . . . . . . . . . . **$3.25**
**Price:** Lock ring 1/4"-28 . . . . . . **$2.13**

**Case-Forming Dies**

Contact RCBS for extensive listing of available case-form dies. From RCBS.

**Price:** . . . . . . **Contact manufacturer.**

**Universal Decap Die**

Precision-machined die to decap uncleaned, unlubed cases from 22- to 45-caliber. Includes die body, decap assembly with lock nut, die lock ring and plastic storage box. From RCBS.

**Price:** . . . . . . . . . . . . . . **$10.70**

## REDDING

**Case-Forming Dies**

Made on a custom basis only to form brass cases from one caliber to another. From Redding Reloading Equipment.

**Price:** . . . . . . **Contact manufacturer.**

**Custom-Made Dies**

All calibers designated "CM" on Redding die chart require Redding custom dies. Die sets for cartridges not listed can be custom made; send them chamber reamer drawing or dimensions and shoulder angle or cartridge for price quote. From Redding Reloading Equipment.

**Price:** 2-die set . . . . . . . . . **$103.50**
**Price:** 2-die set with tapered expander **$109.50**
**Price:** Full-length sizer or neck sizer **$67.50**
**Price:** Deluxe die set . . . . . . **$159.00**
**Price:** Deluxe set with tapered expander . . . . . . . . . . **$165.00**
**Price:** 3-die set . . . . . . . . . **$114.00**
**Price:** Taper crimp die . . . . . . **$49.50**
**Price:** Form die . . . . . . . . . **$49.50**
**Price:** Trim die . . . . . . . . . **$60.00**

**Form & Trim Dies**

Made to chamber dimensions to eliminate resizing when file trimming. Pistol trim dies require extended shellholder. From Redding Reloading Equipment.

**Price:** Series A . . . . . . . . . **$27.00**
**Price:** Series B . . . . . . . . . **$36.00**
**Price:** Series C . . . . . . . . . **$42.00**
**Price:** Series D . . . . . . . . . **$49.50**

### RCBS *Bullet Moulds*

| Caliber | Size | Mould #/Grs./Bullet Type | Top Punch # |
|---|---|---|---|
| **PISTOL MOULDS** | | | |
| 45 Colt | .454 | 45-250-FN | 190 |
| | .454 | 45-255-SWC | 424 |
| | .452 | 45-300-SWC | 424 |
| **RIFLE MOULDS** | | | |
| 40 | .410 | 40-300-SP | 378 |
| | .410 | 40-350-SP-CSA | 378 |
| | .410 | 40-400-SP-CSA | 378 |
| | .458 | 45-500-BPS | 607 |

SWC = Semi-Wadcutter;SP = Semi-Point; CSA = C Sharps Arms.

### RCBS *Rifle/Pistol Dies*

| Caliber | Die Group | Shellholder/ Shellplate # |
|---|---|---|
| 32-20 Win. | B | 1 |
| 32-40 Win. | D | 2 |
| 38-40 Win. | E | 35* |
| 38-55 Win. & Ballard | F | 2 |
| 44-40 Win. | B | 35* |
| 45 Colt B | 20 | |
| 45-70 Gov't. | C | 14* |
| 50-70 U.S. Government | F | 31** |

Comp.:Competition Dies; RS:Reloader Special Dies. * Auto 4x4 shellplate not available. ** Auto 4x4 and five-station shellplates not available. When two shellholder numbers are shown, the most popular is shown first.

### RCBS *Group B Dies*

| Die/Die Part | Price |
|---|---|
| 3-Die Carbide Set | $39.63 |
| 3-Die Set, Roll/Taper Crimp | 29.63 |
| Carbide Sizer Die | 28.88 |
| Sizer Die | 16.38 |
| Expander Die | 11.75 |
| Seater Die, Roll/Taper Crimp | 15.50 |
| Decapping Unit | 5.59 |
| Decapping Pin Holder | 2.75 |
| Decapping Rod | 1.75 |
| Decapping Pin (5) | 1.75 |
| Expander Assembly | 5.53 |
| Guide Bushing | 1.75 |
| Seater Plug | 4.13 |
| Trim Die | 19.50 |

### RCBS *Group C Dies*

| Die/Die Part | Price |
|---|---|
| 3-Die Carbide Set, Roll or Taper Crimp | $56.00 |
| 3-Die Set, Roll/Taper Crimp | 37.13 |
| Carbide Sizer Die | 42.00 |
| Sizer Die | 19.63 |
| Expander Die | 13.88 |
| Seater Die, Roll/Taper Crimp | 17.88 |
| Decapping Unit | 5.59 |
| Decapping Pin Holder | 2.75 |
| Decapping Rod | 1.75 |
| Decapping Pin (5) | 1.75 |
| Expander Assembly | 5.53 |
| Guide Bushing | 1.75 |
| Seater Plug | 4.13 |

### RCBS *Group D Dies*

| Die/Die Part | Price |
|---|---|
| Full-Length Die Set | $48.50 |
| Full-Length Sizer Die | 34.00 |
| Neck Die Set | 55.75 |
| Neck Sizer Die | 39.88 |
| Seater Die | 26.75 |
| Expander Decapping Unit | 5.20 |
| Expander Ball | 3.33 |
| Expander Decapping Rod | 1.75 |
| Decapping Pin (5) | 1.75 |
| Guide Bushing | 1.66 |
| Seater Plug | 4.13 |
| Trim Die | 35.38 |

### RCBS *Group E Dies*

| Die/Die Part | Price |
|---|---|
| 3-Die Set | $53.10 |
| Sizer Die | 30.90 |
| Expander Die | 18.61 |
| Seater Die | 24.51 |
| Decapping Unit | 5.53 |
| Decap Pin Holder | 2.75 |
| Decapping Rod | 1.66 |
| Decapping Pin (5) | 1.66 |
| Expander Assembly | 5.53 |
| Guide Bushing | 1.66 |
| Seater Plug | 3.94 |

### RCBS *Group F Dies*

| Die/Die Part | Price |
|---|---|
| 3-Die Set | $61.25 |
| Sizer Die | 42.50 |
| Expander Die | 22.38 |
| Seater Die | 27.63 |
| Decapping Unit | 5.59 |
| Decapping Pin Holder | 2.75 |
| Decapping Rod | 1.75 |
| Decapping Pin (5) | 1.75 |
| Expander Assembly | 5.53 |
| Guide Bushing | 1.75 |
| Seater Plug | 4.13 |

**REDDING** ***Rifle/Pistol Dies***

| Caliber | Die Group | Shellholder |
|---|---|---|
| 32-20 Win./30-20 TC | C | 3 |
| 38-40 Win. | C | 9 |
| 40-70 Sharps (Straight) | CM | 18 |
| 38-55 Win. & Ballard | C | 2 |
| 38-56 Win. | D | 18 |
| 41 Long Colt | C | 1 |
| 40-65 Win. | D | 18 |
| 40-82 Win. | D | 18 |
| 40-50 Sharps (Straight) | CM | 8 |
| 40-50 Sharps (Bottleneck) | CM | 18 |
| 40-70 Gov't (SharpsBottleneck 2.1") | CM | 18 |
| 40-70 Sharps (Bottleneck) | CM | 18 |
| 40-90 Sharps (Bottleneck) | CM | 18 |
| 44 Russian | C | 19 |
| 44-40 Win. | A | 9 |
| 11mm Mauser | CM | 16 |
| 45 Colt | A | 23 |
| 45-60 Win. | CM | 18 |
| 45-70 U.S. Gov't | B | 18 |
| 45-90 Win. | D | 18 |
| 45-100 Sharps (Straight) | CM | 18 |
| 45-110 Sharps (Straight) | CM | 18 |
| 45-120 Sharps (Straight) | CM | 18 |

CM:Custom

**REDDING Pistol/Rifle 2-Die Prices**

| DIE SET/DIE PART | SERIES A | SERIES B | SERIES C | SERIES D |
|---|---|---|---|---|
| Full-Length Set | $42.00 | $60.00 | $72.00 | $82.50 |
| Deluxe Set | 69.00 | 94.50 | 112.50 | 129.00 |
| Neck Size Die | 30.00 | 39.00 | 46.50 | 52.50 |
| Full-Length Size Die | 30.00 | 39.00 | 46.50 | 52.50 |
| Decap Rod Assembly | 9.00 | 9.00 | 9.00 | 9.00 |
| Decap Rod | 6.00 | 6.00 | 6.00 | 6.00 |
| Size Button | 5.00 | 5.00 | 5.00 | 5.00 |
| Seating Die | 24.90 | 34.50 | 40.50 | 48.00 |
| Seat Plug | 6.00 | 6.00 | 6.00 | 6.00 |
| Form & Trim Die | 24.90 | 33.00 | 40.50 | 46.50 |

**REDDING Pistol/Rifle 3-Die Prices**

| DIE SET/DIE PART | SERIES A | SERIES B | SERIES C | SERIES D |
|---|---|---|---|---|
| 3-Die Set | $42.00 | $60.00 | $72.00 | $82.50 |
| Sizing Die | 24.00 | 31.50 | 36.00 | 43.50 |
| Decap Rod Assembly | 9.00 | 9.00 | 9.00 | 9.00 |
| Decap Rod | 6.00 | 6.00 | 6.00 | 6.00 |
| Seating Die | 21.90 | 30.00 | 34.50 | 40.50 |
| Seat Plug | 6.00 | 6.00 | 6.00 | 6.00 |
| Expander Die | 16.50 | 22.50 | 25.50 | 30.00 |
| Expander | 7.50 | 7.50 | 7.50 | 7.50 |
| Trim Die | 24.90 | 33.00 | 40.50 | 46.50 |

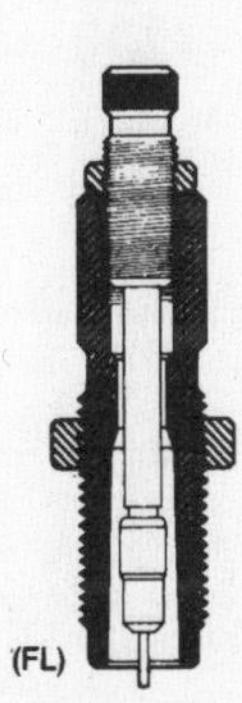


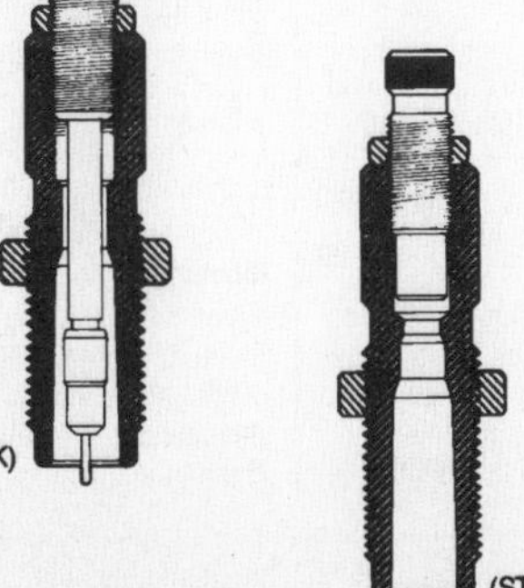


Redding 3-Die Set for Bottleneck Cases

## REDDING

**Pistol/Rifle Steel Dies**

Two- and three-die sets carefully machined to close and uniform tolerances and finish machined on precision lathes. All die parts made of high-grade steel alloy. Knurled outside surface allows hand adjustments. Standard (2-die) and Deluxe (3-die) sets are for bottleneck cases, the Deluxe set containing a separate neck size die. Three-die sets are for straight wall cases and include an expander die. Series A dies are pistol and rifle die sets for most popular calibers; Series B, die sets for slightly less popular calibers; Series C, popular wildcats and less popular rifle/pistol calibers; Series D, obsolete calibers and wildcats. Custom dies upon request. From Redding Reloading Equipment.

**Price:** . . . . . . . . . . . . **See chart.**

## REMINGTON

**Premier Copper Solid Bullets with Sabots**

Copper Solid 45-caliber bullets encased in 50-caliber sabots. From Remington.

**Price:** . . . . . **Contact manufacturer.**

**Premier Golden Lead Round Balls**

Cold-swaged alloy lead round balls plated in brass for cleaner handling and reduced fouling. From Remington.

**Price:** . . . . . **Contact manufacturer.**

**Core-Lokt Saboted Bullets**

Rifle and pistol Core-Lokt bullets encased in four-segment one-piece sabot. From Remington.

**Price:** . . . . . **Contact manufacturer.**

**Gamemaster Bullets**

Pre-lubed alloy lead bullets from 285 grains to 535 grains in calibers 45 to 58. From Remington.

**Price:** . . . . . **Contact manufacturer.**

## SAECO

**Bullet Moulds**

Two- and 4-cavity moulds machined from blocks of copper alloyed pearlitic cast iron for dimensional stability. Cavities cut using same cherrie on digital equipment for uniformity. Steel sprue plate held against mould blocks by high-temperature Inconel spring washers. Mould handles are ductile iron castings with oak grips. From Redding Reloading Equipment.

**Price:** 2-cavity . . . . . . . . . **$75.00**
**Price:** 4-cavity . . . . . . . . . **$135.00**
**Price:** Mould handles . . . . . . **$37.50**

**Magnum Mould Blocks**

Single- and double-cavity moulds made from SAECO double- and triple-cavity blocks with wider spacing for blackpowder silhouette bullets. Available in two calibers: 40 cal., 370- and 410-gr.; 45-cal. 480- and 525-gr. Special-order moulds in any combination of caliber and/or weight. From Redding Reloading Equipment.

**Price:** Single-cavity . . . . . . . **$75.00**
**Price:** Double-cavity . . . . . . . **$96.00**

**Special-Order Moulds**

Three-, 6- and 8-cavity and "magnum" moulds made on special order basis. From Redding Reloading Equipment.

**Price:** 1-cavity magnum . . . . . **$75.00**
**Price:** 2-cavity magnum . . . . . **$96.00**
**Price:** 3-cavity . . . . . . . . **$106.50**
**Price:** 6-cavity . . . . . . . . **$219.00**
**Price:** 8-cavity . . . . . . . . **$312.00**

## SAECO

**Bullet Moulds for Obsolete Cal.**

Special-order moulds available in single-cavity magnum only. Six different bullet styles.

**Style A:** Cylindrical bullet similar to original factory bullets for most blackpowder cartridges. Diameter at front band is same diameter at base band. Rounded grease grooves.

**Style B:** Cylindrical bullet with front wiper band deleted. Rounded grease grooves.

**Style C:** Two diameter bullet with front three bands slightly larger than bore diameter and rear three at groove diameter. Rounded grease grooves.

**Style D:** Two diameter bullet same as Style C, but without front wiper band. Rounded grease grooves.

**Style E:** Tapered bullet with front band near bore diameter tapering to slightly larger than groove diameter. Rounded grease grooves.

**Style F:** Hudson bullet. Two diameter with front bands near bore diameter with two rear bands slightly larger than groove diameter. From Redding Reloading Equipment.

**Price:** . . . . . . **Contact manufacturer.**

## C. SHARPS ARMS

**Sharps Brass**

Unprimed, extruded brass cases for Sharps chamberings or basic brass suitable for the 45-120 3¼-inch or, trimmed and formed, for other Sharps calibers. Unprimed cases come in boxes of 20 for 32-40 Winchester, 38-55 Winchester, 45 Colt, 50-70, 50-90 and others. Sharps basic case, which can be formed to 40-70 Bottleneck, 40-90 BN, 45-90, 45-100 or 45-110. Come 20 to a box. From C. Sharps Arms Co.

**Price:** Basic case . . . . . . . . . **$49.95**

**Price:** Unprimed cases . . . . . **Contact manufacturer.**

## SHILOH CREEK

**Drop Tube**

Adjustable for any length cartridge. Features 24⅜" tube mounted on solid red oak stand with funnel. Mounts easily to any loading bench or table. From Shiloh Creek.

**Price:** . . . . . . . . . . . . . **$45.00**

## SHILOH SHARPS

**Drop Tube**

Used to trickle blackpowder into cartridge case to promote cleaner burning. Consists of 24-inch brass tube ⅜-inch in diameter and set into oak mounting board. Mounts or clamps to any bench or table. From Shiloh Rifle Manufacturing Co., Inc.

**Price:** . . . . . . . . . . . . . **$45.00**

**Wad Punch**

Wad punch for 40, 45 and 50 calibers. From Shiloh Rifle Manufacturing Co., Inc.

**Price:** . . . . . . . . . . . . . **$16.50**

**SPG Bullet Lube**

Developed specifically for blackpowder cartridge shooting, but can be used for smokeless loads. Helps keep fouling soft. Available in hollow stick only. From Shiloh Rifle Manufacturing Co., Inc.

**Price:** 4 tubes . . . . . . . . . **$17.00**

**Price:** 7 tubes . . . . . . . . . **$30.00**

**Nitrated Paper**

Nitrated paper for percussion rifles. Comes in sheets, 100 sheets per package. From Shiloh Rifle Manufacturing Co., Inc.

**Price:** Each . . . . . . . . . . . **$9.00**

SAECO

*Bullet Moulds for Obsolete Calibers*

| Dia. | Wgt. | Style | Mould # |
|---|---|---|---|
| .288 | 137 | E | 539 |
| .310 | 185 | A | 529 |
| .310 | 180 | A | 540 |
| .311 | 160 | B | 534 |
| .322 | 200 | E | 553 |
| .324 | 200 | E | 538 |
| .333 | 210 | E | 541 |
| .336 | 200 | E | 532 |
| .336 | 215 | D | 558 |
| .337 | 220 | F | 559 |
| .338 | 205 | B | 560 |
| .339 | 215 | D | 535 |
| .359 | 250 | B | 561 |
| .359 | 250 | D | 562 |
| .359 | 225 | B | 563 |
| .362 | 275 | E | 565 |
| .375 | 260 | A | 567 |
| .376 | 250 | A | 524 |
| .377 | 300 | B | 570 |
| .380 | 300 | E | 571 |
| .386 | 300 | E | 574 |
| .403 | 250 | A | 576 |
| .403 | 350 | A | 547 |
| .408/.410 | 370 | — | 640 |
| .408/.410 | 410 | — | 740 |
| .414 | 400 | D | 580 |
| .437 | 425 | A | 581 |
| .458/.460 | 460 | — | 645 |
| .458/.460 | 525 | — | 745 |
| .511 | 600 | A | 542 |
| .512 | 650 | A | 583 |
| .518 | 500 | A | 584 |
| .524 | 500 | A | 585 |

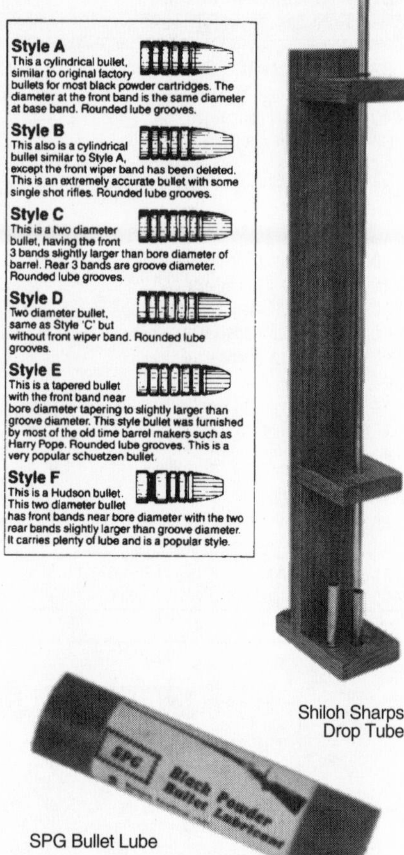


Shiloh Sharps Drop Tube

SPG Bullet Lube

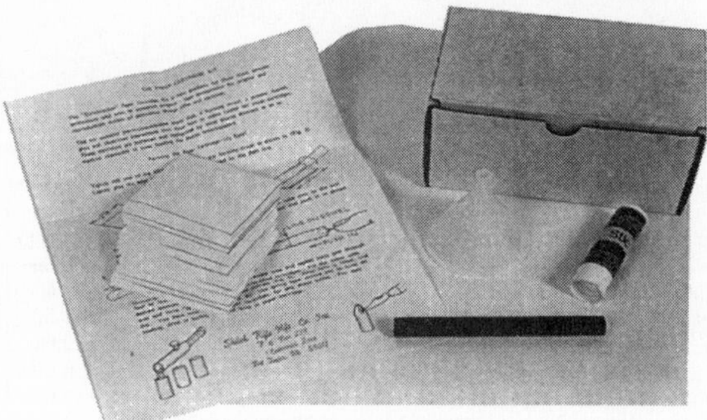

Shiloh Sharps Paper Cartridge Kit

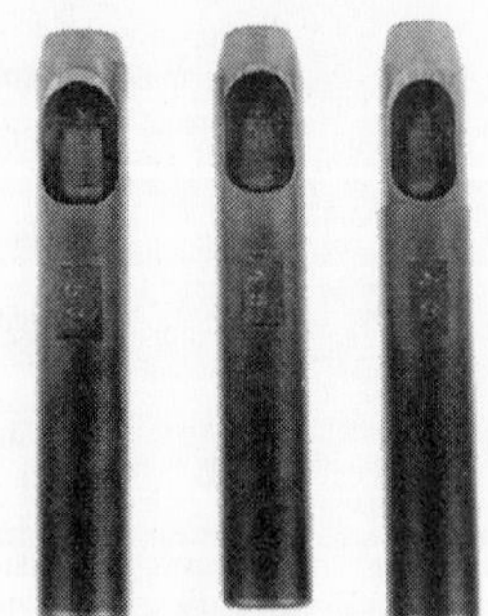

Shiloh Sharps Wad Punch

## SHILOH SHARPS

**Paper Cartridge Kit**

Includes nitrated paper, funnel, glue stick and complete directions. From Shiloh Rifle Manufacturing Co., Inc.

**Price:** Each . . . . . . . . . . **$16.00**

**Tru-Bore Bullet Moulds**

Precision-machined cast iron blocks lathe bored to most any nose design, groove layout or dimension. Available from Shiloh Rifle Manufactuiring Co., Inc.

**Price:** . . . . . . . . . . . . . **$100.00**

## THOMPSON

**Blackpowder Lube**

Semi-tacky lube for blackpowder cartridge bullets. Requires some heat to flow. Comes in 1x4, 1x8 or 2x6 sticks. From Thompson Bullet Lube Co.

**Price:** . . . . . . . . . . . . . **$3.50**

## THOMPSON/CENTER

**Bore Buttons**

Wool wads ⅛" thick, pre-lubed with T/C Natural Lube 1000+ in 50- and 54-caliber and 12-ga. Come 50 to a bag. From Thompson/Center Arms.

**Price:** 50, 54 cals. . . . . . . . . **$7.80**

**Price:** 12 ga. . . . . . . . . . . . **$6.90**

**THOMPSON/CENTER**
***Maxi-Balls/Maxi-Hunters***

| Caliber | Wgt. Grs. | Price/20 |
|---|---|---|
| | **Maxi-Balls** | |
| 45 | 240 | $10.30 |
| 50 | 320 | 10.60 |
| | 370 | 11.25 |
| | 460 | 12.05 |
| 54 | 365 | 11.10 |
| | 430 | 11.45 |
| | 530 | 12.35 |
| 58 | 555 | 13.60 |
| | **Maxi-Hunter** | |
| 45 | 255 | 10.30 |
| 50 | 275 | 10.60 |
| | 350 | 11.25 |
| | 470 | 12.05 |
| 54 | 360 | 11.10 |
| | 435 | 11.45 |
| | 540 | 12.35 |
| 58 | 560 | 13.60 |

## THOMPSON/CENTER

**Break-O-Way Sabots**

Two-piece 50- and 54-caliber sabot held together by pre-lubed woven wool disk encasing 45-caliber 240-, 275- or 300-grain XTP bullet. Sold in packs of 10 or 20. From Thompson/Center Arms.

**Price:** 240-gr. (10) . . . . . . . . . **$6.05**
**Price:** 240-gr. (20) . . . . . . . . . **$9.70**
**Price:** 275-gr. (10) . . . . . . . . . **$6.05**
**Price:** 275-gr. (20) . . . . . . . . . **$10.90**
**Price:** 300-gr. (20) . . . . . . . . . **$11.90**

**Cotton Patches**

Non-toxic, biodegradable .015″ 100% cotton patches available pre-lubed or unlubed for 32, 36, 45, 50, 54, 56, 58 calibers. Come 100 patches to a bag. From Thompson/Center Arms.

**Price:** Pre-lubed . . . . . . . . . . **$5.60**
**Price:** Un-lubed . . . . . . . . . . **$3.80**

**Mould Blocks**

Single-cavity aluminum mould blocks for casting round ball, Maxi-Ball or Maxi-Hunter bullets. Handles constructed of solid brass with hardwood handles. From Thompson/Center Arms.

**Price:** .490, .530 round ball . . . . **$27.00**
**Price:** 45, 50, 54 Maxi-Ball . . . . **$29.70**
**Price:** 50, 54 Maxi-Hunter . . . . **$38.00**

**Natural Lube 1000+ Bore Butter**

Biodegradable, all-natural patch and bullet lube with no petroleum or oil-based additives. Comes in 5-oz. squeeze tubes in natural or pine scent. From Thompson/Center Arms.

**Price:** Natural . . . . . . . . . . . . **$6.94**
**Price:** Pine . . . . . . . . . . . . . **$7.78**

**Pillow Ticking Patches**

Tight weave 100% cotton ticking patches .015″ thick in 45-, 50-, 54- and 58 caliber. Come 100 to a bag. From Thompson/Center Arms.

**Price:** . . . . . . . . . . . . . . . . **$4.10**

## TRADITIONS

**Saboted Pistol Bullets**

Jacketed, hollowpoint, flatbase pistol bullets in 44- and 45-calibers loaded in 50- and 54-caliber self-lubricating sabots. Come 8 per pack. From Traditions, Inc.

**Price:** . . . . . . . . . . . . . . . . **$5.50**

Thompson/Center Break-O-Way Sabots

Thompson/Center Maxi-Balls

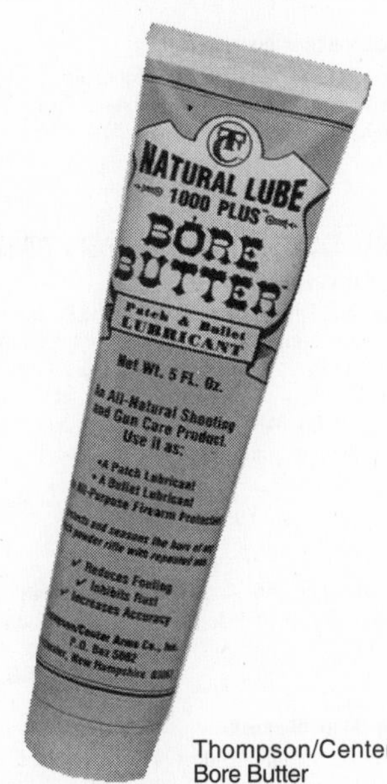


Thompson/Center Bore Butter

## TRADITIONS

**Conical Lead Bullets**

Pure lead, hollowpoint, hollow base conicals in 50 (385 grs.) and 54 (425 grs.) calibers. Come 12 per pack (50-cal.) or 10 per pack (54-cal.) From Traditions, Inc.

**Price:** . . . . . . . . . . . . . . . . **$5.50**

**Cotton Patches**

Dry cotton patches in 32- and 36-caliber. Come 100 per pack. From Traditions, Inc.

**Price:** . . . . . . . . . . . . . . . . **$3.50**

**Pillow Ticking Patches**

Dry 100% cotton patches .015″ thick for 50- and 54-caliber. Come 100 per pack. From Traditions, Inc.

**Price:** . . . . . . . . . . . . . . . . **$4.00**

**Swaged Round Balls**

Pure lead 32-, 50- and 54-caliber round balls. Come 20 or 100 per pack. From Traditions, Inc.

**Price:** 20 . . . . . . . . . . . . . **$2.50**
**Price:** 100 . . . . . . . . . . . . **$10.50**

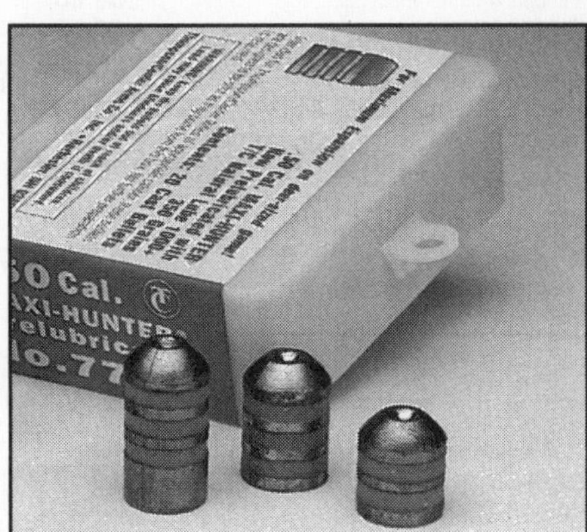


Thompson/Center Maxi-Hunter

Traditions Pillow Ticking Patches

Traditions Saboted Pistol Bullets

## TRADITIONS

**Wonderlube 1000 Plus**

All-natural patch lubricant. Available in 4 oz. jar or 5 oz. squeeze tube. From Traditions, Inc.

**Price:** Jar . . . . . . . . . . . . **$5.50**
**Price:** Tube . . . . . . . . . . . **$8.00**

**Wonderlake 1000 Plus Patches**

100% cotton patches pre-lubed with Wonderlake 1000 Plus for 50 and 54 calibers. Come 100 per pack. From Traditions, Inc.

**Price:** . . . . . . . . . . . . . . **$5.00**

**Wonder Wads**

100% wool wads impregnated with Wonderlake 1000 Plus for 44-, 45-, 50- and 54-caliber or 12-ga. From Traditions, Inc.

**Price:** 44-, 45-cal. . . . . . . . . **$5.50**
**Price:** 50-, 54-cal. . . . . . . . . **$6.50**
**Price:** 12-ga. . . . . . . . . . . . **$7.25**

## JOHN WALTERS

**Pre-Cut Wads**

Made of biodegradable vegetable fibers in .408″ and .458″ diameters 1/16″. Cut to tolerances of no more than .001″ on 40-caliber and .002″ on 45-caliber. Come in bags of 100. From John Walters.

**Price:** 1000 . . . . . . . . . . . **$20.00**

## WARREN MUZZLELOADING

**Conical Pistol Bullets**

Pistol bullets in 31-caliber (105-gr.), 36-caliber (123-gr.) and 44-caliber (200 gr.). Come in packages of 50. From Warren Muzzleloading Co., Inc.

**Price:** 31 and 36 cal. . . . . . . . **$6.40**
**Price:** 44 cal. . . . . . . . . . . . **$6.75**

**Hunting Bullets**

Pre-coated 36- (128-gr.), 45- (240-gr.), 50- (325-gr.), 54- (440-gr.) and 58-caliber (610-gr.) hunting bullets. Come in packages of 10, 20 or 30. From Warren Muzzleloading Co., Inc.

**Price:** 36 cal. (30) . . . . . . . . **$6.20**
**Price:** 45 cal. (20) . . . . . . . . **$5.50**
**Price:** 45 cal. (10) . . . . . . . . **$2.94**
**Price:** 50 cal. (20) . . . . . . . . **$6.25**
**Price:** 50 cal. (10) . . . . . . . . **$3.35**
**Price:** 54 cal. (20) . . . . . . . . **$6.95**
**Price:** 54 cal. (10) . . . . . . . . **$3.95**
**Price:** 58 cal. (20) . . . . . . . . **$7.70**

**Sabot Magnum Bullets**

Soft lead 45-, 50- and 54-caliber hunting bullets encased in magnum sabots. Bullet grain weights: 45 (135-gr.); 50 (180-, 240-gr.); and 54 (180-, 240-gr.). Come in packages of 10 or 20. From Warren Muzzleloading Co., Inc.

**Price:** 45 cal. (20) . . . . . . . . **$6.95**
**Price:** 45 cal. (10) . . . . . . . . **$3.95**
**Price:** 50 cal., 180-gr. (20) . . . . **$7.50**
**Price:** 50 cal., 180-gr. (10) . . . . **$4.25**
**Price:** 50 cal., 240-gr. (20) . . . . **$7.50**
**Price:** 50 cal., 240-gr. (10) . . . . **$4.50**
**Price:** 54 cal., 180-gr. (20) . . . . **$7.25**
**Price:** 54 cal., 180-gr. (10) . . . . **$4.25**
**Price:** 54 cal., 240-gr. (20) . . . . **$7.50**
**Price:** 54 cal., 240-gr. (10) . . . . **$4.50**

## WARREN MUZZLELOADING

**Swaged Predator Bullets**

Saged lead hunting bullets in either hollow base or solid base configurations. Available calibers: 45 (200- 300-gr.); 50 (300-, 400-gr.); 54 (400-, 500-gr.); 58 (500-, 600-gr.). Come in packages of 10, 19 or 20. From Warren Muzzleloading Co., Inc.

**Price:** 45 cal., 200 HB (20) . . . . . **$6.00**
**Price:** 45 cal., 200 HB (10) . . . . . **$3.95**
**Price:** 45 cal., 300 SB (20) . . . . . **$6.75**
**Price:** 45 cal., 300 HB (10) . . . . . **$4.95**
**Price:** 50 cal., 300 HB (20) . . . . . **$6.85**
**Price:** 50 cal., 300 HS (10) . . . . . **$4.95**
**Price:** 50 cal., 400 SB (20) . . . . . **$7.55**
**Price:** 50 cal., 400 SB (10) . . . . . **$5.95**
**Price:** 54 cal., 400 HB (20) . . . . . **$7.70**
**Price:** 54 cal., 400 HB (10) . . . . . **$6.30**
**Price:** 54 cal., 500 SB (19) . . . . . **$8.25**
**Price:** 54 cal., 500 SB (10) . . . . . **$6.30**
**Price:** 58 cal., 500 HB (19) . . . . . **$8.35**
**Price:** 58 cal., 500 HB (10) . . . . . **$6.30**
**Price:** 58 cal., 600 SB (19) . . . . . **$9.60**
**Price:** 58 cal., 600 SB (10) . . . . . **$6.95**

**Sabot Jacketed Bullets**

Jacketed bullets in 45 (158-gr.), 50 (180-, 240-gr.), 54 (240-gr.) and 58 (240-gr.) calibers. From Warren Muzzleloading Co., Inc.

**Price:** . . . . . . . . . . . . . . **$7.95**

## WHITE SHOOTING SYSTEMS

**Muzzle-Loading Bullets**

Super Slug and Buckbuster lead bullets manufactured to .0001″ tolerances. Feature flatnose, straight sidewalls and boattail base. Available calibers: 41 (280-, 320-, 400-gr.); 45 (360-, 400-, 460-, 490-, 520-gr.); 50 (430-, 460-, 480-, 600-gr.); 54 (545). Come 20 per box. From White Shooting Systems.

**Price:** . . . . . . . . . . . . . . **$7.95**

**Sabots**

Patented design 45- and 50-caliber sabots. Come in packages of 50. From White Shooting Systems.

**Price:** . . . . . . . . . . . . . . **$6.95**

**Shooting Star Sabot**

Saboted 45/40 (350-gr.) and 50/45 (435-gr.) bullets. Come in packages of 20. From White Shooting Systems.

**Price:** . . . . . . . . . . . . . . **$9.95**

**SuperLube 2000**

Muzzle-loading rifle and bullet lube. Comes in 4-oz. tin. From White Shooting Systems.

**Price:** . . . . . . . . . . . . . . **$6.00**

## WOLF'S WESTERN TRADERS

**Rifle Dies**

Three- and 5-die sets in 45-70-caliber for the U.S. Models 1873 and 1884 Trapdoor Springfield. All dies made by Lee Precision. Three-die set includes .458-inch expander and compression plug; 5-die set includes taper crimp die and compression die. From Wolf's Western Traders.

**Price:** 3-die set . . . . . . . . . **$30.00**
**Price:** 5-die set . . . . . . . . . **$50.00**
**Price:** Expander die with .458" plug and compression plug . . . . . . . . . **$15.00**
**Price:** Compression die only . . . . **$12.00**
**Price:** Taper crimp die only . . . . **$12.00**
**Price:** Compression die plug . . . . **$4.00**
**Price:** Expander plug .458″ . . . . . **$4.50**

## YESTERYEAR ARMORY

**Pre-Cut Paper Patches**

Made of 100% rag paper in 40- and 45-caliber. Come in packs of 20 sheets with 15 patches per sheet lubed or unlubed. From Yesteryear Armory.

**Price:** . . . . . . . . . . . . . . **$6.00**

White Shooting System Bullets

Traditions Wonderlube 1000 Plus

# SHOTSHELL RELOADING
## TOOLS & ACCESSORIES

# Section 2: Shotshell Reloading

**DILLON SL 900**

**Press Type:** Progressive
**Avg. Rounds Per Hour:** NA
**Weight:** NA
**Features:** 12-ga. only; factory adjusted to load AA hulls; extra large 25-pound capacity shot hopper; fully-adjustable case-activated shot system; hardened steel starter crimp die; dual-action final crimp and taper die; tilt-out wad guide; auto prime; auto index; strong mount machine stand. From Dillon Precision Products.
**Price:** . . . . . . . . . . . . . . . **Contact manufacturer.**

**HOLLYWOOD Automatic Shotshell Press**

**Press Type:** Progressive
**Avg. Rounds Per Hour:** 1,800
**Weight:** 100 lbs.
**Features:** Ductile iron frame; fully automated press with shell pick-up and ejector; comes completely set up for one gauge; one starter crimp; one finish crimp; wad guide for plastic wads; decap and powder dispenser unit; one wrench for inside die lock screw; one medium and one large spanner wrench for spanner nuts; one shellholder; powder and shot measures. Available for 10, 12, 20, 28 or 410. From Hollywood Engineering.
**Price:** . . . . . . . . . . . . . . . . . . . . **$3,600.00**

**HOLLYWOOD Progressive Press**

**Press Type:** Progressive
**Avg. Rounds Per Hour:** 400
**Weight:** 100 lbs.
**Features:** Made of ductile iron; comes completely equipped to reload one gauge; one starter crimp; one finish crimp; wad guide for plastic wads; decap and powder dispenser unit; one wrench for inside die lock screw; one medium and one large spanner wrench for spanner nuts; one shellholder; powder and shot measures. Available for 10, 12, 16, 20, 28 or 410. From Hollywood Engineering.
**Price:** . . . . . . . . . . . . . . . . . . . . **$2,800.00**

**HOLLYWOOD Senior Turret Press**

**Press Type:** Turret
**Avg. Rounds Per Hour:** 200
**Weight:** 50 lbs.
**Features:** Multi-stage press constructed of ductile iron comes completely equipped to reload one gauge; one starter crimp; one finish crimp; wad guide for plastic wads; decap and powder dispenser unit; one wrench for inside die lock screw; one medium and one large spanner wrench for spanner nuts; one shellholder; powder and shot measures. Available for 10, 12, 16, 20, 28 or 410. From Hollywood Engineering.
**Price:** . . . . . . . . . . . . . . . . . . . . **$785.00**

**HOLLYWOOD Shotshell Die Sets**

Complete $1^1/_2$ die set for one gauge to include: starter crimp; finish crimp; wad guide for plastic wads; decap and powder dispenser unit; wrench for inside die lock screw; medium and large spanner wrench for spanner nuts; shellholder. Available for 10, 12, 16, 20, 28 and 410. From Hollywood Engineering.
**Price:** . . . . . . . . . . . . . . . . . . . . **$195.00**

**HORNADY 366 Auto**

**Press Type:** Progressive
**Avg. Rounds Per Hour:** NA
**Weight:** 25 lbs.
**Features:** Heavy-duty die cast and machined steel body and components; auto primer feed system; large capacity shot and powder tubes; adjustable for right- or left-hand use; automatic charge bar with shutoff; swing-out wad guide; primer catcher at base of press; interchangeable shot and powder bushings; lifetime warranty. Available for 12, 20, 28 $2^3/_4''$ and 410 $2^1/_2''$. From Hornady Mfg. Co.
**Price:** . . . . . . . . . . . . . . . . . . . . **$463.20**
**Price:** Die set, 12, 20, 28 . . . . . . . . . . . . . **$93.65**
**Price:** Magnum conversion dies, 12, 20 . . . . . . . **$20.55**

**HOLLYWOOD**
**Shotshell Die Parts**

| DIE/DIE PART | PRICE |
|---|---|
| Finish Crimp | $45.00 |
| Crimp Start, w/lock ring, steel star | 50.00 |
| Steel Star, 6 & 8 point | 15.00 |
| Locking Screw, start crimp die | 2.00 |
| Decap/Powder Dispenser Unit | 75.00 |
| Decap Powder Pin | 20.00 |
| Locking Screw, decap powder pin | 2.00 |
| Lock Collar, wad guide spring finger | 6.00 |
| Lock Ring | 5.00 |
| Set Screw, lock ring | .40 |
| Wad Guide Spring Finger | 2.50 |
| Wad Pressure Spring | 3.00 |
| Wad Ram | 20.00 |
| Wad Receiver, complete | 70.00 |
| Wad Receiver, stripped | 45.00 |
| Primer Rod Buffer Spring | 2.00 |
| Primer Rod Lock Ring, small | 2.00 |
| Primer Rod Lock Ring, large | 2.50 |

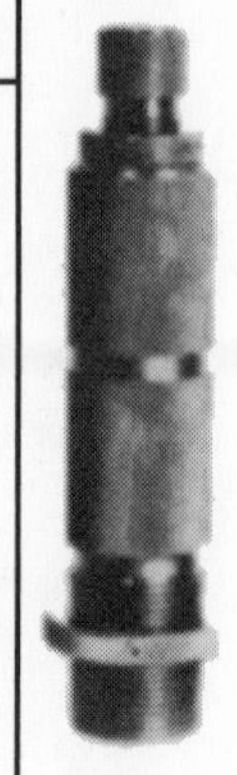

Hollywood Automatic Shotshell Press

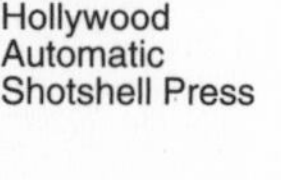

Hollywood Progressive Press

Hollywood Senior Press

Hornady 366 Auto

SHOTSHELL/Presses

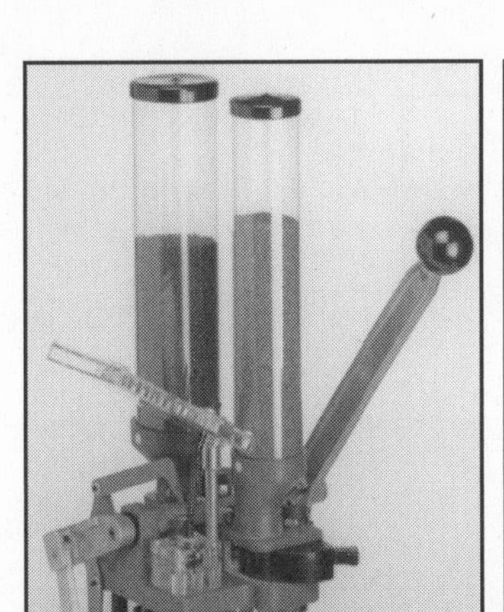
Hornady Apex 3.1 Gas Assist Auto

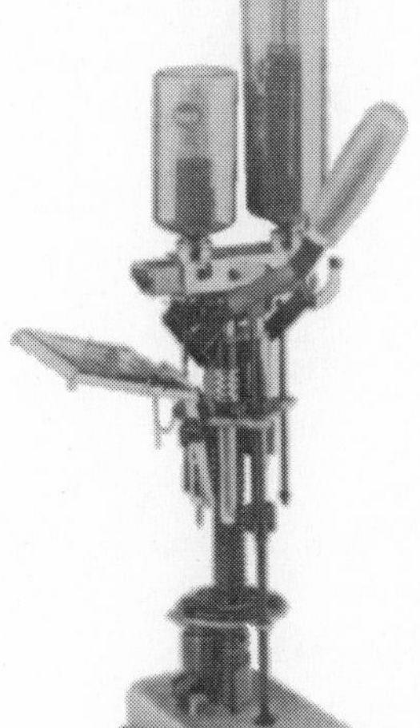
MEC Grabber

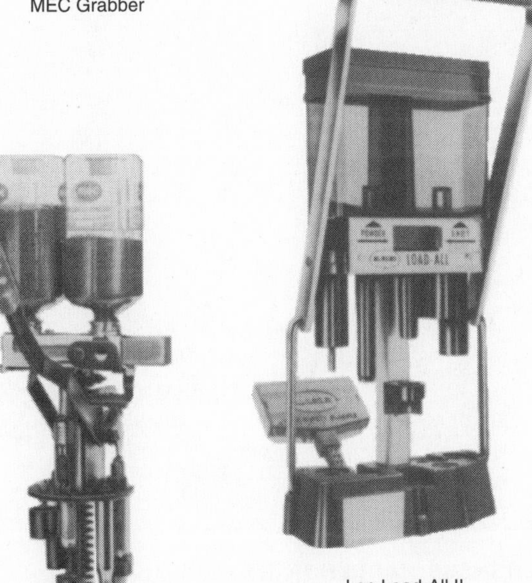
Lee Load-All II

MEC 600 Jr.

**HORNADY Apex 3.1 Auto**

**Press Type:** Auto
**Avg. Rounds Per Hour:** NA
**Weight:** 15 lbs.
**Features:** Features shell retainer system; full-length collet size die to automatically size the full length of brass; shell-actuated auto primer feed; shell-actuated automatic powder/shot drop with shell detect; cam-activated dual-action crimp/taper die; auto index converts single stage shellplate to progressive. Available for 12, 20, 28 gauges or 410 bore. From Hornady Mfg. Co.
**Price:**12, 20 . . . . . . . . . . . . . . . . . . **$299.95**
**Price:**28, 410 . . . . . . . . . . . . . . . . . . **$329.95**

**HORNADY Apex 3.1 Assist Auto**

**Press Type:** Auto
**Avg. Rounds Per Hour:** NA
**Weight:** 15 lbs.
**Features:** Includes all the features of the Apex 3.1 plus a gas-assist indexing assembly which rotates the shellplate smoothly regardless of handle speed. Comes installed on press or as an add-on. From Hornady Mfg. Co.
**Price:** 12, 20 . . . . . . . . . . . . . . . . . . **$349.95**
**Price:** 28, 410 . . . . . . . . . . . . . . . . . . **$369.95**

**LEE Load-All II**

**Press Type:** Single stage
**Avg. Rounds Per Hour:** 100
**Weight:** 3 lbs., 3 oz.
**Features:** Loads steel or lead shot; built-in primer catcher at base with door in front for emptying; recesses at each station for shell positioning; optional primer feed. Comes with safety charge bar with 24 shot and powder bushings. Available for 12-, 16- or 20-gauge. From Lee Precision, Inc.
**Price:** . . . . . . . . . . . . . . . . . . . . **$49.98**

**MEC 600 Jr. Mark V**

**Press Type:** Single stage
**Avg. Rounds Per Hour:** 200
**Weight:** 10 lbs.
**Features:** Spindex crimp starter for shell alignment during crimping; a cam-action crimp die; Pro-Check to keep charge bar properly positioned; adjustable for three shells. Available in 10, 12, 16, 20, 28 gauges and 410 bore. Die set not included. From Mayville Engineering Company, Inc.
**Price:** . . . . . . . . . . . . . . . . . . . . **$162.62**
**Price:** Die set . . . . . . . . . . . . . . . . . . **$59.38**

**MEC 650**

**Press Type:** Progressive
**Avg. Rounds Per Hour:** 400
**Weight:** NA
**Features:** Six-station press; does not resize except as separate operation; auto primer feed standard; three crimping stations for starting, closing and tapering crimp. Die sets not available. Available in 12, 16, 20, 28 and 410. From Mayville Engineering Company, Inc.
**Price:** . . . . . . . . . . . . . . . . . . . . **$319.80**

**MEC 8567 Grabber**

**Press Type:** Progressive
**Avg. Rounds Per Hour:** 400
**Weight:** 15 lbs.
**Features:** Ten-station press; auto primer feed; auto-cycle charging; three-stage crimp; power ring resizer returns base to factory specs; resizes high and low base shells; optional kits to reload three shells and steel shot. Available in 12, 16, 20, 28 gauge and 410 bore. From Mayville Engineering Company, Inc.
**Price:** . . . . . . . . . . . . . . . . . . . . **$458.78**
**Price:** 3 kit, 12-ga. . . . . . . . . . . . . . . . . **$39.19**
**Price:** 3 kit, 20-ga. . . . . . . . . . . . . . . . . **$24.00**
**Price:** Steel shot kit . . . . . . . . . . . . . . . **$23.22**

### MEC 9000G

**Press Type:** Progressive
**Avg. Rounds Per Hour:** 400
**Weight:** 18 lbs.
**Features:** All same features as the MEC Grabber, but with auto-indexing and auto-eject. Finished shells automatically ejected from shell carrier to drop chute for boxing. Available in 12, 16, 20, 28 and 410. From Mayville Engineering Company, Inc.
**Price:** . . . . . . . . . . . . . . . . . . . . . . **$557.02**
**Price:** 3 kit, 12-ga. . . . . . . . . . . . . . . . . **$39.19**
**Price:** 3 kit, 20-ga. . . . . . . . . . . . . . . . . **$24.00**
**Price:** Steel shot kit . . . . . . . . . . . . . . . **$23.22**

### MEC 9000H

**Press Type:** Progressive
**Avg. Rounds Per Hour:** 400
**Weight:** 23 lbs.
**Features:** Same features as 9000G with addition of foot pedal-operated hydraulic system for complete automation. Operates on standard 110v household current. Comes with bushing-type charge bar and three bushings. Available in 12, 16, 20, 28 gauge and 410 bore. From Mayville Engineering Company, Inc.
**Price:** . . . . . . . . . . . . . . . . . . . . . **$1,345.72**
**Price:** Steel shot kit . . . . . . . . . . . . . . . **$22.54**

### MEC Sizemaster

**Press Type:** Single stage
**Avg. Rounds Per Hour:** 150
**Weight:** 13 lbs.
**Features:** Power ring eight-fingered collet resizer returns base to factory specs; handles brass or steel, high or low base, heads; auto primer feed; adjustable for three shells. Available in 10, 12, 16, 20, 28 gauges and 410 bore. From Mayville Engineering Company, Inc.
**Price:** . . . . . . . . . . . . . . . . . . . . . . **$245.04**
**Price:** Die set, 12, 16, 20, 28, 410 . . . . . . . . . **$88.67**
**Price:** Die set, 10-ga. . . . . . . . . . . . . . . . **$104.06**
**Price:** Steel shot kit . . . . . . . . . . . . . . . **$14.34**
**Price:** Steel shot kit, 12-ga. 3½″ . . . . . . . . . . **$70.27**

### MEC Steelmaster

**Press Type:** Single stage
**Avg. Rounds Per Hour:** 150
**Weight:** 13 lbs.
**Features:** Same features as Sizemaster except can load steel shot. Press is available for 3½″ 10-ga. and 12-ga. 2¾″, 3 or 3½. For loading lead shot, die sets available in 10, 12, 16, 20, 28 and 410. From Mayville Engineering Company, Inc.
**Price:** . . . . . . . . . . . . . . . . . . . . . . **$255.00**
**Price:** 3½″ . . . . . . . . . . . . . . . . . . . . **$280.66**

### PONSNESS/WARREN Du-O-Matic 375C

**Press Type:** Progressive
**Avg. Rounds Per Hour:** NA
**Weight:** 31 lbs.
**Features:** Steel or lead shot reloader; large shot and powder reservoirs; bushing access plug for dropping in shot buffer or buckshot; positive lock charging ring to prevent accidental flow of powder; double-post construction for greater leverage; removable spent primer box; spring-loaded ball check for centering size die at each station; tip-out wad guide; two-gauge capacity tool head. Available in 10 (extra charge), 12, 16, 20, 28 and 410 with case lengths of 2½, 2¾, 3 and 3½ inches. From Ponsness/ Warren.
**Price:** . . . . . . . . . . . . . . . . . . . . . . **$225.00**
**Price:** 12-ga. 3½″; 3″ 12, 20, 410 . . . . . . . . . **$240.00**
**Price:** 12, 20 2¾² . . . . . . . . . . . . . . . . . **$307.95**
**Price:** 10-ga. press . . . . . . . . . . . . . . . . **$249.00**

### PONSNESS/WARREN Hydro-Matic

Add-on hydraulic system for Ponsness/Warren 800 or 900 Series presses. Features ½-hp electric motor; ⅓-gallon reservoir tank; variable-speed foot control; dual cylinder system for equal load pressure on press; cycling of 1000 per hour; interchangeablility from press to press. Cylinder kits available for use on second machine. Kits supplied with quick-disconnect hose attachments and all mounting hardware. From Ponsness/Warren.
**Price:** . . . . . . . . . . . . . . . . . . . . . . **$849.95**
**Price:** Cylinder kit . . . . . . . . . . . . . . . . **$349.95**

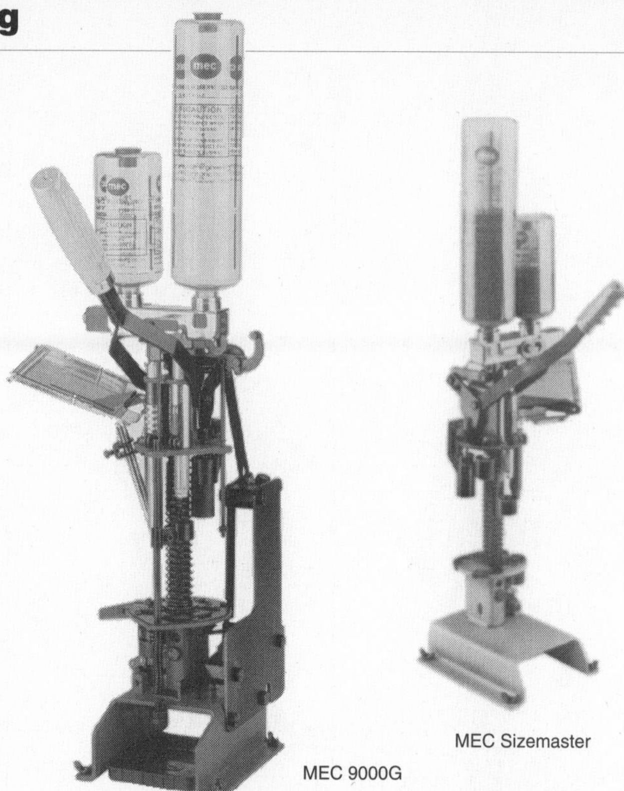

MEC 9000G

MEC Sizemaster

Ponsness/Warren Hydro-Multispeed

### PONSNESS/WARREN Hydro-Multispeed

Hydraulic system developed for the Ponsness/Warren L/S-1000. Also usable for the 950, 900 and 800 series presses. Three reloading speed settings operated with variable foot pedal control. Features stop/reverse at any station; automatic shutdown with pedal control release; fully adjustable hydraulic cylinder rod to prevent racking or bending of machine; quick disconnect hoses for ease of installation. Comes preassembled with step-by-step instructions. From Ponsness/Warren.
**Price:** . . . . . . . . . . . . . . . . . . . . . . **$849.95**
**Price:** Cylinder kit . . . . . . . . . . . . . . . . **$349.95**

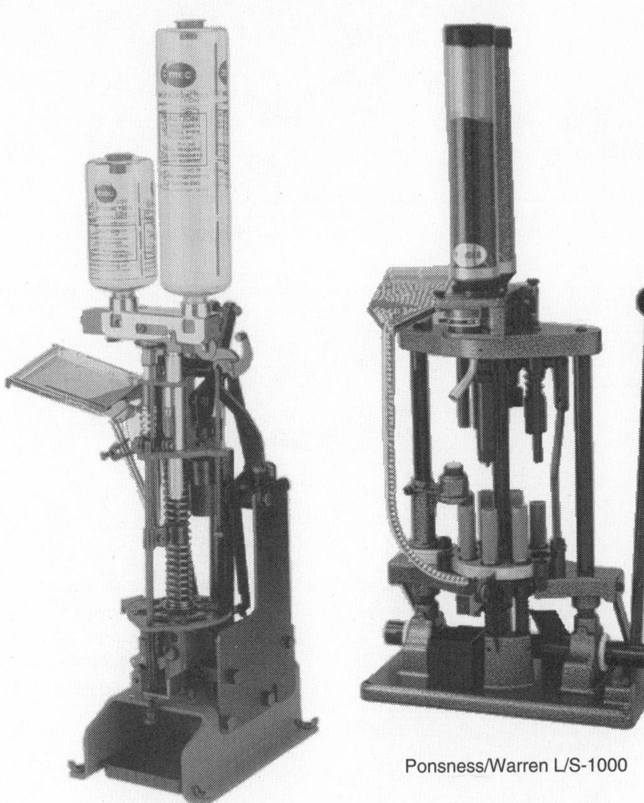

Ponsness/Warren L/S-1000

MEC Steelmaster

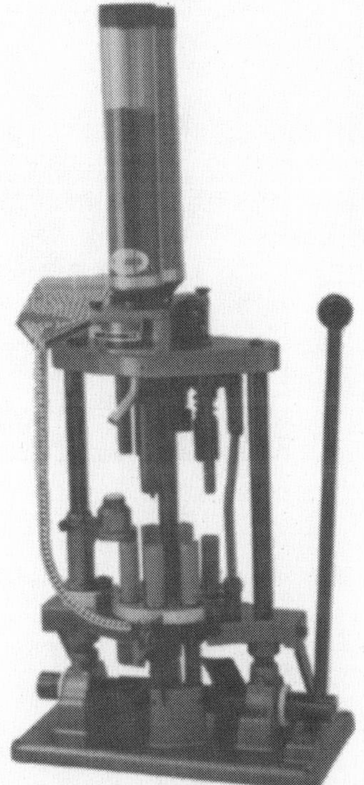

Ponsness/Warren 950 Elite

Ponsness/Warren
Du-O-Matic 375C

**PONSNESS/WARREN L/S-1000**

**Frame:** Die cast aluminum
**Avg. Rounds Per Hour:** NA
**Weight:** 55 lbs.
**Features:** Fully progressive press to reload steel, bismuth or lead shot. Equipped with new Uni-Drop shot measuring and dispensing system which allows the use of all makes of shot in any size. Shells automatically resized and deprimed with new Auto-Size and De-Primer system. Loaded rounds drop out of shellholders when completed. Each shell pre-crimped and final crimped with Tru-Crimp system. Available in 10-gauge $3^{1}/_{2}$" or 12-gauge $2^{3}/_{4}$" and 3". 12-gauge $3^{1}/_{2}$ conversion kit also available. 20-gauge $2^{3}/_{4}$" and 3" special order only. From Ponsness/Warren.
**Price:** 12 ga. . . . . . . . . . . . . . . . . . . . **$669.00**
**Price:** 10 ga. . . . . . . . . . . . . . . . . . . . **$689.00**
**Price:** Conversion kit . . . . . . . . . . . . . . . **$44.95**

**PONSNESS/WARREN Size-O-Matic 900 Elite**

**Press Type:** Progressive
**Avg. Rounds Per Hour:** 500-800
**Weight:** 49 lbs.
**Features:** Progressive eight-station press; frame of die cast aluminum; center post design index system ensures positive indexing; timing factory set, drilled and pinned. Automatic features include index, deprime, reprime, powder and shot drop, crimp start, tapered final crimp, finished shell ejection. Available in 12, 20, 28 and 410. 16-ga. special order. Conversion kit converts the 900 press to the new 950 Elite. Kit includes the new shellholders, seating port, resize/primer knockout assembly and new crimp assembly. From Ponsness/Warren.
**Price:** . . . . . . . . . . . . . . . . . . . . **$599.00**
**Price:** 950 Conversion kit . . . . . . . . . . . . **$169.00**

**PONSNESS/WARREN Size-O-Matic 900 Elite Grand**

**Press Type:** Progressive
**Avg. Rounds Per Hour:** 500-800
**Weight:** 55 lbs.
**Features:** Same as the Elite, but with all the add-on accessories. Includes 25-lb. shot tube; shell counter; bushing access top plate; die cleaner bracket and swab; shot and powder bushing kit; shot and powder measure kit; pinpoint applicator; STOS 2-oz. jar; die cleaner brush; dust cover; die cleaner bracket and swab. From Ponsness/Warren.
**Price:** 12, 20, 28 . . . . . . . . . . . . . . . . **$769.50**
**Price:** 410 . . . . . . . . . . . . . . . . . . . **$775.00**

**PONSNESS/WARREN 950 Elite**

**Press Type:** Progressive
**Avg. Rounds Per Hour:** 500-800
**Weight:** 55 lbs.
**Features:** Same as the 900 Elite, but comes with the L/S 1000 shellholder and resizing system which automatically seats shells into new shellholders and resizes them in primer knockout station. Conversion kit allows converting 900 Elite to 950. Handles both high and low brass with no alteration. Available in 12, 20 and 28 gauges. From Ponsness/Warren.
**Price:** . . . . . . . . . . . . . . . . . . . . **$599.00**
**Price:** Tooling 12, 20, 28 ga. . . . . . . . . . . **$195.00**
**Price:** Conversion kit . . . . . . . . . . . . . . **$169.00**

**PONSNESS/WARREN 950 Elite Grand**

**Press Type:** Progressive
**Avg. Rounds Per Hour:** 500-800
**Weight:** 55 lbs.
**Features:** Same as the 950 Elite, but comes with 25-lb. shot tube, primer tray extension kit, bushing access plate, dust cover, bushing kit, shot and powder measure kit, automatic shell counter, PENX Lube and STOS grease. From Ponsness/ Warren.
**Price:** . . . . . . . . . . . . . . . . . . . . **$769.00**

# Section 2: Shotshell Reloading

## BALLISTIC PRODUCTS

**Accuracy Powder System**

Ballistic Products combines the Hornady Multi-Deluxe powder measure with their powder measure adaptor unit to fit any Ponsness/Warren shotshell press. Weight 5.9 lbs. From Ballistic Products, Inc.

**Price:** . . . . . . . . . . . . . . **$89.99**

**Powder Measure Adaptor**

Adaptor unit for Hornady Multi-Deluxe powder measure to any Ponsness/Warren loading press. Weight: 1lb. From Ballistic Products, Inc.

**Price:** . . . . . . . . . . . . . . **$29.99**

## HOLLYWOOD

**Standard Shot Measure**

Ductile iron body with ground hardened steel drum. Comes complete with one drop tube, 8″ transparent cylinder and cylinder cover. From Hollywood Engineering.

**Price:** . . . . . . . . . . . . . **$150.00**

## HORNADY

**Apex 3.1 Dust Cover**

Nylon cover for the Apex Standard or Auto reloading press. From Hornady Mfg. Co.

**Price:** Each . . . . . . . . . . . **$7.95**

**Interchangeable Charge Bushings**

Machined from nonferrous metal to assure spark-free operation. Fit all Hornady shot presses. Designed so shot and powder bushings cannot be reversed in charge bar. Made for both powder and lead shot. From Hornady Mfg. Co.

**Price:** . . . . . . . . . . . . . . **$3.49**

**Lead Shot Field Load Bushings**

Bushings for different shot sizes to compensate for tighter packing of small sizes. For all Hornady presses. From Hornady Mfg. Co.

**Price:** . . . . . . . . . . . . . . **$3.49**

**Powder and Shot Baffles**

Extra set of two plastic baffles for 366 press. From Hornady Mfg. Co.

**Price:** . . . . . . . . . . . . . . **$5.30**

**Steel Shot Charge Bushings**

Adapt to Hornady Models 155 and 266 presses for use with steel shot. From Hornady Mfg. Co.

**Price:** . . . . . . . . . . . . . . **$4.95**

**Target Load Bushings**

Calibrated to measure maximum legal loads for trap and Skeet shooting. From Hornady Mfg. Co.

**Price:** . . . . . . . . . . . . . . **$3.49**

**366 Primer Tube Filler**

Attaches to feed tube of automatic priming system. Holds full box of shotshell primers. Will not drop upside-down primers into feed tube. Weight: 1 lb. From Hornady Mfg. Co.

**Price:** . . . . . . . . . . . . . . **$12.25**

**366 Riser Legs**

Replaces the I-beam 366 riser blocks. A set of four polymer columns with steel locking bolts to raise the press 3″ off the loading bench. From Hornady Mfg. Co.

**Price:** . . . . . . . . . . . . . . **$6.45**

**366 Wad Guide Spring Fingers**

Plastic fingers force case mouth open to prevent wad tipping and tearing. Standard on Hornady press and fit wad guides of most other makes. Available in 10, 12, 16, 20, 28 gauges and 410 bore. From Hornady Mfg. Co.

**Price:** . . . . . . . . . . . . . . **$1.95**

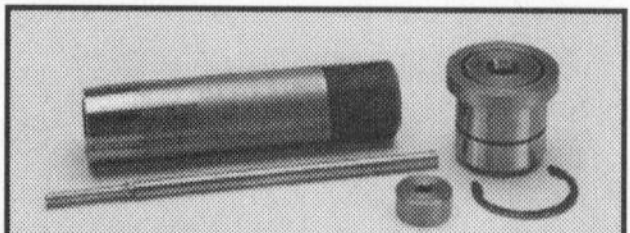

Hornady Collet Size Die

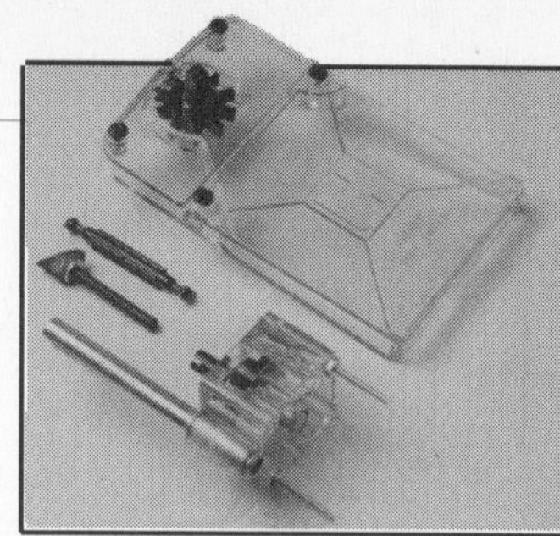

Hornady Auto Primer Drop

Hornady 2-Stage Crimp Die

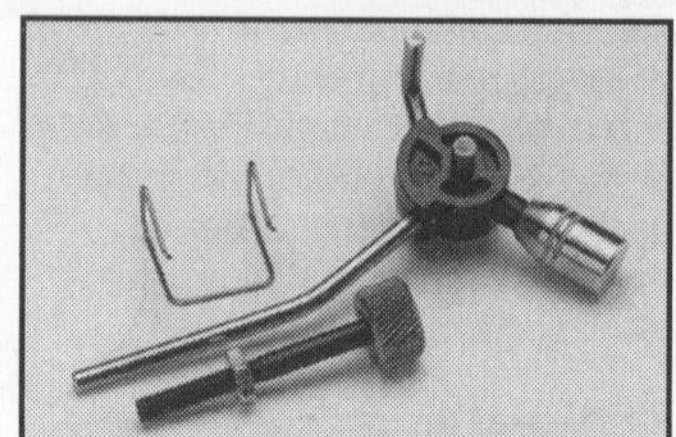

Hornady Auto Index

Hornady Apex 3.1 Dust Cover

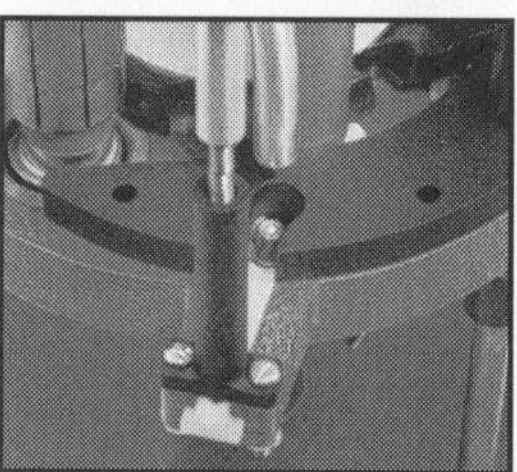

Hornady 3.1 Priming System

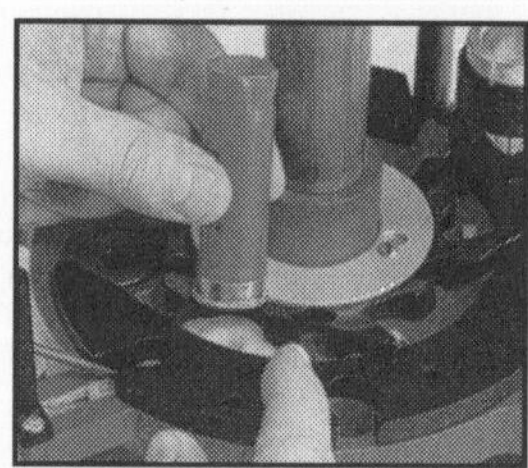

Hornady 3.1 Shell Retainer

**HORNADY Target Load Bushings**

| Charge | Bushing |
|---|---|
| 1/2 oz. | 9 |
| 3/4 oz. | 9 |
| 7/8 oz. | 9 |
| 1 oz. | 7 1/2 |
| 1 oz. | 8 |
| 1 1/8 oz. | 7 1/2 |
| 1 1/8 oz. | 8 1/2 |
| 1 1/8 oz. | 8 1/2 |
| 1 1/8 oz. | 9 |

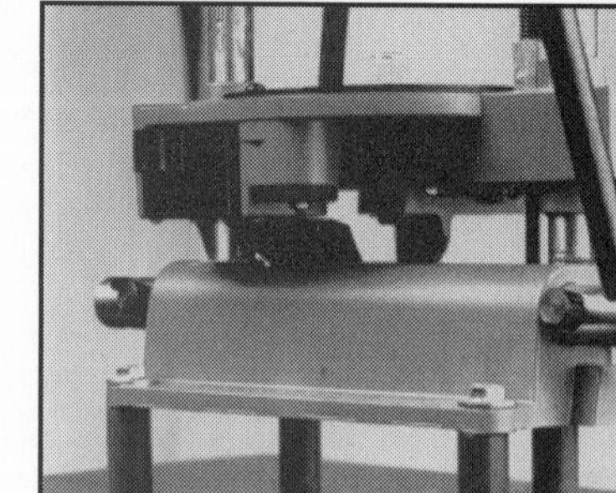

Hornady 366 Riser Legs

## HORNADY

**366 Giant Shot/Powder Hoppers**

Large 2-foot hoppers hold twice the volume of conventional hoppers. From Hornady Mfg. Co.

**Price:** Each . . . . . . . . . . . **$11.30**

**Universal Crimp Starter**

Engineered for cases with poorly defined memory. Improved radius for tight crimp. Available in 6- and 8-point for 12 and 20 gauges and 6-point only for 10, 28 and 410. From Hornady Mfg. Co.

**Price:** . . . . . . . . . . . . . . **$11.15**

## LEE

**Load-All II Conversion Kit**

For converting Load-All II to another gauge. Includes die carrier, steel sizer, wad guide, shellholder, load data and instructions. Available in 12-, 16- and 20-gauge. From Lee Precision, Inc.

**Price:** . . . . . . . . . . . . . . **$19.98**

## LEE

**Load-All II Primer Feed**

Optional attachment for Lee Load-All II to automatically feed primers. From Lee Precision, Inc.

**Price:** . . . . . . . . . . . . . . **$9.98**

**Load-All II Primer Feed With Update Kit**

Upgrade kit for the older Lee Load-All presses. Converts press to Load-All II. Includes the new base with primer catcher; column mounting screws; shellplates for 12-, 16- and 20-gauge; instructions and primer feed. From Lee Precision, Inc.

**Price:** . . . . . . . . . . . . . . **$23.98**

MEC Spindex Crimp Starter

Hornady 366 Wad Guide Spring Fingers

Hornady Crimp Starter

| HORNADY Field Load Bushings |
|---|
| 1/2-oz. |
| 11/16-oz. |
| 5/8-oz. |
| 3/4-oz. |
| 7/8-oz. |
| 1 oz. |
| 1 1/8 oz. |
| 1 1/4 oz. |
| 1 3/8 oz. |
| 1 1/2 oz. |
| 1 5/8 oz. |
| 1 3/4 oz. |
| 1 7/8 oz. |
| 2 oz. |
| 2 1/8 oz. |

Hornady Interchangeable Bushings

**HORNADY Steel Shot Bushings**

| Charge | Bushing # | Size |
|---|---|---|
| 1 oz. | 4,6 | .712 |
| 1 1/8 oz. | 4,6 | .757 |
| 1 1/4 oz. | 4,6 | .792 |
| 1 oz. | 1,2 | .733 |
| 1 1/8 oz. | 1,2 | .777 |
| 1 1/4 oz. | 1,2 | .817 |

Hornady Steel Shot Charge Bushings

MEC Conversion Short Kit

## MEC

**Charge Bars**

Quick-change charge bar with removable powder charger bushings. Bars equipped with soft insert to eliminate shearing when using larger shot sizes and hard lead shot. Fits all MEC presses. From Mayville Engineering Company, Inc.

**Price:** . . . . . . . . . . . . . **$11.80**

**Dust Cover**

Machine washable canvas duck dust cover made to fit Grabber, Hustler, Sizemaster and 9000 series presses equipped with 12″ shot bottles. From Mayville Engineering Company, Inc.

**Price:** . . . . . . . . . . . . . **$34.51**

## MEC

**E-Z Load Handle**

Add-on wood handle reduces downward pressure and increases leverage of downstroke. Fits older MEC progressive machines; comes standard on newer presses. From Mayville Engineering Company, Inc.

**Price:** . . . . . . . . . . . . . . **$5.99**

**E-Z Prime "V" and "S"**

E-Z prime "S" for progressive presses; "V" for 600 Jr. Mark V and Versa MEC 700 except in 410. Standard feature on all MEC presses except 600 Jr. Mark V. Automatically transfers primers to prime station. From Mayville Engineering Company, Inc.

**Price:** . . . . . . . . . . . . **$39.71**

**Hydraulic Conversion for Grabber to Hustler**

No. 3 hydraulic kit includes pump, motor cylinder, controls, base, links and bolt required to attach to Grabber press. From Mayville Engineering Company, Inc.

**Price:** . . . . . . . . . . . . **$931.12**

**Powder Bushings**

MEC offers 47 different bushings to accommodate different powders and loads. From Mayville Engineering Company, Inc.

**Price:** . . . . . . . . . . . . . **$2.18**

**Shotshell Checker**

Precision stainless steel "Go No-Go" measuring tool for shotshells to test for size and roundness. From Mayville Engineering Company, Inc.

**Price:** . . . . . . . . . . . . . **$8.43**

**Conversion Short Kit**

Allows converting 12- or 20-gauge 600 Jr., Sizemaster or Steelmaster presses set up to load 3″ or 3 1/2″ shells to load shells of shorter length. From Mayville Engineering Company, Inc.

**Price:** . . . . . . . . . . . . . **$25.75**

**Spindex Crimp Starter**

Rotates automatically and realigns on orginal crimp of shell. Adjustable for 6- or 8-point crimp. Precision, one-piece Celcon unit standard on MEC reloaders. Adaptable to all MEC presses. From Mayville Engineering Company, Inc.

**Price:** 12-, 16-, 20-ga. . . . . . . . **$4.99**
**Price:** 10-, 28-ga., 410 . . . . . . . **$4.37**

**Steel Conversion Kits 12-Ga. 3 1/2″**

Converts 600 Jr., 600 Jr. Mark V, Versamec, Sizemaster and Steelmaster to steel shot reloaders. From Mayville Engineering Company, Inc.

**Price:** 600 Jr., 600 Jr. Mark V, Versamec . . . . . . . . . **$52.69**
**Price:** Sizemaster and Steelmaster . . . . . . . . . **$70.27**

**Steel Shot Charge Bars**

Designed specifically for loading steel shot reloads using MEC presses. Twenty shot charge bars available. From Mayville Engineering Company, Inc.

**Price:** . . . . . . . . . . . . . **$12.80**

## MULTI-SCALE CHARGE

**Universal Charge Bars**

Precision die cast zinc, fully adjustable replacement steel and lead shot charge bars for MEC shotshell presses. Capacity with No. 4 low antimony shot is from 1/2-oz.to 2 1/4-oz.; powder capacity 12 to 55 grains. Features bottom guides for powder and shot valves and simplified method for reading and adjusting scales. Four models available: Model D for MEC 650 and Grabber; Model D Steel Shot for MEC 650 and Grabber; Model C for MEC 600 Jr., 700 Versamec, Sizemaster 77, MEC 600, 400, 250 and 250 Super, Mark V and the Texan LT, GT and FW; Model C Steel Shot fits same presses as Model C. From Multi-Scale Charge Ltd.

**Price:** . . . . . . . . . . . . . . **$24.95**

**Powder Baffle**

Now spring loaded for automatic powder seal between powder bottle and charge bar of MEC presses for even powder density. Made of die cast zinc. From Multi-Scale Charge Ltd.

**Price:** . . . . . . . . . . . . . . **$5.95**

**Shuttlebars**

Model C and CS steel shot shuttlebars work with same MEC presses as Universal Charge Bar. Made of precision die cast zinc and comes with adjustable shot cavity from 1/2-oz. to 2 1/4 oz. and works with all gauges. From Multi-Scale Charge Ltd.

**Price:** . . . . . . . . . . . . . . **$24.95**

## PATTERN CONTROL

**MEC Powder Baffle**

Designed for MEC presses to maintain consistent powder charge regardless of powder level in powder hopper. Spring-loaded insert prevents powder leakage between baffle and shot/powder bar. From Pattern Control.

**Price:** . . . . . . . . . . . . . . **$5.95**

**Pacific Powder Baffle**

Designed to fit Pacific No. 155, 266 or 366 presses with shot/powder tubes 1 7/8″ in diameter. From Pattern Control.

**Price:** . . . . . . . . . . . . . . **$2.95**

**PC Organizer**

Plastic holder for bushings and charge bars with 15 small and two large pegs. From Pattern Control.

**Price:** . . . . . . . . . . . . . . **$5.95**

## PONSNESS/WARREN

**25-Pound Shot Tube**

Fits any 800 or 900 P/W reloader. Capacity for full bag of shot. Tube is 19″ long and 3″ in diameter. Includes a baffle. From Ponsness/Warren.

**Price:** . . . . . . . . . . . . . **$20.95**

**375 Tool Head**

Extra tool head for gauge conversion. From Ponsness/Warren.

**Price:** . . . . . . . . . . . . . **$39.95**

**800B Taper Crimp Kits**

For P/W 800B press. Includes new sizing dies, final crimp assembly and finish shell knockout. Available in 12, 20, 28 or 410. From Ponsness/Warren.

**Price:** . . . . . . . . . . . . **$152.25**

**950 Elite Conversion Kit**

Converts 900 "Elite" to 950 "Elite" system. Kit includes eight shellholders, one 2-piece shell seating post, resizing/primer knockout assembly and new final crimp assembly. Available for 12, 20 and 28 gauges. From Ponsness/ Warren.

**Price:** . . . . . . . . . . . . **$169.00**

Multi-Scale Shuttle Bar

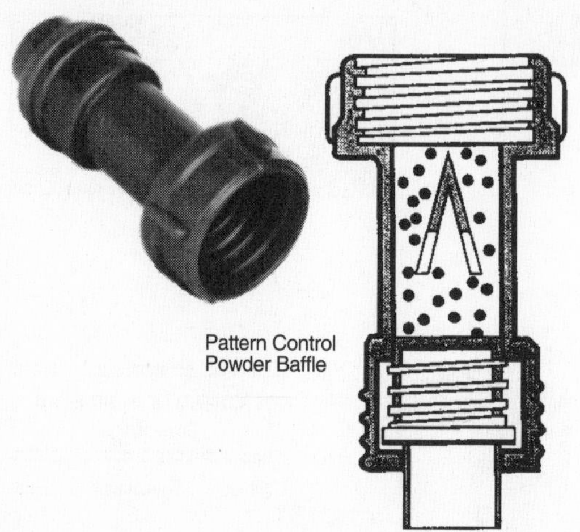

Pattern Control Powder Baffle

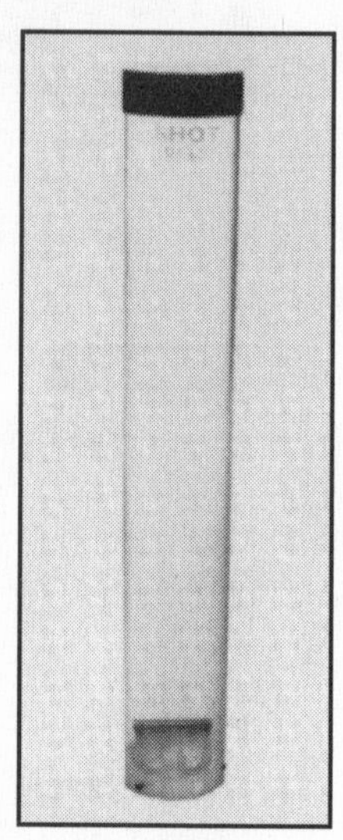

Ponsness/Warren 25-lb. Shot Tube

Ponsness/Warren 800B Taper Crimp Kits

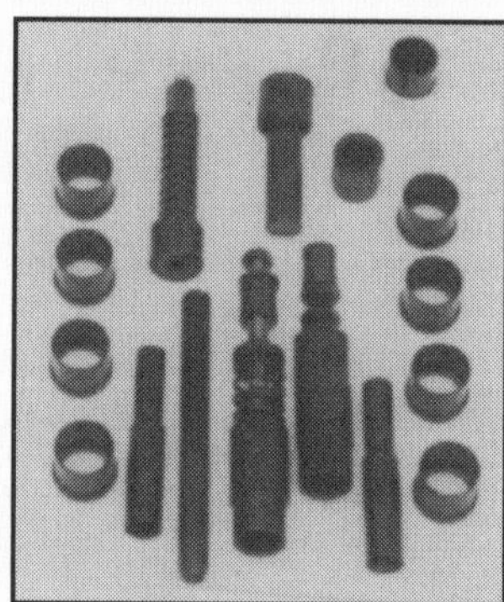

Ponsness/Warren 950 Elite Additional Tool Set

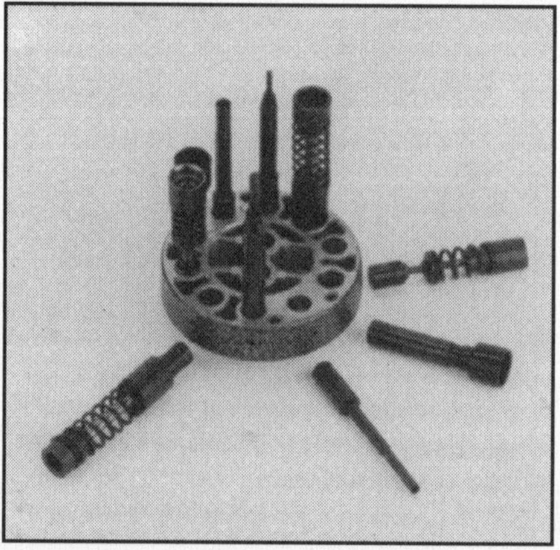

Ponsness/Warren 375 Tool Head

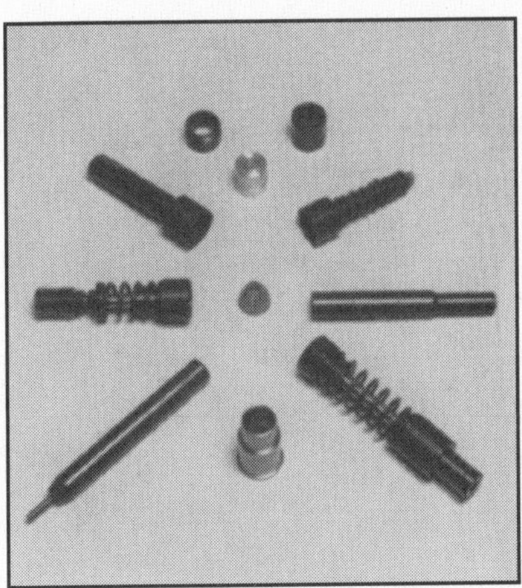
Ponsness/Warren Du-O-Matic Tool Sets

## PONSNESS/WARREN

**950 Elite Additional Tool Set**

For the 900 or 950 series presses and available in 12-, 20- or 28-ga. Includes shellholders, resizing/primer knockout assembly, shot and powder drop tubes, shell seating assembly, wad ram, wad guide cup, wad guide finger, crimp start assembly, final crimp assembly, and shot and powder bushings. From Ponsness/Warren.

**Price:** . . . . . . . . . . . . . . **$195.00**

**Steel Shot Conversion Kit**

Converts the 800, 900 and 950 presses from lead to steel shot reloaders. Kit includes uni-drop steel shot top plate assembly and new wad ram assembly. Ram asssembly fully adjustable for seating steel shot wads. Handles $1^{1}/_{8}$ oz. No. 6 or smaller steel shot. From Ponsness/Warren.

**Price:** . . . . . . . . . . . . . . **$199.95**

Ponsness/Warren Du-O-Matic 375 Conversion Kits

Ponsness/Warren Bushing Access Top Plate

Ponsness/Warren L/S-1000 Shot Bushing

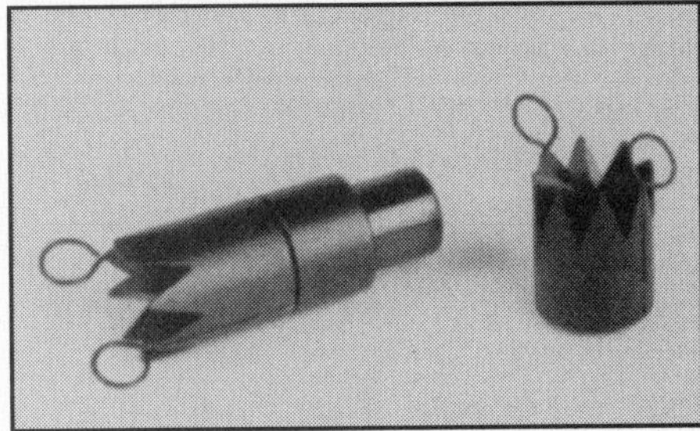
Ponsness/Warren Crimp Starters

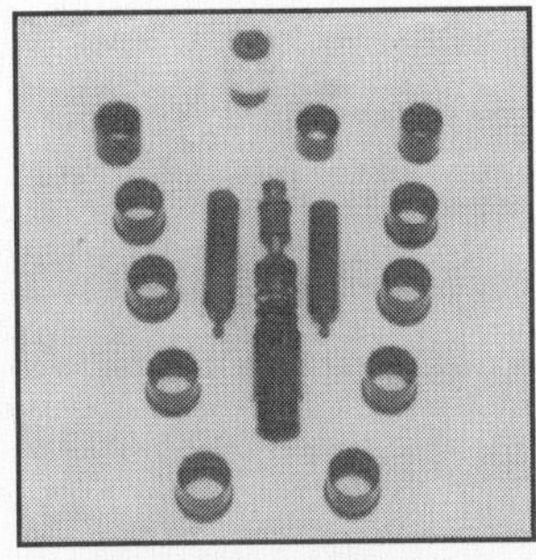
Ponsness/Warren L/S-1000 Additional Tooling Set

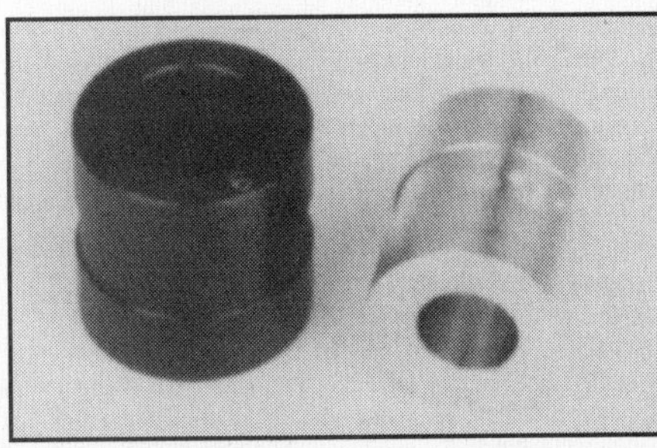
Ponsness/Warren Shot and Powder Bushings

## PONSNESS/WARREN

**Bushing Access Top Plate**

Allows access to bushings without removal of shot and powder tubes. Comes with shot and powder bushing pullers. For Size-O-Matic presses. From Ponsness/Warren.

**Price:** . . . . . . . . . . . . . **$49.95**

**Crimp Starters**

Six- and 8-point crimp starters, ball bearing lined with auto pick-up for perfect alignment and crimp. Comes complete or head only. From Ponsness/Warren.

**Price:** Complete . . . . . . . . **$34.75**
**Price:** Head only . . . . . . . . **$17.75**

**Du-O-Matic 375 Conversion Kits**

Allows conversion to 3″, $3^{1}/_{2}$″ or $2^{1}/_{2}$″ shells. Specify B or C machine. From Ponsness/Warren.

**Price:** $3^{1}/_{2}$″, 12 . . . . . . . . . **$49.95**
**Price:** 3″, 12, 20, 410 . . . . . . . **$31.45**

**Du-O-Matic Additional Tool Sets**

Tooling comes complete in 12, 16, 20, 28 or 410. Includes sizing die, finish shell knockout, primer knockout, shot and powder drop tube assembly, finish crimp assembly, shell seating cup and assembly, wad cup, wad fingers, shot and powder bushing, and a Tru-Start crimp start assembly in 12 and 20 gauge. Metal crimp start assembly in 28 and 410. Special 10-ga. $3^{1}/_{2}$″ magnum tooling set available. 10-ga. tooling set also includes tool head, wad guide housing and 6-point crimp starter. Weight: 5 lbs. From Ponsness/Warren.

**Price:** . . . . . . . . . . . . . . **$82.95**
**Price:** 10-ga. Magnum . . . . . **$103.95**

**Dust Cover**

Made of sturdy canvas comes in large, X-large and small sizes to fit all Ponsness/Warren presses. From Ponsness/Warren.

**Price:** X-Large . . . . . . . . . . **$29.95**
**Price:** Large . . . . . . . . . . . **$27.95**
**Price:** Small . . . . . . . . . . . **$20.95**

**Paper Final Crimp Assembly**

For Du-O-Matic and Size-O-Matic presses (C-type tooling only). Crimp conversion kit for reloading paper shells. From Ponsness/Warren.

**Price:** . . . . . . . . . . . . . **$29.95**

**Shell and Wad Hopper**

Adaptable to any reloading press. Shell hopper holds 500 shells. From Ponsness/Warren.

**Price:** . . . . . . . . . . . . . **$79.95**

**Shot and Powder Bushings**

Distinctly different diameters to eliminate possibility of being reversed. Powder bushings made of aluminum to assure no sparking. Both clearly etch-marked. From Ponsness/Warren.

**Price:** . . . . . . . . . . . . . **$2.99**
**Price:** Set of 10 . . . . . . . . . **$22.95**

**L/S-1000 Shot Bushings**

Steel shot bushings for the L/S-1000 press. Nineteen bushings to load BB to No. 8 steel shot. From Ponsness/Warren.

**Price:** . . . . . . . . . . . . . **$4.49**

**L/S-1000 Additional Tooling Set**

Available for 10- or 12-ga. Kit includes shellholders, shell resizing ring, shell seating cup, wad guide cup, wad guide fingers, crimp start housings, final crimp assembly, and shot and powder bushings. From Ponsness/Warren.

**Price:** . . . . . . . . . . . . . **$169.00**

## PONSNESS/WARREN

**L/S-1000 3 1/2″ Conversion Kit**

Converts 12-ga. L/S-1000 to reload 12-ga. 3 1/2″ shells. Comes with final crimp assembly, wad carrier block and crimp starter housing. From Ponsness/Warren.

**Price:** . . . . . . . . . . . . . **$44.95**

**Shot and Powder Measure Kit**

For checking shot and powder charges during press operation. Available in single-gauge kits or as four-gauge kit, 12, 20, 28 and 410. From Ponsness/Warren.

**Price:** Single gauge kit . . . . . . **$4.25**
**Price:** Four gauge kit . . . . . . **$14.95**

**Sizing Die Cleaner Bracket**

Attaches to 800 or 900 series reloaders. Automatically cleans with brush or swab sizing dies during press operation. Available for 12, 20/28 or 410. From Ponsness/Warren.

**Price:** Bracket . . . . . . . . . **$17.95**
**Price:** Brush . . . . . . . . . . **$1.25**
**Price:** Swab . . . . . . . . . . **$1.50**

**Size-O-Matic Primer Tray Extension Kit**

Increases primer tray capacity to 300 primers. From Ponsness/Warren.

**Price:** . . . . . . . . . . . . . **$22.95**

**Size-O-Matic Shell Counter**

Counts shells automatically and attaches to 800 or 900 series presses. From Ponsness/Warren.

**Price:** . . . . . . . . . . . . . **$22.95**

**Size-O-Matic Shovel Handle**

Made of high-quality aluminum casting with wood grip. Replaces standard ball-type grip that comes standard on the press. From Ponsness/Warren.

**Price:** . . . . . . . . . . . . . **$28.95**

**Size-O-Matic Additional Tool Sets**

For all Size-O-Matic convertible models. Comes complete in 12, 16, 20, 28 or 410. Includes sizing dies, finish shell knockout, primer knockout, shot and powder drop tube assembly, final crimp assembly, shell seating cup and assembly, wad cup, wad fingers, shot and powder bushings, and Tru-Start crimp start assembly in 12- and 20-gauge. Metal crimp start assembly in 28 and 410. Weight: 7 lbs. From Ponsness/Warren.

**Price:** . . . . . . . . . . . . . **$177.00**

**Primer Swing Tray**

Allows filling of primer tray without removing tray cover. Cover swings to the left by loosening wing nut for filling. For the Size-O-Matic presses. From Ponsness/Warren.

**Price:** . . . . . . . . . . . . . **$12.95**

**375 Taper Crimp Kits**

Converts older model Du-O-Matic 375 to the new taper crimp assembly. Includes sizing die, final crimp assembly and finish shell knockout. Available in 12, 20, 28 and 410. From Ponsness/Warren.

**Price:** . . . . . . . . . . . . . **$52.50**

## PONSNESS/WARREN

**Thumb Screws**

For the top plate on older 800 series presses; standard on the 900 press. These screws allow access to shot and powder bushings and to clean gears. Come in sets of four. From Ponsness/ Warren.

**Price:** . . . . . . . . . . . . . **$5.75**

**Tru-Crimp Package**

Final crimp assembly comes complete with Tru-Start crimp starter and Tru-Crimp final crimp package. For all Ponsness/Warren shot presses. From Ponsness/Warren.

**Price:** . . . . . . . . . . . . . **$37.95**

**Tru-Start Crimp Starter**

Specially designed for plastic shotshells. Unique "lead and spin" system ensures shells are precrimped in original folds. Available in 6- or 8-point crimps. Available for any P/W shotshell reloader producing a tapered final crimp. From Ponsness/Warren.

**Price:** . . . . . . . . . . . . . **$14.95**
**Price:** Head only . . . . . . . . . **$6.25**

**Wad Guide Fingers**

Wad guide fingers available in 10, 12, 16, 20, 28 and 410. From Ponsness/Warren.

**Price:** . . . . . . . . . . . . . **$1.50**
**Price:** 10-ga. . . . . . . . . . . **$2.99**

## PRECISION RELOADING

**MEC Powder/Shot Containers**

Ten-inch lead or steel shot and powder bottle assemblies for MEC press. Available filled with 10 lbs. of PR steel shot. From Precision Reloading, Inc.

**Price:** . . . . . . . . . . . . . **$4.50**

**Oak Baseboards**

Oak veneer baseboards 16″x19″x3/4″ designed to make MEC presses portable. Bases have polyurethane finish and have rubber feet to prevent sliding. Weight: 7 lbs. From Precision Reloading, Inc.

**Price:** . . . . . . . . . . . . . **$19.95**

**Oak Baseboard with Brackets**

Same as above with PR aluminum Quick Change brackets installed. Available with either 4″ or 7″ width brackets. From Precision Reloading, Inc.

**Price:** With aluminum brackets . . **$36.95**
**Price:** With brass brackets . . . . **$41.95**

**Quick Change Brackets**

Solid brass 1″x 3/8″x 8″ or aluminum 1″x 1/2″x 8″ brackets allow removing and replacing MEC press with another of similar size base. From Precision Reloading, Inc.

**Price:** Aluminum . . . . . . . . **$17.95**
**Price:** Brass . . . . . . . . . . **$22.95**

**Powder and Shot Bottles for MEC Presses**

Intermediate size 10″ lead and steel shot bottle/powder bottle for MEC presses. Will accommodate 10 lbs. of steel shot. From Precision Reloading, Inc.

**Price:** . . . . . . . . . . . . . **$4.50**

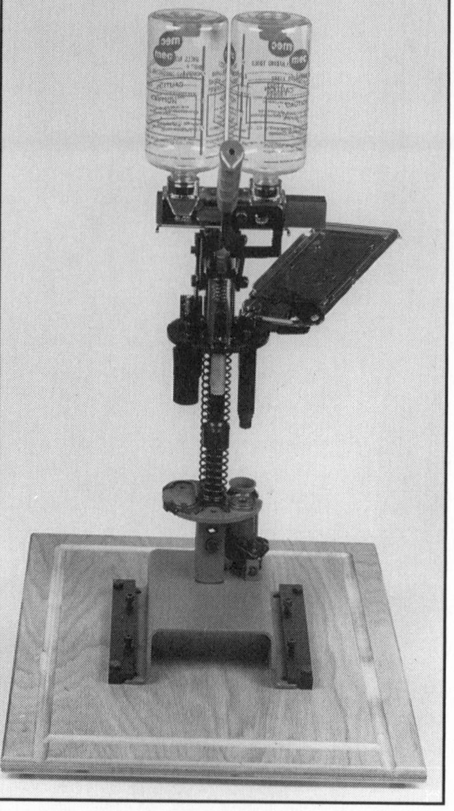

Precision Reloading Oak Baseboard with Brackets

## PRECISION RELOADING

**12-Ga. Spacer Bushings**

Designed for the MEC 600 Jr. and Sizemaster or Steelmaster presses to load 3 1/2″ or 3″ hulls. Eliminates press readjustment when loading shells of shorter length. Brass spacers allow loading from 3″ to 2 3/4″ cases with A, B, E, F spacers; or 3 1/2″ down to 3″ with C spacers; or 3 1/2″ down to 2 3/4″ with D spacer. A (1/4″); B (1/4″); C (1/2″); D (3/4″); E (1/4″); F (1/4″). From Precision Reloading, Inc.

**Price:** A, B . . . . . . . . . . . **$8.95**
**Price:** C . . . . . . . . . . . . **$9.95**
**Price:** D . . . . . . . . . . . . **$10.95**
**Price:** E . . . . . . . . . . . . **$24.95**
**Price:** F . . . . . . . . . . . . **$29.95**

**Quick Change Charge Bar and Spring Anchor Knobs**

Knurled knobs customized to replace the stop screw or anchor bolt on MEC single stage or progressive presses. MMQCBK1 charge bar knob is for the 9000G, 9000H, Grabber and 650 presses; MMQCBK2 charge bar knob is for the Sizemaster 77, Steelmaster and 600 Jr.; MMQCBK3 replaces spring anchor bolt of 9000G, 9000H, Grabber and 650 presses. Made of aircraft aluminum and turned on a lathe to precise specifications. From Precision Reloading, Inc.

**Price:** . . . . . . . . . . . . . **$5.95**

## BALLISTIC PRODUCTS

**Adjustable Shot Dipper**
Tough plastic shot dipper screw-adjusts to measure and drops 1-oz. or 1 7/8 oz. lead shot. Also can be used to measure steel shot. From Ballistic Products, Inc.
**Price:** . . . . . . . . . . . . . . . **$4.49**

**Angle Wad Slitter**
Aluminum tube with choice of three or four slits and tube base for angle-slitting shotcups. Cutting length is adjustable with movable stop. Available for 12-ga. Ranger-Plus, 12-ga. BP12 or BP12-TUFF and 10-ga. BPD or BPD-TUFF wads. X-Acto knife and blades extra. From Ballistic Products, Inc.
**Price:** Angle Cutter . . . . . . . . **$26.95**
**Price:** X-Acto knife . . . . . . . . **$2.95**
**Price:** X-Acto blades (15) . . . . . . **$3.95**

**Buffer Dipper**
Use to pour polyethylene shot buffer into shell. From Ballistic Products, Inc.
**Price:** . . . . . . . . . . . . . . . **$.89**

**Hull Marks**
Round self-adhesive labels for load marking. Come in five colors to code loads or mark with pen. Place on side of shell or base. From Ballistic Products, Inc.
**Price:** 500 . . . . . . . . . . . **$3.95**

**Hull Shape-Up Tool**
Expands the mouth of 20- to 10-ga. hulls for easier loading and will straighten out most bad crimps for hull re-use. From Ballistic Products, Inc.
**Price:** . . . . . . . . . . . . . . . **$7.50**

**Hull Vise**
Firmly grips an empty shell during reloading and crimping process. Adjustable locking action for no spilled loads. Fits all gauges from 10 to 410 bore. From Ballistic Products, Inc.
**Price:** . . . . . . . . . . . . . . . **$34.95**

**Loading Block**
Wood reloading block holds 25 or 50 rounds in upright, brass-down position. Available in 10-ga. through 410 bore. From Ballistic Products, Inc.
**Price:** 25-round . . . . . . . . . **$7.99**
**Price:** 50-round . . . . . . . . . . **$12.99**

**Loading Tray**
Plastic stackable load tray holds 50 shells with brass end up. Can be used in conjunction with MTM 100-rd. or 200-rd. shell cases. Available in 10-, 12-, 16- or 20-ga. From Ballistic Products, Inc.
**Price:** . . . . . . . . . . . . . . . **$2.95**

**Load Log Book**
Four color-coded sections for recording load and hunting information. From Ballistic Products, Inc.
**Price:** . . . . . . . . . . . . . . . **$9.95**

**Mylar Wrap**
For the steel shot reloader. Mylar wraps inside the wad provide barrel protection. Available in either regular thickness (.010″) or extra thin (.003″). From Ballistic Products, Inc.
**Price:** .010″/50 . . . . . . . . . . **$2.99**
**Price:** .003″/100 . . . . . . . . . **$3.99**

Ballistic Products Hull Vice

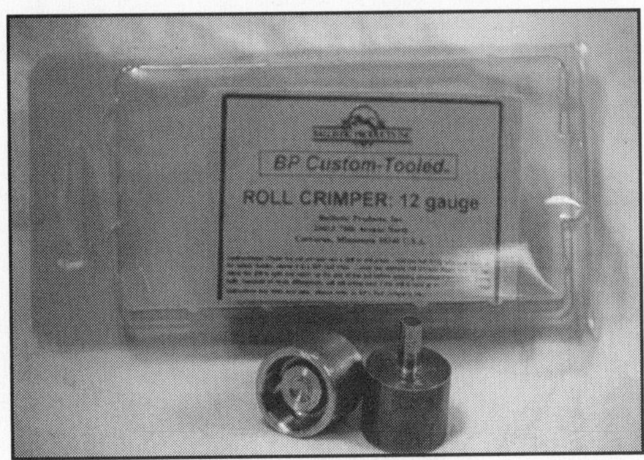


Ballistic Products Roll Crimper

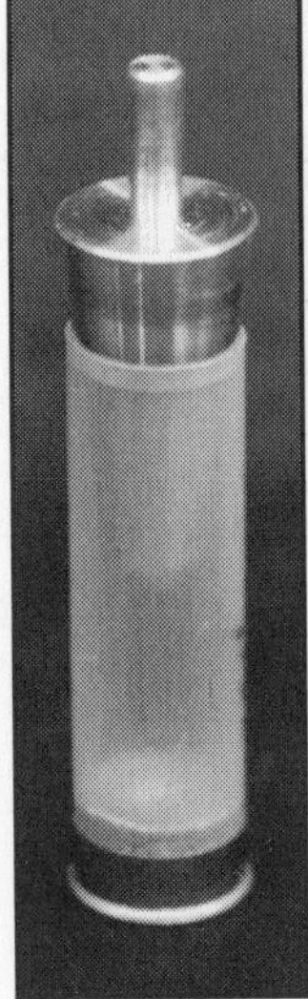

Ballistic Products Spin Doctor

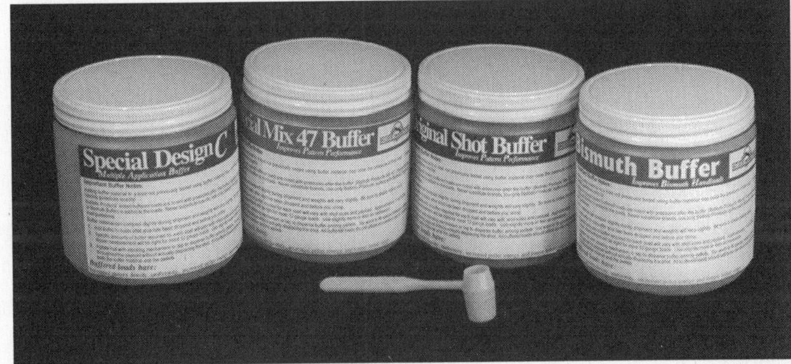


Ballistic Products Shot Buffers

## BALLISTIC PRODUCTS

**Roll Crimper**
Shell crimping tool available in 10-, 12-, 16-, 20- and 28-gauge. Will fit any 1/4″ drill chuck either hand-held or drill press. From Ballistic Products, Inc.
**Price:** . . . . . . . . . . . . . . . **$19.95**

**Shot Buffers**
Fine ground polyethylene shot buffer in original mix, special mix #47 or SD-C for buckshot and large pellets. Both available in plastic jars with buffer to load 150 shells. From Ballistic Products, Inc.
**Price:** Original Mix . . . . . . . . . **$4.99**
**Price:** 5 or more . . . . . . . . . **$4.49**
**Price:** Mix #47 . . . . . . . . . . **$5.49**
**Price:** 5 or more . . . . . . . . . **$4.99**
**Price:** SD-C . . . . . . . . . . . . **$5.99**
**Price:** 5 or more . . . . . . . . . **$5.49**

## BALLISTIC PRODUCTS

**Skiver**
Reams and tapers the mouth of a new hull for better fold or roll crimps. Made of aluminum oxide abrasive. From Ballistic Products, Inc.
**Price:** . . . . . . . . . . . . . . . **$7.95**

**Spin Doctor**
Durable aluminum tool designed to open the mouths of damaged or stubborn once-fired hulls. From Ballistic Products, Inc.
**Price:** . . . . . . . . . . . . . . . **$12.95**

**Super Slick**
Liquid silicone treatment applied to hulls and wads for slippery surface for consistent patterns, pressures and increased velocity. Single application lasts the life of the hull. 12-oz. bottle. From Ballistic Products, Inc.
**Price:** . . . . . . . . . . . . . . . **$12.95**

# Section 2: Shotshell Reloading

## BALLISTIC PRODUCTS

**Teflon Wraps**

For use in 10- and 12-ga. low pressure magnum loads, buckshot loads and slug loads. Helps speed up load velocity, protect the shot column or slug from deformation and barrel scrub, and reduce slug wandering. Packs of 50. From Ballistic Products, Inc.

**Price:** . . . . . . . . . . . . . . . **$8.95**

## HORNADY

**Stack 'N' Pack**

Holds 25 shells. Stacks them for packing into boxes. Includes two 12-gauge shotshell boxes. From Hornady Mfg. Co.

**Price:** . . . . . . . . . . . . . . . **$7.95**

**Wad/Hull Dispenser**

Cardboard dispenser holds up to 200 wads or hulls. Frees up workspace while reloading. From Hornady Mfg. Co.

**Price:** . . . . . . . . . . . . . . . **$6.95**

## LYMAN

**12-Gauge Roll Crimper**

A drill press adapter for roll crimping shotgun slugs. From Lyman Products Corporation.

**Price:** . . . . . . . . . . . . **$20.00**

## MEC

**E-Z Pack**

Reloaded shells stack in E-Z Pack as if in box. Slip box over full stacker, turn stacker upside down. Available in 12, 16, 20, 28 and 410. From Mayville Engineering Company, Inc.

**Price:** . . . . . . . . . . . . . . . **$9.70**

**Shotshell Checker**

Measure precision of reloaded shells for proper chambering. Precision machined holes labeled "Go" "No-Go" test for size and roundness. Made of durable stainless steel and accommodates 10, 12, 16, 20, 28 and 410. From Mayville Engineering Company, Inc.

**Price:** . . . . . . . . . . . . . . . **$8.43**

**Steel Shot Adapter Kit**

To upgrade MEC 600 Jr. Mark V, Versamec, Sizemaster, 650 and Grabber reloading presses to handle steel shot components. Kits for progressive presses also available. Includes wide-mouthed shot bottle, metal drop tube and large diameter rammer tube. Steel shot charge bar available separately depending on powder and shot size desired. From Mayville Engineering Company, Inc.

**Price:** Single stage . . . . . . . **$14.34**
**Price:** Progressive steel shot kit . . **$23.22**

**Super-Sizer**

Resizes shotshell base back to factory specifications. Eight steel fingers encircle base and draw it back to original size. Heavy-duty construction with sure grip plastic handle. Available in 10, 12, 16, 20, 28 and 410. From Mayville Engineering Company, Inc.

**Price:** . . . . . . . . . . . . . **$91.24**
**Price:** Collet and pad for gauge change **$28.10**

## PRECISION RELOADING

**520 Buffer**

Nearly identical to Tru-Square and MEC #520 plastic buffer. Can be subtituted in same charge weight. Comes in 8- or 16-oz. bags. From Precision Reloading, Inc.

**Price:** 8 oz. . . . . . . . . . . . . **$4.99**
**Price:** 16 oz. . . . . . . . . . . . **$8.99**

## PRECISION RELOADING

**All-Gauge Multi-Tool**

Hull mouth restoration and wad seating tool constructed of aircraft aluminum turned by hand. For 10-ga. through 410. From Precision Reloading, Inc.

**Price:** . . . . . . . . . . . . . . **$12.95**

**D-Loader**

Reclaim powder, shot, primer and wad from bad reloads. Made of hard maple with replaceable cutter, D-Loader will also trim the overall length of 10- and 12-ga. TUFF-type wads. From Precision Reloading, Inc.

**Price:** . . . . . . . . . . . . . . **$10.95**

**Hull Saver**

Solid aircraft aluminum 7" tool with knurled handle, tapered to accommodate 10-ga. through 410. Designed to restore the mouths of once-fired hulls. From Precision Reloading, Inc.

**Price:** . . . . . . . . . . . . . . . **$9.95**

**Motor Mica**

Anti-friction dry compound to use as additive to lead and steel shot to avoid bridging; lubricate wads to decrease bore scrub. Comes in 8-oz., 1-lb. or 4½-lb. can. From Precision Reloading, Inc.

**Price:** 8 oz. . . . . . . . . . . . . **$4.95**
**Price:** 1 lb. . . . . . . . . . . . . **$7.95**
**Price:** 4½ lbs. . . . . . . . . . . **$33.95**

**Mylar Shot Wrap**

Plastic mylar wrap available in two thicknesses .010 or .0075 for 10- or 12-gauge. Come in packages of 50 or 500 or 8½ x 11 sheets. From Precision Reloading, Inc.

**Price:** 10-ga./.010, 50 . . . . . . . **$2.95**
**Price:** 10-ga./.010, 500 . . . . . . **$21.90**
**Price:** 10-ga./.0075, 50 . . . . . . . **$2.70**
**Price:** 10-ga./.0075, 500 . . . . . **$20.90**
**Price:** 12-ga./.0075, 50 . . . . . . . **$2.50**
**Price:** 12-ga./.0075, 500 . . . . . **$17.90**
**Price:** 12-ga./.010, 50 . . . . . . . **$2.75**
**Price:** 12-ga./.010, 500 . . . . . . **$18.95**
**Price:** 12-ga./.0075, 50 . . . . . . . **$2.60**
**Price:** 12-ga./.0075, 500 . . . . . **$18.50**
**Price:** Sheet, .010 . . . . . . . . **$1.75**
**Price:** Sheet, .0075 . . . . . . . . **$1.50**

## PRECISION RELOADING

**Over-shot/Over-buffer Tight Seal**

Over-shot material conforms to hull shape and eliminates buffer migration; assists in even crimp opening on combustion. Creates no chamber pressure increases. Comes in packs of 500 for 10- and 12-gauge. From Precision Reloading, Inc.

**Price:** . . . . . . . . . . . . . . . **$5.95**

**Spherical Shotshell Buffer**

Spherical buffer available with or without C-6, a graphite additive, or Motor Mica, an anti-friction compound. Comes in plastic storage bottles. From Precision Reloading, Inc.

**Price:** 10 oz. . . . . . . . . . . . **$4.99**
**Price:** 20 oz. . . . . . . . . . . . **$6.99**
**Price:** 10 oz. w/C-6 or MM . . . . **$5.49**
**Price:** 20 oz. w/C-6 or MM . . . . **$7.69**

## RELOADING SPECIALTIES

**All Seal**

Primer and crimp sealant to weatherproof shells or preserve for storage. Comes in ½-oz. bottle. From Reloading Specialties, Inc.

**Price:** . . . . . **Contact manufacturer.**

**Super Sam Buffer**

Specifically designed for steel shot loads. Granulated plastomers available in 8-oz. bag. From Reloading Specialties, Inc.

**Price:** . . . . . . . . . . . . . . . **$5.95**

## WILLIAMS

**Primer Pocket Conditioner**

Resizes shotshell primer pockets to standard 209 size. Tool and anvil device. From Ballistic Products, Inc.

**Price:** . . . . . . . . . . . . . . . **$9.95**

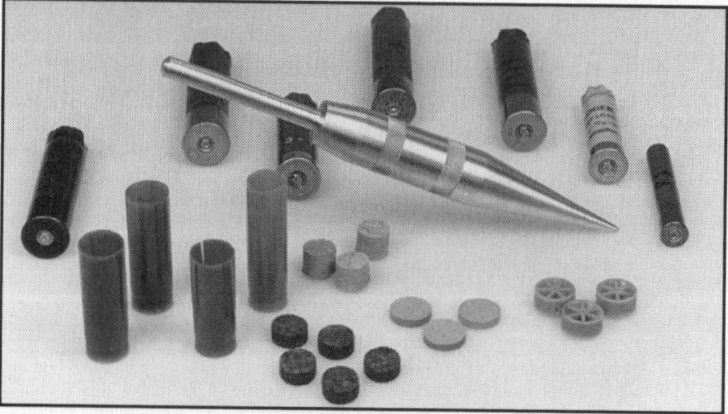

Precision Reloading All-Gauge Multi-Tool

Ballistic Products D-Loader

PART 1 2 3 4 5 6 7

# BULLET SWAGING
## TOOLS & ACCESSORIES

# Section 3: Bullet Swaging



### BULLET SWAGING SUPPLY B.S.S.P. Press

**Frame:** Cast Aluminum
**Frame Type:** O-Type
**Die Thread:** $\frac{5}{8}$-24
**Ram Stroke:** $2\frac{1}{16}$
**Weight:** 8 lbs.
**Features:** O-frame design allows easy access to working area; horizontally mounted; linkage system engineered to reduce stress on the press frame by 95%, thus eliminating press spring and aiding swaging accuracy; ejects on the up-stroke for swaging speed. Dimensions: $11\frac{1}{2}$x 5x $2\frac{5}{8}$. Will accept dies from the Corbin Mity Mite with no modifications; dies from the SAS Mity Mite need ejection punch replacement in the point form die. Steel dies available from 14-45 cal. Carbide point forming and core seating dies available in 224, 243 and 308 calibers in two configurations: Set #1 includes carbide point forming die, carbide core seating die and steel core swage die; Set #2 includes carbide point forming die, steel core seating die and steel core swage die. From Bullet Swaging Supply, Inc.
**Price:** Press . . . . . . . . . . . . . . . . . . . . **$125.00**
**Price:** Press and steel 3-die set . . . . . . . . . . . **$375.00**
**Price:** Press and Set #1, carbide dies . . . . . . . **$1,295.00**
**Price:** Press and Set #2, carbide dies . . . . . . . **$1,040.00**
**Price:** 14- and 17-caliber dies, add per set . . . . . . **$20.00**

### CORBIN CSP-1 Series II

**Frame:** Machined steel
**Frame Type:** H-frame
**Die Thread:** $\frac{7}{8}$-14
**Ram Stroke:** 2 swaging; 4 drawing or jacket making.
**Weight:** 22 lbs.
**Features:** Adaptable for swaging and reloading. Features a ram extender that accepts standard shellholders and guides spent primers into a removable tray; four precision roller bearings mounted in heavy-duty steel links, bearing on hardened tool steel pins; oil-impregnated bronze bearings surrounding ram; dual stroke operation; left- or right-hand handle positioning; ordnance steel alloy supports and ram; machined frame; electrostatic powder-coated, baked-on finish. Swages bullets from 14- to 458-caliber. Maximum bullet length, 1.25; maximum pressure, over 200,000 psi. Comes with floating punch holder for use with external punches of swage dies. Made for use with Corbin M or S type dies. From Corbin Manufacturing & Supply, Inc.
**Price:** . . . . . . . . . . . . . . . . . . . . . **$269.50**
**Price:** Bench stand with storage shelf . . . . . . . . **$49.50**
**Price:** Anvil set (ram and head) . . . . . . . . . . **$25.00**
**Price:** Floor stand (150 lbs.) . . . . . . . . . . . **$239.00**
**Price:** Extra floating punch holder . . . . . . . . . **$20.00**
**Price:** Extra reloading adapter for ram . . . . . . . **$20.00**
**Price:** Extra stop pin . . . . . . . . . . . . . . . **$5.00**

### CORBIN Series II Press Swaging System

Series II CSP-1 press, 3-die FJFB-3-S swaging set, LW-10 lead wire, CSL-2 swaging lube and PCS-1 core cutter. From Corbin Manufacturing & Supply, Inc.
**Price:** . . . . . . . . . . . . . . . . . . . . . **$712.50**

### CORBIN Hydro-Press CHP-1 Swaging System

Includes Hydro-Press, 3-die FJFB-3-H swaging set, LED-1 lead wire extruder, CSL-2 swaging lube, CTJM-1-H lubing jacketmaker, PCM-1 power cannelure tool, CCB-16 core bond, and HTO-2 heat treatment oven. Any caliber from 224-20mm including 50 BMG and shotgun slug. From Corbin Manufacturing & Supply, Inc.
**Price:** . . . . . . . . . . . . . . . . . . . . **$5,950.00**

### CORBIN CSP-2 Mega Mite

**Frame:** Steel
**Frame Type:** H-frame
**Die Thread:** $1\frac{1}{2}$-12
**Ram Stroke:** 3
**Weight:** 55 lbs. (press); 160 lbs. (press and floor stand)
**Features:** Roller bearing linkage; hardened tool steel pivots; precision bronze bushings on polished steel guide rods. Dual stroke operation from 5.5-inch to 3-inch for reloading up to 50 BMG. Can swage hard lead bullets up to .475 diameter and soft lead to .600. Maximum pressure, 180,000 psi; maximum bullet length, $1\frac{1}{2}$; maximum jacket wall, 0.50 copper. Made for use with Corbin H dies. Comes with thick steel floor stand with 4-inch diameter iron tube and punch holder. Height with floor stand is 66. From Corbin Manufacturing & Supply, Inc.
**Price:** . . . . . . . . . . . . . . . . . . . . . **$899.00**
**Price:** Without floor stand . . . . . . . . . . . . **$750.00**

Corbin CSP-2 Mega Mite

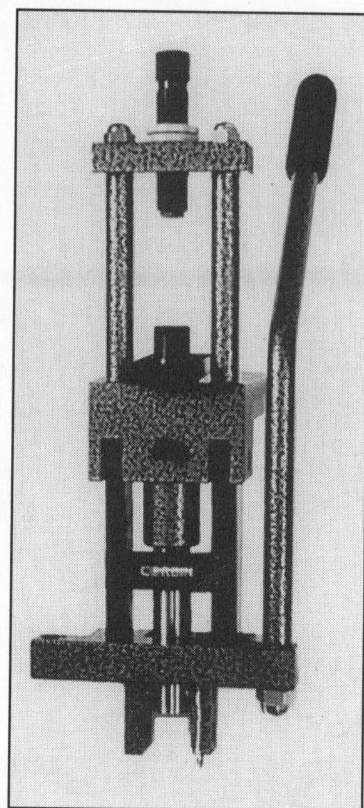

Corbin CSP-1 Series II
Roller Bearing Press

### CORBIN CSP-2H Mega Mite

Hydraulic version of Mega-Mite. Featues same cabinet as the Hydro-press without electronic timing, position sensing and automatic pressure sensing features; use to extrude lead wire, swage bullets, make base guards, tubing jackets and drawn strip jackets; accepts H-type dies. From Corbin Manufacturing & Supply, Inc.
**Price:** . . . . . . . . . . . . . . . . . . . . **$3,450.00**

### CORBIN Silver Press

**Frame:** Ductile iron (80,000 psi)
**Frame Type:** Horizontal
**Die Thread:** $\frac{5}{8}$-24
**Ram Stroke:** 2
**Weight:** 13 lbs.
**Features:** Horizontal stroke, self-ejection and self-alignment. Swages bullets from 14- to 458-caliber; calibers above 308 necessitate use of soft lead. Maximum pressure, 80,000 psi; maximum bullet length, 1.25; maximum bullet weight depends on ogive shape and caliber but is approximately 450 grains with 1-E ogive .458 copper tubing (.030 wall) bullet. Made for use with Corbin M dies. Comes with spare floating punch holder. From Corbin Manufacturing & Supply, Inc.
**Price:** . . . . . . . . . . . . . . . . . . . . . **$189.50**

### CORBIN Silver Press CSP-3 Swaging System 1

Includes Silver Press CSP-3, 3-die FJFB-3-M swaging set (any caliber from 14 to 458), LW-10 lead wire, CSL-2 swaging lube, and PCS-1 core cutter (calibers from 14 to 458). From Corbin Manufacturing & Supply, Inc.
**Price:** . . . . . . . . . . . . . . . . . . . . . **$552.50**

### CORBIN Silver Press CSP-3 Swaging System 2

Includes CSP-3 press, LSWC-1-M swage die in any caliber (270-458), CSL-2 swaging lube, LW-10 lead wire, and PCS-1 core cutter. From Corbin Manufacturing & Supply, Inc.
**Price:** . . . . . . . . . . . . . . . . . . . . . **$333.50**

## ATLANTIC ROSE

**Custom Swaging Dies**

Custom dies for odd-size and weight bullets for ex-Soviet import pistols: 9x18mm, 30 Tokarev and 30 Mauser. From Atlantic Rose, Inc.

## BULLET SWAGING SUPPLY

**22 Jacket-Maker Die**

Makes 22-caliber jackets out of 22-caliber cases. Designed to remove rims from fired 22 Short, Long or Long Rifle cases. Good jackets if velocity is below 3200 fps. From Bullet Swaging Supply, Inc.

**Price:** . . . . . . . . . . . . . **$55.00**

**Boattail Form Die**

Boattail preform die with external boattail punch for point form die. From Bullet Swaging Supply, Inc.

**Price:** . . . . . . . . . . . . . **$110.00**

**Carbide Dies**

Carbide dies made to exact standards for match-quality bullets. Point form and core seating dies available for 224, 243 and 308 calibers. Three-die set includes carbide point form and core seating die and steel core swage die. Also available as kit with press (see Bullet Swaging/Miscellaneous). From Bullet Swaging Supply, Inc.

**Price:** 3-die set . . . . . . . . **$1040.00**
**Price:** Carbide point form die . . . **$795.00**
**Price:** Carbide core seating die . . **$325.00**

**Core Seating Die**

Offered in steel or carbide, threaded 5/8-24 and available for both rifle and pistol calibers 14 through 458. Used to seat the lead core in the jacket. Most calibers in stock; custom dies made to order. Send sample jacket so external punch can be machined to fit and specify bullet weight. From Bullet Swaging Supply, Inc.

**Price:** Steel . . . . . . . . . . **$70.00**
**Price:** Carbide . . . . . . . . . **$325.00**

**Core Swage Die**

Steel swage die, threaded 5/8-24 and available for both rifle and pistol calibers 14 through 458. Most calibers in stock; custom dies made to order. From Bullet Swaging Supply, Inc.

**Price:** . . . . . . . . . . . . . **$70.00**

**Lead Tip Form Die**

Steel die designed for spire point or spitzer rifle bullets to form lead bullet tip. From Bullet Swaging Supply, Inc.

**Price:** . . . . . . . . . . . . . **$85.00**

**Point Form Die**

Gives bullet its final shape and diameter. Offered in steel or carbide, threaded 5/8-24 and available for both rifle and pistol calibers 14 through 458. Most calibers in stock; custom dies made to order. From Bullet Swaging Supply, Inc.

**Price:** Steel . . . . . . . . . . **$120.00**
**Price:** Carbide . . . . . . . . . **$795.00**

**Jacket Reducing Die**

Designed to reduce jacket diameter of commonly available jackets to those not readily available. For example, 284- to 270-caliber. Comes with die, holder and punch. From Bullet Swaging Supply, Inc.

**Price:** . . . . . . . . . . . . . **$55.00**
**Price:** Extra ring dies . . . . . . **$25.00**

Bullet Swaging Supply Tubing Die

Bullet Swaging Supply Jacket Draw Die

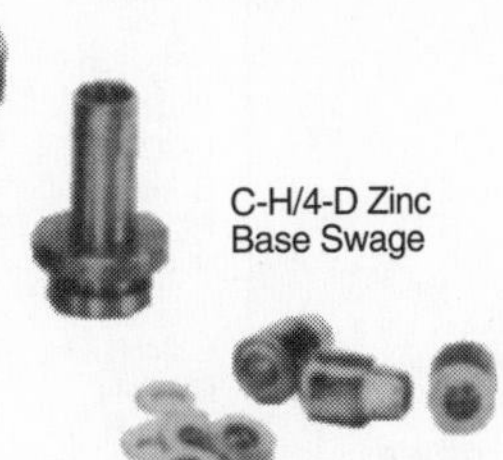

C-H/4-D Zinc Base Swage

## C-H/4-D

**105-Z Zinc Base Swage Die**

Swage 38/357 bullets with zinc bases to prevent leading and to preserve bore life. Semi-wadcutter nose punch and washers extra. Can be used with any standard loading press. From C-H Tool & Die/4-D Custom Die.

**Price:** Die . . . . . . . . . . . **$55.00**
**Price:** Nose punch . . . . . . . . **$9.50**
**Price:** Zinc base washers/1000 . . . **$23.20**

**Half-Jacket Bullet Swage Die**

Forms and swages bullet with half jacket, automatically bleeds off excess lead. Available in .308, .355, .357, .429 and .451 diameters with either round-nose or semi-wadcutter nose punches. Can be used in any loading press that accepts snap-in type shellholder and standard 7/8-14 threads. From C-H Tool & Die/4-D Custom Die.

**Price:** Includes nose punch . . . . **$55.00**
**Price:** Nose punch . . . . . . . . **$9.50**

**Jacket Reducing Die**

Only way to form 7.35 Carcano, 41 Magnum or 40 S&W/10mm jackets. Reduces jackets down to .298″, .408″ or .379″ diameter. Fits any loading press with 7/8-14 threads. From C-H Tool & Die/4-D Custom Die.

**Price:** . . . . . . . . . . . . . **$59.95**

**BULLET SWAGING SUPPLY**

*RIFLE DIES*

| CALIBER | BULLET DIA./TYPE |
|---|---|
| 14 | SP |
| 17 | SP |
| 20 | SP |
| 22 | .223/.224 |
| | .224 |
| | .228/SP |
| 25 | .257 |
| 264 | SP |
| 270 | .277/SP |
| 7mm | .284 |
| 30 | .308 |
| 303 | .311 |
| 8mm | .318 |
| | .323 |
| | .329 |
| 348 | FN, RN |
| 358 | .358/FN, RN, SP |
| 365 | SP |
| 375 | .375/FN, RN, SP |
| 401 Win. | RN |
| 408 | FN, RN |
| 416 | .416/FN, RN |
| 423 | FN, RN |
| 435 | FN, RN |
| 458 | FN, RN, SP |
| 475 | FN, RN |
| 482 | FN, RN |
| 510 | FN, RN, SP |
| 585 | FN, RN |

*PISTOL DIES*

| CALIBER | BULLET TYPE |
|---|---|
| 224 | FN, RN |
| 251 | FN, RN |
| 277 | FN, RN |
| 284 | FN, RN |
| 308 | |
| 310 | |
| 323 | FN, RN |
| 355 | |
| 357 | |
| 358 | WC |
| 400 | |
| 410 | |
| 429 | |
| 451 | |
| 500ae | FN, RN |

## C-H/4-D

**No. 101 Jacketed Softpoint/Hollowpoint Swage Dies**

Forms any full-jacketed pistol bullet from 110 to 250 grains weight. Jacket is swaged up over ogive of bullet. Dies threaded 7/8-14 for use on any press capable of full-length sizing. Punches for solid or hollowpoint. Available in 308, 355, 38/357, 41 S&W, 44 Magnum and 45 ACP. From C-H Tool & Die/4-D Custom Die.

**Price:** . . . . . . . . . . . . . **$99.00**
**Price:** Custom calibers . . . . . **$165.00**
**Price:** Extra punch . . . . . . . . **$5.00**

## CORBIN

**50-Caliber Kit**

For making 50 AE and similar 50-caliber jacketed pistol bullets. Includes heavy-duty bullet swaging press, set of jacket-making dies; spool of lead wire; lead wire cutter; set of three bullet making dies. From Corbin Manufacturing & Supply, Inc.

**Price:** . . . . . **Contact manufacturer.**

## CORBIN

### 224 Kit

For making 224 bullets from fired 22 cases and scrap lead. Includes BSD-224R, RFJM-22R, CM-4 and CSL-2 dies plus instructions. From Corbin Manufacturing & Supply, Inc.

**Price:** . . . . . . . . . . . . . **$349.50**
**Price:** For 6mm . . . . . . . . **$349.50**
**Price:** Upgrade 224 kit to 6mm . . **$239.00**

### Base Guard Bullet Swage Die Kit

To make copper base guard swaged bullets with base-guard design that utilizes precision of 0.001-inch to ensure good seal. Includes Econo-Swage die, Base Guard die, lead wire (70,000-grain spool), magnum core cutter with die and 2-ounce bottle Corbin swage lube. From Corbin Manufacturing & Supply, Inc.

**Price:** . . . . . . . . . . . . . **$372.50**

### H-Type Swaging Dies

Designed to fit only Corbin Hydro-Press or Mega-Mite CSP-2 press. Type-H dies are 1½" in diameter. From Corbin Manufacturing & Supply, Inc.

**Price:** . . . . . . . . . . . . . **See chart.**

### M-Type Swage Dies

For use with Corbin Silver Press or Series II press for any caliber 14 to 458. Only soft lead (Bhn 5) can be used to avoid die breakage. Max bullet length is 1.25"; max bullet weight depends on ogive shape and caliber but is approximately 450 grains with 1E ogive .458 copper tubing (.030" wall) bullet. From Corbin Manufacturing & Supply, Inc.

**Price:** . . . . . . . . . . . . . **See chart.**

### S-Type Swaging Dies

Available in calibers from 308 to 458. Warrantied for use with lead hardness between 5.0 and 8.5 Bhn with up to 0.035" jackets. Recommended for 429- to 458-caliber. From Corbin Manufacturing & Supply, Inc.

**Price:** . . . . . . . . . . . . . **See chart.**

**CORBIN H-Type Swage Dies**

| DIE | DESCRIPTION | PRICE |
|---|---|---|
| CSW-1-H | Core swage die and punch | $160.00 |
| SC-1-H | Core seating die and punch | 160.00 |
| PF-1-H | Point forming die and punch | 229.00 |
| LT-1-H | Lead tip forming die and punch | 160.00 |
| RBT-2-H | Rebated boattail add-on set | 508.00 |
| LSWC-1-H | Lead SWC pistol bullet set | 160.00 |
| JSWC-2-H | 2-die SWC pistol bullet set | 320.00 |
| FJFB-3-H | 3-die flat base open tip | 549.00 |
| LTFB-4-H | 4-die flat base lead tip or open tip | 709.00 |
| RBTO-4-H | 4-die rebated boattail open tip set | 897.00 |
| RBTL-5-H | 5-die rebated boattail, lead tip or open tip set | 1,057.00 |
| FRBO-5-H | 5-die flat base, or rebated boattail open tip | 1,057.00 |
| FRBL-6-H | 6-die all-style package | 1,217.00 |
| DDS-1-H | Dual diameter bullet sizer | 229.00 |
| CTJM-1-H | Tubing jacketmaker | 649.00 |
| CTJM-2-H | Partitioned jacketmaker | 649.00 |
| CTJM-P-H | Partition add-on for CTJM-1-H | 250.00 |
| PUNCH-H | Standard punch for any H-die | 50.00 |
| DCD-1-H | Disk cutter die for copper sheet | 149.00 |
| BGK-1-H | Base guard kit | 198.00 |
| JRD-1-H | Jacket reducing die | 149.00 |
| BRD-1-H | Bullet reducing die | 160.00 |
| LED-1 | Lead wire extruder die set | 469.00 |

Corbin Base Guard Kit

**CORBIN R-Type Swage Dies**

| DIE | DESCRIPTION | PRICE |
|---|---|---|
| RFJM-22R | Turns 22 cases into 224 bullet jackets | $69.50 |
| RFJM-6MR | Turns 22 cases into 6mm bullet jackets | 69.50 |
| SPJM-25R | Turns shotgun primers into 25 ACP jackets | 69.50 |
| JRD-1-R | Jacket reducing die | 79.50 |
| BRD-1-R | Bullet reducing die | 89.50 |
| DCD-1-R | Disk cutter die (copper sheet) | 89.50 |
| BGK-1-R | Base guard bullet kit | 149.50 |
| EC-1 | Econo swage for lead, gas check, or base guard bullets from 224-caliber to 512 | 149.00 |
| CSW-1-R | Core swage die | 89.50 |
| CS-1-R | Core seating die | 89.50 |
| PF-1-R | Point forming die | 129.50 |
| LT-1-R | Lead tip shaping die | 89.50 |
| BSD-xxxR | Core seat and point form die set for rifle 6-S ogive flat base bullets in 224, 243 and 257 calibers; pistol 3/4-E ogive flat base in 251, 308, 312, 355 and 357 calibers | 219.00 |
| Punch-R | Optional or spare punches | 20.00 |

**CORBIN M-Type Swage Dies**

| DIE | DESCRIPTION | PRICE |
|---|---|---|
| CSW-1-M | Core swage die and punch | $89.50 |
| CS-1-M | Core seating die and punch | 89.50 |
| PF-1-M | Point forming die and punch | 129.50 |
| LT-1-M | Lead tip forming die and punch | 89.50 |
| RBT-2-M | Rebated boattail add-on set | 279.00 |
| LSWC-1-M | Lead SWC pistol bullet set | 89.50 |
| JSWC-2-M | 2-die SWC pistol bullet set | 179.00 |
| FJFB-3-M | 3-die flat base open tip | 308.50 |
| LTFB-4-M | 4-die flat base lead tip or open tip | 398.00 |
| RBTO-4-M | 4-die rebated boattail open tip set | 498.00 |
| RBTL-5-M | 5-die rebated boattail lead tip or open tip set | 587.50 |
| FRBO-5-M | 5-die flat base or rebated boattail open tip set | 587.50 |
| FRBL-6-M | 6-die all-style package | 677.00 |
| DDS-1-M | Dual diameter bullet sizer | |
| CTJM-1-M | Tubing jacketmaker (.030 wall) | 338.50 |
| PUNCH-M | Standard punch for any M-die | 20.00 |
| LED-2 | Lead extruder die set, sub-calibers | 169.00 |
| DCD-1-M | Disk cutter die, for copper sheet | 89.50 |
| BGK-1-M | Base guard kit | 149.00 |
| JRD-1-M | Jacket reducing die | 79.50 |
| BRD-1-M | Bullet reducing die | 89.50 |
| Rfjm-22M | 224 rimfire case jacketmaker | 69.50 |
| Rfjm-6MM | 6mm rimfire case jacketmaker | 79.50 |
| Spjm-25M | 25 ACP shotbun primer jacketmaker | 69.50 |
| Rfjm-D | 224 ring die insert (spare) | 30.00 |
| Rfjm-KO | Knock-out rod for jacketmaker | 5.00 |
| Rfjm-P-M | Punch for jacketmaker | 20.00 |
| Rfjm-ROD | 224 screw-in hardened rod | 2.00 |

**CORBIN S-Type Swage Dies**

| DIE | DESCRIPTION | PRICE |
|---|---|---|
| CSW-1-S | Core swage die and punch | $119.50 |
| CS-1-S | Core seating die and punch | 119.50 |
| PF-1-S | Point forming die and punch | 149.50 |
| LT-1-S | Lead tip forming die and punch | 119.50 |
| RBT-2-S | Rebated boattail add-on set | 319.50 |
| LSWC-1-S | Lead SWC pistol bullet set | 119.50 |
| JSWC-2-S | 2-die SWC pistol bullet set | 239.00 |
| FJFB-3-S | 3-die flat base open tip | 388.50 |
| LTFB-4-S | 4-die flat base lead tip or open tip | 508.00 |
| RBTO-4-S | 4-die rebated boattail open tip set | 558.00 |
| RBTLO-5-S | 5-die rebated boattail lead tip or open tip set | 707.50 |
| FRBO-5-S | 5-die flat base or rebated boattail open tip set | 707.50 |
| FRBL-6-S | 6-die all-style package | 827.00 |
| DDS-1-S | Dual diameter bullet sizer | 149.50 |
| CTJM-1-S | Tubing jacketmaker (.030 wall) | 398.50 |
| PUNCH-S | Internal punch for any S-die | 20.00 |

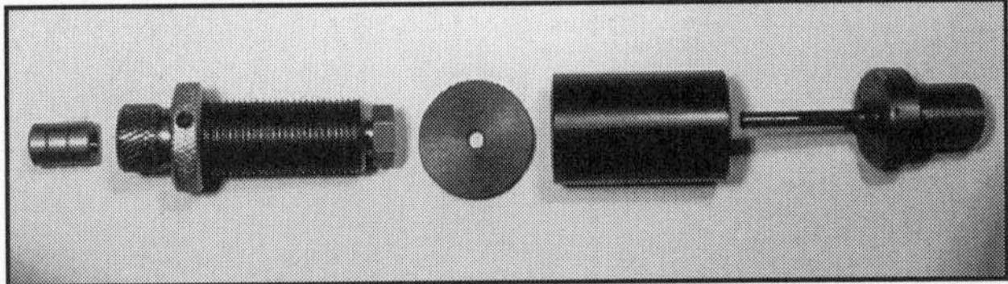

Sport Flite 22 Derim Jakcet Form Die

**W.B. NIEMI ENGINEERING Benchrest Dies**

| | FLAT BASE | BOATTAIL 22, 6mm, 25 | BOATTAIL 6.5, 7mm, 30 |
|---|---|---|---|
| Core Form Die | $350.00 | $350.00 | $425.00 |
| Core Seat Die | 425.00 | 650.00 | 700.00 |
| Point-Up Die | 750.00 | 750.00 | 750.00 |
| Extra Punches | 35.00 | 35.00 | 35.00 |
| Pre-Form Punch/Stripper | | 110.00 | |
| Boattail Ram Punch | | | 65.00 |
| Complete Die Set | 1,550.00 | 1,750.00 | 2,050.00 |

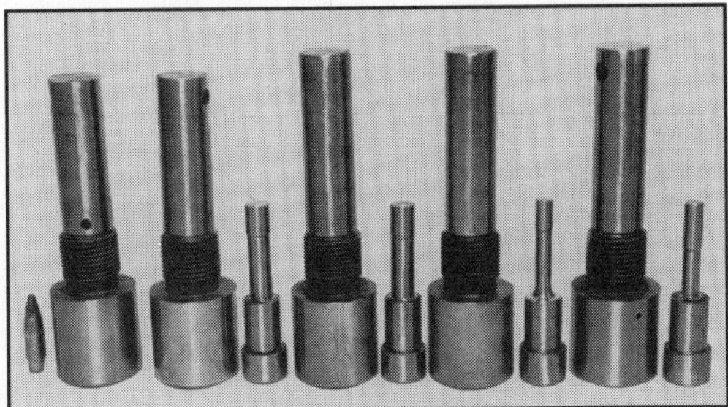

Corbin 5-Die Boattail Rifle Set

Sport Flite 3-Die Set

Corbin Swage Die

Corbin Base Guard Bullet Swage Die Kit

## CORBIN

**R-Type Swage Dies**

Corbin R-type dies fit a standard 7/8-14 threaded reloading press head and the external punch fits into a standard RCBS-style shellholder slot in the ram. Ejection is either by tapping the knock-out rod with mallet or using the Corbin PE-1 power ejector. Jacket makers are designed to fit presses with round 1-1/8″ or smaller diameter ram. Optional oversize ejection tubes are available to fit larger rams. Not for use on light-duty turret presses, or those with universal shellholders instead of T-slot ram. From Corbin Manufacturing & Supply, Inc.

**Price:** . . . . . . . . . . . . **See chart.**

## HOLLYWOOD

**Swaging Dies**

Rifle and pistol swaging dies for lead and alloy bullets or jacketed rifle bullets. Also available for 50 BMG. For use on Hollywood presses only. From Hollywood Engineering.

**Price:** Lead, pistol/rifle . . . . . **$130.00**
**Price:** Jacketed, rifle . . . . . . **$160.00**
**Price:** Special calibers, lead . . . **$150.00**
**Price:** Special calibers, jacketed . . **$180.00**
**Price:** 50 BMG . . . . . . . . **$275.00**

## W.B. NIEMI ENGINEERING

**Carbide Dies**

Custom designed carbide dies with 7/8-14 thread to produce tangent ogive style benchrest bullets. Three-die sets available for flat base and boattail designs. 17 and 22 calibers, flat base only; 6mm, 25, 6.5, 7mm and 30 calibers, flat base and boattail. Complete flat base die sets include steel core forming die, carbide flat base core seater die, one core seating punch and carbide point-up die. Boattail 22, 6mm and 25 die set comes with steel core form die, carbide point-up die. 6.5, 7mm and 30 die sets include same three dies plus boattail ram punch. Available as complete sets or individually. From W.B. Niemi Engineering.

**Price:** . . . . . . . . . . . . **See chart.**

## SPORT FLITE

**22 or 6mm Die Set**

Jacketed bullet three-die 22- and 6mm caliber set made of hardened tool steel. Consists of form die to form lead core to proper diameter, length and weight; core seat die to secure core in copper jacket; and finish die to give bullet final shape. Unique automatic ejection feature with special 1″ diameter ram, ejector pin, top punch holder, lock ring and lock nut available only for RCBS Rock Chucker and Lyman Orange Crusher. 22-caliber bullet has nose of 6-caliber ogive; 6mm with 7-caliber ogive. From Sport Flite Manufacturing Co.

**Price:** . . . . . . . . . . . . **$111.00**

**Derim Jacket Form Die**

For producing 22 or 6mm bullet jackets from 22 Long, Long Rifle or Short cartridge cases. Threaded 7/8-14 to fit any standard reloading press. Available in two configurations: with ram adaptor for threaded support for bottom punch when using 1″ diameter special ram for Sport Flite jacketed bullet die set; or bottom punch to fit universal shellholder. From Sport Flite Manufacturing Co.

**Price:** . . . . . . . . . . . . . **$35.00**

**Pistol Swage Die**

Hardened to 52 Rockwell "C" and adjustable to full range of bullet weights and types, round-nose, semi-wadcutter, wadcutter or spitzer. Form zinc base or jacketed bullets. Jackets cannot be formed into ogive or nose of bullet. Dies fit any standard 7/8-14 thread reloading press. Die sets for 30 (.308-.310), 9mm (.355-.357), 38/357 (.357-.358), 44 (.429-.431) and 45 (.452-.454) available. From Sport Flite Manufacturing Co.

**Price:** . . . . . . . . . . . . . **$24.95**

## BULLET SWAGING SUPPLY

**Carbide Kit #1**

Includes BSSP press, carbide point form die, carbide core seating die and steel core swage die. From Bullet Swaging Supply, Inc.

**Price:** . . . . . . . . . . . . **$1,295.00**

**Carbide Kit #2**

Includes BSSP press, carbide point form die, steel core seating die and steel core swage die. From Bullet Swaging Supply, Inc.

**Price:** . . . . . . . . . . . . **$1,040.00**

**Core and Bullet Lube**

Contains 50% lanolin and 50% castor oil. Comes in 1½-oz. container. From Bullet Swaging Supply, Inc.

**Price:** . . . . . . . . . . . . . . . **$2.50**

**Conversion Kit**

Kit to convert RCBS Rockchucker, Lyman Orange Crusher and Pacific 007 reloading presses to bullet swaging press. Includes modified ram, punch holder and efector pin. From Bullet Swaging Supply.

**Price:** . . . . . . . . . . . . . . **$75.00**

**Core Cutter**

Designed to cut any core wire with cutting die for each diameter. Adjustable for desired core weight. Includes one set of dies. From Bullet Swaging Supply, Inc.

**Price:** . . . . . . . . . . . . . . **$59.00**
**Price:** Extra cutters . . . . . . . **$12.00**

**Core Moulds**

Adjustable weight 4-cavity moulds for turning out lead cores. Made in 1/32″ steps from 5/32″ to 3/8″ From Bullet Swaging Supply, Inc..

**Price:** 3/16, 1/4, 5/16 . . . . . . . . **$75.00**
**Price:** 5/32, 7/32, 3/8 . . . . . . . . **$85.00**

## C-H/4-D

**Cannelure Tool**

Solid steel precision machined tool to roll cannelure groove on jacketed bullets from 17- to 45-caliber. Features cutting wheel hardened to 59C Rockwell. From C-H Tool & Die/4-D Custom Die.

**Price:** . . . . . . . . . . . . . . **$49.50**

**Universal Core Cutter**

Trims bullet cores on wire up through 3/8″. Features adjustable lock nut screw. Can be mounted to feed wire from left or right, top or bottom. From C-H Tool & Die/4-D Custom Die.

**Price:** . . . . . . . . . . . . . . **$44.00**

## CORBIN

**Bullet Balls**

Linear polyethylene spheres of precise weight for insertion into bullet jacket as shock-absorbing tip or to make lightweight projectiles. Available in sizes for calibers 224 to 50. Come 1,000 to a box. From Corbin Manufacturing & Supply, Inc.

**Price:** 1/8″, 224- to 270-cal. . . . . **$25.00**
**Price:** 3/16″, 224- to 284-cal. . . . . **$30.00**
**Price:** 1/4″, 30- to 35-cal. . . . . . **$35.00**
**Price:** 5/16″, 351- to 40-cal. . . . . . **$40.00**
**Price:** 3/8″, 41- to 50-cal. . . . . . **$45.00**

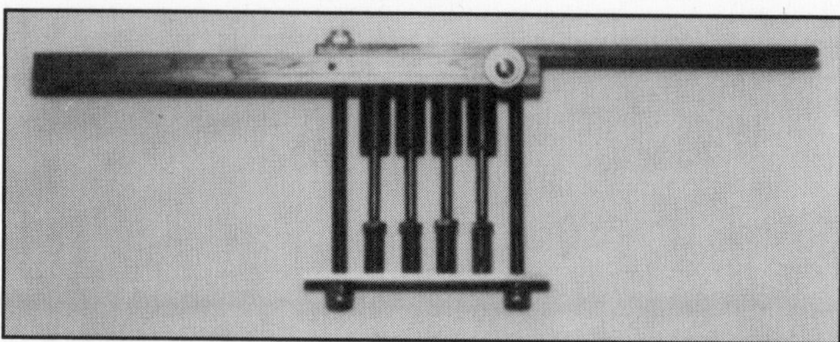

Bullet Swaging Supply Core Mould

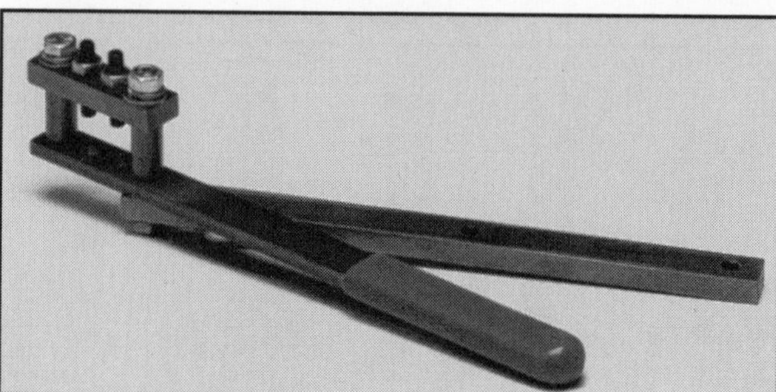

C-H/4-D Core Cutter

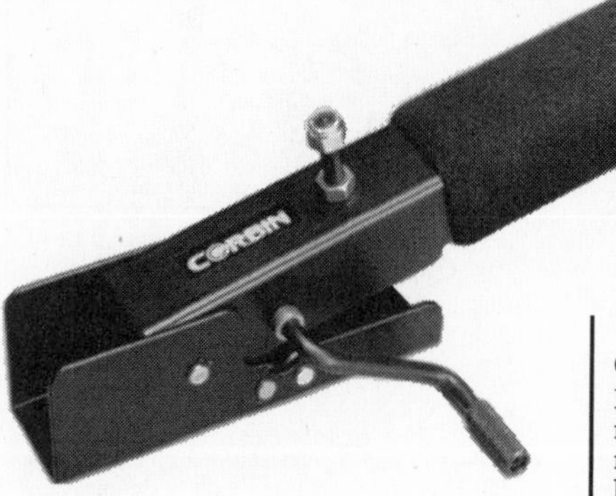


Corbin Cannelure Tool

## CORBIN

**Bullet Dip Lube**

Liquid lube that dries to clear hard wax finish. Available in 4-, 16-oz. and 1-gallon containers. From Corbin Manufacturing & Supply, Inc.

**Price:** 4-oz. . . . . . . . . . . . . **$6.00**
**Price:** 16-oz. . . . . . . . . . . . **$20.00**
**Price:** 1-gallon . . . . . . . . **$125.00**

**Core-Bond**

Liquid flux used to bond lead core to jacket. Comes in 2-oz., 16-oz. or gallon sizes. From Corbin Manufacturing & Supply, Inc.

**Price:** 2-oz. . . . . . . . . . . . . **$4.00**
**Price:** 16-oz. . . . . . . . . . . . **$18.00**
**Price:** 1-gal. . . . . . . . . . . . **$80.00**

**Core Cutter**

Die-type cutter with two hardened tool steel dies in steel frame with fine thread stop screw. Cutting accuracy to 0.1-grain. Two sizes available: standard tool for .185-.365; magnum cutter for .185-.500. From Corbin Manufacturing & Supply, Inc.

**Price:** Standard cutter . . . . . **$39.50**
**Price:** Custom die inserts . . . . **$45.00**
**Price:** Magnum cutter . . . . . **$69.50**
**Price:** Die inserts . . . . . . . **$20.00**

## CORBIN

**Core Mould**

Four-cavity standard caliber and 3-cavity magnum caliber core moulds. Fully adjustable, bench mountable moulds that require no handles or mallets to eject lead cores from precision honed tool steel die cavities. Available in all calibers. From Corbin Manufacturing & Supply, Inc.

**Price:** 4-cavity . . . . . . . . . . **$59.00**
**Price:** 3-cavity magnum . . . . . **$89.00**

**Hand Cannelure Tool**

Duplicates factory bullet cannelure on calibers 224 to 460. Depth and position are adjustable. Features padded handle; positive depth stop; horizontal V-way rollers to prevent bullet creep; positive position stop; heavy-duty crankshaft bearings. Works with lead or jacketed bullets. From Corbin Manufacturing & Supply, Inc.

**Price:** . . . . . . . . . . . . . . **$49.50**
**Price:** .05″ cannelure wheel . . . . **$15.00**
**Price:** Lead bullet knurling tool . . **$49.50**
**Price:** Lead knurling roller set . . . **$25.00**

**HTO-2 Heat Treatment Furnace**

Electronically controlled furnace for heat-treating steel and copper, making bonded-core bullets and other metallurgical heating jobs. Features include fast heat up time, temperature range of 2 to 2000° F., forced-air cooling, dual meters to read both absolute temperature and deviation from selected set-point. Cavity size is 4.5″ x 4.5″ x 6″. Available in 115-volt or 220-volt. From Corbin Manufacturing & Supply, Inc.

**Price:** . . . . . . . . . . . . . **$995.00**

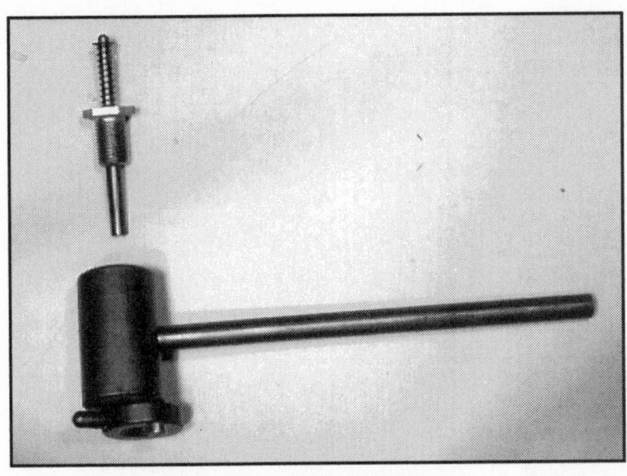

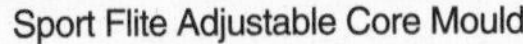
Sport Flite Adjustable Core Mould

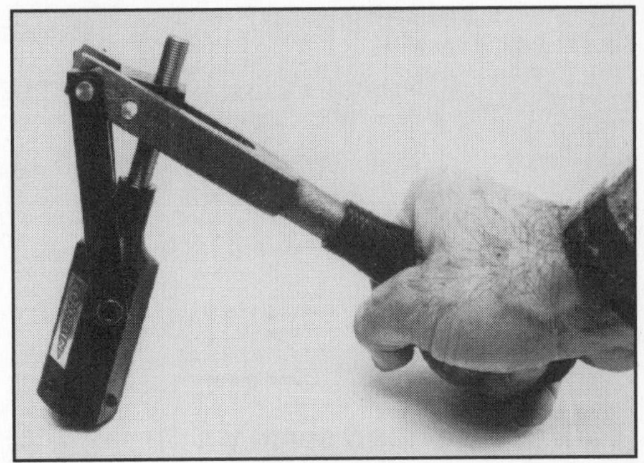

Corbin Power Ejector

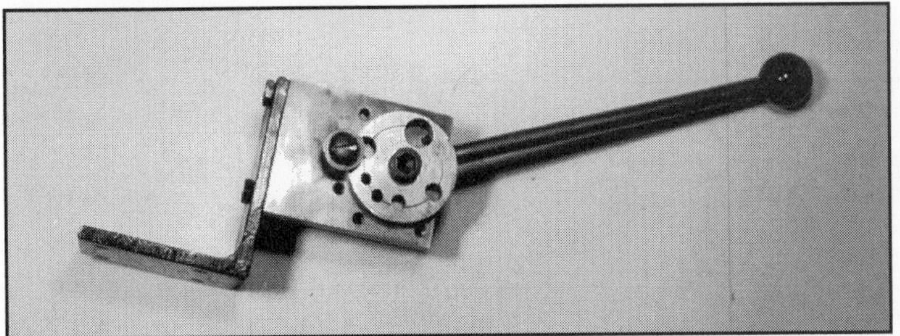

Sport Flite Wire Core Cutter

## CORBIN

**Hydro-Press JMK-2-H Jacket Making Kit**

Designed for semi-automatic 14- to 700-caliber jacket production, kit includes automatic strip feeder with lubrication and motorized part conveyer to fit CHP-1 Hydro-Press. From Corbin Manufacturing & Supply, Inc.

**Price:** . . . . . . . . . . . . **$4,950.00**

**Hydro-Press JMK-1-H Jacket Making Kit**

Dies and punches for Hydro-Press operation to make any thickness and width copper strip into bullet jackets from 14- to 700-caliber. From Corbin Manufacturing & Supply, Inc.

**Price:** . . . . . . . . . . . . **$1,950.00**

**Power Cannelure Machine**

Cannelures 100 lead or jacketed bullets per minute. Cabinet is 10″ high with 6″x 8″ top work space. Includes one cannelure wheel for all calibers and guide plate for one caliber. Caliber plates available from 22 to 512. From Corbin Manufacturing & Supply, Inc.

**Price:** . . . . . . . . . . . . . **$469.00**
**Price:** Custom cannelure wheel . . . **$75.00**
**Price:** Position spacer, .025″ or .048″ . **$10.00**
**Price:** Spare back plate . . . . . . **$40.00**
**Price:** Lead knurling back plate . . **$75.00**

**Swage Lube**

Liquid lubricant for bullet swage dies. Reduces force needed to swage and provides film between die and components to prolong die life. Also works as case size and jacket-making lubricant. Apply by hand or by rolling on impregnated pad. Available in 2- or 16-oz. bottles. From Corbin Manufacturing & Supply, Inc.

**Price:** 2-oz. . . . . . . . . . . . **$5.00**
**Price:** 16-oz. . . . . . . . . . . . **$29.50**

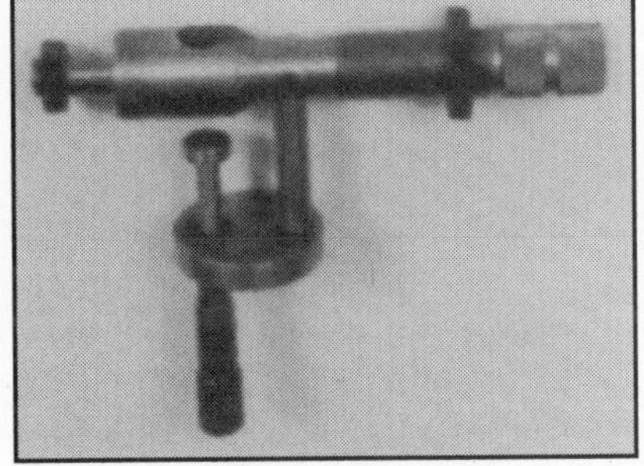

Hollywood Lead Core Cutter

## HOLLYWOOD

**Lead Core Cutter**

Comes with or without micrometer. Accurately cuts lead cores from 22- to 45-caliber. For use on the Hollywood Senior press. Micrometer thimble allows lengths and weight referencing. From Hollywood Engineering.

**Price:** . . . . . . . . . . . . . **$85.00**
**Price:** With micrometer . . . . . **$100.00**

## ROOSTER

**Bullet Film Lube**

Emulsified liquid lube bonds tightly to cast or swaged bullets. Designed for low velocity pistol loads. Apply by dipping, tumbling or flood-coating. Lubes 100,000 bullets. Available in 16-oz., 1/2-oz. or 1-gallon quantities. From Rooster Laboratories.

**Price:** 16-oz. . . . . . . . . . . . **$7.50**
**Price:** 1/2-gal. . . . . . . . . . . **$18.50**
**Price:** 1-gal. . . . . . . . . . . . **$30.00**

Corbin Power Cannelure

## SPORT FLITE

**Adjustable Core Mould**

For casting 30-, 38- and 44/45-caliber cores. Adjustable to provide cores of desired length and weight. From Sport Flite Manufacturing Co.

**Price:** . . . . . . . . . . . . . **$15.50**

**Lead Core Cutter**

Hardened steel body of new design cuts lead wire of 22 (.172) and 30 (.250); 9mm, 38, 357 (.300) and 44, 45 (.365) to length. Length regulated by adjustable stop. Weight: 4 3/4 lbs. From Sport Flite Manufacturing Co.

**Price:** . . . . . . . . . . . . . **$35.00**

## BALLARD

**Copper Tubing Jackets**

Copper tubing jackets in 1″, 1-1/8″, 1-1/4″, and 1-1/2″ lengths in .030 or .050 wall thickness for 475 and 510 calibers. From Ballard Built Custom Bullets.

**Price:** .475 . . . . . . . . . . . . **$25.00**
**Price:** .510 . . . . . . . . . . . . **$23.00**

## BERGER

**Rifle Jackets**

Berger offers a complete range of J-4 rifle bullet jackets from .172-.308 diameter. From Berger Bullets.

**Price:** . . . . . . . . . . . . . **See chart.**

## BULLET SWAGING SUPPLY

**Gas Check**

BSS supplies gas checks for 40-, 41- and 50-caliber bullets from NEI and Colorado Shooters Supply moulds. Price is for 1,000. From Bullet Swaging Supply.

**Price:** 40-41 cal. . . . . . . . . . **$18.00**
**Price:** 50-cal. . . . . . . . . . . . **$34.00**

**Jackets**

Jackets for 22-, 40-, 41- and 50-caliber. Come in quantities of 1000. From Bullet Swaging Supply.

**Price:** . . . . . . . . . . . . **See chart.**

## C-H/4-D

**Rifle and Pistol Copper Jackets**

Copper jackets inspected to ensure concentricity of .0000 to .0003 at a point .110 from base and .0000 to .0005 at a point .125 from mouth. From C-H Tool & Die/4-D Custom Die.

**Price:** . . . . . **Contact manufacturer.**

## CORBIN

**Base Guard Disks**

Conical shaped disks available from 30- to 458-caliber. Hole in center lets lead extrude into rivet and secures disk in place. Available in boxes of 1,000. From Corbin Manufacturing & Supply, Inc.

**Price:** 30-cal. to 38-cal. . . . . . . **$20.00**
**Price:** 40 to 458 . . . . . . . . . **$24.00**

**Base Guard Kit BGK-1**

Die and punch set for any standard slotted ram reloading press or Corbin swage press. Accepts copper strip in .026-.040″ range. From Corbin Manufacturing & Supply, Inc.

**Price:** . . . . . . . . . . . . . **$149.50**

**Copper Strip**

For making base guards, gas checks and bullet jackets. Pure copper, fully annealed with fine grain structure suitable for deep draw operations. Strips have smooth edges, close tolerance widths and thicknesses. Come in 5-lb. bundles or 100-lb. pancake coils. From Corbin Manufacturing & Supply, Inc.

**Price:** 5 lbs. . . . . . . . . . . . . **$35.00**
**Price:** 100 lbs. . . . . . . . . . . . **$500.00**

**Copper, Steel and Brass Bullet Jackets**

Cut to length, deburred copper, brass and steel jackets. Wall thickness of .030, .050 and .065. Come 250 per box. From Corbin Manufacturing & Supply, Inc.

**Price:** . . . . . . . . . . . . . **$20.00**

**BERGER J-4 PISTOL JACKETS**

| Caliber | Length | Price/1000 |
|---|---|---|
| 9mm* | .465 | $49.46 |
| | .505 | |
| | .530 | |
| | .580 | |
| 38 | .437 | 41.60 |
| | .500 | 41.60 |
| | .500, control H.S. | 41.60 |
| | .580 | 41.60 |
| | .700 | 60.80 |
| | .700, scored expan. | |
| 44 | .550 | 62.10 |
| | .550, control H.S. | |
| | .700 | |
| 45 | .550 | 62.10 |
| | .580 | |
| | .700 | |
| | .580 Long | 35.70 |

*Thin wall FMJ

**BERGER J-4 RIFLE JACKETS**

| Caliber | Length | Price/1000 |
|---|---|---|
| .172 | .460 | $42.30 |
| | .500 | |
| | .560 | |
| | .635 | |
| .224 | .600 | 45.10 |
| | .640 | |
| | .705 | |
| | .800 | |
| | .930 | |
| | 1.000 | |
| | 1.060 | |
| | 1.120 | |
| .243 | .750 | 47.30 |
| | .790 | |
| | .825 | |
| | .900 | |
| | 1.050 | 59.40 |
| | 1.400 | 59.40 |
| .257 | .780 | 66.30 |
| | .850 | |
| | .920 | |
| | .940 | |
| | 1.020 | |
| | 1.125 | |
| .264 | 59.40 | |
| .284 | 1.000 | 64.60 |
| | 1.400 | |
| | 1.500 | |
| .308 | .925 | 64.60 |
| | 1.080 | |
| | 1.150 | 68.00 |
| | 1.200 | 68.00 |
| | 1.300 | 68.00 |
| | 1.400 | 68.00 |

Berger J-4 Jackets

**BULLET SWAGING SUPPLY C-H/4-D PISTOL COPPER JACKETS**

| Caliber | Length | Price/1000 |
|---|---|---|
| 9mm/38 | .240 | $48.00 |
| | .460 | 48.00 |
| | .480 | 48.00 |
| | .580 | 48.00 |
| 40 | .580 | 69.00 |
| 44 | .240 | 69.00 |
| | .620 | 69.00 |
| 45 | .230 | 69.00 |
| | .580 | 69.00 |

Corbin Large Caliber Jackets

**CORBIN COPPER TUBING**

| | Price | | | |
|---|---|---|---|---|
| Wall Thickness | 500 Pieces | Custom | 24″ Section | Custom |
| .030 | $150.00 | $5.00 | $200.00 | $175.00 |
| .050 | 175.00 | 6.00 | 225.00 | 200.00 |
| .065 | 200.00 | 7.00 | 250.00 | 225.00 |

## CORBIN

**Copper Tubing**

Cut and trimmed tubing to standard lengths. Custom cutting available. Standard diameters are 3/8″ for 378-caliber down to 338-caliber and 1/2″ for 50-caliber down to 379-caliber; wall thicknesses available, .032″, .049″, .065″. Minimum run, 500 pieces. From Corbin Manufacturing & Supply, Inc.

**Price:** Depending on length and thickness . . . . . . . . . **See chart.**

## HANNED LINE

**PB FreeChec Die**

Cutting die to make gas checks from aluminum can stock for use with plain-base cast bullets. From The Hanned Line.

**Price:** . . . . . . **Contact manufacturer.**

**PB PlastiChec Die**

Precision tool to produce plastic disks of special low-density polyethylene for bases of cast bullets to protect against gas-cutting. From The Hanned Line.

**Price:** . . . . . . **Contact manufacturer.**

## HORNADY

**Crimp-On Gas Checks**

Open edge thicker than side wall for more sure crimp. Come in bags of 1,000. From Hornady Mfg. Co.

**Price:** 22, 25, 35, 6mm, 6.5, . . . . **$10.65**
**Price:** 270, 7mm, 30, 32, 8mm, 338, 348, 375 . . . . . . . . . . **$12.05**
**Price:** 416, 44, 45 . . . . . . . . **$15.30**

## LIGHTNING PERFORMANCE

**Jackets**

Copper tubing jackets for 338-caliber in various lengths. Minimum order 500. From Lightning Performance Innovations, Inc.

**Price:** 1.25″ . . . . . . . . . . **$250.00**
**Price:** 1.37″ . . . . . . . . . . **$300.00**

## LYMAN

**Gas Checks**

Guilding metal cups for 22- through 45-caliber. Come in boxes of 1,000. Weight: 1 1/2 lbs. From Lyman Products Corporation.

**Price:** 22- through 35-caliber . . . **$24.75**
**Price:** 375- through 45-caliber . . . **$29.75**

## NECO

**P-Wads and Wad Insertion Tool**

Precision, hand cut plastic P-Wads for plain base cast bullets to act as gas seal for prevention of gas cutting. Precision stainless steel and tool steel insertion tool designed to seat the P-Wad squarely and uniformly in case mouth. P-Wads comes 100 to a bag. From NECO.

**Price:** . . . . . . . . . . . . . . . **$39.75**
**Price:** P-Wads (22-39) . . . . . . . **$3.75**
**Price:** P-Wads (40-44) . . . . . . . **$5.50**

## R.I.S.

**Copper Tubing**

Copper tubing for swaging bullet jackets. From R.I.S. Co., Inc.

**Price:** . . . . . **Contact manufacturer.**

## SILVER EAGLE

**Graphite Wax Wads**

Designed to be loaded between bullet and powder to lessen copper bore fouling and throat erosion. Come in 3/4″x4″ strips, 10 strips to a pack. Available from E. Arthur Brown Company.

**Price:** . . . . . . . . . . . . . . . **$7.50**

## SPORT FLITE

**Zinc Bases**

For 30-, 9mm, 38-, 357-, 44- and 45-caliber bullets. Come in quantities of 1,000. From Sport Flite Manufacturing, Co.

**Price:** 30, 9mm, 38, 357 . . . . . **$14.50**
**Price:** 44, 45 . . . . . . . . . . . **$16.00**

Lyman Gas Checks

**RCBS GAS CHECKS**

| Caliber | Qty. | Price |
|---|---|---|
| 22 | 1000 | $24.63 |
| 6mm | 1000 | 24.63 |
| 25 | 1000 | 24.63 |
| 6.5 | 1000 | 24.63 |
| 270 | 1000 | 27.25 |
| 7mm | 1000 | 27.25 |
| 30 | 1000 | 27.25 |
| 32-8mm | 1000 | 27.25 |
| 348 | 1000 | 27.25 |
| 35 | 1000 | 27.25 |
| 375 | 1000 | 27.25 |
| 416 | 1000 | 30.38 |
| 44 | 1000 | 32.25 |
| 45 | 1000 | 32.25 |

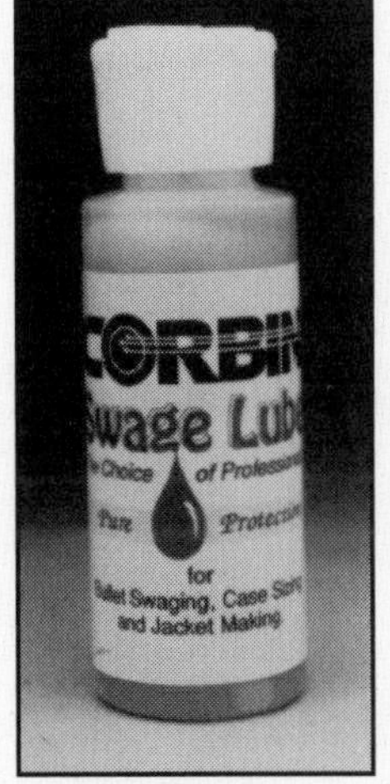


Corbin Swage Lube

Corbin Copper Tubing

Corbin Copper, Steel and Brass Jackets

Corbin 44-Caliber Bullet Jackets

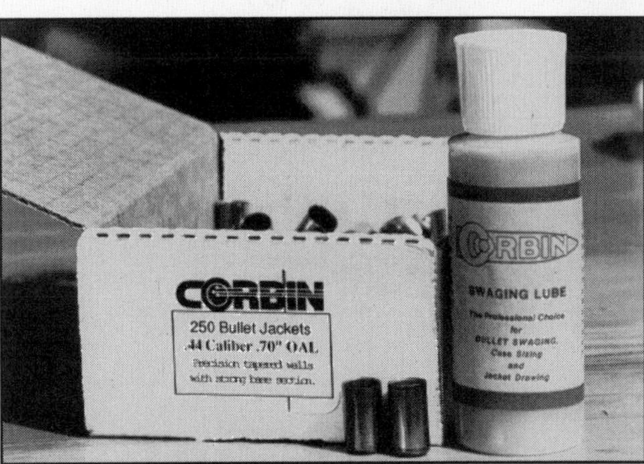


BULLET SWAGING/Jackets & Gas Checks

## BALLARD

**Lead Wire**

Produced in 17″ to 20″ sticks and packaged in 10-lb. quantities. Available sizes: .185, .250, .300, .305, .360 and .390. From Ballard Built Custom Bullets.

**Price:** . . . . . . . . . . . . . . **$20.00**

## BERGER

**Lead Wire**

Rifle bullet lead wire, laboratory certified and 99 percent pure lead with .5 percent antimony. From Berger Bullets.

**Price:** Per lb. . . . . . . . . . . . . **$1.15**

## BULLET SWAGING SUPPLY

**Lead Wire**

Available in .187, .218, .250, and .312 diameters. Price for 25 lbs. From Bullet Swaging Supply, Inc.

**Price:** . . . . . . . . . . . . . . **$30.00**

## C-H/4-D

**Lead Wire**

Diameters: .250 for 30-32 caliber; .312 for 35-38 caliber; .365 for 44-45 caliber. Available in 10-pound roll or 50-pound spool. From C-H Tool & Die/4-D Custom Die.

**Price:** Roll . . . . . . . . . . . . **$19.25**
**Price:** Spool . . . . . . . . . . . . **$66.00**

**Harder Alloy Lead Wire**

Available on special order only and in most common alloys and sizes. Minimum order 500 lbs. per size and type. From C-H Tool & Die/4-D Custom Die.

**Price:** . . . . . **Contact manufacturer.**

## CORBIN

**Lead Wire**

Diameters: .125″, .185″, .218″, .250″, .275″, .312″, .340″, .365″ or .390″ diameters. Available in 10-pound spools. From Corbin Manufacturing & Supply, Inc.

**Price:** . . . . . . . . . . . . . . **$20.00**

## CORBIN

**LED-1 Lead Wire Extruder Kit**

For the CHP-1 Hydro-Press to extrude wire in any diameter from 1/8″ to 1/2″. Includes package of four sample lead bullets (3/4″ diameter x 4″ long), bullet mould with extra tubes, extruder body, floating alignment punch, retainer for dies and package of four heat-treated dies for 22-, 30-, 38-, 44/45-caliber wire. From Corbin Manufacturing & Supply, Inc.

**Price:** . . . . . . . . . . . . . **$469.00**
**Price:** Die insert . . . . . . . . . **$25.00**
**Price:** Extra billet mould tube . . . **$10.00**

**LED-2 Lead Wire Extruder Kit**

Sub-caliber (14-20) lead extrusion kit. Includes four-cavity adjustable-weight mould to make 3/8″ billets, a punch, die body, retainer bushing and set of extruder dies. From Corbin Manufacturing & Supply, Inc.

**Price:** . . . . . . . . . . . . . **$169.00**

## EICHELBERGER

**Lead Wire**

Lead wire for sub-caliber 14 in .100 diameter. Price is per pound. From Eichelberger.

**Price:** . . . . . . . . . . . . . . . **$3.50**

## LIGHTNING PERFORMANCE

**Lead Wire**

Lead wire for swaging 338-caliber bullets. Minimum order to 20 lbs. From Lightning Performance Innovations, Inc.

**Price:** . . . . . . . . . . . . . . **$40.00**

## R.I.S

**Lead Wire**

Lead wire for swaging 223- to 704-caliber bullets. From R.I.S. Co., Inc.

**Price:** . . . . . **Contact manufacturer.**

## SPORT FLITE

**Lead Wire**

Lead wire .177″ diameter for 30, 38, 44/45 calibers. Available in 10- or 25-lb. quantities. Price is for 1 lb. From Sport Flite Manufacturing Co.

**Price:** . . . . . . . . . . . . . . . **$2.15**

Corbin LED-1 Lead Wire Extruder Kit

PART 1 2 3 4 5 6 7

# BULLET CASTING
## TOOLS & ACCESSORIES

# Section 4: Bullet Casting



## BILL FERGUSON

**Lead Pot**

High-quality 50-lb. capacity cast iron plumbers pot with bale handle. Designed to fit Ferguson's Plumbers Furnace and adaptable for use with other heat sources. From Bill Ferguson.

**Price:** . . . . . . . . . . . . . . **$32.00**

**Plumbers Furnace**

Well constructed lead melting furnace with over 43,000 BTUs of thermal capacity. High pressure regulator and vapor hose required. From Bill Ferguson.

**Price:** . . . . . . . . . . . . . . **$101.00**

**High Pressure Vapor Regulator**

For use with Ferguson Plumbers Furnace using LP cylinder P.O.L. valve. Adjustable pressure from 0-45 psi with P.O.L. spud and nut, 1/4″ NPT outlet for optional pressure gauge. From Bill Ferguson.

**Price:** . . . . . . . . . . . . . . **$33.00**

**Plumbers Furnace Kit**

Casting furnace that features 43,000 BTU thermal capacity, adjustable LP regulator with fittings, 6″ long high pressure hose, pressure gauge, cast iron plumbers pot and heat shield. Melts a full pot of lead in 7 minutes. Comes complete with wide stand and bale handle. LP cylinder with standard P.O.L. valve required. From Bill Ferguson.

**Price:** . . . . . . . . . . . . . . **$195.00**
**Price:** Magnum Casting Furnace . . **$249.50**

**LP Pressure Gauge**

Fits in gauge port of Ferguson High Pressure Vapor Regulator for accurate LP vapor pressure control for Plumbers Furnace. Scale range 0-100 psi. From Bill Ferguson.

**Price:** . . . . . . . . . . . . . . **$12.50**

**Heat Shield**

Heavy gauge steel heat shield for use with Ferguson Plumbers Furnace and lead melting pot. Saves energy by keeping hot gases close to pot. Diameter: 7 5/8″. From Bill Ferguson.

**Price:** . . . . . . . . . . . . . . **$11.00**

**LP Vapor Hose**

For use with Plumbers furnace. Comes complete with female 9/16-8 LH fittings for furnace and regulator. Rated 300 psi maximum vapor pressure. Comes in 6-, 10- and 12-foot lengths. From Bill Ferguson.

**Price:** 6 ft. . . . . . . . . . . . . **$15.95**
**Price:** 10 ft. . . . . . . . . . . . . **$22.95**
**Price:** 12 ft. . . . . . . . . . . . . **$26.95**

## LEE

**Lead Pot**

Drawn steel pot with capacity for 4 lbs. lead. Flat bottom for stability and good contact with heat supply. From Lee Precision, Inc.

**Price:** . . . . . . . . . . . . . . **$3.98**

**Precision Melter**

High speed melter for ingot moulds with infinite heat control. Pot capacity of 4 lbs. 500 watts, AC only. From Lee Precision, Inc.

**Price:** 110-volt . . . . . . . . . **$32.98**
**Price:** 220-volt . . . . . . . . . **$36.98**

**Lead Pot**

Cast iron pot with 10-lb. capacity and flat bottom to prevent tipping. Weight: 1-lb. From Lyman Products Corporation.

**Price:** . . . . . . . . . . . . . . **$15.00**

Lee Pro 20

Lee Pro 4-20

## LEE

**Pro 20**

Large diameter, high-capacity 20-lb. melting pot. Features remote sensing thermostat; 700-watt tubular heating element; micro-adjustable flow control valve; front mounted replaceable valve spout. From Lee Precision, Inc.

**Price:** . . . . . . . . . . . . . . **$79.98**

**Pro 4-20**

Same features as the Pro 20 except an extra 4″ of clearance under the spout to accept all brands of bullet moulds and most sinker moulds. Also includes an adjustable mould guide for quick, accurate positioning of mould. From Lee Precision, Inc.

**Price:** 110-volt . . . . . . . . . **$89.98**
**Price:** 220-volt . . . . . . . . . **$94.98**

**Production Pot**

Capacity for 10 lbs. lead. Melt time is less than 20 minutes using 500 watts power and less to maintain heat level. Large stable base with 2″ clearance between up-front spout and base. Features infinite heat control thermostat mounted away from melt pot. Also available in 220-volt export model. From Lee Precision, Inc.

**Price:** 110-volt . . . . . . . . . **$53.98**
**Price:** 220-volt . . . . . . . . . **$58.98**

**Production Pot IV**

Has same features as Lee Production Pot except for 4″ clearance between base and spout. From Lee Precision, Inc.

**Price:** 110-volt . . . . . . . . . **$57.98**
**Price:** 220-volt . . . . . . . . . **$61.98**

## LYMAN

**Master Casting Kit**

Includes Lyman Mini-Mag 8-lb. capacity furnace; Model 450 sizer/lubricator; long-handled casting dipper; ingot mould; and *The Lyman Cast Bullet Handbook*. Weight: 8 lbs., 4 oz. From Lyman Products Corporation.

**Price:** . . . . . . . . . . . . . . **$152.00**

**Mag 20 Electric Furnace**

Capacity for 20 lbs. lead. Features bottom pour valve system; adjustable mould guide for single or multiple cavity moulds; warming shelf for pre-heating blocks; industrial grade thermostat with indicator light; 800-watt heating system melts metal in 20 minutes. Weight: 15 lbs. 110- or 220-volt. From Lyman Products Corporation.

**Price:** . . . . . . . . . . . . . . **$250.00**

Ferguson Lead Pot

## LYMAN

**Lead Pot**

Cast iron pot with 10-lb. capacity and flat bottom to prevent tipping. Weight: 1-lb. From Lyman Products Corporation.

**Price:** . . . . . . . . . . . . . . **$12.95**

**Magdipper Furnace**

Designed for ladle caster with 4 3/8″ diameter pot and 20-lb. capacity. Has same body construction, heating system and tip-resistant base of Lyman Mag 20. Weight: 10 lbs. 110-volt only. From Lyman Products Corporation.

**Price:** . . . . . . . . . . . . . . **$204.95**

**Mini-Mag Furnace**

Electric 8-lb. capacity casting furnace. Melts full load in 30 minutes. Weight: 4 lbs., 4 oz. 110- or 220-volt. From Lyman Products Corporation.

**Price:** 110 . . . . . . . . . . . **$47.50**
**Price:** 220 . . . . . . . . . . . **$50.00**

## RCBS

**Lead Pot**

Heavy-duty cast iron pot holds up to 10 pounds of molten metal. Features a flat bottom, bail handle, pouring spout and tab lifter for gripping with tongs. From RCBS.

**Price:** . . . . . . . . . . . . . . **$13.63**

**Pro-Melt Furnace**

Features 22-lb. capacity melting pot with temperature range of 450° to 850° controlled by industrial-grade thermostat. Pot is made of steel with stainless steel liner and bottom pour valve. Fully adjustable mould guide. Can be set up for right- or left-hand use. 800 watts. From RCBS.

**Price:** 120 VAC . . . . . . . . **$251.50**
**Price:** 240 VAC . . . . . . . . **$273.38**

## RAPINE

**RSS20 Lead Pot**

Stainless steel 20-lb. capacity thermostatically controlled lead pot. From Rapine Bullet Mould Mfg. Co.

**Price:** . . . . . . . . . . . . . . **$179.95**

## BROWNELLS

**Marvelux**

Lead alloy fluxing agent non-corrosive to iron and steel. Reduces dross formation and increases fluidity of bullet alloys. Non-smoking, flameless and odorless. From Brownells, Inc.

**Price:** 1/2-lb. . . . . . . . . . . . **$4.80**
**Price:** 1-lb. . . . . . . . . . . . . **$8.98**
**Price:** 4 lbs. . . . . . . . . . . . **$20.25**

**Industrial Thermometer**

Constructed of 304 stainless steel, all welded construction. 2″ dial, 8″ long stem for immersion in liquids. Guaranteed accurate to .5 of 1% 200° to 1000° in 10°-increments. From Brownells, Inc.

**Price:** . . . . . . . . . . . . . **$31.10**

## CFVENTURES

**Soft Gas Checks**

Soft wax blend with 125-degree Fahrenheit melting point for making gas checks for cast bullets. Come in 5-lb. boxes.

**Price:** . . . . . . . . . . . . . **$50.00**

## BILL FERGUSON

**Casting Thermometer**

Constructed of corrosion resistant type 304 stainless steel with 8″ stem. Temperature range of 200° to 1000° Fahrenheit. Accuracy to within +/-1% of total scale range. From Bill Ferguson.

**Price:** 1/2-lb. . . . . . . . . . . . **$9.95**

**Lets Alloyer's Flux**

Heavy-duty flux developed and formulated to introduce pulverized pure antimony to lead solution at very low working temperatures, 750° to 800° F, in 3 minutes. One pound dissipates 25 lbs. of pulverized antimony. Comes in 1-, 3-, 5- and 50-lb. containers. From Bill Ferguson.

**Price:** 1-lb. . . . . . . . . . . . . **$6.00**
**Price:** 3 lbs. . . . . . . . . . . . **$12.00**
**Price:** 5 lbs. . . . . . . . . . . . **$22.50**
**Price:** 50 lbs. . . . . . . . . . . **$190.00**

**Lets Flux**

Low fuming, minimal odor, non-toxic, crystalline general purpose flux designed for bullet casting. Working temperatures of 550° to 850° F. Non-corrosive and contains no chlorides. Will not disipate pulverized antimony. Comes in 1-, 2-, 4- and 50-lb. containers. From Bill Ferguson.

**Price:** 1-lb. . . . . . . . . . . . . **$3.95**
**Price:** 2 lbs. . . . . . . . . . . . **$6.50**
**Price:** 4 lbs. . . . . . . . . . . . **$10.95**
**Price:** 50 lbs. . . . . . . . . . . **$129.00**

**Clip and Debris Skimmer**

Long handled skimmer for removing debris safely from molten lead. Comes in four diameters, 3″, 4″, 5″ and 6″. From Bill Ferguson.

**Price:** 3″ . . . . . . . . . . . **$14.00**
**Price:** 4″ . . . . . . . . . . . **$15.95**
**Price:** 5″ . . . . . . . . . . . **$18.50**
**Price:** 6″ . . . . . . . . . . . **$23.50**

**Lets Pure Virgin Bar Tin**

Come in 12″ 1-lb. bars. Assay 99.85%+. Calculate the number of inches of tin needed for the casting mix, mark the 12″ bar and dip into molten lead until exact amount melts off. From Bill Ferguson.

**Price:** . . . . . . . . . . . . . **$7.50**

**Lets Pure Pulverized Antimony**

Designed for use with Lets Alloyers Flux to add antimony to molten lead at low working temperatures of 750° to 775°, 400° F. less than the melting point of antimony itself. Comes in 6-, 12.5- and 65-lb. containers. From Bill Ferguson.

**Price:** . . . . . . . . . . . . . **$4.50**

Bill Ferguson Casting Thermometer

Bill Ferguson Clip & Debris Skimmer

Lyman Casting Thermometer

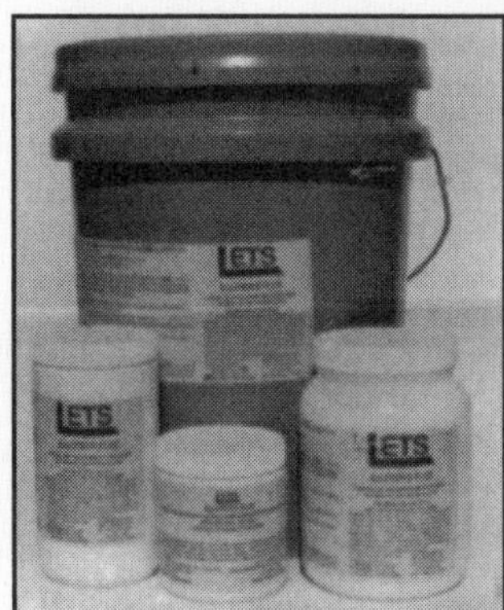


Bill Ferguson Lets Alloyer's Flux

## BILL FERGUSON

**Doe Run Primary Virgin Link Lead**

For the Schuetzen blackpowder cartridge or muzzleloader caster. 99.98%+ pure. Each ingot approximately 5 lbs. From Bill Ferguson.

**Price:** Per pound . . . . . . . . . **$1.00**

## LBT

**Hardness Tester**

Rugged all-steel welded construction. Tests hardness of any cast bullet 1/2″ to 1″ long. Hardness scale runs from 6 BHN (pure lead) to 40 BHN (copper). Features direct scale readout and guaranteed accuracy to 1 BHN. From Lead Bullets Technology.

**Price:** . . . . . . . . . . . . . **$69.00**

**Mould Lube**

Colloidial graphite in beeswax carrier extruded into 1/4″ diameter sticks for application to friction points on mould. Eliminates wear and keeps mould working smoothly. One stick supplied with each LBT mould. Comes in packages of four. From Lead Bullets Technology.

**Price:** . . . . . . . . . . . . . **$4.00**

## LEE

**Ingot Mould**

Lightweight aluminum body with wood handles and cavities for two 1/2-lb. and two 1-lb. ingots. From Lee Precision, Inc.

**Price:** . . . . . . . . . . . . . **$13.98**

**Lead Ladle**

Convenient size ladle with wooden handle for bullet casting. Pour spout on either side for left- or right-hand use. From Lee Precision, Inc.

**Price:** . . . . . . . . . . . . . **$2.98**

## LYMAN

**Casting Dipper**

Features cast iron head, long stem and wooden handle. Weight: 6 oz. From Lyman Products Corporation.

**Price:** . . . . . . . . . . . . . **$12.95**

## LYMAN

**Casting Thermometer**

Stainless steel thermometer with measuring range from 200° Fahrenheit to 1000° F. Features 6″ stem and scale on face showing proper casting ranges for most popular alloys and pure lead. From Lyman Products Corporation.

**Price:** . . . . . . . . . . . . . **$30.00**

**Ingot Mould**

Forms four ingots weighing 1-lb. each. Sides of mould have 30° draft for easy ingot ejection. Weight: 1-lb. From Lyman Products Corporation.

**Price:** . . . . . . . . . . . . . **$15.75**

**Mould Guide**

For use with bottom pour furnaces. Provides precise set-screw adjustments to hold and align moulds. Compatible with Lyman moulds and those of similar design. Weight: 1-lb. From Lyman Products Corporation.

**Price:** . . . . . . . . . . . . . **$16.50**

## MAGMA

**Master Lubricant**

Protects moulds from rust. Comes in 4-oz., 8-oz. or 16-oz. containers. Smaller containers have spray nozzle. From Magma Engineering Co.

**Price:** 4-oz. . . . . . . . . . . . **$16.50**
**Price:** 8-oz. . . . . . . . . . . . **$22.00**
**Price:** 16-oz. . . . . . . . . . . **$40.00**

**Flux**

All synthetic flux. Small amount will flux 20 lbs. of metal. Comes in 1-lb. bricks. From Magma Engineering Company.

**Price:** . . . . . . . . . . . . . **$14.25**

## MI-TE

**Acculoy Bullet Metal**

Premium bullet metal of tin-antimony-lead with 0.5% silver. Silver helps alloy flow, filling contours of mould cavity for sharp, filled-out bullets. Low operating temperature 600° to 625°. Comes in 8½-lb. bars. From Mi-Te Bullets.

**Price:** 1-5, each . . . . . . . . . . **$9.50**
**Price:** 6-10, each . . . . . . . . . **$9.00**
**Price:** 11+, each . . . . . . . . . . **$8.50**

## MIDWAY

**Drop Out Mould Release**

Lubricant and rust prohibitor with Du Pont Teflon for bullet casters. Comes in 6-oz. aerosol can. From Midway Arms, Inc.

**Price:** . . . . . . . . . . . . . . . **$6.99**

**Rust Guard**

Aerosol lubricant and rust preventative with Du Pont Teflon for protecting moulds. Comes in 6-oz. can. From Midway Arms, Inc.

**Price:** . . . . . . . . . . . . . . . **$5.99**

**Rust Inhibitor Chips**

Impregnated 1″x 1″ rust inhibitor chips to protect moulds. Each chip protects up to 20 cubic inches of aluminum or steel. Come in packages of 50 or 200. From Midway Arms, Inc.

**Price:** 50 . . . . . . . . . . . . . **$5.99**
**Price:** 200 . . . . . . . . . . . . **$16.99**

## NEI

**Flux**

Flake-type fluxing agent for removing dross from molten lead. Comes in 4-oz. bag. From NEI Handtools, Inc.

**Price:** . . . . . . . . . . . . . . . **$7.50**

**Mould Prep**

Liquid rust preventative for iron moulds. Contains isopropyl alcohol. Comes in 2-oz. plastic bottle. From NEI Handtools, Inc.

**Price:** . . . . . . . . . . . . . . . **$4.95**

**SP Lube**

Sprue plate lube to prevent galling. Comes in 2-oz. bottle. From NEI Handtools, Inc.

**Price:** . . . . . . . . . . . . . . . **$3.00**

## RAPINE

**Mould Prep**

Micro-graphite, isopropyl alcohol suspension liquid designed to inhibit rust and corrosion. Comes in 2-oz. bottles. From Rapine Associates.

**Price:** . . . . . . . . . . . . . . . **$3.99**

## RCBS

**Bullet Mould Handles**

Solid steel frames with extra-long hardwood handles. One size fits all RCBS bullet moulds. From RCBS.

**Price:** . . . . . . . . . . . . . . **$26.38**

**Ingot Mould**

Heavy-duty iron mould to form four ingots. From RCBS.

**Price:** . . . . . . . . . . . . . . **$13.63**

**Lead Dipper**

Large-capacity bowl with tapered pouring spout and hardwood grip. Convertible for left-hand use. From RCBS.

**Price:** . . . . . . . . . . . . . . **$13.63**

Midway Drop Out Mould Release

RCBS Ingot Mould

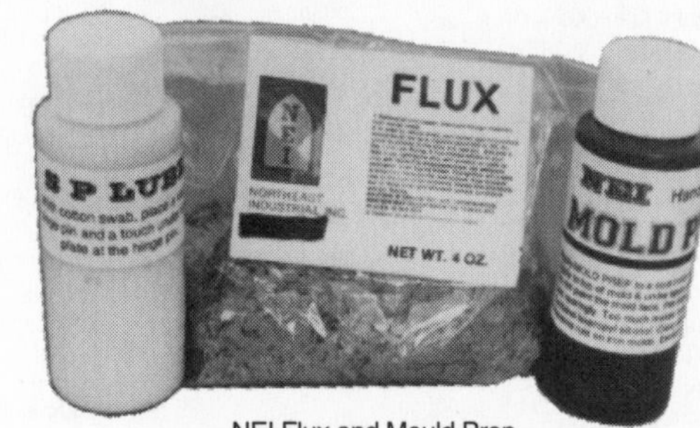


NEI Flux and Mould Prep

**ROWELL LADLES**

| Ladle No. | Capacity (lbs.) | Bowl Dia. (ins.) | Bowl Depth (ins.) | Handle (ins.) | Ladle (ins.) | Weight (lbs.) | Price |
|---|---|---|---|---|---|---|---|
| 1 | 1 | 2¼ | 1 | 9 | 16 | ¾ | $19.95 |
| 2 | 2 | 2½ | 1½ | 10 | 17¼ | 1 | 20.25 |
| 3 | 4 | 3 | 2¼ | 12½ | 15½ | 2 | 26.25 |
| 4 | 4½ | 4 | 2 | 16 | 20 | 4 | 31.25 |
| 5 | 9 | 5 | 2½ | 24 | 31 | 5 | 35.50 |
| 6 | 18 | 6 | 3 | 29 | 35 | 9 | 45.25 |
| 7 | 25 | 7 | 4½ | 29 | 36 | 10 | 51.50 |
| 8 | 40 | 8 | 4½ | 29 | 37 | 13 | 57.75 |
| 9 | 60 | 9 | 5 | 29 | 38 | 20 | 77.75 |
| 10 | 90 | 10 | 5¼ | 29 | 39 | 25 | 88.50 |

No. 9 and No. 10 can be equipped with two handles for $19.75.

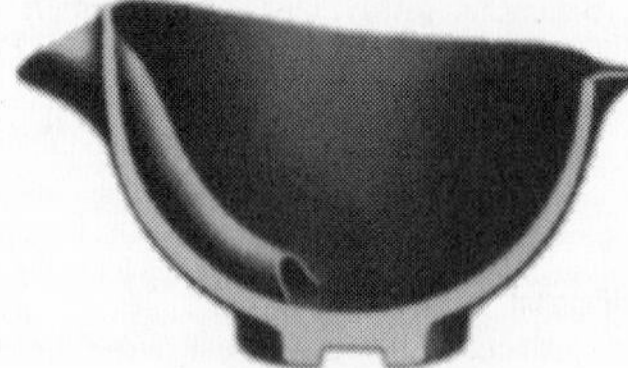

Rowell Bottom Pour Ladle

## RCBS

**Lead Thermometer**

A 1000° range and 1% accuracy thermometer. Features 6″ probe and 1½″ glass-covered face. Comes with an adjustable 6″ handle. From RCBS.

**Price:** . . . . . . . . . . . . . **$33.88**

## REDDING

**Ingot Mould**

Cast iron ingot mould with capacity to cast four ingots. From Redding Reloading Equipment.

**Price:** . . . . . . . . . . . . . **$16.50**

## ROWELL

**Bottom Pour Ladle**

Clean pouring ladle eliminates skimming and wasted metal by delivering lead from the bottom of the ladle bowl. Internal trough inside bowl brings metal from the bottom to the side-pouring spout. Made of durable cast iron with flat base to prevent tipping when set down. Comes in ten sizes. Sizes 1 and 2 have steel bar handle with wood hand grip. Sliding iron sleeve on sizes 4 and up stays cool, protecting user from burns. From Advance Car Mover, Co.

**Price:** . . . . . . . . . . . . . **See chart.**

## SAECO

**Lead Hardness Tester**

Precision instrument to accurately determine hardness of bullet casting alloy. Measures hardness by determining depth of penetration of hardened steel indenter into bullet. Vernier scale calibrated in arbitrary units from 0 for pure lead to Saeco hardness of 10. From Redding Reloading Equipment.

**Price:** . . . . . . . . . . . . . **$135.00**

## SOURCES OF BULLET CASTING METAL

**Action Bullets**
1811 West 13th Ave.
Denver, CO 80204

**Ames Metal Co.**
4324 South Western Blvd.
Chicago, IL
312-523-3230

**A Brigante & Co.**
475 Rt. 32
Highland Mills, NY 10930

**Buffalo Arms Co.**
123 S. Third, Suite 6
Sandpoint, ID 83864
208-263-6953

**Brownells, Inc.**
200 S. Front St.
Montezuma, IA 50171
515-623-5401

**C.J. Ballistics**
P.O. Box 132
Acme, WA 98220
206-595-5001

**Dillon Precision Products**
8009 E. Dillon's Way
Scottsdale, AZ 85260

**Essex Metals**
1000 Brighton St.
Union, NJ 07083
800-282-8369

**Fry Metals**
4100 6th Ave.
Altoona, PA 16602
814-946-1611

**Bill Ferguson, Metallurgist**
P.O. Box 1238
Sierra Vista, AZ 85636
520-458-5321/FAX:520-458-9125

**Art Green**
485 South Robertson Blvd.
Beverly Hills, CA 90211
310-274-1283

**Liberty Metals**
2233 East 16th
Los Angeles, CA 90021
213-581-9171/FAX: 213-581-9351

**Mi-Te Bullets**
R.R. 1 Box 230
Ellsworth, KS 07439

**Peerless Metals**
1445 Osage St.
Denver, CO 80204
303-825-6394

**RSR**
720 South 7th Ave.
City of Industry, CA 91746-3124
818-330-2294

**RSR Dallas**
1111 West Mockingbird Lane
Dallas, TX 75247
214-631-6070

**Signet Metal Corp.**
551 Stewart Ave.
Brooklyn, NY 11222
718-384-5400/FAX: 718-388-7488

**TCSR**
3998 Hoffman Rd.
White Bear Lake, MN 55110-4626
800-328-5323

**TR Metals**
1 Pavillion Ave.
Riverside, NJ 08075
609-461-9000/
FAX:609-764-6340

**KTS Mfg.**
2611 Hwy. 40 East
Inglis, FL 34449
904-447-3571

## CORBIN

**Core Moulds**

Four-cavity and three-cavity moulds for standard and magnum cast cores. Mount to bench; requires no handles or mallets; eject fully-adjustable weight cores from precision honed cavities in tool steel dies. All calibers available. From Corbin Manufacturing & Supply, Inc.

**Price:** 4-cavity . . . . . . . . . . **$59.00**
**Price:** Insert, 4-cavity . . . . . . **$10.00**
**Price:** 3-cavity . . . . . . . . . . **$89.00**
**Price:** Insert, 3-cavity . . . . . . **$25.00**

## DONALD EAGAN

**MX Mould**

Nose-pour benchrest bullet moulds available in conventional and tapered designs. Cavity is machined in the block including the base. There is no bottom plate or plug. Base is at true perpendicular to the axis of the bullet. Features brass block and 1/4″ steel sprue plate that swings on eccentric bushing for sprue hole to nose gate adjustment. Optional stainless steel plate available. Cut to fit Lyman handles. Dimensions: 1.4″x 1.5″x 1.5″. Send $2.00 for detailed sketches of bullet designs. From Donald Eagan.

**Price:** . . . . . . . . . . . . . **$70.00**
**Price:** Stainless steel plate . . . . **$27.00**

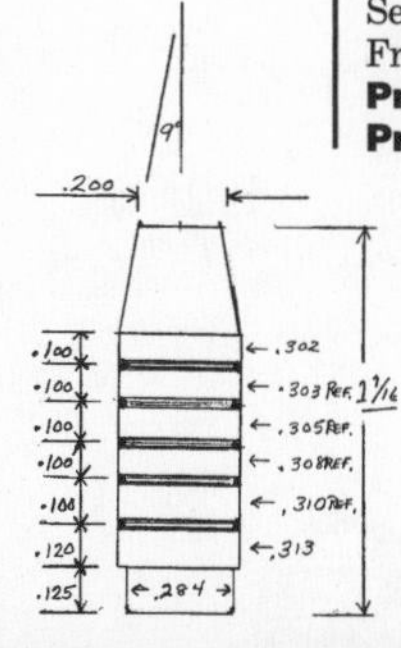


## DONALD EAGAN Bullet Moulds

| Caliber | As Cast Diameter | As Cast Wgt. Grs | Type | Mould |
|---|---|---|---|---|
| 22 | .225 | 43 | GC | MX-2-22 |
| | .225 | 55 | GC | MX-2-22Z |
| | .221-.227 | 55 | Straight Tapered, GC | MX-3-22 |
| 6mm | .238-.246 | 65 | Tapered, GC | MX-3-24X |
| | .244 | 80 | GC | MX-2-243 |
| | .250-.260 | 100 | Straight Tapered, GC | MX-3-25X |
| 7mm | .276-.287 | 145 | Straight Tapered, GC | MX-3-28X |
| 30 | .300-.310 | 155 | For short drive band bullets, GC | MX-2-30W |
| | .301-.310 | 160 | Taper nose for all 30/30 and 30 WCF, GC | MX-2-30C |
| | .311 | 175 | GC | MX-2-308 |
| | .310 | 180 | GC | MX-2-30 |
| | .310 | 185 | For 30-06 and 30-40, GC | MX-2-30H |
| | .304-.315 | 165 | Straight tapered, GC | MX-3-30BR |
| | .3062-.312 | 165 | Straight tapered, GC | MX-3-30KBR |
| | .302-.313 | 175 | Straight tapered, GC | MX-3-30X |
| | .304-.312 | 155 | Straight tapered, GC | MX-3-30J |
| | .304-.313 | 172 | Straight tapered, GC | MX-3-30V |
| | .301-.313 | 190 | Straight tapered, GC | MX-3-30G |
| | .299-.313 | 196 | Straight tapered, GC | MX-3-30US |
| | .310 | 120 | GC | MX-2-30CAR |
| | .304-.313 | 155 | Straight tapered, GC | MX-3-30RJ |
| | .311 | 166 | Tapered, GC | MX-3-30AR |
| | .313 | 188 | Tapered | MX-3-30ARD |
| | .302-.312 | 190 | Tapered, GC | MX-4-30A |
| | .302-.313 | 180 | Tapered, plain base | MX-3-30S |
| | .304-.319 | 180 | Tapered, plain base | MX-2-32C |
| 32 | .314-.324 | 190 | Straight tapered, plain base | MX-3-32S |
| | .315-.325 | 210 | GC | MX-4-32A |
| 33 | .329-.340 | 250 | Straight tapered, GC | MX-3-338 |
| 35 | .359-.364 | 220 | Straight tapered, GC | MX-3-35M |

Donald Eagan MX Bullet Mould

## HENSLEY & GIBBS

**Bullet Moulds**

Handcast moulds in 2-, 4- or 6-cavity designs. Standard moulds cut .001″ to .002″ over sizing diameter in alloy specified. Custom moulds closer to sizing diameter or over .002″ larger than specified alloy. Standard matched moulds are cut consecutively with 1/2-grain maximum variance between the two. Custom matched moulds are same as standard match but will resurface-grind and recherry as needed. All custom moulds an additional $20.00. Moulds can be ordered complete with handles or without. From Hensley & Gibbs.

**Price:** . . . . . **See chart on page 355.**

## HENSLEY & GIBBS Bullet Moulds

| | Bullet | | | Mould | |
|---|---|---|---|---|---|
| Caliber | Dia. | Wgt. Grs. | Type | # | Comments |
| 25 ACP | .252 | 50 | PB | 117 | RGG |
| | .252 | 55 | PB | 306 | RGG; SM |
| 25-20 | .257 | 58 | | 32GC | SGG; OCG; MM; GC |
| | .257 | 65 | | 32GC | SGG; OCG; MM; GC |
| 7mm Nambu | .280 | 60 | PB | 134 | RGG; OCG |
| 8mm Nambu | .323, .321 | 100 | PB | 116 | RGG |
| 8mm Lebel Rev. | .323 | 125 | PB | 226 | RGG; OCG; NDB; SM |
| 30 Luger | .310 | 90 | PB | 93 | SGG; MM |
| | .310 | 92 | PB | 113 | RGG |
| 30 M1 Carbine | .308 | 113 | | | RGG; GC base |
| | .308 | 115 | BB | 254 | RGG |
| 32 Auto | .309 | 83 | PB | | RGG |
| 32 Revolver | .312, .313 | 40 | PB | 354 | RGG; LM |
| | .312, .313 | 90 | PB | 299 | RGG; SM |
| | .312, .313 | 85 | PB | 26-4 | RGG; OCG; 4DB |
| | .312, .313 | 98 | PB | 26-5 | RGG; OCG; 5DB |
| | .312, .313 | 98 | PB | 65 | RGG; OCG; BB; SWS; MM |
| | .312, .313 | 98 | PB | 252 | RGG; OCG; BB |
| | .312, .313 | 90 | PB | S216 | RGG; OCG; MM; RSWS |
| | .312, .313 | 100 | PB | 216 | RGG; OCG; MM; RSWS |
| | .312, .313 | 200 | PB | 220 | RGG; OCG; MM; RSWS |
| | .312, .313 | 115 | PB | 361 | RGG; OCG; SM |
| 32 S&W Long | .312 | 100 | PB | 66 | RGG; OCG; LM; SWS BB |
| | .312 | 100 | BB | 353 | SGG; LEEF; LM |
| | .312 | 105 | | | RGG; square corners, no bevels. |
| 32-20 | .312 | 105 | PB | 89 | RGG; OCG; LM |
| | .312 | 115 | | 89 | RGG; OCG; LM |
| | .312 | 115 | PB | 67 | RGG; MM |
| | .312 | 115 | BB | 388 | RGG; OCG; MM |
| 32 H&R Mag. | .313 | 106 | PB | | SGG; OCG; SWS; LM |
| 380 Auto | .356 | 100 | PB | S55 | RGG; BB |
| 9mm Luger | .356 | 98 | BB | 279 | RGG; SM |
| | .356 | 115 | PB | 307 | SGG |
| | .356 | 115 | PB | 308 | RGG |
| | .356 | 125 | PB | 7 | RGG |
| | .356 | 125 | BB | 115 | RGG |
| | .356 | 125 | BB | 264 | RGG; SWS; SM |
| | .356 | 125 | BB | 275 | RGG; SWS; MM |
| | .356 | 125 | PB | 309 | RGG; LM; BB |
| | .356 | 125 | PB | 310 | RGG; BB |
| | .356 | 125 | PB | 318 | RGG; RSWS; LM |
| | .356 | 125 | BB | 331 | RGG |
| | .356 | 128 | BB | 317 | RGG; LM |
| | .356 | 135 | BB | 286 | RGG; MM |
| | .356 | 135 | BB | 314 | RGG; German army Ogival. |
| | .356 | 140 | | 313 | RGG; OCG; also for revolver; SM |
| | .356 | 147 | PB | 378 | RGG; SM |
| | .356 | 150 | PB | 363 | SGG; LM |
| | .356 | 150 | PB | 377 | RGG |
| 9mm Makarov | .364 | 105 | PB | 375 | RGG |
| 38 Super | .356 | 115 | BB | 262 | RGG; SWS; LM |
| | .356 | 130 | PB | 81 | RGG; SWS; LM |
| | .356 | 130 | PB | 157 | RGG; MM; RSWS |
| | .356 | 130 | PB | 583 | RGG; OCG; SWS; MM |
| | .356 | 135 | PB | 55 | BB |
| | .356 | 135 | PB | 161 | RGG; MM; RSWS |
| | .356 | 145 | PB | 73 | BB; SGG; OCG; SWS; SM |
| | .356 | 145 | PB | 123 | RGG; SWS |
| | .356 | 150 | PB | 355 | SGG; SWS; SM |
| | .356 | 152 | BB | 335 | SGG; SWS; MM |
| | .356 | 155 | BB | 370 | SGG; MM |
| | .356 | 158 | BB | 39BB | RGG; OCG |
| | .356 | 158 | BB | 316BB | SGG; OCG; MM |
| 38 Special | .356 | 145 | PB | 219 | RGG; LEEF; LM |
| | .356 | 145 | BB | 259 | RGG; SWS |
| | .356 | 146 | PB | 244 | BB; RGG; OCG; LM |
| | .356 | 150 | PB | 248 | RGG; OCG; SWS; LM |
| 38 Gold Cup | .356 | 148 | BB | | BB; RGG; OCG; SWS; LM |
| 38 Spl./357 Mag. | .358 | 62 | PB | | RGG; LM |
| | .356 | 148 | BB | 251 | RGG; LM |
| | .356 | 148 | BB | 334 | SGG; LEEF; LM |
| | .358 | 100 | | 234 | GC base; RGG; OCG; SWS; MM |
| | .358 | 110 | PB | 41 | BB; RGG; OCG; SWS; LM |
| | .358 | 130 | PB | 246 | SGG; SWS; MM |
| | .358 | 135 | PB | 272 | SGG; OCG |

RGG = Round Grease Groove; SGG = Square Grease Groove; SM = Small Meplat; MM = Medium Meplat; LM = Large Meplat; OCG = One Crimp Groove; TCG = Two Crimp Grooves; PB = Plain Flat Base; BB = Bevel Base; GC = Gas Check; SWS = Semi- or Wadcutter Shoulder; 1DB = One Driving Band; 2DB = Two Driving Bands; 3DB = Three Driving Bands; 4DB = Four Driving Bands; 5DB = Five Driving Bands; RSWS = Rounded Semi-Wadcutter Shoulder; SBB = Short Bevel Base; LBB = Long Bevel Base; EB = Extended Base; OD = Oversize Diameter; NDB = No Driving Band in front of Crimp Groove; LEEF = Loaded Either End Forward; BRN = Bore Riding Nose. *Extra fee for special cross-venting for this design.

**See page 355 for prices.**

## HENSLEY & GIBBS Bullet Moulds

| Caliber | Bullet Dia. | Bullet Wgt. Grs. | Bullet Type | Mould # | Mould Comments |
|---|---|---|---|---|---|
| 38 Spl./357 Mag. | .358 | 140 | BB | 392 | RGG; OCG; NDB |
| | .358 | 140 | BB | 313BB | RGG; OCG; also for rev. bullet; SM |
| | .358 | 125 | PB | 313PB | RGG; OCG; also for rev. bullet; SM |
| | .358 | 140 | | 393 | GC; RGG; OCG; LM |
| | .358 | 140 | BB | 511 | SGG; OCG; MM |
| | .358 | 145 | PB | 63 | BB; RGG; OCG |
| | .358 | 145 | PB | 73 | BB; SGG; OCG; SM |
| | .358 | 146 | | 159 | RGG; OCG; SWS; tapered boattail; LM |
| | .358 | 148 | PB | 50 | BB; RGG; OCG; SWS; LM |
| | .358 | 150 | PB | 9 | BB; RGG; OCG; SWS; LM |
| | .358 | 130 | PB | 12C | GC; RGG; MM |
| | .358 | 140 | PB | 12B | GC; RGG; MM |
| | .358 | 150 | PB | 12A | GC; RGG; MM |
| | .358 | 150 | PB | 27 | BB; RGG; OCG |
| | .358 | 150 | PB | 61 | SGG; SWS; LM |
| | .358 | 150 | PB | 527 | BB; RGG; SWS; LM |
| | .358 | 156 | | 135 | GC; RGG; TCG; SWS; LM |
| | .358 | 156 | PB | 218 | RGG; OCG; SWS; LM |
| | .358 | 158 | PB | 28 | BB; RGG; OCG |
| | .358 | 158 | PB | 36 | RGG; OCG; SWS; LM |
| | .358 | 158 | PB | 39 | BB and GC base; RGG; OCG |
| | .358 | 158 | PB | 48 | BB; RGG; OCG; LM |
| | .358 | 158 | PB | 49 | BB; RGG; OCG; MM |
| | .358 | 158 | PB | 52 | RGG |
| | .358 | 158 | PB | 260 | RGG; SM |
| | .358 | 158 | PB | 316 | BB; SGG; OCG; MM |
| | .358 | 160 | PB | 51 | BB and GC base; SGG; OCG; LM |
| | .358 | 160 | | 236 | GC; RGG; OCG; SWS; LM |
| | .358 | 160 | PB | 290 | BB; SGG; OCG; SWS; LM |
| | .358 | 160 | BB | 801BB | SGG; OCG; SWS; LM |
| | .358 | 163* | PB | 64 | SGG; OCG; SWS; MM |
| | .358 | 165* | PB | 37 | BB; RGG; OCG; SWS; LM |
| | .358 | 165* | PB | 56 | RGG; OCG; TCG; SWS; LM |
| | .358 | 165* | | 268 | RGG; OCG; SWS; LM |
| | .358 | 170* | | 30 | GC; RGG |
| | .358 | 170* | | 394 | GC; RGG; OCG; LM |
| | .358 | 173* | PB | 43 | SGG; OCG; SWS; LM |
| | .358 | 185* | | 376 | RGG; OCG; LM |
| | .358 | 190* | PB | 395 | RGG; OCG; LM |
| | .358 | 125* | | 322-3 | RGG; OCG; 3DB; SM |
| | .358 | 158* | | 322-4 | RGG; OCG; 4DB; SM |
| | .358 | 190* | | 322-4GC | RGG; OCG; 3DB; SM; GC |
| | .358 | 175* | PB | 57-3 | RGG; OCG; 3DB; LM |
| | .358 | 200* | PB | 57-4 | RGG; OCG; 4DB; SM |
| | .358 | 200* | PB | 138 | RGG; OCG |
| | .358 | 215* | PB | 257 | |
| | .358 | 230* | BB | 127 | SGG; OCG; LM |
| 357 Maximum | .357/.358 | 200* | | 319 | SGG; OCG; SWS; LM |
| | .357/.358 | 200* | | 320 | GC; OCG; MM |
| | .357/.358 | 200* | | 321 | SGG; OCG; boattail bevel base; MM |
| 375 Super Mag. | .376 | 165* | | 380-3 | SGG; OCG; 3DB; MM |
| | .376 | 185* | | 380-3GC | SGG; OCG; 3DB; MM; GC |
| | .376 | 210* | | 380-4 | SGG; OCG; 4DB; MM |
| | .376 | 235* | | 380-4GC | SGG; OCG; 4DB; MM; GC |
| | .376 | 270* | | 380-5 | SGG; OCG; 5DB; MM |
| 38-40 | .401 | 180 | | 6 | BB; RGG; OCG |
| 41 Long Colt | .401 | 185 | PB | 121 | RGG |
| 40 S&W/10mm | .401 | 125 | PB | 365 | SGG |
| | .401 | 135 | BB | 374 | RGG; SWS; SM |
| | .401 | 145 | PB | 360 | SGG; revolvers/single shots only. |
| | .401 | 155 | PB | 373 | RGG; SM |
| | .401 | 155 | BB | S359BB | RGG; MM |
| | .401 | 175 | PB | 332 | BB; RGG; SWS; MM |
| | .401 | 155 | PB | S359PB | RGG; MM |
| | .401 | 180 | BB | 359BB | RGG; MM |
| | .401 | 190 | BB | 324 | SGG; LM |
| | .401 | 200 | PB | 315 | RGG; LM |
| | .401 | 200* | PB | 396 | RGG; OCG; LM |
| | .401 | 220* | PB | 397 | RGG; OCG; LM |
| 41 AE | .410 | 180 | BB | 342BB | RGG; SWS; medium shoulder |
| 41 Magnum | .410 | 79 | PB | 368 | RGG; SWS; LM |
| | .410 | 175 | PB | 255 | RGG; OCG; SWS; LM |
| | .410 | 175 | PB | 291 | SGG; OCG |
| | .410 | 210 | PB | 253 | RGG; LM |
| | .410 | 210 | PB | 256 | BB and GC; RGG; OCG; SWS; LM |
| | .410 | 210* | PB | 261 | RGG; OCG; SWS; MM |
| | .410 | 210* | PB | 263 | RGG; OCG |

RGG = Round Grease Groove; SGG = Square Grease Groove; SM = Small Meplat; MM = Medium Meplat; LM = Large Meplat; OCG = One Crimp Groove; TCG = Two Crimp Grooves; PB = Plain Flat Base; BB = Bevel Base; GC = Gas Check; SWS = Semi- or Wadcutter Shoulder; 1DB = One Driving Band; 2DB = Two Driving Bands; 3DB = Three Driving Bands; 4DB = Four Driving Bands; 5DB = Five Driving Bands; RSWS = Rounded Semi-Wadcutter Shoulder; SBB = Short Bevel Base; LBB = Long Bevel Base; EB = Extended Base; OD = Oversize Diameter; NDB = No Driving Band in front of Crimp Groove; LEEF = Loaded Either End Forward; BRN = Bore Riding Nose. *Extra fee for special cross-venting for this design.

See page 355 for prices.

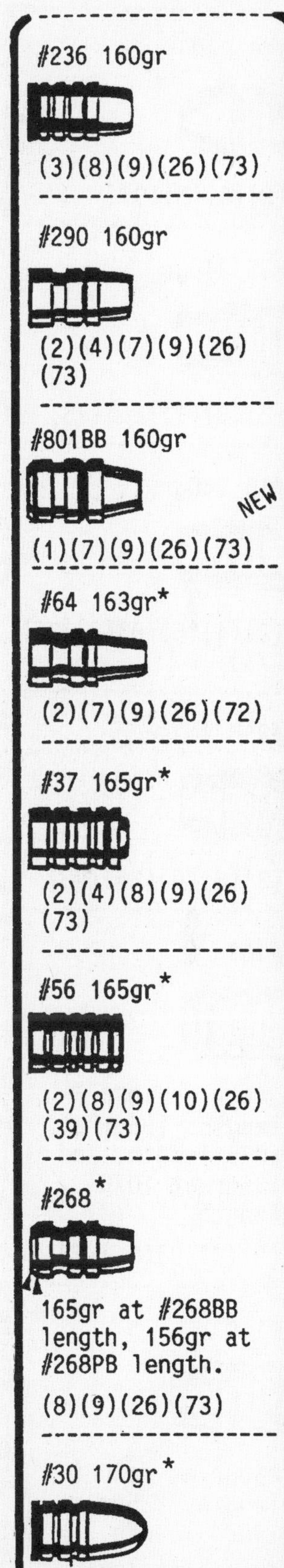

#15 240gr

(2)(6)(8)(9)

#35 240gr

(2)(8)(9)(26)(73)

#45 240gr

(2)(4)(6)(8)(9)(26)(73)

#235 240gr*

(3)(8)(9)(26)(73)

#107 *

245gr at 107A length, 185gr at 107B length, and 135gr at 107C length.

(2)(8)(9)(26)(73)

#140 *

250gr at #140GC length, 225gr at 140PB length.

(7)(9)(26)(73)

## HENSLEY & GIBBS Bullet Moulds

| | Bullet | | | Mould | |
|---|---|---|---|---|---|
| Caliber | Dia. | Wgt. Grs. | Type | # | Comments |
| 41 Magnum | .410 | 220* | PB | 258 | SGG; OCG; SWS; LM |
| 44-40 | .427 | 210 | PB | 44 | RGG; OCG; NDB; LM |
| | .427 | 250 | PB | 44GC | RGG; OCG; NDB; LM |
| | .427 | 210 | PB | 44BB | RGG; OCG; NDB; LM |
| 44 | .429/.431 | 85 | BB | 443 | RGG; LM |
| | .429/.431 | 87 | PB | 350 | RGG; LM |
| | .429/.431 | 180 | PB | 180 | RGG; LM; RSWS |
| | .429/.431 | 180 | PB | 273 | SGG; OCG |
| | .429/.431 | 185 | PB | 245 | RGG; SWS; MM |
| | .429/.431 | 185 | BB | 366 | SGG; LEEF; LM |
| | .429/.431 | 195 | PB | 340 | SGG; OCG; SM |
| | .429/.431 | 200 | | 237 | GC; RGG; OCG; SWS; LM |
| | .429/.431 | 200 | PB | 239 | RGG; OCG; LM |
| | .429/.431 | 200 | | 240 | GC; RGG; OCG |
| | .429/.431 | 200 | PB | 241 | RGG; OCG; SWS; LM |
| | .429/.431 | 205 | PB | 23 | RGG; LM |
| | .429/.431 | 205 | BB | 330 | RGG; OCG; SWS; LM |
| | .429/.431 | 210 | BB | 271 | RGG; SWS |
| | .429/.431 | 220 | PB | 247 | RGG; SWS |
| | .429/.431 | 225 | BB | 341 | SGG; OCG; LM |
| | .429/.431 | 190 | PB | 142PB | RGG; SWS; LM |
| | .429/.431 | 230 | | 142GC | RGG; SWS |
| | .429/.431 | 240 | PB | 15 | GC; RGG; OCG |
| | .429/.431 | 240 | PB | 35 | RGG; OCG; SWS; LM |
| | .429/.431 | 240 | PB | 45 | BB and GC; RGG; OCG; SWS; LM |
| | .429/.431 | 240* | | 235 | GC; RGG; SWS; LM |
| | .429/.431 | 135* | PB | 107C | RGG; OCG; SWS; LM |
| | .429/.431 | 185* | PB | 107B | RGG; OCG; SWS; LM |
| | .429/.431 | 245 | PB | 107A | RGG; OCG; SWS; LM |
| | .429/.431 | 225 | PB | 140PB | SGG; OCG; SWS; LM |
| | .429/.431 | 250 | | 140GC | SGG; OCG; SWS; LM |
| | .429/.431 | 225* | PB | 521PB | RGG; OCG; SWS; LM |
| | .429/.431 | 250* | | 521GC | RGG; OCG; SWS; LM |
| | .429/.431 | 270* | PB | 326 | SGG; OCG; SWS; LM |
| | .429/.431 | 280* | PB | 367 | RGG; OCG; LM |
| | .429/.431 | 280* | PB | 503S | SGG; OCG; SWS; EB band; LM |
| | .429/.431 | 300* | BB | 327 | RGG; OCG; MM |
| | .429/.431 | 300* | PB | 328 | SGG; OCG; SWS; LM |
| | .429/.431 | 300* | BB | 343 | SGG; OCG; LM |
| | .429/.431 | 300* | BB | 369 | SGG; OCG; LM |
| | .429/.431 | 320* | PB | 356 | RGG; OCG; LM |
| | .429/.431 | 95* | | 352-2 | SGG; 2DB; LM |
| | .429/.431 | 130* | | 352-2GC | SGG; 2DB; LM |
| | .429/.431 | 155* | | 352-3 | SGG; 3DB; LM |
| | .429/.431 | 195* | | 352-3GC | SGG; 3DB; LM |
| | .429/.431 | 240* | | 352-4 | SGG; 4DB; LM |
| | .429/.431 | 280* | | 352-4GC | SGG; 4DB; LM |
| | .429/.431 | 335* | | 352-5 | SGG; 5DB; LM |
| | .429/.431 | 255* | BB | 379-3GC | SGG; 3DB; OCG; LM |
| | .429/.431 | 300* | BB | 379-4GC | SGG; 4DB; OCG; LM |
| | .429/.431 | 335* | BB | 379-5 | SGG; 5DB; OCG; LM |
| 45 Auto | .452 | 155* | PB | 358PB | RGG; SWS; SM |
| | .452 | 155* | BB | 358BB | RGG; SWS; SM |
| | .452 | | PB | S242 | RGG; SWS; MM |
| | .452 | 170 | PB | 938 | SGG |
| | .452 | 172 | PB | 229 | RGG; SWS |
| | .452 | 180 | PB | 293 | RGG; SWS; LM |
| | .452 | 180 | PB | 337 | RGG; SWS; MM |
| | .452 | 185 | PB | 130 | BB; RGG; LM; RSWS |
| | .452 | 185 | PB | 163 | 2RGG; LM; RSWS |
| | .452 | 185 | PB | 242 | RGG; SWS; MM |
| | .452 | 200 | PB | 68 | BB; RGG; SWS; MM |
| | .452 | 200 | PB | 249 | RGG |
| | .452 | 200 | BB | 265 | SGG; SWS |
| | .452 | 200 | BB | 519 | Available with PB; RGG |
| | .452 | 215 | PB | 78 | BB; RGG; SWS; LM |
| | .452 | 215 | PB | 118 | BB; RGG; SWS |
| | .452 | 215 | BB | 351 | RGG; SWS; long tapered boattail; MM |
| | .452 | 220 | BB | 294 | RGG; SWS; long tapered boattail; MM |
| | .452 | 230 | PB | 34 | BB; RGG |
| | .452 | 230 | PB | 292 | BB; SGG |
| | .452 | 240 | PB | 329 | RGG; SWS; LM |
| | .452 | 219 | BB | 68BBA | SBB; 207-gr. lino; RGG; EB; SWS; MM |
| | .452 | 232 | BB | 68BBB | LBB; 219-gr. lino; RGG; EB; SWS; MM |
| | .452 | 231 | PB | 68S | 218-gr. lino; RGG; EB; SWS; MM |
| | .452 | 239 | BB | 68BBS | LBB; 226-gr. lino; RGG; EB; SWS; MM |

RGG = Round Grease Groove; SGG = Square Grease Groove; SM = Small Meplat; MM = Medium Meplat; LM = Large Meplat; OCG = One Crimp Groove; TCG = Two Crimp Grooves; PB = Plain Flat Base; BB = Bevel Base; GC = Gas Check; SWS = Semi- or Wadcutter Shoulder; 1DB = One Driving Band; 2DB = Two Driving Bands; 3DB = Three Driving Bands; 4DB = Four Driving Bands; 5DB = Five Driving Bands; RSWS = Rounded Semi-Wadcutter Shoulder; SBB = Short Bevel Base; LBB = Long Bevel Base; EB = Extended Base; OD = Oversize Diameter; NDB = No Driving Band in front of Crimp Groove; LEEF = Loaded Either End Forward; BRN = Bore Riding Nose. *Extra fee for special cross-venting for this design.

See page 355 for prices.

## HENSLEY & GIBBS Bullet Moulds

| Caliber | Bullet Dia. | Bullet Wgt. Grs. | Bullet Type | Mould # | Mould Comments |
|---|---|---|---|---|---|
| 45 L.C./45 A.R. | .454/.452 | 160 | PB | 193 | RGG; OCG; LM |
| | .454/.452 | 195 | PB | 312 | SGG; OCG |
| | .454/.452 | 200 | PB | 21 | RGG; OCG; MM |
| | .454/.452 | 200 | PB | 155 | RGG; OCG; SWS; LM |
| | .454/.452 | 215 | BB | 529 | RGG; OCG; SWS; LM |
| | .454/.452 | 230 | PB | 16 | RGG; OCG |
| | .454/.452 | 230 | PB | 371 | RGG; OCG; SWS |
| | .454/.452 | 240 | PB | 46 | BB and GC; RGG; OCG; SWS; LM |
| | .454/.452 | 240 | PB | 502 | SGG; OCG; SWS; LM |
| | .454/.452 | 250* | PB | 22 | RGG; MM |
| | .454/.452 | 255* | BB | 387 | RGG; OCG; LM |
| | .454/.452 | 260* | PB | 501 | SGG; OCG; SWS; LM |
| | .454/.452 | 265* | BB | 339 | RGG; OCG; LM |
| 454 Casull | .4515 | 300* | PB | 338 | SGG; OCG; SWS; LM |
| | .4515 | 219* | PB | 372-2GC | SGG; 2DB; LM |
| | .4515 | 257* | PB | 372-3 | SGG; 3DB; LM |
| | .4515 | 290* | PB | 372-3GC | SGG; 3DB; LM |
| | .4515 | 340* | PB | 372-4 | SGG; 4DB; LM |
| 45-70 | .458 | 350* | PB | 389 | RGG; MM |
| | .458 | 355* | PB | 348GC | RGG; OCG; SM |
| | .458 | 280* | PB | 348 | RGG; OCG; SM |
| | .458 | 300* | BB | 348BB | RGG; OCG; SM |
| | .458 | 355* | PB | 348GC | RGG; OCG; SM |
| | .458 | 275* | PB | 345-3 | SGG; 3DB; MM |
| | .458 | 325* | PB | 345-4 | SGG; 4DB; MM |
| | .458 | 395* | PB | 345-5 | SGG; 5DB; MM |
| | .458 | 285* | PB | 344-3 | SGG; 3DB; MM |
| | .458 | 340* | PB | 344-4 | SGG; 4DB; MM |
| | .458 | 405* | PB | 344-5 | SGG; 5DB; MM |
| | .458 | 360* | PB | 346 | RGG; TCG |
| | .458 | 380* | BB | 346 | RGG; TCG |
| | .458 | 405* | | 346GC | RGG; TCG |
| | .458 | 250* | PB | 349-2 | SGG; 2DB; OD; MM |
| | .458 | 300* | PB | 349-3 | SGG; 3DB; OD; MM |
| | .458 | 355* | PB | 349-4 | SGG; 4DB; OD; MM |
| | .458 | 405* | PB | 349-5 | SGG; 5DB; OD; MM |
| | .458 | 350* | PB | 390-4 | RGG; 4DB; BRN; SM |
| | .458 | 410* | PB | 390-5 | RGG; 5DB; BRN; SM |
| | .458 | 320* | PB | 364-3GC | SGG; 3DB; MM |
| | .458 | 345* | PB | 364-4 | SGG; 4DB; MM |
| | .458 | 375* | PB | 364-4GC | SGG; 4DB; MM |
| | .458 | 410* | PB | 364-5 | SGG; 5DB; MM |
| | .458 | 195* | PB | 347-2 | RGG; 2DB; MM |
| | .458 | 260* | PB | 347-3 | RGG; 3DB; MM |
| | .458 | 335* | PB | 347-4 | RGG; 4DB; MM |
| | .458 | 400* | PB | 347-5 | RGG; 5DB; MM |
| | .458 | 415* | PB | X347-5 | RGG; 5DB; MM |
| | .458 | 400* | PB | 391-5 | RGG; 5DB; MM |
| | .458 | 425* | PB | X391-5 | RGG; 5DB; MM |

RGG = Round Grease Groove; SGG = Square Grease Groove; SM = Small Meplat; MM = Medium Meplat; LM = Large Meplat; OCG = One Crimp Groove; TCG = Two Crimp Grooves; PB = Plain Flat Base; BB = Bevel Base; GC = Gas Check; SWS = Semi- or Wadcutter Shoulder; 1DB = One Driving Band; 2DB = Two Driving Bands; 3DB = Three Driving Bands; 4DB = Four Driving Bands; 5DB = Five Driving Bands; RSWS = Rounded Semi-Wadcutter Shoulder; SBB = Short Bevel Base; LBB = Long Bevel Base; EB = Extended Base; OD = Oversize Diameter; NDB = No Driving Band in front of Crimp Groove; LEEF = Loaded Either End Forward; BRN = Bore Riding Nose. *Extra fee for special cross-venting for this design.

**See page 355 for prices.**

### HENSLEY & GIBBS *Price Structure*

| Mould/Mould Part | 2 | 4 | 6 |
|---|---|---|---|
| Complete, light/short bullets | $101.00 | $135.00 | $175.00 |
| Complete, heavy/long bullets | 111.00 | 145.00 | 190.00 |
| Mould, no handles | 85.00 | 122.00 | 148.00 |
| Sprue cutter w/screws, trough-style | 18.00 | 30.00 | 31.00 |
| Sprue cutter w/screws, individual hole | | 40.00 | |
| Handles | 34.00 | 34.00 | 52.00 |
| Blocks, only | 68.00 | 93.00 | 118.00 |
| Sprue cutter hinge or stop screw | 2.00 | 2.00 | 2.00 |
| Front/rear lock screws (2) | 1.50 | 1.50 | 1.50 |
| Handle retainer screws (2) | 4.00 | 4.00 | 4.00 |
| Handle pivot bolt/nut | 1.50 | 1.50 | 2.00 |
| Complete set of screws | 9.50 | 9.50 | 10.50 |
| Complete set of screws plus handle pivot bolt/nut | 10.50 | 10.50 | 11.50 |
| Wood Grips | 5.00 | 5.00 | 6.00 |

## LOWETH

**Webley Mark II Mould**

Moulds to produce Webley Mark II .455″ 265-grain round-nose hollow base bullet and an exact copy of the naval bullet developed for the British Royal Navy Shooting Team; and 220-grain 455 Special Target bullet. Moulds made to original British government drawings of bullet. From Richard H. A. Loweth Firearms.

**Price:** . . . . . **Contact manufacturer.**

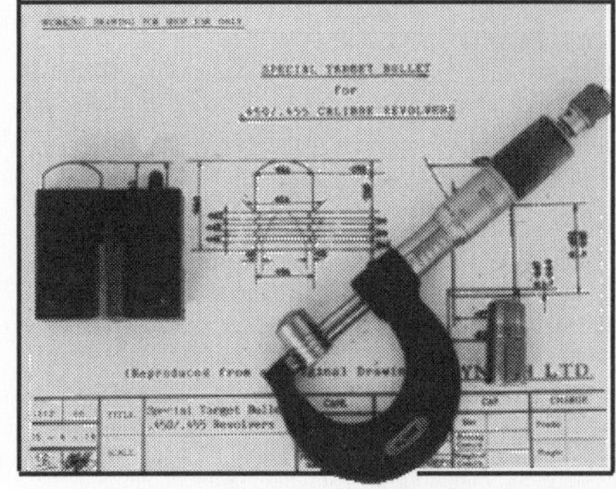


Loweth 455 Special Target Mould Design

Loweth Special Target Bullets

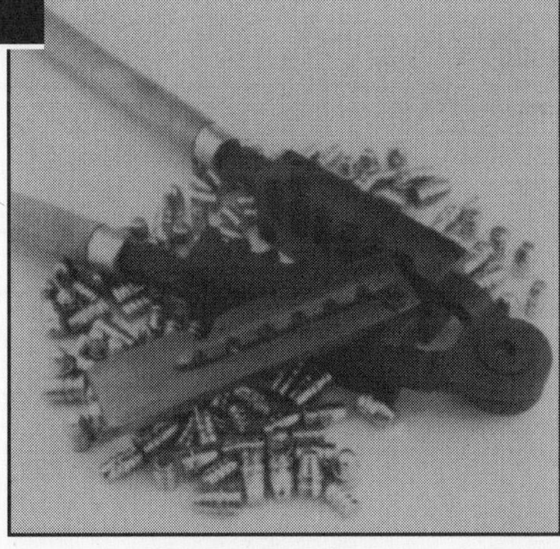

Hensley & Gibbs 6-Cavity Mould

# Section 4: Bullet Casting

## LBT

### Bullet Moulds

Custom 1-, 2- and 4-cavity mould blocks made of hard, stress-relieved 2024-T-351 aluminum with blued machine steel sprue plate. Blocks are larger than necessary to provide more heat radiating surface, higher caloric content and more precise block alignment. Pins are large and spaced further apart. Scientifically designed dual spring tension sprue plate and four-way venting eliminates bullet porosity and base out of squareness. A 60° shoulder angle on pivot screw bears side thrust of knocking sprues without loosening. Available in most popular handgun and rifle calibers. From Lead Bullets Technology.

**Price:** 1- or 2-cavity . . . . . . . **$55.00**
**Price:** 4-cavity . . . . . . . . . . **$95.00**

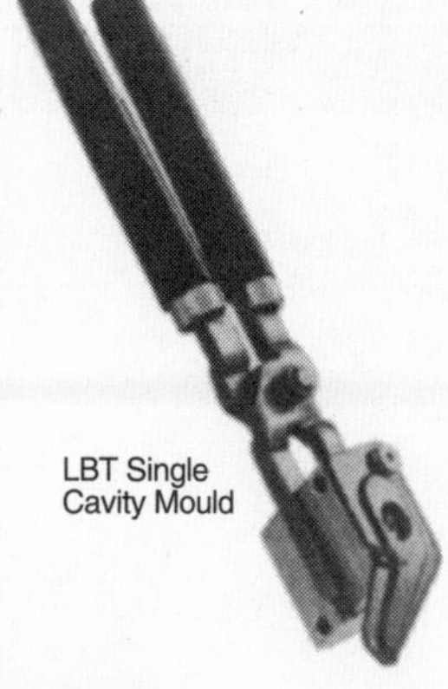

LBT Single Cavity Mould

## LEE

### Bullet Moulds

Aluminum 1- and 2-cavity mould blocks lathe bored to roundness of .001″ or less. Most bullets from Lee moulds can be used as cast without sizing. Lee single-cavity, double-cavity, hollowpoint and hollow base single-cavity moulds come with sprue plate and wood handles. Hollowpoint and hollow base moulds have self-centering automatic core pins. From Lee Precision, Inc.

**Price:** 1-cavity . . . . . . . . . . **$19.98**
**Price:** 2-cavity . . . . . . . . . . **$23.98**
**Price:** Hollowpoint/hollow base . . . **$24.98**
**Price:** Shotgun slug mould base . . **$25.98**

### Mould Handles

Precision steel mould handles fit all Lee moulds as well as most other brands of one- and two-cavity moulds. From Lee Precision, Inc.

**Price:** . . . . . . . . . . . . . **$14.98**

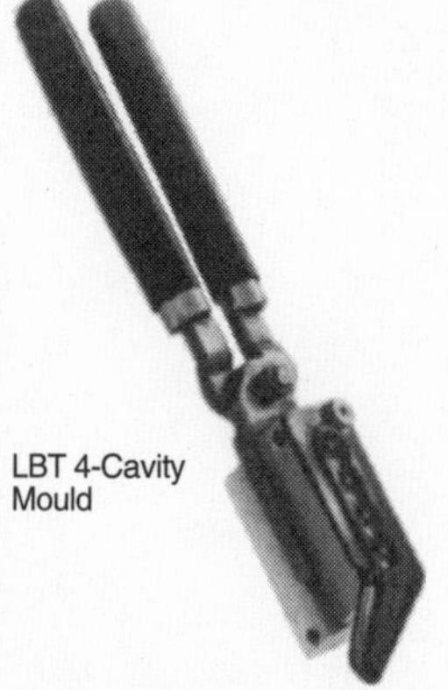

LBT 4-Cavity Mould

## LEE Rifle Bullet Moulds

| Dia. | Wgt. Grs. | Type | Ogive | Gas Check (C) | |
|---|---|---|---|---|---|
| Mould | Micro Bands (M) | | | | |
| **270-CALIBER** | | | | | |
| .277 | 125 | R | 1 | C | 1-cavity |
| **7MM CALIBER** | | | | | |
| .285 | 130 | R | 1 | C | 1-cavity |
| **30-CALIBER** | | | | | |
| .309 | 113 | F | | C | 2-cavity |
| .309 | 120 | R | 1 | C | 2-cavity |
| .309 | 130 | R | 1 | C | 1-cavity |
| .309 | 150 | F | | C | 1-cavity |
| .309 | 160 | R | 1 | C | 1-cavity |
| .309 | 170 | F | | C | 1-cavity |
| .309 | 180 | R | 1 | C | 1-cavity |
| .309 | 200 | R | 1 | C | 1-cavity |
| **7.62x39 CALIBER** | | | | | |
| .312 | 155 | R | 2 | | 1-cavity |
| .312 | 160 | R | 2 | M | 1-cavity |
| **7.65MM, 7.7MM, 303 BRITISH CALIBERS** | | | | | |
| .312 | 185 | R | 1 | | 1-cavity |
| **338-CALIBER** | | | | | |
| .338 | 220 | R | 1 | C | 1-cavity |
| **45-70 CALIBER** | | | | | |
| .457 | 340 | F | | | 1-cavity |
| .457 | 405 | F | | | 1-cavity* |
| .457 | 405 | HB | | | 1-cavity |
| .457 | 450 | F | | | 1-cavity |
| .457 | 500 | F | | | 1-cavity |
| **50-70 CALIBER** | | | | | |
| .515 | 450 | F | | | 1-cavity |
| .515 | 500 | F | | | 1-cavity |

R = Round Nose; F = Flat. *Hollow Point

## LEE Pistol Bullet Moulds

| Dia. | Wgt. Grs. | Type | Ogive | Micro Bands (M) Gas Check(C) | Mould |
|---|---|---|---|---|---|
| **32-20, 32 S&W LONG, 32 COLT NEW POLICE** | | | | | |
| .311 | 93 | R | 1 | | 2-, 6-cavity |
| .311 | 100 | R | 2 | | 2-cavity |
| .314 | 85 | WC | | M | 2-, 6-cavity |
| .314 | 90 | SWC | | M | 2-, 6-cavity |
| **38 SPECIAL, 38 S&W, 38 COLT NEW POLICE** | | | | | |
| .358 | 148 | WC | | | 2-, 6-cavity |
| .358 | 105 | SWC | | | 2-, 6-cavity |
| .358 | 140 | SWC | | | 2-, 6-cavity |
| .358 | 166 | SWC | | | 2-, 6-cavity |
| .358 | 148 | WC | | M | 2-, 6-cavity |
| .358 | 158 | SWC | | M | 2-, 6-cavity |
| .358 | 158 | SWC | | C | 2-, 6-cavity* |
| .358 | 158 | R | 2 | M | 2-, 6-cavity |
| .358 | 150 | R | 1 | | 2-, 6-cavity |
| .358 | 150 | WC | 1 | | 2-, 6-cavity |
| **9MM LUGER, 38 SUPER AUTO, 380 AUTO** | | | | | |
| .356 | 102 | R | 1 | | 2-, 6-cavity |
| .356 | 111 | R | 1 | | 2-, 6-cavity |
| .356 | 124 | R | 2 | M | 2-, 6-cavity |
| .356 | 124 | TC | | M | 2-, 6-cavity |
| .356 | 120 | TC | | | 2-, 6-cavity |
| .356 | 125 | R | 2 | | 2-, 6-cavity |
| .356 | 153 | R | 2 | | 2-, 6-cavity |
| **9MM MAKAROV** | | | | | |
| .365 | 95 | R | 1 | | 2-cavity |
| **10MM AUTO** | | | | | |
| .401 | 145 | SWC | | | 2-cavity |
| .401 | 175 | SWC | | M | 2-, 6-cavity |
| .401 | 175 | TC | | | |
| **41 MAGNUM, 41 ACTION EXPRESS** | | | | | |
| .410 | 195 | SWC | | M | 2-, 6-cavity |
| .410 | 240 | SWC | | | 2-, 6-cavity |
| .410 | 210 | SWC | | M | 2-, 6-cavity |
| .410 | 175 | SWC | | M | 2-, 6-cavity |
| **45 ACP, 45 AUTO RIM** | | | | | |
| .452 | 200 | SWC | | | 2-, 6-cavity |
| **44 SPECIAL, 44 MAGNUM, 44-40 (.427)** | | | | | |
| .429 | 200 | RF | | | |
| .429 | 208 | WC | | | 2-, 6-cavity |
| .429 | 214 | SWC | | | 2-, 6-cavity* |
| .429 | 240 | SWC | | C | 2-, 6-cavity* |
| .429 | 255 | SWC | | | 2-, 6-cavity |
| .429 | 214 | R | 1 | | 2-, 6-cavity |
| .429 | 240 | R | 2 | | 2-, 6-cavity |
| .429 | 240 | SWC | | M | 2-, 6-cavity |
| .430 | 310 | RF | | | 2-, 6-cavity |
| **45 ACP, 45 AUTO RIM** | | | | | |
| .452 | 155 | SWC | | | 2-, 6-cavity |
| .452 | 190 | SWC | | | 2-, 6-cavity |
| .452 | 200 | SWC | | M | 2-, 6-cavity |
| .452 | 228 | R | 1 | | 2-, 6-cavity* |
| .452 | 230 | R | 2 | | 2-, 6-cavity |
| .452 | 230 | TC | | | 2-, 6-cavity |
| .452 | 230 | TC | | | 2-, 6-cavity |
| .452 | 252 | SWC | | | 2-, 6-cavity |
| .452 | 255 | RF | | | 2-, 6-cavity |
| **45 COLT REVOLVER, 45 AUTO RIM** | | | | | |
| .452 | 252 | SWC | | | 2-, 6-cavity |
| .452 | 255 | RF | | | 2-, 6-cavity |

WC = Wadcutter; SWC = Semi-wadcutter; RF = Round with flat; RN = Round Nose; TC = Truncated Cone; M = Micro Bands Radius; C = Gas Check. *Hollow Point.

## LEE

### Six-Cavity Commercial Moulds

Designed for heavy-duty volume production. Mould and blocks have steel bushing and alignment pins. Cam-operated sprue plate is hard anodized and held with wave washers at each end. Handles not included. From Lee Precision, Inc.

**Price:** . . . . . . . . . . . . . **$50.00**

### Shotgun Slug Mould

The Lee 12-gauge Slug Mold features an exclusive "drive key" divider in the hollow base which serves to keep the wad from penetrating into the hollow base and ensures rotation of both wad and slug in a rifled barrel. Available for 1- or 7/8-oz. slug weights. Designed to be loaded in conventional trap hulls with standard trap wads. Comes complete with handles. From Lee Precision, Inc.

**Price:** . . . . . . . . . . . . . **$25.98**

## LBT Bullet Moulds

| Caliber | Wgt. Grs. | Type | Ogive* | Meplat | Length |
|---|---|---|---|---|---|
| **HANDGUN / AUTO PISTOL** | | | | | |
| 25 Auto | 50 | FN | SA | .200 | |
| 32 ACP | 75 | FN | SA | .200 | |
| 380 Auto | 100 | FN | SA | .200 | |
| | 100 | RN | SA | .200 | |
| | 110 | FN | SA | .200 | |
| | 120 | FN | SA | .200 | |
| 9MM | 90 | FN | SA | .200 | |
| | 95 | TC | SA | .200 | |
| | 110 | TC | SA | .200 | |
| | 125 | TC | SA | .200 | |
| | 140 | BR | SA | .200 | |
| | 120 | FNBR | SA | .200 | |
| 10mm Auto | 180 | TC | SA | .200 | |
| | 185 | FNB | SA | .200 | |
| | 165 | SWC | SA | .200 | |
| 45 Auto | 200 | SWC | SA | .200 | |
| | 190 | FNB | SA | .200 | |
| | 220 | FNB | SA | .200 | |
| | 230 | B | SA | .200 | |
| **HANDGUN / REVOLVER / WADCUTTERS** | | | | | |
| 32 | 100 | WC | NA | NA | |
| 38 | 150 | WC | NA | NA | |
| 375 | 170 | WC | NA | NA | |
| 41 | 200 | WC | NA | NA | |
| 44 | 230 | WC | NA | NA | |
| 45 | 260 | WC | NA | NA | |
| **HANDGUN / REVOLVER / SFN SERIES** | | | | | |
| 32 | 90 | SFN | .160 | .080 | |
| | 90 | FN | .250 | .090 | |
| | 100 | SFN | .160 | .080 | |
| | 115 | FN | .250 | .090 | |
| | 140 | FN | .250 | .090 | |
| 38 | 140 | FN | .250 | .090 | |
| | 160 | FN | .250 | .090 | |
| | 180 | FN | .250 | .090 | |
| | 200 | FN | .250 | .090 | Crimp to nose .350 & .400 |
| 375 | 240 | WFN | .250 | .090 | |
| 41 | 200 | WFN | .250 | .090 | |
| | 220 | WFN | .250 | .090 | |
| | 250 | WFN | .250 | .090 | |
| | 300 | WFN | .250 | .090 | |
| 44 | 230 | WFN | .250 | .090 | |
| | 260 | WFN | .250 | .090 | |
| | 280 | WFN | .250 | .090 | |
| | 300 | WFN | .250 | .090 | |
| 45 | 250 | WFN | .250 | .090 | |
| | 280 | WFN | .250 | .090 | |
| | 325 | WFN | .250 | .090 | |
| 475 | 400 | WFN | .250 | .090 | |
| 500 | 400 | WFN | .250 | .090 | |
| **HANDGUN / REVOLVER / WLN SERIES** | | | | | |
| 38 | 180 | WLN | .400 | .090 | |
| 41 | 230 | WLN | .400 | .090 | |
| 44 | 300 | WLN | .400 | .090 | |
| 45 | 320 | WLN | .400 | .090 | |
| **HANDGUN / REVOLVER / LFN SERIES** | | | | | |
| 358 | 180 | LFN | .130 | .340 | .725 |
| | 210 | LFN | .130 | .340 | .840 |
| 375 | 210 | LFN | .130 | .340 | .770 |
| | 225 | LFN | .130 | .340 | .818 |
| | 240 | LFN | .130 | .340 | .240 |
| 41 | 210 | LFN | .130 | .340 | .660 |
| | 230 | LFN | .130 | .340 | .715 |
| | 250 | LFN | .130 | .340 | .774 |
| 44 | 250 | LFN | .130 | .340 | .675 |
| | 280 | LFN | .130 | .340 | .775 |
| | 300 | LFN | .130 | .340 | .820 |
| | 320 | LFN | .130 | .340 | .860 |
| | 350 | LFN | .130 | .340 | .920 |
| 45 | 260 | LFN | .130 | .340 | .675 |
| | 300 | LFN | .130 | .340 | .775 |
| | 320 | LFN | .130 | .340 | .820 |
| | 340 | LFN | .130 | .340 | .870 |
| 475 | 380 | LFN | .130 | .340 | .855 |
| | 400 | LFN | .130 | .340 | .940 |
| | 420 | LFN | .130 | .340 | .955 |
| | 440 | LFN | .130 | .340 | .970 |
| 500 | 400 | LFN | .130 | .340 | .820 |
| | 420 | LFN | .130 | .340 | .820 |
| | 450 | LFN | .130 | .340 | .855 |
| **HANDGUN / REVOLVER / K SERIES** | | | | | |
| 44 | 250 | K | | .340 | |
| 45 | 260 | K | | .340 | |
| | 315 | K | | .340 | |

| Caliber | Wgt. Grs. | Type | Ogive* | Meplat | Length |
|---|---|---|---|---|---|
| **RIFLE & SINGLE SHOT HANDGUN / LFN SERIES** | | | | | |
| 257 | 90 | LFN | .130 | .340 | .745 |
| | 100 | LFN | .130 | .340 | .820 |
| | 117 | LFN | .130 | .340 | .950 |
| 270 | 120 | LFN | .130 | .340 | .840 |
| | 140 | LFN | .130 | .340 | .950 |
| | 150 | LFN | .130 | .340 | 1.010 |
| 7mm | 130 | LFN | .130 | .340 | .835 |
| | 150 | LFN | .130 | .340 | .955 |
| | 170 | LFN | .130 | .340 | 1.070 |
| 310 | 150 | LFN | .130 | .340 | .820 |
| | 170 | LFN | .130 | .340 | .940 |
| | 180 | LFN | .130 | .340 | .955 |
| | 200 | LFN | .130 | .340 | 1.010 |
| 323 | 150 | LFN | .130 | .340 | .754 |
| | 170 | LFN | .130 | .340 | .840 |
| | 200 | LFN | .130 | .340 | .971 |
| 338 | 200 | LFN | .130 | .340 | .990 |
| | 225 | LFN | .130 | .340 | .880 |
| | 250 | LFN | .130 | .340 | 1.090 |
| 348 | 200 | LFN | .130 | .340 | .850 |
| | 250 | LFN | .130 | .340 | 1.035 |
| 358 | 210 | LFN | .130 | .340 | .840 |
| | 225 | LFN | .130 | .340 | .880 |
| | 250 | LFN | .130 | .340 | .965 |
| 375 | 225 | LFN | .130 | .340 | .880 |
| | 240 | LFN | .130 | .340 | .865 |
| | 275 | LFN | .130 | .340 | .978 |
| | 300 | LFN | .130 | .340 | 1.057 |
| 40/416 | 350 | LFN | .130 | .340 | 1.025 |
| | 375 | LFN | .130 | .340 | 1.070 |
| | 400 | LFN | .130 | .340 | 1.155 |
| 458 | 300 | LFN | .130 | .340 | .775 |
| | 340 | LFN | .130 | .340 | .870 |
| | 450 | LFN | .130 | .340 | 1.072 |
| | 500 | LFN | .130 | .340 | 1.192 |
| **RIFLE & SINGLE SHOT / SPITZER** | | | | | |
| 223 | 50 | SP | .264 | | .300 |
| | 55 | SP | .264 | | .350 |
| | 60 | SP | .264 | | .400 |
| | 66 | SP | .264 | | .450 |
| 227 | 65 | SP | .275 | | .410 |
| | 75 | SP | .275 | | .410 |
| 243 | 75 | SP | .295 | | .420 |
| | 90 | SP | .295 | | .530 |
| | 100 | SP | .295 | | .610 |
| 257 | 80 | SP | .303 | | .370 |
| | 90 | SP | .303 | | .440 |
| | 100 | SP | .303 | | .510 |
| | 120 | SP | .303 | | .650 |
| 264 | 100 | SP | .310 | | .500 |
| | 120 | SP | .310 | | .620 |
| | 130 | SP | .310 | | .680 |
| | 150 | SP | .310 | | .800 |
| 270 | 90 | SP | .317 | | .380 |
| | 100 | SP | .317 | | .440 |
| | 110 | SP | .317 | | .500 |
| | 130 | SP | .317 | | .600 |
| 7mm | 110 | SP | .322 | | .435 |
| | 120 | SP | .322 | | .500 |
| | 140 | SP | .322 | | .550 |
| | 150 | SP | .322 | | .670 |
| 7.35/302 | 150 | SP | .335 | | .565 |
| | 170 | SP | .335 | | .670 |
| | 194 | SP | .335 | | .800 |
| 310 | 140 | SP | .341 | | .620 |
| | 160 | SP | .341 | | .675 |
| | 180 | SP | .341 | | .730 |
| | 206 | SP | .341 | | .800 |
| 323 | 150 | SP | .350 | | .480 |
| | 150 | SP | .350 | | .480 |
| | 175 | SP | .350 | | .590 |
| | 200 | SP | .350 | | .700 |
| | 220 | SP | .350 | | .800 |
| 338 | 200 | SP | .360 | | .610 |
| | 225 | SP | .360 | | .710 |
| | 246 | SP | .360 | | .800 |
| 358 | 200 | SP | .375 | | .500 |
| | 250 | SP | .375 | | .730 |
| 375 | 275 | SP | .385 | | .700 |
| | 310 | SP | .385 | | .800 |
| 405-410 | | SP | .400 | | .500 |
| | 300 | SP | .400 | | .600 |
| | 370 | SP | .400 | | .800 |
| 458 | 350 | SP | .425 | | .535 |
| | 400 | SP | .425 | | .640 |
| | 500 | SP | .425 | | .850 |
| 475 | 400 | SP | .430 | | .550 |
| | 510 | SP | .430 | | .800 |
| 512 | 500 | SP | .450 | | .600 |
| | 600 | SP | .450 | | .800 |

SA = Small Auto; FN = Flat Nose; RN = Round Nose; LFN = Long Flat Base; WFN = Wide Flat Nose; FNB = Flat Nose Ball; SP = Spitzer; K = Keith-style

# Section 4: Bullet Casting



## LYMAN

**Ideal Moulds**

Machined from high-grade steel; blocks are hand fit for precision alignment. Pistol bullet moulds available for all popular bullet designs and come in 2- or 4-cavity blocks. Rifle moulds available in 2-cavity only except where bullet size necessitates single cavity. From Lyman Products Corporation.

**Price:** Pistol, 2-cavity . . . . . . **$49.95**
**Price:** Pistol, 4-cavity . . . . . . **$76.50**
**Price:** Rifle . . . . . . . . . . . **$49.95**

**Shotgun Slug Moulds**

Available for 12- or 20-gauge slugs. Mould casts hollow-base slugs which require no rifling. Single-cavity only and cut into the larger double cavity block. Require double cavity handles. From Lyman Products Corporation.

**Price:** . . . . . . . . . . . . **$49.95**

**Mould Rebuild Kit**

Includes sprue cutter, washer, all screws for mould block and handle. From Lyman Products Corporation.

**Price:** 1- and 2-cavity . . . . . . . **$5.00**
**Price:** 4-cavity . . . . . . . . . . **$6.50**

**Mould Box**

Made of tough plastic with snap-lock cover. Impervious to moisture, bore cleaner or oil. Fits single- and double-cavity moulds only. From Lyman Products Corporation.

**Price:** . . . . . . . . . . . . . . **$2.00**
**Price:** 10 . . . . . . . . . . . . **$15.00**

## LYMAN Rifle Bullet Moulds

| Bullet # | Caliber | Dia. | Wgt. Grs. | Top Punch # | Gas Check # | # Cavity Mould |
|---|---|---|---|---|---|---|
| 225438 | 22 | .225 | 44 | 438 | GC | 2 |
| 225415 | | .225 | 55 | 415 | GC | 2 |
| 225646 | | .225 | 55 | 415 | GC | 2 |
| 245496 | 6mm | .245 | 84 | 203 | GC | 2 |
| 257420 | 25 | .257 | 65 | 420 | GC | 2 |
| 266469 | 6.5mm | .266 | 140 | 463 | GC | 2 |
| 268645 | | .268 | 150 | 463 | GC | 2 |
| 280642 | 270 Win. | .280 | 150 | 359 | | 2 |
| 287346 | 7mm | .287 | 135 | 346 | GC | 2 |
| 287641 | | .287 | 160 | 359 | GC | 2 |
| 311359 | 30 M1/7.62x39mm | .311 | 115 | 359 | GC | 2 |
| 311410 | | .311 | 130 | 467 | | 2 |
| 311466 | 30 | .311 | 152 | 467 | GC | 2 |
| 311291 | | .311 | 170 | 465 | GC | 2 |
| 311041 | | .311 | 173 | 8 | GC | 2 |
| 311332 | | .311 | 180 | 413 | GC | 2 |
| 311644 | | .311 | 190 | 359 | GC | 2 |
| 311284 | | .311 | 210 | 467 | GC | 2 |
| 311316 | 32-20 | .311 | 112 | 8 | GC | 2 |
| 311008 | | .311 | 115 | 8 | | 2 |
| 314299 | 314 | .314 | 200 | 467 | GC | 2 |
| 323470 | 8mm | .323 | 165 | 470 | GC | 2 |
| 358315 | 35 | .358 | 204 | 311 | GC | 2 |
| 358009 | | .358 | 280 | 430 | GC | 2 |
| 375248 | 375/38-55 | .375 | 249 | 449 | | 2 |
| 375449 | | .375 | 264 | 449 | GC | 2 |
| 403169 | | .403 | 240 | 43 | | 2 |
| 410660 | | .410 | 385 | 658 | | 2 |
| 410655 | 40 | .410 | 400 | 449 | | 2 |
| 429434 | 44-40 | .429 | 215 | 43 | GC | 2 |
| 439186 | 43 Spanish | .439 | 370 | 251 | 2 | |
| 457191 | 45 | .457 | 292 | 191 | | 2 |
| 457122 | 45 HP | .457 | 330 | 191 | | 2 |
| 457124 | | .457 | 385 | 374 | | 2 |
| 457643 | | .457 | 400 | 191 | | 2 |
| 457193 | | .457 | 405 | 191 | | 2 |
| 457406 | | .457 | 475 | 374 | GC | 2 |
| 457658 | | .457 | 480 | 658 | | 2 |
| 457125 | | .457 | 500 | 374 | | 2 |
| 457132 | 45 Postell | .457 | 535 | 132 | | 2 |
| 515141 | 50 | .515 | 425 | 141 | | 2 |

## LYMAN Pistol Bullet Moulds

| Mould # | Caliber | Dia. | Wgt. Grs. | Top Punch # | Gas Check | # Cavity Mould |
|---|---|---|---|---|---|---|
| 25235 | 25 | .252 | 50 | 203 | | 2 |
| 311252 | 30 | .311 | 75 | 465 | | 2 |
| 313249 | 32 | .313 | 85 | 226 | | 2 |
| 313631 | | .313 | 100 | 8 | GC | 2 |
| 35642 | 9mm | .356 | 90 | 311 | | 2 |
| 356632 | | .356 | 100 | 402 | | 2, 4 |
| 356402 | | .356 | 120 | 402 | | 2, 4 |
| 356242 | | .356 | 120 | 311 | | 2, 4 |
| 356634 | | .356 | 130 | 402 | | 2, 4 |
| 356637 | | .356 | 147 | 429 | | 2, 4 |
| 358345 | 38/357 | .358 | 115 | 429 | | 2 |
| 358093 | | .358 | 125 | 93 | | 2 |
| 358495 | | .358 | 140 | 495 | | 2, 4 |
| 358212 | | .358 | 145 | 311 | | 2 |
| 358091 | | .358 | 150 | 495 | | 2, 4 |
| 358477 | | .358 | 150 | 429 | | 2, 4 |
| 358156 | | .358 | 155 | 429 | GC | 2, 4 |
| 358665 | | .358 | 158 | 495 | | 2 |
| 358311 | | .358 | 160 | 311 | | 2, 4 |
| 357446 | | .357 | 165 | 429 | | 2, 4 |
| 358429 | | .358 | 170 | 429 | | 2, 4 |
| 358430 | | .358 | 195 | 430 | | 2 |
| 358627 | 357 Max. | .358 | 215 | 429 | GC | 2 |
| 364653 | 9mm Mak. | .364 | 95 | 226 | | 2 |
| 401654 | 40 S&W/10mm | .401 | 150 | 43 | | 2 |
| 401638 | | .401 | 175 | 43 | | 2, 4 |
| 401043 | | .401 | 175 | 43 | | 2 |
| 401633 | | .401 | 200 | 43 | | 2 |
| 410610 | 41 | .410 | 215 | 43 | GC | 2 |
| 427098 | 44-40 | .427 | 205 | 43 | | 2 |
| 427666 | | .427 | 200 | 649 | | 2 |
| 429348 | 44/44 Mag. | .429 | 180 | 348 | | 2 |
| 429303 | | .429 | 200 | 303 | GC | 2 |
| 429215 | | .429 | 210 | 421 | GC | 2, 4 |
| 429360 | | .429 | 235 | 360 | | 2 |
| 429667 | | .429 | 240 | 649 | | 2 |
| 429421 | | .429 | 245 | 421 | | 2, 4 |
| 429383 | | .429 | 245 | 251 | | 2 |
| 429244 | | .429 | 255 | 421 | GC | 2, 4 |
| 429640 | | .429 | 275 | 421 | GC | 2 |
| 429650 | | .429 | 300 | 421 | GC | 2 |
| 429649 | | .429 | 325 | 360 | GC | 2 |
| 452460 | 45 | .452 | 200 | 460 | | 2, 4 |
| 452630 | | .452 | 200 | 460 | | 2, 4 |
| 452374 | | .452 | 225 | 374 | | 2, 4 |
| 452424 | | .452 | 255 | 424 | | 2 |
| 452490 | | .452 | 255 | 424 | GC | 2 |
| 452651 | | .452 | 325 | 424 | GC | 2 |
| 452664 | 45 LC | .452 | 250 | 649 | | 2 |
| 454190 | 45 Colt | .454 | 250 | 190 | | 2 |
| | | **Hollowpoint Bullets** | | | | |
| 356637 | 9mm | .356 | 125 | 429 | | |
| 401638 | 10mm | .401 | 155 | 43 | | |
| 429640 | 44 | .429 | 250 | 421 | GC | |
| 452374 | 45 | .452 | 180 | 374 | | |

## LYMAN

**Mould Handles**

*Lyman no longer manufactures small single cavity mould blocks. All current Lyman single- and double-cavity moulds are now made using standard large mould blocks and require large mould handles.* Solid metal frame with hardwood handles designed to provide uniform grip. Three sizes available: small, for older single cavity moulds; large, for current manufacture large block single-cavity and double-cavity moulds; and four-cavity for Lyman four-cavity moulds. From Lyman Products Corporation.

**Price:** 1- and 2-cavity . . . . . . **$24.00**
**Price:** 4-cavity . . . . . . . . . . **$28.00**

**Sabot Slug Mould**

A 20-gauge 350-grain slug designed to fit standard Winchester wads and be star crimped. Comes complete with load data. From Lyman Products Corporation.

**Price:** . . . . . . . . . . . . . **$48.75**

Lyman Pistol Bullet Moulds

| Pistol | .25 | .30 | .32 | | 9mm | | | | | | .38/.357 | | |
|---|---|---|---|---|---|---|---|---|---|---|---|---|---|
| Bullet Number | 252435 | 311252 | 313249 | 313631 | 356242 | 356632 | 356402 | 356242 | 356634 | 356637 | 358345 | 358093 | 358495 |
| Weight (#2 Alloy) | 50 gr. | 75 gr. | 85 gr. | 100 gr. | 90 gr. | 100 gr. | 120 gr. | 120 gr. | 130 gr. | 147 gr. | 115 gr. | 125 gr. | 140 gr. |
| Double Cavity Part # | 2660435 | 2660252 | 2660249 | 2660631 | 2661242 | 2660632 | 2660402 | 2660242 | 2660634 | 2660637 | 2660345 | 2660093 | 2660495 |
| Top Punch Number | 203 | 465 | 226 | 6 | 311 | 402 | 402 | 311 | 402 | 429 | 429 | 93 | 495 |
| Top Punch Part # | 2786748 | 2786742 | 2786703 | 2786690 | 2786710 | 2786723 | 2786723 | 2786710 | 2786723 | 2786731 | 2786731 | 2786754 | 2786789 |
| Four Cavity Part # | — | — | — | — | — | 2670632 | 2670402 | — | 2670634 | 2670637 | — | — | 2670495 |

| Pistol (cont'd) | .38/.357 | | | | | | | | .357 max | 9mm mak. | 40 S&W/10mm | | | |
|---|---|---|---|---|---|---|---|---|---|---|---|---|---|---|
| Bullet Number | 358212 | 358091 | 358477 | 358156 | 358311 | 357446 | 358429 | 358430 | 358627 | 364663 | 401654 | 401638 | 401043 | 401633 |
| Weight (#2 Alloy) | 145 gr. | 150 gr. | 150 gr. | 155 gr. | 160 gr. | 165 gr. | 170 gr. | 195 gr. | 215 gr. | 95 gr. | 150 gr. | 175 gr. | 175 gr. | 200 gr. |
| Double Cavity Part # | 2660212 | 2660091 | 2660477 | 2660156 | 2660311 | 2660446 | 2660429 | 2660430 | 2660627 | 2660663 | 2660654 | 2660638 | 2660043 | 2660633 |
| Top Punch Number | 311 | 495 | 429 | 429 | 311 | 429 | 429 | 430 | 429 | 226 | 43 | 43 | 43 | 43 |
| Top Punch Part # | 2786710 | 2786769 | 2786731 | 2786731 | 2786710 | 2786731 | 2786731 | 2786732 | 2786731 | 2786703 | 2786691 | 2786691 | 2786691 | 2786691 |
| Four Cavity Part # | — | 2670091 | 2670477 | 2670156 | 2670311 | 2670446 | 2670429 | — | — | — | — | 2670638 | — | — |

| Pistol (cont'd) | .41 | .44/40 | .44 & .44 mag | | | | | | | | | | .45 | |
|---|---|---|---|---|---|---|---|---|---|---|---|---|---|---|
| Bullet Number | 410610 | 427098 | 429348 | 429303 | 429215 | 429360 | 429421 | 429383 | 429244 | 429640 | 429650 | 429649 | 452460 | 452630 |
| Weight (#2 Alloy) | 215 gr. | 205 gr. | 180 gr. | 200 gr. | 210 gr. | 235 gr. | 245 gr. | 245 gr. | 255 gr. | 275 gr. | 300 gr. | 325 gr. | 200 gr. | 200 gr. |
| Double Cavity Part # | 2660610 | 2660098 | 2660348 | 2660303 | 2660215 | 2660360 | 2660421 | 2660383 | 2660244 | 2660640 | 2660650 | 2660649 | 2660460 | 2660630 |
| Top Punch Number | 43 | 43 | 348 | 303 | 421 | 360 | 421 | 251 | 421 | 421 | 421 | 649 | 460 | 460 |
| Top Punch Part # | 2786691 | 2786691 | 2786716 | 2786709 | 2786729 | 2786717 | 2786729 | 2786704 | 2786729 | 2786729 | 2786729 | 2786778 | 2786740 | 2786740 |
| Four Cavity Part # | — | — | — | — | 2670215 | — | 2670421 | — | 2670244 | — | — | — | 2670460 | 2670630 |

| Pistol (cont'd) | .45 | .45 Colt .454 dia. | .45 Colt .452 dia. | .45 Colt .452 dia. | .45 |
|---|---|---|---|---|---|
| Bullet Number | 452374 | 454190 | 452424 | 452490 | 452651 |
| Weight (#2 Alloy) | 225 gr. | 250 gr. | 255 gr. | 255 gr. | 325 gr. |
| Double Cavity Part # | 2660374 | 2660190 | 2660422 | 2660490 | 2660651 |
| Top Punch Number | 374 | 190 | 424 | 424 | 424 |
| Top Punch Part # | 2786719 | 2786700 | 2786730 | 2786730 | 2786730 |
| Four Cavity Part # | 2670374 | — | — | — | — |

| Hollow Point Bullets | 9mm | .10mm | .44 | .45 |
|---|---|---|---|---|
| Bullet Number | 358637 | 401638 | 429640 | 452374 |
| Weight (#2 Alloy) | 125 gr. | 155 gr. | 250 gr. | 180 gr. |
| Mould # | 2658637 | 2650638 | 2650640 | 2658374 |
| Top Punch Number | 429 | 43 | 421 | 374 |
| Top Punch Part # | 2786731 | 2786691 | 2786729 | 2786719 |

**DEVASTATOR H.P. BULLETS**
"Big Mouth" hollow point bullets were designed for maximum expansion at handgun velocities when cast from softer alloys like wheelweight metal.

NOTE: All standard rifle and pistol moulds use handles #2735793, and four-cavity moulds use handle #2735794.
Bullet weights listed are nominal and may well vary from bullets dropped from a given mould. Variations between listed nominal weights and actual as-cast weights have absolutely no effect on accuracy.
These bullet illustrations are artists' renderings. They are for general reference only and are not intended to be precise representation.

Lyman Rifle Bullet Moulds

| Rifle | .22 | | | 6mm | .25 | 6.5mm | | .270 Win. | 7mm | | .30 M1/ 7.62x39mm | | .30 | |
|---|---|---|---|---|---|---|---|---|---|---|---|---|---|---|
| Bullet Number | 225438 | 225415 | 225646 | 245496 | 257420 | 266469 | 266645 | 280642 | 287346 | 287641 | 311359 | 311410 | 311466 | 311291 |
| Weight (#2 Alloy) | 44 gr. | 55 gr. | 55 gr. | 84 gr. | 65 gr. | 140 gr. | 150 gr. | 150 gr. | 135 gr. | 160 gr. | 115 gr. | 130 gr. | 152 gr. | 170 gr. |
| Mould # | 2660438 | 2660415 | 2660646 | 2660496 | 2660420 | 2660469 | 2660645 | 2660642 | 2660346 | 2660641 | 2660359 | 2660410 | 2660466 | 2660291 |
| Top Punch Number | 438 | 415 | 415 | 203 | 420 | 463 | 463 | 359 | 346 | 359 | 359 | 467 | 467 | 465 |
| Top Punch Part # | 2786733 | 2786726 | 2786726 | 2786748 | 2786728 | 2786741 | 2786741 | 2786772 | 2786715 | 2786772 | 2786772 | 2786743 | 2786743 | 2786742 |

| Rifle cont'd. | .30 | | | | 32/20 | | .314 dia. | 8mm | .35 | | .375/ .38-55 | | .40 Cal. .406 dia. | .40 Cal. .410 dia. ★ |
|---|---|---|---|---|---|---|---|---|---|---|---|---|---|---|
| Bullet Number | 311041 | 311332 | 311644 | 311284 | 311316 | 311008 | 314299 | 323470 | 358315 | 358009 | 375248 | 375449 | 403169 | 410655 |
| Weight (#2 Alloy) | 173 gr. | 180 gr. | 190 gr. | 210 gr. | 112 gr. | 115 gr. | 200 gr. | 165 gr. | 204 gr. | 280 gr. | 249 gr. | 264 gr. | 240 gr. | 400 gr. |
| Mould # | 2660041 | 2660332 | 2660644 | 2660284 | 2660316 | 2660008 | 2660299 | 2660470 | 2660315 | 2660009 | 2660248 | 2660449 | 2660169 | 2640655 |
| Top Punch Number | 8 | 413 | 359 | 467 | 8 | 8 | 467 | 470 | 311 | 430 | 449 | 449 | 43 | 449 |
| Top Punch Part # | 2786690 | 2786725 | 2786772 | 2786743 | 2786690 | 2786690 | 2786743 | 2786745 | 2786710 | 2786732 | 2786736 | 2786736 | 2786691 | 2786736 |

| Rifle cont'd. | .44/ 40 | .43 Span. ★ | .45 ★ | H.P. ★ | ★ | ★ | ★ | ★ | ★ NEW | ★ | .50 ★ | Shotgun Slugs | | NEW Sabot Slug |
|---|---|---|---|---|---|---|---|---|---|---|---|---|---|---|
| Bullet Number | 429434 | 439186 | 457191 | 457122 | 457124 | 457643 | 457193 | 457406 | 457658 | 457125 | 515141 | 20 ga. | 12 ga. | 12 ga. |
| Weight (#2 Alloy) | 215 gr. | 370 gr. | 292 gr. | 330 gr. | 385 gr. | 400 gr. | 405 gr. | 475 gr. | 480 gr. | 500 gr. | 425 gr. | 345 gr. | 475 gr. | 525 gr. |
| Mould # | 2660434 | 2640186 | 2640191 | 2650122 | 2640124 | 2640643 | 2640193 | 2640406 | 2640658 | 2640125 | 2640141 | 2654020 | 2654012 | 2654112 |
| Top Punch Number | 43 | 251 | 191 | 191 | 374 | 191 | 191 | 374 | 658 | 374 | 141 | — | — | Use with |
| Top Punch Part # | 2786691 | 2786704 | 2786701 | 2786701 | 2786719 | 2786701 | 2786701 | 2786719 | 2786755 | 2786719 | 2786696 | — | — | Win. Wads |

## MAGMA

**Bullet Moulds**

For use with the Magma Master Caster automatic casting machine and manual Bullet Master. Over 40 bullet styles available. From Magma Engineering Co.

**Price:** . . . . . . . . . . . . . . **$65.00**

## MAGMA Bullet Moulds

| Caliber | Wgt. Grs. | Type | Caliber | Wgt. Grs. | Type |
|---|---|---|---|---|---|
| 30 | 115 | RNBB | | 155 | RN SWC |
| 32 | 78 | RN BB | BB | | |
| | 100 | SGG BB | 10mm | 155 | SWC BB |
| | 98 | WC BB | | 170 | SWC BB |
| 32-20 | 115 | FP BB | | 175 | SWC BB |
| 380 | 95 | RN BB | | 180 | FP BB |
| 9mm Mak. | 93 | RN | | 200 | FP BB |
| 9mm | 115 | RN BB | 41 | 215 | SWC BB |
| | 122 | FP BB | 44 | 180 | FP BB |
| | 125 | CN BB | | 215 | SWC BB |
| | 125 | RN BB | | 240 | SWC BB |
| | 135 | RN BB | | 240 | RN BB |
| | 147 | FP BB | | 240 | FP BB |
| 38 Spl. | 145 | RN FB | | 300 | FP BB |
| | 150 | RN FB | 44-40 | 200 | RN FP |
| | 160 | RN BB | 45 | 150 | SWC BB |
| | 150 | SWC BB | | 155 | SWC |
| | 160 | SWC BB | BB&FB | | |
| 38 | 105 | WCD BB | | 160 | SWC FB |
| | 125 | FP BB | | 175 | SWC BB |
| | 148 | WC DBB | | 180 | SWC BB |
| SSG | | | | 185 | SWC BB |
| | 148 | WC DBB | | 200 | SWC BB |
| | 148 | WC BB | | 225 | FP BB |
| | 150 | SWC BB | | 230 | RN BB |
| | 158 | SWC BB | 45 LC | 250 | RN FP BB |
| | 158 | RN BB | | 255 | SWC BB |
| | 180 | FP BB | | 300 | FP BB |
| 38-40 | 180 | RN FP BB | 45-70 | 350 | FP BB |
| 10mm | 140 | RN FP BB | | 405 | FP BB |

RN = Round Nose; BB = Bevel Base; WC = Wadcutter: FP = Flat Point: SWC = Semi-Wadcutter; FB = Flat Base.

Magma 38-40, 44-40 and 4566.

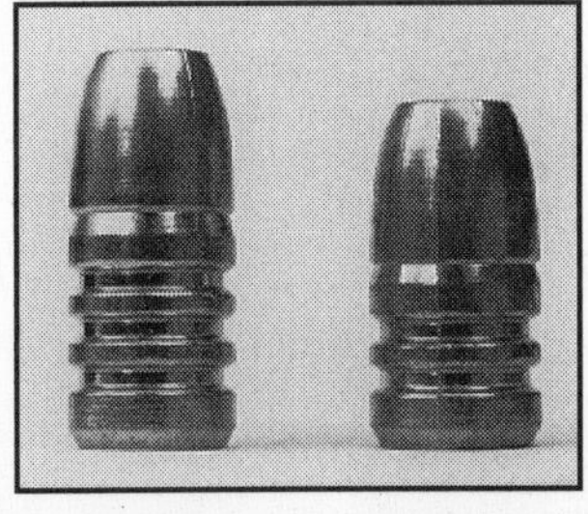

Magma 45-70 350-gr. and 405-gr. Bullets for Cowboy Action Shooting

Magma 30 Carbine, 9x21, 38 Special

# Section 4: Bullet Casting

## NEI

**Bullet Moulds**

Aluminum alloy single- and double-cavity bottom pour, four-cavity, single- and double-cavity nose pour, and customer design moulds with steel alignment pins, steel sockets, and steel sprue plates (1-, 2- and select 4-cavity only).

**Price:** 1- and 2-cavity . . . . . . **$59.95**
**Price:** Large caliber double cavity . **$69.95**
**Price:** Large caliber triple cavity . . **$79.95**
**Price:** Hollow base nose pour . . . **$79.95**
**Price:** 4-cavity . . . . . . . . . . **$89.95**
**Price:** 1-cavity nose pour . . . . . **$79.95**
**Price:** Extra for 2 different cuts . . . **$15.00**
**Price:** Extra for 2 different weights . . **$8.00**
**Price:** Extra tall mould block . . . **$15.00**
**Price:** Custom, cherry NEI property . . . . . . . . . . . . **$175.00**
**Price:** Custom, cherry customer property . . . . . . . . . . . **$250.00**

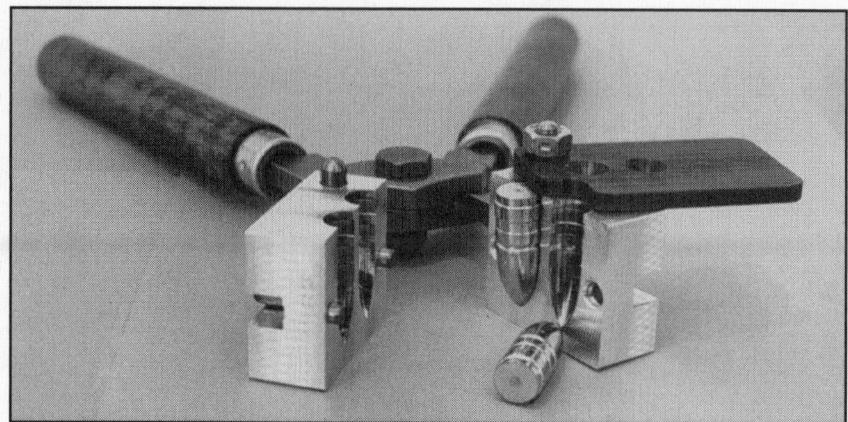

NEI Bullet Mould

## NEI Bullet Moulds

| Caliber | Dia. | Wgt.Grs. | Mould # | Caliber | Dia. | Wgt.Grs. | Mould # |
|---|---|---|---|---|---|---|---|
| 22 Hornet | .224 | 39 | 224-39-GC | | .308 | 173 | 308-173-GC |
| 22 | .224 | 45 | 224-45-GC | | .308 | 176 | 308-176-GC |
| 22 CF | .224 | 54 | 224-54-GC | | .308 | 178 | 308-178-GC |
| | .224 | 62 | 224-62-GC-DD | | .308 | 180 | 308-180-GC |
| | .224 | 72 | 224-72-GC-DD | | .308 | 180 | 308-180-GC-Hornet |
| 223 | .224 | 55 | 224-55-GC | Most 30s | .308 | 182 | 308-182-GC |
| 22 High Power | .228 | 60 | 228-60-GC | All 30s | .308 | 186 | 308-186-GC |
| | .231 | 65 | 231-65-GC | | .308 | 188 | 308-188-GC-DD |
| 6mm | .244 | 63 | 244-63-GC | Most 30s | .308 | 189 | 308-189-GC |
| | .244 | 65 | 244-65-GC | | .308 | 190 | 308-190-GC |
| | .244 | 75 | 244-75-GC | | .308 | 191 | 308-191-GC |
| | .244 | 92 | 244-92-GC | All 30s | .308 | 210 | 308-210-GC |
| | .244 | 95 | 244-95-GC | Fast Twist 30s | .308 | 210 | 308-210-GC |
| | .244 | 100 | 244-100-GC | 30s | .309 | 100 | 309-100-BB |
| 25 ACP | .251 | 51 | 251-51-PB | 30 Carbine | .309 | 115 | 309-115-GC |
| 257 Bores | .257 | 70 | 257-70-GC | 30s | .310 | 78 | 310-78-GC |
| 25 Cal. | .257 | 75 | 257-75-GC | 7.62x39 | .311 | 145 | 311-145-GC |
| 25-20 Win. | .257 | 89 | 257-89-GC | Some 30s | .311 | 154 | 311-154-GC |
| 257 Bolt | .257 | 100 | 257-100-GC | 7.62x39 | .311 | 155 | 311-155-GC |
| 25-35 Win. | .257 | 114 | 257-114-GC | 303 British | .311 | 190 | 311-190-GC |
| 257 Bolt | .257 | 115 | 257-115-GC-DD | 7.62 Mauser | .312 | 108 | 312-108-GC |
| 25 Cal. | .257 | 115 | 257-115-GC | 32-20 | .312 | 115 | 312-115-GC |
| 6.5mm | .264 | 125 | 264-125-GC-DD | 32 LC | .313 | 95 | 313-95-HEEL |
| 265 Cal. | .264 | 130 | 264-130-GC | 32 Pistol | .312 | 115 | 312-115-BB |
| 264 Cal. | .264 | 160 | 264-160-GC | 32s | .312 | 125 | 312-125-GC |
| 6.5x55mm | .270 | 130 | 270-130-GC | 7.7 Jap | .312 | 145 | 312-145-GC |
| 270 | .277 | 130 | 277-130-GC | 32s | .313 | 90 | 313-90-GC |
| 270 Win. | .277 | 100 | 277-100-GC-DD | 32 Cal. | .313 | 95 | 313-95-BBWC |
| | .277 | 125 | 277-185-GC-DD | 32 Pistol | .313 | 100 | 313-100-BB |
| 284/7mm | .277 | 145 | 277-145-PP | 32-20 | .313 | 114 | 313-114-GC |
| 7mm Nambu | .280 | 62 | 280-62-PB | | .313 | 115 | 313-115-GC |
| 284/7mm | .284 | 130 | 284-130-GC-DD | | .313 | 122 | 313-122-GC |
| | .284 | 140 | 284-140-GC | 7.7 Jap | .313 | 165 | 313-165-GC |
| 7mm | .284 | 150 | 284-150-GC | 7.62 Mauser | .313 | 180 | 313-180-GC |
| | .284 | 150 | 284-150-GC-DD | 32 Colt | .315 | 95 | 315-95-BB |
| | .284 | 154 | 284-154-GC | 32 | .315 | 110 | 315-110-BB |
| 7.35 Carcano | .299 | 135 | 299-135-GC | 8mm | .316 | 160 | 316-160-GC |
| | .300 | 140 | 300-140-GC | 303 British | .316 | 200 | 316-200-GC |
| 308 | .301 | 162 | 301-162-PP | 8mm | .318 | 175 | 318-175-GC |
| 30 Cal. | .301 | 167 | 301-167-PP | 32-40 32 SP | .321 | 175 | 321-175-GC |
| | .301 | 175 | 301-175-PP | 32 SPL | .322 | 160 | 322-160-GC |
| | .304 | 209 | 304-209-PP | | .322 | 165 | 322-165-GC-DD |
| | .308 | 80 | 308-80-GC | 8mm | .322 | 180 | 322-180-GC |
| | .308 | 102 | 308-102-GC | 32 Win. SP | .322 | 185 | 322-185-GC |
| | .308 | 108 | 308-108-GC | | .322 | 205 | 322-205-GC |
| | .308 | 110 | 308-110-GC | 7.92 Kurtz | .324 | 125 | 324-125-GC |
| | .308 | 121 | 308-121-GC | 8mm | .324 | 167 | 324-167-GC |
| | .308 | 125 | 308-125-GC | | .324 | 205 | 324-205-GC |
| | .308 | 135 | 308-135-GC | 8mm Kropechec | .326 | 220 | 326-220-GC |
| | .308 | 142 | 308-142-GC | Roth-Steyr | .330 | 116 | 330-116-BB |
| | .308 | 150 | 308-150-GC | 318 Rimless | .330 | 245 | 330-245-GC |
| | .308 | 152 | 308-152-GC | Large 8mm | .331 | 200 | 331-200-GC-DD |
| | .308 | 155 | 308-155-GC | | .331 | 220 | 331-220-GC |
| | .308 | 160 | 308-160-GC | | .338 | 200 | 338-200-GC |
| | .308 | 161 | 308-161-GC | | .338 | 215 | 338-215-GC-DD |
| | .308 | 162 | 308-162-GC | 338 | .338 | 245 | 338-245-GC |

## NEI Bullet Moulds

| Caliber | Dia. | Wgt.Grs. | Mould # |
|---|---|---|---|
| | .338 | 283 | 338-283-GC |
| Ballard | .344 | 210 | 344-210-PB |
| | .348 | 220 | 348-220-GC-DD |
| 348 Win. | .348 | 225 | 348-225-GC |
| | .348 | 240 | 348-240-GC |
| | .348 | 250 | 348-250-GC |
| 35 Win. SL | .351 | 172 | 351-172-GC |
| Rossi 357 | .354 | 160 | 354-160-BB |
| | .354 | 171 | 354-171-GC |
| 9mm | .355 | 69 | 355-69-PB |
| | .356 | 92 | 356-92-GC |
| | .356 | 116 | 356-116-T |
| | .356 | 120 | 356-120-GC |
| | .356 | 120 | 356-120-BB |
| | .356 | 122 | 356-122-BB |
| | .356 | 124 | 356-124-GC |
| | .356 | 125 | 356-125-BB |
| Long Bearing | .356 | 125 | 356-125-BB |
| 9mm | .356 | 129 | 356-129-BB |
| 9mm/38 Sup. | .356 | 140 | 356-140-BB |
| 9mm | .356 | 142 | 356-142-BB |
| | .356 | 144 | 356-144-TRN |
| 9mm/38 Sup. | .356 | 147 | 356-147-BB |
| | .356 | 155 | 356-155-BB |
| | .356 | 175 | 356-175-BB |
| | .357 | 120 | 357-120-BB |
| 38/357 | .357 | 142 | 357-142-GC |
| 38 Special | .357 | 185 | 357-185-GC |
| 38/357 | .358 | 77 | 358-77-BB |
| | .358 | 115 | 358-115-BB |
| 38/357-9mm | .358 | 124 | 358-124-BB |
| 38/357 | .358 | 125 | 358-125-GC |
| 38/9mm | .358 | 125 | 358-125-BB |
| | .358 | 128 | 358-128-BB |
| 38/357 | .358 | 135 | 358-135-BB |
| 38/9mm | .358 | 140 | 358-140-PB |
| 38/357 | .358 | 148 | 358-148-GC |
| | .358 | 148 | 358-148-DEB |
| | .358 | 148 | 358-148-BB |
| | .358 | 150 | 358-150-BB |
| | .358 | 151 | 358-151-BB |
| | .358 | 154 | 358-154-GC |
| | .358 | 154 | 358-154-BB |
| | .358 | 155 | 358-155-GC |
| | .358 | 158 | 358-158-BB |
| | .358 | 158 | 358-158-GC |
| | .358 | 160 | 358-160-PB |
| | .358 | 166 | 358-166-PB |
| | .358 | 167 | 358-167-BB |
| | .358 | 170 | 358-170-GC |
| | .358 | 170 | 358-170-PB |
| | .358 | 171 | 358-171-GC |
| | .358 | 175 | 358-175-GC-152 |
| | .358 | 175 | 358-175-GC-153 |
| | .358 | 175 | 358-175-RNGC |
| 38 S&W | .358 | 180 | 358-180-PB |
| | .358 | 180 | 358-180-BB |
| 38/357 | .358 | 180 | 358-180-GC |
| | .358 | 180 | 358-180-PB |
| | .358 | 186 | 358-186-BT |
| | .358 | 188 | 358-188-GC |
| | .358 | 191 | 358-191-GC |
| 358 Rifle | .358 | 190 | 358-190-PB |
| 35 Rifle | .358 | 208 | 358-208-GC |
| | .358 | 210 | 358-210-PB |
| 35 Cal. Rifles | .358 | 220 | 358-220-GC |
| 35 Rifle | .358 | 232 | 358-232-GC |
| | .358 | 268 | 358-268-GC-DD |
| | .358 | 282 | 358-282-GC |
| | .358 | 300 | 358-300-GC |
| 9mm Makarov | .363 | 115 | 363-115-PB |
| | .363 | 130 | 363-130-PB |
| Stevens | .363 | 210 | 363-210-PB |
| 35 | .363 | 300 | 363-300-GC |
| 9.3mm Rifle | .366 | 260 | 366-260-GC-DD |
| 9.3mm | .366 | 304 | 366-304-GC |
| 38 LC/38 Rook | .375 | 171 | 375-171-PB |
| 375s | .375 | 200 | 375-200-GC |
| | .375 | 210 | 375-210-GC |
| | .375 | 255 | 375-255-GC |
| | .375 | 277 | 375-277-PB |
| | .375 | 280 | 375-280-GC |
| | .375 | 290 | 375-290-GC-DD |
| | .375 | 290 | 375-290-PP |
| | .375 | 304 | 375-304-GC |
| | .375 | 310 | 375-310-GC |
| | .375 | 316 | 375-316-PB |
| | .375 | 320 | 375-320-GC |
| Old 38-55 | .378 | 245 | 378-245-GC |
| 38-55 | .379 | 245 | 379-245-GC |
| | .380 | 236 | 380-236-BB |
| | .380 | 240 | 380-240-BB |
| 41 Long Colt | .386 | 165 | 386-165-BB |
| | .388 | 198 | 388-198-PB |
| 40 Cal. Paper Patch | .395 | 320 | 395-320-PP |
| | .396 | 240 | 396-240-GC |
| 40 Sharps | .400 | 330 | 400-330-PP |
| | .400 | 370 | 400-370-PP |
| 40 S&W 10mm | .401 | 160 | 401-160-BB |
| | .401 | 180 | 401-180-GC |
| | .401 | 200 | 401-200-BB |
| | .403 | 300 | 403-300-GC |
| 40-60 Win. | .404 | 210 | 404-210-GC |
| 40 Cal. Win. | .404 | 211 | 404-211-GC |
| 40 Win. | .404 | 250 | 404-250-GC |
| 40-XX Win. & Rem. | .405 | 300 | 405-300-GC |
| 40-XX Win. | .405 | 365 | 405-365-GC |
| | .406 | 260 | 406-260-GC |
| | .406 | 325 | 406-325-PB |
| | .408 | 215 | 408-215-GC |
| 40-82 | .408 | 260 | 408-260-GC |
| 408s | .408 | 285 | 408-285-BB |
| | .408 | 330 | 408-330-PB |
| | .408 | 360 | 408-360-GC-DD |
| 40-65 | .408 | 400 | 408-400-PB |
| 41 Long Colt | .410 | 200 | 410-200-LC |
| | .41 | 200 | 41-200-LC |
| 41 Colt | .41 | 205 | 41-205-LC |
| 405 Win. | .410 | 410 | 410-410-GC |
| Modern 40 cal. | .410 | 385 | 410-385-PB |
| 41 Mag. | .411 | 190 | 411-190-WC |
| | .411 | 195 | 411-195-GC |
| | .411 | 205 | 411-205-GC |
| | .411 | 210 | 411-210-GC |
| 41 S&W Mag. | .411 | 220 | 411-220-PB |
| | .411 | 225 | 411-225-GC |
| | .411 | 230 | 411-230-PB |
| | .411 | 238 | 411-238-PB |
| | .411 | 240 | 411-240-GC |
| 405 Win. | .411 | 350 | 411-350-GC |
| 405 Win. STD | .412 | 300 | 412-300-GC |
| 405 Win. | .412 | 325 | 412-325-GC-DD |
| | .415 | 330 | 415-330-GC |
| | .415 | 350 | 415-350-PB |
| 416s | .416 | 290 | 416-290-GC |
| | .416 | 320 | 416-320-PP |
| | .416 | 375 | 416-375-GC-DD |
| 416 Rem. | .416 | 380 | 416-380-GC |
| 404 Jeffery | .421 | 390 | 421-390-GC |
| | .422 | 370 | 422-370-BT |
| 10.3mm | .423 | 375 | 423-375-GC-DD |
| 10.75mm | .423 | 455 | 423-455-PP |
| 10.75x57 | .424 | 350 | 424-350-GC |
| 44-40 WCF | .427 | 190 | 427-190-BB |
| 44-40 | .427 | 205 | 427-205-GC |
| 44-40 WCF | .427 | 245 | 427-245-GC |
| | .427 | 250 | 427-250-PB |
| | .429 | 80 | 429-80-STACK |
| | .429 | 185 | 429-185-WC |
| | .429 | 185 | 429-185-DEWC |
| | .429 | 196 | 429-196-GC |
| | .429 | 198 | 429-198-BB |
| | .429 | 220 | 429-220-BB |
| Hi Vel. 44s | .429 | 220 | 429-220-GC |
| 44-40 | .429 | 222 | 429-220-HB |
| | .429 | 225 | 429-225-GC |
| | .429 | 230 | 429-230-GC |
| | .429 | 235 | 429-235-GC |
| | .429 | 235 | 429-235-PB |
| STD 44 | .429 | 240 | 429-240-BB |
| | .429 | 240 | 429-240-GC |
| Ash Can | .429 | 245 | 429-245-WC |

## NEI Bullet Moulds

| Caliber | Dia. | Wgt.Grs. | Mould # |
|---|---|---|---|
| | .429 | 248 | 429-248-WC |
| | .429 | 250 | 429-250-GC |
| | .429 | 260 | 429-260-GC |
| | .429 | 270 | 429-270-PB |
| | .429 | 270 | 429-270-GC |
| 44 Russian | .429 | 278 | 429-278-GC |
| | .429 | 280 | 429-280-GC |
| | .429 | 290 | 429-290-PB |
| | .429 | 295 | 429-295-GC |
| | .429 | 320 | 429-320-PB-SSK |
| | .429 | 330 | 429-330-GC |
| | .429 | 335 | 429-335-GC-DD |
| 444 Marlin | .429 | 362 | 429-362-GC |
| 44 Mag. | .429 | 325 | 429-325-BBJDJ |
| | .438 | 540 | 438-540-PP |
| 43 Spanish | .439 | 375 | 439-375-GC-DD |
| | .439 | 375 | 439-375-GC |
| 44 Long Colt | .44 | 220 | 44-220-LC |
| | .44 | 225 | 44-225-LC-HEEL |
| 44 Sharps | .440 | 480 | 440-480-PP |
| | .440 | 492 | 440-492-PP |
| 44 Long Colt | .445 | 208 | 445-208-LC |
| 44-77 Sharps | .446 | 485 | 446-485-PB |
| 44-60 ETC | .447 | 380 | 447-380-GC-DD |
| 45-70 ETC | .45 | 410 | 45-410-PP |
| 45-90 ETC | .45 | 500 | 45-500-PP |
| | .45 | 520 | 45-520-PP |
| | .45 | 599 | 45-599-PP |
| 45 ACP | .451 | 160 | 451-160-BB |
| | .451 | 170 | 451-170-GC |
| | .451 | 175 | 451-175-BB |
| | .451 | 180 | 451-180-BB |
| | .451 | 190 | 451-190-BB |
| | .451 | 192 | 451-192-PB |
| | .451 | 200 | 451-200-BB |
| .725 OAL | .451 | 200 | 451-200-SP |
| | .451 | 202 | 451-202-BB |
| | .451 | 205 | 451-205-N |
| | .451 | 208 | 451-208-BB |
| | .451 | 210 | 451-210-BB |
| | .451 | 215 | 451-215-BB |
| Ash Can | .451 | 220 | 451-220-BBWC |
| | .451 | 225 | 451-225-BB |
| | .451 | 225 | 451-225-BBWC |
| | .451 | 225 | 451-225-PB |
| | .451 | 226 | 451-226-BB |
| | .451 | 229 | 451-229-BB |
| | .451 | 230 | 451-230-BB |
| | .451 | 230 | 451-230-GI |
| | .451 | 231 | 451-231-BB |
| | .451 | 236 | 451-236-GC |
| | .451 | 240 | 451-240-PB |
| | .451 | 245 | 451-245-BB |
| | .451 | 250 | 451-250-PB |
| | .451 | 255 | 451-255-GC |
| | .451 | 255 | 451-255-BB |
| | .451 | 260 | 451-260-PB |
| | .451 | 263 | 451-263-GC |
| | .451 | 272 | 451-272-BB |
| | .451 | 275 | 451-275-PB |
| | .451 | 275 | 451-275-GC |
| | .451 | 300 | 431-300-BB |
| | .451 | 305 | 451-305-GC |
| | .451 | 310 | 451-310-PB |
| | .451 | 325 | 451-325-PB |
| | .451 | 345 | 451-345-PB |
| Hand Cannon | .451 | 370 | 451-370-GC |
| | .451 | 380 | 451-380-GC |
| | .452 | 520 | 452-520-PB |
| 1860 Army | .454 | 220 | 454-220-C&B |
| 45 Long Colt | .454 | 230 | 454-230-HB |
| Old 45 Colt | .454 | 255 | 454-255-PB |
| | .454 | 270 | 454-270-PBK |
| | .454 | 315 | 454-315-PB |
| Keith Style | .454 | 325 | 454-325-PB |
| | .454 | 368 | 454-368-PB |
| 577/450 | .454 | 475 | 454-475-PB |
| 455 Webley | .455 | 350 | 455-350-GC |
| | .456 | 170 | 456-170-PB |
| | .456 | 250 | 456-250-PB |
| | .458 | 300 | 458-300-GC |
| 458 Win. | .458 | 300 | 458-300-GC |
| | .458 | 333 | 458-333-GC |

| Caliber | Dia. | Wgt.Grs. | Mould # |
|---|---|---|---|
| Light 45-70 | .458 | 350 | 458-350-GC-DD |
| | .458 | 355 | 458-355-GC |
| | .458 | 360 | 458-360-GC-DD |
| | .458 | 385 | 458-385-BB |
| Also 405 GR PB | .458 | 405 | 458-405-GC |
| | .458 | 405 | 458-405-RNGC |
| | .458 | 405 | 458-405-PP |
| 45-70 | .458 | 405 | 458-405-HB |
| Gonic Arms | .458 | 405 | 458-405-PB |
| | .458 | 425 | 458-425-BT |
| | .458 | 440 | 458-440-GC |
| | .458 | 440 | 458-440-GC-DD |
| Orig. 45-70 | .458 | 500 | 458-500-PB |
| 458 Win. | 458 | 500 | 458-500-GC-Hornet |
| | .458 | 510 | 458-510-GC |
| | .458 | 525 | 458-525-GC-DD |
| | .458 | 560 | 458-560-PB |
| 458 SS | .458 | 600 | 458-600-PB |
| 460 Weatherby | .458 | 645 | 458-645-GC |
| 45-70 | .460 | 480 | 460-480-GC |
| 460 Weatherby | .460 | 505 | 460-505-GC |
| Old 45-70 | .462 | 455 | 462-455-GC |
| 500/465 Nitro | .466 | 475 | 466-475-GC |
| 475 Revolver | .475 | 420 | 475-420-PB |
| 475 Pistol | .475 | 435 | 475-435-PB |
| 470 Nitro | .475 | 480 | 475-480-PB |
| | .475 | 435 | 475-435-PB |
| 50 Action Exp. | .500 | 320 | 500-320-GC |
| | .500 | 325 | 500-325-BB |
| 50 Sharps Ring | .500 | 410 | 500-410-SH |
| 505 Gibbs | .505 | 540 | 505-540-GC |
| | .508 | 856 | 508-856-GC |
| 50 Webley | .510 | 300 | 510-300-PB |
| | .510 | 430 | 510-430-GC |
| | .510 | 490 | 510-490-GC |
| 50 Paper Patch | .510 | 500 | 510-500-PP |
| | .510 | 550 | 510-550-GC |
| | .510 | 625 | 510-625-GC-DD |
| | .510 | 625 | 510-625-PP |
| | .510 | 775 | 510-775-GC-DD |
| 50 MG | .510 | 860 | 510-860-GC |
| | .511 | 300 | 511-300-GC |
| 50 Hand Cannon | .511 | 450 | 511-450-PB |
| | .511 | 680 | 511-680-GC |
| | .512 | 420 | 512-420-PB |
| 50-110 Win. | .512 | 435 | 512-435-GC |
| 500 Nitro | .512 | 600 | 512-600-GC |
| | .512 | 640 | 512-640-PB |
| 50-140 Sharps | .515 | 620 | 515-620-PB |
| 50 Maynard | .540 | 524 | 524-524-BB |
| 54 Sharps | .54 | 440 | 54-440-SH |
| | .540 | 475 | 540-475-SH |
| | .54 | 490 | 54-490-NS |
| | .54 | 490 | 54-490-OS |
| | .54 | 515 | 54-515-RT |
| | .543 | 490 | 543-490-SH |
| | .543 | 670 | 543-670-SH |
| 534, 545, 552 | .544 | 525 | 544-525-SH |
| 56-50 Spencer | .556 | 420 | 556-420-PB |
| 56 Orig. Sharps | .56 | 500 | 56-500-OS |
| 58 Muzzle Load | .575 | 500 | 575-500-PB |
| 58 Cal. | .575 | 595 | 575-595-PB |
| 58 Cal. | .577 | 450 | 577-450-HB |
| 577 Nitro | .577 | 900 | 577-900-PB |
| | .584 | 850 | 584-850-DD |
| 58 Berdan | .586 | 725 | 586-725-PB |
| 577 Nitro | .586 | 780 | 586-780-PB |
| | .587 | 1150 | 587-1150-PB |
| 600 Nitro | .622 | 900 | 622-900-PB |
| 12 Bore Paradox | .732 | 835 | 732-835-PB |
| 12 Ga. Shot Gun | .734 | 570 | 734-570-PB |
| 12 Bore | .740 | 725 | 740-725-PB |
| 12 Bore Paradox | .746 | 840 | 746-840-PB |
| 10 Bore | .774 | 1080 | 774-1080-PB |
| | .774 | 900 | 774-900-PB |
| 10 Bore Paradox | .804 | 945 | 804-945-PB |
| | .820 | 1350 | 820-1350-PB |
| 8 Bore | .835 | 1186 | 835-1186-PB |
| | .843 | 2800 | 843-2800-PB |
| | .875 | 1540 | 875-1540-PB |
| | .943 | 2250 | 943-2250-PB |
| 4 Bore | .970 | 2000 | 970-2000-PB |
| | .999 | 3000 | 999-3000 |

## OLD WEST

**Bullet Moulds**

Custom lathe or cherry cut single-, double- or triple-cavity moulds for obsolete and modern rifles and handguns in calibers from 22- to 54-caliber. Nose pour or base pour styles available. Cherry cut moulds are base pour and made of brass. Lathe bored nose pour moulds have minimum bullet length, .950″; maximum length, 1.4″. Lathe bored base pour moulds, any length up to 1.4″. Max number driving bands is six; minimum diameter meplat .1″. Sprue plate of 1/8″ thick steel but 3/16″ thick plates available. Single and double cavity moulds fit RCBS or Lyman handles; for three-cavity only RCBS handles. Economy moulds with each cavity a different caliber or bullet weight also offered. From Old West Bullet Moulds.

**Price:** Cherry cut single, 25 to 50 cal. . . . . . . . . . . . **$55.00**
**Price:** Lathe bored single, nose pour . **$72.00**
**Price:** Lathe bored single, base pour . **$65.00**
**Price:** Cherry cut, 2-cavity, 25 to 45 cal. . . . . . . . . . . . **$68.00**
**Price:** Cherry cut, 2-cavity economy, 25 to 45 cal. . . . . . . . . . . **$76.00**
**Price:** Cherry cut, 3-cavity, 25 to 45 cal. . . . . . . . . . . **$82.00**
**Price:** Hollow base, single cavity . . **$103.00**
**Price:** Adjustable 22 to 54 cal. . . . **$150.00**

## RAPINE

**Bullet Moulds**

Single- and double-cavity moulds machined from high-strength aluminum alloy to precise caliber with highly-polished finish. Come with long wooden handles placed close together to reduce fatigue. From Rapine Bullet Mould Mfg. Co.

**Price:** Plain Base . . . . . . . . . **$59.75**
**Price:** Hollow Base . . . . . . . **$69.95**

## OLD WEST Bullet Moulds

| Caliber | Cast Size | Wgt. Grs. | Type | OAL | Caliber | Cast Size | Wgt. Grs. | Type | OAL |
|---|---|---|---|---|---|---|---|---|---|
| 25 | .253 | 56 | PB | 0.460 | 375 | .377 | 260 | PB | 0.970 |
| | .259 | 95 | PB | 0.770 | | .377 | 294 | GC | 1.072 |
| | .259 | 106 | GC | 0.860 | 38-55 | .381 | 255 | PB | 0.925 |
| 25-20 | .259 | 75 | PB | 0.590 | | .381 | 286 | GC | 1.025 |
| | .259 | 82 | GC | 0.680 | 40 | .402 | 170 | PB | 0.570 |
| 6.5mm | .266 | 130 | PB | 1.00 | | .402 | 205 | GC | 0.680 |
| | .266 | 145 | GC | 1.10 | 41 | .407 | 250 | PB | 0.810 |
| 270 | .279 | 140 | PB | 1.00 | | .407 | 280 | GC | 0.930 |
| | .279 | 155 | GC | 1.10 | 40/41 | .405 | 160 | | 0.530 |
| 7mm | .286 | 145 | PB | 0.940 | | .411 | 210 | PB | 0.680 |
| | .286 | 160 | GC | 1.04 | | .411 | 240 | GC | 0.760 |
| | .287 | 160 | PB | 1.00 | | .411 | 275 | PB | 0.950 |
| | .287 | 176 | GC | 1.10 | | .411 | 310 | GC | 0.950 |
| 30 | .310 | 180 | PB | 1.00 | | .413 | 240 | PB | 0.750 |
| | .310 | 198 | GC | 1.10 | | .413 | 280 | PB | 0.860 |
| 30 Carbine | .311 | 114 | PB | 0.665 | | .413 | 310 | GC | 0.980 |
| | .311 | 130 | GC | 0.765 | 416 | .419 | 360 | PB | 1.190 |
| 30-30 | .311 | 170 | PB | 0.920 | | .419 | 400 | GC | 1.190 |
| | .311 | 190 | GC | 1.015 | 44 | .429 | 215 | PB | 0.670 |
| 32-20 | .313 | 100 | PB | 0.545 | | .429 | 270 | PB | 0.810 |
| | .313 | 118 | GC | 0.645 | | .430 | 240 | PB | 0.700 |
| | .314 | 85 | PB | 0.490 | | .430 | 275 | GC | 0.810 |
| | .314 | 100 | GC | 0.570 | | .430 | 315 | GC | 0.830 |
| 303 | .316 | 195 | PB | 1.00 | | .431 | 220 | PB | 0.680 |
| | .316 | 210 | GC | 1.10 | | .431 | 280 | PB | 0.820 |
| 32-40 | .323 | 172 | PB | 0.865 | | .431 | 320 | GC | 0.910 |
| | .323 | 189 | GC | 0.950 | | .432 | 215 | PB | 0.650 |
| 8mm | .326 | 190 | PB | 1.00 | | .432 | 255 | GC | 0.740 |
| | .326 | 215 | GC | 1.10 | 45 | .454 | 281 | GC | |
| 33 | .340 | 215 | PB | 0.950 | | .454 | 310 | PB | 0.770 |
| | .340 | 230 | GC | 1.04 | | .454 | 390 | PB | 0.970 |
| 348 | .350 | 220 | PB | 0.960 | | .454 | 490 | PB | 1.20 |
| | .350 | 245 | GC | 1.020 | 45-70 | .462 | 255 | PB | 0.650 |
| | .360 | 150 | PB | 0.660 | | .462 | 320 | PB | 0.850 |
| | .360 | 170 | GC | 0.760 | | .462 | 360 | GC | 0.950 |
| 35 | .350 | 220 | GC | 0.890 | 50 | .515 | 385 | PB | 0.830 |
| | .360 | 240 | PB | 1.00 | | .515 | 470 | PB | 1.070 |
| | .360 | 270 | GC | 1.10 | | .515 | 525 | PB | 1.180 |

PB = Plain Base; GC = Gas Check.

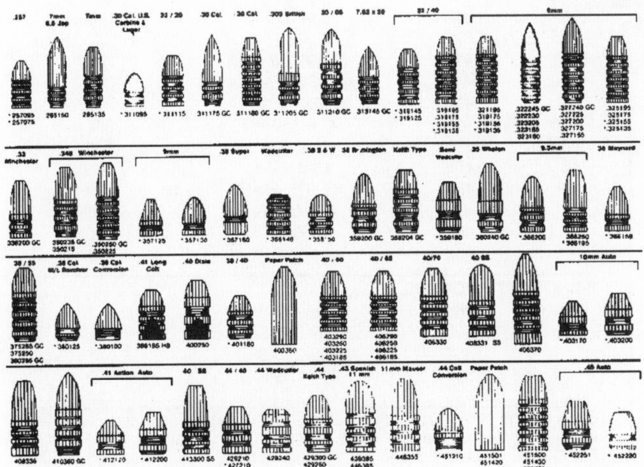

Rapine Bullet Moulds

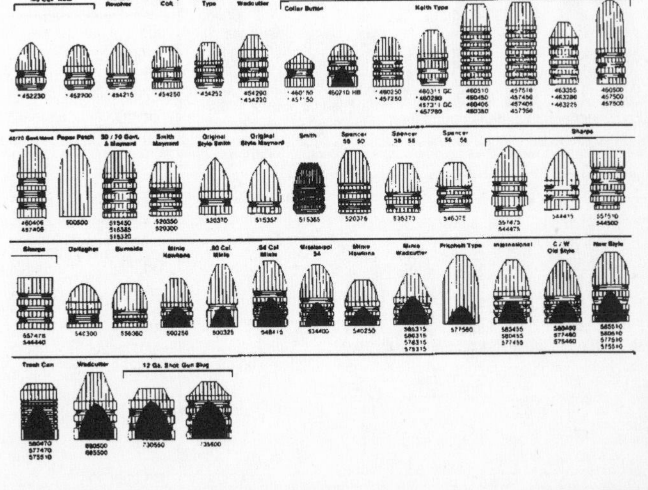

BULLET CASTING/Moulds

## RCBS

### Bullet Moulds

Hand-machined from blocks of precision-cast, malleable iron. Hardened pins ensure permanent alignment. The sprue cutter is solid carbon steel, locked in place with Allen setscrew. Bullet roundness tolerance to .001″. 200 different moulds available. From RCBS.

**Price:** Pistol or round ball . . . . . **$48.36**
**Price:** Rifle or silhouette . . . . . **$50.11**

### Mould Handles

Solid steel frames with extra long wood handles. One size fits all RCBS moulds. From RCBS.

**Price:** . . . . . . . . . . . . . . **$25.03**

| Caliber | 32 | 32 | 32 | 38 | 9mm |
|---|---|---|---|---|---|
| Size | .311″ | .314″ | .314″ | .356″ | .356″ |
| Mould | 32-77-RN Part 82021 | 32-098-WC Part 82060 | 32-098-SWC Part 82061 | 38-90-RN Part 82057 | 09-115-RN Part 82026 |
| Sizer Die | .311″ dia. Part 82214 | .314″ dia. Part 82216 | .314″ dia. Part 82216 | .356″ dia. Part 82221 | .356″ dia. Part 82221 |
| Top Punch | #465 Part 82536 | #445 Part 82543 | #444 Part 82542 | #311 Part 82513 | #115 Part 82504 |

| 38/357 | 38/357 | 38/357 | 40/10mm | 10mm | 10mm | 41 | 44 | 44 | 44 | 44 | 44 | 44 | 45 Auto |
|---|---|---|---|---|---|---|---|---|---|---|---|---|---|
| .358″ | .358 | .358″ | .401″ | .400″ | .400″ | .410″ | .430″ | .430″ | .430″ | .430″ | .430″ | .430″ | .452″ |
| 38-150-SWC Part 82032 | 38-158-RN Part 82064 | 38-158-SWC Part 82065 | 40-180-FN Part 82066 | 10mm-170-SWC Part 82067 | 10mm-200-SWC Part 82068 | 41-210-SWC Part 82039 | 44-225-SWC Part 82041 | 44-240-SWC Part 82042 | 44-245-SWC Part 82043 | 44-250-K Part 82080 | 44-250-SWC Part 82044 | 44-300-SWC Part 82079 | 45-185-BB-SWC Part 82052 |
| .358″ dia. Part 82223 | .358″ dia. Part 82223 | .358″ dia. Part 82223 | .401″ dia. Part 82245 | .400″ dia. Part 82243 | .400″ dia. Part 82243 | .410″ dia. Part 82226 | .430″ dia. Part 82229 | .430″ dia. Part 82229 | .430″ dia. Part 82229 | .430″ dia. Part 82229 | .430″ dia. Part 82229 | .430″ dia. Part 82229 | .452″ dia. Part 82233 |
| #429 Part 82529 | #311 Part 82513 | #429 Part 82529 | #558 Part 85558 | #518 Part 85518 | #518 Part 85518 | #420 Part 82541 | #421 Part 82527 | #421 Part 82527 | #421 Part 82527 | #421 Part 82527 | #421 Part 82527 | #421 Part 82527 | #680 Part 82545 |

| 9mm | 9mm | 9mm | 9mm | 9mm Makarov | 38/357 | 38/357 |
|---|---|---|---|---|---|---|
| .356″ | .356″ | .356″ | .356″ | .365″ | .358″ | .358″ |
| 9mm-124-RN Part 82062 | 09-124-RN-TG Part 82063 | 09-124-CN Part 82027 | 9mm-147-FN Part 82077 | 9mm-100-RN Part 82084 | 38-148-WC-DE Part 82030 | 38-148-WC Part 82031 |
| .356″ dia. Part 82221 | .356″ dia. Part 82221 | .356″ dia. Part 82221 | .356″ dia. Part 82221 | .365″ dia. Part 82248 | .358″ dia. Part 82223 | .358″ dia. Part 82223 |
| #401 Part 82521 | #115 Part 82504 | #402 Part 82522 | #556 Part 85556 | #551 Part 82551 | #344 Part 82515 | #429 Part 82529 |

| 45 Auto | 45 Auto | 45 | 45 Auto | 45 Colt | 45 Colt | 45 |
|---|---|---|---|---|---|---|
| .452″ | .452″ | .454″ | .452″ | .454″ | .454″ | .452″ |
| 45-200-SWC Part 82046 | 45-201-SWC Part 82047 | 44-225-CAV Part 82081 | 45-230-RN Part 82048 | 45-250-FN Part 82049 | 45-255-SWC Part 82050 | 45-300-SWC Part 82083 |
| .452″ dia. Part 82233 | .452″ dia. Part 82233 | .454″ dia. Part 82234 | .452″ dia. Part 82233 | .454″ dia. Part 82234 | .454″ dia. Part 82234 | .452″ dia. Part 82233 |
| #460 Part 82534 | #680 Part 82545 | #552 Part 85552 | #374 Part 82519 | #190 Part 82506 | #424 Part 82528 | #424 Part 82528 |

| Caliber | 22 | 6mm | 25 | 270 | 7mm | 30 | 30 | 30 | 30 | 7.62mm | 35 | 375, 38-55 |
|---|---|---|---|---|---|---|---|---|---|---|---|---|
| Size | .225″ | .244″ | .258″ | .278″ | .285″ | .309″ | .309″ | .309″ | .309″ | .309″ | .358″ | .376″ |
| Mould | 22-055-SP Part 82007 | 243-095-SP Part 82015 | 257-120-SP Part 82016 | 270-150-SP Part 82017 | 7mm-168-SP Part 82018 | 30-115-SP Part 82009 | 30-150-FN Part 82019 | 30-180-SP Part 82020 | 30-180-FN Part 82014 | 7.62-130-SPL Part 82022 | 35-200-FN Part 82028 | 37-250-FN Part 82029 |
| Sizer Die | .225″ dia. Part 82240 | .244″ dia. Part 82202 | .258″ dia. Part 82204 | .278″ dia. Part 82206 | .285″ dia. Part 82209 | .309″ dia. Part 82212 | .309″ dia. Part 82212 | .309″ dia. Part 82212 | .309″ dia. Part 82212 | .309″ dia. Part 82212 | .358″ dia. Part 82223 | .376″ dia. Part 82225 |
| Top Punch | #506 Part 85506 | #509 Part 85509 | #515 Part 85515 | #529 Part 85529 | #531 Part 85531 | #535 Part 85535 | #546 Part 85546 | #541 Part 85541 | #546 Part 85546 | #554 Part 85554 | #565 Part 85565 | #570 Part 85570 |

| 40 | 40 | 40 | 416 | 44-40 | 45 | 45 | 45 | 45 |
|---|---|---|---|---|---|---|---|---|
| .410″ | .410″ | .410″ | .417″ | .428″ | .458″ | .458″ | .458″ | .458″ |
| 40-300-SP-CSA Part 82070 | 40-350-SP-CSA Part 82072 | 40-400-SP-CSA Part 82074 | 416-350-FN Part 82075 | 44-200-FN Part 82036 | 45-300-FN Part 82051 | 45-325-FN-U Part 82065 | 45-405-FN+ Part 82053 | 45-500-FN+ Part 82054 |
| .410″ dia. Part 82226 | .410″ dia. Part 82226 | .410″ dia. Part 82226 | .417″ Part 82246 | .428″ dia. Part 82244 | .458″ dia. Part 82236 | .458″ dia. Part 82236 | .458″ dia. Part 82236 | .458″ dia. Part 82236 |
| #378 Part 82520 | #378 Part 82520 | #378 Part 82520 | #562 Part 85562 | #595 Part 85595 | #600 Part 85600 | #383 Part 85583 | #600 Part 85600 | #600 Part 85600 |

| Caliber | 7mm | 308 | 308 | 357 | 44 |
|---|---|---|---|---|---|
| Size | .285″ | .309″ | .309″ | .358″ | .430″ |
| Mould | 7mm-145-SIL Part 82150 | 308-165-SIL Part 82152 | 308-200-SIL Part 82153 | 357-180-SIL Part 82154 | 429-240-SIL Part 82156 |
| Sizer Die | .285″ dia. Part 82209 | .309″ dia. Part 82212 | .309″ dia. Part 82212 | .358″ dia. Part 82223 | .430″ dia. Part 82229 |
| Top Punch | #531 Part 85531 | #541 Part 85541 | #541 Part 85541 | #430 Part 82530 | #422 Part 82526 |
| Seater Plug | 7mm SIL Part 09696 | 308 SIL Part 09697 | 308 SIL Part 09697 | 357 SIL Part 09698 | 44 SIL Part 09699 |

### RCBS Cast Bullets *Alternate Sizes*

| Caliber | Size |
|---|---|
| 22 | .244 |
| 6mm | .243 |
| 25 | .257 |
| 270 | .277 |
| 7mm | .284 |
| 30 | .308 |
| | .310 |
| | .311 |
| 32 | .312 |
| | .313 |
| | .314 |
| 38/357 | .354 |
| | .355 |
| 38 | .356 |
| 357 | .357 |
| 375/38-55 | .375 |
| 44-40 | .427 |
| 44 | .429 |
| | .431 |
| 45 | .450 |
| | .451 |
| 45 Colt | .454 |
| 45 | .457 |

## RCBS Bullet Moulds

| Caliber | Size | Mould #/Grs./Bullet Type | Top Punch # |
|---|---|---|---|
| **PISTOL MOULDS** | | | |
| 32 | .311 | 32-077-RN | 465 |
| | .314 | 32-098-WC | 445 |
| | .314 | 32-098-SWC | 444 |
| 38 | .356 | 38-090-RN | 311 |
| 9mm | .356 | 09-115-RN | 115 |
| | .356 | 9mm-124-RN | 401 |
| | .356 | 09-124-RN-TG | 115 |
| | .356 | 09-124-CN | 402 |
| | .356 | 9mm-147-FN | 556 |
| 9mm Mak. | .365 | 9mm-100-RN | 551 |
| 38/357 | .358 | 38-148-WC | 429 |
| | .358 | 38-148-WC-DE | 344 |
| | .358 | 38-150-SWC | 429 |
| | .358 | 38-158-RN | 311 |
| | .358 | 38-158-SWC | 429 |
| 40/10mm | .401 | 40-180-FN | 558 |
| 10mm | .400 | 10mm-170-SWC | 518 |
| | .400 | 10mm-200-SWC | 518 |
| 41 | .410 | 41-210-SWC | 420 |
| 44 | .430 | 44-225-SWC | 421 |
| | .430 | 44-240-SWC | 421 |
| | .430 | 44-245-SWC | 421 |
| | .430 | 44-250-K | 421 |
| | .430 | 44-250-SWC | 421 |
| | .430 | 44-300-SWC | 421 |
| 45 Auto | .452 | 45-185-BB-SWC | 680 |
| | .452 | 45-200-SWC | 460 |
| | .452 | 45-201-SWC | 680 |
| 45 | .454 | 45-225-CAV | 552 |
| 45 Auto | .452 | 45-230-RN | 374 |
| 45 Colt | .454 | 45-250-FN | 190 |
| | .454 | 45-255-SWC | 424 |
| 45 | .452 | 45-300-SWC | 424 |
| **RIFLE MOULDS** | | | |
| 22 | .225 | 22-055-SP | 506 |
| 6mm | .244 | 243-095-SP | 509 |
| 25 | .258 | 257-120-SP | 515 |
| 270 | .278 | 270-150-SP | 529 |
| 7mm | .285 | 7mm-168-SP | 531 |
| 30 | .309 | 30-115-SP | 535 |
| | .309 | 30-150-FN | 546 |
| | .309 | 30-180-SP | 541 |
| | .309 | 30-180-FN | 546 |
| 7.62mm | .309 | 7.62-130-SPL | 554 |
| 35 | .358 | 35-200-FN | 565 |
| 375,38-55 | .376 | 37-250-FN | 570 |
| 40 | .410 | 40-300-SP-CSA | 378 |
| | .410 | 40-350-SP-CSA | 378 |
| | .410 | 40-400-SP-CSA | 378 |
| 416 | .417 | 416-350-FN | 562 |
| 44-40 | .428 | 44-200-FN | 595 |
| 45 | .458 | 45-300-FN | 600 |
| | .458 | 45-325-FN-U | 383 |
| | .458 | 45-405-FN+ | 600 |
| | .458 | 45-500-FN+ | 600 |
| | .458 | 45-500-BPS+ | 607 |
| **SILHOUETTE MOULDS** | | | |
| 7mm | .285 | 7mm-145-SIL | 531 |
| 308 | .309 | 308-165-SIL | 541 |
| | .309 | 308-200-SIL | 541 |
| 357 | .358 | 357-180-SIL | 430 |
| 44 | .430 | 429-240-SIL | 422 |

RN = Round Nose; WC = Wadcutter; SWC = Semi-Wadcutter; FN = Flat Nose; K = Keith Type; BB = Bevel Base; CAV = Cavalry; SP = Semi-Point; SPL = Special; CSA = C Sharps Arms; U = Universal; SIL = Silhouette; TG = Target; DE = Double End; CN = Conical Nose; PT = Pointed.

## SAECO

### Bullet Moulds

Two- and 4-cavity moulds machined from blocks of copper alloyed pearlitic cast iron for dimensional stability. Cavities cut using same cherrie on digital equipment for uniformity. Steel sprue plate held against mould blocks by high-temperature Inconel spring washers. Mould handles are ductile iron castings with oak grips. Handles ordered separately. From Redding Reloading Equipment.

**Price:** 2-cavity . . . . . . . . . . **$75.00**
**Price:** 4-cavity . . . . . . . . . **$135.00**
**Price:** Mould handles . . . . . . **$37.50**

### Special Order Moulds

Three-, 6- and 8-cavity and "magnum" moulds made on special order basis. From Redding Reloading Equipment.

**Price:** 1-cavity magnum . . . . . **$75.00**
**Price:** 2-cavity magnum . . . . . **$96.00**
**Price:** 3-cavity . . . . . . . . . **$106.50**
**Price:** 6-cavity . . . . . . . . . **$219.00**
**Price:** 8-cavity . . . . . . . . . **$312.00**

### Bullet Moulds for Obsolete Cal.

Special order moulds available in single cavity magnum only. Six different bullet styles.

**Style A:** Cylindrical bullet similar to original factory bullets for most blackpowder cartridges. Diameter at front band is same diameter at base band. Rounded grease grooves.

**Style B:** Cylindrical bullet with front wiper band deleted. Rounded grease grooves.

**Style C:** Two diameter bullet with front three bands slightly larger than bore diameter and rear three at groove diameter. Rounded grease grooves.

**Style D:** Two diameter bullet same as Style C but without front wiper band. Rounded grease grooves.

**Style E:** Tapered bullet with front band near bore diameter tapering to slightly larger than groove diameter. Rounded grease grooves.

**Style F:** Hudson bullet. Two diameter with front bands near bore diameter with two rear bands slightly larger than groove diameter. From Redding Reloading Equipment.

**Price:** . . . . . **Contact manufacturer.**

### Magnum Mould Blocks

Single- and double-cavity moulds made from SAECO double- and triple-cavity blocks with wider spacing for blackpowder silhouette bullets. Available in two calibers: 40 cal., 370- and 410-gr.; 45-cal. 480- and 525-gr. Special order moulds in any combination of caliber and/or weight. From Redding Reloading Equipment.

**Price:** Single-cavity . . . . . . . **$75.00**
**Price:** Double-cavity . . . . . . . **$96.00**
**Price:** Special order, add . . . . . **$20.00**

| No. | 221 | 243 | 257 | 264 | 270 | 281 | 078 | 071 | 073 | 382 | 254 | 316 | 311 |
|---|---|---|---|---|---|---|---|---|---|---|---|---|---|
| Designation | 60gr. SPGC | 85gr. TCGC | 100gr. TCGC | 140 gr. SPGC | 140gr. TCGC | 145gr. FPGC | 145gr. TCGC | 160gr. TCGC | 165gr. SPGC | 120gr. RNGC | 115gr. RNBB | 150gr. FPGC | 165gr. TCGC |
| Sizing Die | .225 | .244 | .258 | .265 | .278 | .285 | .285 | .285 | .285 | .309 | .309 | .309 | .309 |
| Top Punch | 22498 | 24243 | 25258 | 26264 | 27270 | 28311 | 28520 | 28520 | 28520 | 30467 | 30467 | 30530 | 30301 |
| Description | Works Well in .223 Semi Autos | For all .243 & .244 Cal. | .25 Cal. Silhouette | | Two perfect 60's shot at Reg. 6 IHMSA | Standard for 7mm | Silhouette | 200 meters Silhouette | Heavy 7mm Bullet | For 30 MI, GC | For 30 MI | For 30-30 | |

| | 30 CAL. (cont.) | | | 31 CAL. | 32 CAL. | | | | | | 8 mm | 9 mm/38 SUPER | |
|---|---|---|---|---|---|---|---|---|---|---|---|---|---|
| No. | 307 | 315 | 301 | 305 | 327 | 323 | 325 | 326 | 321 | 322A | 081 | 380 | 922 |
| Designation | 180gr. FPGC | 175gr. TCGC | 196gr. TCGC | 180gr. FPGC | 75gr. RN | 95 gr. WC | 95 gr. SWC | 100gr. SWCBB | 95gr. RN | 118gr. FP | 190gr. RNGC | 95gr. RNBB | 115gr. RNBB |
| Sizing Die | .309 | .309 | .309 | .311 | .313 | .313 | .313 | .313 | .313 | .313 | .323/.324 | .356 | .356 |
| Top Punch | 30301 | 30329 | 30301 | 30301 | 32465 | 32323 | 32467 | 32467 | 32465 | 30254 | 30530 | 35465 | 35311 |
| Description | | Bench Rest Style "E" Taper | Duplicates Original RG4 | 303 British | .32 ACP | Good .32 Long Target Bullet | | | .32 S&W Long | .32-20 Bullet | 8 mm Rifle | Good .380 bullet | |

| | 9 mm/38 SUPER (cont.) | | | | | | | | | | 9.2 mm | 38/357-35 CAL. | |
|---|---|---|---|---|---|---|---|---|---|---|---|---|---|
| No. | 925 | 377 | 384 | 115 | 924 | 383 | 928 | 929 | 910 | 930 | 940 | 052 | 053 |
| Designation | 115gr. SWBB | 122gr. TCBB | 122gr. RN | 122 gr. RNBB | 124gr. SWCGC | 140gr. SWC | 145gr. RNBB | 145gr. SWCBB | 150gr. RN | 154gr. SWCBB | 100gr. RNBB | 148gr. WCBB | 148gr. WC |
| Sizing Die | .356 | .356 | .356 | .356 | .356 | .356/.357 | .356/.357 | .356/.357 | .356 | .356/.357 | .365 | .358 | .358 |
| Top Punch | 35925 | 35375 | 35311 | 35311 | 35925 | 35429 | 35311 | 35925 | 35311 | 35925 | 35465 | 35550 | 35381 |
| Description | | Good Ballistics for 9mm | Good Feeding 9mm | | Good Feeding SWC | | 38 Super | 38 Super | | 38 Super Wilson Design | 9mm Makarov | Target Bullet | GAR Design |

| | 38/357-35 CAL. (cont.) | | | | | | | | | | | | |
|---|---|---|---|---|---|---|---|---|---|---|---|---|---|
| No. | 387 | 348 | 382 | 388 | 363 | 390 | 391 | 398 | 353 | 354 | 396 | 399 | 351 |
| Designation | 148gr. WCDBB | 148gr. DBBWC | 158gr. SWC | 158gr. SWCBB | 162gr. SWCGC | 158gr. RN | 158gr. RNBB | 158gr. TC | 180gr. FP | 180gr. FPGC | 180gr. TC | 180gr. TCGC | 200 gr. FP |
| Sizing Die | .358 | .358 | .358 | .358 | .358 | .358 | .358 | .358 | .358 | .358 | .358 | .358 | .358 |
| Top Punch | 35344 | 35344 | 35429 | 35429 | 35429 | 35311 | 35311 | 35399 | 35353 | 35353 | 35399 | 35399 | 35311 |
| Description | 148gr. Double Bevel Base WC | Single Groove DBB | Keith Design | Most Popular | | Standard .38 Bullet | | | Super Long Range Bullet | GC Version of Popular 353 | | | Heavy .357 Bullet |

| | 41 CAL. (cont.) | | | | | | | 416 CAL. | 44 CAL. | | | |
|---|---|---|---|---|---|---|---|---|---|---|---|---|
| No. | 412 | 417 | 409 | 413 | 415 | 410 | 418 | *916 | 944 | 420 | 444 | 446-A |
| Designation | 185gr. SWC | 210gr. SWC | 190gr. TC | 210gr. TCBB | 220gr. TCGC | 220gr. FP | 220gr. SWCBB | 365gr. RNGC | 200gr. WC | 200 gr. TC | 200gr. FPSWC | 200gr. SWC |
| Sizing Die | .411 | .411 | .411 | .411 | .411 | .411 | .411 | .417 | .430 | .430 | .428 | .430 |
| Top Punch | 41610 | 41610 | 41415 | 41415 | 41415 | 41415 | 41610 | 41916 | 44944 | 44428 | 44191 | 44191 |
| Description | | | | | | Pistol Silhouette | Bevel Base Keith Style | 416 Rifles | GAR Design | Jim Hubert Design | 44-40 | |

| | 45 CAL. | | | | | | | | | | | | |
|---|---|---|---|---|---|---|---|---|---|---|---|---|---|
| No. | 062-B | 062 | 065 | 130 | 131 | 066 | 068 | 069 | 058 | 285 | 067 | 456 | 457 |
| Designation | 160gr. SPL | 170gr. SPLBB | 180gr. SWCBB | 185gr. SWC | 185gr. SWCBB | 180gr. SWC | 200gr. SWCBB | 200gr. SWC | 215gr. SWCBB | 210gr. RNWC | 225gr. TCBB | 225gr. RN | 225gr. RNBB |
| Sizing Die | .452 | .452 | .452 | .452 | .452 | .452 | .452 | .452 | .452 | .452 | .452 | .452 | .452 |
| Top Punch | 45452 | 45452 | 45429 | 45421 | 45421 | 45429 | 45429 | 45429 | 45424 | 45265 | 45375 | 45701 | 45701 |
| Description | Behn Design | -V-MAXX .45 Behn Design | Lt. Wt. IPSC | Most Popular Lt. Target | | | Most Popular Combat Bullet | | Bowling Pin Bullet | Best Feeding .45 ACP | | Standard Round Nose | |

| | | | | 375 CAL. | 40 CAL./10 mm | | | | | | 41 CAL. | |
|---|---|---|---|---|---|---|---|---|---|---|---|---|
| No. | 356 | 395 | 352 | 373 | 040 | 043 | 045 | 047 | 048 | 401 | 416 | 419 |
| Designation | 200 gr. FPGC | 200gr. TCGC | 245gr. FPGC | 265gr. FPGC | 155gr. SWCBB | 170gr. TCBB | 170gr. SWCBB | 200gr. TCBB | 200gr. SWCBB | 190gr. | 170gr. SWCBB | 200gr. SWCBB |
| Sizing Die | .358 | .358 | .358 | .376 | .401 | .401 | .401 | .401 | .401 | .401 | .411 | .411 |
| Top Punch | 35311 | 35399 | 35311 | 37570 | 40048 | 40047 | 40048 | 40047 | 40048 | 40101 | 41447 | 41447 |
| Description | Handgun Silhouette | Silhouette | | Rifle | 10mm Auto | 10mm Auto | 10mm Auto | 10mm Auto | 10mm Auto | .38-40 | 41 Auto Petty Design | 41 Auto Petty Design |

| No. | 445 | 442 | 441 | 440 | 439 | 429 | 424 | 428 | 431 | 430 | 432 | 433 |
|---|---|---|---|---|---|---|---|---|---|---|---|---|
| Designation | 220gr. SWCBB | 246gr. RN | 240gr. SWC | 240gr. SWCBB | 240gr. SWCGC | 240gr. FP | 240gr. TCGC | 240gr. TC | 250gr. FPGC | 265gr. FP | 265gr. FPGC | 300gr. FPGC |
| Sizing Die | .430 | .430 | .430 | .430 | .430 | .430 | .430 | .430 | .430 | .430 | .430 | .430 |
| Top Punch | 44191 | 44374 | 44421 | 44421 | 44421 | 44191 | 44428 | 44428 | 44191 | 44191 | 44191 | 44191 |
| Description | | Standard 44 Spec. Bullet | Standard Wt. 44 Mag Keith Style | | | Superb Long Range Bullet | GC Version of Popular 428 | Most Popular Silhouette | 444 Marlin | Superb Long Range Bullet | | Silhouette |

| | | | | | | 45 CAL. RIFLE | | | | | | | |
|---|---|---|---|---|---|---|---|---|---|---|---|---|---|
| No. | 453 | 945 | 458 | 452 | 454 | 915 | *917 | *918 | *919 | *923 | *921A | *922 | *920 |
| Designation | 225gr. WC | 255gr. SWCGC | 255gr. SWC | 255gr. SWC | 300gr. SWCGC | 300gr. FP | 350gr. FPGC | 405gr. FP | 450gr. FPGC | 375gr. SP | 405gr. SPGC | 500gr. FP | 540gr. FPGC |
| Sizing Die | .452 | .452 | .452 | .455 | .452 | .458 | .458 | .458 | .458 | .458 | .458 | .458 | .458 |
| Top Punch | 45424 | 45424 | 45424 | 45452 | 45424 | 45015 | 45015 | 45015 | 45015 | 45702 | 45702 | 45610 | 45610 |
| Description | Jan Libourel Design | For 45 Colt | For .45 Colt w/.452 Bore | For .45 Colt w/.454 Bore | Heavy .45 Colt & .454 Casull | | | | | | | | |

BULLET CASTING/Moulds

## SAECO Bullet Moulds

| Caliber | Bullet Grs. Wgt. | Bullet Type | Gas Check | Sizing Die | Top Punch |
|---|---|---|---|---|---|
| 22 | 60 | SP | GC | .225 | 22498 |
| 243 | 85 | TC | GC | .244 | 24243 |
| 25 | 100 | TC | GC | .258 | 25258 |
| 6.5mm | 140 | SP | GC | .265 | 26264 |
| 270 | 140 | TC | GC | .278 | 27270 |
| 7mm | 145 | FP | GC | .285 | 28311 |
| | 145 | TC | GC | .285 | 28520 |
| | 160 | TC | GC | .285 | 28520 |
| | 165 | SP | GC | .285 | 28520 |
| 30 | 120 | RN | GC | .309 | 30467 |
| | 115 | RNBB | | .309 | 30467 |
| | 150 | FP | GC | .309 | 30530 |
| | 165 | TC | GC | .309 | 30301 |
| | 180 | FP | GC | .309 | 30530 |
| | 175 | TC | GC | N.R. | 30329 |
| | 196 | TC | GC | .309 | 30530 |
| 31 | 180 | FP | GC | .311 | 30301 |
| 32 | 75 | RN | | .313 | 32465 |
| | 95 | WC | | .313 | 32323 |
| | 95 | SWC | | .313 | 32467 |
| | 100 | SWCBB | | .313 | 32467 |
| | 95 | RN | | .313 | 32465 |
| | 118 | FP | | .313 | 30254 |
| 8mm | 190 | RN | GC | .323/.324 | 30530 |
| 9mm/38 Super | 95 | RNBB | | .356 | 35465 |
| | 115 | RNBB | | .356 | 35311 |
| | 115 | SWBB | | .356 | 35925 |
| | 122 | TCBB | | .356 | 35375 |
| | 122 | RN | | .356 | 35311 |
| | 122 | RNBB | | .356 | 35311 |
| | 124 | SWC | GC | .356 | 35925 |
| | 140 | SWC | | .356/.357 | 35429 |
| | 145 | RNBB | | .356/.357 | 35311 |
| | 145 | SWCBB | | .356/.357 | 35925 |
| | 150 | RN | | .356 | 35311 |
| | 154 | SWCBB | | .356/.357 | 35925 |
| 9.2mm | 100 | RNBB | | .365 | 35465 |
| 38/357-35 | 148 | WCBB | | .358 | 35550 |
| | 148 | WC | | .358 | 35381 |
| | 148 | WCDBB | | .358 | 35344 |
| | 148 | DBBWC | | .358 | 35344 |
| | 158 | SWC | | .358 | 35429 |
| | 158 | SWCBB | | .358 | 35429 |
| | 162 | SWC | GC | .358 | 35429 |
| | 158 | RN | | .358 | 35311 |
| | 158 | RNBB | | .358 | 35311 |
| | 158 | TC | | .358 | 35399 |
| | 180 | FP | | .358 | 35353 |
| | 180 | FP | GC | .358 | 35353 |
| | 180 | TC | | .358 | 35399 |
| | 180 | TC | GC | .358 | 35399 |
| | 200 | FP | | .358 | 35311 |
| | 200 | FP | GC | .358 | 35311 |
| | 200 | TC | GC | .358 | 35399 |
| | 245 | FP | GC | .358 | 35311 |
| 375 | 265 | FP | GC | .376 | 37570 |
| 40/10mm | 155 | SWCBB | | .401 | 40048 |
| | 170 | TCBB | | .401 | 40047 |
| | 170 | SWCBB | | .401 | 40048 |
| | 200 | TCBB | | .401 | 40047 |
| | 200 | SWCBB | | .401 | 40048 |
| | 190 | | | .401 | 40101 |
| 41 | 170 | SWCBB | | .411 | 41447 |
| | 200 | SWCBB | | .411 | 41447 |
| | 185 | SWC | | .411 | 41610 |
| | 210 | SWC | | .411 | 41610 |
| | 190 | TC | | .411 | 41415 |
| | 210 | TCBB | | .411 | 41415 |
| | 220 | TC | GC | .411 | 41415 |
| | 220 | FP | | .411 | 41415 |
| | 220 | SWCBB | | .411 | 41610 |
| 416 | 365 | RN | GC | .417 | 41916 |
| 44 | 200 | WC | | .430 | 44944 |
| | 200 | TC | | .430 | 44428 |
| | 200 | FPSWC | | .428 | 44191 |
| | 200 | SWC | | .430 | 44191 |
| | 220 | SWCBB | | .430 | 44191 |
| | 246 | RN | | .430 | 44374 |
| | 240 | SWC | | .430 | 44421 |
| | 240 | SWCBB | | .430 | 44421 |
| | 240 | SWCGC | | .430 | 44421 |
| | 240 | FP | | .430 | 44191 |
| | 240 | TC | GC | .430 | 44428 |
| | 240 | TC | | .430 | 44428 |
| | 250 | FP | GC | .430 | 44191 |
| | 265 | FP | | .430 | 44191 |
| | 265 | FP | GC | .430 | 44191 |
| | 300 | FP | GC | .430 | 44191 |
| 45 | 160 | SPL | | .452 | 45452 |
| | 170 | SPLBB | | .452 | 45452 |
| | 180 | SWCBB | | .452 | 45429 |
| | 185 | SWC | | .452 | 45421 |
| | 185 | SWCBB | | .452 | 45421 |
| | 180 | SWC | | .452 | 45429 |
| | 200 | SWCBB | | .452 | 45429 |
| | 200 | SWC | | .452 | 45429 |
| | 215 | SWCBB | | .452 | 45424 |
| | 210 | RNWC | | .452 | 45265 |
| | 225 | TCBB | | .452 | 45375 |
| | 225 | RN | | .452 | 45701 |
| | 225 | RNBB | | .452 | 45701 |
| | 225 | WC | | .452 | 45424 |
| | 255 | SWC | GC | .452 | 45424 |
| | 255 | SWC | | .452 | 45424 |
| | 255 | SWC | | .455 | 45452 |
| | 300 | SWC | GC | .452 | 54524 |
| 45 Rifle | 300 | FP | | .458 | 45424 |
| | 350 | FP | GC | .458 | 45015 |
| | 405 | FP | | .458 | 45015 |
| | 465 | FP | GC | .458 | 45015 |
| | 375 | SP | | .458 | 45702 |
| | 405 | SP | GC | .458 | 45702 |
| | 500 | FP | | .458 | 45525 |
| | 540 | FP | GC | .458 | 45525 |

BB = Bevel Base; DBB = Double End Bevel Base; FB = Flat Base; FP = Flat Point; GC = Gas Check; NR = Not Required; RN = Round Nose; SP = Spitzer Point; SWC = Semi-Wadcutter; TC = Truncated Cone; WC = Wadcutter.

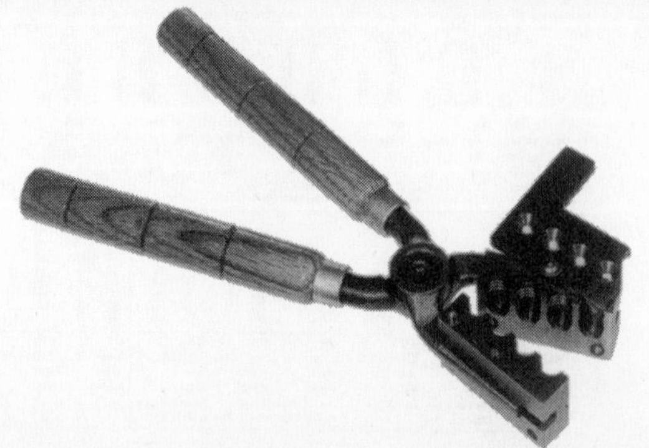

SAECO 4-Cavity Mould

## ACTION BULLETS

**Bullet Lubricant**

Blend of 45% commercial beeswax, 45% paraffin and 10% Action Bullet formula. Available in 1x4, 2x6 or 2x12 hollow or solid sticks. From Action Bullets.

**Price:** 1x4, each . . . **$3.50**
**Price:** 2x6 solid, each . . . **$8.00**
**Price:** 2x12 solid, each . . . **$15.00**

## ANDELA

**Bullet Lubricator**

Lubricates but does not size bullets for cast bullet accuracy. Accepts hollow stick lubricants and Lyman dies if applicable. Custom made to lubricate cylindrical bullets inserted base first or tapered and two diameter bullets nose first. Comes with brass blank die for bullet fitting. Send casting and Andela will fit a die to bullet. From Andela Tool & Machinery.

**Price:** . . . **$150.00**
**Price:** Die fitting . . . **$25.00**

## E. ARTHUR BROWN

**EbcoJacket Lube**

Dry lube puts hard coating on cast bullets. Dip, tumble or flood coat bullets. Comes in 4 oz. plastic bottle. From E. Arthur Brown Company.

**Price:** . . . **$3.50**

## DONALD EAGAN

**MX Lube Die**

Designed for Donald Eagan MX bullets and can be used with Lyman 450 or RCBS lube-sizers. Available for all MX tapered bullets. From Donald Eagan.

**Price:** . . . **$35.00**
**Price:** Top punch, MX2 . . . **$6.00**
**Price:** Top punch, MX3 . . . **$10.00**

**Sizing T-Dies**

Sizing dies designed for use with Donald Eagan MX3 bullets. Can be used with Lyman and RCBS lube-sizers. From Donald Eagan.

**Price:** 30T, 28T, 32T, 30TS . . . **$14.00**
**Price:** 24T, 26T . . . **$18.00**
**Price:** 22T . . . **$24.00**

## HANNED LINE

**NozeFirst Top Punch**

Features a flat face to eliminate lubrisizer misalignment. Available in two formats to fit popular Saeco-type or Lyman/RCBS-type sizers. From The Hanned Line.

**Price:**RCBS/Lyman . . . **$15.40**
**Price:**Saeco . . . **$17.20**

## HOWELL

**Rotary Bullet Feeder**

Designed to fit the Star lubesizer. Feeds 22-, 25-, 30-, 33-, 9mm, 38-, 41- or 45-caliber bullets nose or base first at a rate of 100 bullets per minute. Capacity for 700 to 900 bullets. 14″, 16″ and 20″ bowls available. Powered by 110-volt completely enclosed assembly. Comes set up and ready to run for one or two calibers. From Howell CNC & Machine.

**Price:** 14″, one size base first . . . **$995.00**
**Price:** 14″, two sizes base first . . **$1,225.00**
**Price:** 14″, one size nose first . . **$1,150.00**
**Price:** 14″, two sizes nose first . . **$1,375.00**
**Price:** 14″, one size nose or base first . . . **$1,475.00**
**Price:** 14″, two sizes nose or base first . . . **$1,750.00**
**Price:** 16″, one size base first . . **$1,350.00**
**Price:** 16″, two sizes base first . . **$1,625.00**
**Price:** 16″, one size nose first . . **$1,500.00**
**Price:** 16″, two sizes nose first . . **$1,750.00**
**Price:** 16″, one size nose or base first . . . **$1,750.00**
**Price:** 16″, two sizes nose or base first . . . **$2,150.00**
**Price:** 20″, one size base first . . **$2,375.00**
**Price:** 20″, one size nose first . . **$2,673.00**

## JAVELINA

**Super Lube**

NRA developed formula of 50% Alox 2138F and 50% pure yellow beeswax. Comes in 1.5 oz. hollow tube to fit most lubrisizers. From Brownells, Inc.

**Price:** Each . . . **$1.85**
**Price:** 12 . . . **$22.20**

## LBT

**Blue Lube**

Non-toxic lubricant that flows at room temperature into bullet grooves .015 or deeper. Comes in hollow or solid sticks. From Lead Bullets Technology.

**Price:** 1 to 4 sticks, each . . . **$4.00**
**Price:** 5 or more, each . . . **$3.75**

## LBT

**Blue Soft Lube**

Semi-soft lube designed to flow at lower temperatures down to 60° Fahrenheit. Has higher melting temperature but gives good performance in extreme cold. Comes in hollow or solid sticks. From Lead Bullets Technology.

**Price:** 1 to 4 sticks, each . . . **$4.00**
**Price:** 5 or more, each . . . **$3.75**

**Commercial Lube**

LBT Blue lube but firmer formula. Lubri-sizers need be warmed to about 100° for good flow. Comes in hollow or solid sticks. From Lead Bullets Technology.

**Price:** 1 to 4 sticks, each . . . **$4.00**
**Price:** 5 or more, each . . . **$3.75**

**Lubricator Heater**

Works with all non-commercial lubricators, Lyman, RCBS, Star, Saeco, Pitzer. Rugged aluminum block 1″x 1½″ containing heavy-duty industrial cartridge heater designed for use in plastic injection dies. Suitable for up to 240 volts, AC or DC with use of dimmer switch. From Lead Bullets Technology.

**Price:** . . . **$30.00**

**Lubricator Nose Punches**

Two styles available. Lyman and RCBS sizer lubricator nose punches. Flat face works well with 20 BHN and harder flat-nosed handgun bullets. Fitted punches for LBT bullets only for use with soft bullets under 20 BHN and all rifle bullets under 35-caliber. From Lead Bullets Technology.

**Price:** Lyman, RCBS punch . . . **$5.00**
**Price:** LBT custom . . . **$8.00**

**Magnum Lube**

Performance limit to 2600 fps on conventional bullet designs. Semi-solid lube that flows well down to 45° Fahrenheit. Comes in hollow or solid sticks. From Lead Bullets Technology.

**Price:** 1 to 4 sticks, each . . . **$4.00**
**Price:** 5 or more, each . . . **$3.75**

Donald Eagan Lube Die

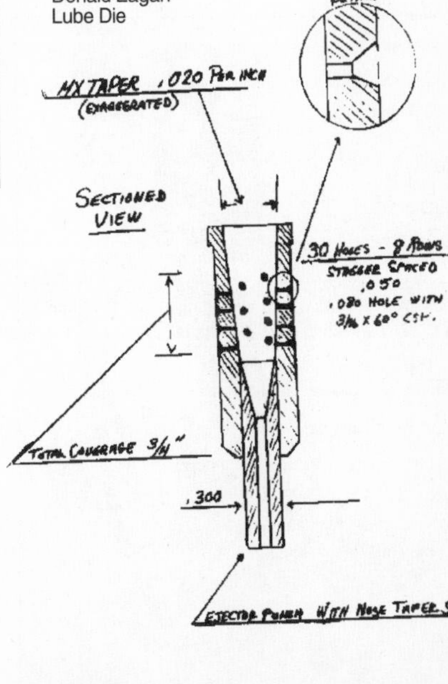

LBT Blue Lube

Hanned Top Punch

Andela Bullet Lubricator

## LEE

**Lube and Sizing Kit**

Standard threaded size die with integral container. Bullets pushed through sizing die nose first. Gas checks automatically seated and crimped. Sized bullets are captured in special container. Comes complete with lube for single bullet size. From Lee Precision, Inc.

**Price:** . . . . . . . . . . . . . . **$15.98**

**Liquid Alox**

Liquid lube coats entire bullet and dries to varnish-like finish. Eliminates need for sizing of most cast bullets. Comes in 4-oz. bottle—enough to lube 1,000 bullets. From Lee Precision, Inc.

**Price:** . . . . . . . . . . . . . . . **$2.75**

**NRA Formula Alox**

Contains 50% alox 2138F and 50% commercial A-1 beeswax. Hollow stick fits most lubricators. Packed in tubes. From Lee Precision, Inc.

**Price:** . . . . . . . . . . . . . . . . **$3.50**

**Price:** 12 sticks . . . . . . . . . . **$36.00**

## LITHI BEE

**Bullet Lube**

Lithium-based grease blended with pure beeswax. Requires no heating of lube-sizer and will fill bullet lube grooves at temperatures to 58° Fahrenheit. Remains solid at 150° Fahrenheit. Available in 1"x 4" hollow or solid sticks. From Lithi Bee Bullet Lube.

**Price:** Each . . . . . . . . . . . . **$2.75**

**Price:** 3-5 boxes (24 per box) . . . . **$62.00**

**Price:** 6 or more boxes . . . . . . **$53.00**

## LYMAN

**#450 Bullet Sizer/Lubricator**

Short stroke, power link leverage system sizes, lubes and seats gas checks. C-type iron-steel cast frame is line bored for die alignment. Comes with gas check seater and Alox lubricant. Adaptable to all bullets by change of size die. Weight: 7³/₄ lbs. From Lyman Products Corporation.

**Price:** . . . . . . . . . . . . . **$125.00**

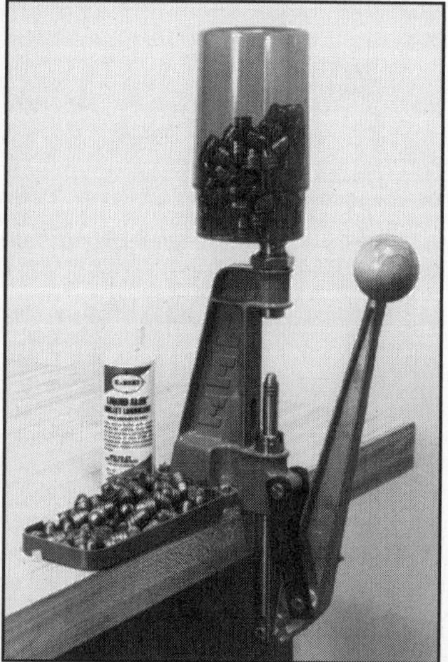

Lee Lube and Sizing Kit

Lee Liquid Alox

Lyman Lube/Sizer Heater

Lyman Orange Magic Bullet Lube

Lyman Liquid Alox

Lithi Bee Bullet Lube

Lyman #450 Bullet Sizer/Lubricator

**LYMAN Lube Size Dies**

| PISTOL | | RIFLE | |
|---|---|---|---|
| **CALIBER** | **DIAMETER** | **CALIBER** | **DIAMETER** |
| 22 Jet | .224, .225 | 244 | .243, .244 |
| 221 Fireball | .224, .225 | 6mm | .243, .244 |
| 25 ACP | .251 | 25 | .257, .258 |
| 30 Luger | .310 | 264 Win. Mag. | .264, .266 |
| 30 Herrett | .310 | 6.5mm | .264, .266 |
| 30 Mauser | .310 | 270 Win. | .277, .278 |
| 32 ACP | .311, .312, .313, .314 | 7mm | .284, .285 |
| 32-20 | .311, .312, .313, .314 | 280 Rem. | .284, .285 |
| 32 S&W | .311, .312, .313, .314 | 284 Win. | .284, .285 |
| 32 H&R Mag. | .311, .312, .313, .314 | 30 | .308, .309, .310 |
| 9mm Luger | .354, .355, .356 | 7.62 Russian | .310 |
| 38 | .354, .355, .356 | 32-20 Win. | .310 |
| 38 Super Auto | .354, .355, .356 | 7.65mm Mauser | .311 |
| 380 Auto | .354, .355, .356 | 303 British | .313, .314 |
| 38 S&W | .357, .358, .359, .360 | 32 Win. Spl. | .321 |
| 38 Spl. | .357, .358, .359, .360 | 32 Win. SL | .321 |
| 357 Mag. | .357, .358, .359, .360 | 32 Rem. | .321 |
| 357 Max. | .357, .358, .359, .360 | 8mm Mauser | .323, .325 |
| 38-40 | .400, .401 | 338 Win. | .338 |
| 10mm Auto | .400, .401 | 9mmx56 | .354, .355, .356 |
| 40 S&W | .400, .401 | 9mmx57 | .354, .355, .356 |
| 41 S&W Mag. | .410 | 35 | .357, .358, .359 |
| 41 AE | .410 | 375 H&H Mag. | .375, .377, .378 |
| 44 S&W Spl. | .429, .430, .431 | 375 Win. | .375, .377, .378 |
| 44 Mag. | .429, .430, .431 | 38-55 | .379 |
| 45 ACP | .450, .451, .452 | 38-40 | .400, .401 |
| 45 Auto Rim | .450, .451, .452 | 44-40 | .427, .428 |
| 45 Colt | .450, .451, .452 | 44 Spl. | .429, .430 |
| 45 Win. Mag. | .450, .451, .452 | 44 Mag. | .429, .430 |
| 45 Colt | .454 | 444 Marlin | .430, .431 |
| 445 Webley | .454 | 45-70 | .457, .458, .459 |
| 22 | .224, .225 | 458 Winchester | .457, .458, .459 |
| 243 | .243, .244 | 50 | .509, .512 |

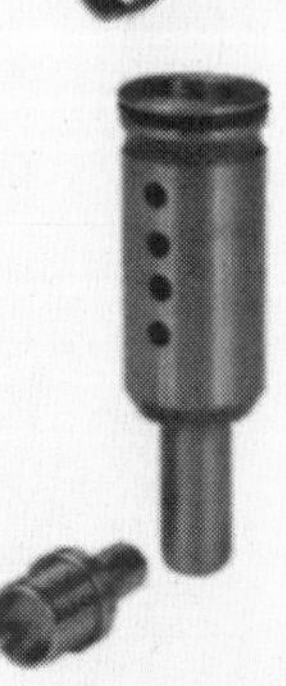

Lyman Size Die and Top Punch

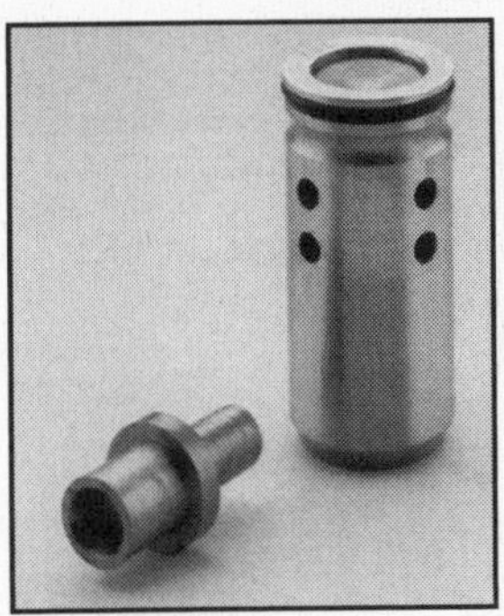

Lyman Lube/Size Die and Top Punch

Midway Lubricator Heater

Magma Star Helper

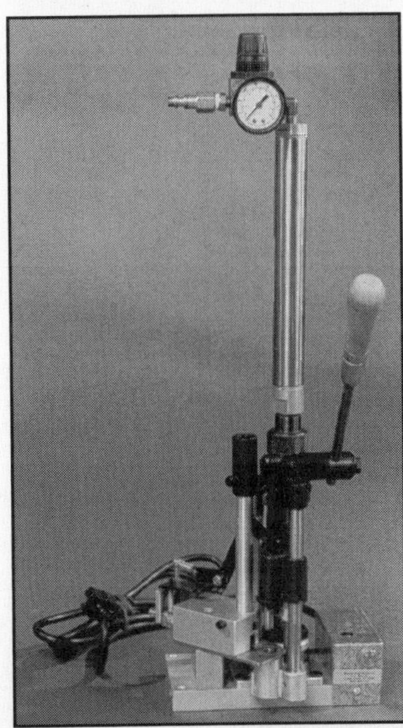

## LYMAN

**Alox Lube**

Comes in tubular form and fits all standard lube sizers. Best for rifle bullets. Weight: 1-oz. From Lyman Products Corporation.

**Price:** . . . . . . . . . . . . . . . **$3.50**

**Ideal Lubricant**

Designed to increase accuracy and eliminate barrel leading. Available in solid or hollow sticks and will fit Lyman 40 sizer/lubricator and other similar tools. From Lyman Products Corporation.

**Price:** . . . . . . . . . . . . . . . **$3.50**

**Liquid Alox**

For both cast and swaged bullets. Coat bullets and allow to dry overnight. Comes in 4-oz. bottle. From Lyman Products Corporation.

**Price:** . . . . . . . . . . . . . . . **$2.95**

**Lube/Sizer Heater**

Aluminum mounting plate/heating block drilled to accept Lyman, RCBS, Saeco and Star lubrisizers. 110-volt. From Lyman Products Corporation.

**Price:** 110 . . . . . . . . . . . . **$40.00**
**Price:** 220 . . . . . . . . . . . . **$44.00**

**Orange Magic Bullet Lube**

High temperature lube designed to allow higher cast bullet velocities without leading. From Lyman Products Corporation.

**Price:** . . . . . . . . . . . . . . . **$4.00**

**Lube/Size Dies and Top Punch**

Now features 90° hole spacing for lubing bullets with hard lubricants. Precisely machined top punch fits bullet nose shape exactly (refer to chart in bullet mould section for correct bullet top punch). Tapered mouth and hardened interior of size die forms and lubes bullets. Interior dimension of size die corresponds to suggested diameters for all popular rifle and pistol calibers. From Lyman Products Corporation.

**Price:** Top Punch . . . . . . . . . **$6.50**
**Price:** Sizing die . . . . . . . . . **$16.00**

## MAGMA

**Star Lube-Sizer**

Accessories for the Star Auto Lubricator/Sizer. Heated base for new hard wax bullet lubes; bullet feeder to automatically feed bullets from plastic tube; hard wax bullet lube. Bullet feeder includes setup for one caliber: small, 38-9mm; large, 10mm, 41, 44, 45. Special transfer bars and feed tubes required for short bullets, e.g. 25, 32, 380. From Magma Engineering Company.

**Price:** . . . . . . . . . . . . . . **$337.50**
**Price:** Heated base . . . . . . . **$85.00**
**Price:** Bullet feeder . . . . . . . **$95.00**
**Price:** Star lube, per pound . . . . . **$9.90**

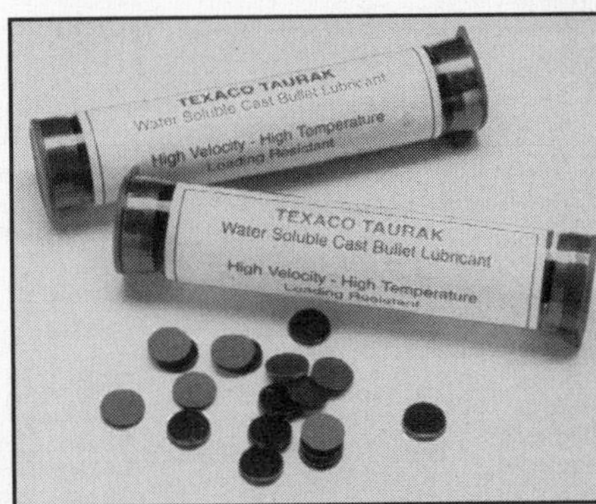


NECO Taurak Bullet Lube

## MIDWAY

**Lubricator Heater**

Thermostatically controlled baseplate heater precisely drilled and tapped for Lyman, RCBS, Saeco and Star lubrisizers. Features industrial-grade heating element and precision thermostat to control lube temperature to within 5°. Mounted on high aluminum plate with cork insulation pad on bottom. Designed to melt hardest lubes. From Midway Arms, Inc.

**Price:** . . . . . . . . . . . . . . **$49.99**

## NECO

**Taurak Bullet Lube**

Thick water soluable, high melting point, block grease lube for cast lead bullets to prevent leading at velocities in excess of 2200 fps. Available in 1″ diameter sticks with or without a center hole. From NECO.

**Price:** . . . . . . . . . . . . . . . **$3.50**

## NEI

**SP Lube**

Sprue plate lube eliminates galling. Comes in 2-oz. container. From NEI Handtools, Inc.

**Price:** . . . . . . . . . . . . . . . **$3.00**

## RAPINE

**Bullet Press Sizer**

Designed specifically for large Civil War bullets, hollow base and solid base carbine bullets but can be used with other calibers. Sizes bullets to .001″ increments using a series of size dies. Comes with one pusher for flat base or hollow base bullets. From Rapine Associates.

**Price:** . . . . . . . . . . . . . **$41.95**
**Price:** Sizing die . . . . . . . **$11.49**

**Bullet Lube**

Bullet lubricant for both blackpowder and modern bullets. Comes in 4-oz. bottle. From Rapine Associates.

**Price:** . . . . . . . . . . . . . . . **$2.95**

## REDDING

**Double "C" Clamps**

Designed for clamping the Saeco lubri-sizer to benchtop. Will accommodate bench thickness of up to 2 1/4″. From Redding Reloading Equipment.

**Price:** . . . . . . . . . . . . . **$19.50**

## RCBS

**Bullet Lube**

Designed for RCBS Lube-A-Matic and other lube-sizers that use hollow-stick lubricant. Non-toxic, temperature-resistant blend of Alox and beeswax to NRA specifications. From RCBS.

**Price:** . . . . . . . . . . . . . . . **$3.38**

**Lube-A-Matic-2**

Auto pressure control with finger tip adjustments for depth of sizing. Uses either Lube-A-Matic or Lyman dies. Will also seat gas checks. Sizer die and top punch not included. From RCBS.

**Price:** . . . . . . . . . . . . . **$128.13**
**Price:** Bullet sizer die . . . . . . **$17.25**
**Price:** Top punch . . . . . . . . . **$6.50**
**Price:** Accessory Base Plate-2 . . . **$22.63**

## ROOSTER

**Bullet Film Lube**

Emulsified liquid lube bonds tightly to cast or swaged bullets. Designed for low velocity pistol loads. Apply by dipping, tumbling or flood-coating. Lubes 100,000 bullets. Available in 16-oz., 1/2-gal. or 1-gallon quantities. From Rooster Laboratories.

**Price:** 16-oz. . . . . . . . . . . . . **$7.50**
**Price:** 1/2-gal. . . . . . . . . . . **$18.50**
**Price:** 1-gal. . . . . . . . . . . . **$30.00**

**Bullet Lubes**

Lubri-sizer high-melt cannelure lubes in choice of hardnesses. Zambini is hard tough lube intended for pistol bullets; melting point of 220° Fahrenheit. Comes in 2″x 6″ commercial-size sticks and 1″x 4″ hollow or solid sticks. HVR is soft but firm and designed for high-velocity rifle bullets; melting point of 220° Fahrenheit. Available in 1″x 4″ sticks only. From Rooster Laboratories.

**Price:** Zambini 2x6, each . . . . . . **$4.00**
**Price:** Zambini 1x4, each . . . . . . **$3.00**
**Price:** HVR, each . . . . . . . . . . **$3.00**

## SAECO

**Bullet Lubes**

Saeco Gold is alox free formula to reduce leading to a minimum. Saeco Traditional rifle lube is NRA formula with alox and natural beeswax mixture. Saeco Green for both pistol and rifle bullets contains no alox and is slightly harder than the other two lubes. All available in solid or hollow sticks. From Redding Reloading Equipment.

**Price:** Each . . . . . . . . . . . . **$3.90**

**Lubri-Sizer**

Features solid cast iron body; swing-out gas check seater for seating gas checks without sizing; adjustable pressure lubricant; two guide rods for alignment of top punch and sizing die; compound leverage; use with hollow or solid stick lube. Top punches and sizing dies not included. From Redding Reloading Equipment.

**Price:** . . . . . . . . . . . . . . **$175.50**

**Sizing Dies**

Made with unique prelead that fits "as cast" bullet diameter for depth of approximately .3-inch to ensure straight bullet feed alignment in die. Gentle taper constriction between the two diameters eliminates lead shearing. Dies are internally micro-honed. From Redding Reloading Equipment.

**Price:** . . . . . . . . . . . . . . **$31.50**

**Top Punches**

Tapered shoulder punch assures positive alignment with die body. Straight shank-type punches designed for Lyman and RCBS lubrisizers also available. From Redding Reloading Equipment.

**Price:** . . . . . . . . . . . . . . **$12.00**

## SPG

**Bullet Lube**

Developed specifically for blackpowder cartridge shooting but can be used for smokeless loads. Helps keep fouling soft. Available in hollow stick only. From SPG Lubricants.

**Price:** Each . . . . . . . . . . . . **$3.90**

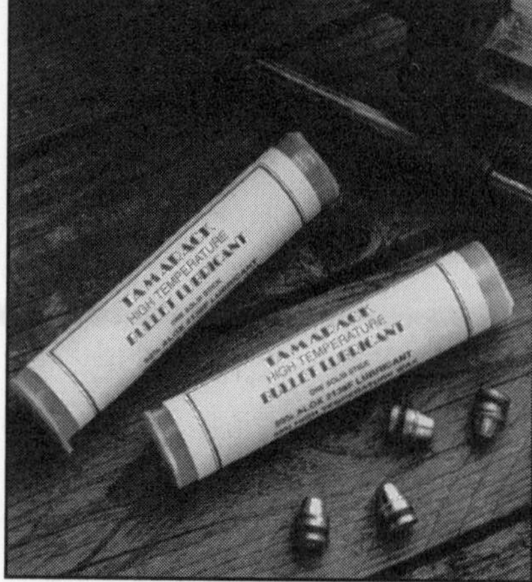


Tamarack Bullet Lube

Robert Stillwell Lube/Size Die

## STAR

**Auto Lubricator/Sizer**

Constructed of aluminum and steel. Features storage pressure system in grease reservoir to feed high pressure pump which forces lube onto bullet grooves. Single pressure screw setting lubes 200 bullets. Bullet forced through hardened universal sizer die by next bullet in line. Specify manufacturer's mould number when ordering. From Star Machine Works.

**Price:** . . . . . . . . . . . . . . **$157.50**

## ROBERT STILLWELL

**Lube/Size Dies**

Custom-made 257 through 530 dies for Star lubricator/sizer. Heat-treated to 60-62 C. From Robert Stillwell.

**Price:** . . . . . . . . . . . . . . **$32.00**
**Price:** Top punch (flat) . . . . . . **$10.00**
**Price:** Top punch (to fit) . . . . . **$16.00**

## TAMARACK

**Hi Temp Bullet Lube**

Lube 50% alox 2138-F and 50% hi-temp A-1 beeswax for pistol and rifle bullets with same hardness as NRA formula so no heating is required. Both hollow and solid sticks 1″x 5″ and 2″x6″ available. Contact manufacturer for bulk prices. From Tamarack Products, Inc.

**Price:** Each . . . . . . . . . . . . **$2.95**
**Price:** 6, each . . . . . . . . . . . **$1.75**
**Price:** 20, each . . . . . . . . . . **$1.45**
**Price:** 50, each . . . . . . . . . . **$1.30**
**Price:** 200+, each . . . . . . . . . **$1.20**

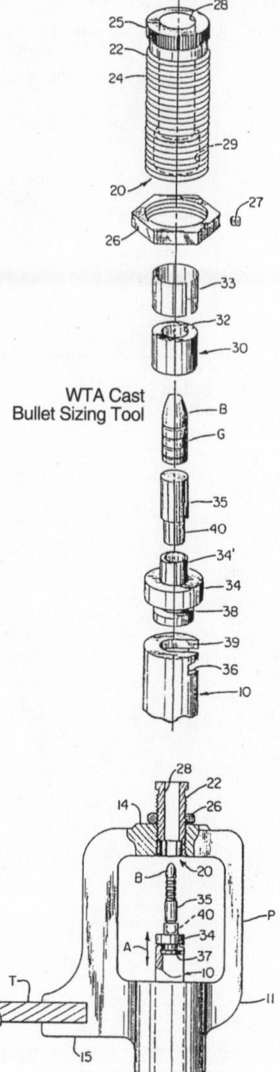


WTA Cast Bullet Sizing Tool

## THOMPSON

**Bullet Lubes**

Five wax-based lube offerings. Bear Lube Cold soft, non-sticky and requires 90° to flow; Bear Lube Heat is medium hard lube flows at 110°; Lazy Lube same as Bear Lube Heat but designed to flow through automated Star Luber; dry, non-sticky Blue Angel for the commercial caster and requires 125° to 140° flow temperature with melt point of 165°; Red Angel melts at 240° and will flow at 180° or lower; PS blackpowder cartridge lube. Available in 1″x 4″, 1″x 8″ or 2″x 6″ sticks. For case and partial case prices contact manufacturer. From Thompson Bullet Lube Co.

**Price:** Bear, Blue Angel, each . . . . **$3.20**
**Price:** Red Angel, each . . . . . . . **$3.50**
**Price:** PS . . . . . . . . . . . . . . **$3.50**

## WTA

**Cast Bullet Sizing Tool**

Consists of a die, flat base and interchangeable bushings for use on any reloading press to size or expand the size of cast bullets. Bushings available in .001 increments. From WTA.

**Price:** . . . . . **Contact manufacturer.**

PART 1 2 3 4 5 6 7

# COMPONENTS

## ACCURATE ARMS

Accurate smokeless powders are listed here in approximate burning order from fastest to slowest. All propellants are double base ball propellants unless described otherwise.

### HANDGUN

**No. 2** Fast burning propellant for use in 38 Special target loads. Also suited to 25 ACP, 32 S&W Long, 32 H&R Magnum, 32/20 Winchester, 380 Auto, 9mm Luger, 38 Super Auto, 357 Magnum, 40 S&W, 41 AE, 10mm Auto, 41 Magnum, 44 Special, 44 Magnum, 45 ACP and 20-gauge shotshell.

**No. 5** Relatively fast burning propellant for use in the 45 ACP. Also suitable for 38 Special, 38 Special +P and 9mm sub-sonic loads. Good for target velocity cast bullet loads in magnum handgun cartridges and for IPSC shooters using the 40 S&W or 41 AE.

**No. 7** Originally developed for 9mm NATO carbine ammo. Best suited to full-power 10mm Auto ammunition. Also good in magnum handgun cartridges such as 357, 41 and 44 Magnum when less than full power loads are preferred.

**No. 9** Popular ball-type 44 Magnum powder. Intended for use in large capacity handgun cartridges (357, 41, 44 Magnum and 454 Casull) but also suited to some small rifle cases (22 Hornet, 30 Carbine) as well as the 410 shotgun. Requires heavy crimp for consistent performance.

### RIFLE

**XMP5744** Double base propellant suitable for large handgun cartridges, small rifle cartridges and large rifle cartridges from the blackpowder era, i.e. 45-70 and 50-70 as well as popular IHSMA-style cartridges.

**1680** Developed specifically for the 7.62x39 and the 30 Herrett. Excellent in the 22 Hornet. Also suitable for small capacity cases such as the T/CU series and the 222 Remington.

**2015BR** Single base, small-grained, extruded propellant developed specifically for benchrest cartridges such as the PPC and BR series. Serves well in other cartridges from the 22 Hornet to 458 Winchester Magnum.

**2230** (Formerly MR-223) A medium-burning propellant developed for the 223 Remington (5.56 NATO). Also suitable to 7mm T/CU, 22/250 Remington, 30/30 Winchester and similar cartridges.

**2460** Medium-burning ball propellant popular with NRA, IHMSA and benchrest shooters. Useful in cartridges from 223 Remington to the 30-06 and good in the 30/30 Winchester. Slightly slower than 2230 and shows a pressure advantage over 2230 in bores 7mm and over. Good choice in 308 Winchester and appropriate with M1 and M14 service rifles.

**2495BR** Similar to 4895. Single base extruded propellant for satisfactory performance in a wide variety of cartridges. Best application is cast bullets in 45-70 Government.

**2520** Medium-slow burning propellant that gives excellent results in medium-capacity cases (308 class) and has certain applications in large bore cartridges. 2520 has a pressure curve appropriate for use with M1 and M14 service rifles.

**2700** Recent ball propellant that fills the gap between 2520 and 4350. Intended for use as a heavy bullet powder in cartridges from 22-250 Remington to the belted magnums.

**4350** Single base, extruded propellent very similar IMR-4350.

**3100** Single base extruded propellant for cartridges from the 243 Winchester to the big magnums. 3100 burn rate is between IMR-4831 and H-4831.

**8700** Slowest powder available. Best suited to magnum rifle cases such as the 264 Winchester Magnum, 7mm Remington Magnum, 257 Weatherby Magnum, 270 Weatherby Magnum and 300 Weatherby Magnum. May also be used in cartridges such as the 25/06 Remington and 270 Winchester.

### SHOTSHELL

**SOLO 1000** Fast clean burning single base disc powder for all automatic pistol and shotguns. Uniform grain size. Similar to Hercules Bullseye for light pistol target shooting and to IMR-700-X or PB for shotshells.

**Nitro 100** Fast burning, double base flake propellant for 1 and 1¹/₈-ounce shot loads in 12-gauge for trap, Skeet and light field. Also applicable in 38 Special, 44 Special, 45 ACP and 45 Long Colt.

**SOLO 1250** Medium rate clean burning single base, disc powder for 12-ga. hunting loads or 20 and 28 ga. Skeet. Similar to IMR SR-7625 and Hercules Unique. Also good for pistol loads in 9mm, 40 S&W and 10mm IPSC.

**4100** Fine-grained, double-based ball propellant developed for use with .410-bore shotshells.

## HERCULES

Alliant Techsystems acquired the Hercules Aerospace Company, including the Commerical Smokeless Powder Group in early 1995. Hercules offers 12 powders for reloading. Within categories, they are listed here in the manufacturer's order of decreasing burning rates. From Alliant Powder.

### SHOTSHELL

**Blue Dot:** Designed for magnum shotshell loads 10, 12, 16, 20 and 28 gauges. Also for use in magnum handgun loads. Available in 1- and 5-lb. canisters.

**Red Dot:** For light to medium shotshells; designed for 12-ga. target loads. Also can be used for handgun loads. Available in 1-, 4- and 8-lb. cannisters.

**Green Dot:** For 12-ga. medium shotshell loads and 20-ga. Skeet loads. Available in 1-, 4- and 8-lb. cannisters.

**Herco:** For high-velocity shotshell loads in heavy and magnum 10-, 12-, 16-, 20-gauge. Also for high performance handgun loads. Available in 1-, 4- and 8-lb. cannisters.

**Unique:** Broad application from light to heavy shotshell loads and medium to light handgun loads. Available in 1-, 4- and 8-lb. cannisters.

### HANDGUN

**Bullseye:** High energy, quick burning powder designed for pistol and revolver. Also for use in 12-gauge 1-oz. target loads. Available in 1-, 4- and 8-lb. cannisters.

**Hercules 2400:** For magnum handguns loads, small-capacity rifle cartridges and 410-bore shotshells. Available in 1-, 4- and 8-lb. cannisters.

### RIFLE

**Reloder 7:** Designed for light rifle loads and also applicable to silhouette loads. Available in 1- and 5-lb. cannisters.

**Reloder 12, 15:** Versatile powders for medium-caliber rifle loads and also usable in silhouette loads.

**Reloder 19, 22:** Powders designed for magnum rifle loads.

# HODGDON POWDER CO.

## HODGDON

Powders are listed in Hodgdon's approximate order of burn rate from fastest to slowest within categories.

### RIFLE

**H4198** An extruded powder with shortened grain size to improve metering and loading density and maintaining ballistic performance. Excellent in the 222 and 7.62x39 Russian and some large straight cases including the 45-70, 444 Marlin and 458 Winchester Magnum.

**H322** Short-grained extruded powder good in all small and medium capacity cases such as the 223 and 222 as well as the 22 and 6mm PPC. Also works well in many TCU and IHMSA cartridges.

**H4895** Versatile extruded powder for the 17 Remington, 22-250, 308 and 458 Winchester. Performance similar to IMR-4895.

**H335** Used by the military for the 223 or 5.56 NATO. Works well in most cases from 30-06 down.

**BL-C2** A spherical propellant best suited for the 308. Performs well in most cases smaller than 30-06.

**Varget** Small extruded grain powder similar to 4064 in burning speed but not interchangeable with 4064. Gives higher velocities in 223, 22-250, 308, 30-06, 375 etc.

**H380** Excellent in the 22-250, 220 Swift, 6mm Remington, 257 Roberts and 30-06. Spherical powder.

**H414** Spherical powder with wide range of use from the 17 Remington to 375 H&H. Designed to be equivalent of H4350 and produces similar results.

**H4350** Extruded powder that provides superior performance in cartridges from 22-250 to 460 Weatherby. Works well with heavier projectiles. H4350 has been changed to the short-cut version for improved metering and loading density. Similar to IMR-4350.

**H450** Relatively slow burning spherical powder designed to be similar in performance to H4831. Works well in 25-06, 7mm Magnum, 30-06, 270, 300 Winchester Magnum and 300 Weatherby Magnum.

**H4831** This slow burning extruded powder is excellent with heavy bullets in many cases including 25-06, 270, 280, 257 Weatherby and 338 Winchester.

**H4831SC** Exact copy of H4831 but with shorter grain size for improved metering and loading density thus the "SC" designation. Load data is same as for H4831.

**H4227** Fastest burning of Hodgdon extruded powders. Well adapted to the 22 Hornet and specialized loading in the 45-70. Excellent in magnum pistol.

**H1000** Extremely slow burning extruded powder with a narrow range of use. Excellent in the 300 Winchester, it also does well in the 270, 30-06, 300 Winchester Magnum and 300 Weatherby Magnum.

**H870** For large capacity big overbore magnum loads. Also used for the 50 BMG.

### SHOTGUN/HANDGUN

**CLAYS** For 12-gauge clay target shooters using $1^{1}/_{8}$- and 1-ounce loads. Also performs well in handgun calibers, 38 Special, 40 S&W and 45 ACP.

**International Clays** For reduced recoil target loads in 12- and 20-gauge.

**HP38** Fastest burning powder in Hodgdon line. Spherical propellant for low velocity and mid-range target loads in 38 Special, 44 Special, 9mm and 45 ACP.

**Universal Clays** Extremely small grain extruded flake powder. For most all straight-wall pistol cartridges as well as 12-gauge $1^{1}/_{4}$-oz. through 28-gauge $^{3}/_{4}$-oz. target loads.

**HS6** Good for all bullet weights in the 9mm. Also performs well in most straight-wall pistol cartridges and is well suited to the 45 ACP. A dual purpose spherical powder that is also applicable to 12-gauge $1^{1}/_{4}$-$1^{1}/_{2}$-ounce shot loads and 20-gauge 1-oz.

**HS7** Primarily a shotgun propellant for heavy field loads. Also can be used to reload steel shot. Will work in some pistol cartridges including the 357 Magnum, 41 Magnum, 44 Magnum and 45 Winchester Magnum.

**H110** True magnum powder for magnum velocities. Top performer in 357 Magnum, 44 Magnum and 410 shotshell. Develops high operating pressures and velocities.

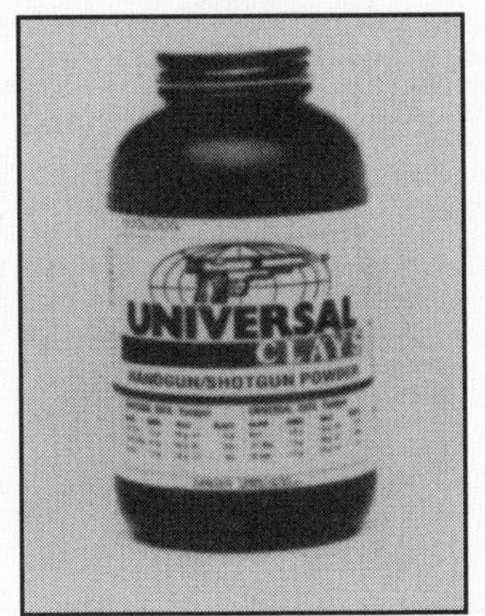


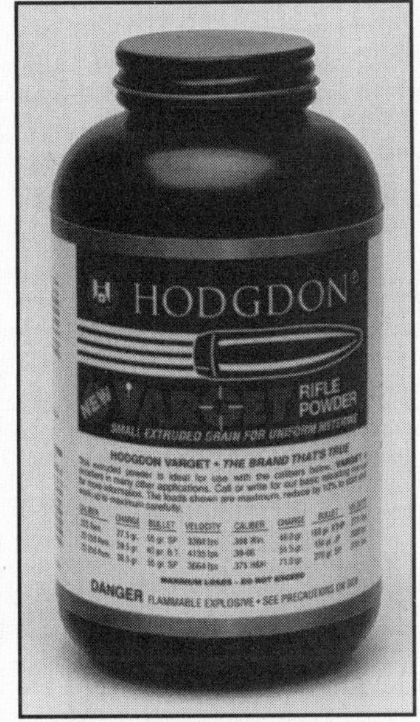

# IMR™

## SHOTGUN/HANDGUN

**Hi-Skor 700X** Shotgun double-base powder developed for 12-ga. components but has found recent applications in high-volume handgun rounds such as the 38 Special, 9mm Luger and 45 ACP.

**Hi-Skor 800X** Slower burning than 700X, it has applications in smaller gauges, target loads, 12-gauge field and heavier handgun loads.

**PB** Named for the porous base structure of its grains, by which the burning rate is controlled, this powder is used for many handgun loads though it was developed for shotshells.

**SR 4756** Designed for magnum shotshells. Good producer in 410-bore target ammo and heavy centerfire handgun ammuntion.

**SR 7625** Clean burning powder with applications in 12-gauge down to 28-gauge target and field loads. Also viable for handgun loads.

## RIFLE

**IMR-4227** Originally intended for small cartridges such as the Hornet and Bee but has proved useful in a wide spread of high performance handgun loads.

**IMR-4198** The powder that showed early 222 shooters, including the benchresters, how good that cartridge was. Also very useful in large caliber, non-bottleneck cases like the 444 Marlin and 45-70.

**IMR-4895** Countless tons of this propellant were used by the U.S. government to load 30-06 ammo during WWII. Probably the most versatile powder ever made. Excellent results with certain bullets in cases from the 17 Remington to the 458 Magnum.

**IMR-4064** Medium-burning powder well suited for a wide range of calibers. Long a favorite of Jack O'Connor in the 220 Swift.

**IMR-4320** Like most medium-burning powders, this one is versatile, giving good results in cases as large as the 460 Weatherby. Meters well.

**SR-4759** Single base powder ideally suited to cast bullet rifle loads.

**IMR-4350** An early slow-burning powder specifically designed for bottlenecked magnum cartridges. Consistent results.

**IMR-4831** Another WWII powder, this slow burner made most of today's high velocity magnum cartridges practical. Excellent in 264 Winchester, 7mm Remington and 338 Magnums.

**IMR-3031** Recommended for medium-size cases such as the 30-30 and 358, it is also useful for mid-range loads and delivers fine results in cases as large as the 460 Weatherby.

**IMR 7828** Slowest burning of the IMR rifle powders, this is at its best with bottlenecked large-capacity cases and heavy bullets.

Cylindrical or flaked powders with 94-98% nitrocellulose content. The powders are presented here in burn rate order from the fastest burning to the slowest burning.

## RIFLE

**N110:** Fast-burning propellant comparable to 2400, H110 or W296 for 22 Hornet, 25-20 Winchester, 357 Mag., 357 Max., 44 Mag. and 45 Mag.

**N120:** Burn rate near various 4227s for light bulleted 22s.

**N130:** Burn rate between IMR-4227 and Win. 680. Used in factory-loaded 22 and 6mm PPC.

**N133:** Burn rate speed close to IMR-4198 for 222 Remington, 223 Remington and 45-70.

**N135:** Moderate burning propellant for 17 Remington through 458 Winchester.

**N140:** Comparable to Reloder 12, IMR-4895 or IMR-4064 for 222 Rem. Mag., 22-250 Rem., 30-30 Win., 308 Win., 30-06 Sprfld., 375 H&H Mag.

**N150:** Moderately slow-burning propellant similar to 760, H414 and IMR 4350.

**N160:** Relatively slow-burning propellant designed for magnum and standard calibers. Similar to Reloder 19, 4831 and 4350.

**N165:** Very slow-burning magnum propellant for use with heavy bullets.

**N170:** Slowest speed propellent available.

**N540:** Burn rate similar to N140. Designed for 308 Winchester.

**N550:** Burn rate similar to N150. Designed for 308 Winchester and 30-06.

**N560:** Burn rate similar to N160. Designed for 270 Winchester and 6.5x55 Swedish Mauser.

**24N41** and **20N29:** Designed for 50 BMG, both are single-base surface-treated powders.

## HANDGUN/SHOTGUN

**N310:** Fast burning propellant similar to Bullseye and AAZ for 25 ACP to 9mm Luger to 44 Mag.

**N320:** Shotgun/handgun propellant with relatively fast burn rate for 9mm Luger, 38 Spl., 357 Mag., 44 Mag., 45 ACP and 45 LC.

**N330:** Handgun propellant with burn rate similar to Green Dot, No. 5 or PB, designed for 9mm Luger, 38 Spl., 40 S&W, 44 S&W Spl., 45 LC.

**N340:** Burn rate similar to W540 or Herco has application for wide variety of handgun calibers.

**N350:** Slow-burning propellant for handgun and shotgun with burn rate similar to Blue Dot, 800-x or AA7.

**3N37:** Designed for high-velocity rimfire cartridges with burn speed between N340 and N350. Also has application in shotshell and cartridges.

**N105 Super Magnum:** Burn rate between N350 and N110 for heavy-bulleted or large case capacity cartridges.

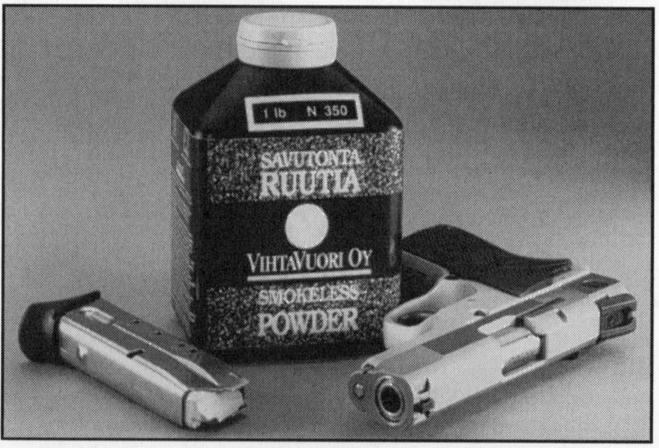

## WINCHESTER

Olin Corporation, of which Winchester has long been a division, has been producing Smokeless Ball powder commercially since 1933. These eleven powders are currently available.

### RIFLE

**748** Rifle powder suitable for 222 Remington and 458 Winchester Magnum. Popular benchrest propellant.

**760** For medium to large cartridges. Broad range of application in medium to large cases.

**WMR** Magnum Rifle ball powder for magnum and high-velocity rifle loads. High density, slow burning and reduced flame powder.

### SHOTGUN/HANDGUN

**231** Fast, high energy, clean burning powder for target and standard velocity loads in handguns.

**296** For 410-bore, magnum pistol and 30 Carbine. Requires heavy bullets and heavy crimps in magnum pistol cartridges.

**540** For heavy shot charges in 12- and 20-gauge. Excellent powder for 28-gauge. Higher density permits easier crimping of heavy loads.

**WAP** Winchester Action Pistol powder designed for handgun calibers such as 9mm Luger, 38 Super, 40 S&W, 10mm Auto and 45 Auto. Clean burning ball powder with low flame temperatures to help extend barrel life.

**WSL Winchester Super-Lite** For target and standard velocity shotshell loads and reloads with reduced recoil.

**WST Winchester Super-Target** Replacement shotshell powder for 452AA. Formulated to produce uniform velocity and pressure.

**WSF Winchester Super-Field** For 20-gauge Skeet and field. Same powder as used in factory 20-ga. AA but can also be used for 12- and 16-gauge.

**WAAP** Lowest charge weight powder Winchester markets for reloading target shotshells.

## NORMA

**N-200** Fastest burning of Norma powders. Best results in small calibers like 22 PPC and 6mm PPC. Also suitable in 9.3x62 with light bullets.

**N-201** Primarily for small-bore centerfire competition in cartridges such as 222, 223 or 6mm.

**N-202** Typically for 30-caliber hunting or competition as in the 308 or 30-06.

**N-204** Intended for use in bottleneck cases with unusually large ratios of powder volume to bullet diameter.

**MRP** For use in the largest of the big-bore magnum rifles.

**R-1** Suitable powder for non-magnum handgun cartridges.

**R-123** Designed for magnum handgun cartridges and certain specialized rifle cartridge applications.

## THUNDERBIRD CARTRIDGE CO.

Thunderbird offers five powders for reloading use. They are listed here in order of decreasing burning rates. Each powder listed is slower burning than those preceding it and faster than those following it. From Thunderbird Cartridge Co.

**T-680:** Ball powder designed for 30 M1 Carbine, 7.62x39 and also applicable to 357 and 44 Magnum.

**T-5020, T-870, T-5070:** Slow burning ball powders for belted magnums, over bore capacity rounds with T-5070 for the 50-calibers.

### SELECTED LOADS

| Cartridge | Bullet Wgt. Grs. | —Load— Grs. | Powder | MV (fps) | Pressure CUP |
|---|---|---|---|---|---|
| 50 BMG | 700 FB | 240 | T-5020 | 3011 | 48,900 |
| | | 243 | T-5020 | 3022 | 49,800 |
| | | 246 | T-5020 | 3078 | 52,700 |
| 50 BMG | 700 FB | 230 | T-870 | 2884 | 45,300 |
| | | 235 | T-870 | 2949 | 48,100 |
| | | 240 | T-870 | 2980 | 48,900 |
| 50 BMG | 700 FB | 238 | T-5070 | 2919 | 45,400 |
| | | 243 | T-5070 | 2970 | 47,500 |
| | | 248 | T-5070 | 3012 | 49,200 |
| | | 250 | T-5070 | 3046 | 51,200 |
| 50 BMG | 750 BT | 200 | T-5020 | 2582 | 39,300 |
| | | 210 | T-5020 | 2693 | 43,625 |
| | | 220 | T-5020 | 2819 | 45,600 |
| | | 225 | T-5020 | 2882 | 48,980 |
| 50 BMG | 750 BT | 220 | T-870 | 2746 | 43,800 |
| | | 225 | T-870 | 2837 | 46,000 |
| | | 230 | T-870 | 2897 | 50,280 |
| 50 BMG | 750 BT | 225 | T-5070 | 2774 | 43,500 |
| | | 230 | T-5070 | 2880 | 45,600 |
| | | 235 | T-5070 | 2900 | 49,320 |

FB = Flat Base; BT = Boattail.

**CAUTION:** Some of these loads are maximum loads. Start low and work up slowly, being alert for signs of excessive pressure.

## BOXER PRIMER PRICES

| Primer | CCI | Price | Federal | Price | Fiocchi | Price | Rem. | Price | RWS | Price | Winchester | Price |
|---|---|---|---|---|---|---|---|---|---|---|---|---|
| Large Rifle | 200 | $22.00/1000 | 210 | $14.40/1000 | 210 | NA | $9\frac{1}{2}$ | $17.20/1000 | 5341 | $14.30/250 | WLR | NA/1000 |
| Magnum Large Rifle | 250 | 23.71/1000 | 215 | 15.40/1000 | | | $9\frac{1}{2}$M | 18.50/1000 | 5333 | 14.30/250 | WLRM | NA/1000 |
| Benchrest Large Rifle | BR2 | 32.43/1000 | 210M | 27.50/1000 | | | | | | | | |
| Benchrest Large Magnum Rifle | 215M | 28.98/1000 | | | | | | | | | | |
| Small Rifle | 400 | 22.00/1000 | 210M | 23.30/1000 | 200 | NA | $6\frac{1}{2}$ | 16.98/1000 | 4033 | 13.10/250 | WSR | NA/1000 |
| Magnum Small Rifle | 450 | 23.71/1000 | 205 | 14.40/1000 | | | | | | | | |
| Benchrest Small Rifle | BR4 | 32.43/1000 | 205M | 27.50/1000 | | | $7\frac{1}{2}$ | 18.50/1000 | | | | |
| Small Pistol | 500 | 21.43/1000 | 100 | 16.50/1000 | 100 | NA | $71\frac{1}{2}$ | 16.98/1000 | 4031 | 13.10/250 | WSP | NA/1000 |
| Magnum Small Pistol | 550 | 21.43/1000 | 200 | 14.00 | | | | | 4047 | 13.10/250 | WSPM | NA/1000 |
| Match Small Pistol | | | 100M | 26.50/1000 | | | | | | | | |
| Large Pistol | 300 | 22.00/1000 | 150 | 14.40/1000 | 150 | NA | $7\frac{1}{2}$ | 17.50/1000 | 5337 | 14.25/250 | WLP | NA/1000 |
| Match Large Pistol | | | 150M | 27.50/1000 | | | | | | | | |
| Magnum Large Pistol | 350 | 23.71/1000 | 155 | 15.40/1000 | | | | | | | | |
| Match Magnum Large Pistol | | | 155M | 28.98/1000 | | | | | | | | |
| 50 BMG | 35 | 110.07/100 | | | | | | | 8212 | 11.30/50 | | |
| Shotshell | 209 | 33.86/1000 | 100M | 22.50 | 209 | NA | 209 | 27.00/1000 | | | W209 | NA/1000 |
| | 209M | 33.86/1000 | | | 410 | 29.08 | | | | | | |
| | 209SC | 33.86/1000 | | | | | | | | | | |
| 410 Premier | | | | | | | | | | | | |
| Percussion Caps | 11 | 33.14/1000 | | | | | 10, 11 | 25.40/1000 | 11 | 4.00/100 | | |
| | 10 | 33.14/1000 | | | | | | | | | | |
| | 11 Magnum | 36.00/1000 | | | | | | | | | | |

## DYNAMIT NOBEL Berdan Primers

| Primer # | Min. Dia. mm | Min. Dia. in. | Max. Hgt. mm | Max. Hgt. in. | Base Thickness mm | Base Thickness in. | Description | Price/Per |
|---|---|---|---|---|---|---|---|---|
| 4506 | 4,50 | .177 | 2,20 | .09 | 0,40 | .0157 | 25 ACP, 32, 380 ACP, some 9mm | $9.85/250 |
| 4520 | 4,50 | .177 | 2,10 | .08 | 0,55 | .0217 | Small rifle, 22 Hornet, 222 Rem., 5.6 | 9.85/250 |
| 4521 | 4,50 | .177 | 2,20 | .09 | 0,40 | .0151 | 9mm Luger (9x19), Steyr | 9.85/250 |
| 5005 | 5,00 | .197 | 2,20 | .09 | 0,40 | .0157 | Non-standard, large caliber pistol | 9.85/250 |
| 5608 | 5,50 | .217 | 2,80 | .11 | 0,70 | .0276 | 7.62 NATO | 13.65/250 |
| 5620 | 5,50 | .217 | 2,65 | .10 | 0,60 | .0236 | | 13.65/250 |
| 6000 | 6,34 | .250 | 2,95 | .11 | 0,79 | .031 | Large dia. for 303 British | 14.90/150 |
| 6504 | 6,45 | .254 | 2,35 | .09 | 0,45 | .0177 | Fits most .254 dia. primed rounds; 577/450, 11.15x58R, etc. | 19.75/150 |
| 6507 | 6,45 | .254 | 3,40 | .133 | 0,33 | .013 | Exact replacement for Eley No. 172 for 500 3″, 577 Nitro, etc. | 5.95/150 |

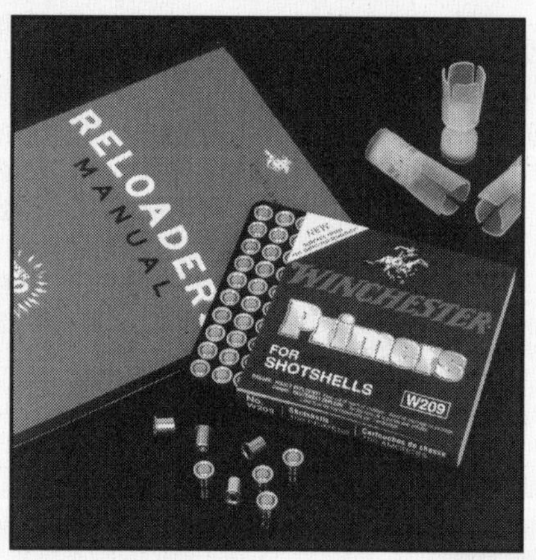


## RWS Berdan Primers

| Primer | # | Description | Price/Per |
|---|---|---|---|
| Small Pistol | 4506 | 25 ACP, 32 ACP, 380 ACP, 9mm | $8.50/250 |
| Small Pistol | 4521 | 9mm Luger, 9x18 Ultra, Steyr | 8.50/250 |
| Large Pistol | 5005 | Large non-standard cases | 8.50/250 |
| Small Rifle | 4520 | Small cases, 22 Hornet, 222 Rem. 5.6mm | 8.50/250 |
| Large Rifle | 5608 | 7.62 NATO | 9.60/250 |
| Large Rifle | 5620 | 5.5mm | 9.60/250 |
| Large Rifle | 6000 | 303 British | 8.50/150 |
| Large Rifle | 6504 | 577 Snider, 577/450 M.H., 43 Egyptian | 8.50/150 |
| Large Rifle | 6507 | British calibers, 500 NE, 577 NE, 450 NE | 8.50/150 |

### DYNAMIT NOBEL

**Berdan Primers**

Berdan primers available for small and large pistol; small and large rifle. See chart for specifications and prices. Come in boxes of 250 and 150. From The Old Western Scrounger.

### M&D MUNITIONS

**Lead Free Primers**

M&D offers lead free small and large pistol primers for reloading. Come in boxes of 2500. From M&D Munitions, Ltd.

**Price: . . . . . Contact manufacturer.**

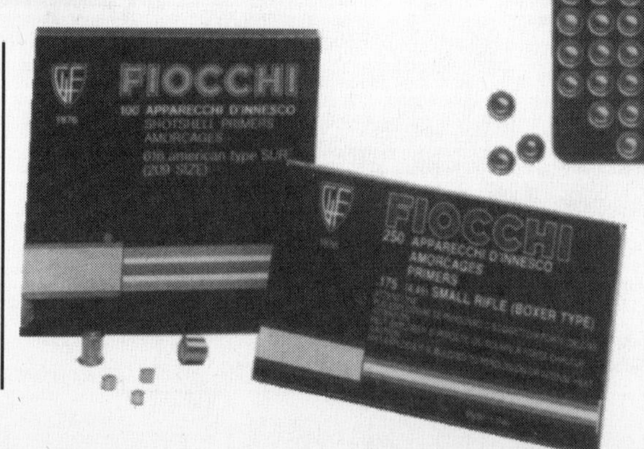

## BRUNO SHOOTER'S SUPPLY

**Lapua and PPC Brass**

Bruno supplies Sako PPC and Lapua brass. From Bruno Shooter's Supply.

**Price:** PPC, per case . . . . . . . . . **$.82**
**Price:** Lapua, 1-449 cases, ea. . . . . . **$1.09**
**Price:** Lapua, 450-999, ea. . . . . . . **$1.04**
**Price:** Lapua, 1000+, ea. . . . . . . . **$1.00**

## BUFFALO ARMS

**Obsolete Caliber Brass**

Brass for obsolete calibers. Brass is drawn, annealed and resized. From Buffalo Arms Co.

**Price:** . . . . . . . . . . . . **See chart.**

## BULL-X

**Once-Fired Pistol Brass**

Processed, commercial or military once-fired brass in 9mm, 38 Special, or 308 calibers. From Bull-X, Inc.

**Price:** . . . . . . . . . . . . **See chart.**

## DAKOTA

**Brass**

Brass cases for Dakota Arms proprietary cartridges, 7mm, 300, 330, 375, 416 and 450 Dakota. From Dakota Arms.

**Price:** . . . . . . . . . . . . . . . **$2.00**

### BULL-X *Once Fired Pistol Brass*

| Caliber | Price 500 | Price 1000 | Comments |
|---|---|---|---|
| 9mm Military | $30.90 | $51.50 | Inspected, deprimed, crimp removed, polished |
| 38 Special | 25.90 | 43.20 | Polished, inspected |
| 308 Military | 28.40 | 47.50 | Polished, inspected |

Bertram Brass

Dakota Brass

### BERTRAM *Pistol Cases*

| Case | Price/20 |
|---|---|
| **PISTOL** | |
| 310 Cattle Killer | $17.98 |
| 7.5mm Swedish Nagant | 17.98 |
| 7.62mm Russian Nagant | 17.98 |
| 7.65 MAS | 17.98 |
| 9mm Browning | 17.98 |
| 41 Long Colt | 17.50 |
| 11.75mm Montenegrin | 19.98 |

From Huntington Die Specialties.

### A-SQUARE *Unprimed Brass*

| Caliber | Packaging | Price |
|---|---|---|
| 7mm STW | B | $39.00 |
| 300 Pegasus | W | 32.00 |
| 338 A-Square | W | 36.00 |
| 338 Excaliber | W | 36.00 |
| 358 STA | B | 39.50 |
| 375 Weatherby | B | 39.50 |
| 375 JRS | B | 39.50 |
| 375 A-Square | W | 27.50 |
| 378 Weatherby | W | 36.00 |
| 450/400 (3″) | W | 45.00 |
| 450/400 (3¼″) | W | 45.00 |
| 416 Taylor | B | 39.50 |
| 416 Hoffman | B | 39.50 |
| 416 Rigby | W | 42.00 |
| 416 Rimmed | W | 53.00 |
| 416 Weatherby | W | 38.00 |
| 404 Jeffery | W | 45.00 |
| 425 Express | B | 39.50 |
| 450 NE(3¼″) | W | 47.00 |
| 450 #2 | W | 58.00 |
| 458 Lott | B | 39.50 |
| 450 Ackley | B | 39.50 |
| 460 Short A-Square | W | 38.00 |
| 460 Weatherby | W | 38.00 |
| 500/465 NE | W | 49.00 |
| 470 NE | W | 48.00 |
| 470 Capstick | B | 41.00 |
| 475 #2 | W | 60.00 |
| 495 A-Square | W | 40.00 |
| 500 NE 3″ | W | 51.00 |
| 505 Gibbs | W | 70.00 |
| 500 A-Square | W | 40.00 |
| 577 NE | W | 70.00 |
| 577 Tyrnsr | W | 80.00 |
| 600 NE | W | 100.00 |
| 700 NE | Bag | 335.00 |

B = Plastic box of 20 rounds; W = Plastic wallet of 10 rounds.

### BUFFALO ARMS Co.

| Case | Price/50 | Price/100 |
|---|---|---|
| 32-40 Win. | $20.00 | $35.00 |
| 32-40 Rem. | 27.00 | 48.00 |
| 33 Win. | 28.00 | 50.00 |
| 35 Win. | 39.00 | 72.00 |
| 38 Colt (.88″) | — | 17.00 |
| 38 Colt (1.03″) | — | 17.00 |
| 38-40 Win. | — | 22.00 |
| 38-56 Win. | 28.00 | 50.00 |
| 38-70 Win. | 41.00 | 77.00 |
| 38-72 Win. | 41.00 | 77.00 |
| 401 Win. SL | 27.00 | 48.00 |
| 40-50 SS | 25.00 | 46.00 |
| 40-60 Win. | 27.00 | 48.00 |
| 40-60 Maynard | 27.00 | 48.00 |
| 40-65 Win. (Rem. Brass) | 27.00 | 47.00 |
| 40-65 Win. (Win. Brass) | 27.00 | 48.00 |
| 405 Win. | 38.00 | 72.00 |
| 40-70x2½ | 38.00 | 72.00 |
| 40-70x2¼ | 41.00 | 77.00 |
| 40-72 Win. | 41.00 | 77.00 |
| 40-82 Win. | 41.00 | 77.00 |
| 40-90 Sharps Bottleneck | 55.00 | 97.00 |
| 41 Colt | 23.00 | $40.00 |
| 43 Dutch Beaumont | 53.00/20 | |
| 43 Spanish | 55.00 | 97.00 |
| 43 Egyptian | 53.00/20 | |
| 44 Colt | 23.00 | 36.00 |
| 44 American (S&W) | — | 20.00 |
| 44-100x2.6 Rem. | 55.00 | 97.00 |
| 45 S&W Schofield | — | 22.00 |
| 44-77 SBN | 55.00 | 97.00 |
| 44-90 SBN | 55.00 | 97.00 |
| 44-90x2.4 Rem. | 41.00 | 77.00 |
| 45-75 Win. | 45.00 | 80.00 |
| 45-100x2.6 Sharps | 55.00 | 97.00 |
| 45-90x2.4 SS | 41.00 | 77.00 |
| 455 Webley | — | 34.00 |
| 455/476 Revolver | — | 34.00 |
| 476 Revolver | — | 34.00 |
| 476 Enfield Revolver MkII | — | 34.00 |
| 476 Eley | — | 34.00 |
| 510 Win. | 55.00 | 97.00 |
| 6.5 Carcano | | 39.00 |
| 6.5x54 MS | 30.00 | 55.00 |
| 7.35 Carcano | | $40.00 |
| 7.7 Japanese | | 26.00 |
| 11.5x57 R Span. Reform. | 55.00 | 97.00 |
| 11.7x51R Danish | 55.00 | 97.00 |
| 11.7x56R Danish | 55.00 | 97.00 |
| **Custom Order Brass** | | |
| 25 Rem. | 14.00 | 24.00 |
| 310 Cadet | 16.00 | 27.00 |
| 32 Win. SL | 17.00 | 30.00 |
| 40-50 SBN | 27.00 | 45.00 |
| 40-70 Win. | 41.00 | 77.00 |
| 44-70 Maynard | 41.00 | 77.00 |
| 455 Colt | — | 34.00 |
| 50-95 Win. | 53.00/20 | 75.00 |
| 6mm Lee Navy | 26.00 | 48.00 |
| 7.65 French | | 22.00 |
| 8x56R Hungarian | 41.00 | 77.00 |
| 8x52R | 39.00 | 72.00 |
| 9mm Steyr | | 24.00 |
| 9.3x72R | 30.00 | 50.00 |

## DILLON

**Mixed Brass**

Mixed brass for 9mm Luger, 40 S&W and 30 Carbine. 9mm and 30 Carbine brass is decapped, primer pocket crimp removed and mixed headstamps. Come in lots of 1000. From Dillon Precision Products, Inc.

**Price:** 9mm . . . . . . . . . . . **$50.00**
**Price:** 40 S&W . . . . . . . . . **$80.00**
**Price:** 30 Carbine . . . . . . . . **$70.00**

## DKT

**New Formed Brass**

Cases for 25x68S Brenneke, 27x68S Brenneke, 8x75R, 300 Rook, 8x60S, 500/465 NE, 475 Ackley Magnum, 475 A&M Magnum, 495 A-Square Magnum, 505 A-Square Magnum, 505 Barnes Supreme and 510 Wells Express. New, fully formed brass ready for fire-forming. From DKT, Inc.

**Price:** . . . . . . . . . . . . **See chart.**

## EICHELBERGER

**14 Caliber Cases**

Formed cases for the 14 Dart, Hornet, Bee Carbine, 14/221, 14/222, 14/222 Mag., 14/H&R Mag. and 14 Cooper. Price for 50 cases. From W.A. Eichelberger.

**Price:** 14 Dart . . . . . . . . . . **$21.50**
**Price:** 14 Hornet, Bee, Carbine, 14/221, 14/222, 14/222 Mag., 14/H&R Mag. **$24.50**
**Price:** 14 Cooper . . . . . . . . **$30.00**

## FREEDOM ARMS

**454 Casull Brass**

Alloyed unprimed brass cases for 454 Casull with small primer pockets. Come in packages of 50. From Freedom Arms, Inc.

**Price:** . . . . . . . . . . . . . . **$25.75**

## GAIN TWIST BARREL CO.

**Obsolete Cases**

High-grade American-made brass cases for obsolete calibers featuring case wall runout average of .00025″; identical case volume batch to batch; double annealed case neck. From Gain Twist Barrel Co.

**Price:** . . . . . **Contact manufacturer.**

## GOODWIN

**New Cases for Obsolete "Everlasting" Calibers**

Solid head cases turned from bar stock and adapted for U.S. Boxer primers. From Jack First Distributors, Inc.

**Price:** Standard . . . . . . . . . **$2.60**
**Price:** Large . . . . . . . **$2.90 - $3.90**

## GRAMPS

**Antique Cartridge Cases**

Distributor for N.D.F.S. Company of England, manufacturer of old Everlasting cases out of solid stock for popular European and British cartridges. From Gramps Antique Cartridges.

**Price:** . . . . . . . . . . . . **See chart.**

## HORNADY

**Unprimed Brass**

Hornady custom pistol ammunition cases are available as component unprimed brass. High-quality SAMMI spec brass in 45 Colt, 45 ACP, 44 Mag., 44 Spl., 40 S&W, 357 Sig and 9x18 Makarov. Come in 100-count bags.

**Price:** . . . . . **Contact manufacturer.**

## BERTRAM *Obsolete Rifle Cases*

| Case | Price/20 | Case | Price/20 |
|---|---|---|---|
| —RIFLE— | | | |
| 222 Rimmed | $23.98 | 400-350 | $70.98 |
| 5.6x33R Rook | 30.98 | 400-360 Purdey | 70.98 |
| 5.6 Vom Hofe Rimmed | 47.98 | 400-360 Westley Richards | 70.98 |
| 240 Flanged | 70.98 | 40-65 WCF | 37.98 |
| 240 Belted | 70.98 | 40-70 Sharps | 36.98 |
| 28-30 Stevens | 50.98 | 40-72 WCF | 36.98 |
| 25-25 Stevens | 47.98 | 40-82 WCF | 37.98 |
| 25-21 Stevens | 47.98 | 404 | 36.98 |
| 25-20 Single Shot | 30.98 | 405 WCF | 47.98 |
| 6.5x53 | 36.98 | 405 Basic 3¹/₄″ | 47.98 |
| 6.5x58R | 47.98 | 40-90 3¹/₄″ | 47.98 |
| 6.5x70R | 47.98 | 43 Spanish | 37.98 |
| 7x33 Sako | 30.98 | 11mm 43 Mauser | 37.98 |
| 7mm Rigby Thick | 70.98 | 10.3x65R Baenziger | 59.98 |
| 7mm H&H Thin | 70.98 | 10.3x60R | 59.98 |
| 7x72R | 47.98 | 10.75x68 | 70.98 |
| 280 Flanged | 70.98 | 10.75x65R | 59.98 |
| 30 Super | 70.98 | 11.15x58R Werndl | 59.98 |
| 30-30 Basic 3¹/₄″ | 47.98 | 11.2x72 Schuler | 70.98 |
| 310 Cadet | 19.98 | 11.7x51 Danish | 59.98 |
| 300 Sherwood | 30.98 | 45-90 WCF | 36.98 |
| 318 Rimless | 70.98 | 45-110 2.8 SS | 61.98 |
| 300 Rook | 30.98 | 45 Basic 2.6″ | 43.98 |
| 32 Ideal | 47.98 | 45 Basic 3¹/₄″ | 70.98 |
| 32 WSL | 30.98 | 50 Sharps | 70.98 |
| 8x64 Brenneke | 47.98 | 450 N.E. Thin | 70.98 |
| 8x56R Hungarian | 37.98 | 450 N.E. Thick | 55.00 |
| 8x58R Danish | 37.98 | 450-400 3″ Rim | 70.98 |
| 8x58 Sauer | 47.98 | 450 #2 | 113.98 |
| 33 WCF | 37.98 | 475 #2 | 113.98 |
| 333 Flanged | 70.98 | 500 Jeffrey | 94.98 |
| 360 Nitro No. 2 | 70.98 | 500 No. 2 | 70.98 |
| 360 No. 2.25 | 70.98 | 500-450 #2 | 94.98 |
| 35 WCF | 37.98 | 505 Gibbs | 94.98 |
| 351 Win. SL | 28.98 | 50-70 | 43.98 |
| 350 Rigby | 70.98 | 50-110 WCF | 61.98 |
| 360 2¹/₄″ | 70.98 | 577 N.E. | 113.98 |
| 9.3x82R | 47.98 | 577-450 MH | 94.98 |
| 375 Flanged 2¹/₄″ | 70.98 | 577-500 NE | 94.98 |
| 375 Mag. Flanged | 70.98 | 585 NYATI | 94.98 |
| 38-56 WCF | 37.98 | 600-577 REWA | 113.98 |
| 38-72 WCF Basic | 36.98 | 12.7x44 | 59.98 |
| 400-375 Belted | 70.98 | 600 NE | 113.98/10 |
| 400 N.E. 3″ | 70.98 | | |

From Huntington Die Specialties.

## EICHELBERGER *14-Caliber Formed Cases*

| Case | Price/50 |
|---|---|
| 14 Dart | $21.50 |
| 14 Hornet | 24.50 |
| 14 Bee | 24.50 |
| 14 Carbine | 22.75 |
| 14/221 | 24.50 |
| 14/222 | 24.50 |
| 14/222 Mag. | 24.50 |
| 14 H&R Mag. | 24.50 |
| 14 Cooper | 30.00 |

## GOODWIN

| Cases | |
|---|---|
| 450-400 2³/₄″ | 11 Mauser |
| 11mm Gras | 43 Egyptian 1.91 |
| 11mm Mauser | 43 Spanish 2.25 |
| 43 Egyptian | 11.15x58R Werndl |
| 43 Spanish | 11.43x55R Turkish |
| 11.43x55R Turkish | 45-75 Winchester |
| 577-450 Martini Henry | 45-90 Winchester |
| #2 Musket | 450 #1 1.5 |
| 461-#1-Gibbs | 450 #1 Carbine |
| 50-70 Government | 450 #1 2.75 Express |
| 50-110 WCF | #2 Musket 2.31 |
| 577 Snider | 455 Auto |
| 8x58R | 455 Webley MkI |
| 8x60R | 455 Webley MkII |
| 450-400 2³/₄″ | 461 Gibbs #1 2.36 |
| 41 LC | 50-70 Govt. |
| 10.15 x 61R Jarman | 50-95 Win. |
| 10.4x38R | 50-110 Win. |
| 10.4x44R | 500 3″ Uniformed |
| 10.4x47R | 577-500 #2 |
| 10.75x58R | 577 Snider 2″ |
| 11x50R Albini Braeudlin | 12.4x44R Norwegian/Swedish |
| 11x52R Dutch Beaumont | |

## DKT, INC. *New Formed Brass*

| Caliber | Price/20 |
|---|---|
| 2R Lovell | $50.00 |
| 5.6x35R Vierling | 22.50 |
| 5.6x50mm | 26.25 |
| 5.6x50R Magnum | 26.25 |
| 5.6x57mm | 30.00 |
| 5.6x57R | 30.00 |
| 5.6x61mm SE Vom Hofe | 48.75 |
| 5.6x61R SE Vom Hofe | 60.00 |
| 5.7mm Spitfire | 18.75 |
| 6.5 JDJ | 18.75 |
| 6.5-06 | 20.62 |
| 6.5-06 Ackley Improved | 25.00 |
| 6.5mm TCU | 18.75 |
| 6.5x53.5 Daudeteau | 33.75 |
| 6.5x53R Dutch | 26.25 |
| 6.5x54mm Mannlicher | 30.00 |
| 6.5x57mm | 26.25 |
| 6.5x57R | 30.00 |
| 6.5x58R | 37.50 |
| 6.5x68mm | 37.50 |
| 6.5x68R | 45.00 |
| 6.5x257 | 22.50 |
| 6.5x284 | 22.50 |
| 6.5x444 | 18.75 |
| 6mm Lee Navy | 26.25 |
| 6mm JDJ | 18.75 |
| 6mm JDJ #2 | 18.75 |
| 6mm Mashburn Improved | 22.50 |
| 6mm TCU | 18.75 |
| 6mm-06 | 18.75 |
| 6mm-284 | 25.00 |
| 6mmx30-30 Ackley | 20.60 |
| 6x47mm | 20.00 |
| 6x61mm Sharpe & Hart | 45.00 |
| 7-30 JDJ | 22.50 |
| 7.5x54mm MAS | 22.50 |
| 7.35 Carcano | 22.50 |
| 7.63mm Mannlicher | 35.00/50 |
| 7.65mm MAS | 30.00/50 |
| 7.65mm French Long | 26.25 |
| 7.92x33 Kurz | 26.25 |
| 7mm Super Mag. | 18.75 |
| 7mm TCU | 18.75 |
| 7mm STW | 30.00 |
| 7mm-06 | 20.62 |
| 7mm-06 Improved | 20.62 |
| 7mm-300 Weatherby | 30.00 |
| 7mmx444 | 18.75 |
| 7R (7mm IHMSA) | 22.50 |
| 7x45 Ingram | 18.75 |
| 7x57 Improved | 22.50 |
| 7x57 Ackley Improved | 30.00 |
| 7x57R | 26.25 |
| 7x64mm | 35.00 |
| 7x65R | 30.00 |
| 7x72R | 41.25 |
| 7x75mm Vom Hofe SE | 48.75 |
| 7x75R Vom Hofe SE | 41.25 |
| 8.15x46R | 30.00 |
| 8.15x53R Finnish | 40.00 |
| 8.63x56R | 56.25 |
| 8mm Gibbs | 26.25 |
| 8mm JDJ | 18.75 |
| 8mm Kropatchek | 33.75 |
| 8mm Nambu | 30.00/50 |
| 8mm Roth-Steyr | 25.00 |
| 8mm-06 | 18.75 |
| 8mm-06 Improved | 18.75 |
| 8x48R Sauer | 41.25 |
| 8x50R | 26.25 |
| 8x50R Siamese | 26.25 |
| 8x51R Lebel Rifle | 30.00 |
| 8x51 Mauser | 22.50 |
| 8x51R Mauser | 26.25 |
| 8x52R Siamese | 26.25 |
| 8x53R Murata | 37.50 |
| 8x54 Krag | 30.00 |
| 8x56mm Mannlicher | 26.25 |
| 8x56R Hungarian | 26.25 |
| 8x57J | 22.50 |
| 8x57JR | $30.00 |
| 8x57JRS | 30.00 |
| 8x57R/360 | 41.25 |
| 8x58R Danish Krag | 26.25 |
| 8x58R Sauer | 41.25 |
| 8x60J | 26.25 |
| 8x60JR | 33.75 |
| 8x60RS | 33.75 |
| 8x60S | 30.00 |
| 8x64S | 40.00 |
| 8x68S Magnum | 45.00 |
| 8x72R | 45.00 |
| 8x75R | 48.75 |
| 9.3x80Rmm | 63.75 |
| 9.3x64mm | 45.00 |
| 9.3x57R Sauer | 37.50 |
| 9.3x57mm | 22.50 |
| 9.3x62mm | 22.50 |
| 9.3x74R | 37.50 |
| 9.3x72R | 33.75 |
| 9.3x82R | 60.00 |
| 9.5x57mm | 35.00 |
| 9mm Bergmann/Bayard | 40.00 |
| 9mm Browning Long | 40.00 |
| 9mm Japanese Revolver | 37.50 |
| 9mm Win. Mag. | 35.00 |
| 9x56mm Mannlicher | 30.00 |
| 9x57mm Mauser | 22.50 |
| 9x57R Mauser | 30.00 |
| 10.3x65R Baenziger | 45.00 |
| 10.4x47R Ital. Vett. | 41.25 |
| 10.75x65R Collath | 37.50 |
| 10mm Wildey Magnum | 30.00 |
| 11.2x60mm Mauser | 75.00 |
| 11.2x72mm Schuler | 75.00 |
| 11.15x65R | 55.00 |
| 11mm French Ord. Revolver | 18.75 |
| 11mm German Service Rev. | 18.75 |
| 11mm Wildey Magnum | 30.00 |
| 11x50R | 37.50 |
| 11x52R Beaumont | 63.75 |
| 11x59R Gras | 60.00 |
| 12.9x63.8mm JDJ | 75.00 |
| 14 Flea | 40.00 |
| 14 Walker Hornet | 40.00 |
| 14-221 | 40.00 |
| 17 Ackley Bee | 25.00 |
| 17 Ackley Hornet | 22.50 |
| 17 Bumble Bee | 22.50 |
| 17 K-Hornet | 22.50 |
| 17 Mach IV | 18.75 |
| 17-221 | 18.75 |
| 17-222 Magnum | 18.75 |
| 17-223 | 18.75 |
| 17-225 Ackley | 22.50 |
| 20-222 | 22.50 |
| 20-223 | 22.50 |
| 20-22-250 Improved | 30.00 |
| 22 Cheetah Mach I | 30.00 |
| 22 Jet | 30.00/50 |
| 22 Snapper Long | 22.50 |
| 22 WCF | 22.50 |
| 22-15-60 | 56.25 |
| 22-284 | 22.50 |
| 22-454 Casull | 30.00 |
| 22-3000 | 45.00 |
| 25 Remington | 22.50 |
| 25 Souper | 18.75 |
| 25-06 Mashburn | 20.62 |
| 25-20 Single Shot | 37.50 |
| 25-21 Stevens | 48.75 |
| 25-25 Stevens | 48.75 |
| 25-35 Ackley | 18.75 |
| 25-36 Marlin | 20.60 |
| 25-284 | 22.50 |
| 28-30-120 | 45.00 |
| 25x68S Brenneke | 48.75 |
| 27x68S Brenneke | 48.75 |
| 30 Gibbs | 26.25 |
| 30 Herrett | 20.60 |
| 30 Newton | $56.25 |
| 30 Wildey Magnum | 30.00 |
| 30-30 Ackley Improved | 18.75 |
| 30-223 | 18.75 |
| 30-284 Winchester | 22.50 |
| 30-338 | 22.50 |
| 300 Rook | 33.75 |
| 32 Ideal | 63.75 |
| 32 Remington | 18.75 |
| 32-40 Remington | 26.25 |
| 32-40 WCF | 18.75 |
| 33 WCF | 30.00 |
| 35 Ackley Short Magnum | 30.00 |
| 35 Newton | 52.50 |
| 35 S&W Auto | 22.50 |
| 35 Whelen Improved | 22.50 |
| 35 Winchester | 45.00 |
| 35 WSL | 22.50 |
| 35-284 | 26.25 |
| 38/56 WCF | 30.00 |
| 38/70 WCF | 37.50 |
| 38/72 | 45.00 |
| 40-60 Marlin | 30.00 |
| 40-60 WCF | 30.00 |
| 40-65 WCF | 35.00 |
| 40-70 Sharps BN | 37.50 |
| 40-70 Sharps Straight | 33.75 |
| 40-70 WCF | 37.50 |
| 40-72 WCF | 41.25 |
| 40-82 WCF | 37.50 |
| 40-90 Sharps BN | 37.50 |
| 43 Berdan | 45.00 |
| 43 Egyptian | 63.75 |
| 43 Mauser | 37.50 |
| 43 Spanish | 37.50 |
| 44 American | 45.00 |
| 44 Auto Mag | 45.00/50 |
| 44 Evans Long | 30.00 |
| 44 Evans Short | 30.00 |
| 44-77 Sharps & Remington | 50.00 |
| 45/60 WCF | 30.00 |
| 45/70 Group III | 22.50 |
| 45/70 WCF Group I/II | 18.75 |
| 45/75 WCF | 37.50 |
| 45/90 WCF | 37.50 |
| 45/120 3¼″ Sharps | 75.00 |
| 50 Alaskan | 45.00 |
| 50 Carbine | 56.25 |
| 50 Special | 37.50 |
| 50-70 Sharps | 52.50 |
| 50-70 Springfield/Sharps | 52.50 |
| 50-90 Sharps | 75.00 |
| 50-95 WCF | 37.50 |
| 50-110 WCF | 37.50 |
| 50-140 3¼″ | 75.00 |
| 70-150 Winchester Express | 15.00/1 |
| 219 Ackley Zipper | 18.75 |
| 219 Donaldson Wasp | 22.50 |
| 219 Improved Zipper | 18.75 |
| 219 Zipper | 18.75 |
| 224 Stark | 22.50 |
| 226 JDJ | 18.75 |
| 240 Apex | 30.00 |
| 240 Cobra | 26.25 |
| 240 Page Super Pooper | 22.50 |
| 244 Ackley Improved | 18.75 |
| 244 Krag | 26.25 |
| 256 Newton | 22.50 |
| 256 Winchester | 37.50/50 |
| 257 Ackley Improved | 22.50 |
| 257 JDJ | 18.75 |
| 270 Ackley Magnum | 26.25 |
| 270 JDJ | 18.75 |
| 270 Ren | 26.25 |
| 270-284 | 22.50 |
| 275 H&H Magnum | 28.12 |
| 276 Dubiel | 30.00 |
| 280 Ross | 67.50 |
| 280 Ross Rimmed | 67.50 |
| 297/250 Rook | 30.00 |
| 303 British Improved | $30.00 |
| 309 JDJ | 18.75 |
| 310 Cadet | 22.50 |
| 333 OKH | 22.50 |
| 333 Jeffrey Rimless | 56.25 |
| 338 Woodswalker | 28.12 |
| 338-350 Remington | 30.00 |
| 338-378 KT | 56.25 |
| 351 WSL | 22.50 |
| 357 Auto Mag | 48.75 |
| 357 Herrett | 20.60 |
| 357 Peterbuilt | 30.00 |
| 357/44 Bain & Davis | 26.25 |
| 358 JDJ | 18.75 |
| 360 NE No. 2 | 93.75 |
| 375 Flanged H&H Mag | 60.00 |
| 375 H&H Ackley Imp | 37.50 |
| 375 JDJ | 18.75 |
| 375 JRS | 20.60 |
| 375 Super Magnum | 22.50 |
| 375 Weatherby | 45.00 |
| 375-284 Winchester | 26.25 |
| 400 Nitro 3″ | 37.50 |
| 401 Herter Power-Mag | 75.00/50 |
| 401 WSL | 33.75 |
| 404 Jeffrey | 60.00 |
| 405 WCF | 37.50 |
| 411 JDJ | 18.75 |
| 411 KDF | 45.00 |
| 416 Hoffman | 56.25 |
| 416 JDJ | 20.60 |
| 416 Remington | 50.00 |
| 416 Rigby | 67.50 |
| 416 Taylor | 56.25 |
| 416/338 | 37.50 |
| 425 Express | 45.00 |
| 425 Wesley-Richards | 97.50 |
| 445 Super Magnum | 26.25 |
| 450 Ackley Magnum | 48.75 |
| 450 Alaskan | 37.50 |
| 450 NE 3¼″ | 78.75 |
| 450 NE No. 2 | 123.75 |
| 450 Watts | 48.75 |
| 450/348 | 37.50 |
| 450/400 Nitro 3″ | 93.75 |
| 450/400 Nitro 3¼″ | 93.75 |
| 454 Casull | 47.50 |
| 455 Colt | 18.75 |
| 455 Webley Auto | 22.50 |
| 458x2″ American | 33.75 |
| 470 Capstick | 45.00 |
| 470 Nitro Express | 71.25 |
| 475 JDJ | 20.60 |
| 475 Ackley Magnum | 56.25 |
| 475 A&M Magnum | 75.00 |
| 475 Magnum | 26.25 |
| 475 Nitro Express | 100.00 |
| 475 No. 2 NE | 123.75 |
| 475 Wildey | 30.00 |
| 495 A-Square | 82.50 |
| 500 Magnum | 37.50 |
| 500 NE 3″ | 90.00 |
| 500 NE 3¼″ | 90.00 |
| 500-450 NE 3¼″ | 75.00 |
| 500-465 NE 3¼″ | 75.00 |
| 505 Barnes Supreme | 78.75 |
| 505 Gibbs | 112.50/10 |
| 505 A-Square Magnum | 67.50 |
| 510 Wells Express | 78.75 |
| 577 Jurras | 112.50 |
| 577 NE | 120.00 |
| 577 Snider | 108.75 |
| 577/450 Martini-Henry | 97.50 |
| 577/500 Magnum 3″ | 112.50 |
| 588 JDJ | 112.50 |
| 585 Nyan | 112.50 |
| 600 SSS 3″ | 93.75 |
| 600 NE | 150.00/10 |
| 700 Nitro Express | 112.50 |
| 700 SSS 3″ | 112.50 |

### GRAYBACK WILDCATS

**Pre-Formed Cases**

Formerly Buzztail Brass. Pre-formed cases using new factory brass. All cases 90% formed to chamber specifications. From Buzztail Brass.

**Price:** . . . . . . . . . . . . **See chart.**

### HARDIN

**7.62mm and 44 AutoMag Cases**

Primarily manufacturers of casings for ChiCim Tokarev 7.62mm and 44-caliber AutoMag pistols. 7.62mm casing will also fit 30-caliber Mauser Broomhandle. Hand-made from surplus military or commercial brass. All cases full-length sized, have military primer crimp removed and tumble cleaned. Packed fifty to a box and priced per 100. From Hardin Specialty Distributors.

**Price:** 7.62mm/30 Mauser . . . . . **$14.50**
**Price:** 44 AutoMag . . . . . . . **$16.50**

### HART

**6mm PPC Norma Brass**

Norma 6mm PPC brass. Price is per case; cases can be ordered in any quantity. From Robert W. Hart & Son, Inc.

**Price:** Norma 6mm . . . . . . . . . **$.75**
**Price:** Brass . . . . . . . . . . . . **$.81**

### MAST TECHNOLOGY

**Obsolete and British Cartridge Brass**

Brass cases for obsolete and British sporting rifle cartridges such as 600 N.E., 404 Jeffrey, 577/450 Martini Henry, 43 Mauser, etc. From Mast Technology, Inc.

**Price:** . . . . . . . . . . . . **See chart.**

### NASS

**Unprimed Beltless Magnum Brass**

Unprimed brass for proprietary Canadian Magnum 7mm, 300, 338, 375 and 458 cartridges. Come in boxes of 20. From Imperial Magnum Corporation.

**Price:** . . . . . . . . . . . . . . **$39.95**

### GOLD MEDAL *Unprimed Brass*

| Caliber | Price/100 | Price/500 |
|---|---|---|
| 223 Rem. (5.56x45mm) | $18.05 | $90.25 |
| 308 Win. (7.62x51mm) | 22.81 | 114.05 |
| 30-06 Springfield (7.62x63mm) | 22.81 | 114.05 |
| 300 Win. Mag. | 33.74 | 168.70 |

From Federal Cartridge Co.

### GOLD MEDAL *Unprimed Brass, Nickel Plated*

| Caliber | Price/100 | Price/500 |
|---|---|---|
| 222 Rem. | $24.63 | $123.15 |
| 223 Rem. | 23.15 | 115.75 |
| 22-250 Rem. | 30.33 | 151.65 |
| 270 Win. Mag. | 27.96 | 148.80 |
| 7-30 Waters | 44.40 | 222.00 |
| 7mm-08 Rem. | 30.33 | 151.65 |
| 7mm Rem. Magnum | 39.94 | 199.70 |
| 308 Win. | 27.10 | 135.50 |
| 30-06 Springfield | 29.30 | 146.50 |
| 300 Win. Mag. | 43.26 | 216.30 |
| 45-70 Government | 34.53 | 172.65 |

From Federal Cartridge Co.

### GRAYBACK *Pre-Formed Factory Cases*

| Caliber | Price/20 | Caliber | Price/20 |
|---|---|---|---|
| 17 Mach IV | $22.00 | 270-45mm | $20.00 |
| 219 Donaldson Wasp | 22.00 | 270-47mm | 20.00 |
| 219 Zipper | 22.00 | 270 Gibbs | 22.00 |
| 219 Zipper Ackley Imp. | 20.00 | 280 Ackley Imp. | 20.00 |
| 22 BR | 22.00 | 7mm STW Win. | 22.00 |
| 22 Cheetah Mk I Lg. Primer | 22.00 | 7mm STW Rem. | 20.00 |
| 22 Cheetah Mk I Sm. Primer | 22.00 | 7mm JRS | 20.00 |
| 22 Cheetah Mk II | 22.00 | 7-30 Waters | 20.00 |
| 22-250 Ackley Imp. | 20.00 | 7mm TCU | 20.00 |
| 22/284 | 22.00 | 7mm Gibbs | 22.00 |
| 243 Ackley Imp. | 20.00 | 7x57 Ackley Imp. | 22.00 |
| 6mm-284 | 20.00 | 7mmx300 Weatherby | 20.00 |
| 6mm TCU | 20.00 | 7mm-08 Ackley Imp. | 20.00 |
| 6mm-257 Ackley Imp. | 20.00 | 7mm-300 Winchester | 20.00 |
| 240 Gibbs | 22.00 | 7-45mm | 20.00 |
| 6mm-45mm | 20.00 | 7-47mm | 20.00 |
| 6mm-47mm | 20.00 | 300 Jarrett | 20.00 |
| 6mm-250 | 20.00 | 30 Gibbs | 22.00 |
| 6mm-250 Ackley Imp. | 20.00 | 30-30 Ackley Imp. | 20.00 |
| 6mm-222 | 20.00 | 30 Herrett | 20.00 |
| 6mm Ackley Imp. | 20.00 | 308 Ackley Imp. | 20.00 |
| 243 Super Rockchucker | 20.00 | 30-06 Ackley Imp. | 20.00 |
| 250 Ackley Improved | 20.00 | 30-284 | 20.00 |
| 257 Weatherby (Rem) | 20.00 | 30-257R | 20.00 |
| 25 Gibbs | 22.00 | 30-257 Ackley Imp. | 20.00 |
| 257 Ackley Imp. (Rem.) | 20.00 | 30-378 Weatherby | 45.00 |
| 257 Ackley Imp. (Win.) | 24.00 | 30x338 | 20.00 |
| 25-06 Ackley Imp. | 20.00 | 8mm-06 | 20.00 |
| 25-45mm | 20.00 | 8mm-06 Ackley Imp. | 20.00 |
| 25-47mm | 20.00 | 8mm Gibbs | 20.00 |
| 6.5mm Gibbs | 22.00 | 338-06 | 20.00 |
| 6.5-06 | 20.00 | 338-06 Ackley Imp. | 20.00 |
| 6.5-06 Ackley Imp. | 20.00 | 338-08 Ackley Imp. | 20.00 |
| 6.5-284 | 20.00 | 338-300 Winchester | 20.00 |
| 6.5 TCU | 20.00 | 338-378 Weatherby | 45.00 |
| 6.5-257R | 20.00 | 338-378 KT | 55.00 |
| 6.5-257 Ackley Imp. | 20.00 | 338 Gibbs | 22.00 |
| 6.5-308 | 20.00 | 338-378 Kubla Kahn | 45.00 |
| 6.5-308 Ackley Imp. | 20.00 | 35 Gibbs | 22.00 |
| 6.5-45mm | 20.00 | 35 Whelen | 20.00 |
| 6.5-47mm | 20.00 | 35 Whelen Ackley Imp. | 20.00 |
| 270 Ackley Imp. | 20.00 | 357 Herrett | 20.00 |
| 270-284 | 20.00 | 375 Weatherby | 28.00 |
| 270-257R | 20.00 | 375 ICL | 20.00 |
| 270-257 Ackley Imp. | 20.00 | 375-06 | 20.00 |
| 270-308 | 20.00 | 375-06 Ackley Imp. | 20.00 |

### MAST *Unprimed Cases*

| Caliber | Price/20 | Price/100 |
|---|---|---|
| 404 Jeffery | $30.00 | $146.00 |
| 404 Basic | | 159.00 |
| 416 Rigby | 31.00 | 152.00 |
| 416 Basic | | 144.00 |
| 50-70 Gov't. | 34.00 | |
| 378 Wea. Basic | | 175.00 |
| 7mm STW | NA | NA |

### WALTER GEHMANN *Obsolete Rifle Brass*

| Case | Price/20 |
|---|---|
| 5.6x61 Vom Hofe | $33.98 |
| 7x66 Vom Hofe | 39.98 |
| 7x75R | 33.98 |

From Huntington Die Specialties.

## N.D.F.S.
### Blackpowder Cartridge Dies

| | | | |
|---|---|---|---|
| 6.5 Carcano | 9.5x47R | 45-90 W.C.F. | 401 S.L.R. |
| 6.5x48 | 9mm M.S. | 50-70 Government | 404 Jeffery |
| 6.5x48 Sauer | 10.4x38 Swiss | 50-95 W.C.F. | 404 Jeffery |
| 6.5x54 Mauser | 10.4x47R | 50-140 3.250″ | 405 Winchester |
| 6.5x54R | 10.15x61R | 50/110 W.C.F. | 416 Rigby |
| 6.5x55 Swedish | 10.66x57R | 240 Apex | 425 W.R. |
| 6.5x57 Mauser | 10.75x58R | 240 Flanged | 450 No. 1 |
| 6.5x68 | 11.15x58R | 242 Vickers | 450 No. 1 CAR |
| 6.5x70 | 11mm Gras | 244 H&H | 450 No. 2 |
| 6mm Lee Navy | 11mm Spanish | 256 Gibbs | 450-400 2.375 |
| 7.5 S/R | 11mm Vickers | 280 Jeffery | 450-400 3″ |
| 7.62x54 Russian | 11x50R | 280 Ross | 450/400 3.250″ |
| 7.92x33 Kurz | 11x52R | 295/300 Rook | 461 No. 1/ No. 2 Gibbs |
| 8.15x46.5R | 12.7x44R | 300 Sherwood | 470 N.E. 3.250″ |
| 8mm Lebel | 26 B.S.A. | 303 Savage | 475 N.E. |
| 8x50 Austrian | 30 Newton | 310 Cadet | 475 No. 2 |
| 8x56R Hungarian | 32 S.L.R. | 318 W.R. | 476 N.E. |
| 8x58R | 33 W.C.F. | 333 Jeffery | 500 Jeffrey |
| 8x60 Portuguese | 35 Winchester | 351 S.L.R. | 500 N.E. 3.250″ |
| 8x60S | 38-56 W.C.F. | 360 N.E. 2.250″ | 500-450 3.250″ |
| 8x68S | 38-72 W.C.F. | 360 No. 2 | 500/465 |
| 9.3x62 Mauser | 40-60 Marlin | 369 Purdey | 505 Gibbs |
| 9.3x64 | 40-60 W.C.F. | 375 Flanged | 577 N.E. 3″ |
| 9.3x72R | 40-70 W.C.F. | 375 H&H | 577/500 |
| 9.3x72R Sauer | 40-82 W.C.F. | 375/303 | 577/500 Mag. |
| 9.3x74R | 43 Egyptian | 400 Purdey | No. 2 Musket |
| 9.5 M.S. | 45-60 W.C.F. | 400-350 | |
| 9.5 Turkish | 45-60 W.C.F. | 400-360 | |
| 9.5x36R | 45-75 W.C.F. | 400/375 | |

## N.D.F.S.

**Obsolete Cases**

Turned brass solid head cases for old, blackpowder cartridges. All cases have Boxer primer pockets. For loading with blackpowder only. See chart for available calibers. From N.D.F.S.

**Price: . . . . . Contact manufacturer.**

## PMC

**Components**

PMC is once again offering component bullets and unprimed brass cases. High-performance Starfire bullets packaged 100 bullets to the box include 95-grain 380 Auto, 125-grain 38 Special, 150-grain 357 Magnum, 124-grain 9mm, 155- and 180-grain 40 S&W, 240-grain 44 Magnum and 230-grain 45 ACP plus a 150-grain 30-caliber flat nose for the 30-30. From their standard line of handgun ammunition they offer sixteen component bullets ranging from 380 Auto to 45 Auto. Total Metal Jacket handgun bullets for target and general shooting include 115-, 124- and 147-grain 9mm round-noses and 200-grain semi-wadcutters plus 165- and 180-grain truncated cone 40 S&Ws. Unprimed handgun brass is available in thirteen calibers from 32 Auto to 45 Colt and unprimed rifle brass in eleven calibers from 222 Remington to 300 Winchester Magnum. Brass is packaged in bags of 200. From PMC.

**Price: . . . . . Contact manufacturer.**

## HUNTINGTON *Miscellaneous Brass*

| Case | Price/Per | Manufacturer |
|---|---|---|
| 22 PPC | $21.98/20 | SAKO |
| 6mm PPC | 21.98/20 | SAKO |
| 375 Black Mesa Express | 47.50/20 | Federal |
| 375 Cylindrical | 22.99/20 | Barnes |
| 416 Chepuis Rimmed | 46.98 | A-Square |
| 50 Basic 3¹/₄″ | 49.98 | El Dorado |
| 454 Casull | 26.98/50 | Freedom Arms |
| 240 Belted Rimless N.E. | 19.98/20 | Kynoch, Boxer primed |
| 300 Dakota | 39.98/20 | Dakota |
| 330 Dakota | 39.98/20 | Dakota |
| 7mm Dakota | 39.98/20 | Dakota |
| 50 Action Express | 28.98/100 | Speer |
| 455 Webley | 19.98/50 | Mountain & Snowden |

From Huntington Die Specialties.

## HUNTINGTON

| Case | Price/20 |
|---|---|
| 280 Ross | $51.98 |
| 280 Ross Basic | 51.98 |
| 375 Flanged | 51.98 |
| 40-70 Sharps | 51.98 |
| 405 Basic 3¹/₄″ | 51.98 |
| 404 Jeffrey | 51.98 |
| 404 Jeffrey Basic | 51.98 |
| 425 Westley Richards | 51.98 |
| 43 Spanish | 51.98 |
| 44 Sharps Basic | 51.98 |
| 45-90 WCF | 51.98 |
| 450 Basic .060″ Rim | 51.98 |
| 450 #2 | 51.98 |
| 450-400 3¹/₄″ | 51.98 |
| 450-400 3″ | 51.98 |
| 475 #2 N.E. | 61.98 |
| 500-465 N.E. | 51.98 |
| 500 N.E. 3¹/₄″ | 51.98 |
| 505 Gibbs | 55.00 |

From Huntington Die Specialties.

## PMC
### *Unprimed Rifle Cases*

| Caliber | Item No. |
|---|---|
| 222 Remington | 222R |
| 223 Remington | 223R |
| 270 Winchester | 270R |
| 22-250 Remington | 22-250R |
| 243 Winchester | 243R |
| 6.5x55 Swedish | 6.5R |
| 7x57 Mauser | 7MR |
| 7mm Rem. Magnum | 7R |
| 7.62x39 Russian | 7.62R |
| 30-30 Winchester | 3030R |
| 308 Winchester | 308R |
| 30-06 Springfield | 3006R |
| 300 Win. Magnum | 300R |
| 303 British | 303R |
| 50 Caliber | 50R |

From PMC.

## LAPUA
### *Unprimed Rifle Brass*

| Caliber | Price/100 |
|---|---|
| 220 Russian | $120.15 |
| 222 Rem. | 50.98 |
| 6mmBR | 38.49 |
| 243 Win. | 45.54 |
| 6.5x55 | 37.47 |
| 270 Win. | 63.33 |
| 7x64 | 64.15 |
| 308 Win. | 33.46 |
| 30-06 | 47.50 |
| 7mm Rem. Mag. | 89.76 |
| 338 Win. Mag. | 89.76 |
| 338 Lapua | 233.70 |

From Keng's Firearms Specialty, Inc.

## LAPUA
### *Unprimed Pistol Brass*

| Caliber | Price/100 |
|---|---|
| 32 S&W Long | $17.92 |
| 357 Mag. | 23.83 |
| 44 Mag. | 64.59 |

From Keng's Firearms Specialty, Inc.

## PMC
### *Unprimed Pistol/Revolver Cases*

| Caliber | Item No. |
|---|---|
| 32 Auto | 32 AR |
| 32 S&W Long | 32SWLR |
| 380 Auto | 380R |
| 38 Special | 38R |
| 38 Super Auto | 38SR |
| 9mm Luger | 9mmR |
| 357 Magnum | 357R |
| 40 Smith & Wesson | 40R |
| 41 Rem. Magnum | 41R |
| 44 S&W Special | 44SR |
| 44 Rem. Magnum | 44R |
| 45 Auto | 45R |
| 45 Long Colt | 45LCR |

From PMC.

## PRECISION COMPONENTS

**Match-Prepped Weight-Matched Brass**

Brass prepped for match-grade accuracy. All brass full-length resized; case necks turned inside/outside to unify case neck wall thickness; trimmed to uniform overall length (+/- .001″); case necks inside/outside deburred; flash hole burrs removed and flash holes unified; primer pockets squared and cut to uniform depth; brass packaged in 1% extreme weight spread boxes. Comes in boxes of 20, 50 or 100 fully prepped and 1% weight matched. 30% average group size reduction, when supplied loading notes are followed. From Precision Components.

**Price:** . . . . . . . . . . . . **See chart.**

## PRECISION RELOADING

**Remington New and Once-Fired Brass**

Remington new unprimed rifle and pistol brass and commercial once-fired brass in select popular calibers. From Precision Reloading, Inc.

**Price:** . . . . . . . . . . . **See charts.**

**Sako Brass**

Uprimed Sako brass for 22 and 6mm PPC. Come in lots of 20, 100 or 500. From Precision Reloading, Inc.

**Price:** 20 . . . . . . . . . . . . **$19.99**
**Price:** 100 . . . . . . . . . . . **$89.99**
**Price:** 500 . . . . . . . . . . . **$399.95**

## RWS

**Unprimed Brass Cases**

High-quality unprimed brass made of MS 72 from 22 Hornet to 404 Jeffery. From The Old Western Scrounger.

**Price:** . . . . . . . . . . . . **See chart.**

## SKIP'S MACHINE

**Lapua Brass**

Match-prepped Lapua 220 Russian brass to customer specifications. Price per case. From Skip's Machine.

**Price:** . . . . . . . . . . . . . . **$2.15**

### NORMA
### *Unprimed Rifle Brass*

| Case | Price/100 |
|---|---|
| 22 PPC | $89.98 |
| 220 Swift | 67.98 |
| 222 Remington | 49.98 |
| 22-250 | 63.98 |
| 243 Winchester | 54.98 |
| 6mm BR | 62.98 |
| 6mm PPC | 62.98 |
| 22 Savage High Power | 86.98 |
| 6.5x50 Japanese | 66.98 |
| 6.5x52 Carcano | 67.98 |
| 6.5x54 M.S. | 59.98 |
| 6.5x55 | 59.98 |
| 270 Winchester | 62.98 |
| 7x57 | 57.98 |
| 7x57R | 61.98 |
| 7x61 Sharp & Hart | 85.98 |
| 7x64 | 65.98 |
| 280 Remington | 59.98 |
| 7mm Remington Mag. | 82.98 |
| 7.5x55 Swiss | 66.98 |
| 7.62x54R Russian | 73.98 |
| 308 Winchester | 61.98 |
| 30-30 | 63.98 |
| 30-06 | 62.98 |
| 300 Winchester | 90.98 |
| 303 British | 69.98 |
| 308 Norma Magnum | 89.98 |
| 7.65x53 Argentine | 63.98 |
| 7.7x58 Japanese | 62.98 |
| 358 Norma | 82.98 |
| 8x57JS | 59.98 |
| 338 Winchester | 79.98 |
| 375 H&H | 90.98 |
| 9.3x57 | 61.98 |
| 9.3x62 | 63.98 |
| 9.3x74R | 85.98 |
| 416 Rigby | 162.98 |
| 470 N.E. | 52.98/20 |

From Huntington Die Specialties.

### NORMA *Brass*

| Caliber | Price/Case |
|---|---|
| 223 Match | $.48 |
| 22-250 | .59 |
| 6mm BR | .60 |
| 6mm PPC | .60 |
| 243 Win. | .52 |
| 6.5x55 | .58 |
| 270 Win. | .59 |
| 280 Rem. | .58 |
| 7x57 | .61 |
| 30-30 Win. | .61 |
| 308 Win. (Match) | .59 |
| 300 Win. Mag. (Match) | .87 |
| 30-06 | .61 |
| 303 British | .67 |

From NECO.

### PRECISION COMPONENTS

| Caliber | Prepped Price/20 | Prepped Price/50 |
|---|---|---|
| 22 Hornet | $34.95 (d) | $72.50 (d) |
| 218 Bee | 34.95 | 72.50 |
| 222 Rem. | 34.95 | 72.50 |
| 222 Rem. Mag. | 34.95 | 72.50 |
| 22-250 | 34.95 | 72.50 |
| 220 Swift | 34.95 | 72.50 |
| 243 Win. | 34.95 | 72.50 |
| 6mm Rem. | 34.95 | 72.50 |
| 250 Savage | 34.95 | 72.50 |
| 257 Roberts | 34.95 | 72.50 |
| 25-06 Rem. | 34.95 | 72.50 |
| 270 Win. | 34.95 | 72.50 |
| 7mm-08 Rem. | 34.95 | 72.50 |
| 280 Rem. | 34.95 | 72.50 |
| 7mm Mauser | 34.95 | 72.50 |
| 7mm Rem. Mag. | 39.95 | 84.50 |
| 7mm Wea. Mag. | 44.95 | 94.50 |
| 30-30 Win. | 34.95 (d) | 72.50 (d) |
| 30-40 Krag | 34.95 | 72.50 |
| 30-06 Sprgfld. | 34.95 | 72.50 |
| 300 Savage | 34.95 | 72.50 |
| 308 Win. | 34.95 | 72.50 |
| 300 H&H Mag. | 44.95 | 94.50 |
| 300 Win. Mag. | 39.95 | 84.50 |
| 300 Wea. Mag. | 44.95 | 94.50 |
| 338 Win. Mag. | 39.95 | 84.50 |
| 35 Rem. | 34.95 | 72.50 |
| 350 Rem. Mag. | 39.95 | 84.50 |
| 35 Whelen | 34.95 | 72.50 |
| 375 H&H Mag. | 39.95 | 84.50 |
| 444 Marlin (c) | 39.95 | 84.50 |
| 45-70 Gov't. (c) | 44.95 | 94.50 |
| 458 Win. Mag. | 44.95 | 94.50 |

(c):Straight wall prepped cases not neck turned; (d):Lightly turned on prepped cases.

### THE OLD WESTERN SCROUNGER
### *Miscellaneous Brass*

| Case | Description | Price/Per |
|---|---|---|
| 219 Zipper Winchester | | $19.00/20 |
| 8mm Japanese Nambu | New/Boxer Primed | 21.65/50 |
| 9mm Makarov Starline | | 6.95/50 |
| 10.3x60 Swiss | Unformed | 47.00/20 |
| 32 H&R Magnum | Starline | 6.95/50 |
| 11mm Beaumont | New | 46.98/20 |
| 445 Super Mag. | Starline | 16.00/50 |
| 45 Basic, 3.25″ | New | 46.98/20 |
| 405 Win. | Basic | 46.98/20 |
| 450 Nitro Express | .040 Rim | 46.98/20 |
| 450 Nitro Express | .060 Rim | 46.98/20 |
| 14 ga. Greener | Primed brass | 2.50/1 |
| 450-400 | 3″ New | 49.98/20 |
| 470 Nitro | New | 49.98/20 |
| 500 Nitro Express | New | 49.98/20 |
| 50 Sharps | Basic 3.25″ | 65.00/20 |
| 50-70 Gov't. | New | 47.98/20 |
| 577 Nitro Express | New | 55.00/20 |
| 600 Nitro Express | New | 65.00/20 |

From The Old Western Scrounger.

## NORMA *Brass*

| Case | Price/20 |
|---|---|
| 220 Swift | $15.05 |
| 222 Remington | 11.80 |
| 22-250 Remington | 15.15 |
| 243 Winchester | 13.00 |
| 5.6mmx52R | 20.80 |
| 6mm PPC | 15.10 |
| 6.5mm Japanese | 16.05 |
| 6.5mm Carcano | 16.25 |
| 6.5mm Swedish | 14.65 |
| 270 Winchester | 14.80 |
| 7mm Remington Magnum | 19.70 |
| 7mmx57 Mauser | 13.85 |
| 7mmx57R | 14.75 |
| 7.5mm Swiss | 15.85 |
| 7x61 Sharpe & Hart | 20.45 |
| 7x64 Brenneke | 15.80 |
| 308 Winchester | 14.75 |
| 308 Norma Magnum | 21.60 |
| 7.62x54R Russian | 17.60 |
| 30-06 | 15.10 |
| 300 Winchester Magnum | 21.65 |
| 303 British | 16.70 |
| 7.65 Argentine | 15.30 |
| 7.7 Japanese | 15.10 |
| 338 Winchester Magnum | 19.05 |
| 358 Norma Magnum | 19.90 |
| 9.3x57 Mauser | 14.90 |
| 9.3x62 Mauser | 15.30 |
| 9.3x74R | 20.65 |
| 375 H&H Magnum | 21.75 |
| 416 Rigby | 39.50 |
| 223 Match | |

From The Old Western Scrounger.

## REMINGTON *Nickel-Plated Rifle Brass*

| Case | Price/20 |
|---|---|
| 17 Rem. | $7.25 |
| 22 Hornet | 3.90 |
| 222 Rem. | 4.60 |
| 223 Rem. | 4.60 |
| 22-250 Rem. | 6.40 |
| 243 Win. | 6.40 |
| 6mm Rem. | 6.90 |
| 257 Roberts | 7.50 |
| 250 Savage | 7.55 |
| 25-06 Rem. | 8.25 |
| 270 Win. | 6.90 |
| 7x57 Mauser | 8.15 |
| 7mm BR | 10.45 |
| 7mm-08 Rem. | 7.75 |
| 280 Rem. | 6.90 |
| 7mm Rem. Mag. | 9.75 |
| 30 M1 Carbine | 3.60 |
| 30-30 Win. | 5.35 |
| 300 Savage | 8.15 |
| 308 Win. | 7.00 |
| 30-06 | 7.00 |
| 300 Win. Mag. | 10.30 |
| 300 Wea. Mag. | 12.65 |
| 303 British | 7.05 |
| 32-20 Win. | 4.60 |
| 8mmx57 Mauser | 7.65 |
| 35 Rem. | 7.50 |
| 35 Whelen | 8.30 |
| 416 Rem. Mag. | 12.95 |
| 444 Marlin | 10.00 |
| 45-70 Gov't. | 11.40 |

From The Old Western Scrounger

## RWS *Formed Cases*

| Case | Price/20 |
|---|---|
| —RIFLE— | |
| 22 Hornet | $20.65 |
| 222 Remington | 26.60 |
| 223 Remington | 25.95 |
| 5.6x50 Magnum | 25.70 |
| 5.6x50R Magnum | 25.70 |
| 5.6x52 | 22.45 |
| 5.6x57 | 28.30 |
| 5.6x57R | 29.30 |
| 243 Winchester | 31.35 |
| 6.5x54 MS | 26.30 |
| 6.5x57 | 25.70 |
| 6.5x57R | 19.95 |
| 6.5x65 | 25.55 |
| 6.5x65R | 32.75 |
| 6.5x68S | 30.60 |
| 6.5x68R | 28.45 |
| 270 Winchester | 23.90 |
| 7x57 | 19.95 |
| 7x57R | 19.95 |
| 7x64 | 19.95 |
| 7x65R | 19.95 |
| 280 Remington | 31.65 |
| 7mm Remington Magnum | 35.20 |
| 308 Winchester | 21.60 |
| 30-06 | 22.50 |
| 30R Blazer | 25.55 |
| 300 Winchester Magnum | 41.85 |
| 7.5x55 Swiss | 31.65 |
| 8x57JS | 20.80 |
| 8x57JR (.318″) | 22.90 |
| 8x57JRS | 26.75 |
| 8x60S | 32.85 |
| 8x68S | 39.55 |
| 9.3x62 | 25.00 |
| 9.3x64 | 33.10 |
| 9.3x72R (.364″) | 23.70 |
| 9.3x74R | 27.10 |
| 375 H&H | 34.80 |
| 404 Jeffrey | 36.00 |
| —PISTOL— | |
| 30 Luger | 23.20 |
| 9x18 Ultra | 16.45 |
| 9x21 Police | 22.20 |

From The Old Western Scrounger.

## BULK PISTOL BRASS

| Caliber | Price/100 |
|---|---|
| 22 Remington Jet | $19.50 |
| 221 Remington Fireball | 27.60 |
| 25 Auto | 12.80 |
| 32 Auto | 13.05 |
| 32 S&W Long | 13.15 |
| 9mm Luger | 13.40 |
| 9mm Win. Mag. | 22.10 |
| 380 Auto | 13.20 |
| 38 Super +P | 14.20 |
| 38 S&W | 13.20 |
| 38 Special | 13.10 |
| 357 Magnum | 14.30 |
| 357 Max. | 16.70 |
| 10mm Auto | 19.10 |
| 40 S&W Auto | 18.10 |
| 41 Rem. Mag. | 18.45 |
| 44 S&W Special | 18.35 |
| 44 Magnum | 18.20 |
| 45 Auto | 17.45 |
| 45 Long Colt. | 19.45 |
| 45 Auto Rim | 17.95 |
| 45 Win. Mag. | 24.90 |

From Old Western Scrounger.

## PRECISION RELOADING *Once-Fired Brass*

| Caliber | Price/100 |
|---|---|
| 223 Remington | $8.00 |
| 243 Winchester | 12.00 |
| 270 Winchester | 11.00 |
| 7mm Remington Magnum | 15.00 |
| 300 Winchester Magnum | 18.00 |
| 30-30 Winchester | 3.00 |
| 308 Winchester | 13.00 |
| 30-06 | 11.00 |
| 35 Remington | 8.00 |

From Precision Reloading Specialties, Inc.

Norma Brass

CASES/Metallic

## SCHARCH

**Commercial or Military Pistol/Rifle Brass**

Processed, cleaned and polished or as is brass for commercial and military pistol and rifle cartridges. From Scharch Mfg., Inc.

**Price:** . . . . . **Contact manufacturer.**

## SCHROEDER

**Brass for Obsolete Cartridges**

Formed cases from virgin or once-fired brass for obsolete or hard-to-find cartridges. From Schroeder Bullets.

**Price:** . . . . . . . . . . . . **See chart.**

## STARLINE

**Pistol Brass**

Unprimed, unplated custom brass from 9mm to 445 Super Magnum. From Starline.

**Price:** . . . . . . . . . . . . **See chart.**

## TALON

**Unfired Military Brass**

Cases recovered from disassembly of surplus military ammunition. Come in lots of 10,000. Calibers include: 50, 30-06, 308, 7.62mm, 30 and 223 Remington. From Talon Manufacturing Company, Inc.

**Price:** . . . . . **Contact manufacturer.**

## THUNDERBIRD CARTRIDGE

**50-Caliber Brass**

Thunderbird offers 50-caliber cleaned military brass, ready to load military brass and primed 50-caliber military brass. Come 100 cases to a bag. From Thunderbird Cartridge Co., Inc.

**Price:** Cleaned . . . . . . . . . **$21.00**
**Price:** Ready to load . . . . . . . **$53.00**
**Price:** Primed . . . . . . . . . **$74.00**

## VOM HOFE

**Brass**

Brass cases for 5.6mmx61, 7mmx66 and 7mmx75R Vom Hofe. Come 20 to a box. From The Old Western Scrounger.

**Price:** 5.6x61, 7mmx75R . . . . . **$31.65**
**Price:** 7mmx66 . . . . . . . . . **$36.00**

### SCHROEDER

***Obsolete Pistol Cartridge Brass***

| Case | Price/Per |
|---|---|
| 7.62/7.63mm Tokarev/Mauser (.30) | $20.00/50 |
| 7.62mm Nagant Revolver | 35.00/50 |
| 7.65mm Parabellum (.30 Luger) | 20.00/50 |
| 7.65mm Mannlicher | 20.00/50 |
| 7.65mm French Mas Long | 20.00/50 |
| .32 Short Colt | 22.00/50 |
| .32 Long Colt | 22.00/50 |
| 8mm Nambu | 16.00/50 |
| 9mm Largo | 20.00/50 |
| 9mm Steyr | 20.00/50 |
| .357 Automag | 25.00/50 |
| .38 Long Colt | 18.00/50 |
| .401 Powermag (Herter) | 25.00/50 |
| .41 Long Colt | 25.00/50 |
| 10.4mm Italian Revolver | 22.00/50 |
| .44 Automag | 25.00/50 |
| .455 Webley Revolver MkII | 23.00/50 |

### REMINGTON

| Caliber | Price/100 | Price/500 |
|---|---|---|
| **RIFLE** | | |
| 17 Remington | $24.00 | $110.90 |
| 22 Hornet | 12.70 | 56.40 |
| 220 Swift | 24.30 | 108.60 |
| 222 Remington | 15.20 | 67.90 |
| 222 Rem. Mag. | 20.70 | 92.30 |
| 223 Rem. | 14.70 | 65.90 |
| 22-250 | 20.90 | 93.60 |
| 6mm Remington | 21.90 | 98.90 |
| 243 Win. | 21.90 | 98.90 |
| 25-06 Remington | 26.70 | 119.90 |
| 25-20 Win. | 14.90 | 66.50 |
| 250 Savage | 26.90 | 120.20 |
| 257 Roberts | 24.50 | 109.80 |
| 6.5x55 SWD MAS | 24.50 | 109.80 |
| 270 Win. | 22.30 | 99.80 |
| 7x64 | 25.30 | 113.80 |
| 280 Rem. | 25.30 | 113.80 |
| 7mm-08 Remington | 25.30 | 113.80 |
| 7mm BR | 34.50 | 154.90 |
| 7mm Rem. Mag. | 31.80 | 142.80 |
| 7mm Wea. Mag. | 40.90 | 183.20 |
| 7mmx57 Mauser | 26.60 | 119.50 |
| 30 Carbine | 11.40 | 50.70 |
| 30 Rem. | 21.70 | 97.40 |
| 30-30 Win. | 16.30 | 72.90 |
| 30-40 Krag | 24.90 | 112.50 |
| 30-06 | 22.70 | 101.60 |
| 300 Savage | 26.70 | 119.90 |
| 300 Win. Mag. | 33.10 | 148.70 |
| 300 Wby. Mag. | 40.80 | 183.30 |
| 303 British | 22.90 | 103.20 |
| 7.62x39 | 22.50 | 101.90 |
| 308 Win. | 22.80 | 102.30 |
| 8mm Mauser | 26.00 | 116.90 |
| 8mm Rem. Mag. | 36.00 | 161.70 |
| 32-20 Win. | 14.80 | 66.20 |
| 32 Win. Spl. | 21.60 | 96.90 |
| 338 Win. Mag. | 33.20 | 149.20 |
| 35 Rem. | 26.00 | 116.90 |
| 350 Rem. Mag. | 33.80 | 151.90 |
| 35 Whelen | 26.80 | 119.80 |
| 375 H&H Mag. | 38.90 | 174.60 |
| 416 Rem. Mag. | 44.70 | 201.40 |
| 444 Marlin | 31.90 | |
| 44-40 | 15.70 | 69.20 |
| 45-70 Government | 35.70 | 160.40 |
| 458 Win. Mag | 38.90 | 174.70 |
| **PISTOL** | | |
| 22 Rem. Jet | 14.20 | 63.70 |
| 221 Remington Fireball | 21.10 | 92.10 |
| 32 S&W | 9.90 | 44.10 |
| 32 ACP | 9.90 | 44.00 |
| 357 Mag. (Brass) | 10.70 | 47.70 |
| 357 Magnum (Nickel) | 11.60 | 51.80 |
| 357 Remington Max. | 12.60 | 56.30 |
| 9mm Luger AP | 10.30 | 45.70 |
| 9mm Luger AP+P | 10.30 | 45.70 |
| 380 Auto Colt | 10.20 | 45.20 |
| 38 Super/+P | 10.10 | 44.80 |
| 38 S&W | 9.50 | 41.20 |
| 38 Spl. (Brass) | 9.80 | 44.20 |
| 40 S&W | 14.40 | 64.10 |
| 10mm | 14.80 | 66.20 |
| 41 Remington Magnum | 13.80 | 61.90 |
| 44 Remington Magnum | 13.90 | 61.90 |
| 44 S&W Special | 13.90 | 61.90 |
| 45 Colt | 14.80 | 65.90 |
| 45 Auto | 13.20 | 58.70 |
| 45 Auto Rim | 13.60 | 60.70 |

From Precision Reloading, Inc.

### SCHROEDER

***Obsolete Rifle Cartridge Brass***

| Case | Price/Per |
|---|---|
| 6.5x50R Arisaka | $12.00/20 |
| 6.5x52 Carcano | 13.00/20 |
| 6.5x54 Mannlicher | 13.00/20 |
| 7.65x54 Mauser | 12.00/20 |
| 7.7x58 Arisaka | 12.00/20 |
| 8mm Lebel | 21.00/20 |
| 351 Win. SL | 22.00/50 |
| 5.45x39mm Russian | 30.00/20 |
| 5.6x57 Mauser | 20.00/20 |
| .22 Savage HP (5.6x52R) | 14.00/20 |
| 6mm Lee Navy | 18.00/20 |
| .256 Winchester | 25.00/50 |
| 6.5x53R Dutch | 18.00/20 |
| 6.5x57 Mauser | 20.00/20 |
| .280 Ross | 20.00/20 |
| 7.35mm Italian | 20.00/20 |
| .303 Savage | 18.00/20 |
| 7.5 French Mas | 22.00/20 |
| 7.5 Swiss | 22.00/20 |
| 7.62x45mm Czech | 20.00/20 |
| 7.62x54R Russian | 18.00/20 |
| .32-40 Winchester | 18.00/20 |
| 7.92x33mm Kurz | 25.00/50 |
| 8x56 Mannlicher | 20.00/20 |
| 8x56R Hungarian | 22.00/20 |
| .33 Winchester | 22.00/20 |
| .35 Win. self load | 22.00/50 |
| 9.5x57(56) Mannlicher | 18.00/20 |
| .38-56 Winchester | 21.00/20 |
| .40-65 Winchester | 20.00/20 |
| 10.4mm Italian | 22.00/20 |
| .50 Alaskan | 25.00/20 |

## REMINGTON/WINCHESTER *Unprimed Brass*

| Case | Price/20 | Case | Price/20 |
|---|---|---|---|
| 17 Rem. | $5.60 | 30-30 Win. | $3.95 |
| 22 Hornet | 3.10 | 30-40 Krag | 6.00 |
| 222 Rem. | 3.75 | 300 Savage | 6.50 |
| 222 Rem. Mag. | 4.80 | 300 H&H Magnum | 8.50 |
| 223 Rem. | 3.65 | 308 Win. | 5.40 |
| 220 Swift | 5.80 | 30-06 Spfld. | 5.50 |
| 225 Win. | 6.55 | 300 Win. Mag. | 7.75 |
| 22-250 Rem. | 5.00 | 300 Wea. Mag. | 9.65 |
| 243 Win. | 5.20 | 303 British | 5.70 |
| 6mm Rem. | 5.60 | 32-20 Win. | 3.55 |
| 6mm BR | 8.35 | 32 Win. Spl. | 5.30 |
| 257 Roberts | 5.90 | 8mm Mauser | 6.50 |
| 250 Savage | 6.55 | 8mm Rem. Mag. | 8.35 |
| 25-06 Rem. | 6.50 | 338 Win. Mag. | 7.75 |
| 25-20 Win. | 3.55 | 348 Win. | 10.70 |
| 25-35 Win. | 5.10 | 38-40 Win. | 5.25 |
| 6.5mm Rem. Mag. | 7.90 | 38-55 Win. | 6.20 |
| 264 Win. Mag. | 7.80 | 35 Rem. | 6.55 |
| 270 Win. | 5.45 | 35 Whelen | 6.55 |
| 7mm Mauser | 6.50 | 350 Rem. Mag. | 7.95 |
| 7mm BR | 8.00 | 375 H&H Mag. | 8.70 |
| 7mm-08 Rem. | 6.15 | 416 Rem. Mag. | 10.50 |
| 7.62x39 | 4.60 | 44-40 Win. | 3.80 |
| 280 Rem. | 6.25 | 444 Marlin | 7.75 |
| 7mm Rem. Mag. | 7.75 | 45-70 Gov't | 8.50 |
| 30 M1 Carbine | 2.95 | 458 Win. Mag. | 8.55 |
| 30 Rem. | 5.30 | | |

From The Old Western Scrounger.

## WEATHERBY *Rifle Cases*

| Case | Price/100 |
|---|---|
| 224 Wea. | $75.98 |
| 240 Wea. | 75.98 |
| 257 Wea. | 82.98 |
| 270 Wea. | 78.98 |
| 7mm Wea. | 75.98 |
| 300 Wea. | 69.98 |
| 340 Wea. | 74.98 |
| 378 Wea. | 179.98 |
| 416 Wea. | 166.98 |
| 460 Wea. | 179.98 |

From Huntington Die Specialties.

## WEATHERBY *Unprimed Bass*

| Caliber | Price/20 |
|---|---|
| 224 | $22.70 |
| 240 | 22.70 |
| 257 | 22.70 |
| 270 | 22.70 |
| 7mm | 22.70 |
| 300 | 22.70 |
| 340 | 24.40 |
| 378 | 38.35 |
| 416 | 40.10 |
| 460 | 47.05 |

From Old Western Scrounger.

## WINCHESTER *Bulk Unprimed Rifle Brass*

| Caliber | Price/20 | Price/100 |
|---|---|---|
| 218 Bee | $5.99 | $22.99 |
| 22 Hornet | 3.79 | 13.49 |
| 220 Swift | 6.79 | 25.99 |
| 222 Rem. | 4.59 | 17.49 |
| 223 Rem. | 4.49 | 15.99 |
| 22/250 | 6.49 | 23.99 |
| 243 Win. | 6.49 | 25.99 |
| 6mm Rem. | 6.79 | 27.99 |
| 25-06 | 7.79 | 29.99 |
| 6.5x55 | 7.29 | 25.99 |
| 270 Win. | 6.99 | 26.99 |
| 284 Win. | 9.99 | 42.99 |
| 7mm Rem. Mag. | 9.49 | 36.99 |
| 30-30 Win. | 4.99 | 20.99 |
| 30-06 Sprgf. | 6.99 | 24.99 |
| 308 Win. | 6.79 | 25.99 |
| 300 Win. Mag. | 9.49 | 36.99 |
| 303 British | 6.79 | 28.99 |

## STARLINE *Unprimed Pistol Brass*

| Caliber | Price/500 | Price/1000 |
|---|---|---|
| 9mm | $36.00 | $68.00 |
| 9mm Super Comp | | NA |
| 9mmx21 | 41.00 | 72.00 |
| 9mm Makarov | 39.00 | 70.00 |
| 9mm Largo | 45.00 | 79.00 |
| 9mm Win. Mag. | 60.00 | 105.00 |
| 9mm Super Comp | | NA |
| 38 Super | 41.00 | 72.00 |
| 38 Special | 35.00 | 65.00 |
| 32 H&R Mag. | 48.00 | 91.00 |
| 44 Mag. | 48.00 | 90.00 |
| 45 Auto | 46.00 | 86.00 |
| 45 Colt | 50.00 | 93.00 |
| 44 Special | 48.00 | 91.00 |
| 41 Mag. | 48.00 | 91.00 |
| 10mm | 49.00 | 92.00 |
| 40 S&W | 48.00 | 91.00 |
| 45 Win. Mag. | 66.00 | 119.00 |
| 10mm Mag. | 62.00 | 117.00 |
| 445 Super Mag. | 130.00 | 228.00 |
| 414 Super Mag. | 130.00 | 228.00 |
| 45 S&W Schofield | 56.00 | 96.00 |
| 356 TSW | 51.00 | 89.00 |
| 357 SIG | 53.00 | 94.00 |
| 38/40 | 65.00 | 118.00 |
| 44/40 | 60.00 | 108.00 |

From Starline.

Starline Unprimed Cases

## WINCHESTER *Unprimed Handgun Cases*

| Case | Price/100 |
|---|---|
| 380 Auto | $12.79 |
| 357 Magnum | 13.79 |
| 9mm Luger | 11.49 |
| 38 Special | 12.49 |
| 38 Super | 13.49 |
| 40 S&W 10mm Auto | 17.79 |
| 44 S&W Special | 16.79 |
| 44 Remington Magnum | 15.49 |
| 45 Colt | 16.49 |
| 45 Automatic | 13.79 |

From Midway Arms.

## ACTIV

**Hulls**

Brass-free hull with steel encasement lining to reinforce the head, rim and primer pocket. Steel primer pocket does not expand after repeated firing and hull does not need to be resized when reloading. Mouths are skived for perfect 8-point crimp. Available in 12-, 16-, 20-gauge. From ACTIV Industries, Inc.

**Price:** . . . . . **Contact manufacturer.**

**Starter Kit**

For the first-time reloader or those who would like to test the ACTIV brass-free hull. Kits come with a choice of 25 hulls in 12-, 16- or 20-gauge, 25 wads, ACTIV Reloading Booklet and patch. From ACTIV Industries, Inc.

**Price:** Per kit . . . . . . . . . . . **$3.60**
**Price:** Case of four . . . . . . . . **$11.75**

## PONSNESS/WARREN

**Once-Fired Federal Gold Medal**

Once-fired 2¾″ hulls sold in lots of 100 or 1000. From Ponsness/Warren.

**Price:** 100 . . . . . . . . . . . . **$5.95**
**Price:** 1000 . . . . . . . . . . . **$49.95**

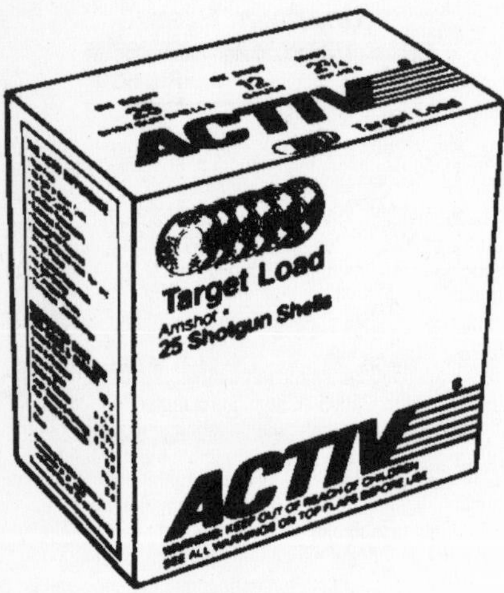


## OLD WESTERN SCROUNGER

| Gauge | Size | Price/25 |
|---|---|---|
| | **Brass Shotshells** | |
| 12 | 2½ | $19.95 |
| 16 | 2½ | 19.95 |
| 20 | 2½ | 19.95 |
| 24 | 2½ | 19.95 |
| 28 | 2½ | 19.95 |
| 32 | 2½ | 19.95 |
| 410 | Long | 19.95 |
| 410 | Short | 19.95 |
| 9.2mm | Long | 19.95 |
| 9.2mm | Short | 19.95 |

### ACTIV *Hull Specifications*

| Model | Gauge | Color |
|---|---|---|
| UH-12 | 12 2¾″ | Red |
| UH-123 | 12 3″ | Red |
| UH-20 | 20 2¾″ | Yellow |
| UH-203 | 20 3″ | Yellow |
| UH-16 | 16 2¾″ | Red |

### PRECISION RELOADING *Once-Fired Hulls*

| Gauge | Size | Description | Crimp | Price/100 | Price/500 | Price/1000 |
|---|---|---|---|---|---|---|
| | | **FEDERAL** | | | | |
| 10 | 3½ | HMH, paper base wad | 6 | $26.00 | | |
| 12 | 3½ | HMH, mag., all plastic | 6 | 12.00 | $52.00 | $96.00 |
| 12 | 3 | HMH, paper basewad | 6 | 10.00 | 48.00 | 90.00 |
| 12 | 2¾ | MBH, paper | 6 | 6.00 | 28.00 | 48.00 |
| 12 | 2¾ | MBH, Gold Medal, all plastic | 8 | 8.00 | 36.00 | 64.00 |
| 12 | 2¾ | HMH, paper base wad | 6 | 6.00 | 28.00 | 52.00 |
| 12 | 2¾ | HMH, all plastic | 6 | 7.00 | 32.00 | 58.00 |
| 20 | 3 | HMH, paper base wad | 6 | 10.00 | 48.00 | 90.00 |
| 20 | 2¾ | HMH, paper base wad | 6 | 6.00 | 28.00 | 52.00 |
| 20 | 2¾ | HMH, paper base wad | 8 | 7.00 | 32.00 | 58.00 |
| | | **REMINGTON** | | | | |
| 8 | 3¼ | HMH, industrial unibody | RC | 15.00 | 70.00 | 125.00 |
| 10 | 3½ | HMH, low inner plastic base wad | 6 | 24.00 | | |
| 10 | 3½ | HMH, high inner plastic base wad | 6 | 24.00 | | |
| 12 | 3½ | HMH, green, plastic base wad | 6 | 12.00 | | |
| 12 | 3½ | HMH, olive drab duplex, plastic base wad | 6 | 14.00 | | |
| 12 | 3 | HMH, green, plastic base wad | 6 | 8.00 | 36.00 | 48.00 |
| 12 | 3 | HMH, olive drab duplex, plastic base wad | 6 | 9.00 | 42.00 | 78.00 |
| 12 | 2¾ | HMH, plastic base wad | 6 | 6.00 | 25.00 | 46.00 |
| 12 | 2¾ | HMH, olive drab duplex, plastic base wad | 6 | 7.00 | 28.00 | 52.00 |
| 12 | 2¾ | HMH, green, plastic base wad | 6 | 7.00 | 28.00 | 52.00 |
| 12 | 2¾ | LBH, premier unibody | 8 | 8.00 | 36.00 | 55.00 |
| 12 | 2¾ | LBH, gold unibody | 8 | 9.00 | 42.00 | 78.00 |
| 12 | 2¾ | LMH, black unibody | 6 | 5.00 | 23.00 | 35.00 |
| 12 | 2¾ | LMH, black unibody | 8 | 6.00 | 25.00 | 46.00 |
| 12 | 2¾ | LMH, green unibody | 6 | 5.00 | 23.00 | 35.00 |
| 12 | 2¾ | LMH, green unibody | 8 | 6.00 | 25.00 | 46.00 |
| 20 | 3 | HMH, unibody | 6 | 9.00 | 42.00 | 78.00 |
| 20 | 3 | LMH, plastic base wad | 6 | 9.00 | 42.00 | 78.00 |
| 20 | 2¾ | LMH, unibody | 6 | 6.00 | 25.00 | 48.00 |
| 20 | 2¾ | HMH, unibody | 6 | 6.00 | 25.00 | 48.00 |
| .410 | 3 | HMH, plastic base wad | 6 | 9.00 | 42.00 | 80.00 |
| .410 | 2½ | HMH, plastic base wad | 6 | 8.00 | 36.00 | 70.00 |
| | | **WINCHESTER** | | | | |
| 10 | 3½ | HBH, plastic base wad | 6 | 24.00 | | |
| 12 | 3½ | HBH, plastic base wad | 6 | 12.00 | | |
| 12 | 3 | HMH, red, black or white, plastic base wad | 6 | 6.00 | 28.00 | 48.00 |
| 12 | 2¾ | LBH, CF, AA trap/Skeet | 8 | 8.00 | 36.00 | 55.00 |
| 12 | 2¾ | LBH, CF, silver, AA trap/Skeet | 8 | 9.00 | 42.00 | 78.00 |
| 12 | 2¾ | HMH, CF, SuperX | 8 | 6.00 | 25.00 | 46.00 |
| 12 | 2¾ | HMH, CF, SuperX | 8 | 7.00 | 28.00 | 52.00 |
| 12 | 2¾ | LMH, PF, plastic base wad | 6 | 5.00 | 20.00 | 30.00 |
| 12 | 2¾ | LMH, PF, plastic base wad | 6 | 5.00 | 23.00 | 35.00 |
| 20 | 3 | HMH, CF, magnum | 8 | 10.00 | 45.00 | 90.00 |
| 20 | 2¾ | LMH, plastic base wad | 6 | 5.00 | 20.00 | 30.00 |

HMH = High Metal Head; LMH = Low Metal Head; CF = Compression formed; HBH = High Brass Head; MBH = Medium Brass Head; LBH = Low Brass Head; PF = Polyformed. From Precision Reloading, Inc.

## BALLISTIC PRODUCTS *Shotshell Hulls*

| Manufacturer | Gauge | Lgth. | Price 50 | Price 100 | Price 500 | Comments |
|---|---|---|---|---|---|---|
| Federal | 12 | 2³/₄″ | $3.79 | $5.99 | $27.90 | Gold Medal, once-fired, 6-point. |
| Fiocchi | 12 | 2³/₄″ | 6.99 | 10.99 | | Clear, high brass |
| Fiocchi | 12 | 2³/₄″ | 6.99 | 10.99 | | Clear, low brass |
| Remington "STS" | 12 | 2³/₄″ | | 7.99 | 36.90 | Once fired, 8-point. |
| Winchester "AA" | 12 | 2³/₄″ | | 7.99 | 37.90 | Once fired, 8-point. |
| Winchester | 12 | 2³/₄″ | 1.99 | 5.99 | 27.90 | AA high-brass, heat crimped, 6-point. |
| Fiocchi | 12 | 2″ | 8.49 | 13.99 | | Assorted colors |
| Fiocchi | 12 | 2¹/₂″ | 8.49 | 13.99 | | Assorted colors |
| Fiocchi | 12 | 3″ | 7.99 | 12.99 | | Brown |
| ACTIV | 12 | 3″ | | 10.99 | 53.00 | New, unprimed, skived. |
| Remington | 12 | 3″ | 6.99 | 11.99 | 54.90 | Once fired, disc base, Type 6, 6-point. |
| ACTIV | 16 | 2³/₄″ | | 9.99 | 49.00 | New, unprimed, skived. |
| Fiocchi | 16 | 2³/₄″ | 8.49 | 13.99 | | Blue |
| Remington | 16 | 2³/₄″ | 7.99 | 13.95 | 68.00 | New, primed. |
| ACTIV | 20 | 2³/₄″ | | 9.99 | 49.00 | New, unprimed. |
| Winchester | 20 | 2³/₄″ | 7.99 | 7.99 | 36.90 | AA, once-fired, Class A, 8-point. |
| Remington | 20 | 2³/₄″ | 7.99 | 13.99 | | New, primed. |
| Fiocchi | 20 | 2³/₄″ | 7.99 | 12.99 | | Yellow |
| Fiocchi | 20 | 3″ | 7.99 | 12.99 | | Yellow |
| ACTIV | 20 | 3″ | | 10.99 | 53.00 | New, primed. |
| Fiocchi | 28 | 2¹/₂″ | 7.99 | 12.99 | | Red |
| Federal | 28 | 2³/₄″ | 4.99 | 7.99 | 36.90 | Fiber base, once-fired, 6-point. |
| Remington | 28 | 2³/₄″ | 7.99 | 13.99 | | NP Comp. |
| Remington | 28 | 2³/₄″ | 7.99 | 13.99 | | New, primed. |
| Remington | 410 | 3″ | 8.99 | 43.90 | | Fiber base, once fired, 6-point. |

New = Never fired; Class A = very clean, once fired.

## PRECISION RELOADING *New Unfired Hulls*

| Gauge | Size | Primed | Description | Price/100 |
|---|---|---|---|---|
| | | | **REMINGTON** | |
| 20 | 2³/₄ | Y | LBH, RTL, plastic base wad | $13.95 |
| 28 | 2³/₄ | Y | LBH, SP, plastic base wad | 13.95 |
| 410 | 2¹/₂ | Y | HMH, SP, plastic base wad | 13.95 |
| | | | **ACTIVE** | |
| 12 | 3 | N | All plastic | 10.95 |
| 12 | 2³/₄ | N | All plastic | 9.95 |
| 16 | 2³/₄ | N | All plastic | 9.95 |
| 20 | 3 | N | All plastic | 10.95 |
| 20 | 2³/₄ | N | All plastic | 9.95 |

HMH = High Metal Head; LBH = Low Metal Head; SP = Soft Point. From Precision Reloading, Inc.

Fiocchi Reifenhauser Three-Piece Hull

### ACCURATE BULLET CO.

**Blackpowder Bullets**

Hand cast, competition quality bullets for metallic blackpowder silhouette shooters. Bullets are weighed and packaged accordingly. From Accurate Bullet Co.

**Price:** . . . . . **Contact manufacturer.**

### ACTION

Hard cast, pressure lubricated pistol bullets sized to exact diameters. Available in 500- or 1000-round boxes. Minimum order of 1000. From Action Bullets, Inc.

**Price:** . . . . . . . . **See chart page 393.**

### ALLRED

Allred specializes in custom, heavy-duty 224 and 308 jacketed rifle bullets designed for hunting, silhouette or target shooting. All have a solid lead core and guilding metal jackets. The 308s feature a copper inner tubing to control penetration and expansion, and provide better weight retention. From Allred Bullet Company.

**Price:** . . . . . . . . **See chart page 408.**

### ALPHA LAFRANCK

Heavyweight 430, 452, 458 and 416 swaged lead bullets are available jacketed or non-jacketed. The 430 bullets are designed for 44 Magnum and 430 JDJ loads in weights from 240 to 370 grs. Two basic jackets, a short .550″ and long .700″, and in three nose designs, wadcutter, semi-wadcutter and round-nose. Ten jacket and weight combinations are standard. Alpha's 452 bullets are designed for revolvers, specifically the 454 Casull and strong 45 Colts in weights from 250 to 400 grs. Three jacket types are available, short .550″, medium .700″ and copper tubing 1.00″ lengths. Fifteen jacket and weight combinations standard. The 458 bullets are offered in over 200 weight, jacket and point form combinations. Seven jacket styles available. "PJ" bullet uses thin .550″ and .700″ jackets for good expansion at low to medium 45/70 velocities. "RJ" jacket available in two lengths, .700″ for 300-gr. and .910″ for 405-gr. bullets. The "SJ" jacket comes in one length, .850″ for 400-gr. "HJ" bullet is offered in 350-gr. with .890″ jacket and 500-gr. 1.285″ jacket. "TJ" bullet has copper tubing jacket of .032″ wall thickness and 1.05″ length. From Alpha LaFranck Enterprises.

**Price:** . . . **See charts pages 393, 408.**

### A-SQUARE

A triad of medium to heavy game bullets either loaded or component form. Monolithic Solids are nonexpanding, made from a single metal with no lead core for the heaviest of game. Dead Tough Soft Points are expanding general purpose bullets for close-range shots. Lion Load Soft Points are designed for less penetration, 18-24 inches, and more expansion. From A-Square Co., Inc.

**Price:** . . . . . **Contact manufacturer.**

### ARMFIELD

Armfield offers 6mm, 25, 6.5mm, 270, 7mm and 308 bonded core guilding or copper jacketed (Plainsbond) bullets for large game; pre-fragmented (Fragcore) guilding jacketed bullets for medium to small game; or solid lead core, guilding jacketed bullets (Standard). All bullets except lead tipped spitzers can be ordered with molycoat for additional $6.00. From Armfield Custom Bullets.

**Price:** . . . . . . . **See chart page 408.**

### ATLANTIC ROSE

Swaged lead alloy and jacketed handgun bullets for ex-Soviet import pistols: 9x18mm; 30 Tokarev; 30 Mauser. The 9x18 bullets are 95 grains and are available in round-nose or lead truncated configuration. The 30 Tokarev and 30 Mauser are 80-gr. bullets and come in flatpoint or hollowpoint. From Atlantic Rose, Inc.

**Price:** . . . . . . . **See chart page 393.**

### AZONE

Quality cast pistol bullets with BHN hardness of 18-19 in calibers 9mm, 38 Super, 38 Revolver, 10mm, 45 ACP, 45 Long Colt and 44 Revolver. Available in 500, 1000, 5000 or 10,000 quantities. From AZone Bullets.

**Price:** . . . . . . . **See chart page 393.**

### BAER HOLLOWS

**Handgun Bullets**

Deep hollowpoint 357 caliber 150-grain cast handgun bullets sized to .358 diameter. In 1996 and 1997 they put into production bullets in 45 ACP, 44, 45-70 and 9mm. Come in quantities of 100 or 1000. From Baer Hollows.

**Price:** 100 . . . . . . . . . . . . **$6.00**
**Price:** 1000 . . . . . . . . . . . **$50.00**

### BALLARD

Swaged jacketed pistol and rifle bullets in 475 and 510 calibers. Premium bullets are bonded core. The 475s have 1E ogive and come in open tip or lead tip depending on weight. Flat-nose and hollowpoints also available. Ogive for 510s is $^3/_4$E with flat-nose and hollowpoint variations. Custom jackets are swaged and come in .030 or .050 thickness. Optional cannelure $2.00 per box. From Ballard Built Custom Bullets.

**Price:** . . . . . . . **See chart page 394.**

### BEARTOOTH

Hand cast rifle and pistol bullets from 22- to 515-caliber made with LBT moulds and heat treated to BHN 21+, hand lubed and sized. DCG: Dual Crimp Groove bullets with grooves set at .450″ and .500″; +P: 38/357 bullets for large frame 38 Specials; LFN: Long Flat Nose profile for high BC and accuracy; WFN: Wide Flat Nose design for non-expanding handgun bullets; WLN: Wide Long Nose for high velocity in handgun bullets; LMN: Wide Medium Nose in 44-caliber with meplat diameter of .320″; FNB: Flat Nose Ball with ogival nose of commercial ball ammunition with meplat for wound potential. From Beartooth Bullets.

**Price:** . . . **See charts pages 394, 409.**

### BERGER

Molybdenum coating is now and option for all bullets. Match-grade lead core jacketed bullets made to very close tolerances from Rorschach and Simonson carbide dies. Jackets drawn from single set of dies using copper strip the width of a single jacket with tolerance of .0003-inch; $^3/_{16}$-inch up from the base. Lead core wire contains .5 percent antimony with dimensional control held to .002-inch. Roundness at the pressure ring held to a standard .001-inch to .00005-inch. From Berger Bullets.

**Price:** . . . . . . . **See chart page 409.**
**Price:** Molycoat 0-149 grains per 100 . **$2.00**
**Price:** Molycoat 150-210 grains per 100 **$4.00**

### BIG BORE BULLETS

Big Bore Bullets of Alaska offers swaged, standard core and core bonded, .032″ jacket, hunting bullets in the following calibers; 458, 375, 452, 429. Lead base guard bullets are available in 9mm, 38/357, 429, and 452 with various tip designs. The SST bullet is a jacketed, serrated tip, hollow point bullet in 452. All bullets are available in custom weights.

**Price:** . . . . . **Contact manufacturer.**

### BITTERROOT

Bonded core rifle hunting bullets for heavy game in eight calibers from 277 to 423. From Bitterroot Bullet Co.

**Price:** . . . . . . . **See chart page 409.**

### BLACK POWDER PRODUCTS

Sized, lubed cast pistol and rifle bullets. Pistol bullets come in packages of 500 in calibers 32 ACP, 380 ACP, 9x18, 9mm, 38/357, 40 S&W, 10mm, 41 Magnum, 44 Magnum, 45 ACP and 45 Long Colt and in a variety of grain weights and nose configurations. Rifle bullets are available in packages of 100 in 7.62x39, 7x57, 30-30, 30-06, 375 Winchester, 45-70 and 50-70. From Black Powder Products.

**Price:** . . . . . . . **See chart page 394.**

### BLUE MOUNTAIN

Multi-stage, tri-jacketed rifle hunting bullets with laminated outer skin for instant expansion upon contact and triple supported shank and base for penetration. Any bullet weight within each caliber range is available. Spitzer (tangential ogive), open tip or hollowpoint styles are offered as well as lead tips. From Blue Mountain Bullets.

**Price:** . . . . . . . **See chart page 410.**

### E. ARTHUR BROWN

LBT-style Bullets. Premium cast wide long nose 44- and 45-caliber hunting bullets fitted with copper base gas checks. Sized to .430 (44-cal.), .452 (45-cal.) and lubed. Available weights: 320-gr. (44-cal.); 335-gr. (45-cal.); 370-gr. (45-cal.). Come 100 to a box. Available from E. Arthur Brown Company.

**Price:** 44-cal., 320-gr. . . . . . . **$18.50**
**Price:** 45-cal., 335-gr. . . . . . . **$18.75**
**Price:** 45-cal., 370-gr. . . . . . . **$20.25**

### BRP

High performance cast handgun bullets from 30- to 50-caliber. Hard alloy in heavy weights and gas checked. Designed for magnum velocities without leading. From BRP, Inc.

**Price:** . . . . . . . **See chart page 395.**

### BRUNO SHOOTER'S SUPPLY

Benchrest bullets hand-swaged in carbide dies. All are of hollowpoint design. From Bruno Shooter's Supply.

**Price:** . . . . . . . **See chart page 410.**

### BUFFALO ARMS CO.

Cast bullets in 38-55 (.375) 250-gr. FN, 40-65 (.406) 245-gr. FN and 43 Spanish (.439) 335-gr. RN lubed with SPG lubricant. From Buffalo Arms Co.

**Price:** 38-55, 40-65/100 . . . . . . **$12.00**
**Price:** 38-40, 43 Spanish/50 . . . . . **$8.50**
**Price:** .406/100 . . . . . . . . . **$30.00**
**Price:** 41 Colt, 44-40/100 . . . . . **$11.50**

## BULLSEYE

Bullseye produces hard cast bullets made from virgin alloy with a 8% tin and anitmony content. From Bullseye Bullets.

**Price:** . . . . . . . **See chart page 396.**

## BULL-X

Hard cast match-grade pistol bullets using virgin alloy with high content of tin and antimony. Bullets are sized to exact diameter required and lubed. Come in boxes of 500. From Bull-X, Incorporated.

**Price:** . . . . . . . **See chart page 395.**

## C.W. CARTRIDGE

Designed for paper Nitro combustible cartridges. Cast of pure lead, three calibers and bullet styles available: 54-, 50- and 45-caliber; solid, hollow-base and hollow-base Minie. From C.W. Cartridge Company.

**Price:** . . . . . . . **See chart page 411.**

**Paper Cartridge Form Kit**

Kit includes 200 precut, nitrated paper sheets, glue stick and 7″ plastic forming dowel to produce combustible cartridge tubes in .542″ diameter for use in 54-caliber Sharps rifles. Refill kit with 500 nitrated sheets and two glue sticks available. From C.W. Cartridge Company.

**Price:** Kit . . . . . . . . . . . . **$15.00**
**Price:** Kit refill . . . . . . . . . . **$24.00**

## JAMES CALHOON

Plastic tipped Saber Tip bullets and 19-caliber bullets are now available for the 19-223 Calhoon and 19 Calhoon Bobcat. Makers of specialized match-grade accuracy varmint rifle bullets featuring double hollowpoint and thin jacket construction for expansion; rebated boattail for improved gas seal; and "silver bullet" coating for reduced fouling. From James Calhoon Bullets.

**Price:** . . . . . . . **See chart page 410.**

## CARROLL BULLETS

Cast rifle and pistol bullets made from custom blend of virgin metals. All bullets come sized and lubed. Lube is non-toxic and alox free.

**Price:** . . . **See charts pages 396, 411.**

## CAST PERFORMANCE BULLET COMPANY

**Handgun Bullets**

LBT design handgun bullets in most popular calibers. From Cast Performance Bullet Company.

**Price:** . . . . . **Contact manufacturer.**

## CHAMPION'S CHOICE

Match-grade lead pistol and jacketed rifle bullets. Come in boxes of 500. From Champion's Choice.

**Price:** . . . **See charts pages 396, 411.**

## CURTIS CAST BULLETS

Hard cast 3% tin, 6% antimony, 91% lead pistol bullets in diameters: .356, .357, .358, .401, .411, .427, .429, .430, .452 and .454. Bullets come lubed with a specially formulated high temperature, non-sticky lube. From Curtis Gun Shop.

**Price:** . . . . . . . **See chart page 397.**

## COPPERHEAD BULLETS

**Swaged Handgun Bullets**

Custom swaged handgun bullets in 260- and 275-grain weights for 44-caliber and in 130- and 160-grain weights for 38-caliber. Medium hard tip controls expansion and ensures deep penetration at handgun velocities. Unique probe and cavity system integrates hard tip and soft core which are custom swaged into premium J-4 jackets. Also available with single, solid core of hard lead. From Copperhead Bullets.

**Price:** . . . . . **Contact manufacturer.**

## DILLON

Premium hard cast handgun bullets of 2% tin, 6% antimony 92% lead. From Dillon Precision Products, Inc.

**Price:** . . . . . . . **See chart page 396.**

## DILLON

Hard swaged lead pistol bullets from hard alloy cores, BHN 16-17, for uniformity in size and weight. From Dillon Precision Products, Inc.

**Price:** . . . . . . . **See chart page 396.**

## D&J BULLET CO.

Competition cast pistol bullets from specially blended 100% pure, virgin alloy with hardness factor rating of 10 and above on the Saeco scale. Designed with longer driving bands for greater accuracy and reduced leading. Velocities of 1350 fps can be achieved without significant lead build-up. Each bullet sized and lubed. Contact D&J for dealer information. From D&J Bullet Co.

**Price:** . . . . . . . **See chart page 397.**

## DKT

Suppliers of cast and jacketed rifle/pistol bullets in a variety of calibers and bullet weights. Cast bullets are made from pure linotype and come sized and lubed. Rooster Red lubricant standard, but LBT may be substitued on request. From DKT, Inc.

**Price:** . . . **See charts pages 397, 410.**

## ELKHORN

Premium swaged bonded core hunting bullets in 7mm, 308-, 338-, 348-, 358-, 375-, 412-, 416- and 458-calibers. Pure lead cores with copper tubing jackets softened to ensure peel back. 348 bullets have .030 jacket tapered to .020 for controlled expansion. 375-458 bullets available with either .030 or .050 jacket thickness. Other bullet weights available on special order. From Elkhorn Bullets.

**Price:** . . . . . . . **See chart page 411.**

## EICHELBERGER

Swaged 14-caliber bullets in spitzer flat-base, 12 and 15 grains, or Spitzer boattail leaded copper in 12.7-grain weight. From Eichelberger.

**Price:** 14-cal. flat-base, per 100 . . . **$45.00**
**Price:** 14-cal. boattail, per 100 . . . **$19.60**
**Price:** 14-cal. boattail, per 1000 . . **$185.00**

## EUBER BULLETS

**6mm Bullets**

Benchrest quality 6mm flat base bullets in 65- and 68-grain weights. Come in packages of 100. From Euber Bullets.

**Price:** . . . . . . . . . . . . . **$12.50**

## FOWLER BULLETS

Match-grade benchrest/varmint bullets formed in Rorschach and Simonson carbide dies. All are flat-base hollowpoint design. The 22 and 6mm bullets have a 7-caliber ogive and the 25-caliber a 9-caliber ogive with .045″ point. From Fowler Bullets.

**Price:** . . . . . . . **See chart page 411.**

## FREEDOM ARMS

Jacketed hollowpoint 240-grain, 260- and 300-grain jacketed flatpoint bullets in 45-caliber and a 300-gr. in 44 Mag. Jacket is .032″ thick; core 10.75% tin and antimony mixture. Come in packages of 50. From Freedom Arms, Inc.

**Price:** 240, 260 . . . . . . . . . **$25.85**
**Price:** 300 . . . . . . . . . . . **$27.25**

## FUSLIER BULLETS

Cast rifle and pistol bullets in two grades with hardness factors of 30-35 BHN for Imperial Fusiliers and 18-30 BHN for Premium. Imperials cast from patented Fusilloy and heat-treated. Bullet nose is annealed for expansion. All Imperials come gas-checked and lubed with teflon-impregnated lube. Premium bullets also cast of Fusilloy and lubed. Can load these bullets to pressures normally associated with jacketed bullets. From Fusilier Bullets.

**Price:** . . . . . . . **See chart page 398.**

## GENTNER BULLETS

**6mm Bullets**

Benchrest-quality 6mm bullets made on Detsch carbide dies. Available in 62- to 68-grain weights with 7 or 8 ogive in boattail or flat base. Come in boxes of 500. From Gentner Bullets.

**Price:** . . . . . . . . . . . . **$70.00**

## GONIC BULLET WORKS

**Bonded Core Bullets**

Bonded-core 357-, 44-, 45- and 30-caliber bullets with various point styles including a plastic point for easy feeding in semi-automatics and lever-actions. From Gonic Bullet Works.

**Price:** . . . . . **Contact manufacturer.**

## GRIZZLY BULLETS

Bonded core, large caliber hunting bullets. Copper jackets are bonded to pure lead core using a chemical-metallurgical fusion technique. From Grizzly Bullets.

**Price:** . . . . . . **See chart page 412.**

## HAMMETT'S VLDS

Very low drag 17- and 6mm caliber target and hunting rifle bullets made with Simonson carbide dies and match-grade jackets. All bullets have a pressure ring at the base of bearing surface for accuracy. From Hammett's.

**Price:** . . . . . . . **See chart page 412.**

## HARRIS

Hunting bullets in 348- (190- and 200-gr. flat points and bonded core), 264- (85-, 100-gr., 120-gr. and 140-gr.) and 224- (55-gr.) calibers. From Harris Enterprises.

**Price:** . . . . . **Contact manufacturer.**

## HAWK LABS, INC.

Precision hunting bullets in calibers and weights from 228 to 577, including hard to find 318, 333, 348, 408, 482 and 505. Soft copper jackets in five thicknesses for improved accuracy through better bore seal and for reduced fouling by lowering barrel friction. No more than 0.5-gr. variation per box of 50. From Hawk Laboratories, Inc.

**Price:** . . . . **See chart pages 413, 414.**

## HOBSON

Cast 357- and 44-caliber two-part bullets with nose cone of very soft flexible alloy joined to a base of super hard alloy to enhance expansion and accuracy. From Hobson Precision Mfg. Co.

**Price:** . . . . . **Contact manufacturer.**

## HT BULLETS

Computer-designed, lathe-turned solid copper hunting bullets. Grooved bearing surface reduces bullet contact area by over 85%. Radial ridges align the bullet and seal the bore. Bullet nose is "reverse radial design" meaning the ogive out toward the tip is concave. Three annealing processes for varied levels of expansion. From HT Bullets.

**Price:** . . . . . . . . **See chart page 415.**

## J&L SUPERIOR Bullets

Lead rifle/pistol bullets dip-lubed with Space Age lube that dries hard and covers bullets completely. From Huntington Die Specialties, Inc.

**Price:** . . . **See charts pages 398, 414.**

## JENSEN BULLETS

Nylon-tipped, bonded single core, jacketed bullets for varminting or big game hunting. Lead core is high temperature flux-bonded to jacket for high weight retention. Jacket is precision machined from pure copper and tapers from thin walls at front to heavy walls where core stops and solid rear shaft begins. Available from 243- to 416-caliber. Other bullet weights available. Minimum order of 100 bullets required for bullet weights not listed. From Jensen Bullets.

**Price:** . . . . . . . **See chart page 415.**

## JLK BULLETS

Competition and varmint 22-caliber, 6mm and 7mm low and very low drag jacketed bullets. Cut lead cores run through squirt die for +/- .1-grain uniformity in weight from bullet to bullet. Bullets swaged in Simonson carbide dies and jacketed using J-4 jackets. (See chart page 414). From JLK Bullets.

**Price:** 22 LD, 6mm per 100 . . . . **$12.00**
**Price:** 22 VLD per 100 . . . . . . **$14.00**
**Price:** 7mm per 100 . . . . . . . **$16.00**

## JRP CUSTOM BULLETS

**Swaged 6mm Bullets**

Benchrest-quality 22-caliber and 6mm swaged bullets with cast lead cores and J-4 jackets. 22-caliber bullets made on Sherman carbide dies; 6mm formed with Niemi and Detsch carbide dies. Available with solid silver point or flat base hollowpoint in various weight grains. From JRP Custom Bullets.

**Price:** Solid Silver Point . . . . . **$16.00**
**Price:** Flat base hollowpoint . . . . **$14.00**

## KAWSER CUSTOM

Pistol bullets utilizing unique saw-tooth nose design. Kawser's Pin-Grabber bullets are designed specifically for bowling pin competition. Pin-Grabbers require special seater plugs for use in Dillon, Lyman, RCBS and Lee presses. Kawser supplies seater/crimper dies in all Pin-Grabber calibers. Perfect Circle bullets come in two bullet styles, jacketed softpoint and jacketed hollowpoint, and three grain weights for the 50 AE Desert Eagle—230-, 300-, 350-grain. Kawser Custom, Inc.

**Price:** Bullets . . . . **See chart page 398.**
**Price:** Seater/crimper die . . . . . **$18.00**
**Price:** Seater plug . . . . . . . . **$12.00**

## KEITH'S

Precision cast bevel base pistol and revolver bullets ranging from 9mm 125-gr. to 45 Long Colt 255-gr. (see chart). Alloy 90% lead, 7% antimony, 3% tin with Brinell hardness of 12. All bullets come sized and Wolverine lubed. (See chart page 398). From Keith's Bullets.

**Price:** . . . . . **Contact manufacturer.**

## KEN'S

Custom swaged hunting bullets in any caliber and bullet type. From Ken's Kustom Kartridges.

**Price:** . . . . . **Contact manufacturer.**

## LANE BULLETS

Cast bullets for the target shooter from 30-caliber up to 45-70. Lead/tin/antimony alloy hard enough to prevent base distortion under high pressure. From Lane Bullets, Inc.

**Price:** . . . . . . . **See chart page 399.**

## LIGHTNING PERFORMANCE INNOVATIONS, INC.

Custom-swaged 338-caliber hunting bullets with pure .030″ copper tubing jackets annealed and softened to support jacket stretch. Bullets lubed with fluoropolymer lubricant impregnated and electrostatically bonded to jacket surface. Available with lead core, aluminum or copper stranded cores or #12, #9, #6 shot cores in Open Tip or Head Tip hollowpoint and partitioned style. From Lightning Performance Innovations, Inc.

**Price:** . . . . . . . **See chart page 417.**

## KLA ENTERPRISES

Unique pre-fragmented, multiple-projectile, self-defense pistol bullets in 38/357 and 9mm calibers. Available in four configurations: Max 70-gr. pre-fragmented jacketed straight walled lead-free hollowpoints in either flat base or stackable hollow bases; Tri-Pro 50-gr., hollow base, pre-fragmented, jacketed semi-wadcutters; Max Round-Nose 60-gr. lead-free, pre-fragmented hollowpoints; Safeguard Wadcutter 50-gr., pre-fragmented, jacketed stackable cylinders. Come in quantities of 21 sections. From KLA Enterprises.

**Price:** Tri-Pro . . . . . . . . **$12.95**
**Price:** Wadcutters . . . . . . . . **$10.95**
**Price:** Max or Max Round-Nose . . **$14.95**

## LIBERTY SHOOTING SUPPLIES

Hand cast rifle and handgun bullets from linotype alloy with BHN of 19-20. Alternate alloys available. Come lubed with Rooster Red. From Liberty Shooting Supplies.

**Price:** . . . **See charts pages 399, 416.**

## M&D MUNITIONS

Hard cast and swaged lead pistol bullets for the target shooter. All lead bullets double dry-lubed for less leading. M&D also offers a plated bullet for lead-free shooting. Plated with copper, .010″ thickness, plating and lead core will not separate but flatten on impact. From M&D Munitions, Ltd.

**Price:** . . . . . . . **See chart page 401.**

## MAGNUS BULLET CO.

Competition pistol bullets from 32- to 45-caliber. From Magnus Bullet Co.

**Price:** . . . . . . . **See chart page 400.**

## MARMIK

Solid A360 brass, long-range 50 BMG 725-gr. spitzer/boattail-style target bullets for both single shot and magazine fed firearms. Length, 2.30\#034\; diameter, .510″; BC, .84; SD, .396; meplat, .100″; OAL, 5.445″; cannelure; and one relief groove. Minimum order is 25 bullets. Price is per bullet. From MarMik, Inc.

**Price:** 25-99 . . . . . . . . . . . **$1.25**
**Price:** 100-500 . . . . . . . . . . **$.90**

## MASTER CLASS

Custom cast handgun bullets of 100% virgin alloy, 2% tin, 6% antimony to 16-17 BHN in calibers, 9mm, 38 Super, 40 S&W, 10mm, 45 ACP, 38 Special, 41, 44 and 45. In 44- and 45-caliber heavy bullets available up to 350 grains. Custom sizing available. From Master Class Bullets.

**Price:** . . . . . . **See chart page 399.**

## MCRW

Custom 6mm bullets in 62-, 65- and 68-grain weights plus 30- and 22-caliber bullets in various grain weights. From MCRW.

**Price:** 100 . . . . . . . . . . . **$13.00**
**Price:** 1000 . . . . . . . . . . . **$125.00**

## R.F. MITCHELL

Premium match-grade 6mm bullets for benchrest or varmint hunting. Forming steps done using carbide dies. 7 ogive bullets in 66-, 68-, 75- and 80-grain; 10 ogive low drag bullets in 64- and 66-grain weights. Come in boxes of 100 or 1000.

**Price:** 100 . . . . . . . . . . . **$12.50**
**Price:** 1000 . . . . . . . . . . . **$116.00**

## MEISTER BULLETS

Hard cast bullets 30- to 45-caliber and swaged pistol bullets for 38/357. Cast bullet alloy of 2% tin, 6% antimony, 92% lead with hardness of 10 Saeco. All bullets come lubed. Swaged hollow base pistol bullets are precast lead cores with hardness of 9 Saeco that are swaged to final shape and diameter. From Meister Bullets. Available from Gander Mountain.

**Price:** . . . . . . . **See chart page 400.**

## MI-TE BULLETS

Quality hard cast pistol bullets of Acculoy—.5% silver, 1.7% tin, 6% antimony, .4% arsenic. Calibers available include 9mm, 38, 40, 41, 44 and 45. From Mi-Te Bullets.

**Price:** . . . . . . . **See chart page 401.**

## MOLOC BULLETS

Cast lead pistol and rifle bullets dry-lubed and sized in calibers 32 through 45 and custom swaged bullets in 32 H&R Mag. .308″ or .312″. From MoLoc Bullets.

**Price:** . . . **See charts pages 401, 416.**

## MONTANA PRECISION SWAGING

Cast rifle and pistol bullets and swaged paper patch bullets. Cast bullets come lubed and sized. From Montanta Precision Swaging.

**Price:** . . . **See charts pages 400, 417.**

## RICK MULHERN BULLETS

Match 30-caliber bullets in popular weights. Standard or rebated 9° boattail design. Made in Simonson carbide dies. Contact for prices. From Rick Mulhern.

**Price:** . . . . . **Contact manufacturer.**

## NORTHERN PRECISION

358- and 375-caliber handgun and rifle bullets are now available. Varmint to dangerous game bullets in 416-, 458- and 429-caliber. 416 bullets come in five styles: Varminter Special—ultra lightweight, thin jacketed, high velocity, high fragmentation bullets; Poly Ball Tip—easy expanding with smooth surface tip either bonded core or matching non-bonded; Long Range Open Country—double-jacket design with easy expansion tip with tough backup slug behind it; Brush Country Big Game—blunt softpoint nose design with tough copper tubing jacket and bonded core; Large and Dangerous Game—spitzer bullets with copper tubing jacket, bonded core and thickened ogive for penetration. Three styles of 458 bullets available: thin jacket round-nose; pure lead base guard; and round-nose with .035″ jacket. The 429s are in four basic styles: thin jacket non-bonded; thin jacket bonded core; pure lead base guard; and tubing jacketed with .025″ or .035″ jacket. From Northern Precision.

**Price:** . . . **See charts pages 403, 419.**

## NATIONAL BULLET CO.

Cast pistol bullets in all popular calibers and select rifle rounds and hard to find imports. Made from alloy mix containing 7% antimony and 2% tin and available in alternate copper-plated version. All bullets come sized and lubed with Thompson bullet lube. From National Bullet Co.

**Price:** . . . . . . . **See chart page 402.**

## THE OLD WESTERN SCROUNGER

Cast lead bullets from .258 to .512 for obsolete blackpowder cartridges. From The Old Western Scrounger.

**Price:** . . . . . . . **See chart page 416.**

## OREGON TRAIL

**Laser-Cast Bullets**

Match-grade cast bullets providing reliable accuracy, less distortion and fewer heavy deposits. From Oregon Trail Bullet Company.

**Price:** . . . . . . . **See chart page 403.**

## PENN

Pistol bullets cast from super strength alloy produced by Penn foundry. Bullets sized to .001″ over nominal or to customer specs. All bullets come Teflon-lubed and in lots of 500 or 1000. From Penn Bullets.

**Price:** . . . . . . . **See chart page 402.**

## PMC

**Components**

PMC is once again offering component bullets and unprimed brass cases. High-performance Starfire bullets packaged 100 bullets to the box include 95-grain 380 Auto, 125-grain 38 Special, 150-grain 357 Magnum, 124-grain 9mm, 155- and 180-grain 40 S&W, 240-grain 44 Magnum and 230-grain 45 ACP plus a 150-grain 30-caliber all copper hollowpoint for the 30-30. From their standard line of handgun ammunition they offer 17 component bullets ranging from 380 Auto to 45 Auto. Bonded Metal Jacket handgun bullets for target and general shooting include 115-, 124- and 147-grain 9mm round-noses and 200-grain semi-wadcutters plus 165- and 180-grain truncated cone 40 S&Ws. Unprimed handgun brass is available in thirteen calibers from 32 Auto to 45 Colt and unprimed rifle brass in 15 calibers from 222 Remington to 50 Browning. Brass is packaged in bags of 200. From PMC.

**Price:** . . . . . **Contact manufacturer.**

## POWELL RIVER LABORATORY

**Rifle Bullets**

Match-grade, non-lead core 30-cal. and 22-cal. bullets with extremely high ballistic coefficients for highpower shooters. The 30-caliber 268- and 250-grain bullets traveling at 2750 fps have B.C.s of .97 and .91 respectively. The 22-cal. 87-grain bullet at 2800 fps has a B.C. of .52. Available in boxes of 20. From PRL.

**Price:** 30-cal. . . . . . . . . . . . **$60.00**
**Price:** 22-cal. . . . . . . . . . . . **$28.00**

## PRECISION BULLET

Cast pistol bullets coated with special dry lube formula that eliminates need for jackets or wax lubricant. Available in calibers from 9mm to 45 Colt. Come in boxes of 1000. From Precision Bullet Co.

**Price:** . . . . . **Contact manufacturer.**

## PRL

Match-grade rifle bullets in 308- (250-, 268-gr.) and 5.56- (87-, 100-gr.) calibers. Come in boxes of 20. From Brown Dog Ent.

**Price:** 308 . . . . . . . . . . . **$60.00**
**Price:** 5.56 . . . . . . . . . . . **$28.00**

## RAINIER BALLISTICS

LeadSafe electroplated virgin and lead alloy pistol bullets. Pure copper jacket completely encloses lead core including base to reduce lead vapor levels and prevent barrel fouling. (See chart page 404). From Rainier Ballistics Corporation.

**Price:** . . . . . **Contact manufacturer.**

## RANGER

Hard cast match-grade pistol bullets in calibers, 380, 9mm, 38 Super, 38 Special, 38/357, 40/10mm, 44-40, 44 and 45. From Ranger.

**Price:** . . . . . . . **See chart page 404.**

## RED CEDAR PRECISION

Cold swaged 357- and 44-caliber pistol bullets for hunters and silhouette shooters. Made from pure chemical lead cores with thin nose (standard bullets) or double walled jackets in the bullet shank (Triple Expansion bullets). Standard hollowpoints and softnoses designed for medium game hunting; Triple Expansion (TX) bullets for slower, controlled expansion. Custom weights and canneluring available upon request. From Red Cedar Precision Manufacturing.

**Price:** . . . . . . . **See chart page 404.**

## R.I.S.

Specialize in match and varmint quality 50 BMG standard and VLD bullets. Available in 750-gr., tangent 10S ogive, standard; secant 15S ogive, 855-gr. VLD. Jackets are pure copper, annealed, drawn and bonded to pure lead core by molecular diffusion process. Come in boxes of 20. From R.I.S. Co., Inc.

**Price:** . . . . . **Contact manufacturer.**

## RUBRIGHT BULLETS

Rifle bullets hand-manufactured using carbide dies and available in 224-, 6mm and 308-calibers on 8 ogive configuration. (See chart page 418). From Brian J. Rubright.

**Price:** 22 . . . . . . . . . . . . **$11.50**
**Price:** 6mm . . . . . . . . . . . **$12.00**
**Price:** 308 . . . . . . . . . . . . **$17.00**

## RWS

Dynamit/Nobel manufactured Brenneke TUG, TIG, Cone Point and H-Mantel bullets from 22- to 375-cal. From The Old Western Scrounger.

**Price:** . . . . . . . **See chart page 420.**

## RHINO

**Big Game Bullets**

Specializing in bonded core big game bullets in .358″, .375″ and .416″ diameters and any grain weight. Bullets jacketed with custom-drawn jackets of annealed copper with the jacket walls two to five times thicker at the rear than at the ogive. From Rhino.

**Price:** . . . . . **Contact manufacturer.**

## ROLSTON

**Cast Bullets**

Hard cast or copper plated handgun bullets ranging in caliber from 9x18 to 45. From Fred W. Rolston, Inc.

**Price:** . . . . . . . **See chart page 405.**

## SCHARCH

Swaged lead pistol bullets. Available unjacketed or with copper jackets for total lead-free shooting. From Scharch Mfg., Inc.

**Price:** . . . . . . . **See chart page 405.**

## SCHROEDER BULLETS

Jacketed bullets for obsolete and obscure cartridges. Examples include: 242 Vickers, 7mm Nambu, 8mm Hungarian rifle, Tokarev, Mauser and Luber pistols. From Schroeder Bullets.

**Price:** . . . **See charts pages 405, 419.**

## SHILEN

Hand swaged flat base varmint bullets in 22-caliber 52-gr. weight and 6mm, 65-gr. weight. Come in boxes of 100 bullets. From Shilen Rifles, Inc.

**Price:** 22 . . . . . . . . . . . . **$12.95**
**Price:** 6mm . . . . . . . . . . . **$13.95**

## STAR

Custom swaged, bonded core heavy game bullets with solid brass or copper jackets. Closed base bullets to ensure core retention. From Star Custom Bullets.

**Price:** . . . . . . . **See chart page 420.**

## STARKE BULLET

**Red Prairie Varmint Bullets**

Pure lead swaged bullets in 224-, 243- or 308-caliber featuring concentricty of .0001″ or less; J4 jackets; variety of ogives and base styles. Come in packages of 100. From Starke Bullet Company.

**Price:** 224 . . . . . . . . . . . . **$13.50**
**Price:** 224, 60-, 70-, 80-gr. . . . . . **$14.00**
**Price:** 243 . . . . . . . . . . . . **$14.50**
**Price:** 308 . . . . . . . . . . . . **$18.00**

## STARKE BULLET COMPANY

Pure lead varmint bullets with core swaged to exacting tolerances and concentricity runout of .0001″ or less. Jacketed with J4 jackets; moly coating available. Come in boxes of 100. From Starke Bullet Company.

**Price:** . . . . . . . . **See chart page 420.**

## SWIFT

Core-bonded safari bullets designed for use on African game. H-frame construction with .055″ copper jacket. From Swift Bullet Co.

**Price:** . . . . . . . . **See chart page 421.**

## TALON

**Bullets**

Bullets recovered from disassembly of surplus U.S. military ammunition. Come in lots of 10,000. Calibers include: 50 BMG, 30-06, 7.62mm, 30 Carbine and 5.56mm. From Talon Manufacturing Company, Inc.

**Price:** . . . . . **Contact manufacturer.**

## TOMBSTONE SMOKE N DEALS

**Copper Plated Bullets**

Designed to shoot at standard velocities and ideal for indoor range shooting. Come in quantities of 500 or 1000. From Tombstone Smoke N Deals.

**Price:** . . . . . . . . **See chart page 407.**

**Cast Lead Bullets**

Super hard cast bullets manufactured with lead alloy composed of 2% tin, 6% anitmony, 92% lead. Come in quantities of 500 or 1000. From Tombstone Smoke N Deals.

**Price:** . . . . . . . . **See chart page 407.**

**Hard Swaged Bullets**

Available for 38/357 and 45 ACP in quantities of 500 or 1000 to a package. From Tombstone Smoke N Deals.

**Price:** . . . . . . . . **See chart page 407.**

## 3-D AMMUNITION & BULLETS

Swaged pistol bullets from 38 Special to 45 ACP with hardness equal to 5% antimony. Produced in carbide dies and come sized and lubed. (See chart page 406). From 3-D Ammunition & Bullets.

**Price:** . . . . . **Contact manufacturer.**

## THUNDERBIRD

Big game and 50-caliber competition solids with patented exterior design. Made from a homogenous alloy, big game bullets range in caliber from 308 to 585 and 180-grain weight to 750; competition 50-caliber spitzer boattail and flatbase bullets available in 700- and 750-grain weight. From Thunderbird Cartridge Co., Inc.

**Price:** . . . . . . . **See chart page 420.**

## TRU-FLIGHT

Super hard cast match-grade bullets manufactured from 100% virgin alloy and lubed with 110v lube. Bullets totally encased in copper. From Tru-Flight Bullet Company.

**Price:** . . . . . . . . **See chart page 406.**

## D.L. UNMUSSIG

Hand-swaged match-grade rifle bullets from .144 to .204 diameter from 15- to 51-grain. From D.L. Unmussig.

**Price:** . . . . . . . . **See chart page 421.**

## VINCENT'S SHOP

Soft-nose, bonded core, dual core and solid pistol bullets in calibers 308 to 416. From Vincent's Shop.

**Price:** . . . . . **Contact manufacturer.**

## VIPER

**Bullets**

Available in 14-, 17-, and 20-calibers in wide range of weights and styles. From Viper Bullet and Brass Works.

**Price:** . . . . . **Contact manufacturer.**

## WATSON

Match 22-caliber bullets made in Rorschach dies and 30-caliber bullets produced in Pindell bullet dies. From Watson Trophy Match Bullets.

**Price:** . . . . . **Contact manufacturer.**

## WESTERN NEVADA WESTCOAST BULLET

Hard cast or copper pistol bullets in 32-, 9mm, 38-, 10mm, 40 S&W, 41-, 44-, 45-, 38-40, 44-40, 45-70 calibers. See chart page 407 for complete listing of calibers and bullet weights. From Western Nevada Westcoast Bullets, Inc.

**Price:** . . . . . **Contact manufacturer.**

## WOODLEIGH

Big game bullets produced by deep drawing copper and steel bullet jackets to proper taper, then jackets are heat-treated. The solids are steel jackets that have been copper-plated; the weld-core soft-nose bullets are made with pure lead cores welded to jacket for maximum retained weight. From Huntington.

**Price:** . . . . . . . . **See chart page 421.**

## WYOMING BONDED

Bonded core medium-weight handgun hunting bullets with specially thinned, annealed jackets in .358 and .375 diameters. Available in 150-gr. (7mm); 200-gr. (35-cal.); and 225-gr. (375-cal.). Come in boxes of 25. Available from E. Arthur Brown Company.

**Price:** . . . . . . . . . . . . . **$25.00**

## ZONIC

Cast handgun hunting bullets. High-quality alloy used to assure shot-to-shot consistency and performance. New bullets for this year include 44-caliber 280-, 300- and 320-grain bullets. From Zonic Bullets.

**Price:** . . . . . **Contact manufacturer.**

Action

Atlantic Rose

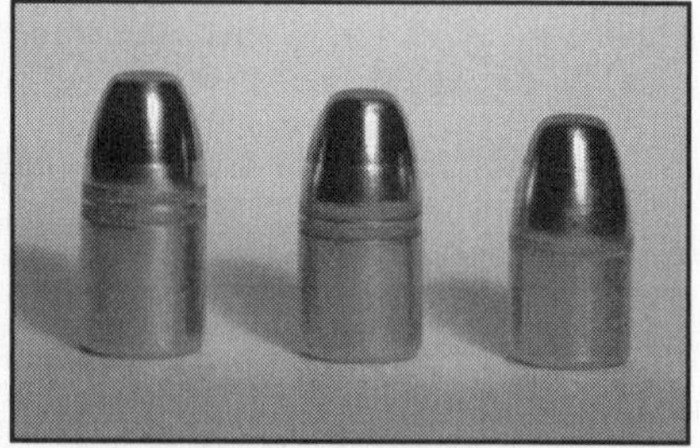

Alpha LaFranck

## ACTION

| Caliber | Wgt. Grs. | Type | Diameter (ins.) | Price 500 | Price 1000 |
|---|---|---|---|---|---|
| 380 Auto | 95 | RNBB | .355/.356 | $17.50 | $33.00 |
| 9m | 125 | FPBB | .355/.356 | 17.50 | 33.00 |
| | 125 | RNBB | .355/.356 | 17.50 | 33.00 |
| 32 | 110 | DEWCBB | .314 | 17.50 | 33.00 |
| 38 | 148 | DEWCBB | .357/.358 | 19.50 | 37.00 |
| | 125 | FPBB | .357/.358 | 17.50 | 33.00 |
| 38/357 | 158 | SWCBB | .357/.358 | 20.00 | 38.00 |
| 10mm/40 S&W | 155 | RNSWCBB | .401 | 19.50 | 37.00 |
| | 180 | FPBB | .401 | 21.50 | 41.00 |
| 38-40 | 180 | RNFPBB | .401/.403 | 21.50 | 41.00 |
| 41 Magnum | 220 | SWC | .410 | 22.00 | 42.00 |
| 44 Magnum | 185 | SWC | .429/.430 | 22.00 | 42.00 |
| | 200 | RNFPBB | .429/.430 | 22.00 | 42.00 |
| | 240 | SWCBB | .429/.430 | 22.50 | 43.00 |
| | 250 | SWC | .429/.430 | 23.50 | 45.00 |
| | 290 | SWC | .429/.430 | 26.50 | 51.00 |
| 45 ACP | 185 | SWCBB | .451/.452 | 22.00 | 42.00 |
| | 195 | SWC | .451/.452 | 22.00 | 42.00 |
| | 200 | SWCBB | .451/.452 | 22.00 | 42.00 |
| | 230 | FP | .451/.452 | 22.50 | 43.00 |
| | 230 | RNBB | .451/.452 | 22.50 | 43.00 |
| 45 Colt | 250 | RNFPBB | .452/.454 | 23.50 | 45.00 |

RNBB = Round-Nose Bevel Base; FPBB = Flat Point Bevel Base; DEWCBB = Double End Wadcutter Bevel Base; SWCBB = Semi-Wadcutter Bevel Base; SWC = Semi-Wadcutter; FP = Flat Point; RNFPBB = Round-Nose Flat Point Bevel Base.

## AZONE Pistol Bullets

| Caliber | Wgt. Grs. | Type | Price/500 | Price/1000 | Price/5000 | Price/10,000 |
|---|---|---|---|---|---|---|
| 9mm/38 Super | 125 | RN | $18.00 | $32.00 | $150.00 | $280.00 |
| | 140 | SWC | 19.00 | 36.00 | 170.00 | 320.00 |
| | 147 | FP | 19.00 | 36.00 | 170.00 | 320.00 |
| | 150 | SWC | 19.00 | 36.00 | 170.00 | 320.00 |
| | 160 | RN | 19.00 | 36.00 | 170.00 | 320.00 |
| 38 Revolver | 148 | DEWC | 19.00 | 36.00 | 170.00 | 320.00 |
| | 148 | SWC | 19.00 | 36.00 | 170.00 | 320.00 |
| | 158 | RN | 19.00 | 36.00 | 170.00 | 320.00 |
| | 158 | SWC | 19.00 | 36.00 | 170.00 | 320.00 |
| 10mm | 155 | SWC | 19.00 | 36.00 | 170.00 | 320.00 |
| | 175 | SWC | 20.00 | 38.00 | 180.00 | 340.00 |
| | 200 | FP | 20.00 | 38.00 | 180.00 | 340.00 |
| 45 ACP | 155 | SWC | 19.00 | 36.00 | 170.00 | 320.00 |
| | 180 | SWC | 20.00 | 38.00 | 180.00 | 340.00 |
| | 200 | SWC | 20.00 | 38.00 | 180.00 | 340.00 |
| | 230 | RN | 22.00 | 42.00 | 200.00 | 380.00 |
| 45 Long Colt | 250 | RNFP | 23.00 | 44.00 | 210.00 | 400.00 |
| 44 Revolver | 215 | SWC | 21.00 | 40.00 | 190.00 | 360.00 |
| | 240 | SWC | 22.00 | 42.00 | 200.00 | 380.00 |
| | 300 | FP | 25.00 | 48.00 | 230.00 | 440.00 |

RN = Round Nose; SWC = Semi-Wadcutter; FP = Flat Point; DEWC = Dead End Wadcutter; RNFP = Round Nose Flat Point.

## ALPHA LAFRANCK Jacketed Bullets

| Jacket | Wgt. Grs. | Type | Price/50 |
|---|---|---|---|
| | **CALIBER: 430** | | |
| S | 240 | WC,SP | $11.00 |
| | 250 | WC,SP | 11.00 |
| | 275 | SWC,SP | 13.00 |
| | 300 | SWC,RN,SP | 15.00 |
| | 300 | SP RAM | 16.00 |
| | 325 | SWC,RN,SP | 17.00 |
| | 350 | SWC,RN,SP | 18.00 |
| | 375 | SWC,RN,SP | 19.00 |
| L | 300 | SWC,RN,SP | 15.00 |
| | 300 | SP RAM | 16.00 |
| | 325 | SWC,RN,SP | 17.00 |
| | 350 | SWC,RN,SP | 18.00 |
| | 370 | SWC,RN,SP | 19.00 |
| | **CALIBER: 452** | | |
| S,L | 250 | RNF | $15.00 |
| | 275 | RNF | 15.00 |
| | 300 | RNF | 15.00 |
| | 325 | RNF | 17.00 |
| | 350 | RNF | 18.00 |
| | 375 | RNF | 19.00 |
| | 400 | RNF | 20.00 |
| TJ | 350 | RNF | 20.00/25 |
| | 375 | RNF | 20.00/25 |
| | 400 | RNF | 20.00/25 |
| | **CALIBER: 357** | | |
| SJ | 180 | RN,HP | $8.00 |
| | 200 | RN,HP | 8.50 |
| | 210 | RN,HP | 9.00 |
| | **CALIBER: 416** | | |
| RJ | 250 | SP | $16.00 |
| | 300 | SP | 16.00 |
| | 350 | SP,RN,HP | 17.00 |
| | 410 | SP,RN,HP | 18.00 |
| DJ | 250 | SP | 20.00 |
| | 300 | SP | 20.00 |
| | 350 | SP,RN,HP | 21.00 |
| | 410 | SP,RN,HP | 22.00 |

HP = Hollowpoint; SP=Spitzer.

## ATLANTIC ROSE Swaged Pistol

| Caliber | Wgt. Grs. | Type | Price/500 | Price/1000 |
|---|---|---|---|---|
| 9x18 | 95 | RN | $23.00 | $35.00 |
| | 95 | TC | 23.00 | 35.00 |
| 30 Tokarev | 80 | FP | 23.00 | 35.00 |
| | 80 | HP | 25.00 | 35.00 |
| 30 Mauser | 80 | FP | 23.00 | 35.00 |
| | 80 | HP | 25.00 | 35.00 |

RN = Round-Nose; TC = Truncated Concial; FP = Flat Point; HP = Hollowpoint.

## BALLARD

| Caliber | Wgt. Grs. | Ogive | Type | Price/25 |
|---|---|---|---|---|
| 475 | 300 | 1E | OT/LT | $25.00 |
| | 500 | 1E | OT/LT | 25.00 |
| 510 | 300 | 3/4E | FN/HP | 25.00 |
| | 500 | 3/4E | FN/HP | 25.00 |
| 44 | 200 | | JHP | 18.50 |
| | 250 | | JHP | 18.50 |
| | 300 | | JHP | 18.50 |
| 45 | 200 | | HP/SP | 20.00 |
| | 250 | | HP/SO | 20.00 |
| | 350 | | HP/SP | 20.00 |
| 475 | 400 | 1E | OT/LT | 27.50 |
| | 400 | 1E | BC | 40.00 |
| 510 | 400 | 1E | OT/LT | 27.50 |
| | 600 | 1E | BC | 40.00 |

OT = Open Tip; LT = Lead Tip; FN = Flat Nose; HP = Hollowpoint; JHP = Jacketed Hollowpoint; BC = Bonded Core.

## BEARTOOTH Pistol

| Caliber | —Bullet— Wgt.Grs. | Type | Gas Check | Price/100 |
|---|---|---|---|---|
| 9mm | 120 | FNB2 | | $9.25 |
| 38/357 | 160 | FNBB | | 9.25 |
| | 180 | WLN+P | GC | 11.00 |
| | 185 | FN | GC | 10.50 |
| | 200 | FN+P | GC | 11.25 |
| | 210 | LFN+P | GC | 11.25 |
| 10mm/38-40 | 200 | FN | GC | 11.25 |
| 41 | 250 | LFN | GC | 12.50 |
| | 280 | WLN | GC | 14.25 |
| 44 | 240 | WFNPB | | 9.75 |
| | 250 | Keith | | 12.25 |
| | 250 | LFN | GC | 12.50 |
| | 280 | WFNPB | | 10.00 |
| | 280 | WFN | GC | 12.50 |
| | 300 | LMNDCG | GC | 12.75 |
| | 325 | LCMN | GC | 13.50 |
| | 325 | WLN | GC | 13.50 |
| | 330 | LFNDCG | GC | 14.00 |
| | 335 | LFNPB | | 11.25 |
| | 355 | WLNDCG | GC | 15.75 |
| | 405 | WLNDCG | GC | 9.25/50 |
| 45 Auto | 225 | FNB | | 9.25 |
| 45 LC/454 Casull | 265 | Keith | | 9.75 |
| | 285 | LMN | GC | 13.75 |
| | 300 | WLN | GC | 14.50 |
| | 340 | LFN | GC | 15.00 |
| | 350 | LCMN | GC | 15.75 |
| | 355 | WLN | GC | 15.75 |
| | 405 | WLN | GC | 9.25/50 |
| 475 Linebaugh | 385 | LFNPB | | 9.50/50 |
| | 420 | LFNPB | | 9.50/50 |
| 50 Linebaugh | 450 | LFNPB | | 9.50/50 |

BB = Bevel Base; DCG = Dual Crimp Groove; FN = Flat Nose; FNB = Flat Nose Ball; FNB2 = Flat Nose Ball 2 (wider meplat); LFN = Long Flat Nose; LMN = Long Medium Nose; LCMN = Long Cylinder Medium Nose; PB = Plain Base; SP = Spitzer Design; WFN = Wide Flat Nose; WLN = Wide Long Nose; +P = Bullets for Magnum Loads.

## BERRY'S Lead-Free Pistol

| Caliber | Wgt. Grs. | Type |
|---|---|---|
| 380 | 95 | RN |
| 9mm | 115 | RN |
| | 124 | RN |
| | 124 | RN |
| | 147 | RN |
| 38 Super | 130 | RN |
| | 135 | RN |
| | 135 | FP |
| | 150 | RN |
| 38/357 | 125 | FP |
| | 148 | DEHB |
| | 148 | DEWC |
| | 158 | FP |
| | 158 | RN |
| 10mm/40 S&W | 165 | FP |
| | 180 | FP |
| 41 | 210 | FP |
| 44 | 180 | FP |
| | 200 | FP |
| | 220 | FP |
| | 240 | FP |
| | 280 | FP |
| 45 | 185 | FP |
| | 200 | FP |
| | 230 | RN |
| 45 LC | 250 | FP |

RN = Round-Nose; FP = Flat Point; DEHB = Double End Hollow Base; DEWC = Double End Wadcutter.

Berry's

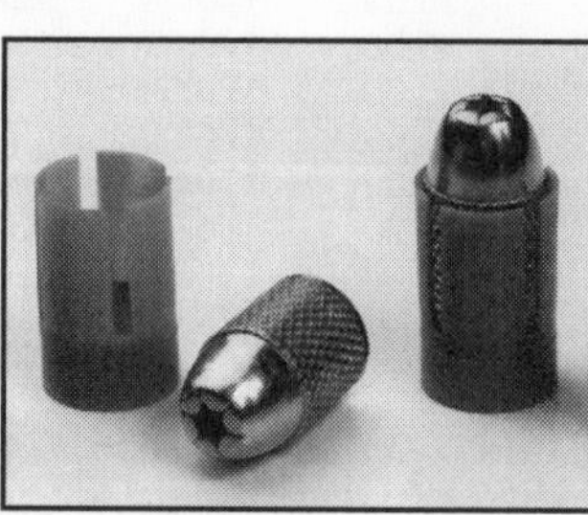

Blackpowder Products

## BLACKPOWDER PRODUCTS

| Caliber | —Bullet— Wgt. Grs. | Type | Price/500 |
|---|---|---|---|
| 32 | 78 | RN,BB | $13.00 |
| 380 | 95 | RNBB | 13.00 |
| 9x18 | 93 | RN | 16.00 |
| 9mm | 122 | FP | 16.00 |
| | 125 | RN | 16.00 |
| | 115 | RN | 16.00 |
| 38/357 | 148 | WCDBB | 20.00 |
| | 158 | SWC | 20.00 |
| | 160 | RN | 20.00 |
| 40 S&W/10mm | 180 | FP | 20.00 |
| | 150 | RN | 20.00 |
| 41 Mag. | 215 | SWC | 23.00 |
| 44 Mag. | 180 | FPBB | 22.50 |
| | 200 | RNFP | 22.50 |
| | 240 | SWCBB | 22.50 |
| | 300 | SWC | 25.00 |
| 44/40 | 180 | FPBB | 22.50 |
| | 200 | RNFP | 22.50 |
| 45 ACP | 175 | SWC | 20.00 |
| | 200 | SWC | 20.00 |
| | 225 | RN | 20.00 |
| | 225 | FPBB | 20.00 |
| | 230 | RN | 23.50 |
| | 230 | FP | 23.50 |
| 45 LC | 225 | FP | 20.00 |
| | 230 | FP | 23.50 |
| | 250 | RNFP | 23.50 |

RN = Roun Nose; FP = Flat Point; DWC = Double End Wadcutter; SWC = Semi-Wadcutter.

## BRP Cast Bullets

| Caliber | Wgt. Grs. | Type | Dia. | Price/100 | Price/1000 |
|---|---|---|---|---|---|
| 50 | 425 | SWCPB | .511 | $14.50 | $130.50 |
| 50 AE | 380 | FPPB | .500 | 13.65 | 122.85 |
| | 345 | FPPB | .500 | 13.40 | 120.60 |
| 475 | 435 | FPPB | .475 | 14.70 | 132.50 |
| | 395 | FPPB | .475 | 13.90 | 125.10 |
| 45-70 | 405 | FPPB | .458 | 16.00 | 144.00 |
| | 405 | FPPB | .458 | 14.20 | 127.80 |
| | 310 | FPGC | .458 | 13.40 | 120.60 |
| 45 | 305 | FPGC | .451 | 13.40 | 120.60 |
| | 260 | SWCGC | .451 | 12.10 | 108.90 |
| | 245 | TCPB | .451 | 8.75 | 78.75 |
| | 210 | ACP | .451 | 8.50 | 76.50 |
| | 205 | ACPGC | .451 | 9.95 | 89.55 |
| 44 | 290 | SWCGC | .430 | 12.85 | 115.65 |
| | 255 | SWCGC | .430 | 12.10 | 108.90 |
| | 245 | SWCPB | .430 | 8.75 | 78.75 |
| | 245 | SILGC | .430 | 11.30 | 101.25 |
| | 223 | SWCGC | .430 | 10.25 | 92.25 |
| 44-40 | 203 | FPPB | .428 | 8.25 | 74.25 |
| 41 | 260 | SWCGC | .411 | 12.10 | 108.96 |
| | 230 | SWCPB | .411 | 8.75 | 78.75 |
| | 213 | SWCGC | .411 | 10.25 | 92.25 |
| 10mm | 190 | TCPB | .401 | 8.00 | 72.00 |
| 35 | 200 | FPGC | .357 | 9.45 | 85.05 |
| | 200 | TCPB | .357 | 8.25 | 74.25 |
| 357 | 180 | SWCGC | .357 | 9.20 | 82.80 |
| | 180 | SILGC | .357 | 9.20 | 82.80 |
| 38/357 | 155 | SWCGC | .357 | 8.40 | 75.60 |
| | 155 | SWCBB | .357 | 7.20 | 64.80 |
| | 145 | WCDBB | .357 | 6.95 | 62.55 |
| 9mm | 115 | SWCPB | .355 | 5.90 | 53.10 |
| 32-20 | 115 | SWCGC | .313 | 7.90 | 71.10 |
| 32 Mag. | 100 | SWCGC | .313 | 7.60 | 68.40 |
| 308 | 173 | FPGC | .308 | 8.65 | 77.85 |
| | 165 | SILGC | .308 | 8.90 | 80.10 |
| 30 | 150 | FPGC | .308 | 8.65 | 77.85 |
| 7mm | 148 | SILGC | .284 | 8.65 | 77.85 |

SWCPB = Semi-Wadcutter Plain Base; FPGC = Flat Point Gas Check; SWCGC = Semi-Wadcutter Gas Check; FPPB = Flat Point Plain Base; SWCBB = Semi-Wadcutter Bevel Base; TCPB = Truncated Cone Plain Base; SILGC = Silhouette Gas Check.

## BIG BORE Pistol

| Caliber | Wgt. Grs. | Price/100 |
|---|---|---|
| 9mm | 120-180 | $20.00 |
| 357 | 120-200 | 20.00 |
| 429 | 180-250 | 20.00 |
| 452 | 180-250 | 20.00 |
| 452 SST | 180-250 | 29.95 |
| 452 SSTJHP | 180-250 | 24.95 |

Big Bore Pistol Bullets

## BULL-X

| | | Bullet | | Price | |
|---|---|---|---|---|---|
| Caliber | Diameter | Wgt. Grs. | Type | 500 | 1000 |
| 30 | .309 | 115 | RN | $23.20 | $38.50 |
| 32 | .313 | 98 | DEWC | 22.65 | 37.70 |
| | .313 | 100 | SWC | 22.65 | 37.70 |
| 9mm | .365 | 93 | RN | 23.50 | 39.20 |
| | .356 | 122 | FP | 24.00 | 40.10 |
| | .356 | 125 | RN | 24.00 | 40.10 |
| | .356/.357/.358 | 147 | FP | 25.80 | 43.10 |
| 380 | .356 | 95 | RN | 23.50 | 39.20 |
| | .356/.357/.358 | 140 | SWC | 26.30 | 43.80 |
| | .358 | 148 | DEWC | 26.05 | 43.50 |
| | .358 | 148 | BN | 26.05 | 43.50 |
| 38 | .358 | 148 | HBWC | 26.05 | 43.50 |
| | .356/.357 | 150 | SWC | 26.30 | 43.80 |
| | .358 | 158 | RN | 27.10 | 45.20 |
| | .358 | 158 | RNFP | 27.10 | 45.20 |
| | .358 | 158 | SWC | 27.10 | 45.20 |
| | .358 | 180 | FP | 30.15 | 50.30 |
| 32-20 | .313 | 115 | RNFP | 23.20 | 38.60 |
| 38-40 | .401 | 180 | RNFP | 30.15 | 50.30 |
| 10mm/ 40 S&W | .401 | 140 | FP | 25.80 | 43.10 |
| | .401 | 175 | SWC | 29.65 | 49.50 |
| | .401 | 180 | FP | 30.10 | 50.20 |
| 10mm | .401 | 200 | FP | 32.10 | 53.60 |
| 41 | .411 | 215 | SWC | 33.95 | 56.60 |
| 44 | .430 | 190 | SWC | 32.40 | 54.10 |
| | .430 | 215 | SWC | 32.40 | 54.10 |
| | .430 | 225 | RNFP | 35.10 | 58.50 |
| | .430 | 240 | SWC | 35.85 | 59.40 |
| | .430 | 300 | FP | 48.30 | 80.50 |
| 44-40 | .427 | 200 | RNFP | 32.20 | 53.80 |
| | .427 | 225 | RNFP | 35.10 | 58.50 |
| | .427 | 240 | RNFP | 35.85 | 59.70 |
| 45 | .452 | 150 | RN, SWC | 32.20 | 53.80 |
| | .452 | 185 | SWC | 30.70 | 51.10 |
| | .452 | 200 | SWC | 32.20 | 53.80 |
| | .452 | 225 | FP | 35.10 | 58.50 |
| | .452 | 230 | RN | 35.10 | 58.50 |
| | .452 | 255 | SWC | 38.30 | 63.80 |
| | .452 | 300 | FP | 48.30 | 80.50 |
| 45-70 | .458 | 405 | FP | 68.50 | 114.00 |

FP = Flat Point; RN = Round Nose; DEWC = Double End Wadcutter; BN = Button Nose; SWC = Semi-Wadcutter.

BRP Bullets

# Section 5: Components

## BULLSEYE

| Caliber | Bullet Diameter | Bullet Wgt. Grs. | Bullet Type | Price 500 | Price 1000 |
|---|---|---|---|---|---|
| 380 | | 95 | RN | $13.00 | $23.00 |
| 9mm | .356 | 125 | RN-BB | 13.00 | 23.00 |
| 9mm Makarov | .365 | 95 | RN-BB | 14.00 | 25.00 |
| 9mm/38 Super | .356 | 147 | FP-BB | 13.00 | 24.00 |
| 38/357 | .357 | 148 | DE-WC | 13.00 | 24.00 |
| | | 148 | BN-WC | 13.00 | 24.00 |
| | | 158 | SWC-BB | 13.00 | 24.00 |
| | | 158 | RN-BB | 13.00 | 24.00 |
| 40/10mm | .401 | 175 | SWC-BB | 16.00 | 29.00 |
| | .401 | 155 | RNSWC-BB | 13.00 | 24.00 |
| 41 | .411 | 215 | SWC-BB | 18.00 | 32.00 |
| 44-40 | .428 | 200 | RNFP | 17.00 | 30.00 |
| 44 | .430 | 200 | RNFP | 17.00 | 30.00 |
| | .430 | 240 | SWC-BB | 18.00 | 33.00 |
| 45 | .452 | 155 | SWC-BB | 15.00 | 26.00 |
| | .452 | 180 | SWC-BB | 17.00 | 30.00 |
| | .452 | 185 | SWC-BB | 17.00 | 30.00 |
| | .452 | 200 | SWC-BB | 17.00 | 30.00 |
| | .452 | 230 | RN-BB | 18.00 | 33.00 |
| 45 LC | .452 | 250 | RNFP | 16.00* | 28.00** |
| | .452 | 255 | SWC-BB | 16.00* | 28.00** |
| 45/70 | .458 | 300 | FP-BC | 18.00* | 34.00** |

* = Price for 400. ** = Price for 800. BB = Bevel Base; RN = Round Nose; FP = Flat Point; DE = Double End; WC = Wadcutter; SWC = Semi-Wadcutter; FB = Flat Base.

## CHAMPION'S CHOICE Match Bullets

| Caliber | Wgt. Grs. | Type | Price/100 |
|---|---|---|---|
| | **Pistol** | | |
| 32 S&W | 83 | LWC | $19.50 |
| 32 S&W | 98 | LWC | 19.50 |
| 38 Spl. | 148 | LWC | 19.50 |
| | **Rifle** | | |
| 6.5mm | 138 | HPBT | 17.00 |
| 7mm | 150 | HPBT | 17.00 |
| | 170 | FMJBT | 19.00 |
| 7.62 (.308) | 170 | FMJBT | 13.25 |
| (.309) | 170 | FMJBT | 13.25 |
| (.308) | 185 | FMJBT | 13.50 |
| (.309) | 185 | FMJBT | 13.50 |
| (.308) | 195 | FMJBT | 15.50 |
| (.308) | 167 | HPBT | 15.50 |
| (.309) | 167 | HPBT | 15.50 |
| (.308) | 185 | HPBT | 18.50 |
| 338 Lapua | 250 | FMJBT | 22.00 |

LWC = Lead Wadcutter; HPBT = Hollowpoint Boattail; FMJBT = Full Metal Jacket Boattail.
From Champion's Choice, Inc.

## DILLON Swaged Pistol

| Caliber | Wgt. Grs. | Type | Price/500 | Price/1000 |
|---|---|---|---|---|
| 38 | 148 | HBWC | $18.95 | $35.45 |
| | 158 | SWC | 18.95 | 35.45 |
| 45 | 200 | SWC | 22.95 | 42.75 |

HBWC = Hollow Base Wadcutter; SWC = Semi-Wadcutter.

## CARROLL

| Caliber | Wgt. Grs. | Type | Price/Per |
|---|---|---|---|
| | **LEAD CAST PISTOL** | | |
| 380 Auto | 95 | RNBB | $15.50/500 |
| 9mm Luger | 125 | RNBB | 15.85/500 |
| | 147 | FNBB | 16.85/500 |
| 38 | 143 | DEWC | 16.20/500 |
| | 148 | WCBB | 16.20/500 |
| 357 | 160 | SWCBB | 17.20/500 |
| 10mm | 175 | SWCBB | 19.25/500 |
| 41 | 215 | SWCBB | 19.90/500 |
| 44 | 240 | SWCBB | 20.60/500 |
| 45 | 185 | SWCFB | 19.25/500 |
| | 200 | SWCBB | 19.25/500 |
| | 225 | FNBB | 19.90/500 |
| | 230 | RNBB | 19.90/500 |
| | 255 | SWCBB | 21.25/500 |
| | **LEAD CAST RIFLE** | | |
| 30 | 190 | FNGC | 7.95/100 |
| 35 | 210 | FNGC | 8.25/100 |
| 45 | 405 | FNPB | 5.35/50 |

RNBB = Round Nose Bevel Base; DEWC = Double End Wadcutter; FNBB = Flat Nose Bevel Base; WCBB = Wadcutter Bevel Base; SWCBB = Semi-Wadcutter Bevel Base; FNGC = Flat Nose Gas Check; FP = Flat Point.

## DILLON Cast Pistol

| Caliber | Wgt. Grs. | Type | Price/500 | Price/1000 |
|---|---|---|---|---|
| 30 M1 | 115 | | $18.25 | $33.75 |
| 32 | 100 | DEWC | 17.95 | 33.45 |
| 380 | 92 | RN | 17.45 | 32.45 |
| 9x18 Makarov | 93 | RN | 17.95 | 33.45 |
| 9mm | 115 | RN | 18.25 | 33.75 |
| | 125 | RN | 18.75 | 44.45 |
| | 135 | | 18.95 | 35.25 |
| | 160 | RN | 18.95 | 35.45 |
| | 148 | WC | 18.95 | 35.45 |
| | 158 | RN | 18.95 | 35.45 |
| | 158 | SWC | 18.95 | 35.45 |
| 10mm | 140 | FP | 19.75 | 36.75 |
| | 155 | SWC | 18.95 | 35.45 |
| | 175 | SWC | 20.75 | 38.75 |
| 38-40 | 180 | RNFT | 23.75 | 43.95 |
| 41 | 215 | SWC | 23.95 | 44.75 |
| 44 | 240 | SWC | 25.75 | 47.75 |
| 44 Mag. | 300 | TC | 16.75 | 31.25 |
| 44-40 (.428) | 205 | RNFT | 24.25 | 44.95 |
| 44-40 (.429) | 205 | RNFT | 24.25 | 44.55 |
| 45 | 155 | SWC | 21.45 | 39.95 |
| | 178 | FBSWC | 23.75 | 44.25 |
| | 200 | SWC | 22.95 | 42.75 |
| | 225 | FPTC | 24.95 | 46.75 |
| | 230 | RN | 25.45 | 47.45 |
| 45 LC | 255 | SWC | 26.95 | 50.25 |
| | 255 | RNFT | 27.95 | 51.75 |
| 45-70 | 300 | FP | 21.25 | 39.25 |
| | 405 | FP | 28.25 | 52.25 |

DEWC = Double End Wadcutter; RN = Round-Nose; SWC = Semi-Wadcutter; HB = Hollow Base; TC = Truncated Cone; FT = Flat Tip; FP = Flat Point.

## CURTIS Pistol

| Bullet # | Wgt. Grs. | Type | Price/Per 1000 |
|---|---|---|---|
| **.356, .357 .358** | | | |
| 115 | 122 | RNBB | $28.00 |
| 377 | 122 | TCBB | 28.00 |
| 9-125 | 125 | RNBB | 28.00 |
| 928 | 145 | RNBB | 29.00 |
| 9-147 | 147 | FPBB | 29.00 |
| 929 | 145 | SWCBB | 29.00 |
| 63 | 145 | RNBB | 29.00 |
| 73 | 145 | SWCBB | 29.00 |
| 316 | 158 | TCBB | 29.00 |
| 052 | 148 | WCBB | 29.00 |
| 348 | 148 | WCDBB | 29.00 |
| 388 | 158 | SWCBB | 29.00 |
| 38-158 | 158 | SWCBB | 29.00 |
| 391 | 158 | RNBB | 29.00 |
| 38-159 | 158 | RNBB | 29.00 |
| 392 | 200 | TCFB | 34.00 |
| 801 | 160 | SWCBB | 33.00 |
| **.401** | | | |
| 043 | 170 | TCBB | 32.00 |
| 40-175 | 175 | SWCBB | 32.00 |
| 045 | 170 | SWCBB | 32.00 |
| 047 | 200 | TCBB | 35.00 |
| **.411** | | | |
| 416 | 170 | SWCBB | 32.00 |
| 419 | 200 | SWCBB | 35.00 |
| 413 | 210 | TCBB | 36.00 |
| 41-215 | 215 | SWCBB | 37.00 |
| **.427** | | | |
| 420 | 200 | TCFB | 35.00 |
| 444 | 200 | FPFB | 35.00 |
| **.429, .430** | | | |
| 420 | 200 | TCFB | 35.00 |
| 444 | 200 | FPFB | 35.00 |
| 445 | 220 | SWCBB | 36.00 |
| 440 | 240 | SWCBB | 39.00 |
| 44-420 | 240 | SWCBB | 39.00 |
| 430 | 265 | FPFB | 41.00 |
| 433 | 300 | FPFB | 51.00 |
| 44-300 | 300 | FPBB | 52.00 |
| 428 | 240 | TCFB | 39.00 |
| **.452** | | | |
| 062 | 170 | SWCBB | 32.00 |
| 065 | 180 | SWCBB | 33.00 |
| 45-185 | 185 | SWCBB | 33.00 |
| 068 | 200 | SWCBB | 35.00 |
| 067 | 225 | TCBB | 36.00 |
| 457 | 225 | RNBB | 36.00 |
| 45-230 | 230 | RNBB | 37.00 |
| 452 | 255 | SWCFB | 40.00 |
| 45-255 | 255 | SWCBB | 40.00 |
| **.454** | | | |
| 452 | 255 | SWCFB | 40.00 |
| 45-255 | 255 | SWCFB | 40.00 |

RNBB = Round-Nose Bevel Base; TCBB = Truncated Cone Bevel Base; FPBB = Flat Point Bevel Base; SWCBB = Semi-Wadcutter Bevel Base; WCBB = Wadcutter Bevel Base; TCFB = Truncated Cone Flat Base; FPFB = Flat Point Flat Base.

## DKT Cast Bullets

| Bullet | Mould | Nom. Wgt. | Std. Dia. | Opt. Dia. | Price/100 |
|---|---|---|---|---|---|
| 600 | LBT | 600 | .477 | .475 | $25.00 |
| 500 | Custom | 500 | .458 | .457 .459 | 25.00 |
| 450 | NEI-SSK | 450 | .512 | .509 .515 | 25.00 |
| 480 | NEI | 450 | .477 | .475 | 25.00 |
| 400 | LBT | 400 | .475 | .477 | 25.00 |
| 385 | NEI | 385 | .417 | | 20.00 |
| 345 | NEI-SSK | 345 | .451 | .450 .452 | 20.00 |
| 340 | Custom | 340 | .452 | .450 .451 | 20.00 |
| 311 | NEI-SSK | 310 | .431 | .429 .430 | 20.00 |
| 310 | NEI-SSK | 310 | .431 | .429 .430 | 20.00 |
| 285 | NEI-SSK | 285 | .431 | .429 .430 | 20.00 |
| 275 | NEI-SSK | 275 | .410 | .412 | 20.00 |
| 270 | NEI-SSK | 270 | .451 | .450 .452 | 20.00 |
| 260 | NEI-SSK | 260 | .431 | .429 .430 | 20.00 |
| 182 | NEI-SSK | 180 | .358 | .357 .359 | 20.00 |
| 115 | Custom | 115 | * | | 20.00 |

*For 310 Cadet.

## D&J

| Wgt. Grs. | Type | Price/1000 |
|---|---|---|
| | **CALIBER: 9mm** | |
| 125 | LRN | $38.13 |
| 125 | FMJ | 65.11 |
| 135 | FMJ | 65.11 |
| 147 | LSWC | 41.88 |
| | **CALIBER: 38 Super** | |
| 125 | FMJ | 65.11 |
| 135 | FMJ | 65.11 |
| 150 | LSWC | 41.88 |
| 160 | LRN | 43.13 |
| | **CALIBER: 38 Revolver** | |
| 148 | LSWC | 41.88 |
| 158 | LSWC | 43.13 |
| | **CALIBER: 10mm/40S&W** | |
| 155 | LRN, SWC | 43.13 |
| | **CALIBER: 44** | |
| 300 | TFP | 60.00 |
| | **CALIBER: 45 ACP** | |
| 175 | LSWC | 45.00 |
| 200 | LSWC | 48.13 |
| 230 | LRN | 51.88 |
| 255 | LSWC | 55.00 |
| 300 | TFP | 60.00 |

LRN = Lead Round Nose; LSWC = Lead Semi-Wadcutter; FMJ = Full Metal Jacket; TFP = Truncated Flat Point.

Dillon

## FUSILIER

| Caliber | Bullet Diameter | Bullet Wgt. Grs. | Type | Price/100 | Price/250 | Price/500 |
|---|---|---|---|---|---|---|
| | | | PISTOL | | | |
| 9mm | .355 | 120 | TC | $7.45 | $18.10 | $35.40 |
| | .355 | 145 | TC | 7.95 | 19.30 | 37.80 |
| | .356 | 120 | TC | 7.45 | 18.10 | 35.40 |
| | .356 | 145 | TC | 7.95 | 19.30 | 37.80 |
| 38 | .357 | 100 | TC | 7.45 | 18.10 | 35.40 |
| | .357 | 125 | TC | 7.75 | 18.80 | 36.85 |
| | .357 | 145 | WCBB | 7.95 | 19.30 | 37.80 |
| | .357 | 158 | SWC, GC | 10.15 | NA | NA |
| | .357 | 180 | TC | 8.45 | 20.50 | 40.15 |
| | .358 | 100 | TC | 7.45 | 18.10 | 35.40 |
| | .358 | 125 | TC | 7.75 | 18.80 | 36.85 |
| | .358 | 145 | WCBB | 7.95 | 19.30 | 37.80 |
| | .358 | 158 | SWC, GC | 10.15 | NA | NA |
| | .358 | 180 | TC | 8.45 | 20.50 | 40.15 |
| 10mm | .401 | 180 | TC | 8.45 | 20.50 | 40.15 |
| | .401 | 200 | TC | 8.95 | 21.70 | 42.55 |
| 44 | .429 | 180 | TC | 8.45 | 20.50 | 40.15 |
| | .429 | 200 | WCFB | 8.95 | 21.70 | 42.55 |
| | .429 | 240 | TC | 9.45 | 22.95 | 44.95 |
| | .429 | 250 | SWCFB | 9.45 | 22.95 | 44.95 |
| | .429 | 300 | TC | 9.95 | 24.15 | 47.30 |
| | .430 | 180 | TC | 8.45 | 20.50 | 40.15 |
| | .430 | 200 | WCFB | 8.95 | 21.70 | 42.55 |
| | .430 | 240 | TC | 9.45 | 22.95 | 44.95 |
| | .430 | 250 | SWCFB | 9.45 | 22.95 | 44.95 |
| | .430 | 300 | TC | 9.95 | 24.15 | 47.30 |
| 45 | .451 | 200 | TC | 8.95 | 21.70 | 42.55 |
| | .451 | 225 | TC | 9.25 | 22.45 | 43.95 |
| | .451 | 300 | TC | 9.95 | 24.15 | 47.30 |
| | .452 | 200 | TC | 8.95 | 21.70 | 42.55 |
| | .452 | 225 | TC | 9.25 | 22.45 | 43.95 |
| | .452 | 300 | TC | 9.95 | 24.15 | 47.30 |

GC = Gas Check; TC = Truncated Cone; FB = Flat Base; WC = Wadcutter; SWC = Semi-Wadcutter; BB = Bevel Base.

## KEITH'S

| Caliber | Wgt. Grs. | Type |
|---|---|---|
| 9mm | 125 | RN |
| | 125 | CN |
| 38 Super | 150 | SWC |
| | 158 | SWC |
| | 158 | RN |
| 10mm | 175 | SWC |
| 41 | 210 | SWC |
| 44 | 240 | SWC |
| 45 | 185 | SWC |
| | 200 | SWC |
| | 230 | RN |
| 45 Colt | 255 | SWC |

RN = Round Nose; CN = Conical Nose; SWC = Semi-Wadcutter.

## J&L SUPERIOR

| Caliber | Diameter | Wgt. Grs. | Type | Price/50 |
|---|---|---|---|---|
| | | PISTOL | | |
| 9mm Makarov | .364 | 110 | RN | $8.98 |
| 455 Webley | .455 | 265 | HB | 11.98 |
| 44-40 | .428 | 200 | FN | 8.98 |

FN = Flat Nose; RN = Round Nose; HB = Hollow Base.

## KASWER Pin-Grabber Bullets

| Cartridge | Wgt. Grs. | Type | Price/100 |
|---|---|---|---|
| 380 Auto | 110 | JHP | $22.00 |
| 9mm Luger | 115 | JHP | 27.00 |
| | 125 | JHP | 22.00 |
| | 150 | JHP | 26.75 |
| 38 Super | 125 | JHP | 22.00 |
| | 150 | JHP | 26.75 |
| 38 Special | 158 | JHP | 24.25 |
| 357 Magnum | 125 | JHP | 22.00 |
| | 150 | JHP | 26.75 |
| | 158 | JHP | 24.25 |
| 357 Maximum | 158 | JHP | 24.25 |
| 40 S&W | 150 | JHP | 30.00 |
| | 170 | JHP | 30.00 |
| 10mm | 170 | JHP | 41.50 |
| | 210 | JHP | 42.00 |
| 41 AE | 170 | JHP | 30.00 |
| | 210 | JHP | 30.00 |
| 41 Magnum | 170 | JHP | 30.00 |
| | 210 | JHP | 30.00 |
| 44 Special | 180 | JHP | 30.50 |
| 44 Magnum | 180 | JHP | 30.50 |
| | 210 | JHP | 35.00 |
| | 240 | JHP | 30.75 |
| | 265 | JHP | 40.00 |
| 45 ACP | 185 | JHP | 32.50 |
| | 200 | JHP | 31.00 |
| | 225 | Lead | 18.50 |
| | 225 | JHP | 32.50 |
| | 250 | JHP | 32.50 |
| | 260 | JHP | 32.50 |
| 45 Win. Magnum | 260 | JHP | 34.50 |
| | 300 | JHP | 36.75* |
| 45 Long Colt | 260 | JHP | 34.50 |
| 454 Casull | 260 | JHP | 35.48 |
| | 300 | JHP | 36.75* |

* = Price for 50. JHP = Jacketed Hollowpoint.

## KASWER Perfect Circle Bullets

| Wgt. Grs. | Type | Price/100 |
|---|---|---|
| | Caliber: 45 ACP | |
| 200 | TC | $11.00 |
| 185 | FMJTC | 21.00 |
| 200 | FMJTC | 21.00 |
| 230 | FMJTC | 17.00 |

TC = Truncated Cone; FMJ = Full Metal Jacket.

## LAPUA Pistol Bullets

| Caliber | Wgt. Grs. | Type | Price/100 |
|---|---|---|---|
| 32 | 83 | LWC | $33.90/500 |
| | 98 | LWC | 33.90/500 |
| 7.65mm | 93 | FMJ | 10.66 |
| 9mm | 120 | CEPP Super | 17.42 |
| | 120 | CEPP Extra | 17.42 |
| 357 | 158 | FN | 21.07 |
| | 240 | HP | 25.66 |

FN = Flat Nose; LWC = Lead Wadcutter; FMJ = Full Metal Jacket; HP = Hollowpoint.

## LANE

| Caliber | Wgt. Grs. | Type | Price/1000 |
|---|---|---|---|
| 30 | 115 | RN | $27.22 |
| 32 | 78 | RN | 26.50 |
| | 100 | DEWC | 26.60 |
| 32-20 | 115 | RN | 27.22 |
| 380 | 95 | RN | 25.80 |
| 9mm | 115 | SWC | 27.22 |
| | 125 | RN | 27.70 |
| | 145 | RN | 29.13 |
| | 147 | FP | 29.18 |
| 10mm | 155 | RN | 30.08 |
| | 175 | SWC | 31.98 |
| | 180 | RN | 32.45 |
| 38 | 145 | RN | 29.13 |
| | 148 | DEWC | 29.13 |
| | 150 | SWC | 29.63 |
| | 158 | SWC | 30.08 |
| | 158 | RN | 30.08 |
| 38-40 | 180 | FP | 32.45 |
| 40 | 347 | RN | 32.93* |
| 41 | 215 | SWC | 29.13 |
| 44 | 240 | SWC | 35.77 |
| | 200 | RNFP | 32.93 |
| 45 | 155 | SWC | 30.08 |
| | 185 | SWC | 32.45 |
| | 200 | SWC | 32.93 |
| | 230 | RN | 35.30 |
| | 250 | RNFP | 36.25 |
| | 255 | SWC | 36.25 |
| 45 | 440 | Ball | 30.00 |
| 45-70 | 405 | FP | 32.93* |
| 50 | 490 | Ball | 40.00 |

* = Price for 500. RN = Round Nose; DEWC = Dead End Wadcutter; SWC = Semi-Wadcutter; FP = Flat Point.

## MASTER CLASS Pistol

| Caliber | Wgt. Grs. | Type | Price/1000 |
|---|---|---|---|
| 9mm | 125 | cn | $28.00 |
| | 135 | RN | 29.00 |
| | 147 | FP | 30.00 |
| 38 Super | 133 | SWC | 30.00 |
| | 160 | RN | 30.00 |
| 40 S&W/10mm | 140 | RN | 29.00 |
| | 155 | RN | 30.00 |
| | 155 | SWC | 30.00 |
| | 170 | SWC | 31.00 |
| | 180 | FP | 33.00 |
| 45 ACP | 160 | SWC | 31.00 |
| | 185 | SWC | 33.00 |
| | 185 | SWC | 33.00 |
| | 200 | SWC | 35.00 |
| | 230 | RN | 39.00 |
| 38 Spec. | 125 | TC | 28.00 |
| | 148 | WC | 30.00 |
| | 158 | SWC | 30.00 |
| 41 | 215 | SWC | 21.00 |
| 44-40 | 200 | RNFP | 35.00 |
| 44 | 240 | SWC | 22.00 |
| 45 LC | 250 | RNFP | 23.00 |

RN = Round-Nose; FP = Flat Point; SWC = Semi-Wadcutter; TC = Truncated Cone; RNFP = Round-Nose Flat Point.

## LIBERTY SHOOTING SUPPLIES Pistol

| Caliber | | Wgt. Grs. | Type | Price 100 | Price 500 |
|---|---|---|---|---|---|
| 25 ACP | .251 | 50 | RN | $5.00 | $22.50 |
| 30 Mauser | .308 | 85 | RN | 6.00 | 27.00 |
| 32 | .311 | 76 | RN | 5.00 | 22.50 |
| | .313 | 92 | WC | 5.00 | 22.50 |
| | .313 | 95 | SWC | 5.00 | 22.50 |
| 32-20 | .313 | 92 | SP | 6.00 | 27.00 |
| | .313 | 112 | GCFP | 6.00 | 27.00 |
| | .313 | 115 | SP | 6.50 | 29.25 |
| 8mm Nambu | .321 | 80 | RN | 8.00 | 36.00 |
| | .321 | 102 | RN | 8.50 | 38.25 |
| 380 | .356 | 95 | BBRN | 5.00 | 22.50 |
| | .356 | 105 | FP | 5.00 | 22.50 |
| 9mm | .356 | 118 | BBFP | 5.00 | 22.50 |
| | .356 | 124 | BBRN | 5.00 | 22.50 |
| | .356 | 124 | BBCON | 5.00 | 22.50 |
| | .356 | 146 | BBFP | 5.50 | 24.75 |
| | .356 | 155 | BBRN | 5.50 | 24.75 |
| 38 | .358 | 73 | WC | 5.00 | 22.50 |
| | .358 | 110 | SWC | 5.00 | 22.50 |
| | .358 | 125 | BBSWC | 5.50 | 24.75 |
| | .358 | 148 | BBWC | 5.50 | 24.75 |
| | .358 | 150 | DEWC | 5.50 | 24.75 |
| | .358 | 158 | BBSWC | 5.50 | 24.75 |
| | .358 | 158 | BBRN | 5.50 | 24.75 |
| | .358 | 180 | GCFP | 6.00 | 27.00 |
| | .358 | 182 | FP | 6.00 | 27.00 |
| | .358 | 190 | RN | 7.00 | 31.50 |
| | .358 | 210 | SWCGC | 6.50 | 29.25 |
| 38 S&W | .360 | 190 | RN | 7.00 | 31.50 |
| 9mm Makarov | .364 | 100 | RN | 7.00 | 31.50 |
| | .376 | 235 | FP | 8.50 | 38.25 |
| 41 Colt | .388-.406 | 202 | RN | 8.00 | 36.00 |
| 40/10mm | .401 | 135 | BBFP | 6.00 | 27.00 |
| | .401 | 165 | BBSWC | 6.00 | 27.00 |
| | .401 | 195 | BBFP | 6.50 | 29.25 |
| | .401 | 200 | BBFP | 6.50 | 29.25 |
| 38/40 | .401 | 165 | FP | 6.00 | 27.00 |
| | | 195 | SWC | 6.50 | 29.25 |
| | | 220 | FP | 7.00 | 31.50 |
| 41 | .410 | 135 | WC | 6.00 | 27.00 |
| | .410 | 165 | RN | 6.00 | 27.00 |
| | .410 | 190 | WC | 6.00 | 27.00 |
| | .410 | 200 | FP | 6.00 | 27.00 |
| | .410 | 215 | BBSWC | 6.00 | 27.00 |
| | | 275 | FP | 5.00* | 22.50* |
| 44/40 | .427 | 200 | FP | 6.50 | 29.25 |
| | .427 | 205 | FP | 6.50 | 29.25 |
| 44 | .429 | 93 | WC | 6.00 | 27.00 |
| | .429 | 180 | WC | 6.00 | 27.00 |
| | .429 | 200 | GCPT | 6.50 | 29.25 |
| | .429 | 205 | FP | 6.50 | 29.25 |
| | .429 | 215 | BBSWC | 6.00 | 27.00 |
| | .429 | 240 | RN | 6.50 | 29.25 |
| | | 240 | WC | 6.50 | 29.95 |
| | | 240 | SWCBB | 6.50 | 29.95 |
| | | 240 | FPGC | 6.50 | 29.95 |
| | | 240 | FP | 7.00 | 31.50 |
| | .429 | 250 | SWC | 7.00 | 31.50 |
| | .429 | 275 | FP | 5.00* | 22.50* |
| | | 300 | SWCGC | 6.50* | 29.25* |
| | | 310 | FP | 6.00* | 27.00* |
| 44 Conquest | .429 | 310 | FP | 6.50* | 29.25* |
| 45 | .451 | 150 | SWC | 7.00 | 31.50 |
| | .451 | 176 | SWC | 6.00 | 27.00 |
| | .451 | 200 | SWCBB | 6.00 | 27.00 |
| | .451 | 220 | FPBB | 6.50 | 29.25 |
| | .451 | 230 | RNBB | 6.50 | 29.25 |
| | .452 | 156 | RN | 6.50 | 29.25 |
| | .452 | 240 | FP | 7.50 | 33.75 |
| | .452 | 250 | WC | 6.50 | 29.25 |
| | .452 | 255 | SWCBB | 7.00 | 31.50 |
| | .452 | 300 | FP | 6.00* | 27.00* |
| | .452 | 325 | FP | 6.50* | 29.25* |
| | .452 | 345 | SWC | 7.00* | 31.50* |
| 45 Colt | .454 | 240 | FP | 7.50 | 33.75 |
| | .454 | 310 | SWCBB | 6.50* | 29.25* |
| Webley | .454 | NA | CBRN | NA | NA |

*Price for 50 and 250.
RN = Round-Nose; WC = Wadcutter; SWC = Semi-Wadcutter; BB = Bevel Base; FP = Flat Point; CON = Conical; DE = Double Ended; GC = Gas Checkable; PT = Pointed; SP = Spire Point; SP = Spire Point; PP = Paper Patch.

## MAGNUS

| Bullet No. | Caliber | Wgt. Grs. | Type | Dia. | Price/500 | Price/1000 |
|---|---|---|---|---|---|---|
| 203 | 30 | 115 | RNBB | .309 | $15.00 | $28.00 |
| 204 | 32 | 98 | WC | .313 | 15.00 | 28.00 |
| 201 | | 100 | SWCBB | .313 | 15.00 | 28.00 |
| 202 | 32-20 | 115 | FP | .313 | 15.00 | 28.00 |
| 205 | 32-30 | 100 | SWC | .314 | 15.00 | 28.00 |
| 401 | 9mm | 122 | FPBB | .355 | 15.00 | 28.00 |
| 402 | | 125 | RNBB | .355 | 15.00 | 28.00 |
| 505 | | 135 | RN | .355 | 15.00 | 28.00 |
| 403 | | 147 | FPBB | .356 | 15.00 | 28.00 |
| 404 | 9mm Mak. | 95 | RN | .356 | 15.00 | 28.00 |
| 506 | 38 Super | 155 | FP | .356 | 17.00 | 31.50 |
| 301 | 380 | 95 | RNBB | .355 | 15.00 | 28.00 |
| 302 | | 100 | FP | .356 | 15.00 | 28.00 |
| 502 | 38/357 | 148 | WC | .357 | 15.00 | 28.00 |
| 503 | | 158 | SWCBB | .357 | 17.00 | 31.50 |
| 504 | | 158 | RNBB | .357 | 17.00 | 31.50 |
| 501 | | 148 | DEWC | .358 | 15.00 | 28.00 |
| 101 | 40/10mm | 180 | FP | .401 | 18.00 | 34.00 |
| 102 | | 155 | RN | .401 | 16.00 | 31.00 |
| 102 | | 155 | SWC | .401 | $16.00 | $31.00 |
| 103 | | 200 | FP | .401 | 20.25 | 38.50 |
| 601 | 41 | 215 | SWCBB | .410 | 21.00 | 40.50 |
| 702 | 44 | 215 | SWCBB | .430 | 21.00 | 40.00 |
| 701 | | 240 | SWCBB | .430 | 19.00 | 35.50* |
| 703 | 44-40 | 210 | RNFP | .440 | 20.25 | 38.50 |
| 805 | 45 | 155 | SWCBB | .452 | 17.00 | 32.00 |
| 806 | | 170 | SPLBB | .452 | 18.00 | 34.00 |
| 801 | | 185 | SWCBB | .452 | 19.00 | 35.50 |
| 802 | | 200 | SWCBB | .452 | 20.00 | 38.50 |
| 807 | | 215 | SWCBB | .452 | 21.00 | 40.00 |
| 803 | | 225 | FPBB | .452 | 22.00 | 42.00 |
| 804 | | 230 | RNBB | .452 | 22.00 | 42.00 |
| 902 | | 250 | RNFP | .452 | 20.00 | 37.50* |
| 901 | | 255 | SWCBB | .452 | 20.00 | 37.50* |
| 905 | 45-70 | 300 | FP | .457 | 29.00 | 54.00 |
| 903 | | 350 | FP | .457 | 29.00 | 54.00 |
| 904 | | 405 | FP | .457 | 36.00 | 68.00 |
| 906 | 45-454 | 300 | FP | .454 | 28.00 | 52.00 |

RNBB = Round Nose Bevel Base; FPBB = Flat Point Bevel Base; DEWC = Dead End Wadcutter; WC = Wadcutter; SWCBB = Semi-Wadcutter Bevel Base; FPBB = Flat Point Bevel Base; FP = Flat Point.

Magnum Bullets

## MONTANA PRECISION SWAGING
### Cast Bullets

| Caliber | Wgt. Grs. | Sized | Tip | Price/100 |
|---|---|---|---|---|
| | | **PISTOL** | | |
| 32 Colt | 93 | .311 | 1R | $7.00 |
| 8mm Nambu | 100 | .323 | 2R | 7.00 |
| 9mm | 111 | .356 | 2R | 7.00 |
| 38 ACP | 111 | .356 | 2R | 7.00 |
| | 150 | .357 | 1R | 7.50 |
| 38/357 | 158 | .358 | SWC | 7.50 |
| | 158 | .358 | GCSWC | 9.10 |
| 38/40 | 170 | .400 | FN | 8.00 |
| 41 Mag. | 195 | .410 | SWC | 8.00 |
| 44 Mag. | 200 | .428 | FN | 8.00 |
| 44-40 | 214 | .428 | 1R | 8.25 |
| 44 Keith | 245 | .429 | FN | 8.75 |
| 45 Colt | 250 | .454 | FN | 8.75 |
| | 255 | .452 | FN | 8.75 |
| | 300 | .452 | GCSWC | 10.85 |

SWC = Semi-Wadcutter; GCSWC = Gas Check Semi-Wadcutter; FN = Flat Nose.

## MEISTER Hard Cast Bullets

| Caliber | Dia. (ins.) | Wgt. Grs. | Type | Price/500 |
|---|---|---|---|---|
| 30 | .308 | 115 | RN | $19.99 |
| 32 | .312 | 100 | DEWC | 18.99 |
| 380 | .355 | 92 | RN | 18.59 |
| 9mm | .356 | 115 | RN | 18.99 |
| | .356 | 125 | RN | 19.69 |
| | .356 | 135 | RN | 19.99 |
| 38 | .357 | 148 | WC | 20.19 |
| | .357 | 150 | SWC | 20.49 |
| | .357 | 158 | RN | 20.19 |
| | .357 | 158 | SWC | 20.19 |
| | .357 | 160 | RN | 20.99 |
| 10mm | .401 | 140 | FP | 21.99 |
| | .401 | 155 | SWC | 21.29 |
| | .401 | 175 | SWC | 21.99 |
| | .401 | 180 | RNFP | 25.99 |
| 41 | .410 | 215 | SWC | 25.49 |
| 44-40 | .428 | 205 | RNFP | 27.99 |
| | .429 | 205 | RNFP | 27.99 |
| 44 | .429 | 240 | SWC | 27.39 |
| | .429 | 300 | FP | 17.89* |
| 45 | .452 | 155 | SWC | 22.79 |
| | .452 | 178 | SWC | 25.19 |
| | .452 | 200 | SWC | 24.29 |
| | .452 | 225 | FP | 26.19 |
| | .452 | 230 | RN | 26.69 |
| | .452 | 255 | SWC | 28.59 |
| | .452 | 255 | RNFP | 29.19 |
| 45 | .458 | 300 | FP | 22.79/250 |
| | .458 | 405 | FP | 29.99/250 |

RN = Round Nose; SWC = Semi-Wadcutter; WC = Wadcutter; RNFP = Round Nose Flat Point; DEWC = Double End Wadcutter; FP = Flat Point.

### M&D MUNITIONS

| Caliber | Wgt. Grs. | Type | Price/1000 |
|---|---|---|---|
| 38/357 | 125 | TMP | $43.50 |
| | 125 | JHP | 51.00 |
| | 135 | FMJ | 45.00 |
| | 148 | LDEW | 22.00 |
| | 148 | LHBWC | 24.50 |
| | 148 | PWC | 46.00 |
| | 158 | TMP | 56.20 |
| | 158 | JHP | 56.00 |
| | 158 | JSP | 55.70 |
| | 158 | LSWC | 24.50 |
| | 158 | LSWCHP | 25.50 |
| | 158 | LRN | 24.50 |
| 9mm | 115 | TMP | 39.20 |
| | 115 | JHP | 52.90 |
| | 124 | TMP | 41.90 |
| | 125 | LRN | 24.50 |
| | 147 | TMP | 54.00 |
| | 147 | JHP | 61.50 |
| 380 ACP | 95 | TMP | 41.00 |
| | 95 | LRN | 20.50 |
| 45 ACP | 200 | MTMP | 73.00 |
| | 200 | LSWC | 29.50 |
| | 230 | TMP | 72.00 |
| | 230 | LRN | 34.50 |
| 45 Long Colt | 250 | FPTMP | 70.00 |
| 44 | 240 | JHP | 72.30 |
| | 240 | SWC | 35.50 |
| 10mm | 175 | SWC | 28.00 |
| | 180 | PHP | 72.00 |
| | 180 | TMP | 60.00 |

TMP = Totally Metal Plated; FMJ = Full Metal Jacket; JHP = Jacketed Hollowpoint; JSP = Jacketed Softpoint; LDEW = Lead Double End Wadcutter; SWC = Semi-Wadcutter; LRN = Lead Round Nose; PHP = Plated Hollowpoint; MTMP = Match Totally Metal Plated; LSWC = Lead Semi-Wadcutter.

### MI-TE Pistol

| Caliber | Wgt. Grs. | Type | Price/500 | Price/1000 |
|---|---|---|---|---|
| 9mm | 125 | RN | $14.65 | $26.75 |
| 38 | 158 | SWC | 16.40 | 30.25 |
| 40 | 155 | SWC | 16.40 | 30.25 |
| 41 | 215 | SWC | 17.55 | 32.60 |
| 44 | 240 | SWC | 18.85 | 35.20 |
| 45 | 200 | SWC | 17.45 | 32.40 |
| | 230 | RN | 18.10 | 33.65 |
| | 255 | SWC | 19.50 | 36.50 |

RN = Round-Nose; SWC = Semi-Wadcutter.

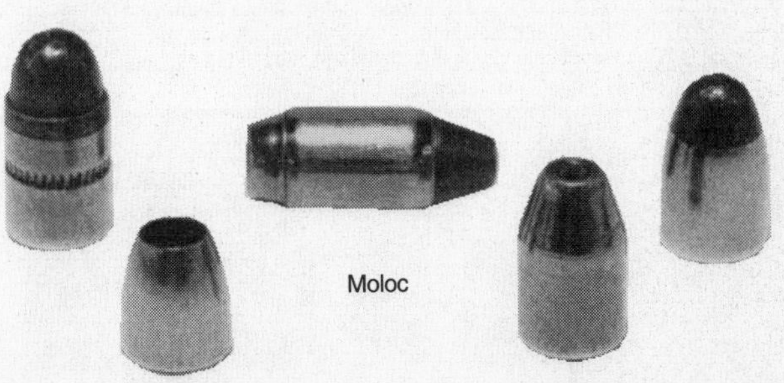

Moloc

### MOLOC Pistol Bullets

| Caliber | Wgt. Grs. | Type | Price/500 |
|---|---|---|---|
| 32 | 100 | SWC | $18.25 |
| 32-20 | 118 | FP | 18.25 |
| 30 Carb. | 115 | RN | 18.25 |
| 380 ACP | 95 | RN | 18.25 |
| 9mm | 125 | RN | 18.25 |
| | 125 | TC | 18.25 |
| 9mm/38 Super | 147 | HTC | 18.90 |
| 38 Super | 160 | RN | 18.90 |
| 38 | 125 | SWC | 18.25 |
| | 148 | BBWC | 18.90 |
| | 158 | SWC | 18.90 |
| | 158 | RN | 18.90 |
| | 180 | FP | 23.60 |
| 10mm | 140 | RNFP | 20.90 |
| | 155 | SWC | 20.90 |
| | 180 | SWC | 23.60 |
| | 180 | FP | 23.60 |
| 41 Mag. | 210 | SWC | 24.30 |
| 44-40 | 200 | FP | 24.30 |
| 44 Mag. | 215 | SWC | 24.30 |
| | 240 | SWC | 26.35 |
| | 275 | FP | 14.77/250 |
| | 300 | FP | 18.00/250 |
| 45 ACP | 155 | SWC | 20.90 |
| | 185 | SWC | 23.60 |
| | 200 | SWC | 24.30 |
| | 230 | RN | 24.95 |
| | 255 | SWC | 27.00 |
| 45 Long Colt | 250 | RNFP | 27.00 |
| 45 Colt/454 Casull | 300 | FP | 18.00/250 |
| 458 | 300 | FP | NA |
| | 405 | FP | NA |

SWC = Semi-Wadcutter; RN = Round Nose; TC = Truncated Cone; BBWC = Bevel Base Wadcutter; FP = Flat Point; RNFP = Round Nose Flat Point.

### MOLOC Swaged Pistol Bullets

| Caliber | Dia. | Wgt. Grs. | Type | Price/100 |
|---|---|---|---|---|
| 32 H&R Mag. | .312 | 85 | HP | $25.22 |
| | | 90-99 | HP | 25.73 |
| | | 100 | HP | 32.45 |
| | | 101-110 | HP | 32.82 |
| | | 90 | SP | 25.73 |
| | | 91-100 | SP | 32.45 |
| | | 101-110 | SP | 33.18 |
| | | 111-120 | SP | 33.55 |
| | | 121-130 | SP | 33.55 |
| | | 90 | FMJ | 36.64 |
| | | 110 | FMJ | 37.55 |
| | | 130 | LRBT | 19.00 |
| | | 100 | PL | 15.00 |
| | | 115 | PL | 15.73 |
| | | 100 | EL | 13.55 |
| | | 115 | EL | 14.27 |
| | .224 | 55-60 | RFJ | 21.91 |
| | | 55-60 | CJ | 23.55 |
| | | 55-60 | Lead | 13.18 |
| 6.5 | .268 | 157 | RNSP | .40/1 |

HP = Hollowpoint; SP = Softpoint; FMJ = Full Metal Jacket; LRBT = Lead Rebated Boattail; PL = Precision Lead; EL = Economy Lead; RNSP = Round Nose Softpoint.

# Section 5: Components



## NATIONAL BULLET CO.

| Caliber | Bullet Dia. | Bullet Wgt. Grs. | Type | Price Hard Cast | Price Copper Plate |
|---|---|---|---|---|---|
| 25 | .250 | 50 | RN | $23.00 | $36.50 |
| 32 | .312 | 77 | RN | 23.00 | 36.50 |
| | .312 | 95 | SWC | 23.00 | 36.50 |
| | .312 | 95 | WC | 23.00 | — |
| | .312 | 100 | HBWC | 25.00 | — |
| 7.62x39 | .311 | 155 | RN | 31.00 | 45.50 |
| 32/20 | .312 | 118 | FP | 25.00 | 39.50 |
| 30 | .308 | 120 | RN | 25.00 | 39.50 |
| | .308 | 165 | FP | 26.00* | 40.50* |
| 380 | .355 | 95 | RN | 23.00 | 36.50 |
| | .355 | 100 | TC | 24.00 | 38.50 |
| 9mm | .356 | 120 | TC | 25.00 | 39.50 |
| | .356 | 125 | RN | 25.00 | 39.50 |
| | .356 | 135 | RN | 26.00 | 40.50 |
| | .356 | 147 | RN | 27.00 | 41.50 |
| 9mm Makarov | .365 | 100 | RN | 24.00 | 38.50 |
| 38 | .357 | 141 | SWC | 26.00 | 40.50 |
| | .357 | 141 | BBWC | 26.00 | — |
| | .357 | 141 | DEWC | 26.00 | — |
| | .357 | 148 | HBWC | 26.00 | — |
| | .357 | 148 | DEWC | 26.00 | 40.50 |
| | .357 | 158 | SWC | 27.00 | 41.50 |
| | .357 | 158 | RN | 27.00 | 41.50 |
| | .357 | 158 | TC | 27.00 | 41.50 |
| | .357 | 180 | TC | 31.00 | 45.50 |
| | .357 | 200 | TC | 33.00 | 47.50 |
| | .357 | 200 | FP | 33.00 | 47.50 |
| 10mm | .401 | 140 | FP | 29.00 | 43.50 |
| | .401 | 155 | SWC | 30.00 | 44.50 |
| | .401 | 170 | SWC | 31.00 | 45.50 |
| | .401 | 180 | TC | 31.00 | 45.50 |
| | .401 | 200 | SWC | 33.00 | 47.50 |
| | .401 | 200 | TC | 33.00 | 47.50 |
| 38-40 | .401 | 180 | RNFP | 32.00 | 45.50 |
| 41 | .410 | 210 | FP | 36.00 | 49.50 |
| | .410 | 225 | SWC | 36.00 | 49.50 |
| 44-40 | .427 | 205 | SWC | 36.00 | 49.50 |
| 44 | .429 | 205 | SWC | 36.00 | 49.50 |
| | .429 | 190 | DEWC | 36.00 | 49.50 |
| | .429 | 205 | RNFP | 36.00 | 49.50 |
| | .429 | 240 | SWC | 37.00 | 50.50 |
| | .429 | 240 | RN | 37.00 | 50.50 |
| | .429 | 265 | SWC | 40.00 | 53.50 |
| | .429 | 300 | FP | 27.00* | 41.50* |
| 45 | .452 | 152 | SWC | 32.00 | 45.50 |
| | .452 | 185 | SWC | 32.00 | 45.50 |
| | .452 | 200 | SWC | 32.00 | 45.50 |
| | .452 | 200 | RNFP | 33.00 | 45.50 |
| | .452 | 215 | SWC | 34.00 | 47.50 |
| | .452 | 230 | RN | 35.00 | 48.50 |
| | .452 | 230 | FP | 35.00 | 48.50 |
| | .452 | .250 | RNFP | 39.00 | 51.50 |
| | .452 | 255 | SWC | 39.00 | 51.50 |
| | .452 | 300 | FP | 27.00* | 41.50* |
| 45-70 | .458 | 300 | FP | 31.00* | 45.50* |
| | .458 | 405 | FP | 38.00* | 52.50* |

RN = Round Nose; SWC = Semi-Wadcutter; WC = Wadcutter; FP = Flat Point; TC = Truncated Cone; BB = Bevel Base; DE = Double End; HBWC = Hollow Base Wadcutter. * = Price for 500.

## PENN Cast Pistol

| Caliber | Wgt. Grs. | Type | Price/500 | Price/1000 |
|---|---|---|---|---|
| 30 | 115 | RNBB | 16.00 | 30.00 |
| 32 | 75 | RNPB | 16.00 | 30.00 |
| | 95 | SWCBB | 16.00 | 30.00 |
| 380 | 95 | RNBB | 16.00 | 30.00 |
| | 100 | TCBT | 16.00 | 30.00 |
| 9mm | 95 | RNBB | 16.00 | 30.00 |
| | 115 | SWCBB | 16.00 | 30.00 |
| | 120 | TCBB | 16.00 | 30.00 |
| | 125 | RNBB | 16.00 | 30.00 |
| | 135 | RNBB | 19.00 | 35.00 |
| | 145 | RNBB | 19.00 | 35.00 |
| | 147 | RNFPBB | 17.00 | 32.00 |
| 38 | 100 | DBBWC | 17.00 | 32.00 |
| | 125 | TCBB | 16.00 | 30.00 |
| | 148 | DBBWC | 17.00 | 32.00 |
| | 158 | SWCBB | 17.00 | 32.00 |
| | 158 | TCBB | 17.00 | 32.00 |
| 10mm | 135 | SWCBB | 18.00 | 34.00 |
| | 155 | SWCBB | 18.00 | 34.00 |
| | 145 | RNBB | 18.00 | 34.00 |
| | 180 | RNFPBB | 19.00 | 36.00 |
| 38-40 | 180 | RNFPBB | 19.00 | 36.00 |
| 41 | 175 | SWCBB | 21.00 | 39.00 |
| | 210 | TCBT | 21.00 | 41.00 |
| 44-40 | 200 | RNFPBB | 21.00 | 41.00 |
| 44 | 180 | TCBB | 21.00 | 41.00 |
| | 185 | DBBWC | 21.00 | 41.00 |
| | 200 | SWCBB | 21.00 | 41.00 |
| | 200 | RNFPBB | 21.00 | 41.00 |
| | 240 | TCBB | 22.00 | 43.00 |
| | 240 | SWCBB | 22.00 | 43.00 |
| | 275 | RNFPBB | — | — |
| 45 | 152 | BB | 20.00 | 37.00 |
| | 180 | SBB | 20.00 | 38.00 |
| | 200 | SWCBB | 21.00 | 39.00 |
| | 230 | RNBB | 21.00 | 40.00 |
| | 230 | TCBB | 21.00 | 40.00 |
| | 255 | RNFPBB | 23.00 | 45.00 |
| 50-AE | 325 | TCBB | 45.00 | 85.00 |
| 357 | 180 | TCBB | 24.00 | 44.00 |
| | 210 | TCBB | 28.00 | 52.00 |
| 41 | 295 | TCBB | 50.00 | 80.00 |
| 44 | 320 | DCGTCBB | 50.00 | 80.00 |
| 45 | 300 | DCGTCBB | 40.00 | 70.00 |
| | 350 | TCBB | 60.00 | 110.00 |
| 454 | 340 | TCBB | 90.00 | 160.00 |
| 45-70 | 300 | FNPB | 60.00 | 130.00 |
| | 360 | FPBB | 65.00 | 140.00 |
| | 370 | SNBB | 65.00 | 140.00 |
| | 405 | FNBB | 60.00 | 150.00 |
| | 500 | RNPB | 75.00 | 175.00 |

RN = Round-Nose; BB = Bevel Base; PB = Plain Base; WC = Wadcutter; SWC = Semi-Wadcutter; FN = Flat Nose; DBB = Double Bevel Base; TC = Truncated Cone; BT = Boattail; FP = Flat Point; SBB = Short Bevel Base; FWC = Full Wadcutter; DCG = Double Crimp Grooves; SN = Spitzer Nose; GC = Gas Check.

National Bullet

## NORTHERN PRECISION Pistol

| Bullet | Wgt. Grs. | Type | Description | Price/Per |
|---|---|---|---|---|
| | | | **CALIBER: 358** | |
| | 200-300 | SP | .025, non-bonded | $20.00/25 |
| | 200-300 | SP | .025 bonded | 25.00/25 |
| | 200-300 | SP | .035, non-bonded | 20.00/25 |
| | 200-300 | SP | .035, bonded | 25.00/25 |
| | | | **CALIBER: 375** | |
| | 200-300 | SP | .025, non-bonded | 20.00/25 |
| | 200-300 | SP | .025, bonded | 25.00/25 |
| | 200-300 | SP | .035, non-bonded | 20.00/25 |
| | 200-300 | SP | .035, bonded | 25.00/25 |
| | 200-300 | | Baseguard | 14.00/50 |
| | 200-300 | RN | Thin jacket, non-bonded | 16.00/50 |
| | 200-300 | RN | Thin jacket, bonded | 25.00/25 |
| | 200-300 | | Flat-tip, thin jacket, non-bonded | 16.00/50 |
| | 200-300 | | Flat-tip, thin jacket, bonded | 25.00/25 |
| | 225-300 | | Poly-Tip, .025, non-bonded | 22.00/25 |
| | 225-300 | | Poly-Tip, .025, bonded | 27.00/25 |
| | | | **CALIBER: 429** | |
| | 180-330 | TC | Flat tip, thin jacket | 14.00/50 |
| | 255 | TC | Flat tip, thin jacket | 25.00/25 |
| | 150-325 | TC | Flat tip, base guard, self-cleaning | 14.00/50 |
| High Performance | 300-375 | TC | Flat tip, .025, bonded core | 25.00/25 |
| High Performance | 300-375 | TC | Flat tip, .025, non-bonded core | 20.00/25 |
| High Performance | 300-375 | TC | Flat tip, .035, bonded core | 25.00/25 |
| High Performance | 300-375 | TC | Flat tip, .035, non-bonded | 20.00/25 |
| | 240-350 | SP | Single shot, thin jacket | 16.00/50 |
| | 240-350 | | Single shot, thin jacket, bonded | 25.00/50 |
| | 275-325 | SP | Base guard, self-cleaning | 14.00/50 |
| | 300-375 | SP | .025, non-bonded | 20.00/25 |
| Polly Tip | 205 | TC | Thin jacket, regular core | 16.00/50 |
| Sabre Star | 215 | TC | Thin jacket, bonded core | 27.00/50 |

HP = Hollowpoint; SP = Spitzer; FT = Flat Tip; RN = Round-Nose; TC = Truncated Cone.

## OREGON TRAIL Cast Bullets

| Caliber | Wgt. Grs. | Type | Price/100 | Price/5000 |
|---|---|---|---|---|
| 32-20 | 115 | FPBB | $5.00 | $15.00 |
| 9mm | 115 | RNBB | 5.00 | 15.00 |
| | 122 | FPBB | 5.00 | 15.25 |
| | 124 | RNBB | 5.00 | 15.25 |
| | 135 | RNBB | 5.00 | 15.25 |
| | 147 | FPBB | 5.00 | 15.25 |
| 38 | 125 | FPBB | 5.00 | 15.25 |
| | 145 | RNBB | 5.00 | 16.00 |
| | 148 | WCDBB, SGG | 5.00 | 16.00 |
| | 158 | | 5.00 | 16.00 |
| 38-40 | 180 | RNFPBB | 5.00 | 16.00 |
| 10mm | 155 | RNSWCBB | 6.00 | 16.00 |
| | 170 | SWCBB | 6.00 | 16.50 |
| | 180 | FPBB | 6.00 | 17.50 |
| 41 | 215 | SWCBB | 6.00 | 19.00 |
| 44-40 | 200 | RNFPBB | 6.00 | 16.00 |
| 44 | 240 | SWCBB | 6.00 | 21.00 |
| 45 | 180 | SWCBB | 6.00 | 17.00 |
| | 200 | SWCBB | 6.25 | 18.50 |
| | 230 | RNBB | 6.00 | 21.00 |
| | 250 | RNFPBB | 6.25 | 23.00 |
| | 300 | FPBB | 6.75 | 24.00 |
| 45-70 | 350 | FPBB | 7.50 | 35.00 |

FP = Flat Point; BB = Bevel Base; RN = Round Nose; WC = Wadcutter; SWC = Semi-Wadcutter; DBB = Double Bevel Base.

## PMC/STARFIRE

| Caliber | Wgt. Grs. | Type |
|---|---|---|
| **Pistol/Revolver/Rifle Bullets** | | |
| 380 Auto | 95 | SFHP |
| 38 Special | 125 | SFHP |
| 357 Magnum | 150 | SFHP |
| 9mm | 124 | SFHP |
| 40 S&W/10mm | 180 | SFHP |
| | 155 | SFHP |
| 44 Magnum | 240 | SFHP |
| 45 Auto | 230 | SFHP |
| 30-30 Win. | 150 | SFHP |
| **Pistol/Revolver Bullets** | | |
| 380 Auto | 90 | FMJ |
| 38/357 | 110 | JHP |
| | 132 | FMJ |
| | 125 | JHP |
| | 158 | JSP |
| 9mm | 124 | FMJ |
| | 115 | FMJ |
| | 115 | JSP |
| 40 S&W/10mm | 165 | TC/FMJ |
| | 170 | JHP |
| | 200 | TC/FMJ |
| 41 Rem. Mag. | 210 | JHP |
| 44 Rem. Mag. | 240 | TC/SP |
| | 240 | SWC/GCK |
| 45 Auto | 185 | JHP |
| | 200 | FMJ/SWC |
| 45 Auto | 230 | FMJ |
| **Plated Pistol/Revolver Bullets** | | |
| 9mm | 115 | RN |
| | 124 | RN |
| | 147 | RN |
| 38/357 | 125 | TC |
| | 158 | TC |
| 40 S&W | 155 | TC |
| | 165 | TC |
| | 180 | TC |
| 45 Auto | 185 | TC |
| | 200 | SWC |

Oregon Trail Pistol Bullets

## RED CEDAR Swaged Pistol

| Caliber | Wgt. Grs. | Type | Price/50 |
|---|---|---|---|
| 357 | 160 | SIL | $17.20 |
| | 175 | FN | 17.70 |
| | 200 | SWCSN | 17.30 |
| | 200 | HP | 18.50 |
| 357 | 230 | SN,HP | 18.50 |
| | 240 | SN,HP | 18.70 |
| | 240 | SNB,HPB | 22.75 |
| | 260 | SN,HP | 19.20 |
| 44 | 245 | HP,SN | 18.50 |
| | 245 | TXHP,TXSN | 18.50 |
| | 265 | SNB | 23.70 |
| | 275 | HP,SN | 19.50 |
| | 275 | TXSN | 27.10 |
| | 300 | HP,SN | 23.70 |
| | 315 | SN | 20.60 |

SIL = Silhouette; FN = Flat Nose; SWC = Semi-Wadcutter; SN = Soft Nose; HP = Hollowpoint.

Red Cedar

## RAINIER BALLISTICS

| Caliber | Wgt. Grs. | Type |
|---|---|---|
| 9mm | 95 | RN |
| | 115 | RN |
| | 124 | FP |
| | 124 | RN |
| | 147 | RN |
| 38 Super Auto | 130 | RN |
| | 151 | RN |
| 38 | 125 | FP |
| | 148 | DEWC |
| | 158 | FP |
| | 158 | RN |
| | 158 | HP |
| 40/10mm | 155 | FP |
| | 180 | FP |
| | 180 | HP |
| 41 | 220 | FP |
| 44 | 240 | FP |
| | 240 | HP |
| 45 | 185 | FP |
| | 200 | SWC |
| | 200 | FP |
| | 200 | HP |
| | 230 | RN |
| 45 LC | 250 | FP |

RN = Round Nose; FP = Flat Point; DEWC = Double End Wadcutter; HP = Hollowpoint; SWC = Semi-Wadcutter.

## RANGER Pistol

| Caliber | Dia. | Wgt. Grs. | Type | Price/1000 |
|---|---|---|---|---|
| 380 | .355 | 95 | RNBB | $25.00 |
| 9mm | .365 | 100 | Makarov | 26.00 |
| | .356 | 115 | RNBB | 25.00 |
| | .356 | 125 | RNBB | 25.00 |
| | .356 | 147 | FP | 26.00 |
| 38 Super | .357 | 147 | FP | 26.00 |
| 38 Special | .358 | 147 | FP | 26.00 |
| 38/357 | .358 | 148 | WCDBB | 26.00 |
| | .358 | 158 | SWCBB | 26.00 |
| | .358 | 158 | RNBB | 26.00 |
| 40/10mm | .401 | 155 | SWCBB | 28.00 |
| | .401 | 155 | RNBB | 28.00 |
| | .401 | 175 | SWCBB | 31.00 |
| 44-40 | .427 | 200 | RNFP | 32.00 |
| 44 | .430 | 240 | SWCBB | 35.00 |
| 45 | .452 | 150 | SWCBB | 28.00 |
| | .452 | 185 | SWCBB | 32.00 |
| | .452 | 200 | SWCBB | 32.00 |
| | .452 | 230 | RNBB | 35.00 |
| | .452 | 250 | RNFPBB | 37.00 |

RNBB = Round-Nose Bevel Base; FP = Flat Point; WCDBB = Wadcutter Double Bevel Base; SWCBB = Semi-Wadcutter Bevel Base; RNFP = Round-Nose Flat Point.

## REMINGTON Pistol Bullets

| Caliber | Wgt. Grs. | Type | Price/2000 |
|---|---|---|---|
| 25 | 50 | MC | $85.75 |
| 32 | 71 | MC | 92.65 |
| 9mm | 124 | Sabre HP | 98.10 |
| | 147 | Sabre HP | 122.30 |
| | 115 | JHP BFB | 85.50 |
| | 115 | MC BFB | 80.55 |
| | 115 | TEMC | 82.50 |
| | 124 | JHP BFB | 90.90 |
| | 124 | MC | 85.50 |
| | 124 | TEMC | 87.70 |
| | 147 | JHP | 113.90 |
| | 147 | MC Match | 113.90 |
| | 147 | TEMC | 116.60 |
| 38 ACP | 102 | Sabre HP | 104.75 |
| | 88 | JHP BFB | 100.10 |
| | 95 | MC BFB | 100.10 |
| | 95 | TEMC | 102.55 |
| | 130 | MC | 100.10 |
| 357 | 125 | Sabre HP | 100.65 |
| 357 Max. | 180 | SJHP | 133.90 |
| 38/357 | 110 | SJHP | 91.20 |
| | 125 | SJHP | 90.90 |
| | 125 | JSP | 95.85 |
| | 130 | TEMC | 102.55 |
| | 140 | SJHP | 104.75 |
| | 158 | SP | 109.70 |
| | 158 | SJHP | 109.70 |
| | 158 | LD SWC | 53.35 |
| | 158 | TEMC | 112.65 |
| | 125 | Sabre | 99.50 |
| 38 | 148 | LD WC | 50.90 |
| | 158 | LD RN | 52.90 |
| | 158 | LD SWC | 55.10 |
| 40/10mm | 165 | Sabre | 78.10* |
| | 180 | Sabre | 87.20* |
| | 155 | JHP | 74.35* |
| | 180 | JHP | 80.05* |
| | 180 | MC | 79.70* |
| | 180 | TEMC | 81.65* |
| 41 | 170 | SJHP | 72.65* |
| | 200 | SJHP | 76.70* |
| | 210 | SP | 78.55* |
| 44 | 180 | SJHP | 152.45 |
| | 180 | JSP | 152.45 |
| | 210 | SJHP | 76.70* |
| | 240 | SP | 84.25* |
| | 240 | SJHP | 84.25* |
| | 240 | LD | 35.80* |
| 45 ACP | 185 | Sabre | 162.60 |
| | 230 | Sabre | 84.90* |
| | 185 | MC WC | 161.60 |
| | 185 | JHP | 157.90 |
| | 230 | MC BFB | 73.60* |
| | 230 | TEMC | 75.50* |
| 45 Colt | 250 | LD | 37.30* |

* = per 1000
SJHP = Semi-jacketed Hollow Point; JHP = Jacketed Hollow Point; SWC = Semi-Wadcutter; WC = Wadcutter; RN = Roundnose; LD = Lead; TEMC = Totally Encapsulated Metal Cased; MC = Metal Cased; SJSP = Semi-Jacketed Soft Point; BFB = Develed Flat Base.

## FRED ROLSTON Handgun Bullets

| Caliber | Wgt. Grs. | Type | Price/500 | Price/1000 |
|---|---|---|---|---|
| | | **Hard Cast** | | |
| 9x18 | 93 | RN | $12.50 | $22.00 |
| 30 Carb. | 120 | RNBB | 12.50 | 22.00 |
| | 155 | RN | 12.50 | 22.00 |
| 380 | 95 | RNBB | 12.50 | 22.00 |
| 9mm | 125 | | 12.50 | 22.00 |
| | 147 | FPBB | 13.00 | 23.00 |
| 38 | 125 | RNBB | 12.50 | 22.00 |
| | 148 | WCBB | 13.00 | 23.00 |
| | 148 | DEWCBB | 13.00 | 23.00 |
| | 158 | SWCBB | 13.25 | 23.50 |
| | 158 | RNBB | 13.25 | 23.50 |
| 40/10mm | 155 | RNSWC | 13.25 | 23.00 |
| | 155 | SWC | 14.50 | 23.50 |
| | 170 | SWCBB | 15.00 | 27.00 |
| | 200 | SWCBB | 14.75 | 27.50 |
| 41 | 215 | SWCBB | 16.25 | 29.50 |
| 44 | 240 | SWCBB | 16.75 | 30.50 |
| 45 | 160 | SWCFB | 13.25 | 24.00 |
| | 185 | SWCBB | 16.00 | 27.00 |
| | 200 | SWCBB | 15.25 | 27.50 |
| | 230 | RNBB | 16.75 | 30.50 |
| | 255 | SWCBB | 17.25 | 31.50 |
| | | **Copper Plated** | | |
| 9x18 | 93 | RN | 16.00 | 29.00 |
| 30 | 120 | RN | 18.75 | 34.50 |
| 30 Carb. | 115 | RN | 16.00 | 29.00 |
| | 120 | RNBB | 16.00 | 29.00 |
| 380 | 95 | RNBB | 16.00 | 29.00 |
| 9mm | 125 | RNBB | 18.75 | 34.50 |
| | 125 | RNBB | 16.00 | 29.00 |
| | 147 | FPBB | 17.00 | 31.00 |
| 38 | 125 | RNBB | 16.25 | 29.50 |
| | 158 | SWCBB | 17.25 | 31.50 |
| | 158 | RNBB | 17.25 | 31.50 |
| 40/10mm | 155 | RN | 17.25 | 31.00 |
| | 155 | SWC | 17.25 | 31.00 |
| | 155 | SWC | 16.75 | 30.50 |
| | 170 | SWCBB | 19.00 | 35.00 |
| | 200 | SWCBB | 19.25 | 35.50 |
| 41 | 215 | SWCBB | 20.75 | 38.50 |
| 44 | 240 | SWCBB | 21.75 | 40.50 |
| 45 | 160 | SWCFB | 17.25 | 32.00 |
| | 185 | SWCBB | 19.00 | 35.00 |
| | 230 | RNBB | 21.75 | 40.50 |
| | 255 | SWCBB | 22.25 | 41.50 |

RN = Round Nose; BB = Bevel Base; FP = Flat Point; WC = Wadcutter; DE = Double End; SWC = Semi-Wadcutter.

Ranger

## SCHARCH Swaged Pistol

| Caliber | Wgt. Grs. | Type | Price/100 | Price/500 |
|---|---|---|---|---|
| 38/357 | 158 | SWC | $5.75 | $23.95 |
| | 158 | RN | 5.75 | 23.95 |
| | 125 | SWC | 4.95 | 20.95 |
| 38 Spl. | 148 | HBWC | 5.25 | 22.95 |
| | 148 | DEWC | 5.25 | 22.95 |
| | 100 | DEWC | 4.95 | 19.45 |
| 44 Mag. | 240 | SWC | 7.75 | 29.95 |
| 9mm | 125 | RN | 4.95 | 19.95 |
| 380 Auto | 115 | RN | 4.75 | 18.95 |
| 40 S&W | 230 | SWC | 6.45 | 25.95 |
| 45 ACP | 230 | RN | 7.45 | 29.95 |
| | 200 | SWC | 6.95 | 27.95 |
| | | **TOTAL COPPER PLATED** | | |
| 380 Auto | 95 | RN | 5.75 | 23.95 |
| 9mm | 115 | RN | 5.75 | 23.95 |
| | 124 | RN | 5.95 | 24.95 |
| | 147 | RN | 6.95 | 27.95 |
| 38/357 | 148 | DEWC | 6.75 | 26.95 |
| | 158 | SWC | 6.95 | 28.95 |
| | 158 | RN | 6.95 | 28.95 |
| 10mm/40 S&W | 155 | SWC | 7.75 | 29.95 |
| | 165 | SWC | 7.95 | 30.95 |
| | 180 | SWC | 8.25 | 32.95 |
| 44 Mag. | 240 | SWC | 9.75 | 39.95 |
| 45 Auto | 200 | SWC | 8.95 | 34.95 |
| | 230 | RN | 9.25 | 37.95 |
| 30 Carbine | 110 | RN | 6.95 | 28.95 |
| 7.62x39 | 113 | RN | 8.25 | 31.95 |

RN = Round-Nose; SWC = Semi-Wadcutter; HBWC = Hollow Base Wadcutter; DEWC = Double End Wadcutter.

## SCHROEDER Obsolete Pistol

| Caliber | Dia. | Wgt. Grs. | Type | Price/100 |
|---|---|---|---|---|
| 7mm Nambu | .280 | 71 | FMJ | $22.00 |
| 7.62, 7.63, 7.65, 30 Tokarev | .308 .309 .310 | 85 | HP | 14.00 |
| | | 90 | HP | 14.00 |
| | | 100 | HP | 14.00 |
| 7.62, 7.63, 7.65, 30 Mauser | .308 .309 .310 | 85 | HP | 14.00 |
| | | 90 | HP | 14.00 |
| | | 100 | HP | 14.00 |
| 7.62, 7.63, 7.65, 30 Luger | .308 .309 .310 | 85 | HP | 14.00 |
| | | 90 | HP | 14.00 |
| | | 100 | HP | 14.00 |
| 8mm Nambu | .320 | 85 | HP,SP | 16.00 |
| | | 90 | HP,SP | 16.00 |
| | | 100 | HP,SP | 16.00 |
| | | 110 | HP,SP | 16.00 |
| | | 110 | FMJ | 16.00 |
| 9mm Makarov | .363 | 90 | HP | 15.00 |
| | | 100 | HP | 15.00 |
| | | 95 | FMJ | 15.00 |
| | | 100 | FMJ | 15.00 |
| | | 95 | HC | 15.00 |
| | | 100 | HC | 15.00 |
| | | 95 | SP | 15.00 |
| | | 100 | SP | 15.00 |

FMJ = Full Metal Jacket; HP = Hollowpoint; SP = Soft Point; HC = Hollow Cavity.

## 3-D Bullets

| Caliber | Diameter | Wgt. Grs. | Type |
|---|---|---|---|
| 38 Spl. | .358 | 158 | SWC |
| | .358 | 158 | RN |
| | .358 | 125 | SWC |
| | .358 | 148 | HBWC |
| | .358 | 148 | DEWC |
| | .358 | 100 | DEWC |
| 357 Mag. | .358 | 158 | SWC |
| 44 Mag. | .430 | 240 | SWC |
| 9mm Luger | .356 | 125 | RN |
| 380 Auto | .356 | 115 | RN |
| 40 S&W | .400 | 180 | SWC |
| 45 ACP | .452 | 230 | RN |
| | .452 | 200 | SWC |

RN = Round Nose; SWC = Semi-Wadcutter; HBWC = Hollow Base Wadcutter; DEWC = Double End Wadcutter.

3-D Swaged Bullets

Winchester Silvertip

## WINCHESTER Pistol Bullets

| Caliber | Wgt. Grs. | Type | Knurl | Price/100 | Price/500 |
|---|---|---|---|---|---|
| 380 | 95 | FMJ | NA | $7.79 | $31.99 |
| 38 | 130 | FMJ | .370 | 8.79 | 32.99 |
| | 145 | STHP | NA | 15.99 | — |
| 9mm | 115 | FMJFB | NA | 6.99 | 27.99 |
| | 115 | FMJ | NA | 6.99 | 27.00 |
| | 115 | JHP | .370 | 7.49 | 29.99 |
| | 115 | STHP | NA | 12.79 | — |
| | 124 | FMJ | NA | 7.79 | 29.99 |
| | 147 | JHP | NA | 10.49 | 39.99 |
| 38/357 | 110 | JHP | .270 | 7.79 | 28.99 |
| | 125 | JHP | .270 | 7.99 | 31.99 |
| | 145 | STHP | NA | 15.99 | — |
| | 158 | JHP | .270 | 9.49 | 36.99 |
| 40/10mm | 155 | STHP | NA | 19.99 | — |
| | 175 | STHP | NA | 19.49 | — |
| | 180 | JHP | NA | 13.49 | 52.99 |
| | 180 | FMJTC | NA | 13.49 | 54.99 |
| 44 | 210 | STHP | NA | 20.99 | — |
| | 240 | HSP | .300 | 14.99 | 59.99 |
| 45 | 230 | FMJ | NA | 12.79 | 48.99 |
| | 230 | JHP | NA | 16.79 | 65.99 |

FMJ = Full Metal Jacket; STHP = Silver Tip Hollowpoint; FB = Flat Base; JHP = Jacketed Hollowpoint; TC = Truncated Cone.
From Midway Arms.

## TRU-FLIGHT

| Caliber | Wgt. Grs. | Type | Price/500 |
|---|---|---|---|
| **TRU-FLIGHT PLUS** | | | |
| 380 | 95 | RN | $23.00 |
| 9mm | 115 | RN | 23.00 |
| | 125 | RN | 25.00 |
| 38 Super/9mm | 147 | RN | 28.00 |
| 38 | 125 | FP | 25.00 |
| | 148 | DEWC | 27.00 |
| | 158 | SWC | 28.00 |
| 10mm | 155 | TC | 34.00 |
| | 180 | TC | 36.00 |
| 41 | 220 | SWC | 38.00 |
| 44 | 240 | FP | 42.00 |
| 45 | 185 | TC | 36.00 |
| | 200 | SWC | 38.00 |
| | 230 | RN | 38.00 |
| 45 LC | 250 | FP | 42.00 |
| **HARD CAST MATCH QUALITY** | | | |
| 32 | 95 | WC | $17.00 |
| 380 | 90 | RN | 17.00 |
| 9mm | 125 | BBTC | 17.00 |
| | 125 | RN | 17.00 |
| 38 Super | 140 | FBSWC | 18.00 |
| | 145 | BBRN | 18.00 |
| 38 Super/9mm | 145 | BBRN | 18.00 |
| 38 | 148 | DEWC | 18.00 |
| | 148 | HBWC | 18.00 |
| | 155 | BBSWC | 18.00 |
| | 180 | FP | 20.00 |
| | 200 | FP | 22.00 |
| 10mm/40 | 155 | BBSWC | 20.00 |
| | 175 | BBSWC | 20.00 |
| 41 | 210 | BBTC | 22.00 |
| 44 | 225 | BBTC | 22.00 |
| 45 | 225 | BBTC | 22.00 |
| | 225 | WC | 22.00 |
| | 165 | FBSWC | 20.00 |
| | 180 | FBSWC | 20.00 |
| | 185 | FBSWC | 20.00 |
| | 200 | BBSWC | 20.00 |
| | 225 | BBSWC | 25.00 |
| | 230 | RN | 25.00 |

RN = Round Nose; FP = Flat Point; DEWC = Double End Wadcutter; SWC = Semi-Wadcutter; TC = Truncated Cone; WC = Wadcutter; BBTC = Bevel Base Truncated Cone; FBSWC = Flat Base Semi-Wadcutter; BBRN = Bevel Base Round Nose; HBWC = Hollow Base Wadcutter; BBTC = Bevel Base Truncated Cone; BBSWC = Bevel Base Semi-Wadcutter.

## TOMBSTONE Copper Plated Bullets

| Caliber | Wgt. Grs. | Type | Price/500 | Price/1000 |
|---|---|---|---|---|
| 30 M1 Carb. | 110 | RN | $27.35 | $50.63 |
| 380 ACP | 100 | RN | 24.01 | 44.46 |
| 9mm | 115 | RN | 24.01 | 44.46 |
| | 122 | RN | 24.01 | 44.46 |
| | 124 | RN | 24.01 | 44.46 |
| 38/357 | 158 | SWC | 27.35 | 50.63 |
| | 158 | RN | 27.35 | 50.63 |
| 40 S&W/10mm | 165 | RN | 31.34 | 58.04 |
| | 180 | FP | 34.68 | 64.22 |
| 44 | 240 | FP | 41.35 | 76.57 |
| 45 | 200 | SWC | 38.02 | 70.39 |
| | 200 | RN | 38.02 | 70.39 |
| | 230 | RN | 39.34 | 72.86 |

RN = Round Nose; FP = Flat Point; SWC = Semi-Wadcutter.

## WESTERN NEVADA Pistol

| Caliber | Wgt. Grs. | Type | Price/500 |
|---|---|---|---|
| | **HARD CAST** | | |
| 32 | 78 | RN | $32.00 |
| | 95 | SWC | 32.00 |
| 380 | 95 | RN | 32.00 |
| 9mm | 122 | FP | 32.00 |
| | 125 | RN | 32.00 |
| | 135 | RN | 32.00 |
| 38 | 148 | WC | 32.00 |
| | 158 | RN | 32.00 |
| | 158 | SWC | 32.00 |
| 38 Super | 160 | RN | 32.00 |
| | 180 | FP | 42.00 |
| 10mm/40 S&W | 155 | SWC | 34.00 |
| | 175 | SWC | 42.00 |
| | 180 | FP | 42.00 |
| 41 | 215 | SWC | 42.00 |
| 44 | 215 | SWC | 42.00 |
| | 240 | SWC | 42.00 |
| | 240 | RN | 42.00 |
| | 300 | FP | 52.00 |
| 45 | 180 | SWC | 41.00 |
| | 185 | SWC | 42.00 |
| | 200 | SWC | 42.00 |
| | 200 | RN | 42.00 |
| | 225 | FP | 44.00 |
| | 230 | RN | 44.00 |
| | 250 | RNFP | 43.00 |
| | 255 | SWC | 46.00 |
| 38-40 | 180 | FP | 42.00 |
| 44-40 | 200 | RNFP | 42.00 |
| 45-70 | 305 | FP | 51.00 |
| | 405 | FP | 62.00 |
| 30 Carbine | 115 | RN | 34.00 |
| | **COPPER** | | |
| 380 | 100 | RN | 32.00 |
| 9mm | 115 | RN | 40.00 |
| | 122 | FP | 41.00 |
| | 124 | RN | 41.00 |
| | 147 | RN | 44.00 |
| 38 | 148 | WC | 46.00 |
| | 158 | RN | 51.00 |
| | 158 | FP | 51.00 |
| | 158 | SWC | 51.00 |
| 41 | 210 | FP | 66.00 |
| 10mm/40 S&W | 165 | RN | 54.00 |
| | 180 | FP | 60.00 |
| 44 | 240 | FP | 69.00 |
| 45 | 185 | FP | 61.00 |
| | 200 | SWC | 65.00 |
| | 200 | RN | 65.00 |
| | 230 | RN | 68.00 |
| 30 Carbine | 110 | RN | 44.00 |
| 7.62x39 | 110 | RN | 53.00 |

RN = Round-Nose; SWC = Semi-Wadcutter; WC = Wadcutter; FP = Flat Point.

## STAR MASTER

| Caliber | Wgt. Grs. | Type | Price/1000 |
|---|---|---|---|
| | **Swaged** | | |
| 38 Spl. | 100 | HBWC | $18.75 |
| | 100 | HBWC Match | 23.75 |
| | 148 | HBWC | 21.25 |
| | 148 | HBWC Match | 26.50 |
| | 158 | SWC | 22.50 |
| | 158 | SWC Match | 27.50 |
| 45 Auto | 185 | SWC | 25.50 |
| | 185 | SWHP | 25.50 |
| | 200 | SWC | 26.50 |
| | 230 | RN | 27.50 |
| | **Jacketed** | | |
| 9mm | 115 | FMJ | 33.00 |
| | 124 | FMJ | 34.00 |
| | 125 | JSP | 34.50 |
| | 147 | FMJ | 35.50 |
| | 147 | TC | 35.50 |
| 38 Spl. | 125 | JHP | 33.00 |
| | 130 | FMJ | 34.00 |
| | 158 | JHP | 37.00 |
| 38 Super | 115 | FMJ | 33.00 |
| | 124 | FMJ | 34.00 |
| | 135 | FMJ | 34.50 |
| 40 S&W/10mm | 165 | JHP | 49.50 |
| | 180 | JHP | 49.50 |
| | 180 | FMJ | 47.00 |
| 44 | 240 | JHP | 62.50 |
| 45 ACP | 185 | JHP | 53.00 |
| | 230 | JHP | 54.00 |
| | 230 | FMJ | 52.00 |
| 380 | 95 | FMJ | 33.00 |
| 357 SIG | 125 | FMJ | 33.00 |

From Star Master

## TOMBSTONE Hard Cast Bullets

| Caliber | Wgt. Grs. | Type | Price/500 | Price/1000 |
|---|---|---|---|---|
| 30 M1 Carb. | 115 | | $17.55 | $32.50 |
| 380 | 92 | RN | 16.85 | 31.20 |
| 9mm | 115 | RN | 17.55 | 32.50 |
| | 125 | RN | 17.55 | 32.50 |
| | 135 | RN | 18.25 | 33.80 |
| 38/357 | 148 | WC | 18.39 | 34.06 |
| | 158 | RN | 18.39 | 34.06 |
| | 158 | SWC | 18.39 | 34.06 |
| 38-40 | 180 | RNFT | 22.89 | 42.38 |
| 40/10mm | 155 | SWC | 18.39 | 34.06 |
| | 175 | SWC | 19.13 | 37.28 |
| 41 | 215 | SWC | 23.31 | 43.16 |
| 44 | 240 | SWC | 24.99 | 46.28 |
| | 300 | TR | 16.29 | 30.16 |
| 44/40 | 205 (.428) | RNFT | 23.45 | 43.42 |
| | 205 (.429) | RNFT | 23.45 | 43.42 |

RN = Round Nose; SWC = Semi-Wadcutter; FT = Flat Tip; TR = Truncated.

## TOMBSTONE Swaged Bullets

| Caliber | Wgt. Grs. | Type | Price/500 | Price/1000 |
|---|---|---|---|---|
| 38/357 | 148 | HBWC | $18.39 | $34.05 |
| | 158 | SWC | 18.39 | 34.05 |
| 45 ACP | 200 | SWC | 22.18 | 41.08 |

HBWC = Hollow Base Wadcutter; SWC = Semi-Wadcutter.

## ALPHA LAFRANCK Jacketed Bullets

| Jacket | Wgt. Grs. | Type | Price/50 |
|---|---|---|---|
| | | **CALIBER: 458** | |
| RJ | 300 | FP,HP,SP | $14.00 |
| | 400 | FP,HP,SP | 18.00 |
| SJ | 400 | FP,SP | 20.00 |
| HJ | 350 | FP,SP | 20.00 |
| | 500 | SP | 20.00 |
| TJ | 400 | SP,FN | 20.00/25 |
| | 437 | SP,FN | 20.00/25 |
| | 450 | SP,FN | 22.00/25 |
| | 500 | SP | 22.00/25 |
| | 550 | SP | 22.00/25 |
| PJ | 250 | FP,SP MACH II | 15.00 |
| | 325 | FP,HP,SP | 15.00 |
| | 350 | FP,HP,SP | 16.00 |
| | 375 | FP,HP,SP | 17.00 |

FP = Flat Point; HP = Hollowpoint; SP=Spitzer; FN = Flat Nose.

## ALPHA LAFRANCK Swaged Lead Bullets

| Caliber | Wgt. Grs. | Price/50 |
|---|---|---|
| 430 | 240-370 | $12.50 |
| 452 | 250-400 | 12.50 |
| 458 | 250-400 | 12.50 |
| 458 | 401-500 | 15.00 |
| 458 | 501-600 | 17.50 |
| 458 | 601-650 | 22.00 |

Alpha LaFranck 458 Spitzers

## ALLRED

| Wgt. Grs. | Type | Price/Per |
|---|---|---|
| | **CALIBER: 224** | |
| 50 | TJ-OT, TC-OT | $12.00/25 |
| 52 | TM-OT | 14.00/100 |
| | DJ-OT, DC-OT | 11.00/25 |
| 55 | TJ-SF, TC-SF | 12.00/25 |
| 60 | DC-OT | 11.00/25 |
| | TJ-LT, TC-LT | 12.00/25 |
| 65 | DC-OT, DJ-OT | 11.00/25 |
| 70 | DC-OT, DJ-OT | 11.00/25 |
| | DJ-LT, DC-OT | 11.00/25 |
| 75 | DC-OT, DJ-LT | 11.00/25 |
| | DC-LT, DJ-SF | 11.00/25 |
| | DC-SF, DJ-OT | 11.00/25 |
| 80 | DC-OT, DC-LT | 11.00/25 |
| | DJ-OT, DJ-SF | 11.00/25 |
| | DJ-LT | 11.00/25 |
| 85 | DC-OT, DJ-OT | 11.00/25 |
| | DC-SF, DJ-SF | 11.00/25 |
| 90 | DC-LT, DJ-LT | 11.00/25 |

Bullet Construction: TM = Single metal jacket; DC = Dual metal jackets, dual core (224); Outer metal jacket, inner copper jacket, dual core (308); DJ = Dual metal jacket, single core (224); Outer metal jacket, inner copper jacket, single core (308); TJ = Triple metal jacket; TC = Triple metal jacket, dual core; SB, CL, SR = Outer metal jacket, inner copper jacket; TSD = Single copper jacket; TDC = Dual copper jacket, dual core; TSB, TCL = Dual copper jacket; LT = Lead tip; OT = Open tip; SF = Small flat tip.

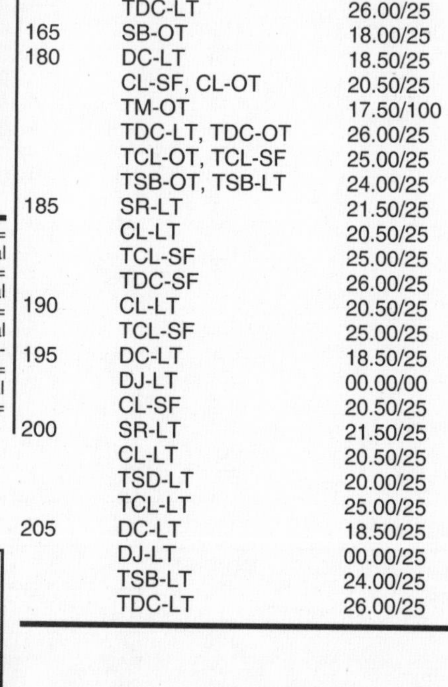

| Wgt. Grs. | Type | Price/Per |
|---|---|---|
| | **CALIBER: 308** | |
| 135 | SB-OT | $18.00/25 |
| 140 | SB-OT | 18.00/25 |
| 145 | SB-SF | 18.00/25 |
| 150 | SB-OT | 18.00/25 |
| | TSD-OT | 20.00/25 |
| | TSB-OT | 24.00/25 |
| | TDC-OT | 26.00/25 |
| 155 | SB-LT | 18.00/25 |
| | TSD-LT | 20.00/25 |
| | TSB-LT | 24.00/25 |
| | TDC-LT | 26.00/25 |
| 165 | SB-OT | 18.00/25 |
| 180 | DC-LT | 18.50/25 |
| | CL-SF, CL-OT | 20.50/25 |
| | TM-OT | 17.50/100 |
| | TDC-LT, TDC-OT | 26.00/25 |
| | TCL-OT, TCL-SF | 25.00/25 |
| | TSB-OT, TSB-LT | 24.00/25 |
| 185 | SR-LT | 21.50/25 |
| | CL-LT | 20.50/25 |
| | TCL-SF | 25.00/25 |
| | TDC-SF | 26.00/25 |
| 190 | CL-LT | 20.50/25 |
| | TCL-SF | 25.00/25 |
| 195 | DC-LT | 18.50/25 |
| | DJ-LT | 00.00/00 |
| | CL-SF | 20.50/25 |
| 200 | SR-LT | 21.50/25 |
| | CL-LT | 20.50/25 |
| | TSD-LT | 20.00/25 |
| | TCL-LT | 25.00/25 |
| 205 | DC-LT | 18.50/25 |
| | DJ-LT | 00.00/25 |
| | TSB-LT | 24.00/25 |
| | TDC-LT | 26.00/25 |

Allred Bullets

## ARMFIELD

| Caliber | Wgt. Grs. | Type | Price/Per |
|---|---|---|---|
| | | **Plainsbond** | |
| 6mm, 25, 6.5mm, 270, 7mm, 308 | up to 140 | FB-OT,SP,RN | $23.91/25 |
| | | RBT(VLD)-OT,SP,RN | 31.30/25 |
| | 140+ | | 25.01 |
| | 180+ | | 34.38 |
| | | **Fragcore** | |
| 6mm, 25, 6.5mm, 270, 7mm, 308 | | FB-OT | $25.85/100 |
| | | RBT(VLD)-OT | 29.15/100 |
| | | **Standard Solid Lead Core** | |
| 6mm, 25, 6.5 270, 7mm, 308 | | FB-OT,SP,RN | $20.90/100 |
| | | RBT(VLD)-OT,SP,RN | 23.10/100 |

FB=Flat Base; OT=Open Tip; RN=Round Nose; RBT=Rebated Boattail; VLD=Very Low Drag; SP=Spitzer; Poly Tip= Polymer (Plastic) Tip.

## BIG BORE BULLETS OF ALASKA Rifle .032″ Copper Jackets

| Caliber | Wgt. Grs. | Core | Price/25 |
|---|---|---|---|
| .458 | 200-500 | Std. | $16.95 |
| .458 | 200-500 | Bonded | 24.95 |
| .375 | 150-350 | Std. | 16.95 |
| .375 | 150-350 | Bonded | 24.95 |
| .308* | 150-250 | Bonded | 19.95 |

*.308 jackets are .020″.

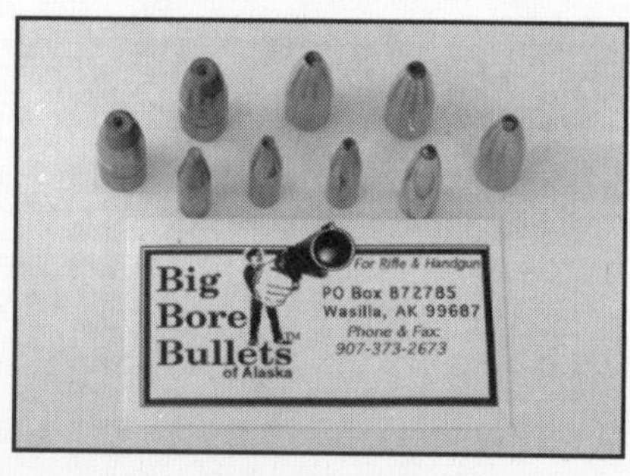


Big Bore Bullets

## BEARTOOTH

| Caliber | Bullet Wgt. Grs. | Bullet Type | Gas Check | Price/100 |
|---|---|---|---|---|
| 22 | 60 | SP | GC | $9.50 |
| 6mm | 80 | LFN | GC | 9.75 |
| | 100 | SP | GC | 9.75 |
| 25 | 105 | LFN | GC | 9.75 |
| 6.5 | 135 | LFN | GC | 10.00 |
| 270 | 120 | SPPB | | 7.75 |
| | 140 | LFN | GC | 10.00 |
| 7mm | 140 | LFN | GC | 10.00 |
| 30 | 115 | FNPB | | 7.50 |
| | 140 | FN | GC | 10.75 |
| | 170 | LMN | GC | 10.75 |
| | 173 | LFN | GC | 10.50 |
| 7.62x39mm | 135 | SP | GC | 10.75 |
| 32-20 | 115 | FNPB | | 7.50 |
| 32 Win. Spl. | 170 | LFN | GC | 10.50 |
| 8mm | 170 | LFN | GC | 10.50 |
| 338 | 235 | LFN | GC | 11.50 |
| | 250 | LFN | GC | 12.50 |
| 348 | 245 | LFN | GC | 12.50 |
| 35 (Rifle) | 185 | FN | GC | 10.50 |
| | 200 | FN | GC | 11.25 |
| | 210 | LFN | GC | 11.25 |
| 375/38-55 | 250 | LFN | GC | 12.50 |
| | 255 | SP | GC | 12.75 |
| 416 | 335 | LFN | GC | 14.00 |
| | 375 | LFN | GC | 17.25 |
| 44-40 | 200 | FNB2 | | 9.50 |
| 45 (Rifle) | 400 | LFNPB | | 8.25/50 |
| | 450 | LFN | GC | 11.25/50 |
| 50 | 475 | LFN | GC | 14.25/50 |
| | 590 | LFNPB | | 9.50/50 |

FN = Flat Nose; FNB = Blat Nose Ball; FNB2 = Flat Nose Ball 2 (wider meplat); LFN = Long Flat Nose; LMN = Long Medium Nose; PB = Plain Base; SP = Spitzer Design.

## BITTERROOT

| Caliber | Wgt. Grs. | B.C. | S.D. | Price/20 |
|---|---|---|---|---|
| 277 | 130 | .385 | .242 | $33.00 |
| | 150 | .450 | .279 | 33.00 |
| 7mm | 140 | .395 | .248 | 33.00 |
| | 160 | .460 | .283 | 33.00 |
| | 175 | .495 | .310 | 33.00 |
| 308 | 165 | .402 | .247 | 33.00 |
| | 180 | .440 | .272 | 33.00 |
| | 200 | .500 | .301 | 35.00 |
| 338 | 200 | .407 | .250 | 35.00 |
| | 225 | .452 | .281 | 37.00 |
| | 250 | .508 | .312 | 39.00 |
| 358 | 225 | .411 | .251 | 37.00 |
| | 250 | .455 | .280 | 39.00 |
| | 275 | .490 | .308 | 41.00 |
| 375 | 250 | .352 | .254 | 39.00 |
| | 275 | .395 | .280 | 41.00 |
| | 300 | .430 | .306 | 43.00 |
| 416 | 335 | .390 | .277 | 45.00 |
| 423 | 335 | .385 | .267 | 45.00 |

S.D. = Standard Deviation; B.C. = Ballistic Coefficient

## BERGER

| Caliber | Wgt. Grs. | Description | Price/Per |
|---|---|---|---|
| 17 | 15 | Small case 17s | $25.20/200 |
| | 18 | Small case 17s | 25.20/200 |
| | 20 | Small case 17s | 25.20/200 |
| | 22 | All CF 17s | 25.20/200 |
| | 25 | All CF 17s | 25.20/200 |
| | 30 | Larger case 17s | 25.20/200 |
| | 37 | Larger case 17s | |
| 22 | 40 | Small case 22s | 12.75/100 |
| 22 | 45 | Small case 22s | 13.25/100 |
| | 50 | All CF 22 cases | |
| | 52 | All CF 22 cases | 13.25/100 |
| | 55 | Same as 52-gr. | 13.25/100 |
| | 60 | Larger CF 22 cases | 13.25/100 |
| | 62 | Same as 60-gr. | 13.25/100 |
| | 64 | Same as 60-gr. | 13.25/100 |
| | 70 VLD | .223 case or larger | 13.75/100 |
| | 70 LTB | .223 case or larger | |
| | 73 LTB | .223 case or larger | |
| | 75 VLD | .223 case or larger | 13.75/100 |
| | 80 VLD | .223 case or larger | 13.75/100 |
| 6mm | 60 | Small capacity cases | 13.25/100 |
| | 62 | Same as 60-gr. | 13.25/100 |
| | 65 | 6mm PPC; 6mm BR | 13.25/100 |
| | 65 Short | 6mm PPC; 6mm BR | 13.25/100 |
| | 65 BT | 6mm PPC; 6mm BR | 13.25/100 |
| | 66 | Same as 65-gr. | |
| | 68 | 6mm PPC; 6mm BR; 243, 6mm Rem. | 13.25/100 |
| | 69* | 6mm PPC; 6mm BR; 243, 6mm Rem. and large capacity cases | 13.25/100 |
| | 70 | Same as 69-gr. | 13.25/100 |
| | 71 | 243; 6mm Rem. and larger cases | 13.25/100 |
| | 74 | 243; 6mm Rem. and large capacity cases | 13.25/100 |
| | 80 | Same as 74-gr. | 13.25/100 |
| | 88* | Same as 74-gr. | 13.25/100 |
| | 90 BT | Same as 74-gr. | |
| | 95 VLD | Same as 74-gr. | 12.10/80 |
| | 105 VLD | Same as 74-gr.; 300-1000 yds. | 12.10/80 |
| | 115 VLD | Same as 105 | |
| 25 | 72 | All 25-caliber | |
| | 78 | All 25 cases | 16.60/100 |
| | 82 | Same as 78-gr. | 16.60/100 |
| | 85 | Same as 78-gr. | 16.60/100 |
| | 87 | Same as 78-gr. | 16.60/100 |
| | 95 | Same as 78-gr. | 16.60/100 |
| | 110 | | 16.60/80 |
| 7mm | 180 VLD | Any 7mm case | |
| 30 | 110 | All 30-cal. cases | 18.70/100 |
| | 125 FB | Same as 110-gr. | 18.70/100 |
| | 135 FB | Same as 110-gr. | 18.70/100 |
| | 150 | Same as 110-gr. | 18.70/100 |
| | 155 VLD | 308 or larger cases | 18.70/100 |
| | 155 LBT | Same as 155-gr. | |
| | 168 LBT | Same as 155-gr. | |
| | 168 VLD | Same as 155-gr. | |
| | 175 VLD | Same as 155-gr. | 18.70/100 |
| 30 | 185 VLD | Same as 155-gr. | 18.70/100 |
| | 190 VLD | Same as 155-gr. | 18.70/100 |
| | 210 VLD | Magnum size cases | 18.70/100 |

*15 Ogive

## BLUE MOUNTAIN

| Caliber | Bullet Wgt. Grs. | Bullet Type |
|---|---|---|
| 172 | 25-28 | Bonded |
| 224 | 55-70 | |
| 244 | 90-105 | Bonded, triple jacket |
| 257 | 87-125 | Bonded, triple jacket |
| 270 | 130-160 | Bonded, triple jacket |
| 284 | 140-175 | Bonded, triple jacket |
| 308 | 150-220 | Bonded, triple jacket |
| 323 | 200-225 | Copper, heavy wall, triple jacket |
| 338 | 215-275 | Copper, heavy wall, triple jacket |
| 358 | 225-300 | Copper, heavy wall, triple jacket |
| 375 | 240-350 | Copper, heavy wall, triple jacket |
| 444 | 240-300 | |

Blue Mountain Bullets

## DKT Jacketed Bullets

| Caliber | Diameter | Wgt. Grs. | Type | Price/50 |
|---|---|---|---|---|
| 22 HP | .228 | 71 | SSP | $24.98 |
| 5.6x51 | .228 | 77 | SSP | 27.98 |
| 6.5x58R | .260 | 120 | RN | 27.98 |
| 6.5 Carcano | .266 | 160 | SSP | 27.98 |
| 280 Ross | .287 | 140/150/160 | SSP | 27.98 |
| 7.35 Carcano | .300 | 140 | HP | 27.98 |
| 8mm | .318 | 150 | SSP | 21.98 |
| | .318 | 175 | SSP | 27.98 |
| | .318 | 196 | RN-SP | 21.98 |
| | .318 | 230 | RN | 31.98 |
| 8.15mm | .324 | 151 | FN-SP | 27.98 |
| 8mm | .329 | 210 | SSP | 27.98 |
| | .329 | 250 | SSP | 29.98 |
| 351 WSL | .351 | 180 | RN | 27.98 |
| 9x57 | .352 | 200 | RN | 27.98 |
| | .352 | 245 | RN | 27.98 |
| | .356 | 200 | SSP | 27.98 |
| 9.3x72R | .364 | 193 | FNSP | 27.98 |
| 401 WSL | .406 | 200/250 | RNSP | 27.98 |
| 40-65/82 | .406 | 260 | FNSP | 27.98 |
| 405 WCF | .411 | 270/300 | RNSSP | 29.98 |
| 45 Revolver | .452 | 300/325 | FN | 31.50 |
| 45-60 WCF | .454 | 300 | FN | 31.50 |
| 50-110 WCF | .510 | 300 | FN | 32.50 |
| | .510 | 450 | FN | 34.50 |
| 500 Linebaugh | .510 | 400-425 | FN | 34.50 |
| 577 NE | .585 | 750 | RN | 37.50 |
| 600 NE | .620 | 900 | RN | 43.50 |
| 700 NE | .700 | 1000 | RN | 49.98 |

HP = Hollowpoint; SP = Softpoint; SSP = Spitzer Softpoint; FN = Flat Nose; RN = Round Nose.

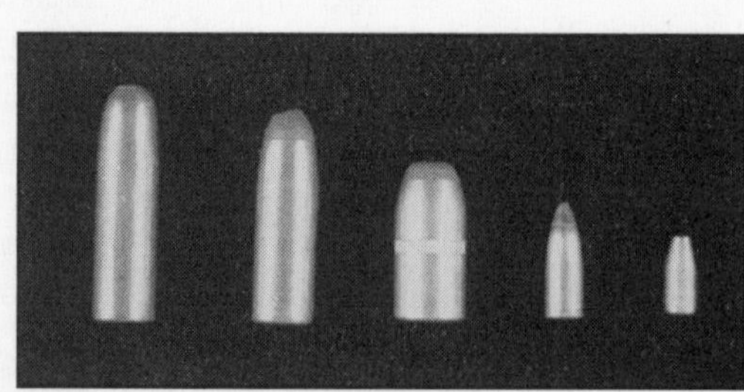

DKT Bullets

## BRUNO SHOOTER'S SUPPLY

| Caliber | Bullet Wgt. Grs. | Bullet Type | Price/100 |
|---|---|---|---|
| 22 | 52, 57 | HPBT | $13.00 |
| | 52, 57 | FB | 12.50 |
| 6mm | 63, 65, 68, 70 | HPFB | 13.95 |
| | 63, 65, 68, 70 | BT | 14.95 |
| 6mm (9/S) | 63, 65, 68 | FB | 13.95 |
| | 63, 65, 68 | BT | 14.95 |
| | 63, 65, 68 | 8-Ogive | 13.95 |

HPBT = Hollowpoint Boattail; FB = Flat Base; HPFB = Hollowpoint Flat Base; BT = Boattail.

Bruno Shooter's Supply

## JAMES CALHOON

| Bullet Wgt. Grs. | Bullet Type | Bullet For | Price 250 | Price 1000 |
|---|---|---|---|---|
| **CALIBER: 17** | | | | |
| 19 | DHP | 17 Cooper to Mach IV | $24.65 | $94.60 |
| 22 | DHP | 17 Cooper to Mach IV | 24.70 | 94.75 |
| 25 | DHP | Mach IV to 17 Remington | 24.95 | 95.80 |
| 28 | DHP | Mach IV to 17 Remington | 25.00 | 96.25 |
| **CALIBER: 22** | | | | |
| 37 | DHP | Hornet to 223 | $22.00 | $84.10 |
| 42 | DHP | Hornet to 223 | 22.15 | 84.55 |
| 45 | HP | Hornet to 223 | 22.25 | 85.00 |
| 50 | DHP | 221 to 22-250 | 22.30 | 85.25 |
| 52 | DHPRBT | 221 to 22-250 | 22.65 | 86.60 |
| 55 | HPRBT | 221 to 22-250 | 21.85 | 83.40 |
| 57 | DHP | 223 to Swift | 24.35 | 93.40 |
| 62 | DHP | 223 to Swift | 25.15 | 96.60 |

HP = Hollowpoint; DHP = Double Hollowpoint; RBT = Rebated Boattail.

## CARROLL

| Caliber | Wgt. Grs. | Type | Price/Per |
|---|---|---|---|
| | LEAD CAST RIFLE | | |
| 30 | 190 | FNGC | $7.95/100 |
| 35 | 210 | FNGC | 8.25/100 |
| 45 | 405 | FNPB | 5.35/50 |

FNGC = Flat Nose Gas Check; FNPB = Flat Nose Plain Base.

C.W. Cartridge 54-Caliber Cartridges

## C.W. CARTRIDGE

| | Bullet | | |
|---|---|---|---|
| Caliber | Wgt. Grs. | Type | Price/20 |
| 54 | 425 | Solid | $5.40 |
| | 415 | Minie | 5.40 |
| | 380 | HB | 5.40 |
| 50 | 380 | Solid | 5.40 |
| | 355 | HB | 5.40 |
| 45 | 300 | Solid | 5.40 |
| | 280 | HB | 5.40 |

## CHAMPION'S CHOICE
### Match Bullets

| Caliber | Wgt. Grs. | Type | Price/100 |
|---|---|---|---|
| 6.5mm | 138 | HPBT | $18.50 |
| 7mm | 170 | FMJBT | 31.00 |
| 7.62 (.308) | 170 | FMJBT | 25.00 |
| (.308) | 185 | FMJBT | 25.00 |
| (.308) | 167 | HPBT | 19.00 |
| (.308) | 185 | HPBT | 30.00 |
| 338 Lapua | 250 | FMJBT | 34.50 |

HPBT = Hollowpoint Boattail; FMJBT = Full Metal Jacket Boattail. From Champion's Choice, Inc.

## FOWLER

| | Bullet | |
|---|---|---|
| Caliber | Wgt. Grs. | Price/100 |
| 7.62x39 | 115 RN | $6.50 |
| 7x57 | | 6.50 |
| 30-30 | 115 RN | 7.50 |
| | 150 RN | 7.50 |
| 30-06 | 130 RN | 7.50 |
| | 190 RN | 8.50 |
| 45/70 | 300 FPBB | 9.50 |
| | 400 FPBB | 10.00 |
| | 450 FP | 11.00 |
| | 500 FP | 12.60 |
| 50/70 | 500 FP | 13.00 |

RN = Round Nose; FP = Flat Point; BB = Bevel Base.

## ELKHORN

| Caliber | Wgt. Grs. | Type | Price/.030 Per 25 | Price/.0505 Per 25 | Price/.065 |
|---|---|---|---|---|---|
| 7mm | 150 | RN, SP | $16.00 | | |
| | 160 | RN, SP | 16.50 | | |
| | 175 | RN, SP | 17.00 | | |
| 308 | 150 | RN, SP | 17.00 | | |
| | 180 | RN, SP | 17.50 | | |
| | 240 | RN, SP | 25.00 | | |
| 338 | 250 | RN, SP | 25.00 | $27.50 | |
| 348 | 200 | FN | 24.00 | | |
| | 250 | FN | 25.00 | | |
| 358 | 250 | RN, SP | 28.00 | 34.00 | |
| 375 | 250 | RN | 28.00 | 34.00 | |
| | 300 | RN | 29.25 | 36.00 | |
| 412 | 300 | RN | 32.00 | 42.00 | |
| 416 | 400 | RN | 32.00 | 42.00 | |
| 458 | 300 | RN, HP | 12.50 | | |
| | 400 | RN | 32.00 | 42.00 | |
| | 450 | RN | 32.50 | 42.50 | |
| | 500 | RN | 33.00 | 43.00 | |
| | 500 | RN | | | $47.00 |

RN = Round Nose; SP = Spitzer; FN = Flat Nose; HP = Hollow Point.

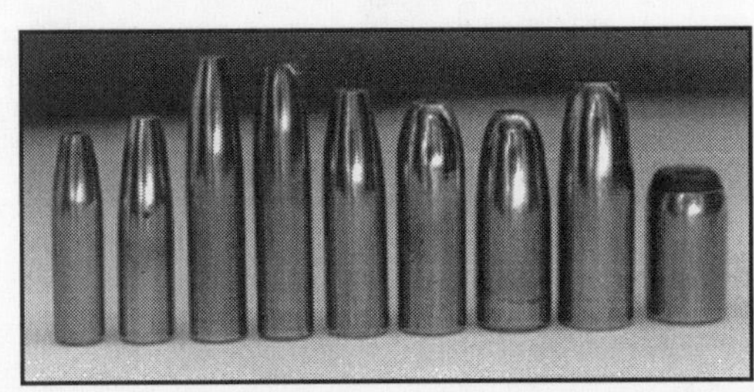

Elkhorn Premium Bonded Core Bullets

## BOB FOWLER
### Muzzleloading

| Caliber | Type | Price/100 |
|---|---|---|
| 44-45 | Pistol | $4.50 |
| 45 | Cal. | 4.50 |
| 50 | Cal. | 4.50 |
| 54 | Cal. | 5.50 |
| 45 | Rifle | 9.00 |
| 50 | Rifle | 9.00 |
| 54 | Rifle | 10.00 |
| 69 | Roundball | 10.00 |
| 69 | Minnie (Federal) | 18.00 |

## FOWLER

| Caliber | Diameter | Wgt. Grs. | Price/100 |
|---|---|---|---|
| 22 | .224 | 52 | $13.50 |
| | | 60 | 14.50 |
| 6mm | .243 | 63 | 13.50 |
| | | 66 | 13.50 |
| | | 68 | 13.50 |
| | | 80 | 14.50 |
| 25 | .257 | 79 | 15.50 |
| | | 85 | 15.50 |
| | | 95 | 16.00 |
| | | 110 | 16.50 |

## FUSILIER

| Caliber | Bullet Diameter | Bullet Wgt. Grs. | Type | Price Imperial |
|---|---|---|---|---|
| 22 | .224 | 55 | MT, GC | $8.95 |
| | .225 | 55 | MT, GC | 8.95 |
| 6mm | .244 | 95 | MT, GC | 9.95 |
| 25 | .258 | 120 | MT, GC | 10.95 |
| 6.5 | .265 | 135 | MT, GC | 10.95 |
| 270 | .278 | 145 | MT, GC | 10.95 |
| 7mm | .285 | 140 | FP, GC | 10.95 |
| | .285 | 145 | MT, GC | 10.95 |
| | .285 | 165 | MT, GC | 11.95 |
| | .285 | 110 | FP | 7.95 |
| 30 | .308 | 130 | PP, GC | 10.95 |
| | .308 | 150 | FP, GC | 10.95 |
| | .308 | 165 | MT, GC | 11.95 |
| | .308 | 170 | FP, GC | 11.95 |
| | .308 | 180 | MT, GC | 11.95 |
| | .309 | 110 | FP | 7.95 |
| | .309 | 130 | PP, GC | 10.95 |
| | .309 | 150 | FP, GC | 10.95 |
| | .309 | 165 | MT, GC | 11.95 |
| | .309 | 170 | FP, GC | 11.95 |
| | .309 | 180 | MT, GC | 11.95 |
| | .310 | 110 | FP | 7.95 |
| | .310 | 130 | PP, GC | 10.95 |
| | .310 | 150 | FP, GC | 10.95 |
| | .310 | 165 | MT, GC | 11.95 |
| | .310 | 170 | FP, GC | 11.95 |
| | .310 | 180 | MT, GC | 11.95 |
| 32-20 | .311 | 110 | FP | 7.95 |
| | .312 | 110 | FP | 7.95 |
| | .313 | 110 | FP | 7.95 |
| | .314 | 110 | FP | 7.95 |
| 32 | .321 | 170 | FP, GC | 11.95 |
| 8mm | .323 | 170 | FP, GC | 11.95 |
| 35 | .358 | 160 | FP, GC | 11.95 |
| | .358 | 180 | FP, GC | 11.95 |
| | .358 | 200 | FP, GC | 12.95 |
| | .358 | 250 | MT, GC | 13.95 |
| 37 | .375 | 250 | FP, GC | 13.95 |
| 416 | .416 | 350 | FP, GC | 17.95 |
| 44 | .427 | 230 | FP, GC | 13.95 |
| | .427 | 275 | FP, GC | 15.95 |
| | .427 | 325 | FP, GC | 16.95 |
| | .428 | 230 | FP, GC | 13.95 |
| | .428 | 275 | FP, GC | 15.95 |
| | .428 | 325 | FP, GC | 16.95 |
| | .429 | 230 | FP, GC | 13.95 |
| | .429 | 275 | FP, GC | 15.95 |
| | .429 | 325 | FP, GC | 16.95 |
| 44 | .430 | 230 | FP, GC | 13.95 |
| | .430 | 275 | FP, GC | 15.95 |
| | .430 | 325 | FP, GC | 16.95 |
| 45 | .457 | 300 | FP, GC | 16.95 |
| | .457 | 340 | FP | 11.95 |
| | .457 | 400 | FP | 13.95 |
| | .457 | 400 | FP, GC | 18.95 |
| | .457 | 475 | FP, GC | 22.95 |
| | .457 | 500 | FP, GC, M | 22.95 |
| | .457 | 525 | FP, GC | 25.95 |
| 45 | .458 | 300 | FP, GC | 16.95 |
| | .458 | 340 | FP | 11.95 |
| | .458 | 400 | FP | 13.95 |
| | .458 | 400 | FP, GC | 18.95 |
| | .458 | 475 | FP, GC | 22.95 |
| | .458 | 500 | FP, GC, M | 22.95 |
| | .458 | 525 | FP, GC | 25.95 |

MT = Mag Tip; FP = Flat Point; GC = Gas Check; MGC = Magnum Gas Check.

## GRIZZLY

| Caliber | Wgt. Grs. | Price/20 |
|---|---|---|
| 308 | 165 | $33.00 |
| | 180 | 33.00 |
| 338 | 225 | 37.00 |
| | 250 | 39.00 |
| 375 | 250 | 39.00 |
| | 300 | 43.00 |
| 416 | 350 | 45.00 |
| 458 | 400 | 47.00* |
| | 500 | 49.00* |

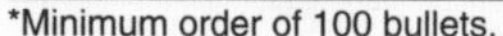

*Minimum order of 100 bullets.

Hammet's VLD 6mm Bullets

## HAMMET'S VLDS

| Caliber | Diameter | Wgt. Grs. | B.C. | Price 100 | Price 250 | Price 1000 |
|---|---|---|---|---|---|---|
| 17 | .172 | 17.0 | .131 | $12.60 | $31.00 | $120.00 |
| | .172 | 18.5 | .148 | 12.60 | 31.00 | 120.00 |
| | .172 | 19.8 | .148 | 12.60 | 31.00 | 120.00 |
| | .172 | 21.9 | .198 | 12.60 | 31.00 | 120.00 |
| | .172 | 25.0 | .219 | 13.00 | 32.00 | 126.00 |
| | .172 | 30.0 | .246 | 13.00 | 32.00 | 126.00 |
| | .172 | 35.0 | — | 18.00 | 43.00 | 175.00 |
| 22 | .224 | 65.0 | — | 15.00 | 36.50 | 145.00 |
| | .224 | 70.0 | — | 15.00 | 36.50 | 145.00 |
| | .224 | 75.0 | — | 15.00 | 36.50 | 145.00 |
| | .224 | 80.0 | — | 15.00 | 36.50 | 145.00 |
| | .224 | 85.0 | — | 16.00 | 37.50 | 155.00 |
| 6mm | .244 | 92.5 | .542 | 16.00 | NA | 155.00 |
| | .224 | 95.0 | .547 | 16.00 | 38.00 | 155.00 |
| | .244 | 103.5 | .572 | 16.00 | NA | 155.00 |
| | .244 | 108.5 | .600 | 16.00 | 38.00 | 155.00 |
| | .244 | 130.0 | .686 | 17.00 | NA | 165.00 |

B.C. = Ballistic Coefficient.

Fusilier

Hawk, Inc.

## HAWK, INC.

| Caliber | Dia. | Wgt. Grs. | Ogive | Jacket | Price/50 |
|---|---|---|---|---|---|
| 6.5mm | .264 | 135 | 2 | .030 | $29.00 |
| | .264 | 160 | 2 | .030 | 30.00 |
| 270 | .277 | 130 | 8 | .030 | 29.00 |
| | .277 | 140 | 8 | .035 | 29.50 |
| | .277 | 150 | 8 | .035 | 30.00 |
| | .277 | 165 | 8 | .035 | 30.50 |
| 7mm | .284 | 140 | 8 | .025 | 28.50 |
| | .284 | 140 | 8 | .035 | 29.50 |
| | .284 | 140 | 8 | .030 | 29.00 |
| | .284 | 150 | SP | .035 | 32.00 |
| | .284 | 160 | 8 | .030 | 30.00 |
| | .284 | 160 | 8 | .035 | 30.50 |
| | .284 | 160 | SP | .035 | 32.50 |
| | .284 | 175 | SP | .035 | 33.50 |
| | .284 | 175 | 8 | .035 | 31.50 |
| 280 | .286 | 160 | 2 | .035 | 31.50 |
| 308 | .308 | 130 | 8 | .025 | 28.50 |
| | .308 | 150 | RT | .025 | 29.00 |
| | .308 | 165 | 8 | .030 | 30.00 |
| | .308 | 165 | 8 | .035 | 30.50 |
| | .308 | 180 | 8 | .030 | 30.00 |
| | .308 | 180 | 8 | .035 | 30.50 |
| | .308 | 200 | 8 | .035 | 31.00 |
| | .308 | 200 | RT | .025 | 30.00 |
| | .308 | 200 | RT | .030 | 30.50 |
| | .308 | 220 | 8 | .035 | 32.00 |
| | .308 | 250 | 8 | .035 | 33.50 |
| | .308 | 150 | SP | .035 | 32.00 |
| | .308 | 165 | SP | .035 | 32.50 |
| | .308 | 180 | SP | .035 | 33.00 |
| | .308 | 200 | SP | .030 | 33.00 |
| | .308 | 200 | SP | .035 | 33.50 |
| 303 | .311 | 180 | SP | .035 | 32.00 |
| | .311 | 200 | SP | .035 | 33.00 |
| 8mm | .318 | 180 | 6 | .030 | 31.00 |
| | .318 | 220 | 6 | .030 | 32.00 |
| 32 | .321 | 170 | FP | .030 | 30.50 |
| 8mm | .323 | 180 | 6 | .025 | 29.00 |
| | .323 | 180 | 6 | .030 | 29.50 |
| | .323 | 180 | 6 | .035 | 30.50 |
| | .323 | 220 | 6 | .030 | 31.00 |
| | .323 | 220 | 6 | .035 | 32.00 |
| | .323 | 250 | 6 | .035 | 33.50 |
| | .329 | 200 | 2 | .035 | 32.50 |
| 333 | .333 | 250 | 2 | .035 | 33.50 |
| 300 | .333 | 300 | RT | | 36.50 |
| 33 Win. | .338 | 180 | FP | .030 | 28.50 |
| | .338 | 200 | FP | .030 | 29.50 |
| 338 | .338 | 200 | 7 | .035 | 30.00 |
| | .338 | 230 | 7 | .035 | 31.00 |
| | .338 | 250 | 7 | .035 | 32.00 |
| | .338 | 275 | 7 | .035 | 33.00 |
| | .338 | 275 | 7 | .050 | 37.50 |
| | .338 | 180 | FP | .030 | 28.50 |
| | .338 | 200 | FP | .030 | 29.50 |
| | .338 | 230 | SP | .035 | 32.00 |
| | .338 | 250 | SP | .035 | 32.50 |
| 348 | .348 | 165 | FP | .030 | 28.50 |
| | .348 | 180 | FP | .030 | 29.00 |
| | .348 | 200 | FP | .035 | 30.00 |
| | .348 | 250 | FP | .035 | 30.50 |
| | .348 | 270 | FP | .035 | 32.00 |
| | .348 | 230 | SP | .030 | 30.50 |
| | .348 | 250 | SP | .030 | 31.50 |
| | .348 | 270 | SP | .050 | 37.50 |
| 351 | .351 | 180 | RN | .025 | 29.00 |
| 9mm | .356 | 200 | 6 | .030 | 31.00 |
| | .356 | 250 | 6 | .030 | 32.00 |
| 358 | .358 | 200 | 8 | .030 | 29.00 |
| | .358 | 225 | 8 | .035 | 30.00 |
| | .358 | 225 | SP | .035 | 28.50 |
| | .358 | 250 | 8 | .030 | 30.00 |
| | .358 | 250 | 8 | .035 | 31.00 |
| | .358 | 250 | 8 | .050 | 36.00 |
| | .358 | 275 | RT | .035 | 32.00 |
| | .358 | 275 | 8 | .050 | 36.50 |
| | .358 | 300 | 8 | .035 | 33.00 |
| | .358 | 300 | 8 | .050 | 37.50 |
| | .358 | 180 | FP | .025 | 28.00 |
| | .358 | 225 | FP | .025 | 29.00 |
| | .358 | 200 | FP | .025 | 28.50 |
| | .358 | 250 | FP | .030 | 29.50 |
| | .358 | 225 | SP | .035 | 31.00 |
| | .358 | 250 | SP | .035 | 32.00 |
| | .358 | 250 | SP | .050 | 36.50 |
| 9.3mm | .365 | 200 | 6 | .030 | 29.50 |
| | .365 | 235 | 6 | .035 | 30.00 |
| | .365 | 250 | 6 | .030 | 30.00 |
| | .365 | 250 | 6 | .035 | 30.50 |
| | .365 | 285 | 6 | .035 | 31.50 |
| | .365 | 285 | 6 | .050 | 38.00 |
| | .365 | 320 | 6 | .030 | 32.50 |
| 375 | .375 | 180 | FP | .025 | 28.50 |
| | .375 | 200 | FP | .025 | 29.00 |
| | .375 | 250 | FP | .025 | 30.00 |
| | .375 | 250 | FP | .035 | 31.00 |
| | .375 | 270 | FP | .050 | 37.50 |
| | .375 | 235 | 6 | .025 | 28.50 |
| | .375 | 235 | 6 | .035 | 29.50 |
| | .375 | 250 | 6 | .035 | 30.50 |
| | .375 | 270 | 6 | .035 | 31.50 |
| | .375 | 270 | 6 | .050 | 37.50 |
| | .375 | 300 | 6 | .035 | 32.00 |
| | .375 | 300 | 6 | .050 | 38.00 |
| | .375 | 325 | 6 | .035 | 33.50 |
| | .375 | 235 | SP | .035 | 31.00 |
| | .375 | 250 | SP | .035 | 32.00 |
| | .375 | 270 | SP | .035 | 33.00 |
| | .375 | 300 | SP | .035 | 34.00 |
| 38-40 Win. | .401 | 200 | HP | .025 | 30.50 |
| 406 | .406 | 235 | FP | .025 | 29.50 |
| | .406 | 270 | FP | .025 | 30.50 |
| | .406 | 300 | FP | .025 | 31.50 |
| | .406 | 300 | 6 | .025 | 32.00 |
| | .406 | 300 | 6 | .035 | 33.00 |
| | .406 | 350 | 6 | .025 | 33.00 |
| | .406 | 350 | 6 | .035 | 36.00 |
| 408 | .408 | 235 | FP | .025 | 29.50 |
| | .408 | 270 | FP | .025 | 30.50 |
| | .408 | 300 | FP | .025 | 31.50 |
| | .408 | 235 | FP | .025 | 29.50 |
| | .408 | 270 | FP | .025 | 30.50 |
| | .408 | 300 | FP | .025 | 31.50 |
| | .408 | 300 | 6 | .025 | 32.00 |
| | .408 | 300 | 6 | .035 | 33.00 |
| | .408 | 350 | 6 | .025 | 33.00 |
| | .408 | 350 | 6 | .035 | 34.00 |
| | .408 | 400 | 6 | .025 | 33.00 |
| | .408 | 400 | 6 | .035 | 34.00 |
| | .408 | 400 | 6 | .050 | 42.00 |
| 410 | .410 | 300 | 6 | .025 | 32.00 |
| | .410 | 300 | 6 | .035 | 33.00 |
| | .410 | 350 | 6 | .025 | 33.00 |
| | .410 | 350 | 6 | .035 | 34.00 |
| | .410 | 400 | 6 | .025 | 33.00 |
| | .410 | 400 | 6 | .035 | 34.00 |
| | .410 | 400 | 6 | .050 | 41.00 |
| 411 | .411 | 300 | 6 | .025 | 32.00 |
| | .411 | 300 | 6 | .035 | 33.00 |
| | .411 | 350 | 6 | .025 | 33.00 |
| | .411 | 350 | 6 | .035 | 34.00 |
| | .411 | 400 | 6 | .025 | 33.00 |
| | .411 | 400 | 6 | .035 | 34.00 |
| | .411 | 400 | 6 | .050 | 41.00 |
| | .411 | 235 | FP | .025 | 29.50 |
| | .411 | 270 | FP | .025 | 30.50 |
| | .411 | 300 | FP | .025 | 31.50 |
| 416 | .416 | 300 | 6 | .025 | 30.00 |
| | .416 | 300 | 6 | .035 | 31.00 |
| | .416 | 300 | 6 | .050 | 36.50 |
| | .416 | 350 | 6 | .025 | 31.00 |
| | .416 | 350 | 6 | .035 | 32.00 |
| | .416 | 350 | 6 | .050 | 37.50 |
| | .416 | 400 | 6 | .035 | 33.00 |
| | .416 | 400 | 6 | .050 | 38.50 |
| | .416 | 400 | 6 | .065 | 52.00 |
| | .416 | 450 | 6 | .050 | 42.50 |
| | .416 | 500 | 6 | .035 | 40.50 |
| | .416 | 350 | SP | .035 | 33.00 |
| | .416 | 350 | SP | .050 | 38.50 |
| | .416 | 400 | SP | .035 | 34.00 |
| | .416 | 400 | SP | .050 | 39.50 |
| 404 Jeffery | .423 | 300 | 6 | .035 | 31.00 |
| | .423 | 300 | RT | .050 | 35.50 |
| | .423 | 350 | 6 | .035 | 32.50 |
| | .423 | 350 | 6 | .050 | 37.00 |
| | .423 | 400 | 6 | .050 | 38.50 |
| | .423 | 400 | 6 | .065 | 51.50 |
| 10.75mm | .424 | 350 | RN | .035 | 35.50 |
| | .424 | 400 | RN | .035 | 40.50 |
| 44/40 | .426 | 200 | HP | .025 | 29.50 |
| 44 Mag. | .430 | 200 | HP | .025 | 27.50 |

BULLETS, CUSTOM/Rifle Prices

## HAWK, INC.

| Caliber | Dia. | Wgt. Grs. | Ogive | Jacket | Price/50 |
|---|---|---|---|---|---|
| | .430 | 240 | HP | .025 | 27.50 |
| | .430 | 265 | HP | .025 | 28.50 |
| | .430 | 300 | HP | .025 | 30.00 |
| 444 Marlin | .430 | 240 | FP | .035 | 28.50 |
| | .430 | 250 | FP | .035 | 29.00 |
| | .430 | 250 | FP | .025 | 27.50 |
| | .430 | 265 | FP | .035 | 29.00 |
| | .430 | 275 | FP | .025 | 28.50 |
| | .430 | 300 | FP | .025 | 29.00 |
| | .430 | 300 | FP | .035 | 30.00 |
| 425 Westley Richards | .435 | 300 | 6 | .035 | 32.00 |
| | .435 | 325 | 6 | .035 | 32.50 |
| | .435 | 350 | 6 | .050 | 38.50 |
| | .435 | 350 | RN | .035 | 33.00 |
| | .435 | 400 | RN | .035 | 38.00 |
| | .435 | 400 | 6 | .050 | 39.50 |
| | .435 | 400 | 6 | .065 | 52.50 |
| | .435 | 450 | 6 | .050 | 41.00 |
| 11.15mm | .439 | 350 | RN | .035 | 36.00 |
| (43 Span.) | .439 | 400 | RN | .035 | 37.00 |
| 11.2mm | .440 | 300 | RN | .035 | 35.00 |
| | .440 | 350 | RN | .035 | 36.00 |
| | .440 | 400 | RN | .035 | 37.00 |
| 43 Mauser | .446 | 350 | FP,HP | .025 | 32.00 |
| | .446 | 400 | FP,HP | .025 | 33.00 |
| 452 | .452 | 300 | FP,HP | .025 | 32.00 |
| | .452 | 350 | FP,HP | .025 | 33.00 |
| 577/450 | .455 | 480 | RN | .025 | 36.00 |
| | .455 | 300 | FP,HP | .025 | 32.00 |
| | .455 | 350 | FP,HP | .025 | 32.00 |
| | .455 | 400 | FP | .025 | 33.00 |
| 458 | .458 | 300 | HP,FP | .025 | 30.00 |
| | .458 | 350 | FP,HP | .025 | 30.50 |
| | .458 | 350 | 4,FP | .035 | 31.50 |
| | .458 | 400 | FP,HP | .025 | 31.00 |
| | .458 | 400 | RN,FP | .035 | 32.50 |
| | .458 | 400 | 4 | .050 | 37.50 |
| | .458 | 400 | 4 | .065 | 52.00 |
| | .458 | 480 | RN | .025 | 34.00 |
| | .458 | 480 | RN | .035 | 36.50 |
| | .458 | 500 | 4 | .035 | 36.50 |
| | .458 | 500 | 4 | .065 | 54.00 |
| 11.4 Danish Rem. | .462 | 400 | RN | .035 | 35.00 |
| | .462 | 300 | HP | .025 | 32.00 |
| | .462 | 350 | HP | .025 | 33.00 |
| 500/465 | .466 | 500 | RN | .035 | 39.00 |
| 475 | .475 | 300 | 1.5, HP | .025 | 30.00 |
| | .475 | 350 | 1.5, HP | .025 | 31.50 |
| | .475 | 350 | 1.5, FP | .035 | 31.50 |
| | .475 | 400 | 1.5, FP | .035 | 32.50 |
| | .475 | 400 | 4 | .035 | 32.50 |
| | .475 | 400 | 4 | .050 | 37.50 |
| | .475 | 400 | 4 | .065 | 52.00 |
| | .475 | 500 | 4 | .050 | 41.50 |
| | .475 | 500 | 4 | .065 | 54.00 |
| | .475 | 600 | 4 | .050 | 45.50 |
| 482 | .482 | 400 | 4 | .035 | 36.50 |
| | .482 | 400 | 4 | .050 | 40.50 |
| | .482 | 500 | 4 | .035 | 38.50 |
| | .482 | 500 | 4 | .050 | 41.50 |
| | .482 | 500 | 4 | .065 | 54.00 |
| 488 | .488 | 400 | 4 | .035 | 35.50 |
| | .488 | 400 | 4 | .050 | 38.50 |
| | .488 | 500 | 4 | .035 | 38.00 |
| | .488 | 500 | 4 | .050 | 42.50 |
| | .488 | 500 | 4 | .065 | 56.50 |
| 50 | .500 | 300 | FP | .025 | 31.50 |
| | .500 | 350 | FP | .025 | 32.50 |
| 505 | .505 | 400 | 2 | .035 | 37.50 |
| | .505 | 400 | 2 | .050 | 43.50 |
| | .505 | 500 | 2 | .035 | 40.50 |
| | .505 | 500 | 2 | .050 | 44.50 |
| | .505 | 500 | 2 | .065 | 53.50 |
| | .505 | 600 | 2 | .050 | 49.50 |
| | .505 | 600 | RN | .065 | 57.00 |
| 510 | .510 | 350 | FP | .025 | 32.50 |
| | .510 | 350 | FP | .035 | 33.50 |
| | .510 | 350 | 2 | .035 | 34.50 |
| | .510 | 400 | 2 | .035 | 36.50 |
| | .510 | 400 | 2 | .050 | 41.00 |
| | .510 | 450 | FP | .035 | 35.00 |
| | .510 | 500 | 2 | .035 | 38.50 |
| | .510 | 500 | 2 | .050 | 42.50 |
| | .510 | 535 | 2 | .065 | 51.50 |
| | .510 | 600 | 2 | .035 | 44.50 |
| | .510 | 600 | RN | .050 | 47.50 |
| 50 BMG | .510 | 700 | SP | .035 | 52.00 |
| | .510 | 700 | SP | .050 | 59.00 |
| 500 Jeffery | .510 | 535 | SCH | .065 | 57.50 |
| 55 | .550 | 500 | RN | .035 | NA |
| | .550 | 700 | RN | .065 | NA |
| 577 | .585 | 560 | RN | .035 | 51.50 |
| | .585 | 560 | RN | .065 | 64.00 |
| | .585 | 750 | RN | .035 | 51.50 |
| | .585 | 750 | RN | .065 | 64.00 |

RN = Round Nose; FP = Flat Point; HP = Hollowpoint.

Hawk Precision Bullets

## JLK

| Bullet | 55 | 60 | 65 | 70 | 75 | 80 | 168 | 180 |
|---|---|---|---|---|---|---|---|---|
| Weight | 55 | 60 | 65 | 70 | 75 | 80 | 168 | 180 |
| Length OL | .765 | .805 | .940 | .980 | 1.050 | 1.120 | 1.420 | 1.520 |
| Bearing Length | .265 | .305 | .340 | .300 | .370 | .340 | .420 | .520 |
| Boattail Length | — | — | — | .180 | .180 | .180 | 230 | .230 |
| Boattail Angle | — | — | — | 9.0° | 9.0° | 9.0° | 7.5° | 7.5° |
| Meplat Dia. | .046 | .046 | .046 | .046 | .046 | .046 | .046 | .046 |
| Ogive Radius | 12 | 12 | 15 | 12 | 12 | 15 | 18 | 18 |
| Ogive Axial Length | .500 | .500 | .600 | .500 | .500 | .600 | .770 | .770 |
| Optimum Twist | 14 | 12 | 10 | 1-9 | 1-8$^1/_2$ | 1-8 | 9.5 | 9 |
| B.C. | .309 | .339 | .397 | .410 | .425 | .510 | .690 | .738 |

## J&L SUPERIOR

| Caliber | Diameter | Wgt. Grs. | Type | Price/50 |
|---|---|---|---|---|
| **RIFLE** | | | | |
| 22 | .224 | 54 | FN | $6.98 |
| 30 | .308 | 130 | RN | 6.98 |
| | .308 | 150 | FN | 7.98 |
| | .308 | 180 | FN | 8.98 |
| 32 | .308 | 115 | FN | 7.98 |
| | .321 | 170 | FN | 8.98 |
| | .323 | 170 | FN | 8.98 |
| 33 | .338 | 200 | FN | 8.98 |
| 348 | .348 | 200 | FN | 8.98 |
| 375 | .376 | 250 | FN | 8.98 |
| 40 | .408 | 260 | FN | 8.98 |
| | .408 | 300 | CSA | 9.98 |
| | .408 | 350 | CSA | 9.98 |
| | .408 | 400 | CSA | 10.98 |
| 38/40 | .401 | 170 | | 8.98 |
| 416 | .416 | 350 | FN | 9.98 |
| 43 Spanish | .439 | 370 | FN | 9.98 |
| 43 Mauser | .446 | 370 | | 9.98 |
| 45 | .458 | 300 | FN | 9.98 |
| | .458 | 325 | FN | 9.98 |
| | .458 | 405 | FN | 10.98 |
| | .458 | 500 | FN | 10.98 |
| 50 | .512 | 450 | FN | 10.98 |
| | .512 | 515 | FN | 10.98 |

FN = Flat Nose; CSA = C. Sharps Arms Design; RN = Round Nose.

## HT

| Caliber | Diameter | Wgt. Grs. | S.D. | B.C. | Price 20 |
|---|---|---|---|---|---|
| 22 | 0.224 | 42 | 0.131 | 0.234 | $30.00 |
| 6mm | 0.243 | 80 | 0.209 | 0.394 | $34.00 |
| 25 | 0.257 | 100 | 0.234 | 0.442 | 34.00 |
| 6.5mm | 0.264 | 120 | 0.266 | 0.502 | 34.00 |
| 270 | 0.277 | 120 | 0.240 | 0.453 | 34.00 |
| | 0.277 | 126 | 0.252 | 0.475 | 34.00 |
| | 0.277 | 130 | 0.261 | 0.492 | 34.00 |
| | 0.277 | 140 | 0.281 | 0.530 | 34.00 |
| 7mm | 0.284 | 120 | 0.230 | 0.434 | 34.00 |
| | 0.284 | 130 | 0.249 | 0.470 | 34.00 |
| | 0.284 | 140 | 0.268 | 0.506 | 34.00 |
| | 0.284 | 150 | 0.288 | 0.543 | 34.00 |
| 30 | 0.308 | 115 | 0.185 | 0.349 | 34.00 |
| | 0.308 | 140 | 0.227 | 0.428 | 34.00 |
| | 0.308 | 150 | 0.243 | 0.458 | 34.00 |
| | 0.308 | 160 | 0.259 | 0.489 | 34.00 |
| | 0.308 | 170 | 0.275 | 0.519 | 34.00 |
| 311 | 0.311 | 180 | 0.284 | 0.516 | 34.00 |
| 338 | 0.338 | 200 | 0.270 | 0.509 | 34.00 |
| | 0.338 | 215 | 0.289 | 0.525 | 34.00 |
| | 0.338 | 225 | 0.304 | 0.574 | 34.00 |
| 358 | 0.358 | 190 | 0.244 | 0.400 | 34.00 |
| | 0.358 | 235 | 0.277 | 0.495 | 34.00 |
| 375 | 0.375 | 235 | 0.252 | 0.450 | 38.00 |
| | 0.375 | 250 | 0.268 | 0.479 | 38.00 |
| | 0.375 | 270 | 0.290 | 0.518 | 38.00 |
| 411 | 0.411 | 320 | 0.284 | 0.507 | 38.00 |
| 416 | 0.416 | 320 | 0.277 | 0.495 | 38.00 |
| | 0.416 | 390 | 0.338 | 0.398 | 30.00 |

S.D. = Sectional Density; B.C. = Ballistic Coefficient

## IMI

| Caliber | Wgt. Grs. | Type | Price/500 |
|---|---|---|---|
| 22 | 55 | FMJ BT | $20.98 |
| | 62 | FMJ BT | 41.98 |
| 30 | 148 | FMJ BT | 47.98 |
| 7.62x39 | 123 | FMJ | 37.98 |
| 50 | 647 | FMJ BT | 120.98* |

FMJ = Full Metal Jacket; BT = Boattail; * = Price for 100. From Huntington Die Specialties.

## LAPUA Rifle Bullets

| Caliber | Wgt. Grs. | Type | Price/100 |
|---|---|---|---|
| 223 | 55 | SP | $19.20 |
| 6mm | 105 | HPBT Scenar | 22.04 |
| 6.5mm | 108 | HPBT Scenar | 21.10 |
| | 139 | HPBT Scenar | 21.10 |
| | 155 | SP Mega | 31.23 |
| 270 | 130 | SP Mira | 27.98 |
| 7mm | 170 | FMJBT Lock Base | 36.22 |
| | 170 | SP Mega | 31.65 |
| 30 | 150 | FMJBT Lock Base | 29.86 |
| | 167 | HPBT Scenar | 21.56 |
| | 170 | FMJBT D46 | 28.50 |
| | 170 | FMJBT D47 | 21.07 |
| | 170 | FMJBT Lock Base | 19.16 |
| | 185 | FMJBT D46 | 29.17 |
| | 185 | FMJBT D47 | 29.17 |
| | 185 | HPBT Scenar | 33.50 |
| | 185 | SP Mega | 34.84 |
| 338 | 250 | Lock Base | 39.41 |
| | 250 | SP Mira | 40.81 |

## JENSEN

| Caliber | Wgt. Grs. | S.D. | B.C. | Price/20 |
|---|---|---|---|---|
| 243 | 80 | .193 | .379 | $43.60 |
| | 100 | .242 | .465 | 44.00 |
| 257 | 100 | .216 | .434 | 44.60 |
| | 120 | .260 | .508 | 45.00 |
| 264 | 125 | .256 | .539 | 45.20 |
| 277 | 130 | .242 | .487 | 45.20 |
| | 150 | .279 | .563 | 45.60 |
| 284 | 140 | .248 | .538 | 45.60 |
| | 154 | .272 | .590 | 45.00 |
| | 175 | .310 | .673 | 46.00 |
| 308 | 165 | .248 | .532 | 46.20 |
| | 180 | .271 | .579 | 47.00 |
| | 200 | .301 | .640 | 48.00 |
| 323 | 210 | .288 | .559 | 48.80 |
| 338 | 200 | .250 | .483 | 48.60 |
| | 225 | .281 | .545 | 49.00 |
| | 250 | .313 | .606 | 49.40 |
| 358 | 225 | .250 | .524 | 49.00 |
| | 250 | .279 | .554 | 49.40 |
| 375 | 225 | .220 | .407 | 54.00 |
| | 250 | .254 | .451 | 54.00 |
| | 300 | .305 | .621 | 54.60 |
| 416 | 335 | .276 | .475 | 58.00 |
| 458 | 400 | .272 | .463 | 62.00 |

S.D. = Sectional Density; B.C. = Ballistic Coefficient.

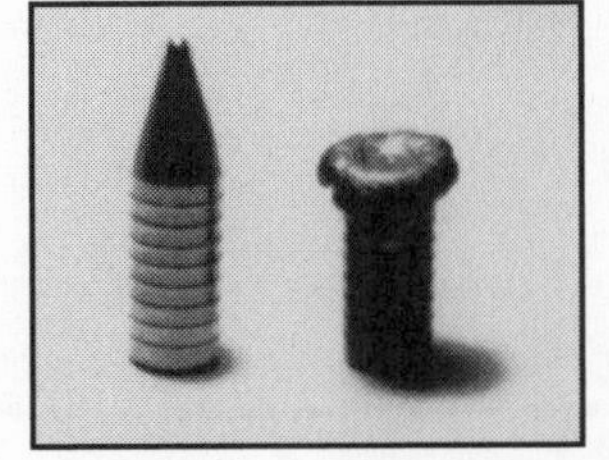

HT Bullets

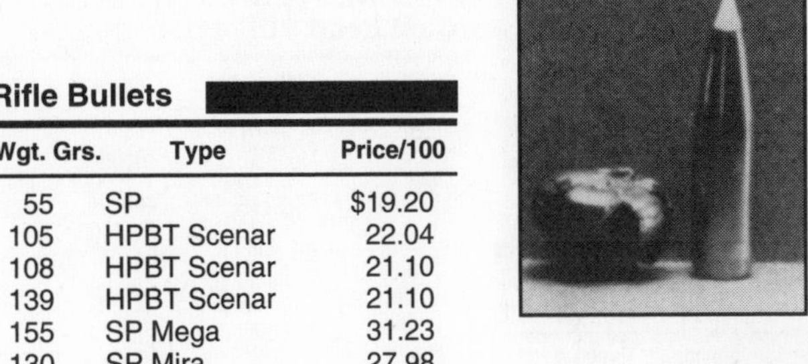

Jensen Bullets

Jensen Big Game Bullets

## LIBERTY SHOOTING SUPPLIES Rifle

| Caliber | Dia. | Wgt. Grs. | Type | Price 100 | Price 500 |
|---|---|---|---|---|---|
| 22 | .224 | 35 | GCSP | $5.50 | $24.75 |
| | .224 | 45 | GCRN | 5.50 | 24.75 |
| | .224 | 55 | GCFP | 5.50 | 24.75 |
| | .224 | 71 | GCFP | 6.50 | 29.25 |
| | .228 | 58 | GCSP | 8.00 | 36.00 |
| | .228 | 77 | PT | 8.00 | 36.00 |
| 6mm | .244 | 77 | GCRN | 6.00 | 27.00 |
| 25 | .258 | 85 | GCFP | 6.50 | 29.25 |
| | .258 | 102 | SP | 7.00 | 31.50 |
| | .258 | 105 | FP | 6.50 | 29.25 |
| 6.5mm | .265 | 136 | GCRN | 6.50 | 29.25 |
| | .265 | 165 | GCRNFP | 7.00 | 31.50 |
| 270 | .278 | 120 | GCPT | 6.50 | 29.25 |
| | .278 | 120 | GCRN | 6.50 | 29.25 |
| 7mm | .285 | 142 | GCRN | 6.00 | 27.00 |
| | .285 | 145 | GCPT | 6.00 | 27.00 |
| 7.35 Carc. | .299 | 145 | GCRN | 8.50 | 38.25 |
| 30 | .303 | 195 | PPSP | 8.00 | 36.00 |
| | .308 | 55 | Sabot | 5.50 | |
| | .309 | 110 | RN | 5.50 | 24.75 |
| | .309 | 130 | GCSP | 6.00 | 27.00 |
| | .309 | 150 | FP | 6.50 | 29.25 |
| | .309 | 150 | GCFP | 6.00 | 27.00 |
| | .309 | 175 | GCFP | 6.50 | 29.25 |
| | .309 | 175 | GCRN | 6.50 | 29.25 |
| | .309 | 210 | GCFP | 8.50 | 38.50 |
| | .311 | 130 | GCSP | 6.50 | 29.25 |
| | .311 | 150 | GCRN | 6.50 | 29.25 |
| | .311 | 175 | GCRN | 7.00 | 31.50 |
| 310 Cadet | .316 | 115 | RN | 8.50 | 38.25 |
| 32-40 | .321 | 155 | FP | 6.50 | 29.95 |
| | .321 | 200 | FP | 8.00 | 36.00 |
| 8mm | .324 | 130 | GCSP | 7.00 | 31.50 |
| | .324 | 160 | FP | 6.50 | 29.95 |
| | .324 | 175 | FP | 7.00 | 31.50 |
| | .324 | 180 | GCFP | 7.00 | 31.50 |
| | .330 | 255 | GCRN | 8.50 | 38.25 |
| 33 | .339 | 215 | FP | 8.00 | 36.00 |
| 348 | .349 | 220 | GCFP | 8.00 | 36.00 |
| | .349 | 245 | GCRN | 8.00 | 36.00 |
| 35 | .358 | 195 | GCRN | 6.50 | 29.25 |
| | .358 | 200 | FP | 6.50 | 29.25 |
| | .358 | 300 | GCFP | 8.50* | 38.25* |
| 375 | .376 | 250 | GCFP | 5.50* | 24.75* |
| | .376 | 255 | RNDD | 7.00* | 31.50* |

| Caliber | Dia. | Wgt. Grs. | Type | Price 100 | Price 500 |
|---|---|---|---|---|---|
| | .376 | 290 | FP | $6.00* | $27.00* |
| 9.3 | .366 | 215 | FP | 8.50 | 38.25 |
| 38-55 | .379 | 250 | GCFP | 6.00* | 27.00* |
| | .379 | 255 | RNDD | 7.50* | 33.75* |
| | .379 | 290 | FP | 6.50* | 29.25* |
| 40 | .396-.406 | 365 | RNPP | 7.00* | 31.50* |
| | .406 | 225 | FP | 6.00* | 27.00* |
| | .406 | 275 | FP | 6.50* | 29.25* |
| | .409 | 350 | PTFP | 7.00* | 21.50* |
| | .410 | 400 | PTFP | 7.00* | 31.50* |
| | .412 | 275 | FP | 7.50* | 33.75* |
| | .412 | 283 | RN | 7.50* | 33.75* |
| 416 | .417 | 385 | GCRN | 8.50* | 38.25* |
| 41 Swiss | .427 | 328 | GCFP | 8.00 | 36.00 |
| 43 Spanish | .439 | 370 | FP | 8.50 | 38.25 |
| 43 Mauser | .446 | 390 | FP | 8.50 | 38.25 |
| 45 | .456 | 300 | RN | 7.00 | 31.50 |
| 45-70 | .458 | 285 | FP | 6.00 | 27.00 |
| | .458 | 300 | RN | 6.50 | 29.25 |
| | .458 | 300 | GCFP | 6.00 | 27.00 |
| | .458 | 360 | RN | 6.50 | 29.25 |
| | .458 | 370 | SP | 7.00 | 31.50 |
| | .458 | 405 | FP | 7.50 | 33.75 |
| | .458 | 405 | CBFPPP | 7.50 | 33.75 |
| | .458 | 425 | BTSP | 8.00 | 36.00 |
| | .458 | 435 | FPPP | 9.00 | 40.50 |
| | .458 | 446 | GCFP | 9.00 | 40.50 |
| | .458 | 455 | SP | 10.00 | 45.00 |
| | .458 | 465 | T | 10.00 | 45.00 |
| | .458 | 490 | GCFP | 11.00 | 49.50 |
| | .458 | 500 | RN | 11.00 | 49.50 |
| | .451 | 500 | RNPP | 11.00 | 49.50 |
| | .451 | 530 | GCFP | 12.00 | 54.00 |
| | .451 | 530 | CBPP | 12.00 | 54.00 |
| | .451 | 580 | T | 13.00 | 58.50 |
| 475 | .476 | 380 | FP | 9.00* | 40.50* |
| 50 | .512 | 340 | FP | 10.00* | 45.00* |
| | .512 | 430 | FP | 10.50* | 47.25* |
| | .512 | 440 | RNFP | 11.00* | 49.50* |
| | .512 | 505 | RNFP | 12.00* | 54.00* |
| | .500 | 535 | FPPPP | 12.50 | 56.25* |
| | .505 | 565 | CBFPPP | 13.00* | 58.50* |
| | .512 | 570 | GCRNFP | 13.00* | 58.50* |
| | .512 | 710 | GCFP | 7.50* | |
| 50 BMG | .512 | 900 | GCSP | .50** | |

*Price for 50 and 250.
**Price for each.
RN = Round-Nose; WC = Wadcutter; SWC = Semi-Wadcutter; BB = Bevel Base; FP = Flat Point; GC = Gas Checkable; PT = Pointed; SP = Spire Point; PP = Paper Patch; T = Taper.

## MOLOC Rifle

| Caliber | Wgt. Grs. | Type | Price/250 |
|---|---|---|---|
| 458 | 305 | FP | $18.00 |
| | 360 | FP | 21.90 |
| | 405 | FP | 25.80 |

FP = Flat Point.

## OLD WESTERN SCROUNGER Cast Lead Bullets

| Diameter | Wgt. Grs. | Type | Price/100 |
|---|---|---|---|
| .258 | 87 | RN | $13.00 |
| .265 | 140 | SPGC | 13.00 |
| .285 | 145 | TCGC | 13.00 |
| .309 | 115 | RNBB | 13.00 |
| | 120 | RNGC | 13.00 |
| | 150 | FPGC | 13.00 |
| | 165 | TCGC | 13.00 |
| | 175 | TCGC | 13.00 |
| | 180 | FPGC | 13.00 |
| .313 | 95 | SWC | 13.00 |
| | 118 | FP | 13.00 |
| .320 | 160 | RN | 15.00 |
| .349 | 185 | FPGC | 16.50 |
| | 220 | FP | 16.50 |
| .358 | 230 | FP | 16.50 |
| .376 | 250 | FP | 16.50 |
| | 250 | FPGC | 16.50 |
| .401 | 172 | FP | 16.50 |
| | 190 | FP | 16.50 |
| | 200 | TCBB | 16.50 |
| .406 | 260 | FP | 16.50 |
| .410 | 215 | SWC | 13.00 |
| | 210 | SWCBB | 13.00 |
| .416 | 350 | FNGC | 17.50 |
| .428 | 210 | FP | 13.00 |

| Diameter | Wgt. Grs. | Type | Price/100 |
|---|---|---|---|
| .430 | 195 | FP | $13.00 |
| | 240 | SWCBB | 13.00 |
| | 240 | SWCGC | 13.00 |
| | 300 | FPGC | 16.50 |
| .439 | 370 | FP | 18.50 |
| .446 | 370 | FP | 18.50 |
| .452 | 250 | RN | 13.00 |
| | 325 | FPGC | 17.50 |
| | 340 | FPGC | 17.50 |
| .458 | 300 | FP | 18.50 |
| | 375 | SP | 18.50 |
| | 405 | FP | 18.50 |
| | 405 | SPGC | 18.50 |
| | 425 | FPGC | 18.50 |
| | 500 | FP | 18.50 |
| | 500 | FPGC | 18.50 |
| | 535 | SPBB | 18.50 |
| .476 | 430 | FP | 18.50 |
| | 440 | FP | 18.50 |
| | 450 | SP | 18.50 |
| .512 | 350 | FP | 18.50 |
| | 400 | FP | 18.50 |
| | 450 | FP | 18.50 |
| | 600 | FPGC | 18.50 |
| | 655 | FP | 18.50 |

BB = Bevel Base; RN = Round Nose; TC = Truncated Cone; GC = Gas Check; SWC = Semi-Wadcutter; SP = Spitzer; FP = Flat Point; BT = Boattail.

## LIGHTNING PERFORMANCE INNOVATIONS, INC.

| Bullet | Wgt. Grs. | Hollow | Bonded Core/25 | Partitioned/25 |
|---|---|---|---|---|
| Open Tip Lead Core | 190 | $37.50 | $53.00 | NA |
| | 225 | 40.00 | 54.00 | NA |
| | 240 | 42.50 | 55.00 | NA |
| | 265 | 45.00 | 56.00 | 51.50 |
| | 290 | 47.50 | 57.00 | 54.50 |
| Twister-Stranded Cores | 125 | 40.25 | | |
| | 140 | 40.25 | | |
| | 160 | 46.75 | | |
| Duster #12, #9, #6 Shot | 160 | 48.75 | | |
| | 180 | 48.75 | | |
| Lead Tips | 250 | 42.50 | 44.00 | |
| | 275 | 47.75 | 50.25 | |
| | 300 | 50.00 | 54.00 | |
| | 300 | — | 55.00 | |
| Lead Tip Hollowpoint | 250 | 43.50 | 45.00 | |
| | 275 | 49.25 | 51.25 | |
| | 300 | 51.25 | 55.00 | |
| | 300 | — | 56.00 | |

## MONTANA PRECISION SWAGING
### Paper Patch Bullets

| Caliber | Wgt. Grs. | Diameter | Type | Base | Price/100 |
|---|---|---|---|---|---|
| | **SWAGED STRAIGHT SIDED UNPATCHED** | | | | |
| 38 | 250 | .365 | RN | Cup | $21.00 |
| | 300 | .365 | RN | Cup | 21.00 |
| 40 | 330 | .395 | RN | Cup | 22.75 |
| | 370 | .395 | RN | Cup | 22.75 |
| | 400 | .395 | RN | Cup | 22.75 |
| | 330 | .399 | RN | Cup | 22.75 |
| | 370 | .399 | RN | Cup | 22.75 |
| | 400 | .399 | RN | Cup | 22.75 |
| 43 Span. | 350 | .439 | RN | Flat, cup | 24.50 |
| | 400-550 | .439 | RN | Flat, cup | 24.50 |
| 44 | 380 | .440 | FN | Cup | 24.50 |
| | 400 | .440 | RN | Cup | 24.50 |
| | 500 | .440 | RN | Cup | 24.50 |
| 45 | 400 | .450 | RN | Cup | 24.50 |
| | 475 | .450 | RN | Cup | 25.0 |
| | 500 | .450 | RN | Cup | 25.00 |
| | 510 | .450 | RN | Cup | 25.00 |
| | 540 | .450 | RN | Cup | 25.00 |
| 50 | 450 | .505 | RN | Cup | 25.50 |
| | 500 | .505 | RN | Cup | 25.50 |
| | 550 | .505 | RN | Cup | 25.50 |
| | **SWAGED TAPER UNPATCHED** | | | | |
| 40 | 330 | .402 | SP | | 27.00 |
| | 350 | .402 | SP | | 27.00 |
| | 370 | .402 | SP | | 27.00 |
| | 420 | .402 | SP | | 27.00 |
| 45 | 450 | .450 | SP | | 27.50 |
| | 510 | .450 | SP | | 27.50 |
| | 540 | .450 | SP | | 27.50 |
| 50 | 450-500 | .503 | SP | | 28.50 |
| | **JACKETED BULLETS FOR BLACK POWDER CARTRIDGE RIFLES** | | | | |
| 40 | 300-350 | .408 Flat | SP | .408 | 24.50/50 |
| 45 | 300-380 | .408 Flat | SP | .458 | 22.50/50 |

RN = Round Nose; SP = Spire Point.

## MONTANA PRECISION SWAGING
### Cast Bullets

| Caliber | Wgt. Grs. | Sized | Tip | Price/100 |
|---|---|---|---|---|
| 257 Roberts | 120 | .257 | SP | $15.50 |
| 8mm | 140 | .284 | FN | 15.50 |
| 32-40 | 200 | .323 | FN | 17.50 |
| | 210 | .376 | RN | 17.50 |
| 38 | 255 | .376 | FN | 17.50 |
| | 255 | .379 | FN | 17.50 |
| | 260 | .406 | SWC | 17.50 |
| | 265 | .381 | FN | 17.50 |
| 40 | 300 | .408 | SP | 17.50 |
| | 350 | .408 | SP | 19.20 |
| | 370 | .408 | SP | 19.20 |
| | 400 | .408 | SP | 19.20 |
| | 410 | .408 | SP | 19.20 |
| 43 | 370 | .440 | RN | 19.20 |
| 44 | 370 | .446 | FN | 19.20 |
| | 485 | .446 | FN | 19.20 |
| 45 | 300 | .458 | FN | 17.50 |
| | 405 | .458 | FN | 21.00 |
| | 385 | .458 | RN | 18.50 |
| | 385 | .405 | FN | 19.20 |
| | 385 | .465 | FN | 19.20 |
| | 480 | .458 | SP | 19.20 |
| | 500 | .458 | FN | 20.30 |
| | 525 | .458 | SP | 20.30 |
| | 550 | .458 | FN | 20.30 |
| 50 | 300 | .510 | RN | 17.50 |
| | 325 | .499 | FN | 17.50 |
| | 365 | .515 | FN | 19.00 |
| | 450 | .510 | FN | 20.30 |
| | 475 | .542 | SP | 20.20 |
| | 640 | .512 | RN | 25.20 |

SWC = Semi-Wadcutter; RN = Round Nose; FN = Flat Nose; SP = Spire Point.

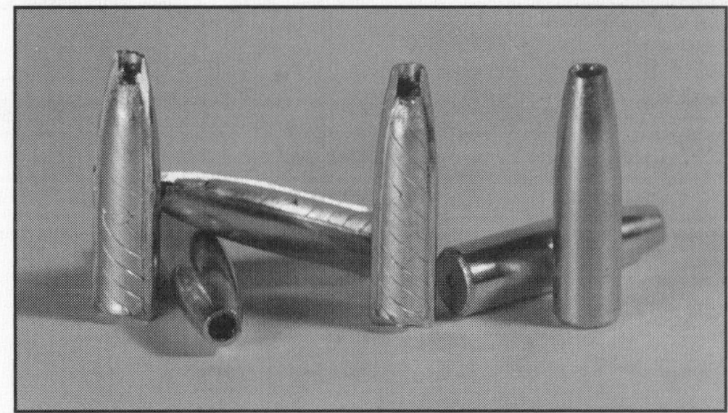

Lightning Performance Innovations 125-gr. Aluminum Core Twister

Lightning Performance Innovations General Product Line

## MIDWAY Plated Bullets

| Caliber | Wgt. Grs. | Type | Price/100 | Price/500 | Price/1000 |
|---|---|---|---|---|---|
| 30 | 110 | RN | $8.79 | $34.99 | $61.99 |
| 7.62x39 | 123 | FMJ | 10.49 | 44.99 | 74.99 |
| 380 ACP | 95 | RN** | 7.79 | 28.99 | 49.99 |
| 9mm | 115 | RN** | 7.79 | 29.99 | 49.99 |
| 115 | HP** | 7.49 | 29.99 | 52.99 | |
| 124 | FP** | 7.79 | 29.99 | 51.99 | |
| 124 | RN** | 7.79 | 29.99 | 51.99 | |
| 147 | RN** | 8.99 | 35.99 | 58.99 | |
| 147 | HP** | 9.29 | 37.99 | 59.99 | |
| 9mm Makarov | 95 | RN** | 7.79 | 28.99 | 49.99 |
| 38 Super | 130 | RN** | 8.99 | 34.99 | 58.99 |
| 151 | RN** | 9.99 | 38.99 | 62.99 | |
| 38/357 | 125 | FP** | 8.49 | 32.99 | 55.99 |
| 125 | HP** | 8.49 | 33.99 | 58.99 | |
| 148 | DEWC** | 9.29 | 36.99 | 59.99 | |
| 158 | FP** | 9.49 | 36.99 | 59.99 | |
| 158 | RN** | 9.49 | 36.99 | 59.99 | |
| 158 | HP** | 9.99 | 39.99 | 64.99 | |
| 40 S&W/10mm | 155 | FP** | 11.99 | 41.99 | 66.99 |
| 180 | FP** | 10.99 | 44.99 | 71.99 | |
| 180 | HP** | 11.99 | 46.99 | 76.99 | |
| 41 Caliber | 220 | FP | 13.49 | 52.99 | 88.99 |
| 44 Caliber | 240 | FP | 13.99 | 52.99 | 87.99 |
| 240 | HP | 13.99 | 55.99 | 92.99 | |
| 45 Caliber | 185 | FP** | 11.99 | 45.99 | 74.99 |
| 185 | HP | 11.99 | 47.99 | 79.99 | |
| 200 | SWC** | 12.49 | 46.99 | 76.99 | |
| 200 | FP** | 12.49 | 46.99 | 76.99 | |
| 200 | HP** | 12.99 | 49.99 | 82.99 | |
| 230 | HP** | 12.49 | 49.99 | 85.99 | |
| 230 | RN** | 12.49 | 48.99 | 79.99 | |
| 250 | FP | 14.49 | 55.99 | 92.99 | |

**These bullets are now re-sized after the final plating process to increase bullet uniformity and to maximize accuracy.

## MIDWAY Extra Hard Cast Bullets

| Caliber | Wgt. Grs. | Type | Dia. | Price/100 | Price/500 | Price/1000 |
|---|---|---|---|---|---|---|
| 32 | 98 | WC | .314 | $5.79 | $19.49 | $34.99 |
| | 100 | SWC | .314 | 5.79 | 19.49 | 34.99 |
| 380 ACP | 95 | RN | .356 | 5.49 | 18.99 | 33.99 |
| 9mm | 122 | FP | .356 | 6.49 | 22.99 | 38.99 |
| | 125 | RN | .356 | 6.29 | 23.99 | 39.99 |
| 9mm Makarov | 93 | RN | .365 | 4.99 | 18.49 | 33.99 |
| 38/357 | 148 | DEWC | .358 | 7.49 | 25.99 | 42.99 |
| | 148 | BN | .358 | 7.49 | 25.99 | 42.99 |
| | 158 | RN | .358 | 7.49 | 26.99 | 44.99 |
| | 158 | SWC | .358 | 7.49 | 26.99 | 44.99 |
| 38/40 WCF | 180 | RN/FP | .401 | 8.29 | 29.99 | 52.99 |
| 40 S&W/10mm | 140 | FP | .401 | 6.99 | 24.99 | 40.99 |
| | 175 | SWC | .401 | 8.29 | 29.99 | 49.99 |
| | 180 | FP | .401 | 8.49 | 31.99 | 51.99 |
| 41 Caliber | 215 | SWC | .411 | 9.49 | 35.99 | 58.99 |
| 44/40 WCF | 200 | RN/FP | .427 | 9.29 | 33.99 | 55.99 |
| | 240 | RN/FP | .427 | 10.49 | 38.99 | 64.99 |
| 44 | 190 | SWC | .430 | 8.79 | 32.99 | 53.99 |
| | 240 | SWC | .430 | 10.49 | 38.99 | 63.99 |
| | 240 | RN/FP | .430 | 9.79 | 37.99 | 63.99 |
| 45 | 185 | SWC | .452 | 8.79 | 34.99 | 52.99 |
| | 200 | SWC | .452 | 8.99 | 32.99 | 55.99 |
| | 230 | RN | .452 | 9.99 | 37.99 | 61.99 |
| | 250 | RN/FP | .452 | 10.99 | 39.99 | 67.99 |
| | 255 | SWC | .452 | 11.49 | 41.99 | 68.99 |

WC = Wadcutter; SWC = Semi-Wadcutter; RN = Round Nose; FP = Flat Point; DEWC = Double Ended Wadcutter.

## RUBRIGHT

| Caliber | Wgt. Grs. | Type | Price/100 |
|---|---|---|---|
| 224 | 52 | FB | $12.00 |
| | 57 | FB | 12.00 |
| 6mm | 63 | FB, BT | 13.00 |
| | 65 | FB, BT | 13.00 |
| | 66 | FB, BT | 13.00 |
| | 68 | FB, BT | 13.00 |
| 308 | 125 | FB | 17.50 |
| | 135 | FB | 17.50 |
| | 150 | FB | 17.50 |

FB = Flat Base; BT = Boattail.

## REMINGTON Rifle Bullets

| Caliber | Wgt. Grs. | Type | Price/2000 |
|---|---|---|---|
| 17 | 25 | PLHP | $250.00* |
| 22 | 45 | SP | 117.40 |
| | 45 | HP | 117.40 |
| | 50 | PLHP | 127.98 |
| | 50 | PSP | 101.05 |
| | 55 | PSP | 93.89 |
| | 55 | MC | 66.95 |
| | 55 | PLHP | 270.30* |
| 6mm | 80 | PSP | 130.45 |
| | 80 | PLHP | 169.50 |
| | 100 | PSPCL | 134.65 |
| 243 | 100 | PSPCL | 134.65 |
| 25 | 87 | PLHP | 169.50 |
| | 86 | SP | 137.15 |
| | 100 | PSPCL | 148.98 |
| | 120 | PSPCL | 160.35 |
| 6.5 | 120 | PSPCL | 172.70 |
| | 140 | PSPCL | 171.95 |
| 270 | 100 | PSP | 148.75 |
| | 130 | PSPCL | 159.10 |
| | 130 | BP | 246.30 |
| | 150 | SPCL | 168.98 |
| 7mm | 140 | PSPCL | 164.55 |
| | 150 | PSPCL | 170.50 |
| | 175 | PSPCL | 182.10 |
| 30 | 110 | SP | 112.15 |
| | 110 | MC | 112.15 |
| | 125 | PSP | 160.85 |
| | 150 | BP | 256.20 |
| | 150 | SPCL | 169.25 |
| | 150 | PSPCL | 169.25 |
| | 165 | PSPCL | 172.45 |
| | 170 | HPCL | 224.70 |
| | 170 | SPCL | 172.45 |
| | 180 | BP | 266.10 |
| | 180 | SPCL | 182.85 |
| | 180 | PSPCL | 182.85 |
| | 125 | PSP | 161.10 |
| 303 | 180 | SPCL | 186.30 |
| 32 | 100 | SP | 148.98 |
| 8mm | 185 | PSPCL | 191.50 |
| 35 | 150 | PSPCL | 172.45 |
| | 200 | SPCL | 101.70** |
| 350 | 200 | PSPCL | 101.70** |
| 44-40 | 200 | SP | 89.45** |
| 45-70 | 405 | SP | 116.98** |
| 45-70 | 300 | JHP | 114.15** |

* = per 4000; ** = per 1000.
PLHP = Power-Lokt Hollow Point; MC = Metal Cased; SPCL = Soft Point Core-Lokt; PSPCL = Pointed Soft Point Core-Lokt; PSP = Pointed Soft Point; SP = Soft Point.

## NORTHERN PRECISION Rifle Bullets

| Bullet | Wgt. Grs. | Type | Description | Price/Per |
|---|---|---|---|---|
| | | | **CALIBER: 358** | |
| | 200-300 | SP | .025, non-bonded | $20.00/25 |
| | 200-300 | SP | .025, bonded | 25.00/25 |
| | 200-300 | SP | .035, non-bonded | 20.00/25 |
| | 200-300 | SP | .035, bonded | 25.00/25 |
| | | | **CALIBER: 375** | |
| | 200-300 | SP | .025, non-bonded | 20.00/25 |
| | 200-300 | SP | .025, bonded | 25.00/25 |
| | 200-300 | SP | .035, non-bonded | 20.00/25 |
| | 200-300 | SP | .035, bonded | 25.00/25 |
| | 200-300 | Baseguard | | 14.00/50 |
| | 200-300 | RN | Thin jacket, non-bonded | 16.00/50 |
| | 200-300 | FT | Thin jacket, non-bonded | |
| | 200-300 | FT | Thin jacket, bonded | 25.00/25 |
| | 225-300 | | Poly Tip, .025 non-bonded | 22.00/25 |
| | 225-300 | | Poly Tip, .025, bonded | 27.00/25 |
| | | | **CALIBER: 416** | |
| Varminter | 198-250 | HP | Thin jacket | 14.00/50 |
| Whitetail | 275-350 | | Thin jacket | 16.00/50 |
| Small Game Getter | 250 | RN | Thin jacket, bonded core | 25.00/25 |
| Polly Ball | 300-375 | SRN | Bonded | 22.00/25 |
| | 300-375 | SRN | Non-bonded | 18.00/25 |
| Long Range | 300-450 | | Double jacket | 27.00/25 |
| Brush Country | 300-450 | | Jacket, bonded core | 25.00/25 |
| Plinker | 250-400 | RN, SP | | 14.00/50 |
| Large Game | 375-450 | SP | Jacket, thick ogive, bonded core | 25.00/25 |
| | 375-450 | SP | Double jacket | 27.00/25 |
| Polly Ball Tip | 300-375 | | .035″ Tube Jacket, non-bonded | 22.00/25 |
| | 300-375 | | .035″ Tube Jacket, bonded | 27.00/25 |
| | | | **CALIBER: 429** | |
| | 150-325 | FT | Baseguard | 14.00/50 |
| | 180-330 | FT | Thin jacket | 14.00/50 |
| | 240-350 | SP | Thin jacket | 16.00/50 |
| | 240-350 | SP | Thin jacket, bonded | 25.00/25 |
| | 255 | FT | Thin jacket, bonded | 25.00/25 |
| | 275-325 | SP | Baseguard | 14.00/50 |
| Large Game | 300-375 | FT | .025 tubing, non-bonded | 20.00/25 |
| Large Game | 300-375 | FT | .025 tubing, bonded | 25.00/25 |
| Large Game | 300-375 | FT | .035 tubing, non-bonded | 20.00/25 |
| Large Game | 300-375 | FT | .035 tubing, bonded | 25.00/25 |
| | 300-375 | SP | .025 tubing, non-bonded | 20.00/25 |
| | 300-375 | SP | .025 tubing, bonded | 25.00/25 |
| Polly Tip | | | Thin jacket | 16.00/50 |
| | | | Thin jacket, bonded | 27.00/25 |
| Sabr Star | | | Thin jacket | 16.00/50 |
| | | | Thin jacket, bonded | 27.00/25 |
| | | | **CALIBER: 458** | |
| Varminter | 265 | RN, FT | Thin jacket | 12.00/50 |
| | 265 | RN, FT | Bonded | 25.00/25 |
| Whitetail/Black Bear | 300-400 | FT, RN | Bonded | 25.00/25 |
| | 300-400 | FT, RN | Thin jacket | 16.00/50 |
| Large Game | 300-500 | RN, FT | Non-bonded | 20.00/25 |
| | 300-500 | RN, FT | Bonded | 25.00/25 |
| Plinker | 250-400 | RN, FT | Baseguard | 14.00/50 |
| | 325-380 | SP | Thin jacket | 16.00/50 |
| | 350-425 | SP | Baseguard | 14.00/50 |
| Large Game | 400-465 | SP | .035 tubing | 25.00/25 |
| Polly Tip | 350-400 | SP | .035 non-bonded | 22.00/25 |
| Tapered Jacket | | SP | .035 bonded | 27.00/25 |

HP = Hollowpoint; SRN = Semi-Round Nose; SP = Spitzer; FT = Flat Tip; RN = Round Nose.

## SCHROEDER Obsolete Rifle

| Caliber | Dia. | Wgt. Grs. | Type | Price/100 |
|---|---|---|---|---|
| 5.45mm | .220 | 52 | HP | $22.00 |
| | .220 | 55 | HP | 22.00 |
| | .220 | 60 | HP | 22.00 |
| | .220 | 69 | HP | 22.00 |
| | .220 | 80 | HP | 22.00 |
| 22 Sav. HP | .228 | 55 | SP | 20.00 |
| | .228 | 60 | SP | 20.00 |
| | .228 | 70 | SP | 20.00 |
| 23 1/2 | .234 | 60 | SP | 20.00 |
| | .234 | 80 | SP | 20.00 |
| | .234 | 100 | SP | 20.00 |
| 242 Vickers | .249 | 100 | SP | 22.00 |
| 6.5mm | .268 | 100 | SP | 20.00 |
| | .268 | 120 | SP | 20.00 |
| | .268 | 129 | SP | 20.00 |
| | .268 | 140 | SP | 20.00 |
| 280 Ross | .287 | 130 | SFP | 22.00 |
| | .287 | 150 | SFP | 22.00 |
| 7.35 Carcano | .298 | 125 | SP | 17.00 |
| | .298 | 130 | SP | 17.00 |
| | .298 | 150 | SP | 17.00 |
| 7.62mm | .310 | 130 | SP | 22.00 |
| | .310 | 150 | SP | 22.00 |
| | .310 | 165 | SP | 22.00 |
| | .310 | 180 | SP | 22.00 |
| 8mm J-Bore | .318 | 150 | SP | 20.00 |
| | .318 | 175 | SP | 20.00 |
| | .318 | 200 | SP | 20.00 |
| | .318 | 220 | SP | 20.00 |
| 32 WSL | .318 | 150 | RN | 20.00 |
| | .318 | 165 | RN | 20.00 |
| | .318 | 170 | RN | 20.00 |
| 303 | .314 | 150 | SP | 22.00 |
| | .314 | 165 | SP | 22.00 |
| | .314 | 180 | SP | 22.00 |
| 32-40 Win. | .3205 | 170 | FN | 22.00 |
| 8mm Hungarian | .329 | 150 | SP | 26.00 |
| | .329 | 175 | SP | 26.00 |
| | .329 | 200 | SP | 26.00 |
| | .329 | 220 | SP | 26.00 |
| 351 WSL | .351 | 180 | RN | 22.00 |
| | .351 | 200 | RN | 22.00 |
| 10.75mm | .423 | 180 | HP | 23.00 |
| | .423 | 200 | HP | 23.00 |
| | .423 | 240 | HP | 23.00 |
| | .423 | 300 | HP | 26.00 |

SP = Spire Point; SFP = Softpoint; RN = Round-Nose; HP = Hollowpoint; FN = Flat Nose.

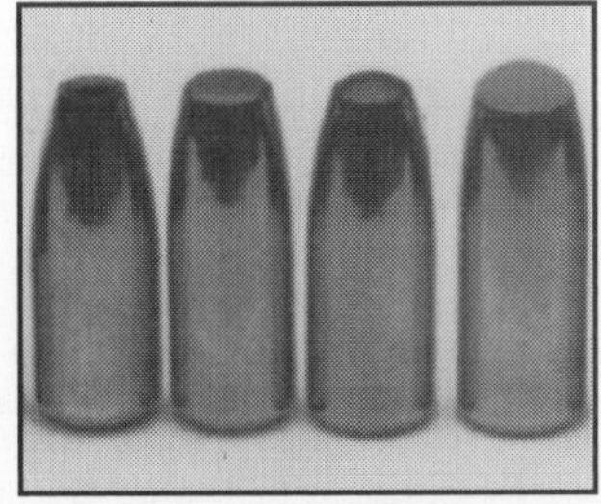

Northern Precision 416-Caliber 200-450-Gr. Bullets

## RWS

| Caliber | Dia. | Wgt. Grs. | Type | Price/Per |
|---|---|---|---|---|
| 22 | .224 | 45 | TG | $21.00/100 |
| | .224 | 46 | SP | 41.70/100 |
| | .224 | 50 | TG | 48.00/100 |
| | .224 | 50 | SP | 41.70/100 |
| | .224 | 74 | CP | 44.30/50 |
| 22 | .228 | 71 | PSP | 36.95/50 |
| 243 | .243 | 70 | TG | 48.00/100 |
| | .243 | 96 | CP | 32.10/50 |
| 264 | .264 | 93 | TG | 48.00/100 |
| | .264 | 93 | SP | 30.45/50 |
| | .264 | 108 | CP | 34.05/50 |
| | .264 | 127 | CP | 49.95/50 |
| | .264 | 159 | SP | 44.60/50 |
| 270 | .277 | 130 | HMHP | 50.10/50 |
| | .277 | 150 | CP | 41.80/50 |
| 7mm | .284 | 123 | CP | 41.80/50 |
| | .284 | 139 | CP | 48.00/100 |
| | .284 | 139 | SP | 32.55/50 |
| | .284 | 162 | CP | 49.85/50 |
| | .284 | 162 | TIG | 36.95/50 |
| | .284 | 173 | HMHP | 67.40/50 |
| | .284 | 177 | TIG | 36.95/50 |
| 30 | .308 | 150 | TIG | 46.00/50 |
| | .308 | 150 | CP | 42.00/50 |
| | .308 | 165 | CP | 49.85/50 |
| | .308 | 181 | HMHP | 73.15/50 |
| | .308 | 181 | TUG | 47.30/50 |
| 8mm | .318 | 196 | SP | 36.85/50 |
| 8mm | .323 | 181 | CP | 36.95/50 |
| | .323 | 187 | HMHP | 77.20/50 |
| | .323 | 196 | SP | 38.70/50 |
| | .323 | 198 | TIG | 45.90/50 |
| | .323 | 224 | CP | 52.90/50 |
| 9.3mm | .364 | 193 | FNSP | 49.70/50 |
| 9.3mm | .366 | 247 | CP | 45.90/50 |
| | .366 | 258 | HMHP | 76.65/50 |
| | .366 | 285 | SP | 40.40/50 |
| | .366 | 293 | TUG | 56.85/50 |
| 375 | .375 | 300 | CP | 60.00/50 |
| | .375 | 300 | FMJ | 33.65/50 |
| | .375 | 300 | TUG | 71.50/50 |
| 10.75mm | .423 | 347 | FMJ | 38.60/50 |
| | .423 | 401 | FMJ | 20.80/20 |

SP = Soft Point; FMJ = Full Metal Jacket; CP = Cone Point; TIG = Brenneke TIG; TUG = Brenneke TUG; HMHP = H-Mantel Hollow Point. From Huntington.

## THUNDERBIRD

| Caliber | Wgt. Grs. | Type | Price/50 |
|---|---|---|---|
| 308 | 180 | RN | $39.00 |
| | 220 | RN | 40.00 |
| 323 | 220 | RN | 43.00 |
| 338 | 250 | RN | 44.00 |
| 9.3mm | 286 | RN | 48.00 |
| 375 | 300 | RN | 49.00 |
| 416 | 400 | RN | 55.00 |
| 423 | 400 | RN | 56.00 |
| 458 | 465 | RN | 60.00 |
| 468 | 480 | RN | 61.00 |
| 475 | 500 | RN | 62.00 |
| 488 | 500 | RN | 64.00 |
| 505 | 525 | RN | 66.00 |
| 510 | 570 | RN | 68.00 |
| 585 | 750 | RN | 77.00 |

## STAR

| Caliber | Dia. | Wgt. Grs. | —Jacket— | C/B | Price/25 |
|---|---|---|---|---|---|
| 7mm | .284, .288 | 139 | .032, .049 | C | $35.00 |
| | .284, .288 | 160 | .032, .049 | C | 35.00 |
| | .284, .288 | 175 | .032, .049 | C | 35.00 |
| 30 | .308 | 180 | .032, .049 | C, B | 35.00 |
| | .308 | 200 | .032, .049 | C, B | 35.00 |
| | .308 | 220 | .032, .049 | C, B | 35.00 |
| | .308 | 250 | .032, .049 | C, B | 35.00 |
| 8mm | .323, .318 | 185 | .032, .049 | C, B | 35.00 |
| | .323, .318 | 200 | .032, .049 | C, B | 35.00 |
| | .323, .318 | 225 | .032, .049 | C, B | 35.00 |
| | .323, .318 | 250 | .032, .049 | C, B | 35.00 |
| 318 | .330 | SO | .032, .049 | C | SO |
| 338 | | 200 | .032, .049, .065 | C, B | 35.00 |
| | | 250 | .032, .049, .065 | C, B | 35.00 |
| | | 275 | .032, .049, .065 | C, B | 35.00 |
| | | 300 | .032, .049, .065 | C, B | 35.00 |
| 35 | .358 | 180 | .032, .049, .065 | C, B | 41.00 |
| | .358 | 250 | .032, .049, .065 | C, B | 41.00 |
| | .358 | 275 | .032, .049, .065 | C, B | 41.00 |
| | .358 | 300 | .032, .049, .065 | C, B | 41.00 |
| 9.3mm | .366 | SO | .049, .065 | C, B | SO |
| 375 | .375 | 270 | .049, .065 | C, B | 41.00 |
| | .375 | 300 | .049, .065 | C, B | 41.00 |
| | .375 | 350 | .049, .065 | C, B | 41.00 |
| 40 | .411 | SO | .049, .065 | C, B | 52.00 |
| 416 | .416 | 300 | .049, .065 | C, B | 52.00 |
| | .416 | 410 | .049, .065 | C, B | 52.00 |
| 404 | .423 | 300 | .049, .065 | C, B | 52.00 |
| | .423 | 410 | .049, .065 | C, B | 52.00 |
| 444 | .429 | SO | .049, .065 | C, B | SO |
| 425 | | SO | .049, .065 | C, B | SO |
| 11.2mm | .440 | 409 | .049, .065 | C, B | 52.00 |
| 458 | .458 | 365 | .032, .049, .065 | C, B | 52.00 |
| | .458 | 400 | .032, .049, .065 | C, B | 52.00 |
| | .458 | 480 | .032, .049, .065 | C, B | 52.00 |
| | .458 | 500 | .032, .049, .065 | C, B | 52.00 |
| | .458 | 600 | .032, .049, .065 | C, B | 52.00 |
| 465 | .468 | SO | .049, .065 | C, B | SO |
| 470 | .475 | 480 | .049, .065 | C, B | 52.00 |
| | .475 | 500 | .049, .065 | C, B | 52.00 |
| | .475 | 520 | .049, .065 | C, B | 52.00 |
| 475 | .488, .483 | SO | .049, .065 | C, B | SO |
| 500 | .505, .510 | 400 | .049, .065 | C, B | 52.00 |
| | .505, .510 | 500 | .049, .065 | C, B | 52.00 |
| | .505, .510 | 535 | .049, .065 | C, B | 52.00 |
| | .505, .510 | 600 | .049, .065 | C, B | 52.00 |
| 50 BMG | .510 | SO | .049, .065 | C | SO |
| 577 | .585 | 650 | .049, .065 | C, B | 52.00 |
| | .585 | 750 | .049, .065 | C, B | 52.00 |
| 600 | .622 | SO | .032, .065 | C, B | SO |

C = Copper; B = Brass; SO = Special Order.

## STARKE

| Caliber | Wgt. Grs. | Price/100 |
|---|---|---|
| 224 | 40,45 | $13.75 |
| | 50,52,55 | 14.25 |
| 243 | 68,70,72 | 14.75 |
| | 75,80,85 | |
| 308 | 125,135,150 | 19.00 |
| | 165,168,172 | |

## WINCHESTER Rifle Bullets

| Caliber | Wgt. Grs. | Type | Knurl | Price/100 | Price/500 |
|---|---|---|---|---|---|
| 22 | 46 | HP | NA | $8.49 | $35.99 |
| | 50 | PSP | NA | 7.49 | 31.99 |
| | 55 | PSP | .460 | 6.99 | 29.99 |
| | 55 | FMJBT | .485 | 4.99 | 19.79 |
| | 64 | PP | NA | 9.49 | 39.99 |
| 243/6mm | 80 | PSP | NA | 10.59 | 42.99 |
| 270 | 130 | PP | .755 | 12.79 | 49.99 |
| | 140 | FS | NA | 19.99 | — |
| 7mm/284 | 150 | PP | .760 | 12.99 | 51.99 |
| | 160 | FS | NA | 23.99 | — |
| 7.62 | 123 | PP | .620 | 12.79 | 51.99 |
| 30 | 147 | FMJBT | .765 | 12.49 | 51.99 |
| | 150 | PP | .685 | 12.69 | 51.99 |
| | 150 | PPFN | .500 | — | — |
| | 180 | PP | .725 | 16.49 | 63.99 |
| | 180 | FS (2700 fps) | NA | 21.99 | — |
| | 180 | FS (3000 fps) | NA | 25.99 | — |
| 44 | 200 | SP | .268 | 17.29 | 64.99 |
| 338 | 230 | FS | NA | 28.99 | — |
| 375 | 270 | FS | NA | 35.99 | — |
| | 300 | FS | NA | 31.99 | — |

HP = Hollowpoint; PSP = Pointed Soft Point; FMJ = Full Metal JAcket; BT = Boattail; PP = Power Point; FS = Fail Safe; FN = Flat Nose.
From Midway Arms.

## SWIFT

| Caliber | Wgt. Grs. | Type | Price/50 |
|---|---|---|---|
| 308 | 165 | SP | $50.25 |
| | 180 | SP | 50.25 |
| | 200 | SP | 50.25 |
| 338 | 225 | SP | 52.30 |
| | 250 | SP | 52.30 |
| | 275 | SP | 52.30 |
| 358 | 225 | SP | 55.60 |
| | 250 | SP | 55.60 |
| 366 | 250 | SP | 56.85 |
| | 300 | SP | 56.85 |
| 375 | 250 | SP | 56.85 |
| | 300 | SP | 56.85 |
| 411 | 350 | SP | 48.95 |
| | 400 | SP | 48.95 |
| 416 | 350 | SP | 64.35 |
| | 400 | SP | 64.35 |
| 458 | 400 | SP | 64.35 |
| | 500 | SP | 64.35 |

From The Old Western Scrounger.

## UNMUSSIG

| Caliber | Wgt. Grs. | Type | Price/100 |
|---|---|---|---|
| 144 | 15 | FB,HP | $27.50 |
| | 16 | FB,HP | 27.50 |
| | 17.5 | FB,HP | 27.50 |
| 172 | 15 | FB,SP | 15.00 |
| | 18 | FB,HP | 15.00 |
| | 21 | FB,HP | 15.00 |
| | 25 | FB,HP | 15.00 |
| | 30 | FB,HP | 15.00 |
| | 35 | BT,SP | 22.50 |
| | 37 | VLD,HP | 22.50 |
| 204 | 32 | FB,SP | 18.50 |
| | 36 | FB,HP | 18.50 |
| | 40 | FB,HP | 18.50 |
| | 44 | FB,HP | 18.50 |
| | 48 | FB,BT,HP | 18.50 |
| | 51 | VLD,HP | 22.50 |

FB = Flat Base; BT = Boattail; HP = Hollow Point; SP = Soft Point; VLD = Very Low Drag.

## WOODLEIGH

| Cartridge | Diameter | Wgt. Grs. | Type | Price/Per |
|---|---|---|---|---|
| 700 Nitro | .700 | 1000 | SN | $102.98/25 |
| | .700 | 1000 | FMJ | 102.98/25 |
| 600 Nitro | .620 | 900 | SN | 50.98/25 |
| | .620 | 900 | FMJ | 60.98/25 |
| 577 Nitro | .585 | 750 | SN | 48.98/25 |
| | .585 | 750 | FMJ | 60.98/25 |
| | .585 | 650 | SN | 41.98/25 |
| 50 BMG | | 750 | SPSN | 60.98 |
| 500 Nitro | .510 | 570 | SN | 36.98/25 |
| | .510 | 570 | SMJ | 46.98/25 |
| | .510 | 535 | SN | 36.98/25 |
| | .510 | 535 | FMJ | 46.98/25 |
| 500 BP Express | .510 | 440 | SN | 34.98/25 |
| 505 Gibbs | .505 | 525 | SN | 36.98/25 |
| | .505 | 525 | FMJ | 46.98/25 |
| 475 N.E. | .483 | 480 | SN | 59.98/50 |
| | .483 | 480 | FMJ | 79.98/50 |
| 475 Jeffery | .488 | 500 | SN | 59.98/50 |
| | .488 | 500 | FMJ | 79.98/50 |
| 475 Nitro | .476 | 480 | SN | 59.98/50 |
| 476 W.R. | .476 | 520 | SN | 59.98/50 |
| | .476 | 520 | FMJ | 79.98/50 |
| | .476 | 480 | SN | 59.98/50 |
| 470 Nitro | .474 | 500 | SN | 59.98/50 |
| | .474 | 500 | FMJ | 79.98/50 |
| 465 Nitro | .468 | 480 | SN | 59.98/50 |
| | .468 | 480 | FMJ | 79.98/50 |
| 450 | .458 | 480 | SN | 59.98/50 |
| | .458 | 480 | FMJ | 79.98/50 |
| 458 Magnum | .458 | 550 | SN | 59.98/50 |
| | .458 | 550 | FMJ | 79.98/50 |
| | .458 | 500 | SN | 59.98/50 |
| | .458 | 500 | FMJ | 79.98/50 |
| | .458 | 400 | SP | 59.98/50 |
| | .458 | 350 | FNSN | 59.98 |
| 11.2X72 Schuler | .440 | 401 | SN | 55.98 |
| 425 W.R. | .435 | 410 | SN | 55.98/50 |
| | .435 | 410 | FMJ | 74.98/50 |
| 404 Jeffrey | .423 | 400 | SN | 55.98/50 |
| | .423 | 400 | FMJ | 74.98/50 |
| | .423 | 350 | SN | 55.98/50 |
| 10.75x68 | .423 | 347 | SN | 55.98/50 |
| | .423 | 347 | FMJ | 74.98 |
| 416 Rigby | .416 | 410 | SN | 55.98/50 |
| | .416 | 410 | FMJ | 74.98/50 |
| | .416 | 340 | SP | 55.98/50 |
| 450/400 Nitro | .411 | 400 | SN | 55.98/50 |
| | .411 | 400 | FMJ | 74.98/50 |
| 375 Magnum | .375 | 300 | SNRN | 55.98/50 |
| | .375 | 300 | SPSN | 55.98/50 |
| | .375 | 300 | FMJ | 74.98/50 |
| | .375 | 300 | RNSN | 55.95 |
| | .375 | 270 | RNSN | 55.98/50 |
| | .375 | 270 | SPSN | 55.98/50 |
| 9.3mm | .366 | 286 | SN | 55.98/50 |
| | .366 | 286 | FMJ | 74.98/50 |
| 35 | .358 | 310 | SN | 55.98/50 |
| | .358 | 310 | FMJ | 74.98/50 |
| | .358 | 250 | SN | 55.98/50 |
| | .358 | 225 | SN | 55.98/50 |
| | .358 | 225 | FMJ | 74.98/50 |
| 338 | .358 | 300 | SN | 55.98/50 |
| | .358 | 300 | FMJ | 74.98/50 |
| | .358 | 250 | SN | 55.98/50 |
| | .358 | 250 | FMJ | 74.98/50 |
| | .358 | 250 | SPSN | 74.98 |
| 333 Jeffrey | .330 | 300 | SN | 55.98/50 |
| | .330 | 300 | FMJ | 74.98/50 |
| | .330 | 250 | SN | 55.98 |
| 318 W.R. | .330 | 250 | SN | 55.98/50 |
| | .330 | 250 | FMJ | 74.98/50 |
| 8mm | .323 | 196 | SN | 55.98 |
| 30 | .308 | 220 | FMJ | 74.98/50 |
| | .308 | 180 | SPSN | 55.98/50 |
| | .308 | 220 | RNSN | 55.98/50 |

SN = Soft Nose; SP = Semi-Point; FMJ = Full Metal Jacket; FN = Flat Nose.
From Huntington Die Specialties.

# BARNES BULLETS

| Caliber | Wgt. Grs. | Type | Price/50 |
|---|---|---|---|
| | RIFLE | | |
| 22 | 45 | SPTS | $21.99 |
| | 45 | BTX | 24.99 |
| | 45 | BTX | 24.99 |
| | 50 | SPTS | 21.99 |
| | 53 | SPX | 24.99 |
| 6mm | 75 | SPTX | 22.99 |
| | 75 | SPTS | 23.99 |
| | 85 | SPTS | 23.99 |
| | 85 | BTX | 24.99 |
| | 90 | SPTX | 23.99 |
| | 95 | SPTX | 23.99 |
| | 115 | RNO | 24.99 |
| 25 | 75 | SPTX | 22.99 |
| | 75 | SPTS | 23.99 |
| | 85 | SPTX | 23.99 |
| | 90 | SPTS | 23.99 |
| | 90 | BTX | 24.99 |
| | 100 | SPTX | 23.99 |
| | 100 | BTX | 25.99 |
| | 115 | SPTX | 24.99 |
| 6.5 | 100 | SPTX | 25.99 |
| | 100 | SPTS | 25.99 |
| | 120 | SPTX | 26.99 |
| | 120 | SPTS | 25.99 |
| | 130 | SPTX | 26.99 |
| | 130 | SPTS | 25.99 |
| | 140 | SPTX | 26.99 |
| 270 | 100 | SPTX | 26.99 |
| | 100 | SPO | 25.99 |
| | 120 | SPO | 25.99 |
| | 120 | SPTX | 26.99 |
| | 120 | BTX | 29.99 |
| | 130 | SPTX | 27.99 |
| | 130 | SPTS | 25.99 |
| | 130 | BTX | 29.99 |
| | 140 | SPTX | 27.99 |
| | 140 | BTX | 29.99 |
| | 150 | SPTX | 27.99 |
| | 150 | RNS | 28.99 |
| | 180 | RNO | 27.99 |
| 7mm | 100 | SPTX | 29.99 |
| | 100 | SPTS | 27.99 |
| | 120 | SPTS | 27.99 |
| | 120 | SPTX | 29.99 |
| | 120 | BTX | 32.99 |
| | 130 | BTX | 32.99 |
| | 140 | SPTX | 31.99 |
| | 140 | SPTS | 28.99 |
| | 140 | BTX | 32.99 |
| | 150 | SPTX | 31.99 |
| | 150 | BTX | 32.99 |
| | 160 | SPTS | 28.99 |
| | 160 | SPTX | 31.99 |
| | 175 | SPTX | 31.99 |
| | 175 | RNS | 29.99 |
| | 195 | SPTO | 28.99 |
| 30-30 | 150 | FNX | 33.99 |
| | 165 | FNX | 32.99 |
| 30 | 110 | SPTX | 29.99 |
| | 110 | SPTS | 27.99 |

| Caliber | Wgt. Grs. | Type | Price/50 |
|---|---|---|---|
| | 125 | SPTS | $27.99 |
| | 125 | SPTX | 29.99 |
| | 130 | BTX | 32.99 |
| | 140 | BTX | 32.99 |
| | 150 | SPTX | 29.99 |
| | 150 | BTX | 32.99 |
| | 165 | SPTS | 28.99 |
| | 165 | SPTX | 29.99 |
| | 165 | BTX | 32.99 |
| | 180 | SPTX | 29.99 |
| | 180 | BTX | 32.99 |
| | 200 | SPTX | 32.99 |
| | 220 | RNS | 37.99 |
| | 250 | RNO | 29.99 |
| 8mm | 180 | SPTX | 31.99 |
| | 200 | SPTX | 32.99 |
| | 220 | SPTX | 33.99 |
| | 220 | RNS | 44.99 |
| 9.3mm | 250 | SPTX | 42.99 |
| | 286 | SPTX | 42.99 |
| | 286 | RNS | 57.99 |
| 338 | 160 | SPTX | 38.99 |
| | 175 | SPTX | 38.99 |
| | 185 | BTX | 39.99 |
| | 200 | SPTX | 39.99 |
| | 200 | SPTO | 49.99 |
| | 210 | SPTO | 49.99 |
| | 210 | BTX | 39.99 |
| | 225 | SPTX | 39.99 |
| | 225 | SPTS | 49.99 |
| | 250 | RNS | 49.99 |
| | 250 | SPTX | 39.99 |
| 348 | 200 | FNX | 39.99 |
| | 200 | FNX | 39.52 |
| | 220 | FPO | 27.99 |
| | 220 | FNX | 39.99 |
| | 250 | FPO | 28.99 |
| 35 | 180 | SPTX | 39.99 |
| | 200 | SPTX | 39.99 |
| | 225 | SPTX | 39.99 |
| | 250 | RNS | 55.99 |
| | 250 | SPTX | 39.99 |
| 38/55 | 255 | FPO(.375) | 28.99 |
| | 255 | FPO(.377) | 28.99 |
| 375 | 210 | SPTX | 39.99 |
| | 220 | FPO | 27.99 |
| | 235 | SPTX | 39.99 |
| | 235 | SPTS | 53.99 |
| | 250 | SPTX | 41.99 |
| | 250 | SPTS | 54.99 |
| | 255 | FPO | 28.99 |
| | 270 | SPTX | 42.99 |
| | 270 | RNS | 55.99 |
| | 300 | RNS | 59.99 |
| | 300 | SPTX | 42.99 |
| 401 | 250 | RNO | 28.99 |
| 404 Jeffery/ 425 Exp. | 350 | SPTX | 44.99 |
| | 400 | SPTX | 46.99 |
| | 350 | RNS | 65.99 |
| | 400 | RNO | 67.99 |

| Caliber | Wgt. Grs. | Type | Price/50 |
|---|---|---|---|
| 411 | 300 | SPTX | $44.99 |
| | 325 | SPTX | 44.99 |
| | 350 | SPTX | 45.99 |
| | 350 | RNS | 65.99 |
| | 400 | SPTX | 46.99 |
| | 400 | RNS | 67.99 |
| 416 | 300 | SPTX | 44.99 |
| | 325 | SPTX | 44.99 |
| | 350 | SPTX | 45.99 |
| | 350 | RNS | 65.99 |
| | 400 | RNS | 67.99 |
| | 400 | SPTX | 46.99 |
| 425 WR | 410 | RNS | 69.99 |
| | 410 | RNO | 49.99 |
| 444 | 250 | JHPO | 25.46 |
| | 275 | JHPO | 25.90 |
| | 300 | JHPO | 26.12 |
| 45/70 | 300 | SSPTO | 28.99 |
| | 300 | FPO | 28.99 |
| | 400 | SSPTO | 36.99 |
| | 400 | FPO | 36.99 |
| 458 | 300 | SPTX | 18.99/20 |
| | 350 | SPTX | 19.99/20 |
| | 400 | SPTX | 19.99/20 |
| | 400 | RNS | 28.99/20 |
| | 450 | SPTX | 20.99/20 |
| | 450 | RNS | 29.99/20 |
| | 500 | RNS | 29.99/20 |
| | 500 | SPTX | 20.99/20 |
| | 600 | RNO | 23.99/20 |
| 465 Nitro | 480 | RNS | 28.99/20 |
| | 480 | RNO | 19.99/20 |
| 470 Nitro | 500 | RNS | 29.99/20 |
| | 500 | RNO | 21.99/20 |
| | 600 | RNO | 23.99/20 |
| 475 No.2 Jeffery | 500 (.488) | RNS | 29.99/20 |
| 500 | 500 (.483) | RNS | 29.99/20 |
| | 500 | RNO | 22.99/20 |
| 50 | 525 (.505) | RNS | 39.99/20 |
| | 600 (.505) | RNS | 39.99/20 |
| | 525 (.510) | RNS | 39.99/20 |
| | 600 (.510) | RNS | 39.99/20 |
| 50/110 Win. | 300 | FPO | 11.99/20 |
| | 450 | FPO | 14.99/20 |
| 50 | 600 | RNO | 34.99/20 |
| | 700 | RNO | 42.99/20 |
| 577 Nitro | 650 | RNS | 57.99/25 |
| | 750 | RNS | 59.99/20 |
| | 750 | RNO | 46.99/20 |
| 600 Nitro | 900 | RNS | 84.95/20 |
| | 900 | RNO | 62.99/20 |
| | PISTOL | | |
| 44 | 200 | PBX | 18.99/20 |
| | 225 | PBX | 19.99/20 |
| | 240 | RNS | 34.99 |
| 45 | 250 | PBX | 19.99/20 |
| | 260 | JHPO | 28.99 |
| | 275 | PBX | 21.99/20 |
| | 300 | JHPO | 29.99 |

BTX = Boattail X-Bullet; HPX = Hollowpoint X-Bullet; SPT = Spitzer; SSPT = Semi-Spitzer; RN = Round Nose; FP = Flat Point; JHP = Jacketed Hollowpoint; O = Original Bullet; S = Barnes Solid; X = X-Bullet.

**BULLETS • RELOADERS • AMMUNITION**

| Caliber | Wgt. Grs. | Type | Price/100 |
|---|---|---|---|
| **RIFLE** | | | |
| 17 | 20 | V-Max | NA |
| | 25 | HP | $12.51 |
| 22 | 40 | Jet | 11.33 |
| | 40 | V-Max BT | 14.90 |
| | 45 | Bee | 10.92 |
| | 45 | Hornet (.223) | 11.33 |
| | 45 | Hornet (.224) | 10.92 |
| | 50 | SPSX | 11.27 |
| | 50 | SP | 10.60 |
| | 50 | V-Max BT | 14.90 |
| | 52 | BTHP Match | 13.71 |
| | 52 | A-Max BT | 15.45 |
| | 53 | HP Match | 13.21 |
| | 55 | SXSP | 11.27 |
| | 55 | SP | 10.70 |
| | 55 | SP w/c | 11.48 |
| | 55 | FMJBT | 11.48 |
| | 55 | V-Max BT | 14.90 |
| | 60 | SP | 11.84 |
| | 60 | HP | 11.84 |
| | 60 | V-Max | 15.42 |
| | 70 | SP (.227) | 15.77 |
| | 75 | A-Max | 15.45 |
| 6mm/243 | 58 | V-Max | NA |
| | 65 | V-Max | 17.93 |
| | 70 | SP | 13.95 |
| | 70 | SXSP | 14.61 |
| | 75 | BTHP Match | 15.11 |
| | 75 | HP | 13.95 |
| | 75 | V-Max | 18.82 |
| | 80 | FMJ | 15.65 |
| | 80 | SP Single Shot | 13.80 |
| | 87 | SP | 14.68 |
| | 87 | BTHP | 15.81 |
| | 87 | V-Max | NA |
| | 100 | SP | 15.31 |
| | 100 | BTSP | 15.77 |
| | 100 | RN | 15.31 |
| | 105 | A-Max | 18.50 |
| 25 | 60 | FP | 14.21 |
| | 75 | HP | 14.21 |
| | 75 | V-Max | 18.82 |
| | 87 | SP | 15.51 |
| | 100 | SP | 15.51 |
| | 117 | RN | 15.51 |
| | 117 | BTSP | 18.35 |
| | 120 | HP | 16.95 |
| 6.5mm | 95 | V-Max | NA |
| | 100 | SP | 18.20 |
| | 129 | SP | 18.20 |
| | 140 | SP | 18.28 |
| | 140 | A-Max | 25.03 |
| | 160 | RN | 22.77 |
| 270 | 100 | SP | 16.80 |
| | 110 | HP | 17.31 |
| | 110 | V-Max | NA |
| | 130 | SP | 15.97 |
| | 140 | BTSP | 19.41 |
| | 150 | SP | 17.52 |
| | 150 | RN | 18.57 |
| 7mm | 100 | HP | 16.80 |
| | 120 | SP | 17.31 |
| | 120 | SSPB | NA |
| | 120 | SP Single Shot | 17.31 |
| | 120 | HP | 17.31 |
| | 120 | V-Max | NA |
| | 139 | SP | 17.45 |
| | 139 | FP | $18.77 |
| | 139 | BTSP | 19.79 |
| | 154 | SP | 19.41 |
| | 154 | RN | 19.41 |
| | 162 | BTSP | 21.01 |
| | 162 | A/MAX | 24.63 |
| | 175 | SP | 20.97 |
| | 175 | RN | 20.97 |
| 30 | 100 | SJ | 10.77 |
| | 110 | SP | 13.72 |
| | 110 | RN | 13.72 |
| | 110 | FMJ | 13.72 |
| | 110 | V-Max | NA |
| | 130 | SP | 17.51 |
| | 130 | SSPB | NA |
| | 130 | SP Single Shot | 16.07 |
| | 150 | SP | 16.80 |
| | 150 | BTSP | 19.53 |
| | 150 | RN (30-30) | 16.80 |
| | 150 | FMJBT | 18.57 |
| | 150 | A-Max | 23.75 |
| | 165 | SP | 18.57 |
| | 165 | BTSP | 19.53 |
| | 168 | BTHP Match | 22.59 |
| | 168 | A-Max | 24.63 |
| | 170 | FP (30-30) | 17.31 |
| | 180 | SP | 18.41 |
| | 180 | BTSP | 21.84 |
| | 180 | RN | 19.05 |
| | 180 | BTHP Match | 23.25 |
| | 180 | A-Max | 25.30 |
| | 190 | BTSP | 21.84 |
| | 220 | RN | 21.84 |
| 7.62x39 | 123 | SP | 17.10 |
| | 123 | FMJ | 17.10 |
| | 123 | SSPB | NA |
| 303/7.7 | 150 | SP | 18.45 |
| | 174 | RN | 19.55 |
| | 174 | FMJBT | 19.55 |
| 32 Spl. | 170 | FP | 18.80 |
| 8mm | 125 | SP | 18.57 |
| | 150 | SP | 18.57 |
| | 170 | RN | 18.87 |
| | 220 | SP | 23.97 |
| 338 | 200 | SP | 23.25 |
| | 200 | FP | 26.88 |
| | 225 | SP | 24.88 |
| | 250 | RN | 26.21 |
| | 250 | SP | 26.21 |
| 348 | 200 | FP | 25.45 |
| 35 | 180 | SP Single Shot | 23.31 |
| | 200 | SP | 23.31 |
| | 200 | RN | 23.11 |
| | 250 | SP | 26.21 |
| | 250 | RN | 26.21 |
| 375 | 220 | FP | 26.21 |
| | 270 | SP | 17.85/50 |
| | 270 | RN | 17.85/50 |
| | 300 | RN | 17.85/50 |
| | 300 | BTSP | 22.33/50 |
| | 300 | FMJ-RN | 33.51 |
| 416 | 400 | RN | 30.04/50 |
| | 400 | FMJ | 41.15/50 |
| 44 | 265 | FP | 24.24 |
| 45 | 300 | HP | 15.77/50 |
| | 350 | RN | 19.53/50 |
| | 500 | RN | 29.21/50 |
| | 500 | FMJRN | 41.15/50 |
| 50 | 750 | A/MAX | $29.00/20 |
| **JACKETED PISTOL** | | | |
| 25 | 50 | FMJRN | $11.07 |
| | 35 | HP/XTP | 11.07 |
| 32 (.311) | 71 | FMJRN | 11.73 |
| | 60 | HPXTP | 11.73 |
| 32 (.312) | 85 | HPXTP | 11.99 |
| | 100 | HP/XTP | 12.19 |
| 9mm | 90 | HP/XTP | 12.04 |
| | 100 | FMJ | 12.19 |
| | 115 | HP/XTP | 11.07 |
| | 115 | FMJRN | 11.99 |
| | 124 | FMJFP | 13.00 |
| | 124 | FMJRN | 12.19 |
| | 124 | HP/XTP | 12.19 |
| | 147 | HP/XTP | 12.24 |
| | 147 | FMJRN | 12.24 |
| 9mm Mak. | 95 | HP/XTP | 12.04 |
| 38 | 110 | HP/XTP | 12.51 |
| | 125 | HP/XTP | 12.19 |
| | 125 | FP/XTP | 12.19 |
| | 140 | HP/XTP | 12.85 |
| | 158 | HP/XTP | 12.65 |
| | 158 | FP/XTP | 12.65 |
| | 160 | CL Sil. | 15.31 |
| | 180 | HP/XTP | 15.60 |
| | 180 | CL Sil. | 15.60 |
| 10mm | 155 | HP/XTP | 15.60 |
| | 180 | HP/XTP | 16.07 |
| | 180 | FMJFP | 16.07 |
| | 200 | HP/XTP | 16.84 |
| | 200 | FMJFP | 16.84 |
| 41 | 210 | CL Sil. | 17.95 |
| | 210 | HP/XTP | 16.84 |
| 44 | 180 | HP/XTP | 16.84 |
| | 200 | HP/XTP | 16.84 |
| | 240 | HP/XTP | 17.28 |
| | 240 | CL Sil. | 18.11 |
| | 300 | HP/XTP | 11.41/50 |
| 45 | 185 | HP/XTP | 16.64 |
| | 185 | SWC Match | 17.28 |
| | 200 | HP/XTP | 16.84 |
| | 200 | FMJ C/T | 17.28 |
| | 230 | HP/XTP | 16.99 |
| | 230 | FMJRN | 16.84 |
| | 230 | FMJFP | 16.84 |
| | 250 | HP/XTP | 17.95 |
| | 300 | HP/XTP | 11.41/50 |
| **LEAD PISTOL** | | | |
| 32 | 90 | SWC | $21.07/500 |
| | 90 | HBWC | 21.07/500 |
| 9mm | 124 | LRN | 22.80/500 |
| 38 | 148 | BBWC | 23.15/500 |
| | 148 | HBWC | 23.15/500 |
| | 148 | DEWC | 23.15/500 |
| | 158 | RN | 24.99/500 |
| | 158 | SWC | 24.99/500 |
| | 158 | SWCHP | 24.99/500 |
| 10mm | 180 | SWC | 28.40/500 |
| | 205 | FP Cowboy | 33.77 |
| 44 | 240 | SWC | 29.84/400 |
| | 240 | SWCHP | 29.84/400 |
| 45 | 200 | SWC | 33.77/500 |
| | 200 | L C/T | 33.77/500 |
| | 230 | LRN | 29.84/400 |
| | 255 | FP Cowboy | 29.84 |

SP = Spire Point; BT = Boattail; FP = Flatpoint; HP = Hollowpoint; JFP = Jacketed Hollowpoint; JTC = Jacketed Truncated Cone; RN = Round Nose; LRN = Lead Round Nose; Sil. = Silhouette; SJ = Short Jacket; FMJ = Full Metal Jacket; SX = Super Explosive; SWC = Semi Wad Cutter; HBWC = Hollow Base Wad Cutter; BBWC = Bevel Base Wad Cutter; DEWC = Double End Wad Cutter; w/c = with cannelure; C/T = Combat Target.

| Caliber | Wgt. Grs. | Type | Caliber | Wgt. Grs. | Type | Caliber | Wgt. Grs. | Type |
|---|---|---|---|---|---|---|---|---|
| | **RIFLE** | | 7mm | 120 | SPTBTSB | | 250 | SPT Par. |
| 22 | 40 | SPTBT | | 120 | FPSBSL | 375 | 260 | SPT Par. |
| | 45 | Hornet SB | | 140 | SPTSBBT | | 300 | SPT Par. |
| | 50 | SPTBT | | 140 | SPT Par. | | **PISTOL** | |
| | 55 | SPTBTSB | | 150 | SPTBTSB | 9mm | 90 | HP |
| 243/6mm | 55 | SPTBTSB | | 150 | SPT Par. | | 115 | FMJ |
| | 70 | SPTBTSB | | 160 | SPT Par. | | 115 | HP |
| | 85 | SPT Par. | | 175 | SPT Par. | 38/357 | 115 | HPIPSC |
| | 85 | SPTBTSB | 30 | 125 | SPTBTSB | | 125 | HP |
| | 95 | SPT Par. | | 150 | SPTBTSB | | 135 | IPSC |
| | 95 | SPTBTSB | | 150 | SPT Par. | | 150 | IPSC |
| | 100 | SPT Par. | | 165 | SPTBTSB | | 150 | JP |
| 25 | 100 | SPTBTSB | | 165 | SPT Par. | | 158 | HP |
| | 100 | SPT Par. | | 170 | RN Par. | | 180 | SIL |
| | 115 | SPT Par. | | 180 | SPTBTSB | 10mm | 135 | HP |
| | 115 | SPTBTSB | | 180 | SPT Par. | | 150 | HP |
| | 120 | SPT Par. | | 180 | PPT Par. | | 170 | HP |
| 6.5mm | 100 | SPBTSB | | 200 | SPT Par. | | 180 | HP |
| | 120 | SPTBTSB | | 220 | SSPT Par. | 41 | 210 | HP |
| | 125 | SPT Par. | 8mm | 200 | SPT Par. | 44 | 200 | HP |
| | 140 | SPT Par. | 338 | 180 | SPTBTSB | | 240 | HP |
| 270 | 130 | SPTBTSB | | 200 | SPTBTSB | | 240 | SP |
| | 130 | SPT Par. | | 210 | SPT Par. | | 300 | HP |
| | 140 | SPBTSB | | 225 | SPT Par. | 45 | 185 | HP |
| | 150 | SPTBTSB | | 250 | SPT Par. | | 230 | FMJ |
| | 150 | SPT Par. | 35 | 225 | SPT Par. | 45 Colt | 250 | HP |
| | 160 | SSPT Par. | | 225 | SPTBTSB | | | |

BT = Ballistic Tip; FMJ = Full Metal Jacket; HP = Hollowpoint; Par = Partition; SB = Solid Base Bullet; SIL = Silhouette; SL = Soft Lead Tip; SP = Softpoint; SPT = Spitzer; SSPT = Semi-Spitzer.

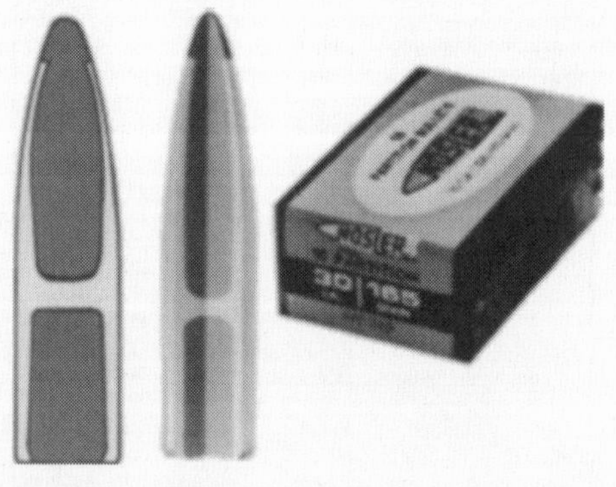

| Caliber | Wgt. Grs. | Type |
|---|---|---|
| **RIFLE** | | |
| 22 | 40 (.223) | Hornet |
| | 40 (.224) | Hornet |
| | 40 (.224) | HP |
| | 45 (.223) | Hornet |
| | 45 (.224) | Hornet |
| | 45 | SMP |
| | 45 | SPT |
| | 50 | SMP |
| | 50 | SPT |
| | 50 | Blitz |
| | 52 | HPBT Match |
| | 53 | HP Match |
| | 55 | Blitz |
| | 55 | SMP |
| | 55 | FMJBT |
| | 55 | SPT |
| | 55 | SBT |
| | 55 | HPBT |
| | 60 | HP |
| | 63 | SMP |
| | *69 | HPBT Match |
| | *80 | HPBT Match |
| 243/6mm | 60 | HP |
| | 70 | HPBT Match |
| | 75 | HP |
| | 80 | Blitz |
| | 85 | SPT |
| | 85 | HPBT |
| | 90 | FMJBT |
| | 100 | SPT |
| | 100 | SMP |
| | 100 | SBT |
| | **107 | HPBT |
| 25 | 75 | HP |
| | 87 | SPT |
| | 90 | HPBT |
| | 100 | SPT |
| | 100 | SBT |
| | 117 | SBT |
| | 117 | SPT |
| | 120 | HPBT |
| 6.5mm | 85 | HP |
| | 100 | HP |
| | 107 | HPBT |
| | 120 | SPT |
| | 120 | HPBT Match |
| | 140 | SBT |
| | 140 | HPBT Match |
| | 142 | HPBT |
| | **155 | HPBT Match |
| | 160 | SMP |
| 270 | 90 | HP |
| | 110 | SPT |
| | 130 | SBT |
| | 130 | SPT |
| | 135 | HPBT |
| | 140 | HPBT |
| | 140 | SBT |
| | 150 | SBT |
| | 150 | RN |
| 7mm | 100 | HP |
| | 120 | SPT |
| | 130 | HPBT |
| | 140 | SBT |
| | 140 | SPT |
| | 150 | SBT |
| | 150 | HPBT Match |
| | 160 | SBT |
| | 160 | HPBT |
| | 168 | HPBT Match |
| | 170 | RN |
| | 175 | SBT |
| 30-30 | 125 | HP/FN |
| | 150 | FN |
| | 170 | FN |
| 30 | 110 | FMJ |
| | 110 | RN |
| | 110 | HP |
| | 125 | SPT |
| | 150 | FMJBT |
| | 150 | SPT |
| | 150 | SBT |
| | 150 | HPBT Match |
| | 150 | RN |
| | 155 | HPBT Palma |
| | 165 | SBT |
| | 165 | HPBT |
| | 168 | HPBT Match |
| | 175 | HPBT Match |
| | 180 | SPT |
| | 180 | SBT |
| | 180 | HPBT Match |
| | 180 | RN |
| | 190 | HPBT Match |
| | 200 | SBT |
| | 200 | HPBT Match |
| | 220 | HPBT Match |
| | 220 | RN |
| | **240 | HPBT |
| 303 | 125 | SPT |
| | 150 | SPT |
| | 174 | HPBT Match |
| | 180 | SPT |
| 8mm | 150 | SPT |
| | 175 | SPT |
| | 220 | SBT |
| 338 | 215 | SBT |
| | 250 | SBT |
| | *300 | HPBT Match |
| 35 | 200 | RN |
| | 225 | SBT |
| 375 | 200 | FN |
| | 250 | SBT |
| | 300 | SBT |
| 45/70 | 300 | HP/FN |
| **PISTOL** | | |
| 25 | 50 | FMJ |
| 32 | 71 | FMJ |
| | 90 | JHC |
| 9mm | 90 | JHP |
| | 95 | FMJ |
| | 115 | JHP |
| | 115 | FMJ |
| | 125 | FMJ |
| | 125 | JHP |
| | 130 | FMJ |
| 9mm Makarov | 95 | JHP |
| | 100 | FPJ |
| 38 Super | 150 | FPJ Match |
| 38 Spl./357 | 110 | JHC Blitz |
| | 125 | JSP |
| | 125 | JHC |
| | 140 | JHC |
| | 158 | JHC |
| | 158 | JSP |
| | 170 | JHC |
| | 170 | FMJ Match |
| | 180 | FPJ Match |
| 10mm | 135 | JHP |
| | 150 | JHP |
| | 165 | JHP |
| | 180 | JHP |
| | 190 | FPJ |
| 41 | 170 | JHC |
| | 210 | JHC |
| | 220 | FPJ Match |
| 44 Spl./Mag. | 180 | JHC |
| | 210 | JHC |
| | 220 | FPJ Match |
| | 240 | JHC |
| | 250 | FPJ Match |
| | 300 | JSP |
| 45 | 185 | JHP |
| | 185 | FPJ Match |
| | 200 | FPJ Match |
| | 230 | FMJ Match |
| | 240 | JHC |
| | 300 | JSP |
| **SINGLE SHOT PISTOL** | | |
| 6mm | 80 | SPT |
| 7mm | 130 | SPT |
| 30 | 135 | SPT |

BT = Boattail; SPT = Spitzer; SBT = Spitzer Boattail; HP = Hollowpoint; HPBT = Hollowpoint Boattail; JHP = Jacketed Hollowpoint; JSP = Jacketed Softpoint; JHC = Jacketed Hollow Cavity; FMJ = Full Metal Jacket; FPJ = Full Profile Jacket; FMJBT = Full Metal Jacket Boattail; FN = Flat Nose; RN = Round Nose; SMP = Semi-Pointed. *For rifles with twist of 1 in 7 to 1 in 10. **For rifles with twist of 1 in 8 or 1 in 9.

# SPEER

| Caliber | Wgt. Grs. | Type | Price/100 |
|---|---|---|---|
| | | **RIFLE** | |
| 223 | 40 | SP (.223, .224) | $10.36 |
| | 45 | SPTZ (.223, .224) | 10.36 |
| | 40 | SP | 10.36 |
| | 45 | SPTZ | 10.36 |
| | 46 | FNSP w/c | 10.36 |
| | 50 | HPTNT | 10.98 |
| | 50 | SPTZ | 10.36 |
| | 52 | HPBT Match | 12.83 |
| | 52 | HP | 11.38 |
| | 55 | SPTZ | 10.46 |
| | 55 | SPTZ w/c | 11.21 |
| | 55 | FMJBT | 11.21 |
| | 62 | FMJBT | 13.42 |
| | 70 | Semi-SPTZ | 14.72 |
| 243/6mm | 70 | TNT | 13.83 |
| | 75 | HP | 13.22 |
| | 80 | SPTZ | 13.47 |
| | 85 | BTSPTZ | 15.14 |
| | 90 | SPTZ | 13.89 |
| | 100 | BTSPTZ | 14.89 |
| | 100 | GS | 16.76/50 |
| | 105 | RN | 14.50 |
| | 105 | SPTZ | 14.50 |
| 25 | 75 | FN w/c | 13.67 |
| | 87 | SPTZ | 14.37 |
| | 87 | TNTHP | 15.10 |
| | 100 | SPTZ | 14.70 |
| | 100 | HP | 15.35 |
| | 100 | BTSPTZ | 17.02 |
| | 120 | GS | 18.16/50 |
| | 120 | BTSPTZ | 17.39 |
| | 120 | SPTZ | 16.31 |
| 6.5mm | 120 | SPTZ | 17.27 |
| | 140 | SPTZ | 17.34 |
| 270 | 90 | TNTHP | 16.62 |
| | 100 | HP | 15.91 |
| | 100 | SPTZ | 15.91 |
| | 130 | BTSPTZ | 17.88 |
| | 130 | SPTZ | 15.10 |
| | 130 | GS | 18.42/50 |
| | 150 | BTSPTZ | 18.74 |
| | 150 | SPTZ | 16.66 |
| | 150 | GS | 19.34/50 |
| 7mm | 110 | TNTHP | 16.85 |
| | 115 | HP | 16.09 |
| | 120 | SPTZ | 16.44 |
| | 130 | SPTZ | 16.58 |
| | 130 | BTSPTZ | 17.74 |
| | 145 | BTSPTZ | 18.76 |
| | 145 | SPTZ | 17.75 |
| | 145 | HPBT Match | 21.71 |
| | 145 | GS | 19.21/50 |
| | 160 | BTSPTZ | 19.93 |
| | 160 | SPTZ | 18.44 |
| | 160 | Mag. Tip | 19.85 |
| | 160 | GS | 21.34/50 |
| | 175 | Mag. Tip | 19.88 |
| | 175 | GS | 21.97/50 |
| 30 | 100 | RNSP | 10.19 |
| | 110 | HP | 12.78 |
| | 110 | RNSP | 12.94 |
| | 110 | RN Carbine | 12.94 |
| | 110 | FMJRN | 12.94 |
| | 110 | SP | 14.69 |
| | 125 | HPTNT | 16.99 |
| | 130 | HP | 16.82 |
| | 130 | FNSP (30-30) | 16.66 |
| | 150 | FNSP (30-30) | 15.91 |
| | 150 | RNSP | 15.91 |
| | 150 | FMJBT w/c | 17.59 |
| | 150 | BTSPTZ | 18.74 |
| | 150 | SPTZ | 15.91 |
| | 150 | Mag. Tip | 20.50 |
| | 150 | GS | 19.21/50 |
| | 165 | RN | 17.97 |
| | 165 | BTSPTZ | 18.54 |
| | 165 | SPTZ | 17.59 |
| | 165 | GS | 19.80/50 |
| | 168 | BT Match | 21.13 |
| | 170 | FN (30-30) | 16.44 |
| | 180 | RNSP | 18.08 |
| | 180 | BTSPTZ | 20.70 |
| | 180 | SPTZ | 17.47 |
| | 180 | Mag. Tip | 23.07 |
| | 180 | GS | 20.70/50 |
| | 190 | Match | 11.06/50 |
| | 200 | SPTZ | 10.49/50 |
| | 200 | GS | 21.85/50 |
| 303 | 123 | FMJ | 16.58 |
| | 125 | SP w/c | 16.58 |
| | 150 | SPTZ | 17.82 |
| | 180 | RN | 18.90 |
| | 200 | GS | 22.91/50 |
| 32 | 170 | FN | 18.16 |
| 8mm | 150 | SPTZ | 17.59 |
| | 170 | Semi-SPTZ | 17.85 |
| | 200 | SPTZ | 11.30/50 |
| 338 | 200 | SPTZ | 11.30/50 |
| | 225 | BTSP | 17.60/50 |
| | 250 | GS | 28.90/50 |
| | 275 | Semi-SPTZ | 12.44/50 |
| | 275 | AGS Solid | 98.09/25 |
| 35 | 180 | FN | 22.09 |
| | 220 | FN | 11.62/50 |
| | 250 | SPTZ | 12.44/50 |
| | 250 | GS | 24.09/50 |
| 9.3mm | 270 | Semi-SPTZ | 12.82/50 |
| 375 | 235 | Semi-SPTZ | 12.73/50 |
| | 270 | BTSP | 21.13/50 |
| | 285 | GS | 37.79/50 |
| | 300 | AGS Solid | 102.95/25 |
| 416 | 350 | Mag. Tip | 23.55/50 |
| 416 | 400 | AGS Solid | 110.66/25 |
| | 400 | AGS | 109.39/25 |
| 45 | 350 | FNSP | 18.54/50 |
| | 400 | FNSP | 17.39/50 |
| | 500 | AGS Solid | 119.69/25 |
| | 500 | AGS | 99.91/25 |
| 50 | 647 | FMJBT | 30.85/20 |
| | | **PISTOL** | |
| 25 ACP | 35 | GDHP | $10.13 |
| | 50 | FMJ | 10.72 |
| 32 | 60 | GDHP | 10.80 |
| | 100 | JHP | 11.79 |
| 9mm | 95 | FMJ | 11.75 |
| | 100 | HP | 11.79 |
| | 115 | FMJ | 10.72 |
| | 115 | HP | 10.72 |
| | 115 | HP GD | 10.94 |
| | 124 | JSP | 11.79 |
| | 124 | TMJ | 11.79 |
| | 124 | SPGD | 11.97 |
| | 147 | TMJ | 11.84 |
| | 147 | HP GD | 12.10 |
| 380 Auto | 90 | HP GD | 10.87 |
| 357 SIG | 125 | TMJ | 11.97 |
| | 125 | HP GD | 11.13 |
| 38/357 | 110 | JHP | 12.07 |
| | 125 | JSP | 11.79 |
| | 125 | JHP | 11.79 |
| | 125 | HP GD | 12.05 |
| | 125 | TMJ | 12.53 |
| | 140 | JHP | 12.45 |
| | 146 | SWCJHP | 12.72 |
| | 158 | TMJ | 14.11 |
| | 158 | JHP | 12.23 |
| | 158 | HP GD | 12.49 |
| | 158 | JSP | 12.23 |
| | 160 | SWCJSP | 12.90 |
| | 180 | FMJ Sil. | 15.03 |
| | 200 | FMJ Sil. | 15.96 |
| 9mm Mak. | 90 | HP GD | 11.58 |
| | 95 | TMJ | 11.46 |
| 10mm | 155 | HP GD | 15.35 |
| | 155 | TMJ | 15.21 |
| | 165 | HP GD | 15.63 |
| | 180 | TMJ | 15.54 |
| | 180 | HP GD | 15.72 |
| | 200 | TMJ | 16.49 |
| 40 S&W | 165 | TMJ | 15.36 |
| 41 AE | 180 | HP | 15.54 |
| 41 | 200 | SWCJHP | 16.72 |
| | 220 | SWCJSP | 17.83 |
| | 210 | TMJ Sil | 17.39 |
| 44 Spl./Mag. | 200 | Mag. JHP | 16.28 |
| | 225 | JHP | 16.50 |
| | 240 | SWCJSP | 16.54 |
| | 240 | Mag. JHP | 16.76 |
| | 240 | Mag. JSP | 16.76 |
| | 240 | TMJ Sil. | 17.56 |
| | 270 | SPGD | 7.93/50 |
| | 300 | SP | 11.68/50 |
| 45 | 185 | HP GD | 16.07 |
| | 185 | SWCTMJ Match | 16.34 |
| | 200 | SWCTMJ Match | 16.76 |
| | 200 | JHP | 16.28 |
| | 225 | Mag. JHP | 17.31 |
| | 230 | HP GD | 16.76 |
| | 230 | TMJ | 16.19 |
| | 260 | JHP | 19.23 |
| | 300 | SP | 11.72/50 |
| 50 AE | 325 | HP | 10.08/50 |
| | | **LEAD HANDGUN** | |
| 9mm | 125 | RN | $7.60 |
| 38 | 148 | BBWC | 7.88 |
| | 148 | HBWC | 7.88 |
| | 158 | HPSWC | 8.17 |
| | 158 | RN | 8.17 |
| | 158 | SWC | 8.17 |
| 44 | 240 | SWC | 11.71 |
| 45 | 200 | SWC | 11.71 |
| | 230 | RN | 11.71 |
| | 250 | SWC | 11.87 |

SP = Softpoint; SPTZ = Spitzer; BT = Boattail; HP = Hollowpoint; PHP = Plated Hollowpoint; HP TNT = Hollowpoint TNT; HPBT = Hollowpoint Boattail; FMJ/BT = Full Metal Jacket Boattail; TMJ = Totally Metal Jacketed; JHP = Jacketed Hollowpoint; JSP = Jacketed Softpoint; PSP = Plated Softpoint; Sil. = Silhouette; FN = Flat Nose; RN = Round Nose; P= Plinker; SWC = Semi Wad Cutter; BBWC = Bevel Base Wad Cutter; HBWC = Hollow Base Wad Cutter; w/c = with cannelure; AGS = African Grand Slam; GS = Grand Slam; GD = Gold Dot.

**ACTIV** *Wad Specifications*

| Model | Gauge | Color | Load |
|---|---|---|---|
| TG-30 | 12 | Red | $1^1/_8$ |
| TG-32 | 12 | Yellow | $1^1/_4$ |
| T-35 | 12 | Blue | $1^1/_4$ & $1^3/_8$ |
| T-42 | 12 | Green | $1^1/_2$ & $1^5/_8$ |
| G-28 | 16 | White | 1 |
| W-28 | 20 | White | $^7/_8$ & 1 |
| W-32 | 20 | Yellow | $1^1/_8$ |

***BALLISTIC PRODUCTS** *European Sporting Wads**

| Wad | Price/200 | Price/1000 | Price/5000 |
|---|---|---|---|
| Competition Special | $3.99 | $14.95 | $72.00 |
| Dispersor-X | 6.79 | 26.95 | 119.00 |
| Brush Wad | 5.79 | 22.95 | 93.00 |
| Light Brush Wad | 4.99 | 19.95 | 88.00 |
| ITD Target Driver | 4.99 | 19.95 | 88.00 |
| Piston Skeet | 4.99 | 19.95 | 88.00 |
| Short Range Crusher | 4.99 | 19.95 | 88.00 |
| Ultra-Short Eurotarget | 5.79 | 22.95 | 93.00 |
| Compact Eurotarget | 5.79 | 22.95 | 93.00 |
| European MightyLlight | 3.99 | 15.99 | 72.00 |
| Super Sport | 5.59 | 21.95 | 89.90 |
| Rex-24 | 5.79 | 22.95 | 93.00 |
| Steel Target Special | 8.99 | 36.95 | 169.00 |

*12-Gauge G/BP.

***BALLISTIC PRODUCTS** *Small Gauge Wads*

| Gauge | Wad | Price/200 | Price/1000 | Price/5000 |
|---|---|---|---|---|
| 16 | Dispersor-X | $6.79 | $26.95 | $119.00 |
| 16 | Sporting 16 | 4.99 | 19.95 | 88.00 |
| 20 | Sporting 20 | 4.59 | 17.95 | 79.00 |
| 24 | Sporting 24 | 5.99 | 24.95 | 99.50 |
| 28 | Sporting 28 | 4.59 | 17.95 | 79.00 |
| 28 | Brush | 4.99 | 19.95 | 88.00 |
| 32 | Sporting 32 | 5.99 | 24.95 | 99.50 |
| 410 | Sporting 410 | 4.59 | 17.95 | 79.00 |
| 410 | Brush Wad 410 | 4.99 | 19.95 | 88.00 |

Ballistic Products Lead Shot Wads

## ACTIV

**Plastic Wads**

Straight wall design for tube resistance. Are color coded to avoid reloading accidents or confusion. Contact your dealer for prices. From ACTIV Industries, Inc.

**Price:** . . . . . **Contact manufacturer.**

## AMERICAN PRODUCTS

**Plastic Wad**

Black wad moulded with a deep, tapered powder cup to give efficient gas seal. The "X" mid-section design provides even pressure on the shot column. For the trap shooter using $1^1/_8$-oz. load, but also works well with 1- or $1^1/_4$-oz. loads. Will fit any standard shell. Load data available. From American Products, Inc.

**Price:** Per 1,000 . . . . . . . . **$14.80**

## BALLISTIC PRODUCTS

**A-Q Slugs**

A 12-ga. $2^3/_4$″ and 3″ lead ball/nylon base 1-oz. slug. Outside base diameter of .740″, slug diameter of .735″. From Ballistic Products, Inc.

**Price:** Per 25 . . . . . . . . . . **$11.99**
**Price:** Per 100 . . . . . . . . . . **$39.90**

**Bismuth Shot**

Exclusive distributor of bismuth shot made by Bismuth Cartridge Company. In concert with this development BPI has developed specialty wads, buffer compounds and loading data for bismuth loads. From Ballistic Products, Inc.

**Price:** . . . . . **Contact manufacturer.**

**BP2 12-Gauge Scattermaster**

Super spreader wad with center column design for better patterns. Come in packs of 200. From Ballistic Products, Inc.

**Price:** . . . . . . . . . . . . **See chart.**

**BP2 Helix Cushion Claymaster Wads**

Four wads designed for the clay target shooter. The Driver #18, #21 and #28 wads feature helix cushions designed to reduce recoil improve pattern uniformity. The BP2 078 Lightning has a multi-mesh cushion design and gas seal for $^7/_8$-oz. loads. Come in packs of 200. From Ballistic Products, Inc.

**Price:** . . . . . . . . . . . . **See chart.**

**BP2 Z21 Trap Commander Wad**

Designed for the high-volume trap shooter with four "cushion towers" and petal design for rapid compression and dense patterns. Come in packs of 200. From Ballistic Products, Inc.

**Price:** . . . . . . . . . . . . **See chart.**

**BP12 Shotcup**

Loads in both the $2^3/_4$″ and 3″ hulls. Ribbed construction allows barrel to act as specially modified "overbored" barrel. Has tapered base. Designed for use with the BPGS gas seal. Comes in bags of 250. From Ballistic Products, Inc.

**Price:** . . . . . . . . . . . . . **$9.95**

**BP12-Tuff Shotcup**

For $^7/_8$- to 1-oz. steel shot or heavy buckshot loads. Designed for use with the BPGS gas seal. Comes in bags of 250. From Ballistic Products, Inc.

**Price:** . . . . . . . . . . . . . **$9.95**

**BPD-10 Shotcup**

Designed for extended range shooting. One-piece construction for $1^1/_2$ to $2^1/_2$-oz. loads. For lead shot, buck shot and slug loads. Bags of 100. From Ballistic Products, Inc.

**Price:** . . . . . . . . . . . . . **$9.95**

## BALLISTIC PRODUCTS

**BPD-10 Tuff**

Patented steel shot wad with vented design for magnum steel shot or heavy lead buckshot loads. Bags of 100. From Ballistic Products, Inc.

**Price:** . . . . . . . . . . . . . **$10.95**

**BPGS Gas Seal**

Designed for use with the BP12 and BP12-Tuff shotcups. Comes in bags of 250. From Ballistic Products, Inc.

**Price:** . . . . . . . . . . . . . **$8.95**

**BPO Overbore Gas Seal**

Designed for use with over-bored 10- and 12-ga. shotguns. Come in packages of 200. From Ballistic Products, Inc.

**Price:** . . . . . . . . . . . . . **$7.99**

**BPO 10-Ga. Gas Seal**

Over powder 10-ga. plastic gas seal for turkey, buckshot, slug and Pagoda loads.

**Price:** . . . . . **Contact manufacturer.**

**Cork Wads**

Lighter, denser and more flexible than cardboard. Wads are $^1/_4$″ thick. Available for 12- and 20-ga. in bags of 200. From Ballistic Products, Inc.

**Price:** . . . . . . . . . . . . . **$6.95**

**Cushioned Steel Driver Wads**

One-piece steel, lead or bismuth wad constructed of tough, durable plastic with variety of preformed shot cup sizes. Available for 12-ga. only $^7/_8$ steel to $1^1/_4$-oz. lead; 1-oz. steel to $1^3/_8$-oz. lead; and $1^1/_8$-oz. steel to $1^1/_2$-oz. lead.

**Price:** 200 . . . . . . . . . . . **$8.99**
**Price:** 1000 . . . . . . . . . . . **$36.95**

**Custom Cut Card and Fiber Wads**

For custom loading applications in 10, 12, 16, 20 and 410. Fiber wads cut $^3/_8$″; card wads cut .070″ and .135″. Fiber wads come in packages of 200; card wads in packages of 400. From Ballistic Products, Inc.

**Price:** Fiber, 10-ga. . . . . . . . . **$5.50**
**Price:** Fiber, 16-, 20-ga. . . . . . . **$4.99**
**Price:** Fiber, 410 . . . . . . . . . **$5.95**
**Price:** Card, 10-, 12-, 20-ga. . . . . . **$7.99**

**Dangerous Game Slugs**

Works in either smoothbore or rifled slug barrels. Available in 12- ($1^1/_8$-oz.), 16- (1-oz.), 20-ga. ($^7/_8$-oz.). Come 25 per pack. From Ballistic Products, Inc.

**Price:** 12, 16, 20 . . . . . . . . **$11.99**

**Felt Wads**

Wool felt wads made to fit the BPD 12-ga. shotcup (20-ga. wad), BPD 10-ga. shotcup (20-ga. wad) and BPD-Tuff 10-ga. cup (12-ga. wad). Comes in $^1/_4$″ and $^1/_8$″ thicknesses in bags of 250. From Ballistic Products, Inc.

**Price:** $^1/_4$″ . . . . . . . . . . . **$7.89**
**Price:** $^1/_8$″ . . . . . . . . . . . **$6.99**

**G/BP 8-Ga. Shotcup**

One of the rarest of shotshell components. Comes in bags of 100. From Ballistic Products, Inc.

**Price:** . . . . . . . . . . . . . **$13.99**

**G/BP 12-Ga. Brush Wad**

Traditional field wad with double ended gas seal with no shotcup. For short-range brush loads. Preferred applications: 10-25 yards; #$8^1/_2$-#10 magnum shot. From Ballistic Products, Inc.

**Price:** . . . . . . . . . . . . **See chart.**

## BALLISTIC PRODUCTS

**G/BP 12 Short Range Crusher Wad**
Designed for fast burn-rated powders. Underside of gas seal has 25 plastic teeth for even, extended-duration burn necessary for 3¼-dram, 1-oz. loads. Three-stage cage design. Preferred application: 15-35 yards; #7½-#9 magnum shot. From Ballistic Products, Inc.
**Price:** . . . . . . . . . . . . **See chart.**

**G/BP 16 Wad**
For 1-oz. 16-ga. loads. Preferred application: 20-45 yards; #6-#8½ copper-plated or magnum shot. From Ballistic Products, Inc.
**Price:** . . . . . . . . . . . . **See chart.**

**G/BP 28-Ga. Brush Wad**
Double-ended gas seal wad with no shotcup. Preferred application: #7 magnum or copper #11. From Ballistic Products, Inc.
**Price:** . . . . . . . . . . . . **See chart.**

**G/BP Compact Eurotarget 12 Wad**
Conducive to loading 2¼ and 2½ English cartridges. Designed for light framed double guns. Preferred applications: 15-35 yards; #6-#9 nickel- and copper-plated shot; #8-#9 magnum. From Ballistic Products, Inc.
**Price:** . . . . . . . . . . . . **See chart.**

**G/BP Competition Special 12 Wad**
For the competitive target shooter using #7½ through #9 magnum shot. Will fit tapered or straight-wall hulls. From Ballistic Products, Inc.
**Price:** . . . . . . . . . . . . **See chart.**

**G/BP 12-Ga. European MightyLight**
Specifically designed for the European 24-gram (⅞-oz.) competition clay target 12-ga. loads. (Chart on page 427.) From Ballistic Products, Inc.
**Price:** . . . . . . . . . . . . **See chart.**

**G/BP Dispersor-X 12 Wad**
One-piece plastic wad with integrated X spreader for quick spreading patterns. Preferred application: 5-25 yards; #8½-#11 shot. (Chart on page 427.) From Ballistic Products, Inc.
**Price:** . . . . . . . . . . . . **See chart.**

**G/BP Dispersor-X 16 Wad**
One-piece plastic wad with integrated X spreader. Preferred application: 5-25 yards; #8½-#11 shot. (Chart on page 427.) From Ballistic Products, Inc.
**Price:** . . . . . . . . . . . . **See chart.**

**G/BP ITD 12 Wad**
For International Trap shooters. Preferred application: 40-60 yards; #6-#8 magnum shot. (Chart on page 427.) From Ballistic Products, Inc.
**Price:** . . . . . . . . . . . . **See chart.**

**G/BP 12-Ga. Light Brush Wad**
Taller than the G/BP 12 Brush. The gas seal only, no shotcup design for short-range spreader loads. (Chart on page 427.) From Ballistic Products, Inc.
**Price:** . . . . . . . . . . . . **See chart.**

**G/BP Instant I.D. Disks**
Clear overshot disks for 12-ga. Come in packs of 500. From Ballistic Products, Inc.
**Price:** . . . . . . . . . . . . . . **$6.95**

**G/BP Light Game Slug .410**
Unique 93-gr. slug and wad column design for small bore shooters. Come in packs of 25, 100, 500 or 2000. From Ballistic Products, Inc.
**Price:** . . . . . . . . . . . . . . **$3.99**
**Price:** 25 . . . . . . . . . . . . **$12.90**
**Price:** 100 . . . . . . . . . . . **$53.00**
**Price:** 500 . . . . . . . . . . . **$199.00**
**Price:** 2000 . . . . . . . . . . **$209.00**

**BALLISTIC PRODUCTS** *Super Buck*

| Shot | Size(in.) | Price/8 lb. | Price/32 lb. |
|---|---|---|---|
| #BB | .170 | $15.99 | $58.00 |
| | .180 | 15.99 | 58.00 |
| #BBB | .190 | 15.99 | 58.00 |
| #T | .200 | 15.99 | 58.00 |
| #TT | .210 | 15.99 | 58.00 |
| #F | .220 | 15.99 | 58.00 |
| #4 | .240 | 15.99 | 58.00 |
| #3½ | .260 | 15.99 | 58.00 |
| #3 | .250 | 15.99 | 58.00 |
| #2½ | .290 | 15.99 | 58.00 |
| #2 | .270 | 15.99 | 58.00 |
| #1 | .300 | 15.99 | 58.00 |
| #0 | .320 | 15.99 | 58.00 |
| #00 | .340 | 15.99 | 58.00 |
| #00½ | .340 | 15.99 | 58.00 |
| #000 | .360 | 15.99 | 58.00 |
| #0000 | .380 | 15.99 | 58.00 |

**BALLISTIC PRODUCTS** *Magnum Lead Shot*

| Shot | Size(in.) | Price/25 lb. | Price/100 lb. |
|---|---|---|---|
| #2 | .150 | $25.87 | $85.24 |
| #4 | .130 | 19.87 | 61.00 |
| #5 | .120 | 19.87 | 61.00 |
| #6 | .110 | 19.87 | 61.00 |
| #7 | .100 | 19.87 | 61.00 |
| #7½ | .095 | 19.87 | 61.00 |
| #8 | .090 | 19.87 | 61.00 |
| #8½ | .085 | 19.87 | 61.00 |
| #9 | .080 | 19.87 | 61.00 |

***BALLISTIC PRODUCTS** *Steel Supreme Grade Shot*

| Shot | Size (in.) | Price/5 lb. | Price/50 lb. |
|---|---|---|---|
| F | .219 | $8.95 | $107.40 |
| BBB | .188 | 8.95 | 107.40 |
| B | .170 | 8.95 | 107.40 |

**BALLISTIC PRODUCTS** *Steel High Grade Shot*

| Shot | Size (in.) | Price/5 lb. | Price/100 lb. |
|---|---|---|---|
| TT | .210 | $8.75 | $109.00 |
| T | .200 | 8.75 | 109.00 |
| BBB | .190 | 8.75 | 109.99 |
| BB | .180 | 8.75 | 109.00 |
| #1 | .160 | 8.75 | 109.99 |
| #2 | .150 | 8.75 | 117.00 |
| #3 | .140 | 8.75 | 117.00 |
| #4 | .130 | 8.75 | 117.00 |
| #5 | .120 | 10.50 | 129.00 |
| #6 | .110 | 11.50 | 159.00 |
| #7 | .100 | 11.50 | 159.00 |

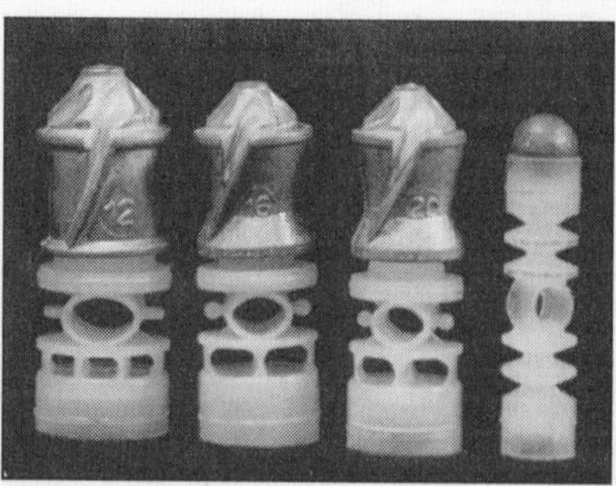
G/BP Dangerous Game Slugs

## BALLISTIC PRODUCTS

**G/BP Magnum 42 12-Gauge**
A 1½-oz. shotcup for magnum field loads. Four-petal shotcup with integrated gas seal/cushion base. Come in packs of 200. From Ballistic Products, Inc.
**Price:** . . . . . . . . . . . . . . **$8.99**

**G/BP Piston Skeet 12 Wad**
Specialized for 1- and ⅞-oz. European design load using compact, high burn-rate powders. "V" petals give dense pattern with short shot string. Preferred application: 20-40 yards; #7½-#8½ magnum shot. (Chart on page 427.) From Ballistic Products, Inc.
**Price:** . . . . . . . . . . . . **See chart.**

**G/BP Rex-24 12 Wad**
For 12-ga. ⅞-oz. target loads. Designed with crush section and multi-level gas seal to insure consistent powder burn. Tear-away petals for consistent patterns and reduced shot deformation. From Ballistic Products, Inc.
**Price:** . . . . . . . . . . . . **See chart.**

**G/BP Sporting 20 Wad**
For field and target high-velocity loads. Preferred application: #5-#7 plated shot for field loads; #8-#9 shot for target loads. (Chart on page 427.) From Ballistic Products, Inc.
**Price:** . . . . . . . . . . . . **See chart.**

**G/BP Sporting 24 Wad**
General target, light field usage with #7½ plated shot. (Chart on page 427.) From Ballistic Products, Inc.
**Price:** . . . . . . . . . . . . **See chart.**

**G/BP Sporting 28 Wad**
A favorite of European field shooters. Preferred applications: 16-19.5 gram field loads; #8½-#9 plated or magnum shot. (Chart on page 427.) From Ballistic Products, Inc.
**Price:** . . . . . . . . . . . . **See chart.**

**G/BP Sporting 32 and 410 Wad**
Preferred applications: the 32 for 32-ga. multi-range loads; the 410 for high-capacity spreader loads. (Chart on page 427.) From Ballistic Products, Inc.
**Price:** . . . . . . . . . . . . **See chart.**

**G/BP Sporting 410 Brush Wad**
For field/target loads. #8½-#10 plated or magnum shot. (Chart on page 427.) From Ballistic Products, Inc.
**Price:** . . . . . . . . . . . . **See chart.**

**G/BP Steel Shot Target Special**
Designed for multi-range steel shot loads. Made of soft, malleable polymer with toughness of steel shot hunting wads. Suitable for any progressive reloading press. From Ballistic Products, Inc.
**Price:** . . . . . . . . . . . . **See chart.**

**G/BP Ultra-Short Eurotarget 12 Wad**
For bulkier powders and English 2¼ and 2½ English cartridges. Has same applications as Compact Eurotarget. (Chart on page 427.) From Ballistic Products, Inc.
**Price:** . . . . . . . . . . . . **See chart.**

**Helix-Cushioned Platform Wad**
Designed for pattern consistency at ranges of 15 and 25 yds. For 12-ga. straight and tapered walled cases. Come in bags of 200. From Ballistic Products, Inc.
**Price:** . . . . . . . . . . . . . . **$4.99**

**BALLISTIC PRODUCTS** *Nickel-Plated Shot*

| Shot | Size (in.) | Price/8 lb. | Price/25 lb. |
|---|---|---|---|
| BB | .180 | $16.95 | $46.95 |
| #3 | .138 | 16.98 | NA |
| #4 | .127 | 16.98 | 39.95 |
| #5 | .120 | 18.95 | 46.95 |
| #6 | .110 | 16.98 | 39.95 |
| #7$^{1}/_{2}$ | .095 | 16.98 | 39.95 |
| #9 | .080 | 16.98 | NA |

**BALLISTIC PRODUCTS** *Copper-Plated Shot*

| Shot | Size (in.) | Price/10 lb. | Price/50 lb. |
|---|---|---|---|
| #4 | .130 | $18.99 | $84.50 |
| #5 | .120 | 18.99 | 84.50 |
| #6 | .110 | 18.99 | 84.50 |
| #7$^{1}/_{2}$ | | 18.99 | 84.50 |

## BALLISTIC PRODUCTS

**Multi-Metal Wads**

High-performance, cold weather hunting wads for steel, lead or bismuth loads. 10- and 12-gauge pre-slit wads come with load data and in boxes of 100. From Ballistic Products, Inc.

**Price:** 12-ga., 2$^{3}/_{4}$″ . . . . . . . . . **$8.99**
**Price:** 12-ga., 3″ . . . . . . . . . **$9.99**
**Price:** 12-ga., 3$^{1}/_{2}$″ . . . . . . . . **$10.99**
**Price:** 10-ga., 3$^{1}/_{2}$″ . . . . . . . . **$10.99**

**Over-Shot Wads**

Designed for use with buffered loads. Three sizes: .100 Nitro Cards; .030 Over-shot Cards; $^{1}/_{2}$ Fiber Cushion Wads. From Ballistic Products, Inc.

**Price:** .030, $^{1}/_{2}$″ . . . . . . . . . **$7.99**
**Price:** .100 . . . . . . . . . . . . **$9.79**

**Ranger-Plus Wads**

Designed for 12-ga. 2$^{3}/_{4}$″, 3″ or 3$^{1}/_{2}$″ lead or steel shot loads. Will hold up to 1$^{1}/_{4}$ oz. steel shot up to BB size; or 1$^{5}/_{8}$ oz. lead. Comes in bags of 100. From Ballistic Products, Inc.

**Price:** . . . . . . . . . . . . . . **$8.95**

**Shock 12 and 20**

Saboted slug designed to work with standard trap wad. Available in 20-ga. 350-gr. and 12-ga. 525-gr. Comes with load data and in boxes of 12 (12-ga.) and 15 (20-ga.). From Ballistic Products, Inc.

**Price:** . . . . . . . . . . . . . . **$5.99**

**Shot**

BPI offers high antimony Super Buck Shot (3% antimony), nickel-plated lead shot manufactured in Italy, high antimony magnum lead shot, copper-plated lead shot and steel shot. From Ballistic Products, Inc.

**Price:** . . . . . . . . . . . . **See chart.**

**Sledgehammer Slugs**

Heavy 10-ga. 730-grain slug. Comes with load data, 25 to a box. From Ballistic Products, Inc.

**Price:** . . . . . . . . . . . . . **$10.99**

**Slugmaster**

Hollowpoint slug with three moulded fracture lines. Available in 20- (275-gr., $^{5}/_{8}$-oz.); 16- (328-gr., $^{3}/_{4}$-oz.); 12- (410-gr., $^{7}/_{8}$-oz.) and 12- (437-gr., 1-oz.) gauges. Come in packs of 25. From Ballistic Products, Inc.

**Price:** . . . . . . . . . . . . . . **$8.99**

## BALLISTIC PRODUCTS

**Spreader-X Wads**

A two-piece cardboard wad that fits together to form four spread chambers. Sits on the base of the wad or atop the gas seal. Opens Full Choke to Improved Cylinder. Available in 10- through 20-ga. for 125 loads. From Ballistic Products, Inc.

**Price:** . . . . . . . . . . . . . . **$5.95**

**Steel Shot Wads**

Made for steel shot loads, the vented design of the 10-ga. Tuff BPD and BP-12 12-ga. wads allow bleed-off at peak pressures. Available in bags of 100 (10-ga.) and 250 (12-ga.) From Ballistic Products, Inc.

**Price:** . . . . . . . . . . . . . **$10.95**

**Thunderbolt Slugs**

Designed for 3″ Chambered Cylinder-choked shotguns. 1$^{7}/_{16}$-oz. slug with attached wad. Come in boxes of 25. From Ballistic Products, Inc.

**Price:** . . . . . . . . . . . . . **$11.99**

**Turkey Ranger Wad**

Heavy plastic wad designed for heavy magnum loads of plated lead shot. Load information provided with wads. Come in bags of 100. From Ballistic Products, Inc.

**Price:** . . . . . . . . . . . . . . **$8.95**

**Tyvex Over-Shot/Over-Cushion Wads**

Designed for 10- and 12-gauge heavy magnum steel shot loads. The 12-ga. $^{5}/_{8}$-inch over-cushion wad prevents steel pellets imbedding in wad base. Over-shot wads, $^{3}/_{4}$″ (10-ga.) and $^{5}/_{8}$″ (12-ga.), contain steel pellets during firing. Come in bags of 500. From Ballistic Products, Inc.

**Price:** . . . . . . . . . . . . . . **$7.99**

**Waxed Hard Wads**

For buckshot, slug and special Skeet loads. $^{1}/_{2}$-, $^{3}/_{8}$-inch thick waxed surface cardboard. Available in 10-, 12-, 16-, 20- and 28-gauges. Come 200 per bag. From Ballistic Products, Inc.

**Price:** 10 . . . . . . . . . . . . . **$7.99**
**Price:** 12, 16, 20 . . . . . . . . . **$6.99**
**Price:** 28 . . . . . . . . . . . . . **$5.99**

## BRENNEKE

**12-, 16-, 20-Ga. Slugs**

Slugs available for 12-, 16- and 20-gauge. 16-gauge offered in 415-grain weight with wad; 20-gauge in 370-grain weight with wad. Come in boxes of 25. From Brenneke of America, Ltd.

**Price:** . . . . . **Contact manufacturer.**

## C&D

**Claybuster Wads**

Straight-wall and tapered-wall target wads in 12-, 20-, 28-gauge and 410 bore. Copies of Winchester, Federal and Remington designs. From C&D Special Products.

**Price:** . . . . . **Contact manufacturer.**

**Shotshell Wads**

For 12-, 20, 28 and 410. Come in bags of 250. From Federal Cartridge Co.

**Price:** . . . . . . . . . . . . . . **$4.36**

## HORNADY

**Buckshot**

Cold-swaged buckshot using lead alloy hardened with 3% antimony. Strict roundness tolerance of +.002. Comes in 5-lb. bag. From Hornady Mfg. Co.

**Price:** . . . . . . . . . . . . . **$10.31**

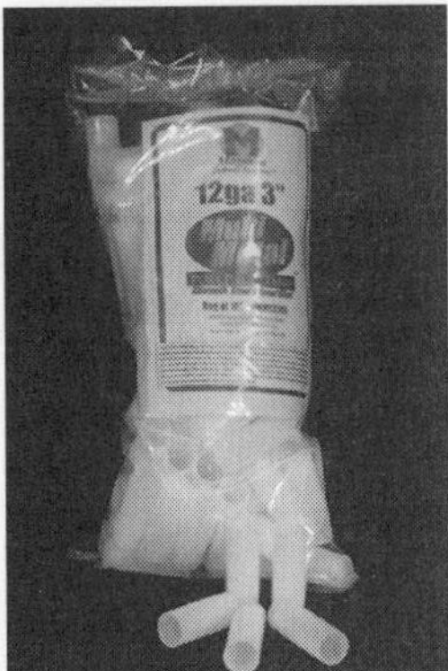

Ballistic Products Multi-Metal Wads

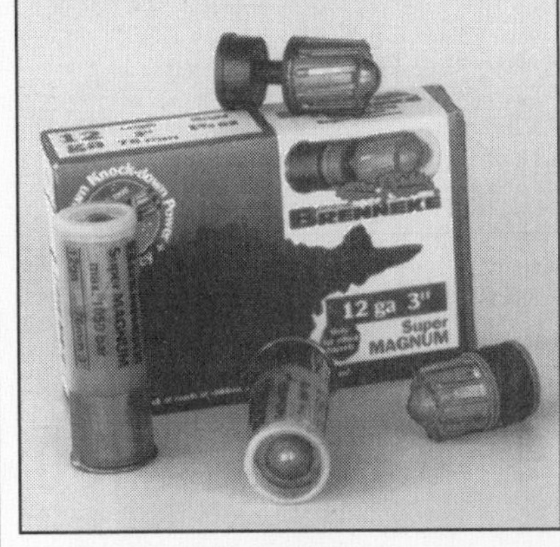


Brenneke Slugs

Hornady Versalite

## HORNADY

**Versalite Wads**

Compressible center section adjusts wad to correct column length. Available in 12- and 20-gauge. Flared shotcup to slip easily over wad seating punch. Come in bags of 250. From Hornady Mfg. Co.

**Price:** 1000 . . . . . . . . . . . **$5.50**

**Shocker Shotgun Sabot Slugs**

Saboted 12- and 20-gauge shotgun slugs designed to fit into standard shotgun wads and old crimped. Wasp-waist design controls expansion and energy transfer. 12-ga. 525-grain, come in 12 pack; 20-ga. 350-grain come in packs of 15. From Lyman Products Corporation.

**Price:** 12-ga. . . . . . . . . . . . **$5.95**
**Price:** 20-ga. . . . . . . . . . . . **$6.50**

## PATTERN CONTROL

**Wads**

Designed especially for Skeet, trap and field loads. Available in 12- (1$^1/_8$, 1 oz.), 20- ($^7/_8$-oz.), 28-gauge ($^3/_4$-oz.) and 410 ($^1/_2$-oz.) in seven styles. Interchangeable with Winchester AA, ACTIV, Federal, Fiocchi and Remington Powder Piston wads. Come in bags of 500. From Pattern Control.

**Price:** . . . . . **Contact manufacturer.**

## POLYWAD

**Spred-R Wad**

Device to open patterns up from Full to Improved Cylinder. Can be used with any wad and size shot. Shaped like thumbtack, Spred-R is inserted into shotshell before crimp with post side down into shot. Installed manually or with rammer tube of shotshell press. A 3-hole 12-ga. size insert is now available for the Sporting Clays shooter. Available in 12-, 16-, 20- or 28-gauges. From Polywad, Inc.

**Price:** 1000 . . . . . . . . . . . **$20.00**
**Price:** 2500 . . . . . . . . . . . **$40.00**

## PRECISION RELOADING

**Alcan Wads**

Card, fiber and felt wads for 12-, 16-, 20-, 28-gauge and 410 loads. Come in bags of 500. From Precision Reloading, Inc.

**Price:** . . . . . . . . . . . . . . **$8.95**

**Alcan Gas Seal Wads**

Air-wedge gas seal wads for 12- and 20-gauge loads. Come in packs of 500. From Precision Reloading, Inc.

**Price:** 12-ga. $^5/_{16}$" air wedge . . . . **$8.95**
**Price:** 20-ga. $^1/_4$" air wedge . . . . . **$7.95**
**Price:** 12-ga. Flite Max. with petals . **$9.95**

**Gualandi 12-Ga. Wad**

A European Super GECO Target wad which is photodegradable to eliminate wad contamination on land, in marshes and waterways. Available for 1- to 1$^1/_8$-oz. loads. Come in packages of 200, 1000 or 5000. From Precision Reloading, Inc.

**Price:** 200 . . . . . . . . . . . **$4.25**
**Price:** 1000 . . . . . . . . . . . **$15.95**
**Price:** 5000 . . . . . . . . . . . **$76.95**

**Steel Tuff Wads**

Wads for reloading steel shot loads for 10-ga. 3$^1/_2$" and 12-ga. 3$^1/_2$", 3" and 2$^3/_4$". Available in packages of 100. From Precision Reloading, Inc.

**Price:** 10-ga. 3$^1/_2$" . . . . . . . . **$11.95**
**Price:** 12-ga. 3$^1/_2$" . . . . . . . . **$11.50**
**Price:** 12-ga. 3" . . . . . . . . . **$9.95**
**Price:** 12-ga. 2$^3/_4$" . . . . . . . . **$7.95**

**Tin-Plated Steel Shot**

Non-toxic tin-plated steel shot. Tin plating provides 40% less friction between pellets and prohibits rust. Available in F, TT, T, BBB. From Precision Reloading, Inc.

**Price:** 10 lbs. . . . . . . . . . . **$23.95**

## PRECISION RELOADING

**U.S. Manufactured Steel Shot**

90 DPH steel shot in sizes T, BBB, BB, B, #1, #2, #3, #4, #6 and #7. Available in 10- or 40-lb. bags. From Precision Reloading, Inc.

**Price:** 10 lbs., T, BBB, BB, B, #1, #2, #3 . . . . . . . . . . **$13.95**
**Price:** 10 lbs., #4 . . . . . . . . **$14.95**
**Price:** 10 lbs., #6 . . . . . . . . **$15.95**
**Price:** 10 lbs., #7 . . . . . . . . **$17.95**
**Price:** 40 lbs., T, BBB, BB, B, #1, #2, #3 . . . . . . . . . . **$54.60**
**Price:** 40 lbs., #4 . . . . . . . . **$55.80**
**Price:** 40 lbs., #6 . . . . . . . . **$58.00**
**Price:** 40 lbs., #7 . . . . . . . . **$66.00**

**Wool Felt Wads**

Felt cushion undershot wads of 100% wool in $^1/_8$", $^3/_8$" and $^1/_4$" sizes. Come in bags of 250. From Precision Reloading, Inc.

**Price:** 24, 28, 32 ($^1/_8$") . . . . . . . **$5.95**
**Price:** 24, 28, 32 ($^1/_4$") . . . . . . . **$6.95**
**Price:** 24, 28, 32 ($^3/_8$") . . . . . . . **$9.95**
**Price:** 12 ($^1/_8$") . . . . . . . . . . **$7.95**
**Price:** 12 ($^1/_4$") . . . . . . . . . . **$9.95**
**Price:** 12 ($^3/_8$") . . . . . . . . . . **$12.95**
**Price:** 20 ($^1/_8$") . . . . . . . . . . **$6.95**
**Price:** 20 ($^1/_4$") . . . . . . . . . . **$7.95**
**Price:** 20 ($^3/_8$") . . . . . . . . . . **$10.95**
**Price:** 410 ($^1/_8$") . . . . . . . . . **$4.95**
**Price:** 410 ($^1/_4$") . . . . . . . . . **$5.95**
**Price:** 410 ($^3/_8$") . . . . . . . . . **$7.95**

**Nickel-Plated Shot**

Nickel shot with 4% antimony in sizes BB, #2, #4, #5, #6, #7$^1/_2$, #8, #9. Come in 10-lb. bags. From Precision Reloading, Inc.

**Price:** . . . . . . . . . . . . . **$19.95**

## RELOADING SPECIALTIES

**Sam I Wads**

Steel shot wads for loading 12-ga. 2$^3/_4$", 3" and 3$^1/_2$"; 10-ga. 3$^1/_2$"; 20-ga. 3". Unique patented design plus conical vaning, focal points and flexible base. Come 100 or 150 per bag. From Reloading Specialties, Inc.

**Price:** . . . . . . . . . . . . . **$7.95**

**Steel Shot**

SAAMI-spec annealed steel shot. Available in 10-lb. bags. From Reloading Specialities, Inc.

**Price:** . . . . . . . . . . . . . **$19.95**

**Super Sam Felt Spacers**

Allows all RS Sam wads to use various payloads. $^1/_8$" thick. Available in bags of 250. From Reloading Specialties, Inc.

**Price:** . . . . . . . . . . . . . **$7.50**

**Super Sam Over-Shot Cards**

For steel shot loads where use of buffer and cards allow better crimp and ignition. Come 1000 per bag. From Reloading Specialties, Inc.

**Price:** . . . . . . . . . . . . . **$7.50**

## REMINGTON

**Power Piston Wads**

One-piece wads feature special compression sections to compensate for seating pressures for uniform crimp with different powder charges. Manufactured to factory standards to duplicate factory performance. From Remington Arms Company, Inc.

**Price:** . . . . . . . . . . . . **See chart.**

## TUCSON MOLD, INC.

**Shotshell Wads**

Shotshell wads for 12-, 20-gauge and 410 bore for 1$^1/_8$, 1 and $^7/_8$ oz. in 12-ga., $^7/_8$ oz. in 20-ga., $^3/_4$ oz. in 28-ga. and $^1/_2$ oz. in 410 bore. Flexible, soft wad design for better gas seal, allowing reduced powder charge and lower chamber pressure with equal velocities. Wad feeding difficulties because of softness can be eliminated with dry lube of silicon on the wad guide. Available in packages of 1000. From Tucson Mold, Inc.

**Price:** . . . . . . . . . . . . . **$10.00**

## VITT/BOOS

**Slugs**

Slug with high, thin helical ribs to tightly fit bore. Weighs 580 grains. Comes in box of 25. From Vitt/Boos.

**Price:** . . . . . . . . . . . . . **$15.00**

## WINCHESTER

**Shotshell Wads**

Winchester AA wads for 12-, 16-, 20-, 28-gauge and 410. See chart for available loads. Available in bags of 1000. From Winchester.

**Price:** . . . . . . . . . . . . . **$22.20**

## WOSENITZ

**Slugs**

Tubular design 490-gr. slug with inside tapered in Venturi shape to cause vacuum as slug passes through air. On impact slug expands to donut shape 1$^1/_4$" in diameter. Come in boxes of ten. From Wosenitz VHP, Inc.

**Price:** . . . . . . . . . . . . . **$9.00**

**REMINGTON** *Shotshell Wads*

| Wad | Gauge | Shot Oz. | Price/250 |
|---|---|---|---|
| PLASTIC TRAP AND SKEET | | | |
| FIG8 | 12 | 1$^1/_8$ | $4.10 |
| RXP12 | 12 | 1$^1/_4$ | 5.45 |
| RXP20 | 20 | $^7/_8$ | 5.45 |
| PT28 | 28 | $^3/_4$ | 5.45 |
| SP410 | 410 | $^1/_2$ | 5.45 |
| PLASTIC FIELD | | | |
| SP10 | 10 | 1$^5/_8$, 2 | 7.00 |
| R12L | 12 | 1 | 5.45 |
| R12H | 12 | 1$^1/_8$ | 5.45 |
| RP12 | 12 | 1$^1/_4$ | 5.45 |
| SP12 | 12 | 1$^1/_4$ | 5.45 |
| SP16 | 16 | 1$^1/_8$ | 5.45 |
| SP20 | 20 | 1 | 5.45 |

Pattern Control Wads

PART

1 2 3 4 5 6 7

# MISCELLANEOUS

**COMPETITION ELECTRONICS ProChrono**

Velocity range from 56 to 9999 fps. Features LCD display, diffuser hoods, optional indoor lighting setup, remote control, infrared thermal printer and printer holder. Records and displays velocity, number of shots and average velocity. Operating temperature range from 32 to 100 degrees Fahrenheit. Mounting hold thread for tripod 1/4x20. Size: 16x4x3 1/4. Guide wire size: 3/16x16". Powered by one 9-volt alkaline battery. Battery not included. From Competition Electronics, Inc.

**Price:** . . . . . . . . . . **$99.95**
**Price:** Indoor lighting setup . . . . . . . **$29.95**
**Price:** Remote control . . . . . . . **$19.95**
**Price:** Infrared thermal printer . . . . . . **$125.00**
**Price:** Printer holder . . . . . . . **$7.50**
**Price:** Extra diffusers . . . . . . . **$4.00**
**Price:** Plastic Diffuser Hoods . . . . . . **$5.00**

**COMPETITION ELECTRONICS Pro-Tach**

Direct readouts from 75 to 4500 fps. Features large LCD display, diffuser hood, optional remote control, low battery indicator. Records number of shots, velocity from shot to shot and average velocity per shot string. Powered by 9-volt battery. Comes with skyscreens and targets. From Competition Electronics, Inc.

**Price:** . . . . . . . . . . **$149.95**
**Price:** Remote control . . . . . . . **$30.00**
**Price:** Additional targets (8) . . . . . . **$7.50**

**CUSTOM CHRONOGRAPH ProShop Meter**

Designed for indoor handgun shooting ranges. Direct Readouts from 100 to 4000 fps. Features 24" tall window; heavy gauge aircraft quality aluminum construction; quartz crystal timing; designed to sit on flat surface. 110 AC. From Custom Chronograph Co.

**Price:** . . . . . . . . . . **$365.00**

**CUSTOM CHRONOGRAPH BulletMeter**

Remote light screen setup with LCD readout chronograph cable attached to screens. Velocity readout from 275 to 4500 fps. Light screen spacing at 22". Features two high frame light screens with plexiglass top, quick disconnect cables for rapid setup and takedown. Automatic update with each shot. Powered by single 9-volt battery. Comes complete with shooting windows, light screens, cables and mounting bracket. Battery and tripod not included. From Custom Chronograph Co.

**Price:** . . . . . . . . . . **$150.00**

**OEHLER 35P Carrying Case**

Hard plastic case holds Model 35P, three skyscreens, 4-foot rail, pair of folding stands, and spare paper and batteries. From Oehler Research.

**Price:** . . . . . . . . . . **$25.00**

**OEHLER BNC/BNC Signal Cable**

30-foot signal cables to connect Model 55 screens to chronograph. From Oehler Research.

**Price:** Each . . . . . . . . . **$15.00**

**OEHLER Diffuser Assembly**

Assembly includes rigid plastic diffuser with two side-rails for one Skyscreen III. From Oehler Research.

**Price:** . . . . . . . . . . **$15.00**

**OEHLER Diffuser Assembly, Lighted**

Clamps to hold tubular 120-volt incandescent bulb to add to diffuser assembly. Includes bulb, socket and cord. From Oehler Research.

**Price:** . . . . . . . . . . **$30.00**

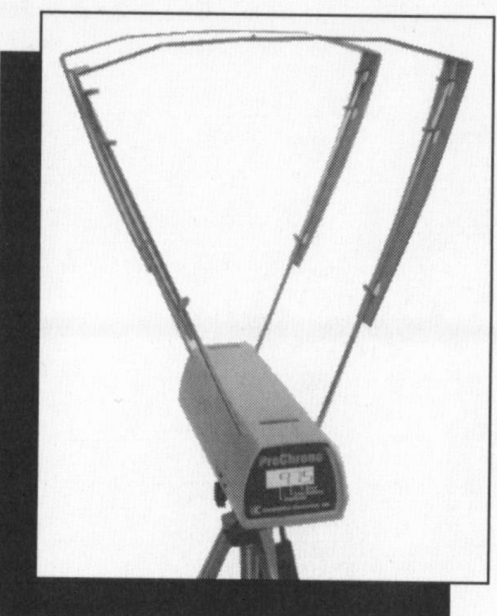


Competition Electronics

Custom Chronograph ProShop Meter

**OEHLER Model 35 Chronograph**

Available with either two or three Skyscreen IIIs. Same features as 35P without printer and, in two skyscreen configuration, without proof channel. Comes with 2-foot mounting rail and battery. From Oehler Research.

**Price:** With 3 Skyscreen III . . . . . . **$225.00**

**OEHLER Model 35BNC Chronograph**

Same unit as Model 35P retaining built-in printer and proof channel but requires Model 55 photoelectric screens and uses 120 vac power instead of battery. From Oehler Research.

**Price:** . . . . . . . . . . **$400.00**

**OEHLER Model 35P Chronograph**

Model 35P uses three Skyscreen III detectors to proof velocity readouts by taking two readings per shot and comparing the two for extreme differences. Includes built-in printer with plain paper printout to record each round as fired. At end of shot string a statistical summary of valid shots with high, low, extreme spread, mean and standard deviation with asterisk denoting possible shot error. Uses 4MHz clock for higher accuracy at short screen spacings. Comes with 2-foot mounting rail and battery. From Oehler Research.

**Price:** . . . . . . . . . . **$345.00**

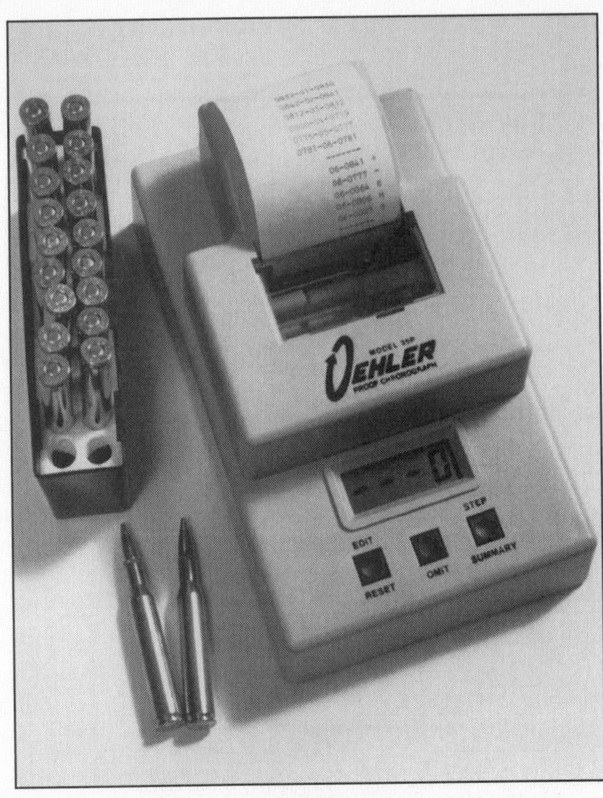


Oehler Model 35P

**OEHLER Model 43 Personal Ballistics Laboratory**

IBM-compatible host computer Model 43 measures firearm pressure curves, muzzle velocity, time-of-flight and downrange velocity using integrated multi-channel electronics; graphically shows point of impact on target with use of Acoustic Target, measures it and makes permanent record. Consists of 9x11x1.4″ metal case connecting to computer via serial port and powered by internal rechargeable battery. Uses one set of three skyscreens near muzzle and second set downrange. Both sets include proof channel. Host computer must be MS-DOS compatible and have CGA, EGA, VGA or Hercules graphics; a serial port; and minimum of 384K of free RAM. Optional equipment includes: Pressure strain gauge starter kit with five gauges, cables and connectors, cleaners and adhesives, soldering iron and other incidentals; Acoustic target with three acoustic sensors; downrange amplifier with 110-yard cable; Skyscreen mounting kit with 4-foot rail and two adjustable stands; set of three downrange Skyscreens. Comes with three Skycreen IIIs, cables, an AC adapter/charger and all software including Ballistic Explorer. From Oehler Research.

**Price:** Model 43 . . . . . . . . . . . . . . . . . . **$600.00**
**Price:** Pressure strain gauge . . . . . . . . . . . **$170.00**
**Price:** Acoustic Target . . . . . . . . . . . . . . . **$600.00**
**Price:** Downrange amplifier . . . . . . . . . . . . **$140.00**
**Price:** Skyscreen mounting kit . . . . . . . . . . . **$50.00**
**Price:** Extra strain gauges, 5 . . . . . . . . . . . **$35.00**

**OEHLER Model 55 Photoelectric Screens**

Steel frame screen of 18″x36″x3″ dimensions with shooting window of 16″x28″. Built-in light source L60 Lumiline lamp. Output is +12; bolt pulse via BNC connector. 120 vac required. From Oehler Research.

**Price:** Two screens . . . . . . . . . . . . . . . **$1,100.00**

**OEHLER Printer Upgrade**

To upgrade Model 35 to 35P by adding plain paper printer. From Oehler Research.

**Price:** . . . . . . . . . . . . . . . . . . . . . . **$145.00**

**OEHLER Skyscreen III**

For use with Oehler Model 12, 33 and 35 chronographs as replacement or spare. Complete with cable and moulded plastic diffuser assembly. From Oehler Research.

**Price:** . . . . . . . . . . . . . . . . . . . . . . **$35.00**

**OEHLER Skyscreen III Plastic Shells**

Four black outside pieces to repair damaged skyscreens. From Oehler Research.

**Price:** . . . . . . . . . . . . . . . . . . . . . . **$15.00**

**OEHLER Skyscreen III Plastic Shell with Lenses**

Kit includes both lenses and two black outside pieces to repair one skyscreen. From Oehler Research.

**Price:** . . . . . . . . . . . . . . . . . . . . . . **$15.00**

**PACT Model 1**

Shot number and velocity alternate on four digit display. Provides statistical summary of average velocity, high and low velocities as well as standard deviation and average deviation. Holds up to 24 shots and recalls any one from memory. Optional infrared print driver allows communication with HP infrared printer. Comes with M5 skyscreens. From PACT.

**Price:** . . . . . . . . . . . . . . . . . . . . . . **$129.99**
**Price:** Infrared print driver . . . . . . . . . . . . **$25.00**
**Price:** Infrared HP printer . . . . . . . . . . . . **$125.00**
**Price:** Skyscreen mounting bracket . . . . . . . . . **$27.99**
**Price:** Light kit . . . . . . . . . . . . . . . . . . **$39.95**
**Price:** Carrying case . . . . . . . . . . . . . . . . **$18.49**

**PACT PC2**

Smaller version of PACT Professional chronograph. Maintains all basic features but with less memory, less powerful software and no printout capability. Optional serial port allows dumping of data to host computer; compatible with RCBS PC Bullet. Optional infrared print driver allows communication with HP battery powered printer. Comes with M5 skyscreens. From PACT.

**Price:** . . . . . . . . . . . . . . . . . . . . . . **$189.99**
**Price:** Infrared print driver . . . . . . . . . . . . **$25.00**
**Price:** Infrared HP printer . . . . . . . . . . . . **$125.00**
**Price:** Skyscreen mounting bracket . . . . . . . . . **$27.99**
**Price:** Light kit . . . . . . . . . . . . . . . . . . **$39.95**
**Price:** Carrying case . . . . . . . . . . . . . . . . **$16.99**

PACT PC2

**PACT Professional Chronograph**

Chronograph with ballistics computer built in. Records in memory and displays each shot, shot number and velocity to tenth of a foot per second at top of 32-character display and current average velocity on lower half of display. Recalculates current string statistics: extreme spread, standard deviation and average deviation. Features "hot key" control to allow user interface with stored data to review any aspect of shot string. Holds up to 300 shots in memory. Ballistics computer features trajectory function to calculate optimal 100-yard zero to tenth of an inch, correcting for altitude and temperature or cross wind; drop tables based on entered data; calculates recoil, ballistic co-efficient; and includes terminal ballistics functions such as kinetic energy, momentum, IPSC power factor, Taylor knock out and Wootters lethality index. Plain paper dot-matrix printer. Comes with M5 14″x12″ skyscreens. Skyscreen mounting bracket and carrying case optional. From PACT.

**Price:** . . . . . . . . . . . . . . . . . . . . . . . . **$279.99**
**Price:** Skyscreen mounting bracket . . . . . . . . . **$27.99**
**Price:** Light kit . . . . . . . . . . . . . . . . . . . **$39.95**
**Price:** Carrying case . . . . . . . . . . . . . . . . **$17.99**
**Price:** Extra printing paper, 6 rolls . . . . . . . . . **$12.00**

**SHOOTING CHRONY MASTER CHRONY**

Include Alpha, Beta, Delta or Gamma chronograph plus remote LCD unit with 16-foot cord. From Shooting Chrony, Inc.

**Price:** F-1 Master . . . . . . . . . . . . . . . . . . **$99.95**
**Price:** Delta Master . . . . . . . . . . . . . . . . . **$109.95**
**Price:** Alpha Master . . . . . . . . . . . . . . . . . **$119.95**
**Price:** Beta Master . . . . . . . . . . . . . . . . . . **$129.95**
**Price:** Gamma Master . . . . . . . . . . . . . . . . **$199.95**

**SHOOTING CHRONY ALPHA CHRONY**

Made of 20-gauge steel, measures 2³/₄x4¹/₄x7¹/₂ and weighs only 2.5 lbs. Set up on table top or tripod. Features velocity range from 30 fps to 5000 fps; accuracy to +99.5%; measures high, low and average velocities, extreme spread and standard deviations; large LCD readout; individually calibrated. Readouts in fps or metric m/s. 1-string, 32-shot memory. Indoor shooting light fixture, stereo jack for optional remote control available. From Shooting Chrony, Inc.

**Price:** . . . . . . . . . . . . . . . . . . . . . . . . **$99.95**

**SHOOTING CHRONY BETA CHRONY**

In addition to all the standard features of the Alpha chronograph, the Beta offers memory for 60 numbered shots; data storage/information retrieval; computer interface. From Shooting Chrony, Inc.

**Price:** . . . . . . . . . . . . . . . . . . . . . . . . **$109.95**

**SHOOTING CHRONY DELTA CHRONY**

The low-priced starter for the Shooting Chrony line of chronographs. Features include LED readout of numbered shot velocities; delivery of high, low and average velocities of string; ability to switch from fps and mps; ability to upgrade to the Alpha Chrony. From Shooting Chrony.

**Price:** . . . . . . . . . . . . . . . . . . . . . . . . **$89.95**
**Price:** Upgrade . . . . . . . . . . . . . . . . . . . . **$25.00**

**SHOOTING CHRONY GAMMA CHRONY**

All the features of the Beta plus 1000-shot memory with optimal 4000-8000-shot available; string size change capability; vapid five mode to measure up to 1800 rounds per minute; IBM interface; remote control.

**Price:** . . . . . . . . . . . . . . . . . . . . . . . . **$199.95**

Shooting Chrony Alpha Chrony

PART 1 2 3 4 5 6 7

# REFERENCE

## SMOKELESS POWDER—COMPOSITION AND BURN RATE
### From Fastest Burning to Slowest

| Manuf. | Powder | Granule Shape | Nitroglyc. % | Bulk Density | Suggested Primers | Primary Uses |
|---|---|---|---|---|---|---|
| Hodg. | Clays | Flake | P | 0.475 | Standard Pistol | Shotgun/Targ. Pistol |
| Norma | R-1 | — | 2 | — | Standard Pistol | Targ. Pistol |
| Scott | Red Diam. | Diamond | 22 | — | Standard Pistol | Shotgun/Light Pistol |
| Vihta. | N310 | Porous base cylin. | 0 | 0.45 | Standard Pistol | Targ. Pistol |
| Herc. | Red Dot | Flake | 20 | 0.480 | Standard Pistol | Shotgun/Light Pistol |
| Herc. | Bullseye | Flake | 40 | 0.620 | Standard Pistol | Light to Med. Pistol |
| Vihta. | N312 | Porous base | 0 | 0.435 | Standard Pistol | Special Blank Powder |
| Win. | 230* | Sphere | UN | 0.715 | Standard Pistol | Light Pistol |
| Scott | 1000 | Flake | 0 | — | Standard Pistol | Light to Med. Pistol/Shotgun |
| Vihta. | N318 | Porous base flake | 0 | 0.430 | — | Shotgun |
| Scott | Nitro-100 | Flake | 27 | 0.510 | Standard Pistol | Shotgun/Light Pistol |
| IMR | 700X | Flake | 29 | 0.500 | Standard Pistol | Shotgun/Light Pistol |
| Win. | 452AA* | Sphere | 13 | 0.555 | Standard Pistol | Shotgun/Light Pistol |
| Scott | 453 | Sphere | 13 | 0.555 | Standard Pistol | Shotgun/Light Pistol |
| Vihta. | N319 | Porous base flake | 0 | 0.430 | — | Shotgun |
| Accur. | AA2 | Sphere | 24 | 0.750 | Standard Pistol | Light to Mod. Pistol |
| Vihta. | N320 | Porous base cylin. | 0 | 0.500 | Standard Pistol | Shotgun/Light to Mod. Pistol |
| Scott | Royal D | — | 0 | — | Standard Pistol | Shotgun/Light to Mod. Pistol |
| Vihta. | N321 | Porous base flake | 0 | 0.450 | — | Shotgun |
| Win. | 231 | Sphere | 22.5 | 0.700 | Standard Pistol | Light to Mod. Pistol |
| Vihta. | N322 | Porous base flake | 0 | 0.430 | — | Shotgun |
| Hodg. | HP-38 | Sphere | P | 0.635 | Standard Pistol | Light to Mod. Pistol |
| Vihta. | N324 | Porous base flake | 0 | 0.470 | — | Shotgun |
| Vihta. | N325 | Porous base flake | 0 | 0.520 | — | Shotgun |
| Win. | WST | Sphere | 20 | 0.535 | Standard Pistol | Shotgun/Targ. Pistol |
| Vihta. | N326 | Porous base flake | 0 | 0.520 | — | Shotgun |
| Hodg. | Int'l clays | Flake | P | 0.525 | — | Shotgun |
| Vihta. | N328 | Porous base flake | 0 | 0.500 | — | Shotgun |
| Herc. | Green Dot | Flake | 20 | 0.515 | — | Shotgun |
| Vihta. | N330 | Porous base cylin. | 0 | 0.600 | Standard Pistol | Light to Mod. Pistol |
| IMR | 7625 | Flake | 0 | 0.640 | Standard Pistol | Shotgun/Pistol |
| IMR | PB | Porous base | 0 | 0.555 | Standard Pistol | Shotgun/Light Pistol |
| Vihta. | N331 | Porous base cylin. | 0 | 0.680 | Standard Pistol | 9mm Luger/Light to Mod. Pistol |
| Scott | Pearl | — | 0 | — | Standard Pistol | Shotgun/Mod. Pistol |
| Win. | WSL | Sphere | 34 | 0.765 | Standard Pistol | Shotgun/Targ. Pistol |
| Hodg. | Univ. clays | Flake | P | 0.650 | Standard Pistol | Shotgun/Pistol |
| Win. | 473AA* | Sphere | UN | 0.665 | — | Shotgun |
| Herc. | Unique | Flake | 20 | 0.610 | Standard Pistol | Mod.-Heavy Pistol/Light Cast-Bullet Rifle |
| Win. | WAP | Sphere | 15 | — | Standard Pistol | Pistol |
| Vihta. | N338 | Porous base cylin. | 0 | 0.540 | — | Blanks/Shotgun |
| Accur. | AA5 | Sphere | 17 | 0.950 | Standard Pistol | Sub-Sonic 9mm Luger/Mod. Pistol |
| Win. | WSF | Sphere | 34 | 0.770 | Standard Pistol | Shotgun/Mod. Pistol |
| Vihta. | N340 | Porous base cylin. | 0 | 0.560 | Standard Pistol | Mod. to Heavy Pistol |
| Win. | 540 | Sphere | 21 | 0.950 | Standard Pistol | Shotgun/Pistol |
| Vihta. | N342 | Porous base cylin. | 0 | 0.560 | Standard Pistol | Shotgun/Pistol |
| Herc. | HERCO | Flake | 20 | 0.570 | Standard Pistol | Shotgun/Mod. Pistol |
| Hodg. | HS6 | Sphere | P | 0.945 | Standard Pistol | Mod. to Heavy Pistol/Shotgun |
| Vihta. | N344 | Porous base flake | 0 | 0.520 | — | Shotgun |
| IMR | 4756 | Flake | 0 | 0.610 | Standard Pistol | Shotgun/Pistol |
| Vihta. | N347 | Porous base flake | 0 | 0.540 | — | Shotgun |
| Scott | 1250 | Flake | 0 | — | Standard Pistol | Shotgun/Mod. Pistol |

## SMOKELESS POWDER—COMPOSITION AND BURN RATE
### From Fastest Burning to Slowest

| Manuf. | Powder | Granule Shape | Nitroglyc. % | Bulk Density | Suggested Primers | Primary Uses |
|---|---|---|---|---|---|---|
| Vihta. | 3N37 | Porous base cylin. | 0 | 0.640 | Standard Pistol | High Vel. 22 RF/Pistol/Shotgun |
| Vihta. | 3N17 | Porous base cylin. | 0 | 0.520 | Standard Pistol | 22 Rimfire |
| Vihta. | 3N36 | Porous base cylin. | 0 | 0.500 | Standard Pistol | 22 Rimfire |
| IMR | 800X | Flake | 29 | — | — | Shotgun |
| Scott | 1500 | Flake | 0 | — | Standard or Mag. Pistol | Mod. to Heavy Pistol |
| Vihta. | N350 | Porous base cylin. | 0 | 0.570 | Standard Pistol | Mod. to Heavy Pistol/Shotgun |
| Hodg. | HS7 | Sphere | P | 0.990 | Standard Pistol | Shotgun/Heavy Pistol |
| Herc. | Blue Dot | Flake | 20 | 0.780 | Standard or Mag. Pistol | Mod. to Heavy Pistol/Shotgun |
| Accur. | AA7 | Sphere | 10.5 | 0.985 | Standard or Mag. Pistol | 9mm Luger/10mm/Mod. to Heavy Pistol |
| Win. | 571 | Sphere | 21 | 0.955 | — | Shotgun |
| Win. | 630* | Sphere | UN | 0.965 | Mag. Pistol | Heavy Pistol |
| Herc. | 2400 | Tubular | 15 | 0.870 | Standard or Mag. Pistol | Heavy and Mag. Pistol |
| Vihta. | N110 | Tubular | 0 | 0.760 | Standard or Mag. Pistol | Heavy and Mag. Pistol |
| Norma | R-123 | — | 0 | — | Standard or Mag. Pistol | Heavy and Mag. Pistol |
| Accur. | AA9 | Sphere | 10 | 0.975 | Mag. Pistol | Mag. Pistol/30 Carb/410 |
| Hodg. | 110 | Sphere | P | 0.975 | Mag. Pistol | Mag. Pistol/30 Carb/410 |
| Win. | 296 | Sphere | 11 | 0.975 | Mag. Pistol | Mag. Pistol/30 Carb/410 |
| IMR | 4759 | Tubular | 0 | 0.675 | Standard/BR Only | Heavy Pistol and Light Cast-Bullet Rifle |
| Vihta. | N120 | Tubular | 0 | 0.820 | Standard Rifle | Light Bullets in 22 Varmint Loads |
| IMR | 4227 | Tubular | 0 | 0.870 | Standard/BR Only | Heavy Pistol/Light Cast-Bullet Rifle |
| Vihta. | N125 | Tubular | 0 | 0.850 | Standard Rifle | 7.62X39 |
| Hodg. | 4227 | Tubular | 0 | 0.870 | Standard/BR Only | Heavy Pistol/Light Cast-Bullet Rifle |
| Vihta. | N130 | Tubular | 0 | 0.850 | Standard Rifle | Factory 22 & 6mm PPC |
| Win. | 680* | Sphere | 10 | 0.950 | Mag. Only | 454 Casull/Small Rifle Cases |
| Accur. | 1680 | Sphere | 10 | 0.950 | Mag. Only | 454 Casull/Small Rifle Cases |
| T-Bird | 680 | Sphere | 10 | 0.950 | Mag. Only | 454 Casull/Small Rifle Cases |
| Vihta. | N132 | Tubular | 0 | 0.860 | Standard Rifle | 5.56 Tracer/Limited Application |
| Norma | 200 | Tubular | 0 | — | Standard Rifle | Small Capacity Rifle |
| Vihta. | N133 | Tubular | 0 | 0.860 | Standard Rifle | 222, 223 & 45-70 |
| IMR | 4198 | Tubular | 0 | 0.850 | Standard Rifle | Excellent Cast-Bullet Rifle |
| Scott** | 4197 | Tubular | 0 | 0.850 | Standard Rifle | Excellent Cast-Bullet Rifle |
| Hodg. | 4198 | Tubular | 0 | 0.850 | Standard Rifle | Excellent Cast-Bullet Rifle |
| Hodg. | 4198SC | Tubular | 0 | 0.880† | Standard Rifle | Excellent Cast-Bullet Rifle |
| B-West | BW-36 | Tubular | 0 | — | Standard Rifle | Mod. Capacity Rifle |
| Herc. | RL7 | Tubular | 7 | 0.890 | Standard Rifle | Mod. Capacity Rifle |
| Vihta. | N134 | Tubular | 0 | 0.860 | Standard Rifle | 7.62mm NATO Tracer |
| Accur. | 2015BR | Tubular | 0 | 0.900 | Std./BR/Mag. Rifle | Mod. Capacity Rifle |
| Scott** | 3032 | Tubular | 0 | 0.880 | Standard Rifle | Mod. Capacity Rifle |
| IMR | 3031 | Tubular | 0 | 0.880 | Standard Rifle | Mod. Capacity Rifle |
| Norma | 201 | Tubular | 0 | — | Standard Rifle | Mod. Capacity Rifle |
| Hodg. | 322 | Tubular | 0 | 0.920† | Standard Rifle | Mod. Capacity Rifle |
| Scott** | 322 | Tubular | 0 | 0.920† | Standard Rifle | Mod. Capacity Rifle |
| B-West | IMR-8208 | Tubular | — | — | Standard Rifle | Mod. Capacity Rifle |
| Accur. | 2230 | Sphere | 10 | — | Std./BR/Mag. Rifle | .223/Mod. Capacity Rifle |
| Win. | 748 | Sphere | 10 | 0.995 | Std./BR/Mag. Rifle | Mod. to Large Rifle |
| Hodg. | 335 | Sphere | P | 1.035 | Mag. Rifle | Mod. to Large Rifle |
| Hodg. | BL-C(2) | Sphere | P | 1.035 | Mag. Rifle | Mod. to Large Rifle |
| Accur. | 2460 | Sphere | 10 | 0.975 | Std./BR/Mag. Rifle | Mod. Capacity Rifle |
| IMR | 4895 | Tubular | 0 | 0.920 | Standard Rifle | Versatile/Gd. Cast Bullet & Reduced Lds. |
| Hodg. | 4895 | Tubular | 0 | 0.920 | Standard Rifle | Versatile/Gd. Cast Bullet & Reduced Lds. |
| Herc. | RL12 | Tubular | 7 | 1.000 | Standard Rifle | Mod. Capacity Rifle |

## SMOKELESS POWDER—COMPOSITION AND BURN RATE
### From Fastest Burning to Slowest

| Manuf. | Powder | Granule Shape | Nitroglyc. % | Bulk Density | Suggested Primers | Primary Uses |
|---|---|---|---|---|---|---|
| Vihta. | N135 | Tubular | 0 | 0.860 | Standard Rifle | 7.62 Ball/Mod. Capacity Rifle |
| IMR | 4064 | Tubular | 0 | 0.905 | Standard Rifle | Mod. Capacity Rifle |
| Scott** | 4065 | Tubular | 0 | 0.905 | Standard Rifle | Mod. Capacity Rifle |
| Accur. | 2520 | Sphere | 10 | 0.970 | Std./BR/Mag. Rifle | Mod. Capacity Rifle |
| IMR | 4320 | Tubular | 0 | 0.935 | Standard Rifle | Mod. to Large Rifle |
| Norma | 202 | Tubular | 0 | — | Standard Rifle | Mod. to Large Rifle |
| Vihta. | N140 | Tubular | 0 | 0.860 | Standard Rifle | Mod. to Large Rifle |
| Vihta. | N540 | Tubular | P | 0.860 | Standard Rifle | Mod. to Large Rifle |
| Accur. | 2700 | Sphere | 10 | 0.960 | Std./BR/Mag. Rifle | Mod. to Large Rifle |
| Herc. | RL15 | Tubular | 7.5 | 0.920 | Standard Rifle | Mod. Capacity Rifle |
| Hodg. | 380 | Sphere | P | 0.967 | Mag. Rifle | Mod. to Large Rifle |
| Scott** | 4351 | Tubular | 0 | 0.910 | Std./BR/Mag. Rifle | Large Rifle |
| Win. | 760 | Sphere | 10 | 1.000 | Std./BR/Mag. Rifle | Large Rifle |
| Hodg. | 414 | Sphere | P | 0.995 | Mag. Rifle | Large Rifle |
| Vihta. | N150 | Tubular | 0 | 0.850 | Std./BR/Mag. Rifle | Large Rifle |
| Vihta. | N550 | Tubular | P | 0.850 | Std./BR/Mag. Rifle | Large Rifle |
| Accur. | 4350 | Tubular | 0 | 0.910 | Std./BR/Mag. Rifle | Large & Mag. Rifle |
| IMR | 4350 | Tubular | 0 | 0.910 | Std./BR/Mag. Rifle | Large & Mag. Rifle |
| Hodg. | 4350 | Tubular | 0 | 0.910 | Std./BR/Mag. Rifle | Large & Mag. Rifle |
| Hodg. | 4350SC | Tubular | 0 | 0.945† | Std./BR/Mag. Rifle | Large & Mag. Rifle |
| Vihta. | 24N64 | Tubular | 0 | — | Mag. Rifle | Large & Mag. Rifle |
| Norma | 204 | Tubular | 0 | 0.990 | Std./BR/Mag. Rifle | Large & Mag. Rifle |
| Herc. | RL19 | Tubular | 11.5 | 0.890 | Std./BR/Mag. Rifle | Large & Mag. Rifle |
| Vihta. | N160 | Tubular | 0 | 0.900 | Mag. Rifle | Large & Mag. Rifle |
| Vihta. | N560 | Tubular | P | 0.900 | Mag. Rifle | Large & Mag. Rifle |
| IMR | 4831 | Tubular | 0 | 0.930† | Std./BR/Mag. Lg. Rifle | Large & Mag. Rifle |
| Hodg. | 450 | Tubular | P | 0.990 | Mag. Lg. Rifle | Large & Mag. Rifle |
| Hodg. | 4831 | Tubular | 0 | 0.930 | Std./BR/Mag. Lg. Rifle | Large & Mag. Rifle |
| Hodg. | 4831SC | Tubular | 0 | 0.960 | Std./BR/Mag. Lg. Rifle | Large & Mag. Rifle |
| Scott** | 4831 | Tubular | 0 | 0.930 | Std./BR/Mag. Lg. Rifle | Large & Mag. Rifle |
| IMR | 7828 | Tubular | 0 | 0.910† | Mag. Lg. Rifle/Fed. 215 | Large & Mag. Rifle |
| Accur. | 3100 | Tubular | 0 | 0.945*** | Std./BR/Mag. Lg. Rifle | Large & Mag. Rifle |
| Win. | 785* | Sphere | — | 1.015 | Mag. Lg. Rifle | Large & Mag. Rifle |
| Norma | MRP | Tubular | 0 | 1.000† | Std./BR/Mag. Lg. Rifle | Large & Mag. Rifle |
| Norma | 205* | Tubular | 0 | 1.000 | Std./BR/Mag. Lg. Rifle | Large & Mag. Rifle |
| Vihta. | N165 | Tubular | 0 | 0.900 | Mag. Lg. Rifle | Large & Mag. Rifle |
| Herc. | RL22 | Tubular | 11.5 | 0.890 | Std./BR/Mag. Lg. Rifle | Large & Mag. Rifle |
| Win. | WMR | Sphere | 13.5 | 1.000 | Mag. Lg. Rifle | Large & Mag. Rifle |
| Hodg. | 1000 | Tubular | 0 | — | Fed-215/Mag. Lg. Rifle | Mag. Rifle |
| Vihta. | 170 | Tubular | 0 | 0.900† | Fed-215 | Mag. Rifle/50 BMG |
| T-Bird | 5020 | Sphere | — | 0.965 | Fed-215 | Mag. Rifle/50 BMG |
| Hodg. | 570* | Tubular | 0 | 0.945 | Mag. Lg. Rifle/Fed-215 | Mag. Rifle/50 BMG |
| Hodg. | 870 | Sphere | P | 0.965 | Fed-215 | Mag. Rifle/50 BMG |
| Accur. | 8700 | Sphere | 10 | 0.960 | Fed-215 | Mag. Rifle/50 BMG |
| T-Bird | 870 | Sphere | 10 | 0.965 | Fed-215 | Mag. Rifle/50 BMG |
| Hodg. | 5010* | Tubular | 0 | 0.910 | Fed-215 | Mag. Rifle/50 BMG |
| T-Bird | 5070 | Sphere | — | 0.965 | Fed-215 | Mag. Rifle/50 BMG |

UN = % unavailable; P = % proprietary; * = Obsolete; ** = Recently Discontinued; *** = Conflicting density data from various sources; † = Estimated
VihtaVuori Oy data was included for completeness but VihtaVuori Oy rankings were based solely on information from their catalogue. Evidently VihtaVuori Oy uses shotgun pressures to compare *all* powders that are intended primarily for use in shotshell loading. Because of the lower pressures involved—compared to the pistol pressures all other powders in this table are compared at—VihtaVuori Oy's rankings for shotgun/pistol type powders differ considerably from those shown here.

## MEASURED POWDER DENSITY

1″ High Circular Column

| —Powder— Name | Type | Listed Bulk Density | Container Dia. (ins.) | Standard Funnel | 6″ Drop Tube | Max. | —Reduction in Volume— 830 psi During | 830 psi After | 3320 psi During | 3320 psi After |
|---|---|---|---|---|---|---|---|---|---|---|
| **Accurate/Scott—** | | | | | | | | | | |
| **N-100** | F | — | .357 | 0.445 | 0.497 | 0.550 | 54.3 | 53 | — | — |
| | | | .410 | 0.477 | 0.509 | 0.543 | | | | |
| | | | .452 | 0.493 | 0.521 | 0.533 | | | | |
| **#2 Imp.** | B | — | .357 | 0.650 | 0.658 | 0.695 | 13.1 | 8 | 33.7 | 28 |
| | | | .410 | 0.663 | 0.676 | 0.707 | | | | |
| | | | .452 | 0.677 | 0.691 | 0.715 | | | | |
| **S1000** | F | — | .357 | 0.450 | 0.486 | 0.497 | 34.3 | 23 | 52.3 | 45 |
| | | | .410 | 0.469 | 0.489 | 0.497 | | | | |
| | | | .452 | 0.465 | 0.483 | 0.488 | | | | |
| **Scot D** | F | — | .357 | 0.460 | 0.470 | 0.501 | 29.4 | 15 | 48.1 | 40 |
| | | | .410 | 0.483 | 0.509 | 0.531 | | | | |
| | | | .452 | 0.472 | 0.517 | 0.528 | | | | |
| **453** | B | 0.555 | .357 | 0.624 | 0.656 | 0.658 | 14.8 | 8 | 37.8 | 33 |
| | | | .410 | 0.631 | 0.656 | 0.690 | | | | |
| | | | .452 | 0.634 | 0.660 | 0.686 | | | | |
| **#5** | B | 0.950 | .357 | 0.893 | 0.897 | 0.920 | 19.6 | 10 | 34.3 | 28 |
| | | | .410 | 0.861 | 0.943 | 0.955 | | | | |
| | | | .452 | 0.875 | 0.943 | 0.974 | | | | |
| **#7** | B | 0.985 | .357 | 0.457 | 1.006 | 1.047 | 7.7 | 2 | 17.3 | 8 |
| | | | .410 | 0.969 | 1.037 | 1.063 | | | | |
| | | | .452 | 0.965 | 1.019 | 1.064 | | | | |
| **#9** | B | 0.975 | .357 | 0.931 | 0.950 | 0.987 | 8.5 | 2 | 18.6 | 10 |
| | | | .410 | 0.937 | 0.963 | 0.986 | | | | |
| | | | .452 | 0.946 | 0.967 | 0.988 | | | | |
| **1680** | B | 0.950 | .357 | 0.976 | 1.009 | 1.047 | 7.5 | 2 | 17.7 | 10 |
| | | | .410 | 0.972 | 1.026 | 1.060 | | | | |
| | | | .452 | 0.979 | 1.038 | 1.061 | | | | |
| **Hercules—** | | | | | | | | | | |
| **Bullseye** | F | 0.620 | .357 | 0.607 | 0.609 | 0.658 | 44.9 | 43 | — | — |
| | | | .410 | 0.605 | 0.656 | 0.707 | | | | |
| | | | .452 | 0.608 | 0.667 | 0.689 | | | | |
| **Red Dot** | F | 0.480 | .357 | 0.400 | 0.447 | 0.467 | 54.9 | 50 | — | — |
| | | | .410 | 0.409 | 0.455 | 0.477 | | | | |
| | | | .452 | 0.417 | 0.474 | 0.485 | | | | |
| **Green Dot** | F | 0.515 | .357 | 0.434 | 0.486 | 0.520 | 50.6 | 46 | — | — |
| | | | .410 | 0.469 | 0.517 | 0.528 | | | | |
| | | | .452 | 0.488 | 0.514 | 0.533 | | | | |
| **Unique** | F | 0.610 | .357 | 0.497 | 0.542 | 0.568 | 43.4 | 43 | — | — |
| | | | .410 | 0.514 | 0.554 | 0.565 | | | | |
| | | | .452 | 0.542 | 0.578 | 0.587 | | | | |
| **Herco** | F | 0.570 | .357 | 0.482 | 0.538 | 0.550 | 41.9 | 35 | — | — |
| | | | .410 | 0.503 | 0.545 | 0.562 | | | | |
| | | | .452 | 0.505 | 0.564 | 0.571 | | | | |
| **Bluedot** | F | 0.780 | .357 | 0.665 | 0.755 | 0.759 | 25.4 | 15 | 44.0 | 40 |
| | | | .410 | 0.707 | 0.744 | 0.766 | | | | |
| | | | .452 | 0.708 | 0.764 | 0.783 | | | | |
| **2400** | F | 0.870 | .357 | 0.837 | 0.871 | 0.901 | 17.1 | 13 | 34.1 | 30 |
| | | | .410 | 0.844 | 0.898 | 0.909 | | | | |
| | | | .452 | 0.842 | 0.901 | 0.910 | | | | |
| **Hodgdon—** | | | | | | | | | | |
| **Clays** | F | 0.475 | .357 | 0.407 | 0.464 | 0.475 | 39.0 | 35 | — | — |
| | | | .410 | 0.449 | 0.486 | 0.494 | | | | |
| | | | .452 | 0.451 | 0.498 | 0.503 | | | | |
| **HP-38** | B | 0.635 | .357 | 0.639 | 0.725 | 0.748 | 27.4 | 20 | 45.3 | 40 |
| | | | .410 | 0.687 | 0.724 | 0.735 | | | | |
| | | | .452 | 0.693 | 0.731 | 0.757 | | | | |
| **Inter** | F | 0.525 | .357 | 0.479 | 0.538 | 0.557 | 36.4 | 30 | — | — |
| | | | .410 | 0.506 | 0.548 | 0.554 | | | | |
| | | | .452 | 0.509 | 0.554 | 0.559 | | | | |

## MEASURED POWDER DENSITY
**1″ High Circular Column**

| —Powder— Name | Type | Listed Bulk Density | Container Dia. (ins.) | Standard Funnel | 6″ Drop Tube | Max. | —Reduction in Volume— 830 psi During | 830 psi After | 3320 psi During | 3320 psi After |
|---|---|---|---|---|---|---|---|---|---|---|
| **Hodgdon—** | | | | | | | | | | |
| **Univ** | F | 0.650 | .357 | 0.591 | 0.624 | 0.658 | 23.6 | 15 | 41.9 | 36 |
| | | | .410 | 0.608 | 0.670 | 0.682 | | | | |
| | | | .452 | 0.618 | 0.672 | 0.684 | | | | |
| **HS6** | F | 0.945 | .357 | 0.893 | 0.957 | 1.002 | 12.3 | 5 | 27.0 | 18 |
| | | | .410 | 0.901 | 0.952 | 0.997 | | | | |
| | | | .452 | 0.903 | 0.974 | 1.004 | | | | |
| **HS7** | B | 0.990 | .357 | 0.897 | 0.972 | 1.021 | 12.3 | 5 | 24.4 | 20 |
| | | | .410 | 0.937 | 0.947 | 1.031 | | | | |
| | | | .452 | 0.915 | 1.000 | 1.040 | | | | |
| **H4227** | B | 0.870 | .357 | 0.811 | 0.879 | 0.897 | 11.8 | 6 | 24.0 | 15 |
| | | | .410 | 0.827 | 0.889 | 0.898 | | | | |
| | | | .452 | 0.837 | .0899 | 0.908 | | | | |
| **H110** | B | 0.975 | .357 | 0.987 | 1.034 | 1.084 | 6.8 | 1 | 17.7 | 5 |
| | | | .410 | 0.994 | 1.054 | 1.088 | | | | |
| | | | .452 | 0.995 | 1.057 | 1.090 | | | | |
| **IMR—** | | | | | | | | | | |
| **PB** | F | 0.555 | .357 | 0.512 | 0.583 | 0.607 | 20.1 | 13 | 41.5 | 33 |
| | | | .410 | 0.537 | 0.594 | 0.611 | | | | |
| | | | .452 | 0.535 | 0.594 | 0.614 | | | | |
| **700X** | F | 0.500 | .357 | 0.471 | 0.523 | 0.583 | 56.0 | 48 | — | — |
| | | | .410 | 0.483 | 0.528 | 0.585 | | | | |
| | | | .452 | 0.488 | 0.554 | 0.583 | | | | |
| **800X** | F | — | .357 | 0.572 | 0.647 | 0.692 | 49.8 | 45 | — | — |
| | | | .410 | 0.594 | 0.653 | 0.705 | | | | |
| | | | .452 | 0.587 | 0.660 | 0.712 | | | | |
| **SR4756** | F | 0.610 | .357 | 0.587 | 0.665 | 0.684 | 18.6 | 8 | 38.1 | 25 |
| | | | .410 | 0.611 | 0.670 | 0.682 | | | | |
| | | | .452 | 0.606 | 0.670 | 0.679 | | | | |
| **IMR4227** | T[1] | 0.870 | .357 | 0.852 | 0.879 | 0.931 | 10.6 | 4 | 21.5 | 10 |
| | | | .410 | 0.869 | 0.946 | 0.955 | | | | |
| | | | .452 | 0.875 | 0.934 | 0.946 | | | | |
| **Winchester—** | | | | | | | | | | |
| **WST** | B | 0.535 | .357 | 0.516 | 0.564 | 0.602 | 26.4 | 18 | 47.1 | 40 |
| | | | .410 | 0.545 | 0.574 | 0.619 | | | | |
| | | | .452 | 0.542 | 0.580 | 0.620 | | | | |
| **WSL** | B | 0.765 | .357 | 0.680 | 0.781 | 0.826 | 36.0 | 34 | — | — |
| | | | .410 | 0.722 | 0.770 | 0.815 | | | | |
| | | | .452 | 0.712 | 0.776 | 0.815 | | | | |
| **231** | B | 0.700 | .357 | 0.645 | 0.714 | 0.748 | 28.4 | 20 | 45.5 | 40 |
| | | | .410 | 0.690 | 0.724 | 0.756 | | | | |
| | | | .452 | 0.691 | 0.733 | 0.750 | | | | |
| **WSF** | B | 0.770 | .357 | 0.707 | 0.781 | 0.821 | 32.3 | 30 | 46.6 | 40 |
| | | | .410 | 0.736 | 0.770 | 0.824 | | | | |
| | | | .452 | 0.731 | 0.792 | 0.833 | | | | |
| **WAP** | B | — | .357 | 0.800 | 0.841 | 0.875 | 12.8 | 2 | 28.0 | 15 |
| | | | .410 | 0.815 | 0.855 | 0.889 | | | | |
| | | | .452 | 0.811 | 0.856 | 0.882 | | | | |
| **540** | B | 0.950 | .357 | 0.893 | 0.961 | 0.998 | 14.5 | 4 | 29.2 | 20 |
| | | | .410 | 0.920 | 0.972 | 1.009 | | | | |
| | | | .452 | 0.920 | 0.995 | 1.017 | | | | |
| **571** | B | 0.955 | .357 | 0.905 | 0.968 | 1.021 | 14.1 | 4 | 28.4 | 19 |
| | | | .410 | 0.929 | 0.991 | 1.020 | | | | |
| | | | .452 | 0.941 | 1.007 | 1.031 | | | | |
| **296** | B | 0.975 | .357 | 0.964 | 1.024 | 1.054 | 8.2 | 1 | 18.3 | 5 |
| | | | .410 | 0.983 | 1.045 | 1.068 | | | | |
| | | | .452 | 0.982 | 1.054 | 1.073 | | | | |

## MEASURED POWDER DENSITY
### Specified Case, Level Full

| —Powder— Name | Type | Listed Bulk Density | Container Dia. (ins.) | Standard Funnel | 6″ Drop Tube | Max. | —Reduction in Volume— 830 psi During | After | 3320 psi During | After |
|---|---|---|---|---|---|---|---|---|---|---|
| **Accurate/Scott—** | | | | | | | | | | |
| **1680** | B | 0.950 | 222 Rem. | 0.998 | 1.030 | 1.058 | 6.4 | 1.5 | 17.0 | 7.5 |
| | | | 308 Win. | 0.984 | 1.026 | 1.054 | 6.4 | 1.5 | 17.0 | 7.5 |
| | | | 7mm Rem.Mag. | 0.986 | 1.041 | 1.053 | 6.4 | 1.5 | 17.0 | 7.5 |
| **2230** | B | — | 222 Rem. | 0.998 | 1.041 | 1.062 | 8.1 | 2.0 | 20.7 | 8.5 |
| | | | 308 Win. | 1.011 | 1.047 | 1.065 | 8.1 | 2.0 | 20.7 | 8.5 |
| | | | 7mm Rem.Mag. | 1.022 | 1.058 | 1.071 | 8.1 | 2.0 | 20.7 | 8.5 |
| **2460** | B | 0.975 | 222 Rem. | 0.928 | 0.965 | 0.991 | 8.3 | 3.0 | 21.2 | 12.0 |
| | | | 308 Win. | 0.928 | 0.965 | 0.977 | 8.3 | 3.0 | 21.2 | 12.0 |
| | | | 7mm Rem.Mag. | 0.943 | 0.978 | 0.993 | 8.3 | 3.0 | 21.2 | 12.0 |
| **2495BR** | T[1] | — | 222 Rem. | 0.839 | 0.871 | 0.885 | 9.4 | 2.0 | 20.9 | 10.5 |
| | | | 308 Win. | 0.876 | 0.910 | 0.913 | 9.4 | 2.0 | 20.9 | 10.5 |
| | | | 7mm Rem.Mag. | 0.887 | 0.918 | 0.929 | 9.4 | 2.0 | 20.9 | 10.5 |
| **2520** | B | 0.970 | 222 Rem. | 0.945 | 0.988 | 1.012 | 7.7 | 1.5 | 20.0 | 12.0 |
| | | | 308 Win. | 0.963 | 1.009 | 1.023 | 7.7 | 1.5 | 20.0 | 12.0 |
| | | | 7mm Rem.Mag. | 0.968 | 1.025 | 1.029 | 7.7 | 1.5 | 20.0 | 12.0 |
| **2700** | B | 0.960 | 222 Rem. | 0.938 | 0.963 | 0.988 | 8.2 | 1.5 | 20.2 | 10.0 |
| | | | 308 Win. | 0.954 | 0.982 | 1.002 | 8.2 | 1.5 | 20.2 | 10.0 |
| | | | 7mm Rem.Mag. | 0.956 | 1.004 | 1.018 | 8.2 | 1.5 | 20.2 | 10.0 |
| **4350** | T[2] | 0.950 | 222 Rem. | 0.850 | 0.878 | 0.896 | 10.4 | 4.0 | 22.9 | 12.0 |
| | | | 308 Win. | 0.888 | 0.916 | 0.929 | 10.4 | 4.0 | 22.9 | 12.0 |
| | | | 7mm Rem.Mag. | 0.905 | 0.925 | 0.938 | 10.4 | 4.0 | 22.9 | 12.0 |
| **3100** | T[2] | 0.945 | 222 Rem. | 0.853 | 0.896 | 0.903 | 8.8 | 2.5 | 20.2 | 9.0 |
| | | | 308 Win. | 0.893 | 0.921 | 0.930 | 8.8 | 2.5 | 20.2 | 9.0 |
| | | | 7mm Rem.Mag. | 0.915 | 0.935 | 0.942 | 8.8 | 2.5 | 20.2 | 9.0 |
| **8700** | B | 0.960 | 222 Rem. | 0.924 | 0.977 | 1.019 | 7.8 | 2.0 | 20.4 | 10.0 |
| | | | 308 Win. | 0.942 | 1.002 | 1.035 | 7.8 | 2.0 | 20.4 | 10.0 |
| | | | 7mm Rem.Mag. | 0.958 | 1.006 | 1.041 | 7.8 | 2.0 | 20.4 | 10.0 |
| **Hercules—** | | | | | | | | | | |
| **2400** | F | 0.870 | 222 Rem. | 0.846 | 0.878 | 0.910 | 16.3 | 9.0 | 32.5 | 26.0 |
| | | | 308 Win. | 0.846 | 0.890 | 0.933 | 16.3 | 9.0 | 32.5 | 26.0 |
| | | | 7mm Rem.Mag. | 0.854 | 0.909 | 0.936 | 16.3 | 9.0 | 32.5 | 26.0 |
| **RX7** | T[3] | 0.890 | 222 Rem. | 0.843 | 0.899 | 0.917 | 10.5 | 3.0 | 22.9 | 14.0 |
| | | | 308 Win. | 0.879 | 0.923 | 0.937 | 10.5 | 3.0 | 22.9 | 14.0 |
| | | | 7mm Rem.Mag. | 0.889 | 0.935 | 0.950 | 10.5 | 3.0 | 22.9 | 14.0 |
| **RX12** | T[3] | 1.000 | 222 Rem. | 0.889 | 0.928 | 0.956 | 9.5 | 2.0 | 21.2 | 10.5 |
| | | | 308 Win. | 0.916 | 0.960 | 0.977 | 9.5 | 2.0 | 21.2 | 10.5 |
| | | | 7mm Rem.Mag. | 0.940 | 0.979 | 0.991 | 9.5 | 2.0 | 21.2 | 10.5 |
| **RX15** | T[3] | 0.920 | 222 Rem. | 0.867 | 0.913 | 0.935 | 10.6 | 5.0 | 22.3 | 12.0 |
| | | | 308 Win. | 0.911 | 0.951 | 0.956 | 10.6 | 5.0 | 22.3 | 12.0 |
| | | | 7mm Rem.Mag. | 0.920 | 0.949 | 0.959 | 10.6 | 5.0 | 22.3 | 12.0 |
| **RX19** | T[2] | 0.890 | 222 Rem. | 0.864 | 0.903 | 0.917 | 13.3 | 7.0 | 26.5 | 17.5 |
| | | | 308 Win. | 0.895 | 0.940 | 0.951 | 13.3 | 7.0 | 26.5 | 17.5 |
| | | | 7mm Rem.Mag. | 0.920 | 0.945 | 0.957 | 13.3 | 7.0 | 26.5 | 17.5 |
| **RX22** | T[2] | 0.890 | 222 Rem. | 0.871 | 0.896 | 0.928 | 13.0 | 7.5 | 25.9 | 18.0 |
| | | | 308 Win. | 0.907 | 0.940 | 0.947 | 13.0 | 7.5 | 25.9 | 18.0 |
| | | | 7mm Rem.Mag. | 0.923 | 0.946 | 0.959 | 13.0 | 7.5 | 25.9 | 18.0 |
| **Hodgdon—** | | | | | | | | | | |
| **H4227** | T[3] | 0.870 | 222 Rem. | 0.818 | 0.871 | 0.882 | 11.8 | 6.0 | 24.0 | 15.0 |
| | | | 308 Win. | 0.837 | 0.876 | 0.890 | 11.8 | 6.0 | 24.0 | 15.0 |
| | | | 7mm Rem.Mag. | 0.843 | 0.887 | 0.898 | 11.8 | 6.0 | 24.0 | 15.0 |
| **H110** | B | 0.975 | 222 Rem. | 0.995 | 1.027 | 1.069 | 6.8 | 1.0 | 17.7 | 5.0 |
| | | | 308 Win. | 1.009 | 1.046 | 1.084 | 6.8 | 1.0 | 17.7 | 5.0 |
| | | | 7mm Rem.Mag. | 1.006 | 1.058 | 1.090 | 6.8 | 1.0 | 17.7 | 5.0 |
| **H4198** | T[1] | 0.880 | 222 Rem. | 0.776 | 0.814 | 0.822 | 10.8 | 2.5 | 24.1 | 10.0 |
| | | | 308 Win. | 0.807 | 0.844 | 0.849 | 10.8 | 2.5 | 24.1 | 10.0 |
| | | | 7mm Rem.Mag. | 0.820 | 0.847 | 0.854 | 10.8 | 2.5 | 24.1 | 10.0 |
| **H4198SC** | T[2] | — | 222 Rem. | 0.850 | 0.896 | 0.906 | 9.5 | 2.5 | 20.3 | 10.0 |
| | | | 308 Win. | 0.890 | 0.923 | 0.930 | 9.5 | 2.5 | 20.3 | 10.0 |
| | | | 7mm Rem.Mag. | 0.892 | 0.933 | 0.946 | 9.5 | 2.5 | 20.3 | 10.0 |

## MEASURED POWDER DENSITY
**Specified Case, Level Full**

| —Powder— Name | Type | Listed Bulk Density | Container Dia. (ins.) | Standard Funnel | 6″ Drop Tube | Max. | —Reduction in Volume— 830 psi During | 830 psi After | 3320 psi During | 3320 psi After |
|---|---|---|---|---|---|---|---|---|---|---|
| **Hodgdon—** | | | | | | | | | | |
| **H322** | T[3] | — | 222 Rem. | 0.885 | 0.917 | 0.931 | 9.4 | 3.0 | 18.6 | 8.0 |
| | | | 308 Win. | 0.897 | 0.942 | 0.953 | 9.4 | 3.0 | 18.6 | 8.0 |
| | | | 7mm Rem.Mag. | 0.906 | 0.959 | 0.968 | 9.4 | 3.0 | 18.6 | 8.0 |
| **BL-C2** | B | 1.035 | 222 Rem. | 0.991 | 1.041 | 1.065 | 6.5 | 1.5 | 16.3 | 6.0 |
| | | | 308 Win. | 1.016 | 1.056 | 1.081 | 6.5 | 1.5 | 16.3 | 6.0 |
| | | | 7mm Rem.Mag. | 1.020 | 1.064 | 1.084 | 6.5 | 1.5 | 16.3 | 6.0 |
| **H335** | B | 1.035 | 222 Rem. | 0.991 | 1.037 | 1.058 | 6.3 | 1.5 | 15.7 | 5.5 |
| | | | 308 Win. | 1.005 | 1.035 | 1.070 | 6.3 | 1.5 | 15.7 | 5.5 |
| | | | 7mm Rem.Mag. | 1.011 | 1.055 | 1.076 | 6.3 | 1.5 | 15.7 | 5.5 |
| **H4895** | T[2] | 0.920 | 222 Rem. | 0.878 | 0.913 | 0.924 | 9.5 | 3.5 | 19.1 | 10.5 |
| | | | 308 Win. | 0.898 | 0.942 | 0.947 | 9.5 | 3.5 | 19.1 | 10.5 |
| | | | 7mm Rem.Mag. | 0.913 | 0.949 | 0.959 | 9.5 | 3.5 | 19.1 | 10.5 |
| **H380** | B | 0.967 | 222 Rem. | 0.917 | 0.952 | 0.981 | 6.9 | 1.5 | 17.4 | 5.5 |
| | | | 308 Win. | 0.944 | 0.974 | 1.007 | 6.9 | 1.5 | 17.4 | 5.5 |
| | | | 7mm Rem.Mag. | 0.951 | 0.981 | 1.008 | 6.9 | 1.5 | 17.4 | 5.5 |
| **H414** | B | 0.995 | 222 Rem. | 0.935 | 0.988 | 1.027 | 6.8 | 1.5 | 17.0 | 7.0 |
| | | | 308 Win. | 0.951 | 1.004 | 1.040 | 6.8 | 1.5 | 17.0 | 7.0 |
| | | | 7mm Rem.Mag. | 0.957 | 1.018 | 1.049 | 6.8 | 1.5 | 17.0 | 7.0 |
| **H4350SC** | T[3] | — | 222 Rem. | 0.899 | 0.935 | 0.945 | 8.9 | 3.0 | 20.2 | 10.0 |
| | | | 308 Win. | 0.926 | 0.963 | 0.969 | 8.9 | 3.0 | 20.2 | 10.0 |
| | | | 7mm Rem.Mag. | 0.940 | 0.982 | 0.988 | 8.9 | 3.0 | 20.2 | 10.0 |
| **H450** | B | 0.990 | 222 Rem. | 0.928 | 0.963 | 0.981 | 7.9 | 1.5 | 19.0 | 8.5 |
| | | | 308 Win. | 0.944 | 0.981 | 1.002 | 7.9 | 1.5 | 19.0 | 8.5 |
| | | | 7mm Rem.Mag. | 0.947 | 1.001 | 1.014 | 7.9 | 1.5 | 19.0 | 8.5 |
| **H4831** | T[2] | 0.930 | 222 Rem. | 0.892 | 0.913 | 0.928 | 8.6 | 2.0 | 20.0 | 9.0 |
| | | | 308 Win. | 0.930 | 0.953 | 0.964 | 8.6 | 2.0 | 20.0 | 9.0 |
| | | | 7mm Rem.Mag. | 0.945 | 0.964 | 0.974 | 8.6 | 2.0 | 20.0 | 9.0 |
| **H4831SC** | T[3] | — | 222 Rem. | 0.906 | 0.928 | 0.945 | 9.0 | 2.5 | 19.7 | 9.5 |
| | | | 308 Win. | 0.940 | 0.958 | 0.976 | 9.0 | 2.5 | 19.7 | 9.5 |
| | | | 7mm Rem.Mag. | 0.952 | 0.982 | 0.992 | 9.0 | 2.5 | 19.7 | 9.5 |
| **H1000** | T[3] | — | 222 Rem. | 0.889 | 0.942 | 0.952 | 8.8 | 3.0 | 19.2 | 10.0 |
| | | | 308 Win. | 0.937 | 0.965 | 0.981 | 8.8 | 3.0 | 19.2 | 10.0 |
| | | | 7mm Rem.Mag. | 0.947 | 0.985 | 0.992 | 8.8 | 3.0 | 19.2 | 10.0 |
| **H570** | T[3] | — | 222 Rem. | 0.857 | 0.899 | 0.917 | 8.2 | 1.5 | 19.5 | 7.5 |
| | | | 308 Win. | 0.912 | 0.939 | 0.947 | 8.2 | 1.5 | 19.5 | 7.5 |
| | | | 7mm Rem.Mag. | 0.927 | 0.959 | 0.972 | 8.2 | 1.5 | 19.5 | 7.5 |
| **H870** | B | 0.965 | 222 Rem. | 0.942 | 0.984 | 0.998 | 9.8 | 2.0 | 18.6 | 6.5 |
| | | | 308 Win. | 0.958 | 1.005 | 1.023 | 9.8 | 2.0 | 18.6 | 6.5 |
| | | | 7mm Rem.Mag. | 0.964 | 1.020 | 1.030 | 9.8 | 2.0 | 18.6 | 6.5 |
| **IMR—** | | | | | | | | | | |
| **IMR4227** | T[3] | 0.870 | 222 Rem. | 0.860 | 0.910 | 0.928 | 10.6 | 4.0 | 21.5 | 10.0 |
| | | | 308 Win. | 0.883 | 0.940 | 0.942 | 10.6 | 4.0 | 21.5 | 10.0 |
| | | | 7mm Rem.Mag. | 0.884 | 0.946 | 0.961 | 10.6 | 4.0 | 21.5 | 10.0 |
| **IMR4198** | T[1] | 0.850 | 222 Rem. | 0.793 | 0.832 | 0.850 | 10.6 | 2.5 | 23.6 | 11.5 |
| | | | 308 Win. | 0.833 | 0.874 | 0.884 | 10.6 | 2.5 | 23.6 | 11.5 |
| | | | 7mm Rem.Mag. | 0.844 | 0.884 | 0.891 | 10.6 | 2.5 | 23.6 | 11.5 |
| **IMR3031** | T[2] | 0.880 | 222 Rem. | 0.814 | 0.860 | 0.885 | 10.2 | 2.5 | 23.9 | 12.5 |
| | | | 308 Win. | 0.853 | 0.893 | 0.902 | 10.2 | 2.5 | 23.9 | 12.5 |
| | | | 7mm Rem.Mag. | 0.858 | 0.894 | 0.904 | 10.2 | 2.5 | 23.9 | 12.5 |
| **IMR4895** | T[2] | 0.920 | 222 Rem. | 0.882 | 0.924 | 0.942 | 8.8 | 2.5 | 19.6 | 9.0 |
| | | | 308 Win. | 0.907 | 0.949 | 0.961 | 8.8 | 2.5 | 19.6 | 9.0 |
| | | | 7mm Rem.Mag. | 0.929 | 0.965 | 0.972 | 8.8 | 2.5 | 19.6 | 9.0 |
| **IMR4064** | T[1] | 0.905 | 222 Rem. | 0.829 | 0.871 | 0.885 | 9.9 | 3.0 | 22.3 | 10.5 |
| | | | 308 Win. | 0.872 | 0.905 | 0.920 | 9.9 | 3.0 | 22.3 | 10.5 |
| | | | 7mm Rem.Mag. | 0.885 | 0.923 | 0.930 | 9.9 | 3.0 | 22.3 | 10.5 |
| **IMR4320** | T[3] | 0.935 | 222 Rem. | 0.903 | 0.942 | 0.952 | 8.3 | 2.0 | 18.5 | 8.0 |
| | | | 308 Win. | 0.923 | 0.974 | 0.981 | 8.3 | 2.0 | 18.5 | 8.0 |
| | | | 7mm Rem.Mag. | 0.942 | 0.979 | 0.992 | 8.3 | 2.0 | 18.5 | 8.0 |

## MEASURED POWDER DENSITY

**Specified Case, Level Full**

| —Powder— Name | Type | Listed Bulk Density | Container Dia. (ins.) | Standard Funnel | 6″ Drop Tube | Max. | —Reduction in Volume— 830 psi During | After | 3320 psi During | After |
|---|---|---|---|---|---|---|---|---|---|---|
| **IMR—** | | | | | | | | | | |
| **IMR4350** | $T^2$ | 0.910 | 222 Rem. | 0.853 | 0.885 | 0.899 | 9.3 | 2.5 | 21.1 | 13.0 |
| | | | 308 Win. | 0.890 | 0.930 | 0.942 | 9.3 | 2.5 | 21.1 | 13.0 |
| | | | 7mm Rem.Mag. | 0.910 | 0.932 | 0.949 | 9.3 | 2.5 | 21.1 | 13.0 |
| **IMR4831** | $T^2$ | 0.930 | 222 Rem. | 0.864 | 0.889 | 0.910 | 8.8 | 2.5 | 20.0 | 8.0 |
| | | | 308 Win. | 0.898 | 0.926 | 0.939 | 8.8 | 2.5 | 20.0 | 8.0 |
| | | | 7mm Rem.Mag. | 0.917 | 0.946 | 0.958 | 8.8 | 2.5 | 20.0 | 8.0 |
| **IMR7828** | $T^2$ | — | 222 Rem. | 0.857 | 0.896 | 0.913 | 9.8 | 4.0 | 20.8 | 10.0 |
| | | | 308 Win. | 0.900 | 0.937 | 0.953 | 9.8 | 4.0 | 20.8 | 10.0 |
| | | | 7mm Rem.Mag. | 0.913 | 0.953 | 0.964 | 9.8 | 4.0 | 20.8 | 10.0 |
| **Norma—** | | | | | | | | | | |
| **N-205** | $T^2$ | — | 222 Rem. | 0.928 | 0.975 | 0.995 | 9.3 | 3.0 | 20.2 | 8.0 |
| | | | 308 Win. | 0.975 | 1.012 | 1.018 | 9.3 | 3.0 | 20.2 | 8.0 |
| | | | 7mm Rem.Mag. | 0.981 | 1.025 | 1.034 | 9.3 | 3.0 | 20.2 | 8.0 |
| **Vihtavuori—** | | | | | | | | | | |
| **N133** | $T^3$ | 0.88 | 222 Rem. | 0.853 | 0.896 | 0.927 | 9.1 | 2.0 | 18.8 | 8.0 |
| | | | 308 Win. | 0.883 | 0.923 | 0.944 | 9.1 | 2.0 | 18.8 | 8.0 |
| | | | 7mm Rem.Mag. | 0.887 | 0.930 | 0.950 | 9.1 | 2.0 | 18.8 | 8.0 |
| **N140** | $T^3$ | 0.92 | 222 Rem. | 0.867 | 0.919 | 0.935 | 9.3 | 2.0 | 19.2 | 8.0 |
| | | | 308 Win. | 0.902 | 0.951 | 0.972 | 9.3 | 2.0 | 19.2 | 8.0 |
| | | | 7mm Rem.Mag. | 0.924 | 0.961 | 0.975 | 9.3 | 2.0 | 19.2 | 8.0 |
| **N150** | $T^3$ | 0.91 | 222 Rem. | 0.860 | 0.882 | 0.920 | 8.6 | 2.0 | 18.5 | 6.0 |
| | | | 308 Win. | 0.902 | 0.940 | 0.956 | 8.6 | 2.0 | 18.5 | 6.0 |
| | | | 7mm Rem.Mag. | 0.915 | 0.943 | 0.954 | 8.6 | 2.0 | 18.5 | 6.0 |
| **N160** | $T^3$ | 0.94 | 222 Rem. | 0.885 | 0.935 | 0.952 | 8.8 | 2.0 | 19.0 | 7.0 |
| | | | 308 Win. | 0.919 | 0.961 | 0.972 | 8.8 | 2.0 | 19.0 | 7.0 |
| | | | 7mm Rem.Mag. | 0.939 | 0.971 | 0.984 | 8.8 | 2.0 | 19.0 | 7.0 |
| **N170** | $T^3$ | — | 222 Rem. | 0.896 | 0.935 | 0.953 | 8.6 | 2.0 | 19.0 | 7.0 |
| | | | 308 Win. | 0.939 | 0.977 | 0.991 | 8.6 | 2.0 | 19.0 | 7.0 |
| | | | 7mm Rem.Mag. | 0.961 | 0.985 | 0.995 | 8.6 | 2.0 | 19.0 | 7.0 |
| **24N64** | $T^3$ | 0.84 | 222 Rem. | 0.818 | 0.867 | 0.889 | 9.0 | 2.0 | 20.1 | 7.0 |
| | | | 308 Win. | 0.882 | 0.905 | 0.918 | 9.0 | 2.0 | 20.1 | 7.0 |
| | | | 7mm Rem.Mag. | 0.895 | 0.905 | 0.924 | 9.0 | 2.0 | 20.1 | 7.0 |
| **Winchester—** | | | | | | | | | | |
| **296** | B | 0.975 | 222 Rem. | 0.963 | 0.991 | 1.062 | 8.2 | 1.0 | 18.3 | 5.0 |
| | | | 308 Win. | 0.984 | 1.026 | 1.068 | 8.2 | 1.0 | 18.3 | 5.0 |
| | | | 7mm Rem.Mag. | 0.985 | 1.023 | 1.069 | 8.2 | 1.0 | 18.3 | 5.0 |
| **748** | B | 0.995 | 222 Rem. | 0.956 | 0.984 | 1.051 | 7.1 | 1.5 | 17.2 | 8.0 |
| | | | 308 Win. | 0.975 | 1.019 | 1.067 | 7.1 | 1.5 | 17.2 | 8.0 |
| | | | 7mm Rem.Mag. | 0.972 | 1.044 | 1.074 | 7.1 | 1.5 | 17.2 | 8.0 |
| **760** | B | 1.000 | 222 Rem. | 0.931 | 0.984 | 1.035 | 7.3 | 1.5 | 17.8 | 7.5 |
| | | | 308 Win. | 0.944 | 0.995 | 1.044 | 7.3 | 1.5 | 17.8 | 7.5 |
| | | | 7mm Rem.Mag. | 0.963 | 1.000 | 1.044 | 7.3 | 1.5 | 17.8 | 7.5 |
| **WMR** | B | — | 222 Rem. | 0.889 | 0.942 | 0.988 | 7.6 | 2.0 | 18.7 | 9.5 |
| | | | 308 Win. | 0.921 | 0.965 | 0.998 | 7.6 | 2.0 | 18.7 | 9.5 |
| | | | 7mm Rem.Mag. | 0.926 | 0.970 | 1.011 | 7.6 | 2.0 | 18.7 | 9.5 |

Listed Bulk Density: As advertised or otherwise estimated, in grams per cubic centimeter (water is 1.00); Reduction in Volume: Percent Reduction in total column volume after listed pressure was applied long enough so that further change was minimal. Pressure was applied to the open top of a cylindrical column of presettled powder; During: Volume loss while pressure applied; After: Stable loss of volume after pressure removed; Experimental Density (measured in listed case or in circular column about 1″ high and of specified diameter): Standard Funnel = Powder dumped through standard handloader's funnel, excess struck off even with top of case; 6″ Drop Tube = Powder dumped through 6″ drop tube, excess struck off even with top of case; Maximum = Powder settled via vibrations as much as possible, excess struck off even with top of case

B = Ball Type (may include any combination of spheres and flattened spheres and may also be porous); PB = Porous Base (porous disks); F = Flake or very short disks (disks: may have one central perforation, may be porous and may be non-flat); $T^1$ = Short tubular granules (Diameter similar to length); $T^2$ = Medium tubular granules (Diameter about one-half length); $T^3$ = Long tubular granules (Diameter less than one-half length)

## MAXIMUM SAAMI CARTRIDGE SPECIFICATIONS

| | | | | | | | | Length (ins.) | | | | | | |
|---|---|---|---|---|---|---|---|---|---|---|---|---|---|---|
| | Case | | Dia. (ins.) | | | | Shoulder | Head to | | Min. | Max. | Twist | | |
| Cartridge | Type | Bullet | Neck | Shoulder | Base | Rim | Angle | Shoulder | Case | OAL | OAL | STD | OPT | Primer |
| **Rifle Cartridges** | | | | | | | | | | | | | | |
| 17 Rem | C | .172 | .199 | .3558 | .3759 | .378 | 23° | 1.3511 | 1.796 | 2.09 | 2.15 | 9 | — | S |
| 22 Hornet | A | .224 | .2425 | .2773 | .2952 | .350 | 5°38´ | .8527 | 1.403 | 1.66 | 1.723 | 16 | — | S |
| 218 Bee | A | .224 | .242 | .3324 | .3491 | .408 | 15° | .9233 | 1.345 | 1.645 | 1.68 | 16 | — | S |
| 222 Rem | C | .224 | .253 | .3573 | .3759 | .378 | 23° | 1.2645 | 1.7 | 2.04 | 2.13 | 14 | — | S |
| 223 Rem | C | .224 | .253 | .3542 | .3759 | .378 | 23° | 1.4381 | 1.76 | 2.165 | 2.26 | 12 | 9 | S |
| 222 Rem Mag | C | .224 | .253 | .3571 | .3754 | .378 | 23° | 1.4636 | 1.85 | 2.22 | 2.28 | 14 | — | S |
| 225 Win | A | .224 | .260 | .406 | .422 | .473 | 25° | 1.53 | 1.93 | 2.42 | 2.5 | 14 | — | L |
| 22-250 | C | .224 | .254 | .4142 | .4668 | .473 | 28° | 1.5148 | 1.912 | 2.29 | 2.35 | 14 | — | L |
| 220 Swift | G | .224 | .260 | .402 | .4449 | .473 | 21° | 1.7227 | 2.205 | 2.65 | 2.68 | 14 | — | L |
| 243 Win | C | .243 | .276 | .454 | .4703 | .473 | 20° | 1.5598 | 2.045 | 2.54 | 2.71 | 10 | — | L |
| 6mm Rem/244 Rem | C | .243 | .276 | .4294 | .4711 | .473 | 26° | 1.7249 | 2.233 | 2.73 | 2.825 | 9 | 12 | L |
| 25-20 Win | A | .257 | .2738 | .3332 | .3492 | .408 | 16°34´ | .8573 | 1.33 | 1.53 | 1.592 | 13 | 14 | S |
| 256 Win Mag | A | .257 | .285 | .368 | .379 | .440 | 25° | .9838 | 1.281 | 1.54 | 1.59 | 14 | — | S |
| 25-35 Win | A | .257 | .2816 | .3642 | .4224 | .506 | 11°34´ | 1.3799 | 2.043 | 2.505 | 2.55 | 8 | — | L |
| 250 Sav | C | .257 | .2856 | .4142 | .4668 | .473 | 26°30´ | 1.5118 | 1.912 | 2.32 | 2.515 | 14 | — | L |
| 257 Rob/257 Rob +P | C | .257 | .290 | .4294 | .4711 | .473 | 20°45´ | 1.7277 | 2.233 | 2.62 | 2.78 | 10 | 12 | L |
| 25-06 Rem | C | .257 | .290 | .441 | .4698 | .473 | 17°30´ | 1.948 | 2.494 | 3.01 | 3.25 | 10 | 12 | L |
| 6.5x55 Swed Mauser | C | .2638 | .2972 | .4350 | .4770 | .479 | 25° | 1.7043 | 2.165 | 3.025 | 3.15 | 7.9 | — | L |
| 6.5mm Rem Mag | E | .2645 | .2980 | .4952 | .5126 | .532 | 25° | 1.7001 | 2.170 | 2.74 | 2.80 | 9 | — | L |
| 264 Win Mag | E | .264 | .298 | .491 | .5127 | .532 | 25° | 2.0401 | 2.52 | 3.16 | 3.34 | 9 | — | L |
| 270 Win | C | .277 | .308 | .441 | .4698 | .473 | 17°30´ | 1.948 | 2.54 | 3.065 | 3.34 | 10 | — | L |
| 7-30 Waters | A | .284 | .3062 | .3991 | .4215 | .506 | 17°12´ | 1.5864 | 2.04 | 2.48 | 2.55 | 9.5 | — | L |
| 7mm-08 | C | .284 | .315 | .454 | .4703 | .473 | 20° | 1.5598 | 2.035 | 2.53 | 2.8 | 9 | — | L |
| 7mm Mauser | C | .284 | .3207 | .4294 | .4711 | .473 | 20°45´ | 1.7277 | 2.235 | 2.94 | 3.065 | 8 | 10 | L |
| 284 Win | I | .284 | .320 | .4748 | .500 | .473 | 35° | 1.7749 | 2.17 | 2.765 | 2.8 | 10 | — | L |
| 280 Rem | C | .284 | .315 | .4412 | .4700 | .473 | 17°30´ | 1.9992 | 2.54 | 3.15 | 3.33 | 10.5 | — | L |
| 7mm Wby Mag | E | .284 | .314 | .492 | .5117 | .5315 | N/A | 2.012 | 2.549 | 3.1 | 3.38 | 12 | 10 | L |
| 7mm Rem Mag | E | .284 | .3150 | .4909 | .5127 | .532 | 25° | 2.04 | 2.5 | 3.15 | 3.29 | 9.5 | — | L |
| 30 Carb | D | .308 | .336 | .336 | .3548 | .360 | — | .9824 | 1.29 | 1.625 | 1.68 | 16 | — | S |
| 30-30 Win | A | .308 | .3301 | .4013 | .4215 | .506 | 15°39´ | 1.4405 | 2.0395 | 2.45 | 2.55 | 12 | — | L |
| 30 Rem | C | .307 | .3318 | .401 | .4207 | .422 | 23° | 1.498 | 2.05 | 2.465 | 2.525 | 12 | — | L |
| 300 Sav | C | .308 | .339 | .4466 | .4706 | .473 | 30° | 1.5586 | 1.871 | 2.495 | 2.6 | 12 | — | L |
| 307 Win | G | .308 | .3435 | .454 | .4703 | .506 | 20° | 1.5598 | 2.015 | 2.53 | 2.56 | 12 | — | L |
| 308 Win | C | .308 | .3435 | .454 | .4703 | .473 | 20° | 1.5598 | 2.015 | 2.49 | 2.81 | 12 | — | L |
| 30-40 Krag | A | .308 | .338 | .419 | .4577 | .545 | 21°6´ | 1.7251 | 2.314 | 2.965 | 3.089 | 10 | — | L |
| 30-06 Sprg | C | .308 | .3397 | .441 | .4698 | .473 | 17°30´ | 1.948 | 2.494 | 2.94 | 3.34 | 10 | — | L |
| 300 H&H Mag | E | .308 | .338 | .4498 | .512 | .532 | 8°30´ | 2.1046 | 2.85 | 3.42 | 3.6 | 10 | — | L |
| 308 Norma Mag | E | .308 | .340 | .489 | .511 | .530 | 25.76° | 2.085 | 2.56 | 3.30 | 3.34 | 10 | 12 | L |
| 300 Win Mag | E | .308 | .3397 | .4891 | .5126 | .532 | 25° | 2.1959 | 2.62 | 3.28 | 3.34 | 10 | — | L |
| 300 Wby Mag | E | .308 | .337 | .492 | .5117 | .5315 | N/A | 2.298 | 2.825 | 3.39 | 3.56 | 12 | — | L |
| 7.62x39 | C | .311 | .337 | .396 | .443 | .447 | 17°30´ | 1.1984 | 1.528 | 2.17 | 2.2 | 9.4 | — | S |
| 303 Sav | A | .311 | .3322 | .4135 | .439 | .505 | 16° | 1.3509 | 2.015 | 2.5 | 2.52 | 12 | — | L |
| 32-20 Win | A | .312 | .3266 | .3424 | .3535 | .408 | 5°42´ | .8812 | 1.315 | 1.54 | 1.592 | 20 | — | S |
| 303 Brit | A | .312 | .338 | .401 | .4601 | .540 | 16°58´ | 1.7901 | 2.222 | 2.915 | 3.075 | 10 | — | L |
| 32-40 Win | A | .321 | .3388 | .3455 | .424 | .506 | — | 1.708 | 2.13 | 2.46 | 2.5 | 16 | — | L |
| 32 Rem | C | .321 | .3437 | .401 | .4207 | .422 | 23° | 1.498 | 2.05 | 2.485 | 2.525 | 14 | — | L |
| 32 Win Spl | A | .321 | .343 | .4014 | .4219 | .506 | 14°31´ | 1.4461 | 2.04 | 2.48 | 2.565 | 16 | — | L |
| 8mm | C | .323 | .3493 | .431 | .4698 | .473 | 20°48´ | 1.8273 | 2.24 | 2.815 | 3.25 | 9 | 10 | L |
| 8mm Rem Mag | E | .323 | .3541 | .4868 | .5126 | .532 | 25° | 2.389 | 2.85 | 3.45 | 3.6 | 9 | — | L |
| 338 Win Mag | E | .338 | .369 | .491 | .5127 | .532 | 25° | 2.04 | 2.5 | 3.28 | 3.34 | 10 | — | L |
| 340 Wby Mag | E | .338 | .367 | .492 | .5117 | .5315 | N/A | 2.298 | 2.825 | 3.39 | 3.56 | 12 | — | L |
| 348 Win | A | .348 | .3757 | .4851 | .553 | .610 | 19°4´ | 1.6499 | 2.255 | 2.77 | 2.795 | 12 | — | L |
| 351 Win SL | H | .351 | .377 | .3775 | .3805 | .410 | — | 1.2 | 1.38 | 1.875 | 1.9 | 16 | — | S |
| 35 Rem | C | .358 | .3838 | .4259 | .4574 | .460 | 23°25´ | 1.5393 | 1.92 | 2.46 | 2.525 | 16 | — | L |
| 356 Win | G | .358 | .388 | .454 | .4703 | .506 | 20° | 1.5598 | 2.015 | 2.53 | 2.56 | 12 | — | L |
| 358 Win | C | .358 | .388 | .454 | .4703 | .473 | 20° | 1.5598 | 2.015 | 2.73 | 2.78 | 12 | — | L |
| 350 Rem Mag | E | .358 | .388 | .4952 | .5126 | .532 | 25° | 1.7001 | 2.17 | 2.73 | 2.8 | 16 | — | L |
| 35 Whelen | C | .358 | .388 | .441 | .4698 | .473 | 17°30´ | 1.948 | 2.494 | 2.97 | 3.34 | 12 | 14 | L |
| 375 Win | B | .375 | .400 | .400 | .4198 | .506 | — | 1.8 | 2.02 | 2.53 | 2.56 | 12 | — | L |

## MAXIMUM SAAMI CARTRIDGE SPECIFICATIONS

| Cartridge | Case Type | Dia. (ins.) Bullet | Neck | Shoulder | Base | Rim | Shoulder Angle | Length (ins.) Head to Shoulder | Case | Min. OAL | Max. OAL | Twist STD | Twist OPT | Primer |
|---|---|---|---|---|---|---|---|---|---|---|---|---|---|---|
| 375 H&H Mag | E | .375 | .402 | .4478 | .5121 | .532 | 15° | 2.4122 | 2.85 | 3.54 | 3.6 | 12 | — | L |
| 38-55 Win | B | .379 | .3922 | .3938 | .421 | .506 | — | 2.013 | 2.085 | 2.47 | 2.51 | 18 | — | L |
| 38-40 Win | A | .401 | .4167 | .4543 | .4695 | .525 | 6°48′ | .9224 | 1.305 | 1.56 | 1.592 | 36 | — | L |
| 416 Rem Mag | E | .416 | .447 | .4868 | .5126 | .532 | 25° | 2.389 | 2.85 | 3.35 | 3.36 | 14 | — | L |
| 416 Rigby | C | .416 | .4461 | .5402 | .589 | .590 | 45° | 2.3557 | 2.9 | 3.63 | 3.75 | 16.5 | — | L |
| 44-40 Win | A | .427 | .443 | .4568 | .4711 | .525 | 4° | .9275 | 1.305 | 1.54 | 1.592 | 20 | 36 | L |
| 44 Rem Mag | B | .429 | .456 | .4561 | .4569 | .514 | — | 1.2 | 1.285 | 1.535 | 1.61 | 20 | — | L |
| 444 Mar | B | .429 | .453 | .4549 | .4698 | .514 | — | 2.0 | 2.225 | 2.5 | 2.57 | 38 | — | L |
| 45-70 Govt | B | .458 | .480 | .4813 | .5055 | .608 | — | 2.0 | 2.105 | 2.49 | 2.55 | 18 | 22 | L |
| 458 Win Mag | F | .458 | .4811 | .4825 | .5126 | .523 | — | 2.4 | 2.5 | 3.28 | 3.34 | 14 | 16 | L |
| 470 NE | A | .475 | .5039 | .5322 | .5728 | .6551 | 7°24′ | 2.3849 | 3.25 | 3.85 | 3.98 | 20 | — | L |
| 50 BMG[1] | C | .510 | .560 | .714 | .804 | .804 | 15°44′ | 3.006 | 3.91 | 5.40 | 5.45 | 16.5 | — | CCI-35 |
| **Pistol and Revolver Cartridges** | | | | | | | | | | | | | | |
| 22 Rem Jet Mag | C | .223 | .251 | .3657 | .3759 | .440 | 6°40′30″ | .5984 | 1.288 | 1.61 | 1.659 | 10 | — | S |
| 221 Rem Fireball | C | .224 | .253 | .3607 | .3759 | .378 | 23° | 1.0707 | 1.4 | 1.78 | 1.83 | 14 | — | S |
| 6mm BR-Rem | C | .243 | .2705 | .4598 | .4703 | .473 | 30° | 1.0749 | 1.56 | 2.08 | 2.2 | 9 | — | S |
| 25 Auto | D | .251 | .278 | — | .278 | .302 | — | — | .615 | .86 | .91 | 16 | — | S |
| 256 Win Mag | A | .257 | .285 | .368 | .379 | .440 | 25° | .9838 | 1.281 | 1.54 | 1.59 | 14 | — | S |
| 7mm BR-Rem | C | .284 | .3085 | .4598 | .4703 | .473 | 30° | 1.0749 | 1.52 | Bullet Dependent | | 9.5 | — | S |
| 30 Luger | C | .308 | .332 | .3785 | .3897 | .394 | 18° | .6257 | .85 | 1.13 | 1.175 | 9.8 | — | S |
| 32 Auto | H | .309 | .3365 | — | .3373 | .358 | — | — | .68 | .94 | .984 | 16 | — | S |
| 32 S&W | B | .312 | .339 | — | .339 | .378 | — | — | .605 | .88 | .93 | 16 | 18 | S |
| 32 CNP | B | .312 | .337 | — | .337 | .375 | — | — | .92 | 1.21 | 1.28 | 16 | — | — |
| 32 S&WL | B | .312 | .337 | — | .337 | .375 | — | — | .92 | 1.23 | 1.28 | 16 | 18 | S |
| 32 H&R Mag | B | .312 | .337 | — | .337 | .375 | — | — | 1.075 | 1.3 | 1.35 | 16 | — | S |
| 32 SC | B | .313 | .318 | — | .318 | .375 | — | — | .65 | .965 | 1.015 | 16 | — | S |
| 32 LC | B | .313 | .318 | — | .318 | .381 | — | — | .916 | 1.165 | 1.216 | 16 | — | S |
| 9mm Luger (+P) | D | .355 | .380 | — | .391 | .394 | — | — | .754 | 1 | 1.169 | 9.8 | — | S |
| 38 Auto,<br>38 Super Auto +P | H | .355 | .384 | — | .384 | .406 | — | — | .9 | 1.23 | 1.28 | 16 | — | S |
| 9mm Win Mag | D | .355 | .379 | — | .391 | .394 | — | — | 1.16 | 1.545 | 1.575 | 10 | — | S |
| 380 Auto | D | .356 | .373 | — | .3739 | .374 | — | — | .68 | .94 | .984 | 12 | 16 | S |
| 38 SC | B | .375[2] | .379 | — | .379 | .440 | — | — | .765 | 1.085 | 1.2 | 16 | 18 | S |
| 38 LC | B | .357 | .378 | — | .3789 | .440 | — | — | 1.035 | 1.305 | 1.36 | 16 | — | S |
| 38 Spc (+P/Match) | B | .357 | .379 | — | .379 | .440 | — | — | 1.155 | 1.4 | 1.55 | 16 | 18 | S |
| 357 Mag | B | .357 | .379 | — | .379 | .440 | — | — | 1.29 | 1.54 | 1.59 | 16 | 18 | S |
| 357 Rem Max | B | .357 | .379 | — | .379 | .440 | — | — | 1.605 | 1.94 | 1.99 | 14 | — | S |
| 38 CNP/38 S&W | B | .361 | .3855 | — | .3863 | .440 | — | — | .775 | 1.16 | 1.24 | 16 | 18 | S |
| 40 S&W | D | .400 | .423 | — | .424 | .424 | — | — | .85 | 1.085 | 1.135 | 16 | — | S |
| 10mm Auto | D | .400 | .423 | — | .425 | .425 | — | — | .992 | 1.24 | 1.26 | 16 | — | L |
| 41 Rem Mag | B | .410 | .434 | — | .4349 | .492 | — | — | 1.29 | 1.54 | 1.59 | $18\frac{3}{4}$ | — | L |
| 41 AE | D | .411 | .434 | — | .435 | .392 | — | — | .866 | 1.1 | 1.152 | $18\frac{3}{4}$ | — | L |
| 44 S&W Spc | B | .429 | .4565 | — | .4569 | .514 | — | — | 1.16 | 1.56 | 1.615 | 20 | — | L |
| 44 Rem Mag | B | .429 | .456 | — | .4569 | .514 | — | — | 1.285 | 1.535 | 1.61 | 20 | — | L |
| 45 Auto (+P/Match) | D | .452 (J)<br>.453 (L) | .473 | — | .476 | .480 | — | — | .898 | 1.19 | 1.275 | 16 | — | L |
| 45 Auto Rim | B | .452 | .472 | — | .4755 | .516 | — | — | .898 | 1.225 | 1.275 | 15 | 16 | L |
| 45 Colt | B | .454 (L) | .480 | — | .480 | .512 | — | — | 1.285 | 1.55 | 1.6 | 16 | — | L |
| 45 Colt[1] | B | .452 (J) | .480 | — | .480 | .512 | — | — | 1.285 | 1.55 | 1.6 | 16 | — | L |
| 45 Win Mag | D | .452 | .473 | — | .476 | .480 | — | — | 1.198 | 1.545 | 1.575 | 16 | — | L |
| 454 Casull[1] | B | .452 | .480 | — | .480 | .512 | — | — | 1.385 | 1.7 | 1.725 | 16 | — | L |
| 50 AE | J | .510 | .529 | .5301 | .543 | .515 | — | 1.2 | 1.285 | 1.555 | 1.595 | 20 | — | L |

[1]Not SAAMI specifications

[2]Evidently a misprint in the SAAMI specifications

A = Rim, bottleneck; B = Rim, straight; C = Rimless, bottleneck; D = Rimless, straight; E = Belted, bottleneck; F = Belted, straight; G = Semi-rimmed, bottleneck; H = Semi-rimmed, straight; I = Rebated, bottleneck; J = Rebated, straight; S = Small; L = Large

All bullet diameters nominal

## CASE CAPACITY FOR CARTRIDGES FIRED IN SPORTING CHAMBERS

| | Case Capacity | | | | | | |
|---|---|---|---|---|---|---|---|
| Max. CC Grs.Water | Make | Bullet Wgt.Grs. | Type | Cart. OAL | Usable CC Grs.Water | Primer+Case Wgt.Grs. | Cartridge |
| **Rifle Cartridges** | | | | | | | |
| 28.4 | H | 25 | SP | 2.15 | 26.5 | 92.1 | 17 Rem. |
| 14.9 | Si | 45 | S | 1.72+ | 12.2 | 54.9 | 22 Hornet |
| 17.9 | Si | 45 | S | 1.68 | 15.5 | 78.6 | 218 Bee |
| 28.6 | Si | 52 | HP | 2.13 | 26.0 | 95.1 | 222 Rem. |
| 31.1 | Si | 52 | HP | 2.26 | 28.8 | 100.5 | 223 Rem. |
| 31.8 | Si | 52 | HP | 2.28 | 29.2 | 98.7 | 222 Rem. Mag. |
| 42.0 | Si | 52 | HP | 2.50 | 40.6 | 148.8 | 225 Win. |
| 44.9 | Si | 52 | HP | 2.35 | 42.5 | 169.4 | 22-250 |
| 51.1 | Si | 52 | HP | 2.68 | 49.0 | 163.5 | 220 Swift |
| 56.7 | Si | 100 | S | 2.71 | 52.8 | 162.2 | 243 Win. |
| 58.4 | Si | 100 | S | 2.82+ | 53.7 | 173.9 | 6mm Rem/244 Rem |
| 23.0 | Sp | 60 | S | 1.59 | 18.1 | 83.6 | 256 Win Mag |
| 39.0 | R | 117 | FP | 2.55 | 33.0 | 133.3 | 25-35 Win |
| 48.2 | Si | 100 | S | 2.51+ | 43.2 | 156.3 | 250 Sav |
| 58.1 | Si | 100 | S | 2.78 | 53.2 | 180.6 | 257 Rob/257 Rob+P |
| 69.1 | R | 120 | S | 3.25 | 64.0 | 197.3 | 25-06 Rem |
| 58.8 | Si | 100 | S | 2.90 | 56.8 | 188.2 | 6.5x55 Swed. Mauser |
| 72.0 | R | 120 | S | 2.80 | 66.0 | 218.5 | 6.5mm Rem Mag |
| 85.8 | W | 120 | S | 3.34 | 81.7 | 242.1 | 264 Win Mag |
| 69.2 | Si | 130 | SBT | 3.34 | 65.4 | 195.2 | 270 Win |
| 57.3 | Sp | 145 | SBT | 2.80 | 51.2 | 165.5 | 7mm-08 |
| 61.5 | Sp | 145 | SBT | 3.06+ | 56.8 | 182.9 | 7mm Mauser |
| 69.6 | Sp | 145 | SBT | 2.80 | 61.3 | 200.3 | 284 Win |
| 73.2 | Sp | 145 | SBT | 3.33 | 67.7 | 191.0 | 280 Rem |
| 85.9 | Sp | 145 | SBT | 3.28 | 80.8 | 223.6 | 7mm Wby Mag |
| 86.7 | Sp | 145 | SBT | 3.29 | 81.3 | 239.7 | 7mm Rem Mag |
| 20.9 | H | 110 | FMJ | 1.68 | 15.5 | 75.5 | 30 Carb |
| 46.7 | Sp | 170 | FSP | 2.55 | 37.8 | 137.8 | 30-30 Win |
| 47.0 | Sp | 170 | FSP | 2.52+ | 37.4 | 131.2 | 30 Rem |
| 55.7 | H | 150 | SPBT | 2.60 | 49.1 | 155.3 | 300 Sav |
| 57.6 | Sp | 170 | FSP | 2.56 | 49.2 | 188.6 | 307 Win |
| 58.0 | H | 150 | SPBT | 2.81 | 52.9 | 167.4 | 308 Win |
| 57.1 | H | 150 | SPBT | 2.81 | 52.0 | 181.9 | 308 Win (Mil) |
| 59.6 | H | 150 | SPBT | 3.09- | 53.8 | 195.2 | 30-40 Krag |
| 70.6 | H | 150 | SPBT | 3.34 | 67.6 | 190.4 | 30-06 Sprg |
| 88.0 | H | 150 | SPBT | 3.60 | 82.2 | 255.4 | 300 H&H Mag |
| 90.9 | H | 165 | SPBT | 3.30 | 80.0 | 249.6 | 308 Norma Mag |
| 93.4 | H | 150 | SPBT | 3.34 | 86.8 | 242.8 | 300 Win Mag |
| 105.7 | H | 150 | SPBT | 3.56 | 98.8 | 229.3 | 300 Wby Mag |
| 35.9 | H | 130 | SP | 2.20 | 31.4 | 108[1] | 7.62x39 |
| 50 | Sp | 170 | FSP | 2.52 | 40.4 | 142.6 | 303 Sav |
| 21.4 | W | 86 | LRN | 1.59+ | 17.1 | 74.1 | 32-20 Win |
| 58.8 | H | 150 | SP | 2.99 | 50.6 | 164.4 | 303 Brit |
| 47.2 | Sp | 170 | FP | 2.50 | 38.1 | 131.0 | 32 Rem |
| 48.3 | Sp | 170 | FSP | 2.56+ | 39.2 | 137.3 | 32 Win Spl |
| 64.4 | H | 170 | RN | 2.81 | 56.9 | 179.7 | 8mm |
| 99.3 | H | 150 | SP | 3.6 | 93.9 | 259.7 | 8mm Rem Mag |
| 88.3 | H | 225 | SP | 3.34 | 78.3 | 237.9 | 338 Win Mag |
| 101.9 | H | 225 | SP | 3.69 | 91.0 | 251.8 | 340 Wby Mag[2] |
| 106.4 | H | 225 | SP | 3.69 | 95.4 | 224.8 | 340 Wby Mag |
| 78.2 | W | 200 | RN | 2.78 | 66.7 | 257.6 | 348 Win |
| 25.0 | W | 180 | RN | 1.90 | 20.2 | 89.4 | 351 Win SL |
| 52.0 | R | 200 | RN | 2.52 | 44.0 | 156.6 | 35 Rem |
| 58.1 | W | 250 | FP | 2.56 | 44.9 | 187.1 | 356 Win |
| 59.2 | Sp | 250 | S | 2.78 | 47.4 | 175.6 | 358 Win |

## CASE CAPACITY FOR CARTRIDGES FIRED IN SPORTING CHAMBERS

| | Case Capacity | | | | | | |
|---|---|---|---|---|---|---|---|
| Max. CC Grs.Water | Make | Bullet Wgt.Grs. | Type | Cart. OAL | Usable CC Grs.Water | Primer+Case Wgt.Grs. | Cartridge |
| 72.7 | — | — | — | — | — | 223.6 | 350 Rem Mag |
| 73.3 | Sp | 250 | S | 3.34 | 63.6 | 189.1 | 35 Whelen |
| 51.1 | H | 220 | FSP | 2.56 | 40.5 | 150.8 | 375 Win |
| 95.3 | Sp | 235 | SS | 3.60 | 86.5 | 258.2 | 375 H&H Mag |
| 51.9 | H | 220 | FSP | 2.51 | 40.2 | 137.9 | 38-55 Win |
| 41.0 | CAST | 180 | FP | 1.59+ | 32.9 | 97.7 | 38-40 Win |
| 107.4 | — | — | — | — | — | 261.2 | 416 Rem Mag |
| 130.5 | — | — | — | — | — | 337.2 | 416 Rigby |
| 42.8 | CAST | 200 | FP | 1.59+ | 32 | 96.4 | 44-40 Win |
| 40.2 | | 240 | JHP | 1.61 | 25.2 | 113.3 | 44 Rem Mag |
| 69.3 | R | 240 | JSP | 2.57 | 51.2 | 199.0 | 444 Mar |
| 76.5 | H | 300 | JHP | 2.55 | 62.7 | 201.0 | 45-70 Govt |
| 95.5 | H | 500 | RN | 3.34 | 74.7 | 229.9 | 458 Win Mag |
| 149.3 | — | — | — | — | — | 321.6 | 470 NE |
| 260 | — | — | — | — | — | 829 | 50 BMG |
| **Pistol and Revolver Cartridges** | | | | | | | |
| 18.9 | H | 45 | SP | 1.65 | 16.2 | 75.3 | 22 Rem Jet Mag |
| 23.7 | Si | 45 | S | 1.83 | 22.0 | 85.0 | 221 Rem Fireball |
| 5.8 | FAC | 50 | FMJ | 0.91 | 4.4 | 28.4 | 25 Auto |
| 23.0 | Sp? | 60 | S | 1.59 | 18.1 | 83.6 | 256 Win Mag |
| 38.9 | Si | 120 | S | 2.18 | 33.7 | 136.8 | 7mm BR-Rem |
| 9.8 | H | 71 | FMJ | 0.98+ | 7.0 | 39.3 | 32 Auto |
| 9.3 | W | 86 | LRN | 0.93 | 6.2 | B-29.1 | 32 S&W |
| 12.1 | H | 71 | FMJ | 1.23 | 12.1 | 48.0 | 32 CNP/32 S&WL |
| 13.8 | W | 86 | LRN | 1.35 | 14.8 | 58.0 | 32 H&R Mag |
| 13.7 | FAC | 100 | JSP | 1.17- | 11.4 | 62.6 | 9mm Luger/+P |
| 18.7 | FAC | 100 | JSP | 1.28 | 15.5 | 60.1 | 38 Auto/+P |
| 22.4 | FAC | 100 | JSP | 1.57 | 20.4 | 81.0 | 9mm Win Mag |
| 11.1 | FAC | 100 | FMJ | 0.98+ | 7.5 | 52.4 | 380 Auto/Super Auto +P |
| 21.5 | CAST | 148 | WC | 1.36 | 14.8 | 64.3 | 38 LC |
| 24.5 | CAST | 148 | WC | 1.55 | 20 | 67.6 | 38 Spc Match |
| 24.5 | H | 158 | JHP | 1.55 | 18.2 | 67.6 | 38 Spc/+P |
| 26.7 | H | 158 | JHP | 1.59 | 17.8 | 84.0 | 357 Mag |
| 34.5 | H | 158 | JHP | 1.99 | 27.7 | 96.9 | 357 Rem Max |
| 15.1 | CAST | 148 | WC | 1.24 | 9.5 | 58.5 | 38 CNP/38 S&W |
| 20.2 | CAST | 180 | RNFP | 1.13+ | 10.6 | 68.3 | 40 S&W |
| 24.7 | CAST | 180 | RNFP | 1.26 | 14.6 | 74.0 | 10mm Auto |
| 35.6 | Si | 210 | JHP | 1.59 | 20.8 | 105.9 | 41 Rem Mag |
| 21.6 | Cast | 180 | RNFP | 1.15+ | 12.3 | 76.3 | 41 AE |
| 35.9 | — | 240 | JHP | 1.61+ | 25.9 | 95.5 | 44 S&W Spc |
| 40.2 | — | 240 | JHP | 1.61 | 25.2 | 113.3 | 44 Rem Mag |
| 27.1 | W | 230 | FMJ | 1.27+ | 17.6 | 84.8 | 45 Auto (+P/Match) |
| 31.0 | W | 230 | FMJ | 1.27+ | 21.5 | 72.4* | 45 Auto Rim |
| 42.0 | H | 250 | JHP | 1.60 | 29.8 | 117.4 | 45 Colt |
| 47.4 | H | 250 | JHP | 1.60 | 35.2 | 87.2* | 45 Colt* |
| 38.8 | H | 250 | JHP | 1.57+ | 29.3 | 109.1 | 45 Win Mag |
| 46.8 | H | 250 | JHP | 1.72+ | 33.8 | 132.8 | 454 Casull* |
| 50.0 | IMI | 300 | JHP | 1.59 | 35.4 | 168.7 | 50 AE |

* = Semi-Balloon Head case

[1] 340 Wby. Mag. made from Win. 375 H&H case.

[2] Steel Berdan primed case.

H = Hornady; Si = Sierra; Sp = Speer; R = Remington; W = Winchester; FAC = Unknown factory bullet; SP = Spire Point; S = Spitzer; HP = Hollowpoint; FP = Flatpoint; SBT = Spitzer Boattail; FMJ = Full Metal Jacket; FSP = Flat- Softpoint; SPBT = Softpoint Boattail; LRN = Lead Round-nose; RN = Jacketed Round-nose; JHP = Jacketed Hollowpoint; JSP = Jacketed Softpoint; WC = Wadcutter; RNFP = Round-nose Flatpoint

**Maximum Case Capacity** is the volume of entire case interior in grains of water

**Usable Case Capacity** is the volume of entire case interior minus volume occupied by seated bullet

**Cartridge OverAll Length** is the length of cartridge with bullet seated normally.

## SELECTED HANDGUN LOADS

| —Bullet— Wgt.Grs. | Type | OAL (ins.) | Load (Grs./Powder) | Velocity (fps) | Energy (ft.lbs.) | Pressure | Barrel (ins.) | Comments |
|---|---|---|---|---|---|---|---|---|
| | | | | **25 Automatic** | | | | |
| 35 | XTP | 0.855 | 2.1/N330 | 1024 | 80 | 22,500 | — | Impressive 25 Auto. performance |
| | | | | **7mm TCU** | | | | |
| 100 | JHP | N/S | 23.0/XMP-5744 | 2320 | 1195 | N/A | 14 Contender | Max. Recommended Load |
| 120 | JSP | N/S | 22.0/XMP-5744 | 2090 | 1160 | N/A | 14 Contender | Max. Recommended Load |
| 130 | JSP | N/S | 20.5/XMP-5744 | 1934 | 1075 | N/A | 14 Contender | Max. Recommended Load |
| 140 | JSBT | N/S | 20.5/XMP-5744 | 1938 | 1165 | N/A | 14 Contender | Max. Recommended Load |
| 145 | Lead | N/S | 20.0/XMP-5744 | 1871 | 1125 | N/A | 14 Contender | Max. Recommended Load |
| 150 | JBT | N/S | 19.0/XMP-5744 | 1772 | 1045 | N/A | 14 Contender | Max. Recommended Load |
| 162 | JBT | N/S | 18.5/XMP-5744 | 1690 | 1092 | N/A | 14 Contender | Max. Recommended Load |
| 175 | JPSP | N/S | 18.0/XMP-5744 | 1623 | 1020 | N/A | 14 Contender | Max. Recommended Load |
| | | | | **32-20 Winchester** | | | | |
| 90 | JHC | N/S | 9.7/XMP-5744 | 920 | 165 | N/A | 6½ Blackhawk | Max. Recommended Load |
| 100 | Lead | N/S | 9.3/XMP-5744 | 900 | 180 | N/A | 6½ Blackhawk | Max. Recommended Load |
| 100 | XTP | N/S | 9.5/XMP-5744 | 930 | 190 | N/A | 6½ Blackhawk | Max. Recommended Load |
| | | | | **380 Auto** | | | | |
| 90 | XTP | 0.980 | 3.6/VN320 | 1097 | 240 | 20,400 PSI | 3½ Test | Impressive, rivals 38 Spc.+ P |
| 100 | FMJ | N/S | 3.4/Universal | 889 | 175 | 16,100 CUP | 3¾ Test | Max. Load |
| | | | | **9mm Luger** | | | | |
| 90 | XTP | 1.063 | 7.3/V3N37 | 1518 | 460 | 33,300 PSI | 4 Test | Max. Load |
| 95 | FMJ | N/S | 6.4/WAP | 1285 | 345 | 33,000 PSI | 4 Test | Max. Load |
| 115 | XTP | 1.083 | 6.9/V3N37 | 1322 | 445 | 33,300 PSI | 4 Test | Max. Load |
| 147 | XTP | 1.142 | 5.1/V3N37 | 1084 | 380 | 33,300 PSI | 4 Test | Max. Load |
| | | | | **38 Super+P** | | | | |
| 115 | XTP | 1.240 | 8.0/V3N37 | 1436 | 525 | 34,700 PSI | 5 Test | Max. Load |
| 115 | JHP | N/S | 7.8/WAP | 1340 | 455 | 34,300 PSI | 5 Test | Max. Load |
| 115 | FMJ | 1.240 | 13.0/No. 9 | 1395 | 495 | 32,800 CUP | 5 Test | Max. Load |
| 147 | XTP | 1.260 | 6.9/V3N37 | 1224 | 485 | 34,700 PSI | 5 Test | Max. Load |
| 147 | JHP | N/S | 4.5/Universal | 961 | 300 | 28,800 CUP | 5 Test | Mod. Pressure, Clean |
| 147 | JHP | N/S | 6.3/WAP | 1110 | 400 | 34,500 PSI | 5 Test | Max. Load |
| 147 | TMJ | 1.230 | 10.2/No. 9 | 1175 | 450 | 29,400 CUP | 5 Test | Mod. Pressure |
| 158 | JHP (Hdy.) | 1.280 | 9.7/No. 9 | 1121 | 440 | 31,000 CUP | 5 Test | Max. Load; Hornady bullet |
| 160 | Lead | N/S | 5.5/WAP | 1035 | 380 | 34,200 PSI | 5 Test | Max. Load |
| 160 | Lead | 1.280 | 9.5/No. 9 | 1116 | 440 | 29,500 CUP | 5 Test | Mod. Pressure |
| | | | | **38 Special** | | | | |
| 110 | XTP | 1.437 | 7.0/VN350 | 1216 | 360 | 16,200 PSI | 6 Test | Near Max. Load |
| 125 | XTP | 1.437 | 6.5/VN340 | 1137 | 355 | 16,200 PSI | 6 Test | Near Max. Load |
| 148 | BBWC | N/S | 3.0/Clays | 906 | 270 | 14,500 CUP | 7 Test | Clean Load |
| 148 | BBWC | N/S | 2.6/WST | 682 | 150 | 14,700 PSI | 4 Vented Test | Clean Load |
| 148 | HBWC | N/S | 2.5/Clays | 836 | 225 | 13,200 CUP | 7 Test | Clean Load |
| 148 | HBWC | N/S | 2.7/WST | 717 | 165 | 15,000 PSI | 4 Vented Test | Clean Load |
| 158 | JHP | 1.437 | 5.8/VN350 | 912 | 290 | 16,200 PSI | 6 Test | Near Max. Load |
| | | | | **357 SIG** | | | | |
| 115 | XTP | 1.135 | 8.7/VN350 | 1400 | 500 | N/A | — | Max. Load |
| 124 | XTP | 1.135 | 8.2/VN350 | 1330 | 485 | N/A | — | Max. Load |
| 147 | XTP | 1.135 | 6.9/VN350 | 1170 | 445 | N/A | — | Max. Load |
| | | | | **357 Magnum** | | | | |
| 110 | XTP | 1.575 | 19.8/VN110 | 1872 | 855 | 33,300 PSI | 7 Test | Max. Load |
| 125 | XTP | 1.575 | 18.1/VN110 | 1738 | 835 | 33,300 PSI | 7 Test | Max. Load |
| 140 | JHP (Speer) | 1.575 | 14.4/No. 9 | 1349 | 565 | 33,600 PSI | 6 S&W 686 | Max. Load |
| 158 | XTP | 1.580 | 13.0/No. 9 | 1261 | 555 | 34,000 PSI | 6 S&W 686 | Max. Load |
| 174 | LSWC | 1.660 | 12.5/No. 9 | 1300 | 650 | 35,000 PSI | 6 S&W 686 | Max. Load, Over SAAMI OAL |
| 180 | LTCGC | 1.675 | 11.5/No. 9 | 1330 | 705 | 35,000 PSI | 6 S&W 686 | Max. Load, Over SAAMI OAL |
| 200 | TMJ (Speer) | 1.697 | 12.1/N110 | 1183 | 620 | 33,300 PSI | 7 Test | Max. Load |
| | | | | **40 S&W** | | | | |
| 135 | JHP | N/S | 7.5/Universal | 1324 | 525 | 32,500 PSI | 4 Test | Max. Load |
| 150 | JHP | N/S | 7.5/WAP | 1190 | 470 | 32,800 PSI | 4 Test | Max. Load |
| 155 | XTP | 1.126 | 8.0/V3N37 | 1267 | 550 | 33,300 PSI | 4 Test | Max. Load |
| 180 | JHP | N/S | 6.2/WAP | 1020 | 415 | 33,200 PSI | 4 Test | Max. Load |
| 180 | JHP (Speer) | 1.126 | 6.6/VN350 | 1126 | 505 | 33,300 PSI | 4 Test | Max. Load |
| 180 | XTP | 1.135 | 11.0/No. 9 | 1019 | 415 | 35,000 PSI | 4 Test | Max. Load |
| 200 | TMJ (Speer) | 1.126 | 5.9/VN350 | 974 | 420 | 33,300 PSI | 4 Test | Max. Load |
| 200 | XTP | 1.130 | 9.2/No. 9 | 863 | 330 | 35,000 PSI | 4 Test | Max. Load |
| 200 | Lead | N/S | 3.5/WST | 760 | 255 | 25,200 PSI | 4 Test | Target Load, Clean |

## SELECTED HANDGUN LOADS

| —Bullet— Wgt.Grs. | Type | OAL (ins.) | Load (Grs./Powder) | Velocity (fps) | Energy (Ft.lbs.) | Pressure | Barrel (ins.) | Comments |
|---|---|---|---|---|---|---|---|---|
| | | | | **10mm Auto** | | | | |
| 135 | JHP (Hdy.) | 1.250 | 17.5/No. 9 | 1507 | 680 | 29,200 PSI | 5 Test | Max. Load |
| 155 | JHP (Hdy.) | 1.250 | 15.9/No. 9 | 1414 | 685 | 32,700 PSI | 5 Test | Max. Load |
| 155 | XTP | 1.256 | 8.6/VN350 | 1331 | 610 | 35,700 PSI | 5 Test | Max. Load |
| 170 | JHP | 1.250 | 15.0/No. 9 | 1341 | 675 | 34,100 PSI | 5 Test | Max. Load |
| 180 | JHP (Speer) | 1.256 | 7.9/V3N37 | 1212 | 585 | 35,700 PSI | 5 Test | Max. Load |
| 200 | XTP | 1.250 | 12.5/No. 9 | 1170 | 605 | 38,000 PSI | 5 Test | Max. Load |
| 200 | FMJ | 1.256 | 6.9/V3N37 | 1084 | 520 | 35,700 PSI | 5 Test | Max. Load |
| | | | | **41 Magnum** | | | | |
| 170 | JHP (Sierra) | 1.565 | 19.7/No. 9 | 1705 | 1095 | 37,800 CUP | 9½ Test | Max. Load |
| 210 | LSWC | 1.675 | 8.3/No. 2 | 1157 | 620 | Moderate | 9½ Test | Targ Load |
| 210 | LSWC | 1.675 | 18.0/No. 9 | 1582 | 1165 | 38,600 CUP | 9½ Test | Max. Load |
| 210 | XTP | 1.570 | 18.0/No. 9 | 1521 | 1075 | 40,000 CUP | 9½ Test | Max. Load |
| 220 | FPJ (Sierra) | 1.560 | 18.0/No. 9 | 1496 | 1090 | 37,700 CUP | 9½ Test | Max. Load |
| 240 | LRN | 1.710 | 17.2/No. 9 | 1483 | 1170 | 39,300 CUP | 9½ Test | Max. Load |
| | | | | **44-40 Winchester** | | | | |
| 200 | Lead | N/S | 17.0/XMP-5744 | 1035 | 475 | N/A | 7½ Test | Max. Recommended Load |
| | | | | **44 Special** | | | | |
| 180 | XTP | 1.469 | 10.7/VN350 | 1173 | 550 | 14,700 PSI | 6 Test | Near Max. |
| 200 | XTP | 1.469 | 10.1/VN350 | 1104 | 540 | 14,700 PSI | 6 Test | Near Max. |
| 250 | Lead | N/S | 12.5/XMP-5744 | 737 | 300 | N/A | 7½ Test | Max. Recommended Load |
| 267 | Lead FN | 1.539 | 5.5/VN320 | 807 | 385 | 11,100 PSI | 6 Test | Target Load |
| 267 | Lead FN | 1.539 | 8.2/VN350 | 942 | 525 | 14,700 PSI | 6 Test | Near Max. |
| | | | | **44 Magnum** | | | | |
| 180 | XTP | 1.602 | 28.4/VN110 | 1837 | 1345 | 34,200 PSI | 7 Test | Max. Load |
| 200 | JHP (Norma) | 1.595 | 25.0/No.9 | 1676 | 1245 | 37,800 CUP | 7½ Redhawk | Max. Load |
| 200 | XTP | 1.602 | 25.7/VN110 | 1698 | 1280 | 34,200 PSI | 7 Test | Max. Load |
| 240 | Lead | N/S | 24.0/XMP-5744 | 1446 | 1110 | N/A | 7½ Redhawk | Max. Recommended Load |
| 240 | XTP | N/S | 24.0/XMP-5744 | 1413 | 1060 | N/A | 7½ Redhawk | Max. Recommended Load |
| 240 | JHP (IMI) | 1.560 | 21.3/No.9 | 1500 | 1200 | 40,000 CUP | 7½ Redhawk | Max. Load |
| 250 | LSWC | N/S | 18.0/No.9 | 1300 | 935 | N/A | — | Mod., powerful; typical revolver vel. |
| 300 | JSP (Sierra) | 1.717 | 18.6/VN110 | 1271 | 1075 | 34,200 PSI | 7 Test | Max. Load |
| 300 | JSP (Sierra) | 1.735 | 19.0/No. 9 | 1257 | 1050 | 40,000 CUP | 7½ Redhawk | Max. Load |
| 300 | XTP | N/S | 20.0/XMP-5744 | 1191 | 940 | N/A | 7½ Redhawk | Max. Recommended Load |
| 300 | XTP | 1.595 | 17.7/No. 9 | 1274 | 1080 | 38,320 CUP | 7½ Redhawk | Max. Load |
| 325 | SWCGC | 1.665 | 17.5/No.9 | 1322 | 1260 | 39,800 | 7½ Redhawk | Max. Load |
| 325 | SWCGC | 1.665 | 20.0/XMP-5744 | 1082 | 845 | N/A | 7½ Redhawk | Max. Recommended Load |
| | | | | **45 Auto** | | | | |
| 154 | LSWC | 1.240 | 6.0/VN320 | 1059 | 380 | 15,000 PSI | 6 | Target Load, Adjust for Accuracy |
| 155 | LSWC | N/S | 5.2/Clays | 1082 | 400 | 17,700 CUP | 5 | Max. Load, Reduce for Accuracy |
| 180 | LSWC | 1.244 | 5.6/VN320 | 998 | 395 | 15,000 PSI | 6 | Target Load, Adjust for Accuracy |
| 185 | XTP | 1.268 | 8.4/VN340 | 1114 | 510 | 19,600 PSI | 6 Test | Max. Load |
| 185 | JHP | N/S | 8.9/WAP | 1045 | 445 | 19,900 PSI | 5 Test | Max. Load |
| 200 | LSWC | N/S | 4.3/Clays | 888 | 350 | 17,000 CUP | 5 | Max. Load, Reduce for Accuracy |
| 200 | LSWC | 1.240 | 4.8/VN320 | 912 | 365 | 15,000 PSI | 6 | Target Load, Adjust for Accuracy |
| 200 | JHP | N/S | 7.7/WAP | 965 | 410 | 20,100 PSI | 5 Test | Max. Load |
| 230 | FMJ | N/S | 7.4/WAP | 885 | 400 | 19,600 PSI | 5 Test | Max. Load |
| 230 | JHP | N/S | 6.6/WAP | 835 | 355 | 20,200 PSI | 5 Test | Max. Load |
| 230 | LRN | N/S | 7.3/WAP | 915 | 425 | 19,600 PSI | 5 Test | Max. Load |
| | | | | **45 AR** | | | | |
| 255 | LSWC | 1.250 | 12.0/No. 9 | 874 | 430 | 14,400 CUP | 6½ S&W 25-2 | Max. Load, seat & crimp normally |
| | | | | **45 Colt** | | | | |
| 180 | LSWC | 1.525 | 5.2/VN310 | 930 | 345 | 10,200 CUP | 6 Test | Target Load |
| 185 | XTP | 1.559 | 9.9/VN320 | 1274 | 665 | 13,800 PSI | 6 Test | Max. Load |
| 255 | Lead RN | 1.600 | 7.8/VN340 | 920 | 475 | 13,600 CUP | 6 Test | Max. Load |
| 255 | Lead | N/S | 17.8/XMP-5744 | 860 | 415 | N/A | 7½ Test | Max. Recommended Load |
| | | | | **454 Casull** | | | | |
| 240 | JHP (Sierra) | 1.705 | 28.0/No. 9 | 1753 | 1635 | 39,800 CUP | 7½ Test | Max. for bullet |
| 240 | JHP (Fed.) | 1.780 | 31.0/No. 9 | 1916 | 1955 | 54,100 CUP | 7½ Test | Max. Load |
| 250 | XTP | 1.700 | 28.0/No. 9 | 1770 | 1740 | 45,800 CUP | 7½ Test | Max. for bullet |
| 300 | JSP (Speer) | 1.765 | 26.0/No. 9 | 1596 | 1695 | 46,200 CUP | 7½ Test | Max. for bullet |
| 300 | XTP | 1.765 | 26.0/No. 9 | 1623 | 1755 | 50,000 CUP | 7½ Test | Max. for bullet |
| 300 | XTP | 1.760 | 26.5/VN110 | 1631 | 1770 | 48,080 CUP | 8 FA Revolver | Max. Load |
| 300 | FA JFP | 1.760 | 26.6/VN110 | 1634 | 1775 | 49,380 CUP | 8 FA Revolver | Max. Load |

## SELECTED RIFLE LOADS

| —Bullet— Wgt.Grs. | Type | Load (Grs./Powder) | Velocity (fps) | Energy (Ft.lbs.) | Pressure | Barrel (ins.) | Comments |
|---|---|---|---|---|---|---|---|
| **222 Remington** | | | | | | | |
| 50 | J | 25.0/Varget | 3114 | 1075 | 40,600 CUP | 26 Test | Mild Load, Compressed |
| 52 | J | 25.0/Varget | 3097 | 1105 | 42,700 CUP | 26 Test | Mild Load, Compressed |
| 53 | J | 25.0/Varget | 3097 | 1125 | 42,700 CUP | 26 Test | Mild Load, Compressed |
| 55 | J | 25.0/Varget | 3095 | 1170 | 43,000 CUP | 26 Test | Mild Load, Compressed |
| **223 Remington** | | | | | | | |
| 50 | J | 27.5/Varget | 3383 | 1270 | 44,800 CUP | 26 Test | Moderate Load, Compressed |
| 55 | J | 27.5/Varget | 3384 | 1395 | 49,700 CUP | 26 Test | Max. Load |
| 60 | J | 26.4/Varget | 3199 | 1360 | 50,700 CUP | 26 Test | Max. Load |
| 64 | J | 26.4/Varget | 3199 | 1455 | 50,700 CUP | 26 Test | Max. Load |
| 70 | J | 25.5/Varget | 2993 | 1390 | 47,700 CUP | 26 Test | Near Max. Load, Compressed |
| 80 | J | 25.0/Varget | 2869 | 1460 | 51,500 CUP | 26 Test | Max. Load |
| **22 PPC** | | | | | | | |
| 40 | J | 29.5/Varget | 3560 | 1125 | 45,700 CUP | 24 Test | Mild Load, Compressed |
| 50 | J | 29.5/Varget | 3408 | 1290 | 48,200 CUP | 24 Test | Near Max. Load, Compressed |
| 52 | J | 28.5/Varget | 3363 | 1305 | 48,900 CUP | 24 Test | Near Max. Load |
| 53 | J | 28.5/Varget | 3363 | 1330 | 48,900 CUP | 24 Test | Near Max. Load |
| 55 | J | 28.5/Varget | 3317 | 1340 | 47,800 CUP | 24 Test | Near Max. Load |
| **22-250 Remington** | | | | | | | |
| 40 | J | 39.5/Varget | 4135 | 1515 | 51,100 CUP | 26 Test | Max. Load |
| 50 | J | 37.5/Varget | 3834 | 1630 | 50,400 CUP | 26 Test | Max. Load |
| 55 | J | 36.5/Varget | 3664 | 1640 | 50,400 CUP | 26 Test | Max. Load |
| **6mm PPC** | | | | | | | |
| 68 | J | 29.0/Varget | 3034 | 1390 | 48,000 CUP | 24 Test | Near Max. Load |
| 70 | J | 29.0/Varget | 3034 | 1430 | 48,000 CUP | 24 Test | Near Max. Load |
| 75 | J | 28.0/Varget | 2906 | 1405 | 47,000 CUP | 24 Test | Near Max. Load |
| 80 | J | 28.0/Varget | 2843 | 1435 | 44,400 CUP | 24 Test | Mild Load, Compressed |
| 85 | J | 28.0/Varget | 2848 | 1530 | 50,000 CUP | 24 Test | Max. Load |
| **6mm BR Remington** | | | | | | | |
| 68 | J | 34.0/Varget | 3342 | 1685 | 49,400 CUP | 24 Test | Max. Load |
| 70 | J | 34.0/Varget | 3342 | 1735 | 49,400 CUP | 24 Test | Max. Load |
| 80 | J | 32.5/Varget | 3159 | 1770 | 50,700 CUP | 24 Test | Max. Load |
| 85 | J | 31.0/Varget | 3007 | 1705 | 50,800 CUP | 24 Test | Max. Load |
| **243 Winchester** | | | | | | | |
| 70 | J | 42.0/Varget | 3600 | 2015 | 50,000 CUP | 26 Test | Max. Load |
| 80 | PSP | 47.5/WMR | 3250 | 1875 | 54,700 PSI | 24 Test | Moderate Pressure |
| 100 | PSP | 44.7/WMR | 3000 | 2000 | 55,500 PSI | 24 Test | Moderate Pressure |
| 105 | J | 43.7/WMR | 2890 | 1945 | 56,500 PSI | 24 Test | Moderate Pressure |
| **6mm Remington** | | | | | | | |
| 60 | J | 42.0/Varget | 3722 | 1845 | 50,500 CUP | 26 Test | Max. Load |
| 70 | J | 42.0/Varget | 3550 | 1960 | 50,000 CUP | 26 Test | Max. Load |
| **25-20 Winchester** | | | | | | | |
| 60 | JFN | 11.4/XMP-5744 | 1953 | 505 | N/A | 24 Test | Max. Recommended Load |
| 65 | Lead | 11.0/XMP-5744 | 1874 | 505 | N/A | 24 Test | Max. Recommended Load |
| 75 | JFN | 11.2/XMP-5744 | 1850 | 565 | N/A | 24 Test | Max. Recommended Load |
| 90 | Lead | 10.0/XMP-5744 | 1675 | 560 | N/A | 24 Test | Max. Recommended Load |
| **257 Rob+P** | | | | | | | |
| 90 | OPE | 48.7/WMR | 2990 | 1785 | 45,200 PSI | 24 Test | Mild Load, Compressed |
| 100 | ST | 48.7/WMR | 2935 | 1910 | 48,300 PSI | 24 Test | Mild Load, Compressed |
| 120 | BT | 45.6/WMR | 2795 | 2080 | 55,000 PSI | 24 Test | Max. Load |
| **25-06 Remington** | | | | | | | |
| 90 | OPE | 58.1/WMR | 3340 | 2230 | 52,700 PSI | 24 Test | Max. Listed Load |
| 100 | ST | 58.1/WMR | 3280 | 2385 | 55,600 PSI | 24 Test | Max. Listed Load |
| 120 | BT | 54.3/WMR | 3055 | 2485 | 60,100 PSI | 24 Test | Max. Load |
| **270 Winchester** | | | | | | | |
| 90 | J | 55.0/Varget | 3596 | 2585 | 51,400 CUP | 26 Test | Max. Load |
| 100 | HP (Speer) | 55.5/VN550 | 3322 | 2450 | 52,200 PSI | 24 1/2 Test | Mild Load |
| 100 | SP | 59.5/WMR | 3120 | 2160 | 45,500 PSI | 24 Test | Very Mild Load |
| 130 | SP (Hdy.) | 58.0/VN560 | 3023 | 2640 | 52,200 PSI | 24 1/2 Test | Mild Load |
| 130 | SP | 58.9/WMR | 3000 | 2600 | 53,500 PSI | 24 Test | Mild Load |

## SELECTED RIFLE LOADS

| —Bullet— Wgt.Grs. | Type | Load (Grs./Powder) | Velocity (fps) | Energy (Ft.lbs.) | Pressure | Barrel (ins.) | Comments |
|---|---|---|---|---|---|---|---|
| **270 Winchester (cont.)** | | | | | | | |
| 140 | SP | 57.6/WMR | 2930 | 2665 | 57,800 PSI | 24 Test | Moderate Load |
| 150 | SP (Hdy.) | 54.4/VN560 | 2809 | 2625 | 52,200 PSI | 24½ Test | Mild Load |
| 150 | SP | 57.5/WMR | 2850 | 2705 | 58,200 PSI | 24 Test | Moderate Load |
| **7mm-08 Remington** | | | | | | | |
| 115 | J | 46.0/Varget | 3138 | 2515 | 49,200 CUP | 24 | Max. Load |
| 120 | J | 46.0/Varget | 3138 | 2625 | 49,200 CUP | 24 | Max. Load |
| 139 | J | 44.0/Varget | 2947 | 2680 | 50,400 CUP | 24 | Max. Load |
| 140 | J | 44.0/Varget | 2947 | 2700 | 50,400 CUP | 24 | Max. Load |
| 154 | J | 40.0/Varget | 2650 | 2400 | 49,700 CUP | 24 | Max. Load |
| 162 | J | 40.0/Varget | 2650 | 2495 | 49,700 CUP | 24 | Max. Load |
| 175 | J | 38.0/Varget | 2420 | 2275 | 50,700 CUP | 24 | Max. Load |
| **280 Remington** | | | | | | | |
| 145 | SP | 60.4/WMR | 2930 | 2765 | 53,500 PSI | 24 Test | Moderate Load |
| 160 | ST | 57.8/WMR | 2795 | 2775 | 56,800 PSI | 24 Test | Moderate Load |
| **30 Carbine** | | | | | | | |
| 100 | J (Speer) | 15.0/XMP-5744 | 1846 | 755 | N/A | 20 Test | Max. Recommended Load |
| 110 | FMJ | 14.5/XMP-5744 | 1787 | 775 | N/A | 20 Test | Max. Recommended Load |
| 125 | Lead | 13.5/XMP-5744 | 1711 | 810 | N/A | 20 Test | Max. Recommended Load |
| **30-30 Winchester** | | | | | | | |
| 152 | Lead | 22.5/XMP-5744 | 2112 | 1505 | N/A | 20 Test | Max. Recommended Load |
| 173 | Lead | 22.0/XMP-5744 | 2035 | 1590 | N/A | 20 Test | Max. Recommended Load |
| **308 Winchester** | | | | | | | |
| 150 | J | 47.0/Varget | 2829 | 2665 | 50,200 CUP | 26 Test | Max. Load |
| 150 | FMJBT (Lap.) | 47.3/VN540 | 2835 | 2675 | 50,800 PSI | 24 Test | Very Mild Load |
| 152 | Lead | 27.0/XMP-5744 | 2230 | 1675 | N/A | 24 Test | Max. Rec. Load |
| 165 | LSIL | 22.0/XMP-5744 | N/A | N/A | N/A | — | Sub-moa 100 yd. groups with scoped rifle |
| 167 | FMJBT (Lap.) | 43.9/VN540 | 2637 | 2575 | 50,800 PSI | 24 Test | Very Mild Load |
| 168 | J | 46.0/Varget | 2731 | 2780 | 50,600 CUP | 26 Test | Max. Load |
| 172 | J | 46.0/Varget | 2731 | 2850 | 50,600 CUP | 26 Test | Max. Load |
| 165 | Lead | 27.0/XMP-5744 | 2165 | 1715 | N/A | 24 Test | Max. Recommended Load |
| 180 | J | 45.0/Varget | 2661 | 2830 | 49,600 CUP | 26 Test | Max. Load |
| **30-06** | | | | | | | |
| 110 | J | 59.0/Varget | 3432 | 2875 | 49,500 CUP | 26 Test | Max. Load |
| 125 | J | 57.2/Varget | 3267 | 2960 | 49,500 CUP | 26 Test | Max. Load |
| 130 | J | 57.2/Varget | 3267 | 3080 | 49,500 CUP | 26 Test | Max. Load |
| 150 | L.FMJBT | 52.4/VN540 | 2944 | 2885 | 49,300 PSI | 24 Test | Very Mild Load |
| 150 | J | 51.5/Varget | 2980 | 2960 | 49,600 CUP | 26 Test | Max. Load |
| 152 | Lead | 33.5/XMP-5744 | 2451 | 2025 | N/A | 24 Test | Max. Recommended Load |
| 165 | J | 50.5/Varget | 2873 | 3025 | 49,700 CUP | 26 | Max. Load |
| 168 | J | 50.5/Varget | 2873 | 3080 | 49,700 CUP | 26 | Max. Load |
| 165 | LSIL | 25.0/XMP-5744 | N/A | N/A | N/A | — | MOA 100 yd. groups with receiver sight |
| 167 | L.HPBT | 49.2/VN540 | 2755 | 2815 | 49,300 PSI | 24 Test | Very Mild Load |
| 180 | Lead | 32.0/XMP-5744 | 2337 | 2180 | N/A | 24 Test | Max. Recommended Load |
| 180 | J | 49.0/Varget | 2700 | 2915 | 49,800 CUP | 26 Test | Max. Load |
| 185 | L.FMJBT | 47.7/VN540 | 2614 | 2805 | 49,300 PSI | 24 Test | Very Mild Load |
| 200 | SP | 55.7/WMR | 2435 | 2630 | 48,200 PSI | 24 Test | Very Mild Load |
| 210 | Lead | 30.0/XMP-5744 | 2021 | 1905 | N/A | 24 Test | Max. Recommended Load |
| 220 | SP | 55.7/WMR | 2380 | 2765 | 51,100 PSI | 24 Test | Moderate Load |
| 220 | J | 45.0/Varget | 2382 | 2770 | 49,400 CUP | 26 Test | Max. Load |
| 225 | J | 45.0/Varget | 2382 | 2835 | 49,400 CUP | 26 Test | Max. Load |
| **300 Winchester** | | | | | | | |
| 110 | J | 72.5/Varget | 3660 | 3270 | 51,700 CUP | 26 Test | Max. Load |
| 125 | J | 68.5/Varget | 3398 | 3205 | 52,100 CUP | 26 Test | Max. Load |
| 130 | J | 68.5/Varget | 3398 | 3330 | 52,100 CUP | 26 Test | Max. Load |
| 165 | SP | 76.0/WMR | 3010 | 3320 | 53,800 PSI | 24 Test | Mod. Load |
| 180 | SP | 74.0/WMR | 2960 | 3500 | 60,300 PSI | 24 Test | Max. Load |
| 190 | SPBT | 74.0/WMR | 2920 | 3595 | 59,500 PSI | 24 Test | Max. Load |
| 200 | SP | 69.0/WMR | 2750 | 3360 | 59,000 PSI | 24 Test | Max. Load |
| 220 | SP | 68.2/WMR | 2665 | 3470 | 59,800 PSI | 24 Test | Max. Load |

## SELECTED RIFLE LOADS

| —Bullet— Wgt.Grs. | Type | Load (Grs./Powder) | Velocity (fps) | Energy (Ft.lbs.) | Pressure | Barrel (ins.) | Comments |
|---|---|---|---|---|---|---|---|
| **22 Miller Short** | | | | | | | |
| 240 | LSP | 9.0/No. 9 | 1170 | 730 | 21,100 PSI | — | Breech Seated, Miller bullet, Schuetzen Chambering |
| **32-40 Winchester (Schuetzen)** | | | | | | | |
| 170 | Lead | 20.0/XMP-5744 | 1802 | 1225 | N/A | 24 Test | Max. Recommended Load |
| 170 | JFN | 20.0/XMP-5744 | 1777 | 1190 | N/A | 24 Test | Max. Recommended Load |
| 200 | Lead | 11.0/XMP-5744 | 1043 | 480 | N/A | 24 Test | Max. Recommended Load |
| 200 | Lead | 12.5/XMP-5744 | 1138 | 575 | N/A | 24 Test | Max. Recommended Load |
| 200 | Lead | 14.0/XMP-5744 | 1243 | 685 | 9700 PSI | 24 Test | Breech Seated, Max. Load |
| 200 | Lead | 15.5/XMP-5744 | 1345 | 800 | N/A | 24 Test | Max. Recommended Load |
| **35 Whelen** | | | | | | | |
| 205 | Lead | 38.0/XMP-5744 | 2452 | 2735 | N/A | 24 Test | Max. Recommended Load |
| 250 | Lead | 36.0/XMP-5744 | 2173 | 2620 | N/A | 24 Test | Max. Recommended Load |
| 280 | Lead | 34.0/XMP-5744 | 2015 | 2525 | N/A | 24 Test | Max. Recommended Load |
| **38-55 Winchester** | | | | | | | |
| 200 | JFN | 25.5/XMP-5744 | 1853 | 1525 | N/A | 24 Test | Max. Recommended Load |
| 220 | JFN | 23.5/XMP-5744 | 1648 | 1325 | N/A | 24 Test | Max. Recommended Load |
| 240 | Lead | 22.0/XMP-5744 | 1601 | 1365 | N/A | 24 Test | Max. Recommended Load |
| **40-65 Winchester** | | | | | | | |
| 260 | Lead | 26.0/XMP-5744 | 1651 | 1570 | N/A | 36 S. Sharps | Max. Recommended Load |
| 300 | Lead | 24.0/XMP-5744 | 1515 | 1525 | N/A | 36 S. Sharps | Max. Recommended Load |
| 300 | CSA | 24.0/XMP-5744 | 1521 | 1540 | N/A | 36 S. Sharps | Max. Recommended Load |
| 350 | CSA | 23.0/XMP-5744 | 1436 | 1600 | N/A | 36 S. Sharps | Max. Recommended Load |
| 400 | CSA | 23.0/XMP-5744 | 1364 | 1650 | 22,000 | 36 S. Sharps | Max. Recommended Load |
| **45-70** | | | | | | | |
| 260 | Lead | 30.0/XMP-5744 | 1494 | 1685 | N/A | 24 Test | Max. Recommended Load |
| 300 | J | 62.0/Varget | 2090 | 2910 | 24,700 CUP | 24 | Max. Load, Compressed |
| 350 | J | 61.0/Varget | 2027 | 3190 | 27,300 CUP | 24 | Max. Load, Compressed |
| 378 | Lead | 28.5/XMP-5744 | 1418 | 1685 | N/A | 24 Test | Max. Recommended Load |
| 405 | Lead | 28.5/XMP-5744 | 1375 | 1700 | N/A | 24 Test | Max. Recommended Load |
| 405 | JFP | 55.0/Varget | 1845 | 3060 | 25,000 CUP | 24 | Max. Load, Compressed |
| 420 | LFN | 28.5/XMP-5744 | 1375 | 1760 | 16,100 | — | C.O.L. 2.600″, suitable for magazine rifles |
| 475 | Lead | 27.0/XMP-5744 | 1253 | 1655 | N/A | 24 Test | Max. Recommended Load |
| 500 | Lead | 26.0/XMP-5744 | 1217 | 1640 | N/A | 24 Test | Max. Recommended Load |
| 530 | LRN | 28.5/XMP-5744 | 1280 | 1925 | 18,400 | — | C.O.L. 2.830″, Single Shot rifles only |
| **458 Winchester** | | | | | | | |
| 500 | J | 71.0/Varget | 2064 | 4730 | 41,600 CUP | 22 | Moderate Load, Compressed |
| 600 | J | 65.0/Varget | 1852 | 4570 | 44,600 CUP | 22 | Moderate Load, Compressed |
| **50-70** | | | | | | | |
| 425 | Lead | 30.0/XMP-5744 | 1419 | 1900 | N/A | 30 S. Sharps | Max. Recommended Load |
| 550 | Lead | 25.0/XMP-5744 | 1208 | 1780 | N/A | 30 S. Sharps | Max. Recommended Load |
| **50-90 (2½″ case)** | | | | | | | |
| 365 | Lead | 37.0/XMP-5744 | 1652 | 2210 | N/A | 30 1875 S. Sharps | Max. Recommended Load |
| 440 | Lead | 33.0/XMP-5744 | 1418 | 1965 | N/A | 30 1875 S. Sharps | Max. Recommended Load |
| 550 | Lead | 30.0/XMP-5744 | 1275 | 1985 | N/A | 30 1875 S. Sharps | Moderate |
| 550 | Lead | 35.0/XMP-5744 | 1400 | 2390 | 20,000 PSI | 30 1875 S. Sharps | Max. Recommended Load |
| **50-140** | | | | | | | |
| 440 | Lead | 55.0/XMP-5744 | 1978 | 3820 | N/A | 30 S. Sharps | Max. Recommended Load |
| 550 | Lead | 50.0/XMP-5744 | 1736 | 3680 | N/A | 30 S. Sharps | Max. Recommended Load |
| 700 | Lead | 48.0/XMP-5744 | 1529 | 3635 | N/A | 30 S. Sharps | Max. Recommended Load |

N/A = Not Available; FA = Freedom Arms; IMI (Israeli Military Industries); J = Jacketed, Unspecified; FPJ = Full Profile Jacketed; LTCGC = Lead Truncated Cone Gas Check; TMJ = Totally Metal Jacketed; JFN = Jacketed Flat Nose

**For detailed loading information, see the latest loading data from the appropriate powder manufacturer. The data listed in this table are generally maximum recommended loads and as such are not load recommendations but are given as an informative reference only. Before handloading any cartridge refer to the data provided—free of charge—by the germane powder manufacturer. Read and follow their instruction exactly. If you do not understand all safety aspects or if you are unwilling to follow recommended safety guidelines do not undertake handloading.**

## SELECTED SHOTSHELL LOADS

| Hull | Shot Wgt. (oz.) | Primer | Powder (Grs./Type) | Wad | Pressure (psi) | Velocity (fps) |
|---|---|---|---|---|---|---|
| **12 Gauge 2¾″ Case, ⅞ oz. shot at 1200 fps** | | | | | | |
| Fio Prpl | 7/8 | CCI-209M | 17.3/Clays | Purple PC | 5700 | 1200 |
| Fio Prpl | 7/8 | F-209A | 16.5/Clays | R-TGT12 | 6400 | 1200 |
| Fio Prpl | 7/8 | Fio-616 | 16.6/Clays | F-12S0 | 6800 | 1200 |
| Fio Prpl | 7/8 | W-209 | 16.8/Clays | W-WAA12SL | 6200 | 1200 |
| **12 Gauge 2¾″ Case, ⅞ oz. shot at 1250 fps** | | | | | | |
| Fio Prpl | 7/8 | CCI-209M | 18.1/Clays | Purple PC | 6300 | 1250 |
| Fio Prpl | 7/8 | F-209A | 17.7/Clays | R-TGT12 | 7300 | 1250 |
| Fio Prpl | 7/8 | Fio-616 | 17.8/Clays | F-12S0 | 7500 | 1250 |
| Fio Prpl | 7/8 | W-209 | 18.0/Clays | W-WAA12SL | 7200 | 1250 |
| **12 Gauge 2¾″ Case, ⅞ oz. shot at 1300 fps** | | | | | | |
| Fio Prpl | 7/8 | CCI-209M | 19.2/Clays | Purple PC | 7700 | 1300 |
| Fio Prpl | 7/8 | F-209A | 18.7/Clays | R-TGT12 | 7400 | 1300 |
| Fio Prpl | 7/8 | Fio-616 | 19.2/Clays | F-12S0 | 8500 | 1300 |
| Fio Prpl | 7/8 | W-209 | 19.0/Clays | W-WAA12SL | 8000 | 1300 |
| **12 Gauge 2¾″ Case, 1 oz. shot at 1180 fps** | | | | | | |
| Activ | 1 | F-209A | 18.0/Clays | F-12S0 | 8400 | 1180 |
| Activ | 1 | Fio-616 | 18.0/Clays | R-TGT12 | 5900 | 1180 |
| Activ | 1 | W-209 | 17.5/Clays | W-WAA12SL | 7800 | 1180 |
| Activ | 1 | CCI-209M | 19.0/Internat'l | A-TG30 | 7400 | 1180 |
| Activ | 1 | F-209A | 19.5/Internat'l | F-12S0 | 7000 | 1180 |
| Activ | 1 | Fio-616 | 19.0/Internat'l | R-TGT12 | 5900 | 1180 |
| Activ | 1 | W-209 | 18.5/Internat'l | WAA12SL | 6500 | 1180 |
| W-CF | 1 | W-209 | 19.5/WST | W-WAA12SL | 7400 | 1180 |
| W-CF | 1 | CCI-209 | 19.0/WST | F-12S0 | 8300 | 1180 |
| F-GM | 1 | W-209 | 20.5/WST | F-12S0 | 7400 | 1180 |
| R-RTL | 1 | CCI-209 | 19.0/WST | W-WAA12SL | 8000 | 1180 |
| W-CF | 1 | W-209 | 19.0/WST | F-12S0 | 8000 | 1180 |
| R-RTL | 1 | W-209 | 19.0/WST | F-12S0 | 8200 | 1180 |
| W-CF | 1 | F-209 | 19.5/WST | F-12S0 | 7900 | 1180 |
| R-RTL | 1 | F-209 | 19.0/WST | W-WAA12SL | 8100 | 1180 |
| **12 Gauge 2¾″ Case, 1 oz. shot at 1235 fps** | | | | | | |
| Activ | 1 | F-209A | 18.7/Clays | F-12S0 | 9200 | 1235 |
| Activ | 1 | Fio-616 | 19.5/Clays | R-TGT12 | 7300 | 1235 |
| Activ | 1 | W-209 | 18.5/Clays | W-WAA12SL | 9100 | 1235 |
| Activ | 1 | CCI-209M | 20.0/Internat'l | A-TG30 | 8500 | 1235 |
| Activ | 1 | F-209A | 21.0/Internat'l | F-12S0 | 8400 | 1235 |
| Activ | 1 | Fio-616 | 21.0/Internat'l | R-TGT12 | 7200 | 1235 |
| Activ | 1 | W-209 | 20.5/Internat'l | WAA12SL | 7900 | 1235 |
| W-CF | 1 | W-209 | 21.0/WST | W-WAA12SL | 8100 | 1235 |
| R-RTL | 1 | W-209 | 19.5/WST | W-WAA12SL | 8000 | 1235 |
| W-CF | 1 | W-209 | 20.5/WST | F-12S0 | 9500 | 1235 |
| F-GM | 1 | W-209 | 22.0/WST | F-12S0 | 8500 | 1235 |
| F-GM | 1 | CCI-209 | 21.0/WST | F-12S0 | 8500 | 1235 |
| W-CF | 1 | CCI-209 | 21.5/WST | W-WAA12SL | 7900 | 1235 |
| R-RTL | 1 | CCI-209 | 20.0/WST | W-WAA12SL | 9000 | 1235 |
| W-CF | 1 | CCI-209 | 20.5/WST | F-12S0 | 9500 | 1235 |
| W-CF | 1 | F-209 | 21.0/WST | W-WAA12SL | 7400 | 1235 |
| R-RTL | 1 | F-209 | 20.5/WST | W-WAA12SL | 9000 | 1235 |
| W-CF | 1 | F-209 | 21.0/WST | F-12S0 | 9300 | 1235 |
| **12 Gauge 2¾″ Case, 1 oz. shot at 1290 fps** | | | | | | |
| Activ | 1 | Fio-616 | 20.5/Clays | R-TGT12 | 9100 | 1290 |
| Activ | 1 | W-209 | 19.5/Clays | W-WAA12SL | 10,400 | 1290 |
| Activ | 1 | CCI-209M | 21.5/Internat'l | A-TG30 | 9600 | 1290 |
| Activ | 1 | F-209A | 22.0/Internat'l | F-12S0 | 9900 | 1290 |
| Activ | 1 | Fio-616 | 22.5/Internat'l | R-TGT12 | 8000 | 1290 |
| Activ | 1 | W-209 | 22.0/Internat'l | WAA12SL | 8900 | 1290 |
| W-CF | 1 | W-209 | 22.0/WST | W-WAA12SL | 9000 | 1290 |

## SELECTED SHOTSHELL LOADS

| Hull | Shot Wgt. (oz.) | Primer | Powder (Grs./Type) | Wad | Pressure (psi) | Velocity (fps) |
|---|---|---|---|---|---|---|
| R-RTL | 1 | W-209 | 21.0/WST | F-12S0 | 9700 | 1290 |
| F-GM | 1 | W-209 | 23.0/WST | F-12S0 | 9300 | 1290 |
| W-CF | 1 | CCI-209 | 22.5/WST | W-WAA12SL | 9400 | 1290 |
| R-RTL | 1 | CCI-209 | 21.0/WST | W-WAA12SL | 10,100 | 1290 |
| F-GM | 1 | CCI-209 | 22.5/WST | F-12S0 | 9500 | 1290 |
| W-CF | 1 | F-209 | 22.5/WST | W-WAA12SL | 8400 | 1290 |
| R-RTL | 1 | F-209 | 21.5/WST | W-WAA12SL | 9700 | 1290 |
| F-GM | 1 | F-209 | 23.0/WST | F-12S0 | 8400 | 1290 |
| W-CF | 1 | W-209 | 21.0/WSL | W-WAA12SL | 9500 | 1290 |
| R-RTL | 1 | W-209 | 21.0/WSL | F-12S0 | 9800 | 1290 |
| W-CF | 1 | CCI-209 | 21.0/WSL | W-WAA12SL | 9400 | 1290 |
| R-RTL | 1 | CCI-209 | 21.0/WSL | F-12S0 | 10,300 | 1290 |
| W-CF | 1 | F-209 | 21.0/WSL | W-WAA12SL | 9300 | 1290 |
| R-RTL | 1 | F-209 | 21.0/WSL | F-12S0 | 9700 | 1290 |
| **12 Gauge 2 3/4″ Case, 1 1/8 oz. shot at 1090 fps** | | | | | | |
| Activ | 1 1/8 | CCI-209 | 18.4/Clays | Activ TG-30 | 5900 lup | 1090 |
| Activ | 1 1/8 | F-209 | 18.3/Clays | F-12S0 | 6300 lup | 1090 |
| Activ | 1 1/8 | R-209P | 18.0/Clays | R-TGT12 | 6100 lup | 1090 |
| Activ | 1 1/8 | W-209 | 18.5/Clays | Purple PC | 5900 lup | 1090 |
| Activ | 1 1/8 | CCI-209M | 19.8/Internat'l | Activ TG-30 | 6600 lup | 1090 |
| Activ | 1 1/8 | F-209 | 21.2/Internat'l | F-12S0 | 6200 lup | 1090 |
| Activ | 1 1/8 | R-209P | 21.1/Internat'l | R-TGT12 | 5800 lup | 1090 |
| Activ | 1 1/8 | W-209 | 20.0/Internat'l | W-WAA12SL | 6400 lup | 1090 |
| **12 Gauge 2 3/4″ Case, 1 1/8 oz. shot at 1145 fps** | | | | | | |
| Activ | 1 1/8 | CCI-209 | 19.5/Clays | Activ TG-30 | 6800 lup | 1145 |
| Activ | 1 1/8 | F-209 | 19.1/Clays | F-12S0 | 7300 lup | 1145 |
| Activ | 1 1/8 | R-209P | 19.1/Clays | R-TGT12 | 6900 lup | 1145 |
| Activ | 1 1/8 | W-209 | 19.5/Clays | Purple PC | 6700 lup | 1145 |
| Activ | 1 1/8 | CCI-209M | 20.5/Internat'l | Activ TG-30 | 7300 lup | 1145 |
| Activ | 1 1/8 | F-209 | 21.8/Internat'l | F-12S0 | 6500 lup | 1145 |
| Activ | 1 1/8 | R-209P | 21.7/Internat'l | R-TGT12 | 6400 lup | 1145 |
| Activ | 1 1/8 | W-209 | 20.6/Internat'l | W-WAA12SL | 7000 lup | 1145 |
| R-RTL | 1 1/8 | W-209 | 19.0/WST | R-Fig-8 | 10,400 | 1145 |
| R-RTL | 1 1/8 | CCI-209 | 18.5/WST | R-Fig-8 | 10,200 | 1145 |
| F-GM | 1 1/8 | CCI-209 | 19.5/WST | F-12S3 | 8500 | 1145 |
| R-RTL | 1 1/8 | F-209 | 18.5/WST | R-RXP12 | 10,000 | 1145 |
| F-GM | 1 1/8 | F-209 | 20.0/WST | F-12S3 | 7700 | 1145 |
| W-CF | 1 1/8 | W-209 | 18.5/WSL | W-WAA12SL | 8000 | 1145 |
| R-RTL | 1 1/8 | W-209 | 18.5/WSL | W-WAA12 | 8300 | 1145 |
| W-CF | 1 1/8 | CCI-209 | 18.5/WSL | W-WAA12SL | 8800 | 1145 |
| R-RTL | 1 1/8 | CCI-209 | 18.0/WSL | F-12S3 | 8600 | 1145 |
| W-CF | 1 1/8 | F-209 | 18.5/WSL | W-WAA12SL | 7800 | 1145 |
| R-RTL | 1 1/8 | F-209 | 18.5/WSL | W-WAA12SL | 8000 | 1145 |
| **12 Gauge 2 3/4″ Case, 1 1/8 oz. shot at 1200 fps** | | | | | | |
| Activ | 1 1/8 | CCI-209 | 20.6/Clays | Activ TG-30 | 7700 lup | 1200 |
| Activ | 1 1/8 | F-209 | 19.9/Clays | F-12S0 | 8400 lup | 1200 |
| Activ | 1 1/8 | R-209P | 20.2/Clays | R-TGT12 | 7600 lup | 1200 |
| Activ | 1 1/8 | W-209 | 20.5/Clays | Purple PC | 7500 lup | 1200 |
| Activ | 1 1/8 | CCI-209M | 21.5/Internat'l | Activ TG-30 | 8100 lup | 1200 |
| Activ | 1 1/8 | F-209 | 23.2/Internat'l | F-12S0 | 7400 lup | 1200 |
| Activ | 1 1/8 | R-209P | 23.4/Internat'l | R-TGT12 | 6800 lup | 1200 |
| Activ | 1 1/8 | W-209 | 21.5/Internat'l | W-WAA12SL | 7800 lup | 1200 |
| Activ | 1 1/8 | CCI-209M | 24.0/Universal | F-12S0 | 8500 | 1200 |
| Activ | 1 1/8 | F-209A | 24.0/Universal | R-TGT12 | 7900 | 1200 |
| Activ | 1 1/8 | W-209 | 24.0/Universal | Activ TG-30 | 8300 | 1200 |
| W-CF | 1 1/8 | W-209 | 20.0/WST | R-RXP12 | 9700 | 1200 |
| F-GM | 1 1/8 | W-209 | 21.0/WST | F-12S3 | 9500 | 1200 |
| F-GM | 1 1/8 | F-209 | 21.5/WST | F-12S3 | 9000 | 1200 |
| F-GM | 1 1/8 | CCI-209 | 21.0/WST | F-12S3 | 10,300 | 1200 |

## SELECTED SHOTSHELL LOADS

| Hull | Shot Wgt. (oz.) | Primer | Powder (Grs./Type) | Wad | Pressure (psi) | Velocity (fps) |
|---|---|---|---|---|---|---|
| W-CF | 1 1/8 | CCI-209 | 20.5/WST | R-Fig-8 | 10,000 | 1200 |
| W-CF | 1 1/8 | W-209 | 20.0/WSL | R-Fig-8 | 9400 | 1200 |
| W-CF | 1 1/8 | W-209 | 20.0/WSL | W-WAA12SL | 9000 | 1200 |
| R-RTL | 1 1/8 | W-209 | 19.5/WSL | W-WAA12SL | 9400 | 1200 |
| W-CF | 1 1/8 | CCI-209 | 19.5/WSL | R-R12L | 9200 | 1200 |
| R-RTL | 1 1/8 | CCI-209 | 19.0/WSL | R-Fig-8 | 9600 | 1200 |
| W-CF | 1 1/8 | F-209 | 20.0/WSL | W-WAA12SL | 9100 | 1200 |
| R-RTL | 1 1/8 | F-209 | 20.0/WSL | R-Fig-8 | 8100 | 1200 |
| W-CF | 1 1/8 | F-209A | 23.0/WSF | W-WAA12SL | 8400 | 1200 |
| **12 Gauge 2 3/4" Case, 1 1/8 oz. shot at 1255 fps** | | | | | | |
| Activ | 1 1/8 | CCI-209M | 22.7/Internat'l | Activ TG-30 | 9300 lup | 1255 |
| Activ | 1 1/8 | F-209 | 24.0/Internat'l | F-12S0 | 8200 lup | 1255 |
| Activ | 1 1/8 | R-209P | 24.3/Internat'l | R-TGT12 | 7500 lup | 1255 |
| Activ | 1 1/8 | W-209 | 22.6/Internat'l | W-WAA12SL | 8700 lup | 1255 |
| Activ | 1 1/8 | CCI-209M | 26.0/Universal | F-12S0 | 9500 | 1255 |
| Activ | 1 1/8 | F-209A | 25.5/Universal | R-TGT12 | 8900 | 1255 |
| Activ | 1 1/8 | W-209 | 25.5/Universal | Activ TG-30 | 9000 | 1255 |
| W-CF | 1 1/8 | W-209 | 21.5/WSL | W-WAA12SL | 10,800 | 1255 |
| R-RTL | 1 1/8 | W-209 | 20.5/WSL | R-RXP12 | 10,500 | 1255 |
| W-CF | 1 1/8 | CCI-209 | 21.0/WSL | R-R12L | 10,600 | 1255 |
| R-RTL | 1 1/8 | CCI-209 | 20.0/WSL | R-Fig-8 | 10,600 | 1255 |
| W-CF | 1 1/8 | F-209 | 21.5/WSL | W-WAA12SL | 10,300 | 1255 |
| R-RTL | 1 1/8 | F-209 | 21.0/WSL | R-Fig-8 | 9180 | 1255 |
| W-CF | 1 1/8 | F-209A | 24.0/WSF | W-WAA12SL | 9100 | 1255 |
| **12 Gauge 2 3/4" Case, 1 1/8 oz. shot at 1275 fps** | | | | | | |
| F-GM | 1 1/8 | CCI-209 | 27.0/WSF | F-12S4 | 9200 | 1275 |
| **12 Gauge 2 3/4" Case, 1 1/8 oz. shot at 1310 fps** | | | | | | |
| Activ | 1 1/8 | CCI-209M | 27.0/Universal | F-12S0 | 10,200 | 1310 |
| Activ | 1 1/8 | F-209A | 26.7/Universal | R-TGT12 | 9700 | 1310 |
| Activ | 1 1/8 | W-209 | 27.0/Universal | Activ TG-30 | 10,100 | 1310 |
| W-CF | 1 1/8 | W-209 | 27.5/WSF | W-WAA12 | 8700 | 1310 |
| W-CF | 1 1/8 | W-209 | 27.5/WSF | F-12S3 | 8500 | 1310 |
| R-RTL | 1 1/8 | W-209 | 27.0/WSF | W-WAA12 | 9700 | 1310 |
| **12 Gauge 2 3/4" Case, 1 1/8 oz. shot at 1365 fps** | | | | | | |
| W-CF | 1 1/8 | W-209 | 29.0/WSF | W-WAA12 | 9900 | 1365 |
| W-CF | 1 1/8 | W-209 | 28.5/WSF | F-12S3 | 9500 | 1365 |
| R-RTL | 1 1/8 | W-209 | 28.0/WSF | F-12S3 | 8900 | 1365 |
| **12 Gauge 2 3/4" Case, 1 1/8 oz. shot at 1400 fps** | | | | | | |
| W-CF | 1 1/8 | W-209 | 30.0/WSF | W-WAA12 | 10,600 | 1400 |
| W-CF | 1 1/8 | W-209 | 29.5/WSF | F-12S3 | 10,800 | 1400 |
| R-RTL | 1 1/8 | W-209 | 29.0/WSF | F-12S3 | 9500 | 1400 |
| **12 Gauge 2 3/4" Case, 1 1/4 oz. shot at 1220 fps** | | | | | | |
| Activ | 1 1/4 | CCI-209M | 25.0/Universal | Activ TG-30 | 9100 | 1220 |
| Activ | 1 1/4 | F-209 | 27.0/Universal | Hor-Versalite | 10,200 | 1220 |
| Activ | 1 1/4 | F-209A | 23.7/Universal | Activ TG-30 | 10,600 | 1220 |
| Activ | 1 1/4 | W-209 | 24.0/Universal | W-WAA12 | 9800 | 1220 |
| W-CF | 1 1/4 | W-209 | 26.0/WSF | F-12S4 | 9000 | 1220 |
| R-RTL | 1 1/4 | F-209 | 26.5/WSF | W-WAA12F114 | 8800 | 1220 |
| **12 Gauge 2 3/4" Case, 1 1/4 oz. shot at 1275 fps** | | | | | | |
| W-CF | 1 1/4 | W-209 | 28.0/WSF | W-WAA12F114 | 9700 | 1275 |
| R-RTL | 1 1/4 | W-209 | 27.5/WSF | W-WAA12F114 | 9700 | 1275 |
| W-CF | 1 1/4 | W-209 | 27.5/WSF | F-12S4 | 10,900 | 1275 |
| R-RTL | 1 1/4 | CCI-209 | 27.0/WSF | W-WAA12F114 | 10,200 | 1275 |
| W-CF | 1 1/4 | CCI-209 | 29.0/WSF | R-RXP12 | 10,400 | 1275 |
| F-GM | 1 1/4 | CCI-209 | 27.0/WSF | F-12S4 | 9200 | 1275 |
| R-RTL | 1 1/4 | F-209 | 28.0/WSF | R-RXP12 | 9500 | 1275 |

## SELECTED SHOTSHELL LOADS

| Hull | Shot Wgt. (oz.) | Primer | Powder (Grs./Type) | Wad | Pressure (psi) | Velocity (fps) |
|---|---|---|---|---|---|---|
| **12 Gauge 2 3/4" Case, 1 1/4 oz. shot at 1310 fps** | | | | | | |
| W-CF | 1 1/4 | F-209A | 27.0/WSF | W-WAA12F114 | 10,700 | 1310 |
| **12 Gauge 2 3/4" Case, 1 1/4 oz. shot at 1330 fps** | | | | | | |
| W-CF | 1 1/4 | W-209 | 29.5/WSF | W-WAA12F114 | 10,600 | 1330 |
| R-RTL | 1 1/4 | W-209 | 29.5/WSF | W-WAA12F114 | 10,400 | 1330 |
| F-GM | 1 1/4 | W-209 | 31.5/WSF | F-12S4 | 9500 | 1330 |
| R-RTL | 1 1/4 | CCI-209 | 28.5/WSF | W-WAA12F114 | 10,900 | 1330 |
| R-RTL | 1 1/4 | F-209 | 29.5/WSF | W-WAA12F114 | 10,200 | 1330 |
| W-CF | 1 1/4 | CCI-209 | 28.0/WSF | R-SP12 | 9800 | 1330 |
| **16 Gauge 2 3/4" Case, 1 oz. shot at 1165 fps** | | | | | | |
| Activ | 1 | CCI-209M | 20.5/Universal | Activ G-28 | 7800 | 1165 |
| W-CF | 1 | W-209 | 20.0/WSF | W-WAA16 | 8400 | 1165 |
| **16 Gauge 2 3/4" Case, 1 oz. shot at 1220 fps** | | | | | | |
| Activ | 1 | CCI-209M | 21.5/Universal | Activ G-28 | 8700 | 1220 |
| W-CF | 1 | W-209 | 21.0/WSF | W-WAA16 | 9000 | 1220 |
| W-CF | 1 | F-209 | 21.5/WSF | W-WAA16 | 8600 | 1220 |
| W-CF | 1 | CCI-209 | 21.0/WSF | W-WAA16 | 8800 | 1220 |
| **16 Gauge 2 3/4" Case, 1 1/8 oz. shot at 1185 fps** | | | | | | |
| W-CF | 1 1/8 | CCI-209 | 20.5/WSF | W-WAA16 | 10,800 | 1185 |
| **20 Gauge 2 3/4" Case, 7/8 oz. shot at 1200 fps** | | | | | | |
| W-CF | 7/8 | W-209 | 17.0/WSF | R-RXP20 | 10,700 | 1200 |
| R-RXP | 7/8 | W-209 | 17.0/WSF | W-WAA20 | 10,500 | 1200 |
| R-RXP | 7/8 | R-209P | 15.8/Universal | R-RXP20 | 9000 | 1200 |
| W-CF | 7/8 | CCI-209 | 17.5/WSF | R-RXP20 | 10,500 | 1200 |
| R-RXP | 7/8 | CCI-209 | 17.5/WSF | R-RXP20 | 9700 | 1200 |
| W-CF | 7/8 | F-209 | 17.0/WSF | R-RXP20 | 10,500 | 1200 |
| **28 Gauge 2 3/4 Case, 3/4 oz. shot at 1200 fps** | | | | | | |
| F-TGT | 3/4 | F-209 | 14.0/Universal | R-PT28 | 10,800 | 1200 |
| F-TGT | 3/4 | F-209A | 14.2/Universal | R-PT28 | 11,400 | 1200 |
| F-TGT | 3/4 | W-209 | 13.8/Universal | PC28 | 10,200 | 1200 |

**For specific details on any of these loads refer to the data manual provided free of charge by the appropriate powder manufacturer or distributor. This shotshell data is only a small sample of the myriad loads that have already been developed with some of the newer powders available. VihtaVuori may eventually market their shotshell powders, for which considerable data is already available, we have not listed any of those loads because the powders are not readily obtainable stateside and many of the components used in VihtaVuori's data are also hard to come by here.**

# THE HANDLOADER'S LIBRARY

**IMPORTANT NOTICE TO BOOK BUYERS**

Books listed here may be bought from the publisher or Ray Riling Arms Books Co., 6844 Gorsten St., P.O. Box 18925, Philadelphia, PA 19119, phone 215-438-2456.

A full variety of books on the subject of handloading are also available from Rutgers Book Center, 127 Raritan Ave., Highland Park, NJ 08904.

***NEW BOOK**

**The AA Hull, Revision V,** Ballistic Products, Hamel, MN, 1995. 19 pp., paper covers, $5.00.
Informative manual about the AA hull and loads for it.

***ABC's of Reloading, 6th Edition,** by C. Rodney James and the editors of *Handloader's Digest*, DBI Books, a division of Krause Publications, Vernon Hills, IL, 1997. 288 pp., illus. Paper covers. $21.95.
The definitive guide to every facet of cartridge and shotshell reloading.

**Accurate Smokeless Powder Loading Guide, Number One,** Accurate Arms, McEwen, TN, 1994. 345 pp. Hard covers. $16.95.
All the loading data collected to date on Accurate smokeless powders for popular rifle and pistol cartridges, plus many wildcats and obsolete cartridges.

**ACTIV Hull Handloads: Complete Loading Guide,** Ballistic Products, Hamel, MN, 1995. Paper covers, $5.00.
Brand-new manual covers history, evolution and loading instructions for the ACTIV hull.

**Advantages III,** Ballistic Products, Hamel, MN, 1987. 72 pp., illus., paper covers, $7.00.
Comprehensive reloading guide for the hunter.

**African Cartridge Reloading Data,** Thunderbird Cartridge Co. Inc., Phoenix, AZ, 1994. 32 pp. Paper covers, $14.95.
Loading techniques and recipes for the 577 Nitro Express 3″ using common American extruded powders with ballistics and cartridge specifications.

**Ammunition Making,** by George E. Frost, National Rifle Association of America, Washington, D.C., 1990. 160 pp., illus. Paper covers. $17.95.
Reflects the perspective of "an insider" with half a century's experience in successful management of ammunition manufacturing operations.

**Barnes Reloading Manual #1,** Barnes Bullets, American Fork, UT, 1995. 350 pp., illus. $24.95.
Data for more than 65 cartridges from 243 to 50 BMG.

**Basic Handloading,** by George C. Nonte, Jr., Outdoor Life Books, New York, NY, 1982. 192 pp., illus. Paper covers. $6.95.
How to produce high-quality ammunition using the safest, most efficient methods known.

**Big Bore Rifles And Cartridges,** Wolfe Publishing Co., Prescott, AZ, 1991. Paper cover. $26.00.
This book covers cartridges from 8mm to .600 Nitro with over 60 chapters containing loading tables and commentary.

**Black Powder Guide, 2nd Edition,** by George C. Nonte, Jr., Stoeger Publishing Co., So. Hackensack, NJ, 1991. 288 pp., illus. Paper covers. $14.95.
How-to instructions for selection, repair and maintenance of muzzleloaders, making your own bullets, restoring and refinishing, shooting techniques.

**Black Powder Loading Manual, The Gun Digest, 3rd Edition,** edited by Sam Fadala, DBI Books, a division of Krause Publications, Inc., Vernon Hills, IL, 1995. 368 pp., illus. Paper covers. $19.95.
Revised and expanded edition of this landmark blackpowder loading book. Covers hundreds of loads for most of the popular blackpowder rifles, handguns and shotguns.

**Blue Dot Powder, Revision IV,** Ballistic Products, Hamel, MN, 1992. 24 pp., paper covers, $4.00.
A discussion of the characteristics of Blue Dot under various conditions.

**Bob Pease Collection Revised Vol. 1,** Bob Pease Accuracy, New Braunfels, TX, 1990. 40 pp., $6.00.
Covers bedding, turning, case sorting and preparation.

**Bob Pease Collection Revised Vol. 2,** Bob Pease Accuracy, New Braunfels, TX, 1990. 40 pp., $6.00.
Info on resting, aiming and sitting techniques, as well as accuracy loading.

**Bob Pease Collection Revised Vol. 3,** Bob Pease Accuracy, New Braunfels, TX, 1990. 40 pp., $6.00.
Answers shooters' questions on troubleshooting and case and rifle preparation.

**Bob Pease Collection Revised Vol. 4,** Bob Pease Accuracy, New Braunfels, TX, 1990. 40 pp., $6.00.
Explains the newest tools and equipment.

**Buckshot Loading II,** Ballistic Products, Hamel, MN. 48 pp., illus. Paper covers. $5.00
Complete overview of buckshot loading technique, application and recipies.

**The Bullet Swage Manual.** by Ted Smith, Corbin Manufacturing and Supply Co., White City, OR, 1988. 45 pp., illus. Paper covers. $10.00.
A book that fills the need for information on bullet swaging.

**Cartridge Case Measurements,** by Dr. Arthur J. Mack, Amrex Enterprises, Vienna, VA, 1990. 300 pp., illus. Paper covers. $49.95.
Lists over 5000 cartridges of all kinds. Gives basic measurements (rim, head, shoulder, neck, length, plus bullet diameter) in both English and Metric. Hundreds of experimental and wildcats.

***Cartridges of the World, 8th Edition,** by Frank Barnes, edited by M. L. McPherson, DBI Books, a division of Krause Publications, Inc., Vernon Hills, IL, 1997. 480 pp., illus. Paper covers. $24.95.
Completely revised edition of the general purpose reference work for which collectors, police, scientists and laymen reach first for answers to cartridge identification questions.

**Cast Bullets,** by Col. E. H. Harrison, A publication of the National Rifle Association of America, Washington, DC, 1979. 144 pp., illus. Paper covers. $12.95.
An authoritative guide to bullet casting techniques and ballistics.

***Complete Blackpowder Handbook, 3rd Edition,** by Sam Fadala, DBI Books, a division of Krause Publications, Inc., Vernon Hills, IL, 1997. 400 pp., illus. Paper covers. $21.95.
Expanded and completely rewritten edition of the definitive book on the subject of blackpowder.

**The Complete Handloader,** by John Wootters, Stackpole Books, Harrisburg, PA, 1989. 224 pp., illus. $29.95.
One of the deans of gun writers shares a lifetime of experience and recommended procedures on handloading for rifles, handguns, and shotguns.

**The Complete Handloader for Rifles, Handguns and Shotguns,** by John Wootters, Stackpole Books, Harrisburg, PA, 1988. 214 pp., $29.95.
Loading-bench know-how.

**Complete Reloading Manuals,** Loadbooks, USA.

**.22 Hornet,** 1990. $7.95.
**.22-250 Remington,** 1990. $7.95.
**.220 Swift,** 1990. $7.95.
**.222 Remington,** 1990. $7.95.
**.223 Remington,** 1990. $7.95.
**.243 Winchester,** 1990. $7.95.
**.25-06 Remington,** 1990. $7.95.
**.270 Winchester,** 1990. $7.95.
**.280 Remington (7mm Exp),** 1990. $7.95.
**.30 M1 Carbine,** 1990. $7.95.
**.30-06 Springfield,** 1990. $7.95.
**.30-30 Winchester,** 1990. $7.95.
**.300 Weatherby,** 1990. $7.95.
**.300 Winchester Magnum,** 1990. $7.95.
**.308 Winchester,** 1990. $7.95.
**.32 H&R,** 1990. $7.95.
**.338 Winchester,** 1990. $7.95.
**.357 Magnum,** 1990. $7.95.
**.38 Special,** 1990. $7.95.
**.38 Super,** 1990. $7.95.
**.380 ACP,** 1990. $7.95.
**.41 Magnum,** 1990. $7.95.
**.44 Magnum,** 1990. $7.95.
**.45 ACP,** 1990. $7.95.
**.45 Colt,** 1990. $7.95.
**.45-70 Gov't,** 1990. $7.95.
**10mm & .41 Handgun,** 1990. $7.95.
**12 Gauge Shotgun,** 1990. $9.95.
**20/28 Gauge/.410 Shotgun,** 1990. $9.95.
**6mm Remington (.244),** 1990. $7.95.
**6.5x55 Swedish,** 1990. $7.95.
**7mm Remington Magnum,** 990. $7.95.
**7x57 Mauser,** 1990. $7.95.
**7mm-08 Remington,** 1990. $7.95.
**7.62x39,** 1990. $7.95.
**8mm Mauser,** 1990. $7.95.
**9mm Luger,** 1990. $7.95.
**Remington XP-100,** 1990. $10.95.
**T/C Contender Pistol,** 1990. $17.95.

**Corbin Technical Bulletins, Vol. I,** Corbin Manufacturing, White City, OR, 1977. 66 pp., $8.00.
Details basic operations and techniques concerning bullet swaging.

**Corbin Technical Bulletins, Vol. II,** Corbin Manufacturing, White City, OR, 1980. 92 pp., $8.00.
Deals with specific calibers, including the obsolete and experimental, detailing the various styles and weights.

**Corbin Technical Bulletins, Vol. III,** Corbin Manufacturing, White City, OR, 1983. 98 pp., $8.00.
Collection of papers describing experimental work on cores, shapes and jacket styles.

**Designing and Forming Custom Cartridges,** by Ken Howell, Ken Howell, Stevensville, MT, 1995. 596 pp., illus. $59.95.
Covers cartridge dimensions and includes complete introductory material on cartridge manufacture and appendices on finding loading data and equipment.

**Discover Swaging,** by David R. Corbin, Stackpole Books, Harrisburg, PA, 1979. 283 pp., illus. $18.95.
A guide to custom swaged bullet design and performance.

**Experiments of a Handgunner,** by Walter F. Roper, Wolfe Publishing, Prescott, AZ, 1989. 202 pp., illus., $37.00.
A limited edition reprint. A listing of experiments with functioning parts of handguns, with targets, stocks, rests, handloading, etc.

**Extended Ballistics for the Advanced Rifleman,** by Art Blatt, Pachmayr, Inc., Los Angeles, CA, 1986. 379 pp. Spiral bound. $15.95.
Enhanced data on all factory centerfire rifle loads from Federal, Hornady, Norma, Remington, Weatherby, and Winchester.

**Federal Gold Medal, 12-Gauge 2¾″,** Ballistic Products, Hamel, MN, 1990. 12 pp., paper covers, $4.00.
More than 23 loads, along with other information.

**Federal Gold Medal 12-Gauge, 3″ Hull, Revision IV,** Ballistic Products, Hamel, MN, 1991. 15 pp., paper covers, $4.00.
Hunting loads for different situations.

**Fiocchi 12-Gauge 2¾″ Hunting Loads, Revision IV,** Ballistic Products, Hamel, MN, 1989. 12 pp., paper covers, $4.00.
Specific loads for cold weather shooting, as well as slug loads.

**Firearms Pressure Factors,** by Dr. Lloyd Brownell, Wolfe Publishing Co., Prescott, AZ, 1990. 200 pp., illus. $14.00.
The only book available devoted entirely to firearms and pressure. Contains chapters on secondary explosion effect, modern pressure measuring techniques in revolvers and rifles, and Dr. Brownell's series on pressure factors.

**Forty Years with the 45-70,** by Paul Matthews, Wolfe Publishing Co., Prescott, AZ, $11.50
Four decades of the author's experience is contained in this text.

**G/BP European Sporting Wads, Revision III,** Ballistic Products, Hamel, MN, 1995. 140 pp., paper covers, $5.00.
High performance loads for use with Europe's finest sporting wads.

**Game Loads and Practical Ballistics for the American Hunter,** by Bob Hagel, Wolfe Publishing Co., Prescott, AZ, 1992. 310 pp., illus. $27.90.

Hagel's knowledge gained as a hunter, guide and gun enthusiast is gathered in this informative text.

**Gibbs' Cartridges and Front Ignition Loading Technique,** by Roger Stowers, Wolfe Publishing Co., Prescott, AZ, 1991. 64 pp., illus. Paper covers. $14.95.
The story of this innovative gunsmith who designed his own wildcat cartridges known for their flat trajectories, high velocity and accuracy.

**Handbook of Bullet Swaging No. 7,** by David R. Corbin, Corbin Manufacturing and Supply Co., White City, OR, 1990. 200 pp., illus. Paper covers. $10.00.
This handbook explains the most precise method of making quality bullets.

**The Handbook of Commercial Bullet Casting, Revised,** by Paul B. Moore, Magma Engineering Co., Queen Creek, AZ, 1993. 169 pp., illus., paper covers. $19.95.
A how-to book outlining the field of commercial bullet casting.

**Handbook for Shooters and Reloaders,** by P.O. Ackley, Salt Lake City, UT, 1970, (Vol. I), 567 pp., illus. (Vol. II), a new printing with specific new material. 495 pp., illus. $17.95 each.

**Handbook of Metallic Cartridge Reloading,** by Edward Matunas, Winchester Press, Piscataway, NJ, 1981. 272 pp., illus. $19.95.
Up-to-date, comprehensive loading tables prepared by four major powder manufacturers.

**Handgun Reloading, The Gun Digest Book of,** by Dean A. Grennell and Wiley M. Clapp, DBI Books, a division of Krause Publications, Inc., Vernon Hills, IL, 1987. 256 pp., illus. Paper covers. $16.95.
Detailed discussions of all aspects of reloading for handguns, from basic to complex. New loading data.

**Handloader's Bullet Making Annual Vol. I,** Wolfe Publishing, Prescott, AZ, 1990. 120 pp., paper covers, $6.95.
Collection of articles from *Handloader's* magazine for the advanced handloader.

**Handloader's Bullet Making Annual Vol. II,** Wolfe Publishing, Prescott, AZ, 1991. 120 pp., paper covers, $6.95.
Collection of articles from *Handloader's* magazine for the advanced handloader.

**Handloader's Bullet Making Annual Vol. III,** Wolfe Publishing, Prescott, AZ, 1992. 120 pp., paper covers, $6.95.
Collection of articles from *Handloader's* magazine for the advanced handloader.

**Handloader's Cast Bullet Special Edition,** Wolfe Publishing Co., Prescott, AZ $6.95
A specialized journal designed for the advanced shooter and handloader.

***Handloader's Digest, 17th Edition,** edited by Bob Bell, DBI Books, a division of Krause Publications, Vernon Hills, IL, 1997. 480 pp., illus. Paper covers. $27.95.
Top writers in the field contribute helpful information on techniques and components. Greatly expanded and fully indexed catalog of all currently available tools, accessories and components for metallic, blackpowder cartridge, shotshell reloading and swaging.

**Handloader's Guide,** by Stanley W. Trzoniec, Stoeger Publishing Co., So. Hackensack, NJ, 1985. 256 pp., illus. Paper covers. $14.95.
The complete step-by-step fully illustrated guide to handloading ammunition.

**Handloader's Manual of Cartridge Conversions,** by John J. Donnelly, Stoeger Publishing Co., So. Hackensack, NJ, 1986. Unpaginated. $49.95.
From 14 Jones to 70-150 Winchester in English and American cartridges, and from 4.85 U.K. to 15.2x28R Gevelot in metric cartridges. Over 900 cartridges described in detail.

**Handloader's Shotgun Special Edition,** Wolfe Publishing, Prescott, AZ, 1992. 96 pp., paper covers, $6.95.
Technical features on the latest in handloading and shotgunning techniques.

**Handloading,** by Bill Davis, Jr., NRA Books, Wash., D.C., 1980. 400 pp., illus. Paper covers. $15.95.
A complete update and expansion of the NRA Handloader's Guide.

***Handloading Bismuth,** Ballistic Products, Hamel, MN, 1996. $5.00.

**Handloading for Hunters,** by Don Zutz, Winchester Press, Piscataway, NJ, 1977. 288 pp., illus. $30.00.
Precise mixes and loads for different types of game and for various hunting situations with rifle and shotgun.

**Hatcher's Notebook,** by S. Julian Hatcher, Stackpole Books, Harrisburg, PA, 1992. 488 pp., illus. $39.95.
A reference work for shooters, gunsmiths, ballisticians, historians, hunters and collectors.

**Hodgdon Data Manual No. 26,** Hodgdon Powder Co., Shawnee Mission, KS, 1993. 797 pp. $22.95.
Includes Hercules, Winchester and Dupont powders; data on cartridge cases; loads; silhouette; shotshell; pyrodex and blackpowder; conversion factors; weight equivalents, etc.

**The Home Guide to Cartridge Conversions,** by Maj. George C. Nonte Jr., The Gun Room Press, Highland Park, NJ, 1976. 404 pp., illus. $24.95.
Revised and updated version of Nonte's definitive work on the alteration of cartridge cases for use in guns for which they were not intended.

**Hornady Handbook of Cartridge Reloading, 4th Edition, Vol. I and II,** Hornady Mfg. Co., Grand Island, NE, 1991. 1200 pp., illus. $28.50.
New edition of this famous reloading handbook. Latest loads, ballistic information, etc.

**Hornady Handbook of Cartridge Reloading, Abridged Edition,** Hornady Mfg. Co., Grand Island, NE, 1991. $19.95.
Ballistic data for 25 of the most popular cartridges.

**Hornady Load Notes,** Hornady Mfg. Co., Grand Island, NE, 1991. $4.95.
Complete load data and ballistics for a single caliber. Eight pistol 9mm-45ACP; 16 rifle, 222-45-70.

**How to Load the 16-Gauge,** Ballistic Products, Hamel, MN, 1991. 14 pp., paper covers, $5.00.
Lead and steel loads for the Sweet Sixteen.

**How to Reload Better for Upland Bird Hunting, Revised,** Ballistic Products, Hamel, MN, 1992. 32 pp., paper covers, $5.00.
More than 18 loads for various winged game under varying conditions.

***How-To's for the Black Powder Cartridge Rifle Shooter,** by Paul A. Matthews, Wolfe Publishing Co., Prescott, AZ, 1995. 45 pp. Paper covers. $22.50.
Covers lube recipes, good bore cleaners and over-powder wads. Tips include compressing powder charges, combating wind resistance, improving ignition and much more.

**The Hunter's Shooting Guide,** by Jack O'Connor, Outdoor Life Books, New York, NY, 1982. 176 pp., illus. Paper covers. $5.95.
A classic covering rifles, cartridges, shooting techniques for shotguns/rifles/handguns.

**The Ideal Handbook of Useful Information for Shooters, No. 15,** originally published by Ideal Manufacturing Co., reprinted by Wolfe Publishing Co., Prescott, AZ, 1991. 142 pp., illus. Paper covers. $10.95.
A facsimile reprint of one of the early Ideal Handbooks.

**The Ideal Handbook, No. 5,** Facsimile reprint by Armory Publications, Oceanside, CA, 1993. 80 pp., illus. Paper covers. $12.95.
A limited reprinting of the rare 1893 edition of the handbook issued by the Ideal manufacturing Co., of New Haven, CT.

**The Illustrated Reference of Cartridge Dimensions,** edited by Dave Scovill, Wolfe Publishing, Prescott, AZ, 1994. 343 pp., illus., paper covers. $19.00.
Comprehensive volume of dimensions for more than 300 cartridges. Standard and metric dimensions have been taken from SAAMI drawings and/or fired cases.

**IMR Handloader's Guide for Smokeless Powders,** IMR Powder Co., Plattsburgh, NY, 1990. 52 pp., paper covers, Free.
Load data for shotshell, rifle and handgun using the various powders the company offers.

**JGS Chamber Reamer Prints,** JGS Precision Tool Mfg., Coos Bay, OR, 1995.
**Wildcat Chamber Prints,** $23.98
**Ackley Chamber Prints,** $14.98
**British Chamber Prints,** $9.98
**American Chamber Prints,** $23.98

**The Law Enforcement Book of Weapons, Ammunition and Training Procedures, Handguns, Rifles and Shotguns,** by Mason Williams, Charles C. Thomas, Publisher, Springfield, IL, 1977. 496 pp., illus. $135.00.
Data on firearms, firearm training, and ballistics.

**Loading the Black Powder Rifle Cartridge,** by Paul A Matthews, Wolfe Publishing Co., Prescott, AZ, 1993. 121 pp., illus. Paper covers. $22.50.
Author Matthews brings the blackpowder cartridge shooter valuable information on the basics, including cartridge care, lubes and moulds, powder charges and developing and testing loads in his usual authoritative style.

**Loading Cartridges for the Original .45-70 Springfield Rifle and Carbine,** by J.S. and Pat Wolf, Wolf's Western Traders, Hill City, SD, 1991. 169 pp., illus. Paper covers. $16.95.
From sighting-in to reloading, this book tells you everything you need to know about the .45-70 Springfield rifle and carbine.

**Loading the Peacemaker—Colt's Model P,** by Dave Scovill, Wolfe Publishing Co., Prescott, AZ, 1996. 227 pp., illus. $24.95.
A comprehensive work about the history, maintenance and repair of the most famous revolver ever made, including the most extensive load data ever published.

**Lyman Black Powder Handbook,** ed. by C. Kenneth Ramage, Lyman Products for Shooters, Middlefield, CT, 1975. 239 pp., illus. Paper covers. $14.95.
Comprehensive load information for the modern blackpowder shooter.

**Lyman Cast Bullet Handbook, 3rd Edition,** edited by C. Kenneth Ramage, Lyman Publications, Middlefield, CT, 1980. 416 pp., illus. Paper covers. $19.95.
Information on more than 5000 tested cast bullet loads and 19 pages of trajectory and wind drift tables for cast bullets.

**Lyman Pistol & Revolver Handbook, 2nd Edition,** edited by Thomas J. Griffin, Lyman Products Co., Middlefield, CT, 1996. 287 pp., illus. Paper covers. $18.95.
The most up-to-date loading data available including the hottest new calibers, like 40 S&W, 9x21, 9mm Makarov, 9x25 Dillon and 454 Casull.

**Lyman Reloading Handbook No. 47,** edited by Edward A. Matunas, Lyman Publications, Middlefield, CT, 1992. 480 pp., illus. Paper covers. $23.00.
"The world's most comprehensive reloading manual." Complete "How to Reload" information. Expanded data section with all the newest rifle and pistol calibers.

**Lyman Shotshell Handbook, 4th Edition,** edited by Edward A. Matunas, Lyman Products Co., Middlefield, CT, 1996. 330 pp., illus. Paper covers. $24.95.
Has 9000 loads, including slugs and buckshot, plus feature articles and a full color I.D. section.

**Lyman's Guide to Big Game Cartridges & Rifles,** by Edward Matunas, Lyman Publishing Corp., Middlefield, CT, 1994. 287 pp., illus. Paper covers. $17.95.
A selection guide to cartridges and rifles for use on big game—antelope to elephant.

**Making Loading Dies and Bullet Molds,** by Harold Hoffman, H&P Publishing, San Angelo, TX, 1993. 230 pp., illus. Paper covers. $24.95.
A good book for learning tool and die making.

**Manual of Pistol and Revolver Cartridges, Volume 2, Centerfire U.S. and British Calibers,** by Hans A. Erlmeier and Jakob H. Brandt, Journal-Verlag, Wiesbaden, Germany, 1981. 270 pp., illus. $34.95.
Catalog system allows cartridges to be traced by caliber or alphabetically.

***Metallic Cartridge Reloading, 3rd Edition,** by M.L. McPherson, DBI Books, a division of Krause Publications, Inc., Vernon Hills, IL., 1996. 384 pp., illus. Paper covers. $21.95.
A true reloading manual with over 10,000 loads fro all popular metallic cartridges and a wealth of invaluable technical data provided by a recognized expert.

**The Mighty 10-Gauge, Revision IV,** by Dave Fackler, Ballistic Products, Hamel, MN, 1987. 65 pp., paper covers, $6.00.
Reloading manual and overview of this big bore.

**Military Rifle & Machine Gun Cartridges,** by Jean Huon, Paladin Press, Boulder, CO, 1990. 392 pp., illus. $34.95
Describes the primary types of military cartridges and their principle loadings, as well as their characteristics, origin and use.

**Modern Handloading,** by Maj. Geo. C. Nonte, Winchester Press, Piscataway, NJ, 1972. 416 pp., illus. $15.00.
Covers all aspects of metallic and shotshell ammunition loading, plus more loads than any book in print.

**Modern Practical Ballistics,** by Art Pejsa, Pejsa Ballistics, Minneapolis, MN, 1990. 150 pp., illus. $24.95.
Covers all aspects of ballistics and new, simplified methods. Clear examples illustrate new, easy but very accurate formulas.

***Modern Reloading,** by Richard Lee, Inland Press, 1996. 510 pp., illus. $24.98.
The how-tos of rifle, pistol and shotgun reloading plus load data for 104 rifle and pistol calibers.

**Modern Shotguns & Loads,** by Charles Askins, Wolfe Publishing, Prescott, AZ, 1992. 432 pp., $30.00.
Shotgun history, ammunition, handloading, and the principles and terms of wingshooting are explained.

**Mr. Single Shot's Cartridge Handbook,** by Frank de Haas, Mark de Haas, Orange City, IA, 1996. 116 pp., illus. Paper covers. $21.50.
This book covers most of the cartridges, both commercial and wildcat, that the author has known and used.

**Nick Harvey's Practical Reloading Manual,** by Nick Harvey, Australian Print Group, Maryborough, Victoria, Australia, 1995. 235 pp., illus. Paper covers. $24.95.
Contains data for rifle and handgun including many popular wildcat and improved cartridges. Tools, powders, components and techniques for assembling optimum reloads with particular application to North America.

**Nosler Reloading Manual No. 3,** edited by Gail Root, Nosler Bullets, Inc., Bend, OR, 1989. 516 pp., illus. $21.95.
All-new book. New format including featured articles and cartridge introductions by well-known shooters, gun writers and editors.
**NRA Firearms Fact Book,** by the editors of NRA, National Rifle Association, Washington, DC, 1991. 330 pp., illus., paper covers, $10.95.
The second, revised edition of the classic *NRA Firearms and Ammunition Fact Book.* Covers gun collecting, firearms safety, ballistics and general references.
**Outdoor Life Gun Data Book,** by F. Philip Rice, Outdoor Life Books, New York, NY, 1987. 412 pp., illus. $27.95.
All the facts and figures that hunters, marksmen, handloaders and other gun enthusiasts need to know.
**Pagoda Design Loads II,** Ballistic Products, Hamel, MN, 1992. 20 pp., illus., paper covers, $5.00.
Special loads using a second gas seal for better powder burning.
**The Paper Jacket,** by Paul Matthews, Wolfe Publishing Co., Prescott, AZ, 1991. Paper covers. $13.50.
Up-to-date and accurate information about paper-patched bullets.
**Pellet Statistics and Ballistics,** Ballistic Products, Hamel, MN. Paper covers, illus., $5.00.
Complete chart and statistical information for the shotgunner, including lead, steel and bismuth.
**Pet Loads, Third Edition,** by Ken Waters, Wolfe Publishing, Prescott, AZ, 1986. Two Volumes, 636 pp., $29.50.
Comprehensive work on over 100 cartridges. Incorporates supplements 1-12.
**Supplements to Pet Loads, Third Edition,** by Ken Waters.
**Supplement No. 1,** $2.70.
**Supplement No. 3,** $3.70.
**Supplement No. 4,** $4.30.
**Supplement No. 5,** $4.10.
**Supplement No. 6,** $4.30.
**Supplement No. 7,** $3.30.
**Supplement No. 8,** $3.90.
**Supplement No. 9,** $4.10.
**Supplement No. 10,** $4.10.
**Supplement No. 11,** $3.90.
**Supplement No. 12,** $4.10.
**Supplement No. 13,** 1989. 16 pp., $8.50.
**Supplement No. 14,** 1990. 16 pp., $8.50.
**Supplement No. 15,** 1990. 16 pp., $8.50.
**Supplement No. 16,** 1991. 36 pp., $8.50.
**Supplement No. 17,** 1992. 36 pp., $10.50.
**Supplement No. 18,** 1993. 36 pp., $10.50.
**Supplement No. 19,** 1994. $10.50.
**Supplement No. 20,** 1995. $10.50.
**The Powder Manual,** Ballistic Products, Hamel, MN, 1991. 56 pp., paper covers, $6.00.
A guide to shotgun powders and when to use them.
**Practical Dope on the .22,** by F.C. Ness, Wolfe Publishing, Prescott, AZ, 1989. 313 pp., $39.00.
History, development, characteristics, ballistics and game killing power of this small bore.
**Practical Handgun Ballistics,** by Mason Williams, Charles C. Thomas, Publisher, Springfield, IL, 1980. 215 pp., illus. $55.00.
Factual information on the practical aspects of ammunition performance in revolvers and pistols.
**Precision Handloading,** by John Withers, Stoeger Publishing Co., So. Hackensack, NJ, 1985. 224 pp., illus. Paper covers. $14.95.
An entirely new approach to handloading ammunition.
**Prices Paid for British Sporting Rifle Cartridges,** by Bill Fleming, Armory Publications, Oceanside, CA, 1992. 31 pp. Paper covers. $15.00.
A list reflecting the relative scarcity of case types, particular load variations, and unusual headstamps of cartridges for British sporting rifles.
**Propellant Profiles New and Expanded, 3rd Edition,** Wolfe Publishing Co., Prescott, AZ, 1991. Paper covers. $16.95.
A collection of reference articles that appeared in *Handloader* magazine, covering 48 powders.
**Ranger-Plus Loads, Revision IV,** Ballistic Products, Hamel, MN, 1992. 34 pp., paper covers, $4.00.
Numerous loads for the Ranger-Plus wad, including steel recipies.
**RCBS Cartridge & Chamber Drawings,** Oroville, CA, 1993. 120 pp., illus., $75.00.
A reference book including the SAAMI drawings for the most popular calibers.
**RCBS Cast Bullet Manual,** Omark Industries, Lewiston, ID, 1986. 172 pp., $9.95.
An introduction to the casting and loading of cast bullets for rifle and handgun.
**Rediscover Swaging,** by David R. Corbin, Corbin Manufacturing, White City, OR, 1989. 240 pp., illus. $24.50.
Covers the swaged bullet making process, along with a brief history.
**Reloader's Guide, 3rd Edition,** by R.A. Steindler, Stoeger Publishing Co., So. Hackensack, NJ, 1984. 224 pp., illus. Paper covers. $11.95.
Complete, fully illustrated step-by-step guide to handloading ammunition.
**Reloaders' Guide for Hercules Smokeless Powders,** Hercules Inc., Wilmington, DE, 1991. 58 pp., paper covers. Free.
Load data using the company's powders for handguns, rifles and shotguns.
***Reloading for Shotgunners, 4th Edition,** by Kurt D. Fackler and M.L. McPherson, DBI Books, a division of Krause Publications, Inc., Vernon Hills, IL, 1997. 320 pp., illus. Paper covers. $19.95.
Expanded reloading tables with over 11,000 loads. Bushing charts for every major press and component maker. All new presentation on all aspects of shotshell reloading by two of the top experts in the field.
**Reloading Tools, Sights and Telescopes for Single Shot Rifles,** by Gerald O. Kelver, Brighton, CO, 1982. 163 pp., illus. Paper covers. $15.00.
A listing of most of the famous makers of reloading tools, sights and telescopes with a brief description of the products they manufactured.
**Remington 12-Gauge 3" Hunting Loads, Revision IV,** Ballistic Products, Hamel, MN, 1989. 15 pp., paper covers, $4.00.
Loads to improve your game shooting.
**Remington Type 5 SP12 12-Gauge 3" Hull Loads for Hunting, Revised,** Ballistic Products, Hamel, MN, 1989. 15 pp., paper covers, $2.00.
A wide spectrum of reloading tips and loads.
**Rifleman's Handbook: A Shooter's Guide to Rifles, Reloading & Results,** by Rick Jamison, NRA Publications, Washington, DC, 1990. 303 pp., illus. $21.95.
Helpful tips on precision reloading, how to squeeze incredible accuracy out of an "everyday" rifle, etc.
**Roll Crimper's Manual,** Ballistic Products, Hamel, MN, 1992. 40 pp., paper covers, $5.00.
The complete loading and instructional manual for roll-crimped loads.
**.17 Caliber Data Book,** Saunders' Gun And Machine Shop, Manchester, IA 1993. $15.00
Load data for 31 different rifles, as well as a listing of .17 accessories.
**Shooting and Hunting Buyer's Guide,** Wolfe Publishing, Prescott, AZ, 1992. 112 pp., paper covers, $6.95.
Critical and scientific evaluations of the year's new products.
**Shooting Black Powder Cartridge Rifle,** by Paul Matthews, Wolfe Publishing Co., Prescott, AZ, 1995. $22.98
A complement to *Loading Black Powder* that offers an understanding on the operation and approach to accurate shooting.
**Shot Shell Boxes: Prices Realized at Auction 1985-1990,** compiled by Bob Strauss, Circus Promotions Corp., Spring, TX, 2nd edition, 1990. 148 pp., illus. Paper covers. $12.00.
Actual prices realized at all major auctions over that time period.
**Shotgun Slug Loading and Field Application,** Ballistic Products, Hamel, MN, 1995. Paper covers. $5.00.
Complete guide for the shotgun slug shooter and loader.
**The Shotshell in the United States,** by Richard J. Iverson, Circus Promotions Corp., Jefferson, ME, 1988. 193 pp., illus. Paper covers. $35.00.
Lists manufacturers, distributors, trade brands, headstamps, gauges, shot sizes, colors and configurations.
**Sierra Handgun Manual, 3rd Edition,** edited by Kenneth Ramage, Sierra Bullets, Santa Fe Springs, CA, 1990. 704 pp., illus. 3-ring binder. $19.95.
New listings for XP-100 and Contender pistols and TCU cartridges...part of a new single shot section. Covers the latest loads for 10mm Auto, 455 Super Mag, and Accurate powders.
**Sierra Rifle Manual, 3rd Edition,** edited by Kenneth Ramage, Sierra Bullets, Santa Fe Springs, CA, 1990. 856 pp., illus. 3-ring binder. $24.95.
Updated load information with new powder listings and a wealth of inside tips.
**Sinclair Precision Reloading Handbook, 9th Edition,** by Fred Sinclair and Bill Garrett, Sinclair International, Inc., Fort Wayne, IN, 1995. 74 pp., $9.00.
Includes info on case selection and preparation, wind reading, load testing, proper use of hand dies.
**Sixgun Cartridges and Loads,** by Elmer Keith, The Gun Room Press, Highland Park, NJ, 1986. 151 pp., illus. $24.95.
A manual covering the selection, uses and loading of the most suitable and popular revolver cartridges. Originally published in 1936. Reprint.
**Slug and Buckshot Manual,** Ballistic Products, Corcoran, MN, 1983. 33 pp., paper covers, $5.00. Addendum $2.00.
A guide to slug reloading with many techniques and tips to improve shooting.
**Speer Reloading Manual Number 12,** edited by members of the Speer research staff, Omark Industries, Lewiston, ID, 1990. 621 pp., illus., $18.95
Reloading manual for rifles and pistols.
**SPG Black Powder Cartridge Reloading Primer,** by Mike Venturino & Steve Garbe, Livingston, MT, 1992. 120 pp., $19.95.
Covers blackpowder reloading and gives individual reloading data.
**The Sporting Ballistics Book,** by Charles W. Matthews, Bill Matthews, Inc., Lakewood, CO, 1992. 182 pp. Wirebound. $19.95.
A useful book for those interested in doing their own exterior-ballistic calculations without the aid of a computer.
**Sporting Clays, Loading and Shooting,** Ballistic Products, Hamel, MN, 1991. 44 pp., paper covers, $5.00.
Information to improve your loads and scores.
**Status of Steel, Revision VII,** Ballistic Products, Hamel, MN, 1995. 94 pp., paper covers, $6.00.
Instructional guide to the use of steel shot.
***Steel Reloading Manual,** Precision Reloading, Inc., Stafford Springs, CT, 1997. $5.95.
An instructional reference guide featuring the newest recipies for steel shot.
**Subject Index to American Rifleman Magazine (1976-1990),** Tioga Engineering Co., Wellsboro, PA, 1992. 68 pp., paper covers. $16.00.
Detailed subject listing of the articles published during that 14-year time span.
**Tables of Bullet Performance,** by Philip Mannes, Wolfe Publishing Co., Prescott, AZ, softbound, $16.95.
Almost any hypothetical ballistic problem may be solved by the tables in this book.
**The .30-'06, A Sourcebook for the Advanced Handloader,** by W.L. Godfrey, Mountain South, Barnwell, SC, 1990. 400+ pp., illus. $24.95.
Source book on this cartridge's ballistics with eight different bullet weights and more than 50 powders, including blackpowder.
***Turkey Ranger Loading Data,** Ballistic Products, Hamel, MN. $2.00.
Loads for the 12-ga. $1^1/_2$ to 2 oz. lead shells.
**28-Gauge Specialist,** Ballistic Products, Hamel, MN, 1989. 12 pp., paper covers, $4.00.
Specific load data information about this special gauge.
**Varmint and Small Game Rifles and Cartridges,** Wolfe Publishing Co., Prescott, AZ, $26.00.
Tells you what shoots and why, describing the basic principles required for top-notch accuracy.
**Why Not Load Your Own?** by Col. T. Whelen, A.S. Barnes, New York, 1957, 4th ed., rev. 237 pp., illus. $20.00.
A basic reference on handloading, describing each step, materials and equipment. Includes loads for popular cartridges.
**Weiderladen,** Dynamit Nobel-RWS, hard-bound, illus., $52.50
Written in German, this is Europe's bible of reloading, including extensive listing of metric calibers and the powders used in them.
**Wildcat Cartridges, Volume I,** Wolfe Publishing Company, Prescott, AZ, 1992. 125 pp. Soft cover. $16.95.
A collection from *Handloader* magazine, the more popular and famous wildcats are profiled.
**Wildcat Cartridges, Volume II,** compiled from *Handloader* and *Rifle* magazine articles written by featured authors, Wolfe Publishing Co., Prescott, AZ, 1992. 971 pp., illus. Paper covers. $34.95.
This volume details rifle and handgun cartridges from the 14-221 to the 460 Van Horn. A comprehensive work containing loading tables and commentary.
**Winchester Reloading Components Catalog, 13th Edition,** Winchester Technical Services Department, East Alton, IL, 1993. 52 pp., illus. Free.
Contains reloading data for shotshell, centerfire rifle and pistol ammunition, as well as detailing their component offerings.
**World Directory of Custom Bullet Makers,** Corbin Manufacturing, White City, OR, 1993, 200 pp., $24.50.
Commercial listing of the names and addresses and what they produce.
**Yours Truly, Harvey Donaldson,** by Harvey Donaldson, Wolfe Publ. Co., Inc., Prescott, AZ, 1980. 288 pp., illus. $19.50.
Reprint of the famous columns by Harvey Donaldson which appeared in "Handloader" from May 1966 through December 1972.

# ORGANIZATIONS & PUBLICATIONS

## ORGANIZATIONS

**Amateur Trapshooting Assn.**
601 W. National Rd., Vandalia, OH 45377

**The Cast Bullet Assn., Inc.**
Ralland J. Fortier, Membership Director, 4103 Foxcraft Dr., Traverse City, MI 49684

**Fifty Caliber Shooters Assn.**
11469 Olive St. Rd., Suite 50, St. Louis, MO 63141/601-475-7545; Fax:601-475-0452

**Handgun Hunters International**
J.D. Jones, Director, P.O. Box 357 MAG, Bloomingdale, OH 43910

**International Ammunition Association, Inc.**
8 Hillock Lane, Chadds Ford, PA 19317/610-358-1258;Fax:610-358-1560

**International Benchrest Shooters**
Joan Borden, RR 1, Box 250BB, Springville, PA 18844/717-965-2366

**IHMSA (Intl. Handgun Metallic Silhouette Assn.)**
Frank Scotto, P.O. Box 5038, Meriden, CT 06450

**National Bench Rest Shooters Assn., Inc.**
Pat Ferrell, 2835 Guilford Lane, Oklahoma City, OK 73120-4404/405-842-9585; Fax: 405-842-9575

**National Muzzle Loading Rifle Assn.**
Box 67, Friendship, IN 47021

**National Reloading Manufacturers Assn.**
One Centerpointe Dr., Suite 300, Lake Oswego, OR 97035

**National Rifle Assn. of America**
11250 Waples Mill Rd., Fairfax, VA 22030

**National Skeet Shooting Assn.**
Mike Hampton, Exec. Director, 5931 Roft Road, San Antonio, TX 78253-9261

**National Sporting Clays Association**
5931 Roft Road, San Antonio, TX 78253-9261/800-877-5338

**Sporting Arms & Ammunition Manufacturers Institute (SAAMI)**
Flintlock Ridge Office Center, 11 Mile Hill Rd., Newtown, CT 06470-2359/203-426-1320; FAX: 203-426-1087

**Sporting Clays of America (SCA)**
Ron L. Blosser, Pres., 9257 Buckeye Rd., Sugar Grove, OH 43155-9632/614-746-8334; Fax: 614-746-8605

**U.S. Practical Shooting Assn./IPSC**
Dave Thomas, P.O. Box 811, Sedro Woolley, WA 98284/360-855-2245

**The Varmint Hunters Assn., Inc.**
Box 759, Pierre, SD 57501/Member Services 800-528-4868

**The Wildcatters**
P.O. Box 170, Greenville, WI 54942

**The Women's Shooting Sports Foundation (WSSF)**
1505 Highway 6 South, Suite 101, Houston, TX 77077

## PUBLICATIONS

**American Firearms Industry**
Nat'l. Assn. of Federally Licensed Firearms Dealers, 2455 E. Sunrise Blvd., Suite 916, Ft. Lauderdale, FL 33304. $35.00 yr. For firearms retailers, distributors and manufacturers.

**American Handgunner**
591 Camino de la Reina, Suite 200, San Diego, CA 92108. $16.75 yr. Articles for handgun enthusiasts, competitors, police and hunters.

**American Rifleman (M)**
National Rifle Assn., 11250 Waples Mill Rd., Fairfax, VA 22030 (Same address for both). Publications Div. $35.00 yr. Firearms articles of all kinds.

**Cartridge Journal (M)**
Robert Mellichamp, 907 Shirkmere, Houston, TX 77008/713-869-0558. Dues $12 for U.S. and Canadian members (includes the newsletter); 6 issues.

**The Cast Bullet*(M)**
Official journal of The Cast Bullet Assn. Director of Membership, 203 E. 2nd St., Muscatine, IA 52761. Annual membership dues $14, includes 6 issues.

**Gun List**
700 E. State St., Iola, WI 54990. $29.95 yr. (26 issues); $54.95 2 yrs. (52 issues). Indexed market publication for firearms collectors and active shooters; guns, supplies and services.

**Gun World**
Gallant/Charger Publications, Inc., 34249 Camino Capistrano, Capistrano Beach, CA 92624. $22.50 yr. For the hunting, reloading and shooting enthusiast.

**Guns & Ammo**
Petersen Publishing Co., 6420 Wilshire Blvd., Los Angeles, CA 90048. $21.94 yr. Guns, shooting, and technical articles.

**Guns**
Guns Magazine, P.O. Box 85201, San Diego, CA 92138. $19.95 yr.; $34.95 2 yrs.; $46.95 3 yrs. In-depth articles on a wide range of guns, shooting equipment and related accessories for gun collectors, hunters and shooters.

**Guns Review**
Ravenhill Publishing Co. Ltd., Box 35, Standard House, Bonhill St., London EC 2A 4DA, England. £20.00 sterling (approx. U.S. $38 USA & Canada) yr. For collectors and shooters.

**Handgunning***
PJS Publications, News Plaza, P.O. Box 1790, Peoria, IL 61656. Cover price $3.95; subscriptions $19.98 for 6 issues. Premier journal for multi-sport handgunners: hunting, reloading, law enforcement, practical pistol and target shooting, and home defense.

**Handloader***
Wolfe Publishing Co., 6471 Airpark Dr., Prescott, AZ 86301. $22.00 yr. The journal of ammunition reloading.

**INSIGHTS***
NRA, 11250 Waples Mill Rd., Fairfax, VA 22030. Editor, John E. Robbins. $15.00 yr., which includes NRA junior membership; $10.00 for adult subscriptions (12 issues). Plenty of details for the young hunter and target shooter; emphasizes gun safety, marksmanship training, hunting skills.

**Muzzle Blasts (M)**
National Muzzle Loading Rifle Assn., P.O. Box 67, Friendship, IN 47021. $30.00 yr. annual membership. For the blackpowder shooter.

**Muzzleloader Magazine***
Rebel Publishing Co., Inc., Dept. Gun, Route 5, Box 347-M, Texarkana, TX 75501. $18.00 U.S.; $22.50 U.S. for foreign subscribers a yr. The publication for blackpowder shooters.

**Precision Shooting**
Precision Shooting, Inc., 222 McKee St., Manchester, CT 06040. $32.00 yr. Journal of the International Benchrest Shooters, and target shooting in general. Also considerable coverage of varmint shooting, as well as big bore, small bore, schuetzen, lead bullet, wildcats and precision reloading.

**Rifle***
Wolfe Publishing Co., 6471 Airpark Dr., Prescott, AZ 86301. $19.00 yr. The sporting firearms journal.

**Safari* (M)**
Safari Magazine, 4800 W. Gates Pass Rd., Tucson, AZ 85745/602-620-1220. $55.00 (6 times). The journal of big game hunting, published by Safari Club International. Also publish *Safari Times*, a monthly newspaper, included in price of $55.00 field membership.

**Second Amendment Reporter**
Second Amendment Foundation, James Madison Bldg., 12500 NE 10th Pl., Bellevue, WA 98005. $15.00 yr. (non-contributors).

**Shooting Times**
PJS Publications, News Plaza, P.O. Box 1790, Peoria, IL 61656/309-682-6626. $23.98 yr. Guns, shooting, reloading; articles on every gun activity.

**The Shotgun News‡**
Snell Publishing Co., Box 669, Hastings, NE 68902. $22.00 yr.; all other countries $110.00 yr. Sample copy $4.00. Gun ads of all kinds.

**Shotgun Sports**
P.O. Box 6810, Auburn, CA 95604/916-889-2220; FAX:916-889-9106. $28.00 yr. Trapshooting how-to's, shotshell reloading, shotgun patterning, shotgun tests and evaluations, Sporting Clays action, waterfowl/upland hunting. Call 1-800-676-8920 for a free sample copy.

**The Sixgunner (M)**
Handgun Hunters International, P.O. Box 357, MAG, Bloomingdale, OH 43910

**The Skeet Shooting Review**
National Skeet Shooting Assn., 5931 Roft Rd., San Antonio, TX 78253. $20.00 yr. (Assn. membership of $30.00 includes mag.) Competition results, personality profiles of top Skeet shooters, how-to articles, technical, reloading information.

**SPG Lubricants/BP Cartridge (Q)**
SPG Lubricant, P.O. Box 761, Livingston, MT 59047. $15 yr. For the blackpowder cartridge enthusiast.

**Sporting Clays Magazine**
5211 South Washington Ave., Titusville, FL 32780/407-268-5010; FAX: 407-267-7216. $29.95 yr. (12 issues).

**Sporting Gun**
Bretton Court, Bretton, Peterborough PE3 8DZ, England. £27.00 (approx. U.S. $36.00), airmail £35.50 yr. For the game and clay enthusiasts.

**Trap & Field**
1200 Waterway Blvd., Indianapolis, IN 46202. $25.00 yr. Official publ. Amateur Trapshooting Assn. Scores, averages, trapshooting articles.

**The U.S. Handgunner* (M)**
U.S. Revolver Assn., 40 Larchmont Ave., Taunton, MA 02780. $10.00 yr. General handgun and competition articles. Bi-monthly sent to members.

**The Varmint Hunter Magazine (Q)**
The Varmint Hunters Assn., Box 759, Pierre, SD 57501/800-528-4868. $24.00 yr.

*Published bi-monthly †Published weekly ‡Published three times per month. All others are published monthly.
M=Membership requirements; write for details. Q=Published Quarterly.

# DIRECTORY

# OF THE HANDLOADER'S TRADE

The **Product Directory** contains a total of 57 handloading product categories. Each category lists manufacturers of that handloading product.

The **Manufacturers' Directory** lists the manufacturers alphabetically with their addresses, phone numbers and FAX numbers, if available.

## DIRECTORY OF THE HANDLOADER'S TRADE INDEX

# PRODUCT DIRECTORY

## AMMUNITION COMPONENTS, BULLETS

Acadian Ballistic Specialties
Accurate Bullet Co.
Action Bullets, Inc.
Alaska Bullet Works, Inc.
Allred Bullet Co.
Alpha LaFranck Enterprises
Armfield Custom Bullets
A-Square Co., Inc.
Atlantic Rose, Inc.
Baer's Hollows
Ballard Built
Banaczkowski Bullets
Barnes Bullets, Inc.
Beartooth Bullets
Beeline Custom Bullets
Bell Reloading, Inc.
Belt MTN Arms
Berger Bullets, Ltd.
Bergman & Williams
Berry's Bullets
Big Bore Bullets of Alaska
Big Bore Express
Bitterroot Bullet Co.
Black Belt Bullets
Black Hills Shooters Supply
Black Mountain Bullets
Black Powder Products
Blount, Inc., Sporting Equipment Div.
Blue Point
Briese Bullet Co., Inc.
Brown Dog Ent.
Brownells, Inc.
BRP, Inc. High Performance Cast Bullets
Bruno Shooters Supply
Buck Stix—SOS Products Co.
Buckeye Custom Bullets
Buckskin Bullet Co.
Buffalo Arms Co.
Bullet, Inc.
Bullet Mills
Bullseye Bullets
Bull-X, Inc.
Calhoon Varmint Bullets, James
Carnahan Bullets
Cascade Bullet Co., Inc.
Cast Performance Bullet Company
Champion's Choice, Inc.
CheVron Bullets
Circle M Custom Bullets
C.J. Ballistics, Inc.
Competitor Corp., Inc.
Cook Engineering Service
Copperhead Bullets, Inc.
Cor-Bon, Inc.
Cummings Bullets
Curtis Cast Bullets
Curtis Gun Shop
Custom Bullets by Hoffman
Cutsinger Bench Rest Bullets
CVA
D&J Bullet Co. & Custom Gun Shop, Inc.
Denver Bullets, Inc.
DKT, Inc.
Dohring Bullets
Double A Ltd.
Eichelberger Bullets, Wm.
Eldorado Cartridge Corp.
Elkhorn Bullets
Enguix Import-Export
Epps, Ellwood
Forkin, Ben
4W Ammunition
Fowler, Bob
Fowler Bullets
Foy Custom Bullets
Freedom Arms, Inc.
Fusilier Bullets
G&C Bullet Co., Inc.
Gander Mountain, Inc.
Gehmann, Walter
Gner's Hard Cast Bullets
Golden Bear Bullets
Gonic Bullet Works
Gotz Bullets
Granite Custom Bullets
Green Mountain Rifle Barrel Co., Inc.
Grier's Hard Cast Bullets
Group Tight Bullets
Gun City
Hammets VLD Bullets
Harris Enterprises
Harrison Bullets
Hart & Son, Inc., Robert W.
Hawk, Inc.
Hawk Laboratories, Inc.
Haydon Shooters' Supply, Russ
Heidenstrom Bullets
Hi-Performance Ammunition Company
Hirtenberger Aktiengesellschaft
Hobson Precision Mfg. Co.
Hornady Mfg. Co.
Hunters Supply
Huntington Die Specialties
HT Bullets
IMI Services USA, Inc.
J&D Components
J&L Superior Bullets
Jensen Bullets
Jericho Tool & Die Co. Inc.
Jester Bullets
JLK Bullets
JRP Custom Bullets
Kasmarsik Bullets
Kaswer Custom, Inc.
Keith's Bullets
Ken's Kustom Kartridges
Keng's Firearms Specialty, Inc.
KLA Enterprises
Knight Rifles
Kodiak Custom Bullets
Lapua Ltd.
Liberty Shooting Supplies
Lightfield Ammunition Corp.
Lightning Performance Innovations, Inc.
Loweth, Richard H.R.
Lomont Precision Bullets
M&D Munitions Ltd.
Magnus Bullets
Maine Custom Bullets
Marchmon Bullets
Markesbery Muzzle Loaders, Inc.
MarMik, Inc.
MAST Technology
Mathews & Son, Inc., George E.
Meister Bullets
Men-Metallwerk Elisenhuette, GmbH
Miller Enterprises, Inc., R.P.
Mitchell Bullets, R.F.
MI-TE Bullets
Modern Muzzleloading, Inc.
MoLoc Bullets
Montana Armory, Inc.
Montana Precision Swaging
Mountain State Muzzleloading Supplies, Inc.
Mt. Baldy Bullet Co.
Mulhern, Rick
Mushroom Express Bullet Co.
Nagel's Bullets
National Bullet Co.
Naval Ordnance Works
Navy Arms Co.
Northern Precision Custom Swaged Bullets
Nosler, Inc.
Oklahoma Ammunition Co.
Old Wagon Bullets
Old Western Scrounger, Inc.
Ordnance Works, The
Oregon Trail Bull Company
Page Custom Bullets
Patrick Bullets
Phillippi Custom Bullets, Justin
Pinetree Bullets
PMC/Eldorado Cartridge Corp.
Precision Cast Bullets
Prescott Projectile Co.
Precision Reloading, Inc.
Price Bullets, Patrick W.
PRL Bullets
Professional Hunter Supplies
Rainier Ballistics Corp.
Ranger Products
Red Cedar Precision Mfg.
Redwood Bullet Works
Remington Arms Co., Inc.
Renner, R.J.
Rhino
R.I.S. Co., Inc.
R.M. Precision, Inc.
Robinson H.V. Bullets
Rolston, Inc., Fred W.
Rubright Bullets
RWS
Scharch Mfg., Inc.
Schneider Bullets
Schroeder Bullets
Shappy Bullets
Sharps Arms Co. Inc., C.
Shilen, Inc.
Shooting Components Marketing
Sierra Bullets
Slug Group, Inc.
SOS Products Co.
Speer Products
Spence, George W.
Spencer's Custom Guns
Stanley Bullets
Star Ammunition, Inc.
Star Custom Bullets
Stark's Bullet Mfg.
Starke Bullet Company
Swift Bullet Co.
Talon Mfg. Co., Inc.
TCCI
3-D Ammunition & Bullets
Traditions, Inc.
Trophy Bonded Bullets, Inc.
True Flight Bullet Co.
Unmussig Bullets, D.L.
USAC
Vann Custom Bullets
Vincent's Shop
Viper Bullet and Brass Works
Warren Muzzleloading Co., Inc.
Watson Trophy Match Bullets
Western Nevada West Coast Bullets
Widener's Reloading & Shooting Supply, Inc.
Williams Bullet Co., J.R.
Winchester Div., Olin Corp.
Winkle Bullets
Woodleigh
Wosenitz VHP, Inc.
Wyant Bullets
Wyoming Armory, Inc.
Wyoming Bonded Bullets
Wyoming Custom Bullets
Yukon Arms Classic Ammunition
Zero Ammunition Co., Inc.
Zonie Bullets

## AMMUNITION COMPONENTS, CASES

A-Square Co., Inc.
Belt MTN Arms
Bertram Bullet Co.
Black Hills Shooters Supply
Brown Co., E. Arthur
Buffalo Arms Co.
Bull-X, Inc.
Buzztail Brass
Calhoon Varmint Bullets, James
Canyon Cartridge Corp.
Cheddite France, S.A.
Colorado Sutlers Arsenal
Competitor Corp., Inc.
Cumberland States Arsenal
Dakota Arms
Denver Bullets, Inc.
DKT, Inc.
Dynamit Nobel-RWS, Inc.
Eichelberger Bullets, Wm.
Eldorado Cartridge Corp.
Enguix Import-Export
Epps, Ellwood
Forkin, Ben
Freedom Arms, Inc.
Gain Twist Barrel Co.
"Gramps" Antique Cartridges
Grayback Wildcats
Hardin Specialty Dist.
Heidenstrom Bullets
Hirtenberger Aktiengesellschaft
Huntington Die Specialties
IMI Services USA, Inc.
Imperial Magnum Corp.
Kaswer Custom, Inc.
Keng's Firearms Specialty, Inc.
KJM Fabritek, Inc.
Lapua Ltd.
Lindsley Arms Cartridge Co.
M&D Munitions Ltd.
Marple & Associates, Dick
MAST Technology
Men-Metallwerk Elisenhuette, GmbH
Naval Ordnance Works
Norma
North American Shooting Systems
North Devon Firearms Services
Northern Precision Custom Swaged Bullets
Oklahoma Ammunition Co.
Old Western Scrounger, Inc.
Pomeroy, Robert
PMC/Eldorado Cartridge Corp.
Precision Components
Professional Hunter Supplies
Remington Arms Co., Inc.
Rifle Works & Armory
R.I.S. Co., Inc.
RWS
Scharch Mfg., Inc.
Schroeder Bullets
Shooting Components Marketing
Silhouette, The
Spence, George W.
Star Custom Bullets
Stewart's Gunsmithing
Talon Mfg. Co., Inc.
TCCI
3-D Ammunition & Bullets
Vihtavuori Oy/Kaltron-Pettibone
Vom Hoffe
Watson Trophy Match Bullets
Weatherby, Inc.
Widener's Reloading & Shooting Supply, Inc.
Winchester Div., Olin Corp.
Yesteryear Armory & Supply
Yukon Arms Classic Ammunition

## AMMUNITION COMPONENTS, POWDERS

Accurate Arms Co., Inc.
Alliant Techsystems
Arco Powder
Black Hills Shooters Supply
DuPont
Enguix Import-Export
GOEX, Inc.
Hercules, Inc.
Hodgdon Powder Co.
IMR Powder Co.
Legend Products Corp.
Norma
Petro-Explo, Inc.
Scot Powder Co.
Scot Powder Co. of Ohio, Inc.
Talon Mfg. Co., Inc.
TCCI
Vihtavuori Oy
Widener's Reloading & Shooting Supply, Inc.
Winchester Div., Olin Corp.

## AMMUNITION COMPONENTS, PRIMERS

Black Hills Shooters Supply
Blount, Inc., Sporting Equipment Div.
CCI
Cheddite France, S.A.
CVA
Dixie Gun Works
Dynamit Nobel-RWS, Inc.
Federal Cartridge Co.
Fiocchi of America, Inc.
Hirtenberger Aktiengesellschaft
Remington Arms Co., Inc.
R.I.S. Co., Inc.
Vihtavuori Oy
Widener's Reloading & Shooting Supply, Inc.
Winchester Div., Olin Corp.

## AMMUNITION COMPONENTS, SHOTSHELL

ACTIV Industries, Inc.
American Products Inc.
Ballistic Products, Inc.
Bismuth Cartridge Co.
Brenneke KG, Wilhelm
Butler Enterprises
C&D Special Products
Cheddite France, S.A.
Claybuster Wads & Harvester Bullets
Colorado Sutlers Arsenal
Cumberland States Arsenal
Estate Cartridge, Inc.
Fiocchi of America, Inc.
Haselbauer Products, Jerry
Kent Cartridge Mfg. Co. Ltd.
Lage Uniwad
Lawrence Brand Shot
Littleton, J.F.
Michael's Antiques
Murmur Corp.
Navy Arms Co.
Pacific Cartridge, Inc.
Pattern Control
Polywad, Inc.
Reloading Specialties, Inc.
Remington Arms Co., Inc.
Seebeck Assoc., R.E.
Steel Reloading Components, Inc.
TMI Products
Trico Plastics
Tucson Mold, Inc.
Vitt/Boos
Walters, John
Widener's Reloading & Shooting Supply, Inc.
Winchester Div., Olin Corp.
Windjammer Tournament Wads, Inc.

## AMMUNITION, COMMERCIAL

ACTIV Industries, Inc.
AFSCO Ammunition
American Ammunition
Arizona Ammunition, Inc.
Arms Corporation of the Philippines
A-Square Co., Inc.
Atlantic Rose, Inc.
Beeline Custom Bullets
Berger Bullets, Ltd.
Bergman & Williams
Big Bear Arms & Sporting Goods, Inc.
Black Hills Ammunition, Inc.
Blammo Ammo
Blount, Inc., Sporting Equipment Div.
Brenneke KG, Wilhelm
Brown Dog Eng.
Buffalo Bullet Co., Inc.
BulletMakers Workshop, The
Bull-X, Inc.
California Magnum
CBC
Chuck's Gun Shop
Colorado Sutlers Arsenal
Cor-Bon, Inc.
Cumberland States Arsenal
Daisy Mfg. Co.
Dead Eye's Sport Center
Delta Frangible Ammunition, LLC
Denver Bullets, Inc.
Diana
Dynamit Nobel-RWS, Inc.
Effebi SNC-Dr. Franco Beretta
Eldorado Cartridge Corp.
Eley Ltd.
Elite Ammunition
Estate Cartridge, Inc.
Federal Cartridge Co.
Fiocchi of America, Inc.
4W Ammunition
Garrett Cartridges, Inc.
Gibbs Rifle Co., Inc.
GOEX, Inc.
Goldcoast Reloaders, Inc.
Grand Falls Bullets, Inc.
Hansen & Co.
Hansen Cartridge Co.
Hart & Son, Inc., Robert W.
Hirtenberger Aktiengesellschaft
Hornady Mfg. Co.
Hunters Supply
ICI-America
IMI
Israel Military Industries Ltd.
Jedediah Starr Trading Co.
Jones, J.D.
Keng's Firearms Specialty, Inc.
Kent Cartridge Mfg. Co. Ltd.
Lapua Ltd.
Lightfield Ammunition Corp.
M&D Munitions Ltd.
Mac-1 Distributors
MagSafe Ammo Co.
Maionchi-L.M.I.
Markell, Inc.
Mathews & Son, Inc., George E.
Men—Metallwerk Elisenhuette, GmbH
Mullins Ammunition
NECO
New England Ammunition Co.
Oklahoma Ammunition Co.
Old Western Scrounger, Inc.
Omark Industries
Pacific Cartridge, Inc.
PMC/Eldorado Cartridge Corp.
Polywad, Inc.
Pony Express Reloaders
Precision Delta Corp.
Pro Load Ammunition, Inc.
Remington Arms Co., Inc.
Rocky Fork Enterprises
Rucker Dist. Inc.
RWS
Shooting Components Marketing
Slug Group, Inc.
Spence, George W.
SSK Industries
Star Reloading Co., Inc.
Talon Mfg. Co., Inc.
Taylor & Robbins
TCCI
Thompson Bullet Lube Co.
3-D Ammunition & Bullets
3-Ten Corp.
USAC
Valor Corp.
Victory USA
Vihtavuori Oy/Kaltron-Pettibone
Voere-KGH m.b.H.
Weatherby, Inc.
Westley Richards & Co.
Widener's Reloading & Shooting Supply, Inc.
Winchester Div., Olin Corp.
Zero Ammunition Co., Inc.
Zonie Bullets

## AMMUNITION, CUSTOM

Accuracy Unlimited (Littleton, CO)
AFSCO Ammunition
Allred Bullet Co.
American Derringer Corp.
Arizona Ammunition, Inc.
Arms Corporation of the Philippines
A-Square Co., Inc.
Atlantic Rose, Inc.
Ballistica Maximus North
Berger Bullets, Ltd.
Bertram Bullet Co.
Black Hills Ammunition, Inc.
Blue Mountain Bullets
Bruno Shooters Supply
Brynin, Milton
Buck Stix—SOS Products Co.
Buckskin Bullet Co.
Bull-X, Inc.
BulletMakers Workshop, The
Calhoon Varmint Bullets, James
Carroll Bullets
CBC
CHAA, Ltd.
Country Armourer, The
Cubic Shot Shell Co., Inc.
Custom Tackle and Ammo
Dakota Arms
Dead Eye's Sport Center
Delta Frangible Ammunition, LLC
DKT, Inc.
Elite Ammunition
Ellis Sport Shop, E.W.
Estate Cartridge, Inc.
4W Ammunition
Freedom Arms, Inc.
GDL Enterprises
Glaser Safety Slug, Inc.
GOEX, Inc.
"Gramps" Antique Cartridges
Grand Falls Bullets, Inc.
Granite Custom Bullets
Gun Accessories
Heidenstrom Bullets
Hirtenberger Aktiengesellschaft
Hoelscher, Virgil
Horizons Unlimited
Hornady Mfg. Co.
Hunters Supply
IMI
Israel Military Industries Ltd.
Jensen Bullets
Jensen's Custom Ammunition
Jensen's Firearms Academy
Jett & Co., Inc.
Kaswer Custom, Inc.
Keeler, R.H.
Kent Cartridge Mfg. Co. Ltd.
KJM Fabritek, Inc.
Kortz, Dr. L.
Lindsley Arms Cartridge Co.
Loch Leven Industries
MagSafe Ammo Co.
MAST Technology
McMurdo, Lynn
Men-Metallwerk Elisenhuette, GmbH
Milstor Corp.
Mountain Rifles Inc.
Mullins Ammunition
Naval Ordnance Works
NECO
Northern Precision Custom Swaged Bullets
Old Western Scrounger, Inc.
Oklahoma Ammunition Company
Oregon Trail Bullet Company
Parts & Surplus
Personal Protection Systems
Precision Cartridge
Precision Delta Corp.
Precision Reloading, Inc.
Precision Munitions, Inc.
Professional Hunter Supplies
Recoilless Technologies, Inc.
Sandia Die & Cartridge Co.
Slings & Arrows
SOS Products Co.
Specialty Gunsmithing
Spence, George W.
Spencer's Custom Guns
Star Custom Bullets
State Arms Gun Co.
Stewart's Gunsmithing
Talon Mfg. Co., Inc.
3-D Ammunition & Bullets
3-Ten Corp.
Unmussig Bullets, D.L.
Vitt/Boos
Vulpes Ventures, Inc.
Warren Muzzleloading Co., Inc.
Weaver Arms Corp. Gun Shop
Wells Custom Gunsmith, R.A.
Worthy Products, Inc.
Wyoming Armory, Inc.
Yukon Arms Classic Ammunition
Zonie Bullets

## AMMUNITION, FOREIGN

AFSCO Ammunition
Ammunition Consulting Services, Inc.
Armscorp USA, Inc.
A-Square Co., Inc.
Atlantic Rose, Inc.
Berger Bullets, Ltd.
Bertram Bullet Co.
BulletMakers Workshop, The
CBC
Cheddite France, S.A.
Cubic Shot Shell Co., Inc.
Dead Eye's Sport Center
Diana
DKT, Inc.
Dynamit Nobel-RWS, Inc.
Fiocchi of America, Inc.
First, Inc., Jack
Fisher, R. Kermit
Fisher Enterprises, Inc.
FN Herstal
Forgett Jr., Valmore J.
Gibbs Rifle Co., Inc.
GOEX, Inc.
Hansen & Co.
Hansen Cartridge Co.
Heidenstrom Bullets
Hirtenberger Aktiengesellschaft
Hornady Mfg. Co.
IMI
IMI Services USA, Inc.
Israel Military Industries Ltd.
JagerSport, Ltd.
Keng's Firearms Specialty, Inc.
Magnum Research, Inc.
MagSafe Ammo Co.
MagTech Recreational Products, Inc.
Maionchi-L.M.I.
MAST Technology
Merkuria Ltd.
Mullins Ammunition
Naval Ordnance Works
Oklahoma Ammunition Co.
Old Western Scrounger, Inc.
Petro-Explo, Inc.
Precision Delta Corp.
R.E.T. Enterprises
Rocky Fork Enterprises
RWS
Sentinel Arms
Southern Ammunition Co., Inc.
Spence, George W.
Stratco, Inc.
SwaroSports, Inc.
T.F.C. S.p.A.
USA Sporting
Vihtavuori Oy/Kaltron-Pettibone
Yukon Arms Classic Ammunition

## BOOKS & MANUALS, PUBLISHERS

Action Direct, Inc.
American Handgunner Magazine
Armory Publications, Inc.
Arms & Armour Press
Arms, Peripheral Data Systems
Ballistic Products, Inc.
Barnes Bullets, Inc.
Blackhawk West
Blacksmith Corp.
Blacktail Mountain Books
Blue Book Publications, Inc.
Blue Ridge Machinery & Tools, Inc.
Brown Co., E. Arthur
Brownell Checkering Tools, W.E.
Bullet'n Press
Calibre Press, Inc.
Cape Outfitters
Colonial Repair
Colorado Sutlers Arsenal
Corbin Mfg. & Supply, Inc.
Cumberland States Arsenal
DBI Books
Flores Publications, Inc., J.
Forgett Jr., Valmore J.
Golden Age Arms Co.
Gun City
Gun Hunter Books
Gun Hunter Trading Co.
Gun List
Gun Parts Corp., The
Gun Room Press, The
Gun Works, The
Guncraft Books
Guncraft Sports, Inc.
Gunnerman Books
GUNS Magazine
H&P Publishing
Handgun Press
Hawk, Inc.
Hawk Laboratories, Inc.
Heritage/VSP Gun Books
Hodgdon Powder Co.
Home Shop Machinist, The
Hornady Mfg. Co.
Hungry Horse Books
Info-Arm
Ironside International Publishers, Inc.
Koval Knives
Krause Publications, Inc.
Lane Publishing
Lapua Ltd.
Lethal Force Institute
Liberty Shooting Supplies
Lyman Instant Targets, Inc.
Lyman Products Corp.
Madis Books
Martin Bookseller, J.
McKee Publications
MI-TE Bullets
Montana Armory, Inc.
Mountain South
New Win Publishing, Inc.
NgraveR Co., The
OK Weber, Inc.
Outdoorsman's Bookstore, The
Pejsa Ballistics
Petersen Publishing Co.
Pettinger Books, Gerald
Pointing Dog Journal
Police Bookshelf
Precision Shooting, Inc.
PWL Gunleather
Quack Decoy & Sporting Clays
Paintball Games International Magazine (Aceville Publications)
Paintball Sports Magazine
Remington Double Shotguns
R.G.-G., Inc.
Riling Arms Books Co., Ray
Rocky Mountain Wildlife Products
Rutgers Book Center
S&S Firearms
Safari Press, Inc.
Saunders Gun & Machine Shop
Semmer, Charles
Sharps Arms Co., Inc. C.
Shootin' Accessories, Ltd.
Sierra Bullets
SPG, Inc.
Stackpole Books
Stewart Game Calls, Inc., Johnny
Stoeger Industries
Stoeger Publishing, Co.
Thomas, Charles C.
Track of the Wolf, Inc.
Trafalgar Square
Trotman, Ken
Vintage Industries, Inc.
VSP Publishers
WAMCO—New Mexico
Wiest, M.C.
Wilderness Sound Products Ltd.
Williams Gun Sight Co.
Winchester Press
Wolfe Publishing Co.
Wolf's Western Traders

## BULLETS, CASE & DIE LUBRICANTS

Blackhawk West
Bonanza
Brown Co., E. Arthur
Camp-Cap Products
Chem-Pak, Inc.
C-H Tool & Die Corp.
Cooper-Woodward
CVA
Denver Bullets, Inc.
Dropkick
Elkhorn Bullets
E-Z-Way Systems
Forster Products
4-D Custom Die Co.
Gozon Corp., U.S.A.
Guardsman Products
HEBB Resources
Hollywood Engineering
Hornady Mfg. Co.
Imperial
Le Clear Industries
Lestrom Laboratories, Inc.
Lithi Bee Bullet Lube
M&N Bullet Lube
Michaels of Oregon Co.
Micro-Lube
MI-TE Bullets
NECO
Paco's
Pease Accuracy, Bob
Ponsness/Warren
Prolix Lubricants
RCBS
Reardon Products
Rooster Laboratories
Rorschach Precision Products

Shay's Gunsmithing
Silver Eagle Machining
Small Custom Mould & Bullet Co.
Tamarack Products, Inc.
Uncle Mike's
Warren Muzzleloading Co., Inc.
Widener's Reloading & Shooting Supply, Inc.
Young Country Arms

## BULLET CASTING, FURNACES & POTS

Advance Car Mover Co., Rowell Div.
Ballisti-Cast, Inc.
Brass and Bullet Alloys
Ferguson, Bill
GAR
Jedediah Starr Trading Co.
Lee Precision, Inc.
Lyman Instant Targets, Inc.
Lyman Products Corp.
Magma Engineering Co.
Necromancer Industries, Inc.
Rapine Bullet Mould Mfg. Co.
RCBS

## BULLET CASTING, LEAD

Action Bullets, Inc.
Ames Metal Products
Atlantic Rose, Inc.
Brass and Bullet Alloys
Bullseye Bullets
D&J Bullet Co. & Custom Gun Shop, Inc.
Denver Bullets, Inc.
Essex Metals
Federated-Fry
Ferguson, Bill
4W Ammunition
Fry Metals
Graphics Direct
Green, Arthur S.
Gun Works, The
Harris Enterprises
Heidenstrom Bullets
Hobson Precision Mfg. Co.
Hunters Supply
Javelina Lube Products
K&S Mfg. Inc.
Lane Bullets, Inc.
Liberty Metals
Liberty Shooting Supplies
Loweth, Richard H.R.
Luch Metal Merchants, Barbara
M&D Munitions Ltd.
Magma Engineering Co.
Miller Enterprises, Inc., R.P.
MI-TE Bullets
Mt. Baldy Bullet Co.
Pedersoli and Co., Davidey20
Peerless Alloy, Inc.
RCBS
R.I.S. Co., Inc.
Rolston, Inc., Fred W.
RSR Corp. (CA)
RSR Corp. (TX)
Seebeck Assoc., R.E.
Signet Metal Corp.
TCSR
Thompson/Center Arms
TR Metals Corp.

## BULLET CASTING, ACCESSORIES

Advance Car Mover Co., Rowell Div.
Ballisti-Cast, Inc.
Brownells, Inc.
Dropkick
Eagan, Donald V.
Ferguson, Bill
Green, Arthur S.
Hanned Line, The
Hanned Precision
Howell Machine
LBT
Lithi Bee Bullet Lube
Lyman Instant Targets, Inc.
Lyman Products Corp.
Magma Engineering Co.
Midway Arms, Inc.
Mountain State Muzzleloading Supplies, Inc.
Paco's
RCBS
Small Custom Mould & Bullet Co.
Thompson Bullet Lube Co.
Wolf's Western Traders

## BULLET JACKETS & GAS CHECKS

Alaska Bullet Works, Inc.
Berger Bullets, Ltd.
Bullet Swaging Supply, Inc.
CFVentures
Elkhorn Bullets
Feken, Dennis
Group Tight Bullets
Hanned Line, The
Hanned Precision
Hornady Mfg. Co.
J-4, Inc.
Lyman Instant Targets, Inc.
Lyman Products Corp.
Northern Precision Custom Swaged Bullets
Professional Hunter Supplies
R.I.S. Co., Inc.
Star Custom Bullets
Wyoming Armory, Inc.

## BULLET PULLERS

Haydon Shooters' Supply, Russ
Hollywood Engineering
Hornady Mfg. Co.
Lyman Instant Targets, Inc.
Lyman Products Corp.
Midway Arms, Inc.
Quinetics Corp.
RCBS

## BULLET TOOLS

Arms Corporation of the Philippines
Eagan, Donald V.
Hart & Son, Inc., Robert W.
Hornady Mfg. Co.
Lyman Instant Targets, Inc.
Lyman Products Corp.
Paco's
RCBS
Small Custom Mould & Bullet Co.
Stoney Point Products, Inc.

## CARTRIDGES FOR COLLECTORS

Ad Hominem
Alpha 1 Drop Zone
Ammunition Consulting Services, Inc.
Buck Stix—SOS Products Co.
Cameron's
Campbell, Dick
Cole's Gun Works
Colonial Repair
Country Armourer, The
DGR Custom Rifles
Duane's Gun Repair
Ed's Gun House
Enguix Import-Export
Epps, Ellwood
First, Inc., Jack
Fitz Pistol Grip Co.
Forty Five Ranch Enterprises
Goergen's Gun Shop, Inc.
"Gramps" Antique Cartridges
Gun Parts Corp., The
Gun Room Press, The
Michael's Antiques
MAST Technology
Montana Outfitters
CFCMountain Bear Rifle Works, Inc.
Pasadena Gun Center
Samco Global Arms, Inc.
San Francisco Gun Exchange
Scott Fine Guns, Inc., Thad
SOS Products Co.
Stone Enterprises, Ltd.
Ward & Van Valkenburg
Yearout, Lewis E.

## CASE CLEANERS & POLISHING MEDIA

American Gas and Chemical Co., Ltd.
Belltown, Ltd.
Birchwood Casey
Blount, Inc., Sporting Equipment Div.
Brown Co., E. Arthur
Davis Products, Mike
Dillon Precision Products, Inc.
Dutchman's Firearms, Inc., The
Flitz International, Ltd.
Goddard, Allen
Graves Co.
Hornady Mfg. Co.
Iosso Products
Lyman Instant Targets, Inc.
Lyman Products Corp.
Pro-Shot Products, Inc.
Range Brass Products Company
Raytech
RCBS
Sierra Specialty Prod. Co.
Sportsman Supply Co.
VibraShine, Inc.
Widener's Reloading & Shooting Supply, Inc.

## CASE PREPARATION TOOLS

Brown Co., E. Arthur
Buck Stix—SOS Products Co.
CONKKO
Custom Products
D.C.C. Enterprises
Dewey Mfg. Co., Inc., J.
Eichelberger Bullets, Wm.
E-Z-Way Systems
Hanned Line, The
Hanned Precision
Hart & Son, Inc., Robert W.
Haydon Shooters' Supply, Russ
Holland's Gunsmithing
Hornady Mfg. Co.
Huntington Die Specialties
Image Ind. Inc.
Imperial
K&M Services
Le Clear Industries
Lee Precision, Inc.
Lyman Instant Targets, Inc.
Lyman Products Corp.
Magma Engineering Co.
MarMik, Inc.
Marquart Precision Co.
Match Prep—Doyle Gracey
McKillen & Heyer, Inc.
MCS, Inc.
Midway Arms, Inc.
Miller Engineering
Mo's Competitor Supplies
MWG Company
Pease Accuracy, Bob
Plum City Ballistic Range
Prime Reloading
Pro-Shot Products, Inc.
R&D Engineering & Manufacturing
RCBS
Redding Reloading Equipment
SAECO
Scharch Mfg., Inc.
Sinclair International, Inc.
SOS Products Co.
Stoney Point Products, Inc.
Time Precision, Inc.
VibraShine, Inc.
Von Minden Gunsmithing Services
Wells Custom Gunsmith, R.A.
Whitetail Design and Engineering Ltd.
Widener's Reloading & Shooting Supply, Inc.
Wilson, Inc., L.E.

## CASE & AMMUNITION PROCESSORS, SEPARATORS, INSPECTORS, BOXERS

Ammo Load, Inc.
Ben's Machines
Brass and Bullet Alloys
Camdex, Inc.
Case Sorting System
Haselbauer Products, Jerry
Hornady Mfg. Co.
Howell Machine
Image Ind. Inc.
Scharch Mfg., Inc.
TMI Products
Tru-Square Metal Prods., Inc.

## CASE TRIMMERS, TRIM DIES & ACCESSORIES

Brown Co., E. Arthur
Chem-Pak, Inc.
C-H Tool & Die Corp.
Custom Products, Neil A. Jones
Dillon Precision Products, Inc.
Forster Products
4-D Custom Die Co.
Fremont Tool Works
GAR
Hollywood Engineering
Hornady Mfg. Co.
Jones Custom Products, Neil A.
Lyman Instant Targets, Inc.
Lyman Products Corp.
Match Prep—Doyle Gracey
North Devon Firearms Services
Pease Accuracy, Bob
Rapine Bullet Mould Mfg. Co.
Raytech
RCBS
Redding Reloading Equipment
SAECO
Sinclair International, Inc.
Stalwart Corp.
Time Precision, Inc.
Watson Trophy Match Bullets
Widener's Reloading & Shooting Supply, Inc.
Wilson, Inc., L.E.

## CASE TUMBLERS, VIBRATORS, MEDIA & ACCESSORIES

Brown Co., E. Arthur
Davis Products, Mike
Dillon Precision Products, Inc.
Graves Co.
Hornady Mfg. Co.
Lortone, Inc.
Lyman Instant Targets, Inc.
Lyman Products Corp.
Midway Arms, Inc.
Original Box, Inc.
Range Brass Products Company
Raytech
RCBS
Rooster Laboratories
Scharch Mfg., Inc.
Tru-Square Metal Prods., Inc.
VibraShine, Inc.
Vibra-Tek Co.
Widener's Reloading & Shooting Supply, Inc.

## CHRONOGRAPHS & PRESSURE TOOLS

Brown Co., E. Arthur
Canons Delcour
Competition Electronics, Inc.
Custom Chronograph, Inc.
D&H Precision Tooling
Hege Jagd-u. Sporthandels, GmbH
Hornady Mfg. Co.
Kent Cartridge Mfg. Co. Ltd.
Oehler Research, Inc.
P.A.C.T., Inc.
Shooting Chrony, Inc.
SKAN A.R.
Stratco, Inc.
Tepeco

## CLEANERS & DEGREASERS

American Gas & Chemical Co., Ltd.
Armite Laboratories
Belltown, Ltd.
Birchwood Casey
Break-Free, Inc.
Brobst, Jim
Brown Co., E. Arthur
Camp-Cap Products
Clenzoil Corp.
Crouse's Country Cover
Davis Products, Mike
Dutchman's Firearms, Inc., The

E&L Mfg., Inc.
Gozon Corp., U.S.A.
Gun Works, The
Hodgdon Powder Co.
Hornady Mfg. Co.
INTEC International, Inc.
Iosso Products
Jonad Corp.
Kleen-Bore, Inc.
Lyman Instant Targets, Inc.
Lyman Products Corp.
RCBS
RIG Products
Shiloh Creek
Shooter's Choice
TDP Industries, Inc.
Tetra Gun Lubricants
Thompson Bullet Lube Co.
United States Products Co.
Venco Industries, Inc.
WD-40 Co.
Widener's Reloading & Shooting Supply, Inc.

## COMPUTER SOFTWARE/VIDEOS, BALLISTICS & RELOADING

Action Target, Inc.
ADC, Inc.
AmBr Software Group Ltd.
Arms, Programming Solutions
Arms Software
Ballistic Engineering & Software, Inc.
Ballistic Program Co., Inc., The
Barnes Bullets, Inc.
Beartooth Bullets
Blackwell, W.
Canons Delcour
Corbin Mfg. & Supply, Inc.
Country Armourer, The
Data Tech Software Systems
Exe, Inc.
FlashTek, Inc.
Hutton Rifle Ranch
Jensen Bullets
J.I.T., Ltd.
JWH: Software
Kent Cartridge Mfg. Co. Ltd.
Load From A Disk
Maionchi-L.M.I.
Oehler Research, Inc.
P.A.C.T., Inc.
PC Bullet/ADC, Inc.
Pejsa Ballistics
Powley Computer
RCBS
Sierra Bullets
Tioga Engineering Co., Inc.
Vancini, Carl
W. Square Enterprises

## DIE ACCESSORIES, METALLIC

Alex, Inc.
Brown Co., E. Arthur
Carbide Die & Mfg. Co., Inc.
Custom Products, Neil A. Jones
Fisher Custom Firearms
Hanned Line, The
Hanned Precision
Hornady Mfg. Co.
Jones Custom Products, Neil A.
LAP Systems Group, N.A.
Lyman Instant Targets, Inc.
Lyman Products Corp.
MTM Moulded Products Co., Inc.
Pease Accuracy, Bob
Ponsness/Warren
Rapine Bullet Mould Mfg. Co.
RCBS
Roberts Products
Widener's Reloading & Shooting Supply, Inc.

## DIES, METALLIC

Bald Eagle Precision Machine Co.
Blount, Inc., Sporting Equipment Div.
Brown Co., E. Arthur
Bull Mountain Rifle Co.
Carbide Die & Mfg. Co., Inc.
C-H Tool & Die Corp.
Custom Products, Neil A. Jones
Davis, Don
Dever Co., Jack
Eagan, Donald V.
First, Inc., Jack
Forster Products
4-D Custom Die Co.
Freedom Arms, Inc.
Fremont Tool Works
"Gramps" Antique Cartridges
Hanned Line, The
Hanned Precision
Harrell's Precision
Heidenstrom Bullets
Hollywood Engineering
Hornady Mfg. Co.
Huntington Die Specialties
Jones Custom Products, Neil A.
King & Co.
Korzinek Riflesmith, J.
LAP Systems Group, N.A.
Lee Precision, Inc.
Lyman Instant Targets, Inc.
Lyman Products Corp.
MCRW Associates Shooting Supplies
Montana Armory, Inc.
Niemi Engineering, W.B.
North Devon Firearms Services
Rapine Bullet Mould Mfg. Co.
RCBS
Redding Reloading Equipment
Roberts Products
Rosenthal, Brad and Sallie
SAECO
Scott, Dwight
Sharps Arms Co. Inc., C.
Silhouette, The
Von Minden Gunsmithing Services
Welsh, Bud
Widener's Reloading & Shooting Supply, Inc.
Wilson, Inc., L.E.
Wolf's Western Traders

## DIES, SHOTSHELL

Hollywood Engineering
Hornady Mfg. Co.
Mayville Engineering Co.
MEC, Inc.
Ponsness/Warren

## DIES, SWAGE

Camdex, Inc.
Bullet Swaging Supply, Inc.
Corbin Mfg. & Supply, Inc.
Cumberland Arms
Custom Products
G&C Bullet Co., Inc.
Eagan, Donald V.
Heidenstrom Bullets
Hollywood Engineering
LAP Systems Group, N.A.
North Devon Firearms Services
Rorschach Precision Products
Sport Flite Manufacturing Co.

## GAUGES, CALIPERS & MICROMETERS

Accuracy Components Co.
Accuracy Den, The
CP Specialties
Clymer Manufacturing Co., Inc.
Forgreens Tool Mfg., Inc.
Hornady Mfg. Co.
Huntington Die Specialties
JGS Precision Tool Mfg.
Lyman Instant Targets, Inc.
Lyman Products Corp.
MarMik, Inc.
Midway Arms, Inc.
NECO
Plum City Ballistic Range
Prairie River Arms
Rapine Bullet Mould Mfg. Co.
RCBS
Sinclair International, Inc.
Stoney Point Products, Inc.
Stratco, Inc.
Varner's Service
Wilson, Inc., L.E.

## GUNS, CLEANING & REFINISHING SUPPLIES

AC Dyna-tite Corp.
Acculube II, Inc.
Accupro Gun Care
American Gas & Chemical Co., Ltd.
Answer Products Co.
Armite Laboratories
Armsport, Inc.
Atlantic Mills, Inc.
Atsko/Sno-Seal, Inc.
Barnes Bullets, Inc.
Birchwood Casey
Blackhawk East
Blue and Gray Products, Inc.
Blount, Inc., Sporting Equipment Div.
Break-Free, Inc.
Bridgers Best
Brown Co., E. Arthur
Camp-Cap Products
Cape Outfitters
CONKKO
Connecticut Shotgun Mfg. Co.
Crane & Crane Ltd.
Creedmoor Sports, Inc.
CRL, Inc.
CRR, Inc./Marble's Inc.
Custom Products
D&H Prods. Co., Inc.
Dara-Nes, Inc.
Decker Shooting Products
Deepeeka Exports Pvt. Ltd.
Dewey Mfg. Co., Inc., J.
Dri-Slide, Inc.
Du-Lite Corp.
Dutchman's Firearms, Inc., The
Dykstra, Doug
E&L Mfg., Inc.
Eezox, Inc.
Ekol Leather Care
Faith Associates, Inc.
Flitz International Ltd.
Fluoramics, Inc.
Frontier Products Co.
G96 Products Co., Inc.
Goddard, Allen
Golden Age Arms Co.
Gozon Corp., U.S.A.
Great Lakes Airguns
Guardsman Products
Half Moon Rifle Shop
Heatbath Corp.
Hoppe's Div.
Hornady Mfg. Co.
Hydrosorbent Products
Iosso Products
Johnston Bros.
Kellogg's Professional Products
Kent Cartridge Mfg. Co. Ltd.
Kesselring Gun Shop
Kleen-Bore, Inc.
Laurel Mountain Forge
Lee Supplies, Mark
LEM Gun Specialties, Inc.
Lewis Lead Remover, The
List Precision Engineering
LPS Laboratories, Inc.
Marble Arms
Micro Sight Co.
Minute Man High Tech. Ind.
Mountain View Sports, Inc.
MTM Molded Products Co., Inc.
Muscle Products Corp.
Nesci Enterprises, Inc.
Northern Precision Custom Swaged Bullets
Now Products, Inc.
Old World Oil Products
Omark Industries
Original Mink Oil, Inc.
Outers Laboratories, Div. of Blount
Ox-Yoke Originals, Inc.
P&M Sales and Service
Pachmayr Ltd.
PanaVise Products, Inc.
Parker Gun Finishes
Pendleton Royal
Penguin Industries, Inc.
Precision Reloading, Inc.
Prolix® Lubricants
Pro-Shot Products, Inc.
R&S Industries Corp.
Radiator Specialty Co.
Rice, Keith
Rickard, Inc., Pete
RIG Products
Rod Guide Co.
Rooster Laboratories
Rusteprufe Laboratories
Rusty Duck Premium Gun Care Products
Saunders Gun & Machine Shop
Sharp Shooter, Inc.
Shiloh Creek
Shooter's Choice
Shootin' Accessories, Ltd.
Silencio/Safety Direct
Sno-Seal, Inc.
Spencer's Custom Guns
Stoney Point Products, Inc.
Svon Corp.
Tag Distributors
TDP Industries, Inc.
Tetra Gun Lubricants
Texas Platers Supply Co.
T.F.C. S.p.A.
Thompson Bullet Lube Co.
Thompson/Center Arms
Track of the Wolf, Inc.
United States Products Co.
Valor Corp.
Van Gorden & Son, Inc., C.S.
Venco Industries, Inc.
VibraShine, Inc.
Warren Muzzleloading Co., Inc.
WD-40 Co.
Wick, David E.
Willow Bend
Young Country Arms
Z-Coat Industrial Coatings, Inc.

## HEARING PROTECTORS

Aero Peltor
Ajax Custom Grips, Inc.
Autauga Arms, Inc.
Brown Co., E. Arthur
Brown Products, Inc., Ed
Browning Arms Co.
Clark Co., Inc., David
CRL, Inc.
E-A-R, Inc.
Electronic Shooters Protection, Inc.
Faith Associates, Inc.
Flents Products Co., Inc.
Gentex Corp.
Hart & Son, Inc., Robert W.
Hoppe's Div.
Kesselring Gun Shop
North Specialty Products
Paterson Gunsmithing
Peltor, Inc.
Penguin Industries, Inc.
R.E.T. Enterprises
Silencio/Safety Direct
Valor Corp.
Wells Custom Gunsmith, R.A.
Willson Safety Prods. Div.

## LABELS, BOXES, CARTRIDGE HOLDERS

Ballistic Products, Inc.
Berry's Mfg. Inc.
Brown Co., E. Arthur
Crane & Crane Ltd.
Del Rey Products
DeSantis Holster & Leather Goods
Fitz Pistol Grip Co.
Flambeau Products Corp.
J&J Products Co.
Kolpin Mfg., Inc.
Liberty Shooting Supplies
Michaels of Oregon Co.
Midway Arms, Inc.
MTM Moulded Products Co., Inc.
Pattern Control
Pendleton Royal
Uncle Mike's

## LEAD WIRE & WIRE CUTTERS

Berger Bullets, Ltd.
Blue Ridge Machinery & Tools, Inc.
Coats, Mrs. Lester
Cook Engineering Service
Green, Arthur S.
Hart & Son, Inc., Robert W.
Hollywood Engineering
Laputa Ltd.
Lightning Performance Innovtions, Inc.
Luch Metal Merchants, Barbara
Professional Hunter Supplies
Rochester Lead Works
Sport Flite Manufacturing Co.
Star Custom Bullets
TCSR
Unmussig Bullets, D.L.

## LOAD TESTING & PRODUCT TESTING, CHRONOGRAPHING & BALLISTIC STUDIES

Ammunition Consulting Services, Inc.
Ballistic Research
Bartlett, Don
Briese Bullet Co., Inc.
Buck Stix—SOS Products Co.
Clearview Products
Clerke Co., J.A.
D&H Precision Tooling
Defense Training International, Inc.
DGR Custom Rifles
Duane's Gun Repair
Gonzalez Guns, Ramon B.
Henigson & Associates, Steve
Hensler, Jerry
Hoelscher, Virgil
Jackalope Gun Shop
Jensen Bullets
Lomont Precision Bullets
Maionchi-L.M.I.
MAST Technology
McMurdo, Lynn
Middlebrooks Custom Shop
Multiplex International
Oil Rod and Gun Shop
Rupert's Gun Shop
SOS Products Co.
Specialty Gunsmithing
Spencer's Custom Guns
Vancini, Carl
Vulpes Ventures, Inc.
Wells Custom Gunsmith, R.A.
White Laboratory, Inc., H.P.
X-Spand Target Systems

## LOADING BLOCKS, METALLIC & SHOTSHELL

Flambeau Products Corp.
Hornady Mfg. Co.
LAP Systems Group, N.A.
Lyman Instant Targets, Inc.
Lyman Products Corp.
Midway Arms, Inc.
MTM Moulded Products Co., Inc.
RCBS
Stalwart Corp.
Trico Plastics
Widener's Reloading & Shooting Supply, Inc.
Wise Guns, Dale

## LUBRISIZERS, DIES & ACCESSORIES

Ben's Machines
Cooper-Woodward
GAR
Hanned Line, The
Hanned Precision
LBT
Lyman Instant Targets, Inc.
Lyman Products Corp.
Magma Engineering Co.
Midway Arms, Inc.
North Devon Firearms Services
Protector Mfg. Co., Inc., The
RCBS
SPG, Inc.
Star Machine Works
Stillwell, Robert
Thompson Bullet Lube Co.
WTA Manufacturing, Bill Wood

## MOULDS & MOULD ACCESSORIES

Brownells, Inc.
Colorado Shooter's Supply
Cumberland Arms
Eagan, Donald V.
Forgett Jr., Valmore J.
GAR
Graf & Sons
Gun Works, The
Hensley & Gibbs
Hoch Custom Bullet Moulds
Jones Moulds, Paul
LBT
Loweth, Richard H.R.
Lyman Instant Targets, Inc.
Lyman Products Corp.
NEI Handtools, Inc.
Old West Bullet Moulds
Paco's
Pedersoli and Co., Davide
Protector Mfg. Co., Inc., The
Rapine Bullet Mould Mfg. Co.
RCBS
Redding Reloading Equipment
SAECO
Small Custom Mould & Bullet Co.
Sport Flite Manufacturing Co.
Thompson/Center Arms
Wolf's Western Traders

## POWDER MEASURES, SCALES, FUNNELS & ACCESSORIES

Blount, Inc., Sporting Equipment Div.
Bonanza
Brown Co., E. Arthur
Bruno Shooters Supply
Custom Products, Neil A. Jones
Denver Instrument Co.
Eichelberger Bullets, Wm.
Fitz Pistol Grip Co.
Forster Products
Fremont Tool Works
GAR
Greenwood Precision
Hoehn Sales, Inc.
Hollywood Engineering
Hornady Mfg. Co.
Jones Custom Products, Neil A.
Lyman Instant Targets, Inc.
Lyman Products Corp.
Mayville Engineering Co.
MCRW Associates Shooting Supplies
MEC, Inc.
Mountain State Muzzleloading Supplies, Inc.
MTM Moulded Products Co., Inc.
Multi-Scale Charge Ltd.
October Country
Pease Accuracy, Bob
Pedersoli and Co., Davide
Quinetics Corp.
RCBS
Rosenthal, Brad and Sallie
Saunders Gun & Machine Shop
Saville Iron Co.
Shiloh Creek
Shiloh Rifles Mfg.
S.L.A.P. Industries
Vega Tool Co., c/o T.R. Ross
Welsh, Bud
Werner, Carl
Widener's Reloading & Shooting Supply, Inc.

## PRESS ACCESSORIES, METALLIC

Ammo Load, Inc.
Blount, Inc., Sporting Equipment Div.
Brown Co. E. Arthur
Camdex, Inc.
C-H Tool & Die Corp.
4-D Custom Die Co.
Hollywood Engineering
Hornady Mfg. Co.
Howell Machine
K&M Services
Kapro Mfg. Co., Inc.
LAP Systems Group, N.A.
Lyman Instant Targets, Inc.
Lyman Products Corp.
MA Systems
MCRW Associates Shooting Supplies
Ponsness/Warren
Quinetics Corp.
RCBS
Redding Reloading Equipment
R.E.I.
SAECO
TTM

## PRESS ACCESSORIES, SHOTSHELL

Ballistic Products, Inc.
Hollywood Engineering
Hornady Mfg. Co.
Multi-Scale Charge Ltd.
Pattern Control
Ponsness/Warren
R.E.I.

## PRESSES, ARBOR

Bald Eagle Precision Machine Co.
Blue Ridge Machinery & Tools, Inc.
B-Square Co., Inc.
Custom Products, Neil A. Jones
Davis, Don
Hart & Son, Inc., Robert W.
Haydon Shooters' Supply, Russ
Jones Custom Products, Neil A.
K&M Services
Pease Accuracy, Bob
Sinclair International, Inc.
Spencer's Custom Guns

## PRESSES, METALLIC

Ammo Load, Inc.
Blount, Inc., Sporting Equipment
Brown Co., E. Arthur
Camdex, Inc.
C-H Tool & Die Corp.
Dillon Precision Products, Inc.
Enguix Import-Export
Forster Products
Fremont Tool Works
4-D Custom Die Co.
Hollywood Engineering
Hornady Mfg. Co.
LAP Systems Group, N.A.
Lee Precision, Inc.
Lyman Instant Targets, Inc.
Lyman Products Corp.
Ponsness/Warren
RCBS
Redding Reloading Equipment
Roberts Products
SAECO
Sharp Shooter Supply
Star Machine Works
Widener's Reloading & Shooting Supply, Inc.

## PRESSES, SHOTSHELL

Ballistic Products, Inc.
Dillon Precision Products, Inc.
Hollywood Engineering
Hornady Mfg. Co.
Lee Precision, Inc.
Mayville Engineering Co.
MEC, Inc.
Ponsness/Warren
Widener's Reloading & Shooting Supply, Inc.

## PRESSES, SWAGE

Bullet Swaging Supply, Inc.
Camdex, Inc.
Corbin Mfg. & Supply, Inc.
G&C Bullet Co., Inc.

## PRIMING TOOLS & ACCESSORIES

Brown Co., E. Arthur
CONKKO
Custom Products, Neil A. Jones
Flambeau Products Corp.
Hornady Mfg. Co.
Huntington Die Specialties
Jones Custom Products, Neil A.
K&M Services
Lyman Instant Targets, Inc.
Lyman Products Corp.
MarMik, Inc.
Montana Armory, Inc.
MTM Moulded Products Co., Inc.
PEM'S Mfg. Co.
Roberts Products
RCBS
Sharps Arms Co. Inc., C.
Simmons, Jerry
Sinclair International, Inc.
Widener's Reloading & Shooting Supply, Inc.
Williams Gun Sight Co.

## REBORING & RERIFLING

Ackley Rifle Barrels, P.O.
A.M.T.
Arcadia Machine & Tool, Inc.
Arundel Arms & Ammunition, Inc., A.
BlackStar AccuMax Barrels
BlackStar Barrel Accurizing
Chicasaw Gun Works
Cochran, Oliver
Ed's Gun House
Flaig's
Gun Works, The
H&S Liner Service
Ivanoff, Thomas G.
Jackalope Gun Shop
K-D, Inc.
Kopp, Terry K.
LaBounty Precision Reboring
NCP Products, Inc.
Matco, Inc.
Pence Precision Barrels
Perazone, Brian
Pro-Port Ltd.
Ranch Products
Redman's Rifling & Reboring
Rice, Keith
Ridgetop Sporting Goods
Shaw, Inc., E.R.
Siegrist Gun Shop
Simmons Gun Repair, Inc.
Swift River Gunworks
300 Gunsmith Service, Inc.
Time Precision, Inc.
Tom's Gun Repair
Van Patten, J.W.
West, Robert G.
White Rock Tool & Die
Zufall, Joseph F.

## RESTS—BENCH, PORTABLE—AND ACCESSORIES

Accuright
Adventure 16, Inc.
Armor Metal Products
Bald Eagle Precision Machine Co.
Bartlett Engineering
Borden's Accuracy
Browning Arms Co.
B-Square Co., Inc.
Bull Mountain Rifle Co.
Canons Delcour
Chem-Pak, Inc.
Clift Mfg., L.R.
Clift Welding Supply
Cravener's Gun Shop
Decker Shooting Products
Desert Mountain Mfg.
Erickson's Mfg., Inc., C.W.
F&A Inc.
Greenwood Precision
Harris Engineering, Inc.
Hart & Son, Inc., Robert W.
Hidalgo, Tony
Hoelscher, Virgil
Hoppe's Div.
Kolpin Mfg., Inc.
Kramer Designs
Midway Arms, Inc.
Millett Sights
MJM Manufacturing
Outdoor Connection, Inc., The
PAST Sporting Goods, Inc.
Pease Accuracy, Bob
Penguin Industries, Inc.
Portus, Robert
Protektor Model
Ransom International Corp
Saville Iron Co.
ShurKatch Corporation
Spencer's Custom Guns
Stoney Point Products, Inc.
Sure Shot of LA, Inc.
Thompson Target Technology
T.H.U. Enterprises, Inc.
Tonoloway Tack Drivers
Varner's Service
Wichita Arms, Inc.
Zanotti Armor, Inc.

### RIFLE BARREL MAKERS

ABS Co. Inc./Lothar Walther
Ackley Rifle Barrels, P.O.
Airrow
A.M.T.
Arcadia Machine & Tool, Inc.
Arundel Arms & Ammunition, Inc., A.
Bauska Barrels
BlackStar AccuMax Barrels
BlackStar Barrel Accurizing
Border Barrels Ltd.
Broad Creek Rifle Works
Broughton Rifle Barrels
Brown Co., E. Arthur
Bullberry Barrel Works, Ltd.
Camas Hot Springs Mfg.
Canons Delcour
Carter's Gun Shop
Christensen Arms
Cincinnati Swaging
Clerke Co., J.A.
Chicasaw Gun Works
Cochran, Oliver
Competition Limited
D&J Bullet Co. & Custom Gun Shop, Inc.
deHaas Barrels
Dilliott Gunsmithing, Inc.
Donnelly, C.P.
Douglas Barrels, Inc.
Gaillard Barrels
Gain Twist Barrel Co.
Getz Barrel Co.
Green Mountain Rifle Barrel Co., Inc.
Gun Works, The
Half Moon Rifle Shop
Harold's Custom Gun Shop, Inc.
Harris Gunworks
Hart Rifle Barrels, Inc.
Hastings Barrels
Hoelscher, Virgil
H-S Precision, Inc.
Jackalope Gun Shop
K-D, Inc.
KOGOT
Kopp, Terry K.
Krieger Barrels, Inc.
LaBounty Precision Reboring
Lilja Precision Rifle Barrels
Lothar Walther Precision Tool, Inc.
Mac's .45 Shop
Matco, Inc.
McGowen Rifle Barrels
McMillan Rifle Barrels
Mid-America Recreation, Inc.
Nowlin Mfg. Co.
Obermeyer Rifled Barrels
Olympic Arms, Inc.
Pac-Nor Barreling
Pell, John T.
Pence Precision Barrels
Raptor Arms Co., Inc.
Rocky Mountain Rifle Works Ltd.
Sabatti S.R.L.
Schneider Rifle Barrels, Inc., Gary
Shaw, Inc., E.R.
Shilen, Inc.
Siskiyou Gun Works
Small Arms Mfg. Co.
Sonora Rifle Barrel Co.
Specialty Shooters Supply, Inc.
Stratco, Inc.
Strutz Rifle Barrels, Inc., W.C.
Swivel Machine Works, Inc.
Unmussig Bullets, D.L.
Verney-Carron
Wells, Fred F.
Wilson Arms Co., The
Wiseman and Co., Bill

### SCOPES, MOUNTS & ACCESSORIES, OPTICAL EQUIPMENT

Accuracy Innovations, Inc.
Ackerman, Bill
ADCO Sales, Inc.
Adventurer's Outpost
Aimpoint U.S.A.
Aimtech Mount Systems
Air Venture
Alley Supply Co.
Anderson Manufacturing Co., Inc.
Apel GmbH, Ernst
Applied Laser Systems, Inc.
A.R.M.S., Inc.
Armscorp USA, Inc.
Autauga Arms, Inc.
Baer Custom, Inc., Les
Barrett Firearms Mfg., Inc.
Bausch & Lomb Sports Optics Div.
Beaver Park Products, Inc.
BEC, Inc.
Blount, Inc., Sporting Equipment Div.
Bohemia Arms Co.
Boonie Packer Products
Borden's Accuracy
Brown Co. E. Arthur
Brownells, Inc.
Brunton U.S.A.
B-Square Co., Inc.
Bull Mountain Rifle Co.
Burris
Bushnell Sports Optics Worldwide
Butler Creek Corp.
California Grip
Celestron International
Center Lock Scope Rings
Clearview Mfg. Co., Inc.
Combat Military Ordnance Ltd.
Compass Industries, Inc.
Concept Development Corp.
Conetrol Scope Mounts
CRDC Laser Systems Group
Creedmoor Sports, Inc.
Crimson Trace
Custom Quality Products, Inc.
D&H Prods. Co., Inc.
D.C.C. Enterprises
Del-Sports, Inc.
DHB Products
Doctor Optic Technologies, Inc.
Eagle International Sporting Goods, Inc.
Edmund Scientific Co.
Ednar, Inc.
Eggleston, Jere D.
EGW Evolution Gun Works
Eclectic Technologies, Inc.
Emerging Techonolgies, Inc.
Europtik Ltd.
Excalibur Enterprises
Farr Studio, Inc.
Forgett Jr., Valmore J.
Fotar Optics
Frankonia Jagd
Fujinon, Inc.
G.G. & G.
Gentry Custom Gunmaker, David
Glaser Safety Slug, Inc.
Great Lakes Airguns
GSI, Inc.
Gun Accessories
Gun South, Inc.
Guns, (Div. of D.C. Engineering, Inc.)
Hakko Co. Ltd.
Hammerli USA
Harris Gunworks
Hart & Son, Inc., Robert W.
Harvey, Frank
Hermann Leather Co., H.J.
Hertel & Reuss
Hiptmayer, Armurier
Hiptmayer, Klaus
Hofmann & Co.
Holland's
Ironsighter Co.
Jaeger, Inc., Paul/Dunn's
JagerSport, Ltd.
Jeffredo Gunsight
Jewell Triggers, Inc.
Kahles USA
KDF, Inc.
Kelbly, Inc.
KenPatable Ent., Inc.
Kesselring Gun Shop
Kimber of America, Inc.
Kmount
Knight's Mfg. Co.
Kowa Optimed, Inc.
Kris Mounts
KVH Industries, Inc.
Kwik Mount Corp.
Kwik-Site Co.
L&S Technologies, Inc.
L.A.R. Mfg., Inc.
Laser Devices, Inc.
Laseraim
LaserMax, Inc.
Leapers, Inc.
Lectro Science, Inc.
Lee Co., T.K.
Leica USA, Inc.
Leupold
Lightforce U.S.A. Inc.
List Precision Engineering
Lite Tek International
Lohman Mfg. Co., Inc.
London Guns Ltd.
Lyte Optronics
Mac's .45 Shop
Masen Co., Inc., John
Maxi-Mount
McCann's Machine & Gun Shop
McMillan Optical Gunsight Co.
MCS, Inc.
MDS
Meier Works
Merit Corp.
Michaels of Oregon Co.
Military Armament Corp.
Millett Sights
Mirador Optical Corp.
Mitchell Optics Inc.
Mo's Competitor Supplies
Mountain Rifles Inc.
MWG Co.
New England Custom Gun Service
Nic Max, Inc.
Nikon, Inc.
Oakshore Electronic Sights, Inc.
Olympic Optical Co.
Optical Services Co.
Orchard Park Enterprise
Oregon Arms, Inc.
Outdoor Connection, Inc., The
Parsons Optical Mfg. Co.
PECAR Herbert Schwarz, GmbH
PEM's Mfg. Co.
Pentax Corp.
Perazone, Brian
Pilkington Gun Co.
Pioneer Research, Inc.
P.M. Enterprises, Inc.
Precise Metalsmithing Enterprises
Precision Sport Optics
Premier Reticles
Ram-Line Blount, Inc.
Ranch Products
Randolph Engineering, Inc.
Ranging, Inc.
Redfield, Inc.
Rice, Keith
Rocky Mountain High Sports Glasses
Rogue Rifle Co., Inc.
RPM
S&K Mfg. Co.
Saunders Gun & Machine Shop
Schmidt & Bender, Inc.
Scope Control Inc.
ScopLevel
Score High Gunsmithing
Seattle Binocular & Scope Repair Co.
Segway Industries
Selsi Co., Inc.
Shepherd Scope Ltd.
Sightron, Inc.
Simmons Enterprises, Ernie
Simmons Outdoor Corp.
Six Enterprises
SKAN A.R.
SKB Shotguns
Slug Group, Inc.
Spencer's Custom Guns
Sportsmatch U.K. Ltd.
Springfield, Inc.
Steiner
STI International
Stoeger Industries
Sure Shot of LA, Inc.
SwaroSports, Inc.
Swarovski Optik North America Ltd.
Swift Instruments, Inc.
TacStar Industries, Inc.
Talley, Dave
Tasco Sales, Inc.
Tele-Optics
Thompson/Center Arms
Trijicon, Inc.
Ultra Dot Distribution
Uncle Mike's
Unertl Optical Co., Inc., John
United Binocular Co.
United States Optics Technologies, Inc.
Valor Corp.
Voere-KGH m.b.H.
Warne Manufacturing Co.
Warren Muzzleloading Co., Inc.
WASP Shooting Systems
Weatherby, Inc.
Weaver Products
Weaver Scope Repair Service
Weigand Combat Handguns, Inc.
Westfield Engineering
Westley Richards & Co.
White Rock Tool & Die
White Muzzleloading Systems
White Shooting Systems, Inc.
Wideview Scope Mount Corp.
Williams Gun Sight Co.
York M-1 Conversions
Zanotti Armor, Inc.
Zeiss Optical, Carl

### SHELLHOLDERS

American Sales & Kirkpatrick
Anderson Manufacturing Co., Inc.
Brown Co., E. Arthur
E&L Mfg., Inc.
F&A Inc.
Fremont Tool Works
Hollywood Engineering
Hornady Mfg. Co.
Lyman Instant Targets, Inc.
Lyman Products Corp.
Marquart Precision Co.
North Devon Firearms Services
Quinetics Corp.
Rapine Bullet Mould Mfg. Co.
RCBS
Redding Reloading Equipment
SAECO
ShurKatch Corporation
Vega Tool Co.

### SHOTSHELL MISCELLANY

American Products Co.
Clearview Products
Colorado Sutlers Arsenal
Cumberland States Arsenal
Haselbauer Products, Jerry
Hornady Mfg. Co.
Kent Cartridge Mfg. Co. Ltd.
Kirkpatrick Leather Co.
Ponsness/Warren
Reloading Specialties, Inc.
TMI Products

### SIGHTS, METALLIC

Accura-Site
All's, The Jim J. Tembelis Co., Inc.
Alpec Team, Inc.
Andela Tool & Machine, Inc.
Anschutz GmbH
Armsport, Inc.
Aro-Tek, Ltd.
Baer Custom, Inc., Les
BEC, Inc.
Bo-Mar Tool & Mfg. Co.
Bond Custom Firearms
Bowen Classic Arms Corp.
Bradley Gunsight Co.
Brown Co., E. Arthur
Brown Products, Inc., Ed
California Sights
Cape Outfitters
Carter's Gun Shop
Center Lock Scope Rings
C-More Systems
Colonial Repair
CRL, Inc.
CRR, Inc./Marble's Inc.
DHB Products
Eagle International Sporting Goods, Inc.
Engineered Accessories
Evans, Andrew
Evans Gunsmithing
Farr Studio, Inc.
Fautheree, Andy
Forgett Jr., Valmore J.
G.G. & G.
Gun Doctor, The
Hank's Gun Shop
Hart & Son, Inc., Robert W.
Heinie Specialty Products
Hesco-Meprolight
Hiptmayer, Armurier
Innovative Weaponry, Inc.
Innovision Enterprises
Jaeger, Inc., Paul/Dunn's
J.P. Enterprises, Inc.
Kris Mounts
Lee's Red Ramps
List Precision Engineering
London Guns Ltd.
L.P.A. Snc
Lyman Instant Targets, Inc.
Lyman Products Corp.
Mac's .45 Shop
Marble Arms
Mayville Engineering Co.
MCS, Inc.
MEC, Inc.
MEC-Gar S.R.L.
Meier Works
Meprolight
Merit Corp.
Mid-America Recreation, Inc.
Middlebrooks Custom Shop
Millett Sights
MMC
Mo's Competitor Supplies
Montana Armory, Inc.
Montana Vintage Arms
New England Custom Gun Service
Novak's Inc.
Oakshore Electronic Sights, Inc.
OK Weber, Inc.
Pachmayr Ltd.
PEM's Mfg. Co.
P.M. Enterprises, Inc.
Quarton USA, Ltd. Co.
Redfield, Inc.
RPM
Sharps Arms Co. Inc., C.
Slug Site
STI International
Stiles Custom Guns
Talley, Dave
T.F.C. S.p.A.
Thompson/Center Arms

Trijicon, Inc.
United States Optics Technologies, Inc.
WASP Shooting Systems
Wichita Arms, Inc.
Williams Gun Sight Co.
Wilson Gun Shop

## STOCKS, COMMERCIAL & CUSTOM

A&W Repair
Accuracy Unlimited (Glendale, AZ)
Ackerman & Co.
Acra-Bond Laminates
Ahlman Guns
Amrine's Gun Shop
Arms Ingenuity Co.
Artistry In Wood
Arundel Arms & Ammunition, Inc., A.
Baelder, Harry
Bain & Davis, Inc.
Balickie, Joe
Bansner's Gunsmithing Specialties
Barnes Bullets, Inc.
Bartlett, Don
Beitzinger, George
Belding's Custom Gun Shop
Bell & Carlson, Inc.
Benchmark Guns
Biesen, Al
Biesen, Roger
Billeb, Stephen L.
Billings Gunsmiths, Inc.
Blount, Inc., Sporting Equipment Div.
Boltin, John M.
Borden's Accuracy
Bowerly, Kent
Boyds'Gunstock Industries, Inc.
Brace, Larry D.
Brgoch, Frank
Brown Co., E. Arthur
Brown Precision, Inc.
Buckhorn Gun Works
Bull Mountain Rifle Co.
Bullberry Barrel Works, Ltd.
Burgess & Son Gunsmiths, R.W.
Burkhart Gunsmithing, Don
Burres, Jack
Butler Creek Corp.
Cali'co Hardwoods, Inc.
Camilli, Lou
Campbell, Dick
Cape Outfitters
Caywood, Shane J.
Chambers Flintlocks Ltd., Jim
Chicasaw Gun Works
Christman Jr., Gunmaker, David
Churchill, Winston
Clark Custom Guns, Inc.
Claro Walnut Gunstock Co.
Clifton Arms, Inc.
Cloward's Gun Shop
Cochran, Oliver
Coffin, Charles H.
Coffin, Jim
Colonial Repair
Colorado Gunsmithing Academy
Colorado School of Trades
Conrad, C.A.
Crane Sales Co., George S.
Creedmoor Sports, Inc.
Curly Maple Stock Blanks
Custom Checkering Service
Custom Gun Products
Custom Gun Stocks
Custom Riflestocks, Inc.
Custom Shop, The
D&D Gunsmiths, Ltd.
D&G Precision Duplicators
D&J Bullet Co. & Custom Gun Shop, Inc.
Dangler, Homer L.
D.D. Custom Stocks
de Treville & Co., Stan
Dever Co., Jack
Devereaux, R.H. "Dick"
DGR Custom Rifles
DGS, Inc.
Dilliott Gunsmithing, Inc.
Dillon, Ed
Dowtin Gunworks
Dressel Jr., Paul G.
Duane Custom Stocks, Randy
Duane's Gun Repair
Duncan's Gun Works, Inc.
Echols & Co., D'Arcy
Eggleston, Jere D.
Erhardt, Dennis
Eversull Co., Inc., K.
Fajen, Inc., Reinhart
Farmer-Dressel, Sharon
Fiberpro/California
Fibron Products, Inc.
Fisher, Jerry A.
Flaig's
Folks, Donald E.
Forster, Kathy
Forster, Larry L.
Forthofer's Gunsmithing & Knifemaking
Frank Custom Classic Arms, Ron
Francotte & Cie S.A., Auguste
Game Haven Gunstocks
Gene's Custom Guns
Gervais, Mike
Gilman-Mayfield, Inc.
Gillmann, Edwin
Giron, Robert E.
Goens, Dale W.
Golden Age Arms Co.
Gordie's Gun Shop
Goudy Classic Stocks, Gary
Grace, Charles E.
Great American Gun Co.
Green, Roger M.
Greene, M.L.
Greene Precision Duplicators
Greenwood Precision
Griffin & Howe, Inc.
Gun Shop, The
Guns
Gunsmithing Ltd.
Hallberg Gunsmith, Fritz
Halstead, Rick
Hamilton, Jim
Hanson's Gun Center, Dick
Harper's Custom Stocks
Harris Gunworks
Hart & Son, Inc., Robert W.
Harwood, Jack O.
Hastings Barrels
Hecht, Hubert J.
Heilmann, Stephen
Hensley, Gunmaker, Darwin
Heppler, Keith M.
Heydenberk, Warren R.
High Tech Specialties, Inc.
Hillmer Custom Gunstocks, Paul D.
Hiptmayer, Armurier
Hiptmayer, Klaus
Hoelscher, Virgil
Hoenig & Rodman
H-S Precision, Inc.
Huebner, Corey O.
Ide, Kenneth G.
Island Pond Gun Shop
Ivanoff, Thomas G.
Jackalope Gun Shop
Jaeger, Inc., Paul/Dunn's
Jamison's Forge Works
Jarrett Rifles, Inc.
Johnson Wood Products
J.P. Gunstocks, Inc.
KDF, Inc.
Keith's Custom Gunstocks
Ken's Rifle Blanks
Kilham & Co.
Klein Custom Guns, Don
Klingler Woodcarving
Knight's Mfg. Co.
Knippel, Richard
Kokolus, Michael M.
Lawson Co., Harry
Lind Custom Guns, Al
Ljutic Industries, Inc.
Lock's Philadelphia Gun Exchange
Lynn's Custom Gunstocks
Lyons Gunworks, Larry
Mac's .45 Shop
Marple & Associates, Dick
Masen Co., Inc., John
McCament, Jay
McCullough, Ken
McDonald, Dennis
McFarland, Stan
McGowen Rifle Barrels
McGuire, Bill
McKinney, R.P.
McMillan Fiberglass Stocks, Inc.
Mercer Custom Stocks, R.M.
Mid-America Recreation, Inc.
Miller Arms, Inc.
Morrison Custom Rifles, J.W.
MPI Fiberglass Stocks
MWG Co.
NCP Products, Inc.
Nelson, Stephen
Nettestad Gun Works
New England Arms Co.
New England Custom Gun Service
Newman Gunshop
Nickels, Paul R.
Norman Custom Gunstocks, Jim
Oakland Custom Arms, Inc.
Oil Rod and Gun Shop
OK Weber, Inc.
Old World Gunsmithing
One Of A Kind
Or-šn
Orvis Co., The
Ottmar, Maurice
P&S Gun Service
Pacific Research Laboratories, Inc.
Pagel Gun Works, Inc.
Paulsen Gunstocks
Pecatonica River Longrifle
PEM's Mfg. Co.
Pentheny de Pentheny
Perazone, Brian
Perazzi USA, Inc.
Pohl, Henry A.
Powell & Son (Gunmakers) Ltd., William
R&J Gun Shop
Ram-Line Blount, Inc.
Rampart International
Raptor Arms Co., Inc.
Reagent Chemical and Research, Inc.
Reiswig, Wallace E.
Richards Micro-Fit Stocks
Rimrock Rifle Stocks
RMS Custom Gunsmithing
Robinson, Don
Robinson Firearms Mfg. Ltd.
Rogers Gunsmithing, Bob
Roto Carve
Royal Arms Gunstocks
Ryan, Chad L.
Sanders Custom Gun Service
Saville Iron Co.
Schiffman, Curt
Schiffman, Mike
Schumakers Gun Shop
Schwartz Custom Guns, David W.
Schwartz Custom Guns, Wayne E.
Score High Gunsmithing
Shell Shack
Sile Distributors, Inc.
Simmons Gun Repair, Inc.
Six Enterprises
Skeoch, Brian R.
Smith, Sharmon
Snider Stocks, Walter S.
Speedfeed, Inc.
Speiser, Fred D.
Stiles Custom Guns
Storey, Dale A.
Strawbridge, Victor W.
Sturgeon Valley Sporters
Swan, D.J.
Szweda, Robert
Swift River Gunworks
Talmage, William G.
Taylor & Robbins
Tecnolegno S.p.A.
T.F.C. S.p.A.
Thompson/Center Arms
Tiger-Hunt
Tirelli
Tom's Gun Repair
Track of the Wolf, Inc.
Trevallion Gunstocks
Tucker, James C.
Turkish Firearms Corp.
Tuttle, Dale
Vest, John
Vic's Gun Refinishing
Vintage Industries, Inc.
Volquartsen Custom Ltd.
Von Minden Gunsmithing Services
Walker Arms Co., Inc.
Walnut Factory, The
Weber & Markin Custom Gunsmiths
Weems, Cecil
Wells, Fred F.
Wells Custom Gunsmith, R.A.
Wenig Custom Gunstocks, Inc.
Werth, T.W.
Wessinger Custom Guns & Engraving
West, Robert G.
Western Gunstock Mfg. Co.
Williams Gun Sight Co.
Williamson Precision Gunsmithing
Windish, Jim
Winter, Robert M.
Working Guns
Wright's Hardwood Gunstock Blanks
Wyoming Bonded Bullets
Yee, Mike
Zeeryp, Russ

## STUCK CASE REMOVERS

Atsko/Sno-Seal, Inc.
Hornady Mfg. Co.
MarMik, Inc.
RCBS
Redding Reloading Equipment
SAECO
Sno-Seal
Widener's Reloading & Shooting Supply, Inc.

## TARGETS

Action Target, Inc.
American Target
American Whitetail Target Systems
A-Tech Corp.
Autauga Arms, Inc.
Barsotti, Bruce
Beomat of America Inc.
Birchwood Casey
Blount, Inc., Sporting Equipment Div.
Blue and Gray Products, Inc.
Camp-Cap Products
Champion Target Co.
Cunningham Co., Eaton
Dapkus Co., Inc., J.G.
Datumtech Corp.
Dayson Arms Ltd.
D.C.C. Enterprises
Detroit-Armor Corp.
Diamond Mfg. Co.
Estate Cartridge, Inc.
Federal Champion Target Co.
Freeman Animal Targets
G.H. Enterprises Ltd.
Gun Parts Corp., The
Hiti-Schuch, Atelier Wilma
Hornady Mfg. Co.
H-S Precision, Inc.
Hunterjohn
Innovision Enterprises
JWH: Software
Kennebec Journal
Kleen-Bore, Inc.
Lakefield Arms Ltd.
Lewis, Ed
Littler Sales Co.
Lyman Instant Targets, Inc.
Lyman Products Corp.
M&D Munitions Ltd.
Mendez, John A.
MSR Targets
National Target Co.
N.B.B., Inc.
North American Shooting Systems
Nu-Teck
Outers Laboratories, Div. of Blount
Ox-Yoke Originals, Inc.
Passive Bullet Traps, Inc.
PlumFire Press, Inc.
Quack Decoy & Sporting Clays
Redfield, Inc.
Remington Arms Co., Inc.
Rockwood Corp., Speedwell Div.
Rocky Mountain Target Co.
R-Tech Corp.
Savage Arms (Canada), Inc.
Savage Range Systems, Inc.
Schaefer Shooting Sports
Seligman Shooting Products
Shooters Supply
Shoot-N-C Targets
Shotgun Shop, The
Thompson Target Technology
Trius Products, Inc.
White Flyer Targets
World of Targets
X-Spand Target Systems
Z's Metal Targets & Frames
Zriny's Metal Targets

## TRIGGERS, RELATED EQUIPMENT

A.M.T.
Arcadia Machine & Tool, Inc.
B&D Trading Co., Inc.
Baer Custom, Inc., Les
Behlert Precision, Inc.
Bond Custom Firearms
Boyds' Gunstock Industries, Inc.
Bull Mountain Rifle Co.
Canjar Co., M.H.
Custom Products
Cycle Dynamics, Inc.
Dayton Traister
Electronic Trigger Systems, Inc.
Eversull Co., Inc., K.
Galati International
Gentry Custom Gunmaker, David
Hastings Barrels
Hawken Shop, The
Hoelscher, Virgil
Holland's
Jacobson, Teddy
Jaeger, Inc., Paul/Dunn's
Jewell Triggers, Inc.
J.P. Enterprises, Inc.
List Precision Engineering
L&R Lock Co.
Mahony, Philip Bruce
Masen Co., Inc., John
Master Lock Co.
Miller Single Trigger Mfg. Co.
NCP Products, Inc.
OK Weber, Inc.
PEM's Mfg. Co.
Penrod Precision
Perazone, Brian
Perazzi USA, Inc.
Raptor Arms Co., Inc.
S&B Industries
Shilen, Inc.
Simmons Gun Repair, Inc.
STI International
Timney Mfg., Inc.
Voere-KGH m.b.H.

# MANUFACTURERS' DIRECTORY

## A

A&W Repair, 2930 Schneider Dr., Arnold, MO 63010/314-287-3725
A.B.S. III, 9238 St. Morritz Dr., Fern Creek, KY 40291
AC Dyna-tite Corp., 155 Kelly St., P.O. Box 0984, Elk Grove Village, IL 60007/847-593-5566; FAX: 847-593-1304
Acadian Ballistic Specialties, P.O. Box 61, Covington, LA 70434
Acculube II, Inc., 4366 Shackleford Rd., Norcross, GA 30093-2912
Accupro Gun Care, 15512-109 Ave., Surrey, BC U3R 7E8, CANADA/604-583-7807
Accuracy Den, The, 25 Bitterbrush Rd., Reno, NV 89523/702-345-0225
Accuracy Innovations, Inc., P.O. Box 376, New Paris, PA 15554/814-839-4517; FAX: 814-839-2601
Accuracy Unlimited, 7479 S. DePew St., Littleton, CO 80123
Accuracy Unlimited, 16036 N. 49 Ave., Glendale, AZ 85306/602-978-9089; FAX: 602-978-9089
Accurate Arms Co., Inc., 5891 Hwy. 230 West, McEwen, TN 37101/615-729-4207, 800-416-3006; FAX 615-729-4211
Accurate Bullet Co., 159 Creek Road, Glen Mills, PA 19342/610-399-6584
Accura-Site (See All's, The Jim Tembelis Co., Inc.)
Accuright, RR 2 Box 397, Sebeka, MN 56477/218-472-3383
Ackerman & Co., 16 Cortez St., Westfield, MA 01085/413-568-8008
Ackerman, Bill (See Optical Services Co.)
Acra-Bond Laminates (See Artistry in Wood)
Action Bullets, Inc., RR 1, P.O. Box 189, Quinter, KS 67752/913-754-3609; FAX: 913-754-3629
Action Direct, Inc., P.O. Box 830760, Miami, FL 33283/305-559-4652; FAX: 305-559-4652
Action Target, Inc., P.O. Box 636, Provo, UT 84603/801-377-8033; FAX: 801-377-8096
Actions by "T", Teddy Jacobson, 16315 Redwood Forest Ct., Sugar Land, TX 77478/281-277-4008
ACTIV Industries, Inc., 1000 Zigor Rd., P.O. Box 339, Kearneysville, WV 25430/304-725-0451; FAX: 304-725-2080
Ad Hominem, 3130 Gun Club Lane, RR Orillia, Ont. L3V 6H3, CANADA/705-689-5303; FAX: 705-689-5303
ADC, Inc., 33470 Chinook Plaza, Scappoose, OR 97056/503-543-5088
ADCO Sales Inc., 10 Cedar St., Unit 17, Woburn, MA 01801/617-935-1799; FAX: 617-935-1011
Advance Car Mover Co., Rowell Div., P.O. Box 1, 240 N. Depot St., Juneau, WI 53039/414-386-4464; FAX: 414-386-4416
Adventure 16, Inc., 4620 Alvarado Canyon Rd., San Diego, CA 92120/619-283-6314
Adventurer's Outpost, P.O. Box 70, Cottonwood, AZ 86326/800-762-7471; FAX: 602-634-8781
Aero Peltor, 90 Mechanic St., Southbridge, MA 01550/508-764-5500; FAX: 508-764-0188
AFSCO Ammunition, 731 W. Third St., P.O. Box L, Owen, WI 54460/715-229-2516
Ahlman Guns, 9525 W. 230th St., Morristown, MN 55052/507-685-4243; FAX: 507-685-4280
Aimpoint U.S.A, 420 W. Main St., Geneseo, IL 61254/309-944-1702
Aimtech Mount Systems, P.O. Box 223, 101 Inwood Acres, Thomasville, GA 31799/912-226-4313; FAX: 912-227-0222
Air Venture, 9752 E. Flower St., Bellflower, CA 90706/310-867-6355
Airrow (See Swivel Machine Works, Inc.)
Ajax Custom Grips, Inc., 9130 Viscount Row, Dallas, TX 75247/214-630-8893; FAX: 214-630-4942; WEB: http://www.ajaxgrips.com
Alaska Bullet Works, Inc., 9978 Crazy Horse Drive, Juneau, AK 99801/907-783-3834; FAX: 907-789-3433
Alex, Inc., Box 3034, Bozeman, MT 59772/406-282-7396; FAX: 406-282-7396
All American Lead Shot Corp., P.O. Box 224566, Dallas, TX 75062
All's, The Jim J. Tembelis Co., Inc., P.O. Box 108, Winnebago, WI 54985-0108/414-725-5251; FAX: 414-725-5251
Alley Supply Co., P.O. Box 848, Gardnerville, NV 89410/702-782-3800
Alliant Techsystems, Smokeless Powder Group, 200 Valley Rd., Suite 305, Mt. Arlington, NJ 07856/800-276-9337; FAX: 201-770-2528
Allred Bullet Co., 932 Evergreen Drive, Logan, UT 84321/801-752-6983; FAX: 801-752-6983
Alpec Team, Inc., 201 Ricken Backer Cir., Livermore, CA 94550/510-606-8245; FAX: 510-606-4279
Alpha LaFranck Enterprises, P.O. Box 81072, Lincoln, NE 68501/402-466-3193
AmBr Software Group Ltd., P.O. Box 301, Reistertown, MD 21136-0301/800-888-1917; FAX: 410-526-7212
American Ammunition, 3545 NW 71st St., Miami, FL 33147/305-835-7400; FAX: 305-694-0037
American Derringer Corp., 127 N. Lacy Dr., Waco, TX 76705/800-642-7817, 817-799-9111; FAX: 817-799-7935
American Gas & Chemical Co., Ltd., 220 Pegasus Ave., Northvale, NJ 07647/201-767-7300
American Handgunner Magazine, 591 Camino de la Reina, Suite 200, San Diego, CA 92108/619-297-5350; FAX: 619-297-5353
American Products Inc., 14729 Spring Valley Road, Morrison, IL 61270/815-772-3336; FAX: 815-772-8046
American Safe Arms, Inc., 1240 Riverview Dr., Garland, UT 84312/801-257-7472; FAX: 801-785-8156
American Sales & Kirkpatrick, P.O. Box 677, Laredo, TX 78042/210-723-6893; FAX: 210-725-0672
American Target, 1328 S. Jason St., Denver, CO 80223/303-733-0433; FAX: 303-777-0311
American Whitetail Target Systems, P.O. Box 41, 106 S. Church St., Tennyson, IN 47637/812-567-4527
Ames Metal Products, 4323 S. Western Blvd., Chicago, IL 60609/773-523-3230; FAX: 773-523-3854
Ammo Load, Inc., 1560 E. Edinger, Suite G, Santa Ana, CA 92705/714-558-8858; FAX: 714-569-0319
Amrine's Gun Shop, 937 La Luna, Ojai, CA 93023/805-646-2376
A.M.T., 6226 Santos Diaz St., Irwindale, CA 91702/818-334-6629; FAX: 818-969-5247
Analog Devices, Box 9106, Norwood, MA 02062
Andela Tool & Machine, Inc., RD3, Box 246, Richfield Springs, NY 13439
Anderson Manufacturing Co., Inc., 22602 53rd Ave. SE, Bothell, WA 98021/206-481-1858; FAX: 206-481-7839
Anics Firm, Inc., 3 Commerce Park Square, 23200 Chagrin Blvd., Suite 240, Beechwood, OH 44122/216-292-4363, 800-556-1582; FAX: 216-292-2588
Anschutz GmbH, Postfach 1128, D-89001 Ulm, Donau, GERMANY
Answer Products Co., 1519 Westbury Drive, Davison, MI 48423/810-653-2911
AO Safety Products, Div. of American Optical Corp. (See E-A-R, Inc., Div. of Cabot Safety Corp.)
Apel GmbH, Ernst, Am Kirschberg 3, D-97218 Gerbrunn, GERMANY/0 (931) 707192
Arcadia Machine & Tool, Inc. (See AMT)
Arco Powder, HC-Rt. 1, P.O. Box 102, County Rd. 357, Mayo, FL 32066/904-294-3882; FAX: 904-294-1498
Arizona Ammunition, Inc., 21421 No. 14th Ave., Suite E, Phoenix, AZ 85727/602-516-9004; FAX: 602-516-9012
Armfield Custom Bullets, 4775 Caroline Drive, San Diego, CA 92115/619-582-7188; FAX: 619-287-3238
Armite Laboratories, 1845 Randolph St., Los Angeles, CA 90001/213-587-7768; FAX: 213-587-5075
Armor Metal Products, P.O. Box 4609, Helena, MT 59604/406-442-5560; FAX: 406-442-5650
Armory Publications, Inc., 2615 N. 4th St., No. 620, Coeur d'Alene, ID 83814-3781/208-664-5061; FAX: 208-664-9906
A.R.M.S., Inc., 230 W. Center St., West Bridgewater, MA 02379-1620/508-584-7816; FAX: 508-588-8045
Arms & Armour Press, Wellington House, 125 Strand, London WC2R 0BB ENGLAND/0171-420-5555; FAX: 0171-240-7265
Arms Corporation of the Philippines, Bo. Parang Marikina, Metro Manila, PHILIPPINES/632-941-6243, 632-941-6244; FAX: 632-942-0682
Arms Ingenuity Co., P.O. Box 1, 51 Canal St., Weatogue, CT 06089/203-658-5624
Arms, Programming Solutions (See Arms Software)
Arms Software, P.O. Box 1526, Lake Oswego, OR 97035/800-366-5559, 503-697-0533; FAX: 503-697-3337
Armscorp USA, Inc., 4424 John Ave., Baltimore, MD 21227/410-247-6200; FAX: 410-247-6205
Armsport, Inc., 3950 NW 49th St., Miami, FL 33142/305-635-7850; FAX: 305-633-2877
Aro-Tek, Ltd., 206 Frontage Rd. North, Suite C, Pacific, WA 98047/206-351-2984; FAX: 206-833-4483
Artistry in Wood, 134 Zimmerman Rd., Kalispell, MT 59901/406-257-9003
Arundel Arms & Ammunition, Inc., A., 24A Defense St., Annapolis, MD 21401/410-224-8683
A-Square Co., Inc., One Industrial Park, Bedford, KY 40006-9667/502-255-7456; FAX: 502-255-7657
A-Tech Corp., P.O. Box 1281, Cottage Grove, OR 97424
Atlantic Mills, Inc., 1295 Towbin Ave., Lakewood, NJ 08701-5934/800-242-7374
Atlantic Research Marketing Systems (See A.R.M.S., Inc.)
Atlantic Rose, Inc., P.O. Box 1305, Union, NJ 07083
Atsko/Sno-Seal, Inc., 2530 Russell SE, Orangeburg, SC 29115/803-531-1820; FAX: 803-531-2139
Audette, Creighton, 19 Highland Circle, Springfield, VT 05156/802-885-2331
Autauga Arms, Inc., Pratt Plaza Mall No. 13, Prattville, AL 36067/800-262-9563; FAX: 334-361-2961
Automatic Equipment Sales, 627 E. Railroad Ave., Salesburg, MD 21801
A Zone Bullets, 2039 Walter Rd., Billings, MT 59105/800-252-3111; 406-248-1961

## B

B&D Trading Co., Inc., 3935 Fair Hill Rd., Fair Oaks, CA 95628/800-334-3790, 916-967-9366; FAX: 916-967-4873
B&G Bullets (See Northside Gun Shop)
Baelder, Harry, Alte Goennebeker Strasse 5, 24635 Rickling, GERMANY/04328-722732; FAX: 04328-722733
Baer Custom, Inc., Les, 29601 34th Ave., Hillsdale, IL 61257/309-658-2716; FAX: 309-658-2610
Baer's Hollows, P.O. Box 284, Eads, CO 81036/719-438-5718
Bain & Davis, Inc., 307 E. Valley Blvd., San Gabriel, CA 91776-3522/818-573-4241, 213-283-7449
Balaance Co., 340-39 Ave. S.E. Box 505, Calgary, AB, T2G 1X6 CANADA
Bald Eagle Precision Machine Co., 101-A Allison St., Lock Haven, PA 17745/717-748-6772; FAX: 717-748-4443
Balickie, Joe, 408 Trelawney Lane, Apex, NC 27502/919-362-5185
Ballard Built, P.O. Box 1443, Kingsville, TX 78364/512-592-0853
Ballard Industries, 10271 Lockwood Dr., Suite B, Cupertino, CA 95014/408-996-0957; FAX: 408-257-6828
Ballistic Engineering & Software, Inc., 185 N. Park Blvd., Suite 330, Lake Orion, MI 48362/313-391-1074
Ballistic Products, Inc., 20015 75th Ave. North, Corcoran, MN 55340-9456/612-494-9237; FAX: 612-494-9236
Ballistic Program Co., Inc., The, 2417 N. Patterson St., Thomasville, GA 31792/912-228-5739, 800-368-0835
Ballisti-Cast, Inc., Box 383, Parshall, ND 58770/701-862-3324; FAX: 701-862-3331
Ballistic Research, 1108 W. May Ave., McHenry, IL 60050/815-385-0037
Ballistica Maximus North, 107 College Park Plaza, Johnstown, PA 15904/814-266-8380
Bansner's Gunsmithing Specialties, 261 East Main St. Box VH, Adamstown, PA 19501/800-368-2379; FAX: 717-484-0523
Barnes Bullets, Inc., P.O. Box 215, American Fork, UT 84003/801-756-4222, 800-574-9200; FAX: 801-756-2465; WEB: http://www.itsnet.com/home/bbullets
Barrett Firearms Manufacturer, Inc., P.O. Box 1077, Murfreesboro, TN 37133/615-896-2938; FAX: 615-896-7313
Bartlett, Don, P.O. Box 55, Colbert, WA 99005/509-467-5009
Bartlett Engineering, 40 South 200 East, Smithfield, UT 84335-1645/801-563-5910
Baumgartner Bullets, 3011 S. Alane St., W. Valley City, UT 84120
Bausch & Lomb Sports Optics Div. (See Bushnell Sports Optics Worldwide)
Bauska Barrels, 105 9th Ave. W., Kalispell, MT 59901/406-752-7706
Beartooth Bullets, P.O. Box 491, Dept. HLD, Dover, ID 83825-0491/208-448-1865
Beaver Park Products, Inc., 840 J St., Penrose, CO 81240/719-372-6744
BEC, Inc., 1227 W. Valley Blvd., Suite 204, Alhambra, CA 91803/818-281-5751; FAX:818-293-7073
Beeline Custom Bullets Limited, P.O. Box 85, Yarmouth, Nova Scotia CANADA B5A 4B1/902-648-3494; FAX: 902-648-0253
Behlert Precision, Inc., P.O. Box 288, 7067 Easton Rd., Pipersville, PA 18947/215-766-8681, 215-766-7301; FAX: 215-766-8681
Beitzinger, George, 116-20 Atlantic Ave., Richmond Hill, NY 11419/718-847-7661
Belding's Custom Gun Shop, 10691 Sayers Rd., Munith, MI 49259/517-596-2388
Bell & Carlson, Inc., Dodge City Industrial Park/101 Allen Rd., Dodge City, KS 67801/800-634-8586, 316-225-6688; FAX: 316-225-9095
Bell Reloading, Inc., 1725 Harlin Lane Rd., Villa Rica, GA 30180
Bell's Gun & Sport Shop, 3309-19 Mannheim Rd, Franklin Park, IL 60131
Belltown, Ltd., 11 Camps Rd., Kent, CT 06757/860-354-5750
Belt MTN Arms, 107 10th Ave. SW, White Sulphur Springs, MT 59645/406-586-4495
Ben's Machines, 1151 S. Cedar Ridge, Duncanville, TX 75137/214-780-1807; FAX: 214-780-0316
Benchmark Guns, 12593 S. Ave. 5 East, Yuma, AZ 85365
Beomat of America Inc., 300 Railway Ave., Campbell, CA 95008/408-379-4829
Beretta S.p.A., Pietro, Via Beretta, 18-25063 Gardone V.T. (BS) ITALY/XX39/30-8341.1; FAX: XX39/30-8341.421
Berger Bullets, Ltd., 5342 W. Camelback Rd., Suite 200, Glendale, AZ 85301/602-842-4001; FAX: 602-934-9083
Bergman & Williams, 2450 Losee Rd., Suite F, Las Vegas, NV 89030/702-642-1901; FAX: 702-642-1540
Berry's Bullets (See Berry's Mfg., Inc.)
Berry's Mfg., Inc., 401 North 3050 East St., St. George, UT 84770/801-634-1682; FAX: 801-634-1683
Bertram Bullet Co., P.O. Box 313, Seymour, Victoria 3660, AUSTRALIA/61-57-922912; FAX: 61-57-991650

Biesen, Al, 5021 Rosewood, Spokane, WA 99208/509-328-9340
Biesen, Roger, 5021 W. Rosewood, Spokane, WA 99208/509-328-9340
Big Bear Arms & Sporting Goods, Inc., 1112 Milam Way, Carrollton, TX 75006/972-416-8051, 800-400-BEAR; FAX: 972-416-0771
Big Bore Bullets of Alaska, P.O. Box 872785, Wasilla, AK 99687/907-373-2673; FAX: 907-373-2673
Big Bore Express, 7154 W. State St., Boise, ID 83703/800-376-4010; FAX:208-376-4020
Billeb, Stephen L., 1101 N. 7th St., Burlington, IA 52601/319-753-2110
Billings Gunsmiths, Inc., 1841 Grand Ave., Billings, MT 59102/406-256-8390
Birchwood Casey, 7900 Fuller Rd., Eden Prairie, MN 55344/800-328-6156, 612-937-7933; FAX: 612-937-7979
Bismuth Cartridge Co., 3500 Maple Ave., Suite 1650, Dallas, TX 75219/800-759-3333, 214-521-5880; FAX: 214-521-9035
Bitterroot Bullet Co., Box 412, Lewiston, ID 83501-0412/208-743-5635
Black Belt Bullets (See Big Bore Express)
Black Hills Ammunition, Inc., P.O. Box 3090, Rapid City, SD 57709-3090/605-348-5150; FAX: 605-348-9827
Black Hills Shooters Supply, P.O. Box 4220, Rapid City, SD 57709/800-289-2506
Black Powder Products, 67 Township Rd. 1411, Chesapeake, OH 45619/614-867-8047
Blackhawk East, Box 2274, Loves Park, IL 61131
Blackhawk West, Box 285, Hiawatha, KS 66434
Blacksmith Corp., 830 N. Road No. 1 E., P.O. Box 1752, Chino Valley, AZ 86323/520-636-4456; FAX: 520-636-4457
BlackStar AccuMax Barrels, 11501 Brittmoore Park Drive, Houston, TX 77041/281-721-6040; FAX: 281-721-6041
BlackStar Barrel Accurizing (See BlackStar AccuMax Barrels)
Blacktail Mountain Books, 42 First Ave. W., Kalispell, MT 59901/406-257-5573
Blammo Ammo, P.O. Box 1677, Seneca, SC 29679/803-882-1768
Blount, Inc., Sporting Equipment Div., 2299 Snake River Ave., P.O. Box 856, Lewiston, ID 83501/800-627-3640, 208-746-2351; FAX: 208-799-3904
Blue and Gray Products, Inc. (See Ox-Yoke Originals, Inc.)
Blue Book Publications, Inc., One Appletree Square, 8009 34th Ave. S., Suite, 175/Minneapolis, MN 55425
800-877-4867, 612-854-5229; FAX: 612-853-1486
Blue Mountain Bullets, HCR 77, P.O. Box 231, John Day, OR 97845/541-820-4594
Blue Ridge Machinery & Tools, Inc., P.O. Box 536-GD, Hurricane, WV 25526/800-872-6500; FAX: 304-562-5311
BMC Supply, Inc., 26051 - 179th Ave. S.E., Kent, WA 98042
Bohemia Arms Co., 17101 Los Modelos, Fountain Valley, CA 92708/619-442-7005; FAX: 619-442-7005
Boltin, John M., P.O. Box 644, Estill, SC 29918/803-625-2185
Bo-Mar Tool & Mfg. Co., Rt. 8, Box 405, Longview, TX 75604/903-759-4784; FAX: 903-759-9141
Bonanza (See Forster Products)
Bond Custom Firearms, 8954 N. Lewis Ln., Bloomington, IN 47408/812-332-4519
Boonie Packer Products, P.O. Box 12204, Salem, OR 97309/800-477-3244, 503-581-3244; FAX: 503-581-3191
Borden's Accuracy, RD 1, Box 250BC, Springville, PA 18844/717-965-2505; FAX: 717-965-2328
Border Barrels Ltd., Riccarton Farm, Newcastleton SCOTLAND U.K. TD9 0SN
Bowen Classic Arms Corp., P.O. Box 67, Louisville, TN 37777/423-984-3583
Bowerly, Kent, 26247 Metolius Meadows Dr., Camp Sherman, OR 97730/541-595-6028
Boyds' Gunstock Industries, Inc., 3rd & Main, P.O. Box 305, Geddes, SD 57342/605-337-2125; FAX: 605-337-3363
Brace, Larry D., 771 Blackfoot Ave., Eugene, OR 97404/503-688-1278
Bradley Gunsight Co., P.O. Box 340, Plymouth, VT 05056/860-589-0531; FAX: 860-582-6294
Brass and Bullet Alloys, P.O. Box 1238, Sierra Vista, AZ 85636/602-458-5321; FAX: 602-458-9125
Break-Free, Inc., P.O. Box 25020, Santa Ana, CA 92799/714-953-1900; FAX: 714-953-0402
Brenneke KG, Wilhelm, Ilmenauweg 2, 30851 Langenhagen, GERMANY/0511/97262-0; FAX: 0511/97262-62
Bridgers Best, P.O. Box 1410, Berthoud, CO 80513
Briese Bullet Co., Inc., RR1, Box 108, Tappen, ND 58487/701-327-4578; FAX: 701-327-4579
Broad Creek Rifle Works, 120 Horsey Ave., Laurel, DE 19956/302-875-5446
Brown Co., E. Arthur, 3404 Pawnee Dr., Alexandria, MN 56308/320-762-8847
Brown Dog Ent., 2200 Calle Camelia, 1000 Oaks, CA 91360/805-497-2318; FAX: 805-497-1618
Brown Precision, Inc., 7786 Molinos Ave., Los Molinos, CA 96055/916-384-2506; FAX: 916-384-1638
Brown Products, Inc., Ed, Rt. 2, Box 492, Perry, MO 63462/573-565-3261; FAX: 573-565-2791
Brownell Checkering Tools, W.E., 9390 Twin Mountain Circle, San Diego, CA 92126/619-695-2479; FAX: 619-695-2479
Brownells, Inc., 200 S. Front St., Montezuma, IA 50171/515-623-5401; FAX: 515-623-3896
Browning Arms Co., One Browning Place, Morgan, UT 84050/801-876-2711; FAX: 801-876-3331
BRP, Inc., High Performance Cast Bullets, 1210 Alexander Rd., Colorado Springs, CO 80909/719-633-0658
Bruno Shooters Supply, 111 N. Wyoming St., Hazleton, PA 18201/717-455-2281; FAX: 717-455-2211
Brunton U.S.A., 620 E. Monroe Ave., Riverton, WY 82501/307-856-6559; FAX: 307-856-1840
Brynin, Milton, P.O. Box 383, Yonkers, NY 10710/914-779-4333
B-Square Company, Inc., P.O. Box 11281, 2708 St. Louis Ave., Ft. Worth, TX 76110/817-923-0964, 800-433-2909; FAX: 817-926-7012
Buck Stix—SOS Products Co., Box 3, Neenah, WI 54956
Buckeye Custom Bullets, 6490 Stewart Rd., Elida, OH 45807/419-641-4463
Buckhorn Gun Works, 8109 Woodland Dr., Black Hawk, SD 57718/605-787-6472
Buckskin Bullet Co., P.O. Box 1893, Cedar City, UT 84721/801-586-3286
Buffalo Arms Co., 3355 Upper Gold Creek Rd., Samuels, ID 83864/208-263-6953; FAX: 208-265-2096
Buffalo Bullet Co., Inc., 12637 Los Nietos Rd., Unit A, Santa Fe Springs, CA 90670/310-944-0322; FAX: 310-944-5054
Buffalo Rock Shooters Supply, R.R. 1, Ottawa, IL 61350/815-433-2471
Bull Mountain Rifle Co., 6327 Golden West Terrace, Billings, MT 59106/406-656-0778
Bullberry Barrel Works, Ltd., 2430 W. Bullberry Ln. 67-5, Hurricane, UT 84737/801-635-9866; FAX: 801-635-0348
Bullet, Inc., 3745 Hiram Alworth Rd., Dallas, GA 30132
Bullet'n Press, 19 Key St., Eastport, Maine 04631/207-853-4116
Bullet Swaging Supply, Inc., P.O. Box 1056, 303 McMillan Rd, West Monroe, LA 71291/318-387-7257; FAX: 318-387-7779
BulletMakers Workshop, The, RFD 1 Box 1755, Brooks, ME 04921
Bullseye Bullets, 1610 State Road 60, No. 12, Valrico, FL 33594/813-654-6563
Bull-X, Inc., 520 N. Main, Farmer City, IL 61842/309-928-2574, 800-248-3845 orders only; FAX: 309-928-2130
Bushnell Sports Optics Worldwide, 9200 Cody, Overland Park, KS 66214/913-752-3400, 800-423-3537; FAX: 913-752-3550
Burgess & Son Gunsmiths, R.W., P.O. Box 3364, Warner Robins, GA 31099/912-328-7487
Burkhart Gunsmithing, Don, P.O. Box 852, Rawlins, WY 82301/307-324-6007
Burres, Jack, 10333 San Fernando Rd., Pacoima, CA 91331/818-899-8000
Burris Co., Inc., P.O. Box 1747, 331 E. 8th St., Greeley, CO 80631/970-356-1670; FAX: 970-356-8702
Bushmann Hunters & Safaris, P.O. Box 293088, Lewisville, TX 75029/214-317-0768
Butler Creek Corp., 290 Arden Dr., Belgrade, MT 59714/800-423-8327, 406-388-1356; FAX: 406-388-7204
Butler Enterprises, 834 Oberting Rd., Lawrenceburg, IN 47025/812-537-3584
Buzztail Brass (See Grayback Wildcats)
B-West Imports, Inc., 2425 N. Huachuca Dr., Tucson, AZ 85745-1201/602-628-1990; FAX: 602-628-3602

## C

C&D Special Products (See Claybuster Wads & Harvester Bullets)
C&T Corp. TA Johnson Brothers, 1023 Wappoo Road, Charleston, SC 29407-5960
Calhoon Varmint Bullets, James, Shambo Rt., 304, Havre, MT 59501/406-395-4079
Calibre Press, Inc., 666 Dundee Rd., Suite 1607, Northbrook, IL 60062-2760/800-323-0037; FAX: 708-498-6869
Cali'co Hardwoods, Inc., 3580 Westwind Blvd., Santa Rosa, CA 95403/707-546-4045; FAX: 707-546-4027
California Magnum, 20746 Dearborn St., Chatsworth, CA 91313/818-341-7302; FAX: 818-341-7304
California Sights (See Fautheree, Andy)
Camdex, Inc., 2330 Alger, Troy, MI 48083/810-528-2300; FAX: 810-528-0989
Cameron's, 16690 W. 11th Ave., Golden, CO 80401/303-279-7365; FAX: 303-628-5413
Camilli, Lou, 600 Sandtree Dr., Suite 212, Lake Park, FL 33403-1538
Campbell, Dick, 20,000 Silver Ranch Rd., Conifer, CO 80433/303-697-0150
Camp-Cap Products, P.O. Box 173, Chesterfield, MO 63006/314-532-4340; FAX: 314-532-4340
Canjar Co., M.H., 500 E. 45th Ave., Denver, CO 80216/303-295-2638; FAX: 303-295-2638
Canons Delcour, Rue J.B. Cools, B-4040 Herstal, BELGIUM/+32.(0)42.40.61.40; FAX: +32(0)42.40.22.88
Canyon Cartridge Corp., P.O. Box 152, Albertson, NY 11507/FAX: 516-294-8946
Cape Outfitters, 599 County Rd. 206, Cape Girardeau, MO 63701/314-335-4103; FAX: 314-335-1555
Carbide Die & Mfg. Co., Inc., 15615 E. Arrow Hwy., Irwindale, CA 91706/818-337-2518
Carnahan Bullets, 17645 110th Ave. SE, Renton, WA 98055
Carroll Bullets (See Precision Reloading, Inc.)
Carter's Gun Shop, 225 G St., Penrose, CO 81240/719-372-6240
Cartridge Transfer Group, Pete de Coux, 235 Oak St., Butler, PA 16001/412-282-3426
Cascade Bullet Co., Inc., 2355 South 6th St., Klamath Falls, OR 97601/503-884-9316
Cascade Shooters, 2155 N.W. 12th St., Redwood, OR 97756
Case Sorting System, 12695 Cobblestone Creek Rd., Poway, CA 92064/619-486-9340
Cast Performance Bullet Company, 12441 U.S. Hwy. 26, Riverton, WY 82501/307-856-4347
Catco-Ambush, Inc., P.O.Box 300, Corte Madera, CA 94926
Caywood, Shane J., P.O. Box 321, Minocqua, WI 54548/715-277-3866 evenings
CBC, Avenida Humberto de Campos, 3220, 09400-000 Ribeirao Pires-SP-BRAZIL/55-11-742-7500; FAX: 55-11-459-7385
CCG Enterprises, 5217 E. Belknap St., Halton City, TX 76117/800-819-7464
CCI, Div. of Blount, Inc., Sporting Equipment Div., 2299 Snake River Ave.,, P.O. Box 856/Lewiston, ID 83501
800-627-3640, 208-746-2351; FAX: 208-746-2915
Celestron International, P.O. Box 3578, 2835 Columbia St., Torrance, CA 90503/310-328-9560; FAX: 310-212-5835
Center Lock Scope Rings, 9901 France Ct., Lakeville, MN 55044/612-461-2114
Century International Arms, Inc., P.O. Box 714, St. Albans, VT 05478-0714/802-527-1252, 800-527-1252; FAX: 802-527-0470; WEB: http://www.centuryarms.com
CFVentures, 509 Harvey Dr., Bloomington, IN 47403-1715
C-H Tool & Die Corp. (See 4-D Custom Die Co.)
CHAA, Ltd., P.O. Box 565, Howell, MI 48844/800-677-8737; FAX: 313-894-6930
Chambers Flintlocks Ltd., Jim, Rt. 1, Box 513-A, Candler, NC 28715/704-667-8361
Champion Target Co., 232 Industrial Parkway, Richmond, IN 47374/800-441-4971
Champion's Choice, Inc., 201 International Blvd., LaVergne, TN 37086/615-793-4066; FAX: 615-793-4070
Champlin Firearms, Inc., P.O. Box 3191, Woodring Airport, Enid, OK 73701/405-237-7388; FAX: 405-242-6922
Cheddite France, S.A., 99, Route de Lyon, F-26501 Bourg-les-Valence, FRANCE/33-75-56-4545; FAX: 33-75-56-3587
Chem-Pak, Inc., 11 Oates Ave., P.O. Box 1685, Winchester, VA 22604/800-336-9828, 703-667-1341; FAX: 703-722-3993
CheVron Bullets, RR1, Ottawa, IL 61350/815-433-2471
CheVron Case Master (See CheVron Bullets)
Chicasaw Gun Works, 4 Mi. Mkr., Pluto Rd., Box 868, Shady Spring, WV 25918-0868/304-763-2848; FAX: 304-763-2848
Chopie Mfg., Inc., 700 Copeland Ave., LaCrosse, WI 54603/608-784-0926
Christensen Arms, 192 East 100 North, Fayette, UT 84630/801-528-7999; FAX: 801-528-7494
Christman Jr., David, Gunmaker, 937 Lee Hedrick Rd., Colville, WA 99114/509-684-1438
Chu Tani Ind., Inc., P.O. Box 2064, Cody, WY 82414-2064
Chuck's Gun Shop, P.O. Box 597, Waldo, FL 32694/904-468-2264
Churchill, Winston, Twenty Mile Stream Rd., RFD P.O. Box 29B, Proctorsville, VT 05153/802-226-7772
Cincinnati Swaging, 2605 Marlington Ave., Cincinnati, OH 45208
Citadel Mfg., Inc., 5220 Gabbert Rd., Moorpark, CA 93021/805-529-7294; FAX: 805-529-7297
C.J. Ballistics, Inc., P.O. Box 132, Acme, WA 98220/206-595-5001
Clark Co., Inc., David, P.O. Box 15054, Worcester, MA 01615-0054/508-756-6216; FAX: 508-753-5827
Clark Custom Guns, Inc., 336 Shootout Lane, Princeton, LA 71067/318-949-9884; FAX: 318-949-9829
Claro Walnut Gunstock Co., 1235 Stanley Ave., Chico, CA 95928/916-342-5188
Claybuster Wads & Harvester Bullets, 309 Sequoya Dr., Hopkinsville, KY 42240/800-922-6287, 800-284-1746, 502-885-8088; FAX: 502-885-1951
Clearview Mfg. Co., Inc., 413 S. Oakley St., Fordyce, AR 71742/501-352-8557; FAX: 501-352-7120
Clearview Products, 3021 N. Portland, Oklahoma City, OK 73107
Clenzoil Corp., P.O. Box 80226, Sta. C, Canton, OH 44708-0226/330-833-9758; FAX: 330-833-4724
Clerke Co., J.A., P.O. Box 627, Pearblossom, CA 93553-0627/805-945-0713
Clift Mfg., L.R., 3821 Hammonton Rd., Marysville, CA 95901/916-755-3390; FAX: 916-755-3393
Clift Welding Supply & Cases, 1332-A Colusa Hwy., Yuba City, CA 95993/916-755-3390; FAX: 916-755-3393
Cloward's Gun Shop, 4023 Aurora Ave. N, Seattle, WA 98103/206-632-2072
Clymer Manufacturing Co., Inc., 1645 W. Hamlin Rd., Rochester Hills, MI 48309-1530/810-853-5555, 810-853-5627; FAX: 810-853-1530
C-More Systems, P.O. Box 1750, 7553 Gary Rd., Manassas, VA 22110/703-361-2663; FAX: 703-361-5881
Coats, Mrs. Lester, 300 Luman Rd., Space 125, Phoenix, OR 97535/503-535-1611
Coffin, Charles H., 3719 Scarlet Ave., Odessa, TX 79762/915-366-4729
Coffin, Jim (See Working Guns)
Cole's Gun Works, Old Bank Building, Rt. 4, Box 250, Moyock, NC 27958/919-435-2345
Colonial Arms, Inc., P.O. Box 636, Selma, AL 36702-0636/334-872-9455; FAX: 334-872-9540
Colonial Repair, P.O. Box 372, Hyde Park, MA 02136-9998/617-469-4951
Colorado Gunsmithing Academy, 27533 Highway 287 South, Lamar, CO 81052/719-336-4099, 800-754-2046; FAX: 719-336-9642
Colorado School of Trades, 1575 Hoyt St., Lakewood, CO 80215/800-234-4594; FAX: 303-233-4723
Colorado Shooter's Supply, 1163 W. Paradise Way, Fruita, CO 81521/303-858-9191
Colorado Sutlers Arsenal (See Cumberland States Arsenal)
Combat Military Ordnance Ltd., 3900 Hopkins St., Savannah, GA 31405/912-238-1900; FAX: 912-236-7570
Companhia Brasileira de Cartuchos (See CBC)
Compass Industries, Inc., 104 East 25th St., New York, NY 10010/212-473-2614, 800-221-9904; FAX: 212-353-0826

Competition Electronics, Inc., 3469 Precision Dr., Rockford, IL 61109/815-874-8001; FAX: 815-874-8181
Competitor Corp., Inc., Appleton Business Center, 30 Tricnit Road, Unit 16, New Ipswich, NH 03071-0508/603-878-3891; FAX: 603-878-3950
Concept Development Corp., 14715 N. 78th Way, Suite 300, Scottsdale, AZ 85260/800-472-4405; FAX: 602-948-7560
Conetrol Scope Mounts, 10225 Hwy. 123 S., Seguin, TX 78155/210-379-3030, 800-CONETROL; FAX: 210-379-3030
CONKKO, P.O. Box 40, Broomall, PA 19008/215-356-0711
Connecticut Shotgun Mfg. Co., P.O. Box 1692, 35 Woodland St., New Britain, CT 06051-1692/860-225-6581; FAX: 860-832-8707
Conrad, C.A., 3964 Ebert St., Winston-Salem, NC 27127/919-788-5469
Cook Engineering Service, 891 Highbury Rd., Vermont VICT 3133 AUSTRALIA
Cooper Arms, P.O. Box 114, Stevensville, MT 59870/406-777-5534; FAX: 406-777-5228
Cooper-Woodward, 3800 Pelican Rd., Helena, MT 59602/406-458-3800
Copperhead Bullets, Inc., P.O. Box 662, Butte, MT 59703/406-723-6300
Corbin Mfg. & Supply, Inc., 600 Industrial Circle, P.O. Box 2659, White City, OR 97503/541-826-5211; FAX: 541-826-8669
Cor-Bon Bullet & Ammo Co., 1311 Industry Rd., Sturgis, SD 57785/800-626-7266; FAX: 800-923-2666
Costa, David (See Island Pond Gun Shop)
Country Armourer, The, P.O. Box .308, Ashby, MA 01431-0308/508-827-6797; FAX: 508-827-4845
CP Bullets, 340-1 Constance Dr., Warminster, PA 18974
Crane & Crane Ltd., 105 N. Edison Way 6, Reno, NV 89502-2355/702-856-1516; FAX: 702-856-1616
Crane Sales Co., George S., P.O. Box 385, Van Nuys, CA 91408/818-505-8337
CRDC Laser Systems Group, 3972 Barranca Parkway, Ste. J-484, Irvine, CA 92714/714-586-1295; FAX: 714-831-4823
Creedmoor Sports, Inc., P.O. Box 1040, Oceanside, CA 92051/619-757-5529
Crimson Trace, 1433 N.W. Quimby, Portland, OR 97209/503-295-2406; FAX: 503-295-0005
Crit'R Call (See Rocky Mountain Wildlife Products)
Crouse's Country Cover, P.O. Box 160, Storrs, CT 06268/860-423-8736
CRR, Inc./Marble's Inc., 420 Industrial Park, P.O. Box 111, Gladstone, MI 49837/906-428-3710; FAX: 906-428-3711
Cubic Shot Shell Co., Inc., 98 Fatima Dr., Campbell, OH 44405/216-755-0349; FAX: 216-755-0349
Cumberland Arms, 514 Shafer Road, Manchester, TN 37355/800-797-8414
Cumberland States Arsenal, 1124 Palmyra Road, Clarksville, TN 37040
Cummings Bullets, 1417 Esperanza Way, Escondido, CA 92027
Cunningham Co., Eaton, 607 Superior St., Kansas City, MO 64106/816-842-2600
Curly Maple Stock Blanks (See Tiger-Hunt)
Curtis Cast Bullets, 119 W. College, Bozeman, MT 59715/406-587-4934
Curtis Gun Shop (See Curtis Cast Bullets)
Custom Barreling & Stocks, 937 Lee Hedrick Rd., Colville, WA 99114/509-684-5686 (days), 509-684-3314 (evenings)
Custom Bullets by Hoffman, 2604 Peconic Ave., Seaford, NY 11783
Custom Checkering Service, Kathy Forster, 2124 SE Yamhill St., Portland, OR 97214/503-236-5874
Custom Chronograph, Inc., 5305 Reese Hill Rd., Sumas, WA 98295/360-988-7801
Custom Gun Products, 5021 W. Rosewood, Spokane, WA 99208/509-328-9340
Custom Gun Stocks, Rt. 6, P.O. Box 177, McMinnville, TN 37110/615-668-3912
Custom Hunting Ammo & Arms (See CHAA, Ltd.)
Custom Products (See Jones Custom Products, Neil A.)
Custom Quality Products, Inc., 345 W. Girard Ave., P.O. Box 71129, Madison Heights, MI 48071/810-585-1616; FAX: 810-585-0644
Custom Riflestocks, Inc., Michael M. Kokolus, 7005 Herber Rd., New Tripoli, PA 18066/610-298-3013
Custom Shop, The, 890 Cochrane Crescent, Peterborough, Ont. K9H 5N3 CANADA/705-742-6693
Custom Tackle and Ammo, P.O. Box 1886, Farmington, NM 87499/505-632-3539
Cutsinger Bench Rest Bullets, RR 8, Box 161-A, Shelbyville, IN 46176/317-729-5360

## D

D&D Gunsmiths, Ltd., 363 E. Elmwood, Troy, MI 48083/810-583-1512; FAX: 810-583-1524
D&G Precision Duplicators (See Greene Precision Duplicators)
D&H Precision Tooling, 7522 Barnard Mill Rd., Ringwood, IL 60072/815-653-4011
D&H Prods. Co., Inc., 465 Denny Rd., Valencia, PA 16059/412-898-2840, 800-776-0281; FAX: 412-898-2013
D&J Bullet Co. & Custom Gun Shop, Inc., 426 Ferry St., Russell, KY 41169/606-836-2663; FAX: 606-836-2663
D&R Distributing, 308 S.E. Valley St., Myrtle Creek, OR 97457/503-863-6850
Daisy Mfg. Co., P.O. Box 220, Rogers, AR 72757/501-636-1200; FAX: 501-636-1601
Dakota Arms, Inc., HC 55, Box 326, Sturgis, SD 57785/605-347-4686; FAX: 605-347-4459
Dangler, Homer L., Box 254, Addison, MI 49220/517-547-6745
Dapkus Co., Inc., J.G., Commerce Circle, P.O. Box 293, Durham, CT 06422
Dara-Nes, Inc. (See Nesci Enterprises, Inc.)
Data Tech Software Systems, 19312 East Eldorado Drive, Aurora, CO 80013
Datumtech Corp., 2275 Wehrle Dr., Buffalo, NY 14221
Davis, Don, 1619 Heights, Katy, TX 77493/713-391-3090
Davis Products, Mike, 643 Loop Dr., Moses Lake, WA 98837/509-765-6178, 509-766-7281 orders only
Dayson Arms Ltd., P.O. Box 532, Vincennes, IN 47591/812-882-8680; FAX: 812-882-8680
Dayton Traister, 4778 N. Monkey Hill Rd., P.O. Box 593, Oak Harbor, WA 98277/360-679-4657; FAX:360-675-1114
DBI Books, Division of Krause Publications, 935 Lakeview Parkway, Suite 101, Vernon Hills, IL 60061/847-573-8530; Fax: 847-573-8534; For consumer orders, see Krause Publications
D.C.C. Enterprises, 259 Wynburn Ave., Athens, GA 30601
D.D. Custom Stocks, R.H. "Dick" Devereaux, 5240 Mule Deer Dr., Colorado Springs, CO 80919/719-548-8468
de Treville & Co., Stan, 4129 Normal St., San Diego, CA 92103/619-298-3393
Dead Eye's Sport Center, RD 1, Box 147B, Shickshinny, PA 18655/717-256-7432
Decker Shooting Products, 1729 Laguna Ave., Schofield, WI 54476/715-359-5873
de Coux, Pete (See Cartridge Transfer Group)
Deepeeka Exports Pvt. Ltd., D-78, Saket, Meerut-250-006, INDIA/011-91-121-512889, 011-91-121-545363; FAX: 011-91-121-542988, 011-91-121-511599
Defense Training International, Inc., 749 S. Lemay, Ste. A3-337, Ft. Collins, CO 80524/303-482-2520; FAX: 303-482-0548
deHaas Barrels, RR 3, Box 77, Ridgeway, MO 64481/816-872-6308
Del Rey Products, P.O. Box 91561, Los Angeles, CA 90009/213-823-0494
Delhi Gun House, 1374 Kashmere Gate, Delhi, INDIA 110 006/(011)2940974+2940814; FAX: 91-11-2917344
Del-Sports, Inc., Box 685, Main St., Margaretville, NY 12455/914-586-4103; FAX: 914-586-4105
Delta Enterprises, 284 Hagemann Drive, Livermore, CA 94550
Delta Frangible Ammunition, LLC, P.O. Box 2350, Stafford, VA 22555-2350/540-720-5778, 800-339-1933; FAX: 540-720-5667
Denver Bullets, Inc., 1811 W. 13th Ave., Denver, CO 80204/303-893-3146; FAX: 303-893-9161
Denver Instrument Co., 6542 Fig St., Arvada, CO 80004/800-321-1135, 303-431-7255; FAX: 303-423-4831
DeSantis Holster & Leather Goods, Inc., P.O. Box 2039, 149 Denton Ave., New Hyde Park, NY 11040-0701/516-354-8000; FAX: 516-354-7501
Desert Mountain Mfg., P.O. Box 2767, Columbia Falls, MT 59912/800-477-0762, 406-892-7772
Detroit-Armor Corp., 720 Industrial Dr. No. 112, Cary, IL 60013/708-639-7666; FAX: 708-639-7694
Dever Co., Jack, 8590 NW 90, Oklahoma City, OK 73132/405-721-6393
Devereaux, R.H. "Dick" (See D.D. Custom Stocks)
Dewey Mfg. Co., Inc., J., P.O. Box 2014, Southbury, CT 06488/203-264-3064; FAX: 203-262-6907
DGR Custom Rifles, RR1, Box 8A, Tappen, ND 58487/701-327-8135
DGS, Inc., Dale A. Storey, 1117 E. 12th, Casper, WY 82601/307-237-2414
DHB Products, P.O. Box 3092, Alexandria, VA 22302/703-836-2648
Diamond Mfg. Co., P.O. Box 174, Wyoming, PA 18644/800-233-9601
Dilliott Gunsmithing, Inc., 657 Scarlett Rd., Dandridge, TN 37725/423-397-9204
Dillon, Ed, 1035 War Eagle Dr. N., Colorado Springs, CO 80919/719-598-4929; FAX: 719-598-4929
Dillon Precision Products, Inc., 8009 East Dillon's Way, Scottsdale, AZ 85260/602-948-8009, 800-762-3845; FAX: 602-998-2786
Division Lead Co., 7742 W. 61st Pl., Summit, IL 60502
DKT, Inc., 14623 Vera Drive, Union, MI 49130-9744/616-641-7120, 800-741-7083 orders only; FAX: 616-641-2015
Doctor Optic Technologies, Inc., 4685 Boulder Highway, Suite A, Las Vegas, NV 89121/800-290-3634, 702-898-7161; FAX: 702-898-3737
Dohring Bullets, 100 W. 8 Mile Rd., Ferndale, MI 48220
Donnelly, C.P., 405 Kubli Rd., Grants Pass, OR 97527/541-846-6604
Double A Ltd., P.O. Box 11306, Minneapolis, MN 55411/612-522-0306
Douglas Barrels, Inc., 5504 Big Tyler Rd., Charleston, WV 25313-1398/304-776-1341; FAX: 304-776-8560
Dowtin Gunworks, Rt. 4, Box 930A, Flagstaff, AZ 86001/602-779-1898
Dressel Jr., Paul G., 209 N. 92nd Ave., Yakima, WA 98908/509-966-9233; FAX: 509-966-3365
Dri-Slide, Inc., 411 N. Darling, Fremont, MI 49412/616-924-3950
Dropkick, 1460 Washington Blvd., Williamsport, PA 17701/717-326-6561; FAX: 717-326-4950
Duane Custom Stocks, Randy, 110 W. North Ave., Winchester, VA 22601/703-667-9461; FAX: 703-722-3993
Duane's Gun Repair (See DGR Custom Rifles)
Du-Lite Corp., 171 River Rd., Middletown, CT 06457/203-347-2505; FAX: 203-347-9404
Duncan's Gun Works, Inc., 1619 Grand Ave., San Marcos, CA 92069/619-727-0515
Dunphy, Ted, W. 5100 Winch Rd., Rathdrum, ID 83858/208-687-1399; FAX: 208-687-1399
DuPont (See IMR Powder Co.)
Dutchman's Firearms, Inc., The, 4143 Taylor Blvd., Louisville, KY 40215/502-366-0555
Dybala Gun Shop, P.O. Box 1024, FM 3156, Bay City, TX 77414/409-245-0866
Dykstra, Doug, 411 N. Darling, Fremont, MI 49412/616-924-3950
Dynamit Nobel-RWS, Inc., 81 Ruckman Rd., Closter, NJ 07624/201-767-7971; FAX: 201-767-1589

## E

E&L Mfg., Inc., 4177 Riddle by Pass Rd., Riddle, OR 97469/541-874-2137; FAX: 541-874-3107
Eagan, Donald V., P.O. Box 196, Benton, PA 17814/717-925-6134
Eagle International Sporting Goods, Inc., P.O. Box 67, Zap, ND 58580/888-932-4536; FAX: 701-948-2282
E-A-R, Inc., Div. of Cabot Safety Corp., 5457 W. 79th St., Indianapolis, IN 46268/800-327-3431; FAX: 800-488-8007
Echols & Co., D'Arcy, 164 W. 580 S., Providence, UT 84332/801-753-2367
Eclectic Technologies, Inc., 45 Grandview Dr., Suite A, Farmington, CT 06034
Ed's Gun House, P.O. Box 62, Minnesota City, MN 55959/507-689-2925
Edmisten Co., P.O. Box 1293, Boone, NC 28607
Edmund Scientific Co., 101 E. Gloucester Pike, Barrington, NJ 08033/609-543-6250
Ednar, Inc., 2-4-8 Kayabacho, Nihonbashi, Chuo-ku, Tokyo, JAPAN 103/81(Japan)-3-3667-1651; FAX: 81-3-3661-8113
Eezox, Inc., P.O. Box 772, Waterford, CT 06385-0772/860-447-8282, 800-462-3331; FAX: 860-447-3484
Effebi SNC-Dr. Franco Beretta, via Rossa, 4, 25062 Concesio, Italy/030-2751955; FAX: 030-2180414
Eggleston, Jere D., 400 Saluda Ave., Columbia, SC 29205/803-799-3402
EGW Evolution Gun Works, 4050 B-8 Skyron Dr., Doylestown, PA 18901/215-348-9892; FAX: 215-348-1056
Eichelberger Bullets, Wm., 158 Crossfield Rd., King of Prussia, PA 19406
Eldorado Cartridge Corp. (See PMC/Eldorado Cartridge Corp.)
Electronic Shooters Protection, Inc., 11997 West 85th Place, Arvada, CO 80005/303-456-8964; 800-797-7791; FAX: 303-456-7179
Electronic Trigger Systems, Inc., P.O. Box 13, 230 Main St. S., Hector, MN 55342/320-848-2760; FAX: 320-848-2760
Eley Ltd., P.O. Box 705, Witton, Birmingham, B6 7UT, ENGLAND/021-356-8899; FAX: 021-331-4173
Elite Ammunition, P.O. Box 3251, Oakbrook, IL 60522/708-366-9006
Elkhorn Bullets, P.O. Box 5293, Central Point, OR 97502/541-826-7440
Emerging Technologies, Inc. (See Laseraim Technologies, Inc.)
Engineered Accessories, 1307 W. Wabash Ave., Effingham, IL 62401/217-347-7700; FAX: 217-347-7737
Enguix Import-Export, Alpujarras 58, Alzira, Valencia, SPAIN 46600/(96) 241 43 95; FAX: (96) (241 43 95) 240 21 53
Ensign-Bickford Co., The, 660 Hopmeadow St., Simsbury, CT 06070
EPC, 1441 Manatt St., Lincoln, NE 68521/402-476-3946
Epps, Ellwood (See "Gramps" Antique Cartridges)
Erhardt, Dennis, 3280 Green Meadow Dr., Helena, MT 59601/406-442-4533
Erickson's Mfg., C.W., Inc., 530 Garrison Ave. N.E., P.O. Box 522, Buffalo, MN 55313/612-682-3665; FAX: 612-682-4328
Essex Metals, 1000 Brighton St., Union, NJ 07083/800-282-8369
Estate Cartridge, Inc., 12161 FM 830, Willis, TX 77378/409-856-7277; FAX: 409-856-5486
Euber Bullets, No. Orwell Rd., Orwell, VT 05760/802-948-2621
Evans, Andrew, 2325 NW Squire St., Albany, OR 97321/541-928-3190; FAX: 541-928-4128
Evans Gunsmithing (See Evans, Andrew)
Eversull Co., K., Inc., 1 Tracemont, Boyce, LA 71409/318-793-8728; FAX: 318-793-5483
Excalibur Enterprises, P.O. Box 400, Fogelsville, PA 18051-0400/610-391-9105; FAX: 610-391-9220
Exe, Inc., 18830 Partridge Circle, Eden Prairie, MN 55346/612-944-7662
E-Z-Way Systems, P.O. Box 4310, Newark, OH 43058-4310/614-345-6645, 800-848-2072; FAX: 614-345-6600

## F

F&A Inc. (See ShurKatch Corporation)
Faith Associates, Inc., 1139 S. Greenville Hwy., Hendersonville, NC 28792/704-692-1916; FAX: 704-697-6827
Fajen, Inc., Reinhart, Route 1, P.O. Box 214-A, Lincoln, MO 65338/816-547-3030; FAX: 816-547-2215
Far North Outfitters, Box 1252, Bethel, AK 99559
Farmer-Dressel, Sharon, 209 N. 92nd Ave., Yakima, WA 98908/509-966-9233; FAX: 509-966-3365
Farr Studio, Inc., 1231 Robinhood Rd., Greeneville, TN 37743/615-638-8825
Fautheree, Andy, P.O. Box 4607, Pagosa Springs, CO 81157/303-731-5003

Federal Cartridge Co., 900 Ehlen Dr., Anoka, MN 55303/612-323-2300; FAX: 612-323-2506
Federal Champion Target Co., 232 Industrial Parkway, Richmond, IN 47374/800-441-4971; FAX: 317-966-7747
Federated-Fry (See Fry Metals)
Feinwerkbau Westinger & Altenburger GmbH (See FWB)
Feken, Dennis, Rt. 2 Box 124, Perry, OK 73077/405-336-5611
Ferguson, Bill, P.O. Box 1238, Sierra Vista, AZ 85636/520-458-5321; FAX: 520-458-9125
Fibron Products, Inc., P.O. Box 430, Buffalo, NY 14209-0430/716-886-2378; FAX: 716-886-2394
Finch Custom Bullets, 40204 La Rochelle, Prairieville, LA 70769
Fiocchi of America, Inc., 5030 Fremont Rd., Ozark, MO 65721/417-725-4118, 800-721-2666; FAX: 417-725-1039
First, Inc., Jack, 1201 Turbine Dr., Rapid City, SD 57701/605-343-9544; FAX: 605-343-9420
Fisher Custom Firearms, 2199 S. Kittredge Way, Aurora, CO 80013/303-755-3710
Fisher Enterprises, Inc., 1071 4th Ave. S., Suite 303, Edmonds, WA 98020-4143/206-771-5382
Fisher, Jerry A., 553 Crane Mt. Rd., Big Fork, MT 59911/406-837-2722
Fisher, R. Kermit (See Fisher Enterprises, Inc.)
Fitz Pistol Grip Co., P.O. Box 610, Douglas City, CA 96024/916-778-0240
Flaig's, 2200 Evergreen Rd., Millvale, PA 15209/412-821-1717
Flambeau Products Corp., 15981 Valplast Rd., Middlefield, OH 44062/216-632-1631; FAX: 216-632-1581
Flents Products Co., Inc., P.O. Box 2109, Norwalk, CT 06852/203-866-2581; FAX: 203-854-9322
Flitz International Ltd., 821 Mohr Ave., Waterford, WI 53185/414-534-5898; FAX: 414-534-2991
Flores Publications, Inc., J. (See Action Direct, Inc.)
Fluoramics, Inc., 18 Industrial Ave., Mahwah, NJ 07430/800-922-0075, 201-825-7035
FN Herstal, Voie de Liege 33, Herstal 4040, BELGIUM/(32)41.40.82.83; FAX: (32)41.40.86.79
Folks, Donald E., 205 W. Lincoln St., Pontiac, IL 61764/815-844-7901
Forgett Jr., Valmore J., 689 Bergen Blvd., Ridgefield, NJ 07657/201-945-2500; FAX: 201-945-6859; E-MAIL: ValForgett@msn.com
Forgreens Tool Mfg., Inc., P.O. Box 990, 723 Austin St., Robert Lee, TX 76945/915-453-2800; FAX: 915-453-2460
Forkin, Ben (See Belt MTN Arms)
Forster, Kathy (See Custom Checkering Service)
Forster, Larry L., P.O. Box 212, 220 First St. NE, Gwinner, ND 58040-0212/701-678-2475
Forster Products, 82 E. Lanark Ave., Lanark, IL 61046/815-493-6360; FAX: 815-493-2371
Forthofer's Gunsmithing & Knifemaking, 5535 U.S. Hwy 93S, Whitefish, MT 59937-8411/406-862-2674
Forty Five Ranch Enterprises, Box 1080, Miami, OK 74355-1080/918-542-5875
Fotar Optics, 1756 E. Colorado Blvd., Pasadena, CA 91106/818-579-3919; FAX: 818-579-7209
Fouling Shot, The, 6465 Parfet St., Arvada, CO 80004
4-D Custom Die Co., 711 N. Sandusky St., P.O. Box 889, Mt. Vernon, OH 43050-0889/614-397-7214; FAX: 614-397-6600
Fowler, Bob (see Black Powder Products)
Fowler Bullets, 806 Dogwood Dr., Gastonia, NC 28054/704-867-3259
Foy Custom Bullets, 104 Wells Ave., Daleville, AL 36322
Francotte & Cie S.A., Auguste, rue du Trois Juin 109, 4400 Herstal-Liege, BELGIUM/32-4-248-13-18; FAX: 32-4-948-11-79
Frank Custom Classic Arms, Ron, 7131 Richland Rd., Ft. Worth, TX 76118/817-284-9300; FAX: 817-284-9300
Frankonia Jagd, Hofmann & Co., D-97064 Wurzburg, GERMANY/09302-200; FAX: 09302-20200
Freedom Arms, Inc., P.O. Box 1776, Freedom, WY 83120/307-883-2468, 800-833-4432 (orders only); FAX: 307-883-2005
Freeman Animal Targets, 5519 East County Road, 100 South, Plainsfield, IN 46168/317-272-2663; FAX: 317-272-2674; E-MAIL: Signs@indy.net; WEB: http://www.freemansighs.com
Fremont Tool Works, 1214 Prairie, Ford, KS 67842/316-369-2327
Europtik Ltd., P.O. Box 319,, Dunmore, PA 18512/717-347-6049; FAX: 717-969-4330
4W Ammunition (See Hunters Supply)
Frontier Products Co., 164 E. Longview Ave., Columbus, OH 43202/614-262-9357
Fry Metals, 4100 6th Ave., Altoona, PA 16602/814-946-1611
FTI, Inc., 72 Eagle Rock Ave., Box 366, East Hanover, NJ 07936-3104
Fujinon, Inc., 10 High Point Dr., Wayne, NJ 07470/201-633-5600; FAX: 201-633-5216
Fusilier Bullets, 10010 N. 6000 W., Highland, UT 84003/801-756-6813
FWB, Neckarstrasse 43, 78727 Oberndorf a. N., GERMANY/07423-814-0; FAX: 07423-814-89

## G

G96 Products Co., Inc., River St. Station, P.O. Box 1684, Paterson, NJ 07544/201-684-4050; FAX: 201-684-3848
G&C Bullet Co., Inc., 8835 Thornton Rd., Stockton, CA 95209/209-477-6479; FAX: 209-477-2813
Gaillard Barrels, P.O. Box 21, Pathlow, Sask., S0K 3B0 CANADA/306-752-3769; FAX: 306-752-5969
Gain Twist Barrel Co., Rifle Works and Armory, 707 12th Street, Cody, WY 82414/307-587-4914; FAX: 307-527-6097
Galati International, P.O. Box 326, Catawissa, MO 63015/314-257-4837; FAX: 314-257-2268
Gamco, 1316 67th Street, Emeryville, CA 94608/510-527-5578
Game Haven Gunstocks, 13750 Shire Rd., Wolverine, MI 49799/616-525-8257
Gander Mountain, Inc., P.O. Box 128, Hwy. "W,", Wilmot, WI 53192/414-862-2331,Ext. 6425
GAR, 590 McBride Avenue, West Paterson, NJ 07424/201-754-1114; FAX: 201-754-1114
Garrett Cartridges, Inc., P.O. Box 178, Chehalis, WA 98532/360-736-0702
GDL Enterprises, 409 Le Gardeur, Slidell, LA 70460/504-649-0693
Gehmann, Walter (See Huntington Die Specialties)
Genco, P.O. Box 5704, Asheville, NC 28803
Gene's Custom Guns, P.O. Box 10534, White Bear Lake, MN 55110/612-429-5105
Gentex Corp., 5 Tinkham Ave., Derry, NH 03038/603-434-0311; FAX: 603-434-3002
Gentner Bullets, 109 Woodlawn Ave., Upper Darby, PA 19082/610-352-9396
Gentry Custom Gunmaker, David, 314 N. Hoffman, Belgrade, MT 59714/406-388-GUNS
George & Roy's, 2950 NW 29th, Portland, OR 97210/503-228-5424, 800-553-3022; FAX: 503-225-9409
Gervais, Mike, 3804 S. Cruise Dr., Salt Lake City, UT 84109/801-277-7729
Getz Barrel Co., P.O. Box 88, Beavertown, PA 17813/717-658-7263
G.G. & G., 3602 E. 42nd Stravenue, Tucson, AZ 85713/520-748-7167; FAX: 520-748-7583
G.H. Enterprises Ltd., Bag 10, Okotoks, Alberta T0L 1T0 CANADA/403-938-6070
Gibbs Rifle Co., Inc., Cannon Hill Industrial Park, Rt. 2, Box 214 Hoffman, Rd./Martinsburg, WV 25401
304-274-0458; FAX: 304-274-0078
Gillmann, Edwin, 33 Valley View Dr., Hanover, PA 17331/717-632-1662
Gilman-Mayfield, Inc., 3279 E. Shields, Fresno, CA 93703/209-221-9415; FAX: 209-221-9419
Gilmore Sports Concepts, 5949 S. Garnett, Tulsa, OK 74146/918-250-4867; FAX: 918-250-3845
Giron, Robert E., 1328 Pocono St., Pittsburgh, PA 15218/412-731-6041
Glaser Safety Slug, Inc., P.O. Box 8223, Foster City, CA 94404/800-221-3489, 510-785-7754; FAX: 510-785-6685
Gner's Hard Cast Bullets, 1107 11th St., LaGrande, OR 97850/503-963-8796
Goddard, Allen, 716 Medford Ave., Hayward, CA 94541/510-276-6830
Goens, Dale W., P.O. Box 224, Cedar Crest, NM 87008/505-281-5419
Goergen's Gun Shop, Inc., Rt. 2, Box 182BB, Austin, MN 55912/507-433-9280
GOEX, Inc., 1002 Springbrook Ave., Moosic, PA 18507/717-457-6724; FAX: 717-457-1130
Goldcoast Reloaders, Inc., 4260 NE 12th Terrace, Pompano Beach, FL 33064/954-783-4849; FAX: 954-942-3452
Golden Age Arms Co., 115 E. High St., Ashley, OH 43003/614-747-2488
Golden Bear Bullets, 3065 Fairfax Ave., San Jose, CA 95148/408-238-9515
Gonic Bullet Works, P.O. Box 7365, Gonic, NH 03839
Gonzalez Guns, Ramon B., P.O. Box 370, 93 St. Joseph's Hill Road, Monticello, NY 12701/914-794-4515
Gordie's Gun Shop, 1401 Fulton St., Streator, IL 61364/815-672-7202
Gotz Bullets, 7313 Rogers St., Rockford, IL 61111
Goudy Classic Stocks, Gary, 263 Hedge Rd., Menlo Park, CA 94025-1711/415-322-1338
Gozon Corp., U.S.A., P.O. Box 6278, Folson, CA 95763/916-983-2026; FAX: 916-983-9500
Grace, Charles E., 1305 Arizona Ave., Trinidad, CO 81082/719-846-9435
Graf & Sons, Route 3 Highway 54 So., Mexico, MO 65265/573-581-2266; FAX: 573-581-2875
"Gramps" Antique Cartridges, Box 341, Washago, Ont. L0K 2B0 CANADA/705-689-5348
Grand Falls Bullets, Inc., P.O. Box 720, 803 Arnold Wallen Way, Stockton, MO 65785/816-229-0112
Granite Custom Bullets, Box 190, Philipsburg, MT 59858/406-859-3245
Graphics Direct, P.O. Box 372421, Reseda, CA 91337-2421/818-344-9002
Graves Co., 1800 Andrews Ave., Pompano Beach, FL 33069/800-327-9103; FAX: 305-960-0301
Grayback Wildcats, 5306 Bryant Ave., Klamath Falls, OR 97603/541-884-1072
Great American Gunstock Co., 3420 Industrial Drive, Yuba City, CA 95993/916-671-4570; FAX: 916-671-3906
Great Lakes Airguns, 6175 S. Park Ave., Hamburg, NY 14075/716-648-6666; FAX: 716-648-5279
Green, Arthur S., 485 S. Robertson Blvd., Beverly Hills, CA 90211/310-274-1283
Green Genie, Box 114, Cusseta, GA 31805
Green Mountain Rifle Barrel Co., Inc., P.O. Box 2670, 153 West Main St., Conway, NH 03818/603-447-1095; FAX: 603-447-1099
Green, Roger M., P.O. Box 984, 435 E. Birch, Glenrock, WY 82637/307-436-9804
Greene Precision Duplicators, M.L. Greene Engineering Services, P.O. Box, 1150/Golden, CO 80402-1150
303-279-2383
Greenwood Precision, P.O. Box 468, Nixa, MO 65714-0468/417-725-2330
Greg's Superior Products, P.O. Box 46219, Seattle, WA 98146
Grier's Hard Cast Bullets, 1107 11th St., LaGrande, OR 97850/503-963-8796
Griffin & Howe, Inc., 33 Claremont Rd., Bernardsville, NJ 07924/908-766-2287; FAX: 908-766-1068
Group Tight Bullets, 482 Comerwood Court, San Francisco, CA 94080/415-583-1550
GSI, Inc., 108 Morrow Ave., P.O. Box 129, Trussville, AL 35173/205-655-8299; FAX: 205-655-7078
Guardsman Products, 411 N. Darling, Fremont, MI 49412/616-924-3950
Gun Accessories (See Glaser Safety Slug, Inc.)
Gun City, 212 W. Main Ave., Bismarck, ND 58501/701-223-2304
Gun Doctor, The, 435 East Maple, Roselle, IL 60172/708-894-0668
Gun Doctor, The, P.O. Box 39242, Downey, CA 90242/310-862-3158
Gun Hunter Books (See Gun Hunter Trading Co.)
Gun Hunter Trading Co., 5075 Heisig St., Beaumont, TX 77705/409-835-3006
Gun List (See Krause Publications, Inc.)
Gun Parts Corp., The, 226 Williams Lane, West Hurley, NY 12491/914-679-2417; FAX: 914-679-5849
Gun Room Press, The, 127 Raritan Ave., Highland Park, NJ 08904/908-545-4344; FAX: 908-545-6686
Gun Shop, The, 5550 S. 900 East, Salt Lake City, UT 84117/801-263-3633
Gun Shop, The, 62778 Spring Creek Rd., Montrose, CO 81401
Gun South, Inc. (See GSI, Inc.)
Gun Works, The, 247 S. 2nd, Springfield, OR 97477/541-741-4118; FAX: 541-988-1097
Guncraft Sports, Inc., 10737 Dutchtown Rd., Knoxville, TN 37932/423-966-4545; FAX: 423-966-4500
Guncraft Books (See Guncraft Sports, Inc.)
Gunnerman Books, P.O. Box 217, Owosso, MI 48867/517-729-7018; FAX: 517-725-9391
Guns, 81 E. Streetsboro St., Hudson, OH 44236/216-650-4563
Guns, Div. of D.C. Engineering, Inc., 8633 Southfield Fwy., Detroit, MI 48228/313-271-7111, 800-886-7623 (orders only); FAX: 313-271-7112
GUNS Magazine, 591 Camino de la Reina, Suite 200, San Diego, CA 92108/619-297-5350; FAX: 619-297-5353
Gunsmith in Elk River, The, 14021 Victoria Lane, Elk River, MN 55330/612-441-7761
Gunsmithing, Inc., 208 West Buchanan St., Colorado Springs, CO 80907/719-632-3795; FAX: 719-632-3493
Gunsmithing Ltd., 57 Unquowa Rd., Fairfield, CT 06430/203-254-0436; FAX: 203-254-1535

## H

H&P Publishing, 7174 Hoffman Rd., San Angelo, TX 76905/915-655-5953
H&S Liner Service, 515 E. 8th, Odessa, TX 79761/915-332-1021
Hakko Co. Ltd., Daini-Tsunemi Bldg., 1-13-12, Narimasu, Itabashiku Tokyo 175, JAPAN/03-5997-7870/2; FAX: 81-3-5997-7840
Half Moon Rifle Shop, 490 Halfmoon Rd., Columbia Falls, MT 59912/406-892-4409
Hallberg Gunsmith, Fritz, P.O. Box 339, 160 N. Oregon St., Ontario, OR 97914/541-889-3135; FAX: 541-889-2633
Halstead, Rick, RR4, Box 272, Miami, OK 74354/918-540-0933
Hamilton, Jim, Rte. 5, Box 278, Guthrie, OK 73044/405-282-3634
Hammerli USA, 19296 Oak Grove Circle, Groveland, CA 95321/209-962-5311; FAX: 209-962-5931
Hammets VLD Bullets, P.O. Box 479, Rayville, LA 71269/318-728-2019
Hammonds Rifles, RD 4, Box 504, Red Lion, PA 17356/717-244-7879
Handgun Press, P.O. Box 406, Glenview, IL 60025/847-657-6500; FAX: 847-724-8831
Hank's Gun Shop, Box 370, 50 West 100 South, Monroe, UT 84754/801-527-4456
Hanned Line, The, P.O. Box 2387, Cupertino, CA 95015-2387
Hanned Precision (See Hanned Line, The)
Hansen & Co. (See Hansen Cartridge Co.)
Hansen Cartridge Co., 244-246 Old Post Rd., Southport, CT 06490/203-259-6222, 203-259-7337; FAX: 203-254-3832
Hanson's Gun Center, Dick, 233 Everett Dr., Colorado Springs, CO 80911
Hardin Specialty Dist., P.O. Box 338, Radcliff, KY 40159-0338/502-351-6649
Harold's Custom Gun Shop, Inc., Broughton Rifle Barrels, Rt. 1, Box 447, Big Spring, TX 79720/915-394-4430
Harper's Custom Stocks, 928 Lombrano St., San Antonio, TX 78207/210-732-5780
Harrell's Precision, 5756 Hickory Dr., Salem, VA 24133/703-380-2683
Harris Engineering, Inc., 999 Broadway, Barlow, KY 42024/502-334-3633; FAX: 502-334-3000
Harris Enterprises, P.O. Box 105, Bly, OR 97622/503-353-2625
Harris Gunworks, 3840 N. 28th Ave., Phoenix, AZ 85017-4733/602-230-1414; FAX: 602-230-1422
Harrison Bullets, 6437 E. Hobart St., Mesa, AZ 85205
Hart & Son, Inc., Robert W., 401 Montgomery St., Nescopeck, PA 18635/717-752-3655, 800-368-3656; FAX: 717-752-1088
Hart Rifle Barrels, Inc., P.O. Box 182, 1690 Apulia Rd., Lafayette, NY 13084/315-677-9841; FAX: 315-677-9610
Harvey, Frank, 218 Nightfall, Terrace, NV 89015/702-558-6998
Harwood, Jack O., 1191 S. Pendlebury Lane, Blackfoot, ID 83221/208-785-5368
Haselbauer Products, Jerry, P.O. Box 27629, Tucson, AZ 85726/602-792-1075
Hastings Barrels, 320 Court St., Clay Center, KS 67432/913-632-3169; FAX: 913-632-6554
Hawk, Inc., 849 Hawks Bridge Rd., Salem, NJ 08079/609-299-2700; FAX: 609-299-2800
Hawk Laboratories, Inc. (See Hawk, Inc.)
Hawken Shop, The (See Dayton Traister)
Haydon Shooters' Supply, Russ, 15018 Goodrich Dr. NW, Gig Harbor, WA 98329/253-857-7557; FAX: 253-857-7884
Heatbath Corp., P.O. Box 2978, Springfield, MA 01101/413-543-3381
HEBB Resources, P.O. Box 999, Mead, WA 99021-09996/509-466-1292
Hecht, Hubert J., Waffen-Hecht, P.O. Box 2635, Fair Oaks, CA 95628/916-966-1020
Heidenstrom Bullets, Urds GT 1 Heroya, 3900 Porsgrunn, NORWAY

Heilmann, Stephen, P.O. Box 657, Grass Valley, CA 95945/916-272-8758
Heinie Specialty Products, 301 Oak St., Quincy, IL 62301-2500/309-543-4535; FAX: 309-543-2521
Henigson & Associates, Steve, P.O. Box 2726, Culver City, CA 90231/310-305-8288; FAX: 310-305-1905
Hensler, Jerry, 6614 Country Field, San Antonio, TX 78240/210-690-7491
Hensley & Gibbs, Box 10, Murphy, OR 97533/541-862-2341
Hensley, Darwin, Gunmaker, P.O. Box 329, Brightwood, OR 97011/503-622-5411
Heppler, Keith M., Keith's Custom Gunstocks, 540 Banyan Circle, Walnut Creek, CA 94598/510-934-3509; FAX: 510-934-3143
Hercules, Inc. (See Alliant Techsystems, Smokeless Powder Group)
Heritage/VSP Gun Books, P.O. Box 887, McCall, ID 83638/208-634-4104; FAX: 208-634-3101
Hermann Leather Co., H.J., Rt. 1, P.O. Box 525, Skiatook, OK 74070/918-396-1226
Hertel & Reuss, Werk für Optik und Feinmechanik GmbH, Quellhofstrasse, 67/34 127 Kassel, GERMANY/0561-83006; FAX: 0561-893308
Hesco-Meprolight, 2139 Greenville Rd., LaGrange, GA 30241/706-884-7967; FAX: 706-882-4683
Heydenberk, Warren R., 1059 W. Sawmill Rd., Quakertown, PA 18951/215-538-2682
Hickman, Jaclyn, Box 1900, Glenrock, WY 82637
Hidalgo, Tony, 12701 SW 9th Pl., Davie, FL 33325/954-476-7645
High Tech Specialties, Inc., P.O. Box 387R, Adamstown, PA 19501/215-484-0405, 800-231-9385
Hillmer Custom Gunstocks, Paul D., 7251 Hudson Heights, Hudson, IA 50643/319-988-3941
Hi-Performance Ammunition Company, 484 State Route 366, Apollo, PA 15613/412-327-8100
Hiptmayer, Armurier, RR 112 750, P.O. Box 136, Eastman, Quebec JOE 1P0, CANADA/514-297-2492
Hiptmayer, Klaus, RR 112 750, P.O. Box 136, Eastman, Quebec J0E 1P0, CANADA/514-297-2492
Hirtenberger Aktiengesellschaft, Leobersdorferstrasse 31, A-2552 Hirtenberg, AUSTRIA/43(0)2256 81184; FAX: 43(0)2256 81807
Hiti-Schuch, Atelier Wilma, A-8863 Predlitz, Pirming Y1 AUSTRIA/0353418278
Hobson Precision Mfg. Co., Rt. 1, Box 220-C, Brent, AL 35034/205-926-4662
Hoch Custom Bullet Moulds (See Colorado Shooter's Supply)
Hodgdon Powder Co., 6231 Robinson, Shawnee Mission, KS 66202/913-362-9455; FAX: 913-362-1307; WEB: http://www.hodgdon.com
Hoehn Sales, Inc., 2045 Kohn Road, Wright City, MO 63390/314-745-8144; FAX: 314-745-8144
Hoelscher, Virgil, 11047 Pope Ave., Lynwood, CA 90262/310-631-8545
Hoenig & Rodman, 6521 Morton Dr., Boise, ID 83704/208-375-1116
Hoffman New Ideas, 821 Northmoor Rd., Lake Forest, IL 60045/312-234-4075
Holland's Gunsmithing, P.O. Box 69, Powers, OR 97466/541-439-5155; FAX: 541-439-5155
Hollywood Engineering, 10642 Arminta St., Sun Valley, CA 91352/818-842-8376
Home Shop Machinist, The, Village Press Publications, P.O. Box 1810, Traverse City, MI 49685/800-447-7367; FAX: 616-946-3289
Hondo Ind., 510 S. 52nd St.,I04, Tempe, AZ 85281
Hoppe's Div., Penguin Industries, Inc., Airport Industrial Mall, Coatesville, PA 19320/610-384-6000
Horizons Unlimited, P.O. Box 426, Warm Springs, GA 31830/706-655-3603; FAX: 706-655-3603
Hornady Mfg. Co., P.O. Box 1848, Grand Island, NE 68802/800-338-3220, 308-382-1390; FAX: 308-382-5761
Howell Machine, 815 1/2 D St., Lewiston, ID 83501/208-743-7418
H-S Precision, Inc., 1301 Turbine Dr., Rapid City, SD 57701/605-341-3006; FAX: 605-342-8964
HT Bullets, 244 Belleville Rd., New Bedford, MA 02745/508-999-3338
Huebner, Corey O., P.O. Box 2074, Missoula, MT 59806-2074/406-721-7168
Hughes, Steven Dodd, P.O. Box 545, Livingston, MT 59047/406-222-9377
Hungry Horse Books, 4605 Hwy. 93 South, Whitefish, MT 59937/406-862-7997
Hunters Supply, Rt. 1, P.O. Box 313, Tioga, TX 76271/800-868-6612; FAX: 817-437-2228
Hunterjohn, P.O. Box 477, St. Louis, MO 63166/314-531-7250
Huntington Die Specialties, 601 Oro Dam Blvd., Oroville, CA 95965/916-534-1210; FAX: 916-534-1212
Hutton Rifle Ranch, P.O. Box 45236, Boise, ID 83711/208-345-8781
Hydrosorbent Products, P.O. Box 437, Ashley Falls, MA 01222/413-229-2967; FAX: 413-229-8743

## I

IAI (See A.M.T.)
ICI-America, P.O. Box 751, Wilmington, DE 19897/302-575-3000
Illinois Lead Shop, 7742 W. 61st Place, Summit, IL 60501
Image Ind. Inc., 864 Lively, Wood Dale, IL 60191/630-616-1340; FAX: 630-616-1341
Image Ind. Inc., 382 Balm Court, Wood Dale, IL 60191/630-766-2402; FAX: 630-766-7373
IMI, P.O. Box 1044, Ramat Hasharon 47100, ISRAEL/972-3-5485617;FAX: 972-3-5406908
IMI Services USA, Inc., 2 Wisconsin Circle, Suite 420, Chevy Chase, MD 20815/301-215-4800; FAX: 301-657-1446
Imperial (See E-Z-Way Systems)
Imperial Magnum Corp., P.O. Box 249, Oroville, WA 98844/604-495-3131; FAX: 604-495-2816
IMR Powder Co., 1080 Military Turnpike, Suite 2, Plattsburgh, NY 12901/518-563-2253; FAX: 518-563-6916
Independent Machine & Gun Shop, 1416 N. Hayes, Pocatello, ID 83201
Info-Arm, P.O. Box 1262, Champlain, NY 12919/514-955-0355; FAX: 514-955-0357
Innovative Weaponry, Inc., 337 Eubank NE, Albuquerque, NM 87123/800-334-3573, 505-296-4645; FAX: 505-271-2633
Innovision Enterprises, 728 Skinner Dr., Kalamazoo, MI 49001/616-382-1681; FAX: 616-382-1830
INTEC International, Inc., P.O. Box 5708, Scottsdale, AZ 85261/602-483-1708
International Shooters Service (See I.S.S.)
Iosso Products, 1485 Lively Blvd., Elk Grove Village, IL 60007/708-437-8400; FAX: 708-437-8478
Iron Bench, 12619 Bailey Rd., Redding, CA 96003/916-241-4623
Ironside International Publishers, Inc., P.O. Box 55, 800 Slaters Lane, Alexandria, VA 22313/703-684-6111; FAX: 703-683-5486
Ironsighter Co., P.O. Box 85070, Westland, MI 48185/313-326-8731; FAX: 313-326-3378
Island Pond Gun Shop, P.O. Box 428, Cross St., Island Pond, VT 05846/802-723-4546
Israel Military Industries Ltd. (See IMI)
I.S.S., P.O. Box 185234, Ft. Worth, TX 76181/817-595-2090
I.S.W., 106 E. Cairo Dr., Tempe, AZ 85282
Ivanoff, Thomas G. (See Tom's Gun Repair)

## J

J-4, Inc., 1700 Via Burton, Anaheim, CA 92806/714-254-8315; FAX: 714-956-4421
J&D Components, 75 East 350 North, Orem, UT 84057-4719/801-225-7007
J&J Products, Inc., 9240 Whitmore, El Monte, CA 91731/818-571-5228, 800-927-8361; FAX: 818-571-8704
J&J Sales, 1501 21st Ave. S., Great Falls, MT 59405/406-453-7549
J&L Superior Bullets (See Huntington Die Specialties)
J&R Enterprises, 4550 Scotts Valley Rd., Lakeport, CA 95453
Jackalope Gun Shop, 1048 S. 5th St., Douglas, WY 82633/307-358-3441
Jaeger, Inc., Paul/Dunn's, P.O. Box 449, 1 Madison Ave., Grand Junction, TN 38039/901-764-6909; FAX: 901-764-6503
JägerSport, Ltd., One Wholesale Way, Cranston, RI 02920/800-962-4867, 401-944-9682; FAX: 401-946-2587
Jamison's Forge Works, 4527 Rd. 6.5 NE, Moses Lake, WA 98837/509-762-2659
Jarrett Rifles, Inc., 383 Brown Rd., Jackson, SC 29831/803-471-3616
Javelina Lube Products, P.O. Box 337, San Bernardino, CA 92402/714-882-5847; FAX: 714-434-6937
Jeffredo Gunsight, P.O. Box 669, San Marcos, CA 92079/619-728-2695
Jensen Bullets, 86 North, 400 West, Blackfoot, ID 83221/208-785-5590
Jensen's Custom Ammunition, 5146 E. Pima, Tucson, AZ 85712/602-325-3346; FAX: 602-322-5704
Jensen's Firearms Academy, 1280 W. Prince, Tucson, AZ 85705/602-293-8516
Jericho Tool & Die Co. Inc., RD 3 Box 70, Route 7, Bainbridge, NY 13733-9494/607-563-8222; FAX: 607-563-8560
Jester Bullets, Rt. 1 Box 27, Orienta, OK 73737
Jewell Triggers, Inc., 3620 Hwy. 123, San Marcos, TX 78666/512-353-2999
J-Gar Co., 183 Turnpike Rd., Dept. 3, Petersham, MA 01366-9604
JGS Precision Tool Mfg., 1141 S. Summer Rd., Coos Bay, OR 97420/541-267-4331; FAX:541-267-5996
J.I.T., Ltd., P.O. Box 230, Freedom, WY 83120/708-494-0937
JLK Bullets, 414 Turner Rd., Dover, AR 72837/501-331-4194
Johnson Wood Products, 34968 Crystal Road, Strawberry Point, IA 52076/319-933-4930
Johnston Bros. (See C&T Corp. TA Johnson Brothers)
Jonad Corp., 2091 Lakeland Ave., Lakewood, OH 44107/216-226-3161
Jones, J.D. (See SSK Industries)
Jones Custom Products, Neil A., 17217 Brookhouser Road, Saegertown, PA 16433/814-763-2769; FAX: 814-763-4228
Jones Moulds, Paul, 4901 Telegraph Rd., Los Angeles, CA 90022/213-262-1510
J.P. Enterprises, Inc., P.O. Box 26324, Shoreview, MN 55126/612-486-9064; FAX: 612-482-0970
J.P. Gunstocks, Inc., 4508 San Miguel Ave., North Las Vegas, NV 89030/702-645-0718
JP Sales, Box 307, Anderson, TX 77830
JRP Custom Bullets, RR2 2233 Carlton Rd., Whitehall, NY 12887/518-282-0084 (a.m.), 802-438-5548 (p.m.)
JRW, 2425 Taffy Ct., Nampa, ID 83687
JWH: Software, 6947 Haggerty Rd., Hillsboro, OH 45133/513-393-2402

## K

K&M Services, 5430 Salmon Run Rd., Dover, PA 17315/717-292-3175
K&P Gun Co., 1024 Central Ave., New Rockford, ND 58356/701-947-2248
K&S Mfg., 2611 Hwy. 40 East, Inglis, FL 34449/904-447-3571
K&T Co., Div. of T&S Industries, Inc., 1027 Skyview Dr., W. Carrollton, OH 45449/513-859-8414
Ka Pu Kapili, P.O. Box 745, Honokaa, HI 96727/808-776-1644; FAX: 808-776-1731
Kahles, A Swarovski Company, 1 Wholesale Way, Cranston, RI 02920-5540/800-426-3089: FAX: 401-946-2587
Kandel, P.O. Box 4529, Portland, OR 97208
Kapro Mfg. Co., Inc. (See R.E.I.)
Kasmarsik Bullets, 4016 7th Ave. SW, Puyallup, WA 98373
Kaswer Custom, Inc., 13 Surrey Drive, Brookfield, CT 06804/203-775-0564; FAX: 203-775-6872
K.B.I., Inc., P.O. Box 6625, Harrisburg, PA 17112/717-540-8518; FAX: 717-540-8567
K-D, Inc., Box 459, 585 N. Hwy. 155, Cleveland, UT 84518/801-653-2530
KDF, Inc., 2485 Hwy. 46 N., Seguin, TX 78155/210-379-8141; FAX: 210-379-5420
Keeler, R.H., 817 "N" St., Port Angeles, WA 98362/206-457-4702
Keith's Bullets, 942 Twisted Oak, Algonquin, IL 60102/708-658-3520
Keith's Custom Gunstocks (See Heppler, Keith M.)
Kelbly, Inc., 7222 Dalton Fox Lake Rd., North Lawrence, OH 44666/216-683-4674; FAX: 216-683-7349
Kellogg's Professional Products, 325 Pearl St., Sandusky, OH 44870/419-625-6551; FAX: 419-625-6167
Ken's Kustom Kartridges, 331 Jacobs Rd., Hubbard, OH 44425/216-534-4595
Ken's Rifle Blanks, Ken McCullough, Rt. 2, P.O. Box 85B, Weston, OR 97886/503-566-3879
Keng's Firearms Specialty, Inc., 875 Wharton Dr., P.O. Box 44405, Atlanta, GA 30336-1405/404-691-7611: FAX: 404-505-8445
Kennebec Journal, 274 Western Ave., Augusta, ME 04330/207-622-6288
KenPatable Ent., Inc., P.O. Box 19422, Louisville, KY 40259/502-239-5447
Kent Cartridge Mfg. Co. Ltd., Unit 16, Branbridges Industrial Estate, East, Peckham/Tonbridge, Kent, TN12 5HF ENGLAND
622-872255; FAX: 622-872645
Kesselring Gun Shop, 400 Hwy. 99 North, Burlington, WA 98233/206-724-3113; FAX: 206-724-7003
Kilham & Co., Main St., P.O. Box 37, Lyme, NH 03768/603-795-4112
Kimber of America, Inc., 1 Lawton St., Yonkers, NY 10705/800-880-2418
King & Co., P.O. Box 1242, Bloomington, IL 61702/309-473-3964
KJM Fabritek, Inc., P.O. Box 162, Marietta, GA 30061/770-426-8251; FAX: 770-426-8252
KLA Enterprises, P.O. Box 2028, Eaton Park, FL 33840/941-682-2829; FAX: 941-682-2829
Kleen-Bore, Inc., 16 Industrial Pkwy., Easthampton, MA 01027/413-527-0300; FAX: 413-527-2522
Klein Custom Guns, Don, 433 Murray Park Dr., Ripon, WI 54971/414-748-2931
Klingler Woodcarving, P.O. Box 141, Thistle Hill, Cabot, VT 05647/802-426-3811
Kmount, P.O. Box 19422, Louisville, KY 40259/502-239-5447
Knight's Mfg. Co., 7750 9th St. SW, Vero Beach, FL 32968/561-562-5697; FAX: 561-569-2955
Knippel, Richard, 1455 Jubal Ct., Oakdale, CA 95361-9669/209-869-1469
Knoell, Doug, 9737 McCardle Way, Santee, CA 92071
Kodiak Custom Bullets, 8261 Henry Circle, Anchorage, AK 99507/907-349-2282
KOGOT, 410 College, Trinidad, CO 81082/719-846-9406
Kokolus, Michael M. (See Custom Riflestocks, Inc.)
Kolpin Mfg., Inc., P.O. Box 107, 205 Depot St., Fox Lake, WI 53933/414-928-3118; FAX: 414-928-3687
Kopp Professional Gunsmithing, Terry K., Route 1, Box 224F, Lexington, MO 64067/816-259-2636
Korzinek Riflesmith, J., RD 2, Box 73D, Canton, PA 17724/717-673-8512
Koval Knives, 5819 Zarley St., Suite A, New Albany, OH 43054/614-855-0777; FAX: 614-855-0945
Kowa Optimed, Inc., 20001 S. Vermont Ave., Torrance, CA 90502/310-327-1913; FAX: 310-327-4177
Kramer Designs, P.O. Box 129, Clancy, MT 59634/406-933-8658; FAX: 406-933-8658
Krause Publications, Inc., 700 E. State St., Iola, WI 54990/715-445-2214; FAX: 715-445-4087; Consumer orders only 800-258-0929
Krieger Barrels, Inc., N114 W18697 Clinton Dr., Germantown, WI 53022/414-255-9593; FAX: 414-255-9586
Kris Mounts, 108 Lehigh St., Johnstown, PA 15905/814-539-9751
KVH Industries, Inc., 110 Enterprise Center, Middletown, RI 02842/401-847-3327; FAX: 401-849-0045
Kwik Mount Corp., P.O. Box 19422, Louisville, KY 40259/502-239-5447
Kwik-Site Co., 5555 Treadwell, Wayne, MI 48184/313-326-1500; FAX: 313-326-4120

## L

L&S Technologies, Inc. (See Aimtech Mount Systems)
Labanu, Inc., 2201-F Fifth Ave., Ronkonkoma, NY 11779/516-467-6197; FAX: 516-981-4112
LaBounty Precision Reboring, P.O. Box 186, 7968 Silver Lk. Rd., Maple Falls, WA 98266/360-599-2047
Lage Uniwad, P.O. Box 2302, Davenport, IA 52809/319-388-LAGE; FAX: 319-388-LAGE
Lake Center, P.O. Box 38, St. Charles, MO 63302/314-946-7500
Lakewood Products, LLC, 275 June St., Berlin, WI 54923/800-US-BUILT; FAX: 414-361-7719
Lane Bullets, Inc., 1011 S. 10th St., Kansas City, KS 66105/913-621-6113, 800-444-7468
Lane Publishing, P.O. Box 459, Lake Hamilton, AR 71951/501-525-7514; FAX: 501-525-7519
Lanphert, Paul, P.O. Box 1985, Wenatchee, WA 98807

Lapua Ltd., P.O. Box 5, Lapua, FINLAND SF-62101/6-310111; FAX: 6-4388991
L.A.R. Mfg., Inc., 4133 W. Farm Rd., West Jordan, UT 84088/801-280-3505; FAX: 801-280-1972
Laseraim Technologies, Inc., P.O. Box 3548, Little Rock, AR 72203/501-375-2227; FAX: 501-372-1445
Laser Devices, Inc., 2 Harris Ct. A-4, Monterey, CA 93940/408-373-0701; FAX: 408-373-0903
LaserMax, Inc., 3495 Winton Place, Bldg. B, Rochester, NY 14623-2807/716-272-5420; FAX: 716-272-5427
Laurel Mountain Forge, P.O. Box 224C, Romeo, MI 48065/810-749-5742
Lawrence Brand Shot (See Precision Reloading, Inc.)
Lawson Co., Harry, 3328 N. Richey Blvd., Tucson, AZ 85716/520-326-1117
LBT, HCR 62, Box 145, Moyie Springs, ID 83845/208-267-3588
Lead Bullets Technology (See LBT)
Leapers, Inc., 7675 Five Mile Rd., Northville, MI 48167/810-486-1231; FAX: 810-486-1430
Le Clear Industries (See E-Z-Way Systems)
Lectro Science, Inc., 6410 W. Ridge Rd., Erie, PA 16506/814-833-6487; FAX: 814-833-0447
Lee Precision, Inc., 4275 Hwy. U, Hartford, WI 53027/414-673-3075; FAX: 414-673-9273
Lee Supplies, Mark, 9901 France Ct., Lakeville, MN 55044/612-461-2114
Lee's Red Ramps, 4 Kristine Ln., Silver City, NM 88061/505-538-8529
Lee Co., T.K., One Independence Plaza, Suite 520, Birmingham, AL 35209/205-913-5222
Legend Products Corp., 21218 Saint Andrews Blvd., Boca Raton, FL 33433-2435
Leica USA, Inc., 156 Ludlow Ave., Northvale, NJ 07647/201-767-7500; FAX: 201-767-8666
LEM Gun Specialties, Inc., The Lewis Lead Remover, P.O. Box 2855, Peachtree City, GA 30269-2024
Lenahan Family Enterprise, P.O. Box 46, Manitou Springs, CO 80829
Lethal Force Institute (See Police Bookshelf)
Lestrom Laboratories, Inc., P.O. Box 628, Mexico, NY 13114-0628/315-343-3076; FAX: 315-592-3370
Leupold & Stevens, Inc., P.O. Box 688, Beaverton, OR 97075/503-646-9171; FAX: 503-526-1455
Lewis Lead Remover, The (See LEM Gun Specialties, Inc.)
Liberty Metals, 2233 East 16th St., Los Angeles, CA 90021/213-581-9171; FAX: 213-581-9351
Liberty Shooting Supplies, P.O. Box 357, Hillsboro, OR 97123/503-640-5518
Lightfield Ammunition Corp. (See Slug Group, Inc.)
Lightforce U.S.A. Inc., 19226 66th Ave. So., L-103, Kent, WA 98032/206-656-1577; FAX:206-656-1578
Lightning Performance Innovations, Inc., RD1 Box 555, Mohawk, NY 13407/315-866-8819, 800-242-5873; FAX: 315-866-8819
Lilja Precision Rifle Barrels, P.O. Box 372, Plains, MT 59859/406-826-3084; FAX: 406-826-3083
Lincoln, Dean, Box 1886, Farmington, NM 87401
Lind Custom Guns, Al, 7821 76th Ave. SW, Tacoma, WA 98498/206-584-6361
Lindsley Arms Cartridge Co., P.O. Box 757, 20 College Hill Rd., Henniker, NH 03242/603-428-3127
List Precision Engineering, Unit 1, Ingley Works, 13 River Road, Barking, Essex 1G11 0HE ENGLAND/011-081-594-1686
Lithi Bee Bullet Lube, 1728 Carr Rd., Muskegon, MI 49442/616-788-4479
Littler Sales Co., 20815 W. Chicago, Detroit, MI 48228/313-273-6889; FAX: 313-273-1099
Littleton, J.F., 275 Pinedale Ave., Oroville, CA 95966/916-533-6084
Ljutic Industries, Inc., 732 N. 16th Ave., Suite 22, Yakima, WA 98902/509-248-0476; FAX: 509-576-8233
Load From A Disk, 9826 Sagedale, Houston, TX 77089/713-484-0935; FAX: 281-484-0935
Loch Leven Industries, P.O. Box 2751, Santa Rosa, CA 95405/707-573-8735; FAX: 707-573-0369
Lock's Philadelphia Gun Exchange, 6700 Rowland Ave., Philadelphia, PA 19149/215-332-6225; FAX: 215-332-4800
Lohman Mfg. Co., Inc., 4500 Doniphan Dr., P.O. Box 220, Neosho, MO 64850/417-451-4438; FAX: 417-451-2576
Lomont Precision Bullets, RR 1, Box 34, Salmon, ID 83467/208-756-6819; FAX: 208-756-6824
London Guns Ltd., Box 3750, Santa Barbara, CA 93130/805-683-4141; FAX: 805-683-1712
Lortone, Inc., 2856 NW Market St., Seattle, WA 98107/206-789-3100
Lothar Walther Precision Tool, Inc., 2190 Coffee Rd., Lithonia, GA 30058/770-482-4253; Fax: 770-482-9344
Loweth (Firearms), Richard H.R., 29 Hedgegrow Lane, Kirby Muxloe, Leics. LE9 2BN ENGLAND/(0)116 238 6295
L.P.A. Snc, Via Alfieri 26, Gardone V.T., Brescia, ITALY 25063/30-891-14-81; FAX: 30-891-09-51
LPS Laboratories, Inc., 4647 Hugh Howell Rd., P.O. Box 3050, Tucker, GA 30084/404-934-7800
Lucas, Mike, 1631 Jessamine Rd., Lexington, SC 29073/803-356-0282
Luch Metal Merchants, Barbara, 48861 West Rd., Wixon, MI 48393/800-876-5337
Lyman Instant Targets, Inc. (See Lyman Products Corp.)
Lyman Products Corp., 475 Smith Street, Middletown, CT 06457-1541/860-632-2020, 800-22-LYMAN; FAX: 860-632-1699
Lynn's Custom Gunstocks, RR 1, Brandon, IA 52210/319-474-2453
Lyte Optronics (See TracStar Industries, Inc.)
Lyons Gunworks, Larry, 110 Hamilton St., Dowagiac, MI 49047/616-782-9478

## M

M&D Munitions Ltd., 127 Verdi St., Farmingdale, NY 11735/800-878-2788, 516-752-1038; FAX: 516-752-1905
M&M Engineering (See Hollywood Engineering)
M&N Bullet Lube, P.O. Box 495, 151 NE Jefferson St., Madras, OR 97741/503-255-3750
MA Systems, P.O. Box 1143, Chouteau, OK 74337/918-479-6378
Mac-1 Distributors, 13974 Van Ness Ave., Gardena, CA 90249/310-327-3582
Mac's .45 Shop, P.O. Box 2028, Seal Beach, CA 90740/310-438-5046
Madis Books, 2453 West Five Mile Pkwy., Dallas, TX 75233/214-330-7168
Mag-Na-Port International, Inc., 41302 Executive Dr., Harrison Twp., MI 48045-1306/810-469-6727; FAX: 810-469-0425
Magma Engineering Co., P.O. Box 161, 20955 E. Ocotillo Rd., Queen Creek, AZ 85242/602-987-9008; FAX: 602-987-0148
Magnum Grips, Box 801G, Payson, AZ 85547
Magnum Power Products, Inc., P.O. Box 17768, Fountain Hills, AZ 85268
Magnum Research, Inc., 7110 University Ave. NE, Minneapolis, MN 55432/800-772-6168, 612-574-1868; FAX: 612-574-0109; WEB:http://www.magnumresearch.com
Magnus Bullets, P.O. Box 239, Toney, AL 35773/205-420-8359; FAX: 205-420-8360
MagSafe Ammo Co., 2725 Friendly Grove Rd NE, Olympia, WA 98506/360-357-6383; FAX: 360-705-4715
MagTech Recreational Products, Inc., 5030 Paradise Rd., Suite A104, Las Vegas, NV 89119/702-736-2043; FAX: 702-736-2140
Maine Custom Bullets, RFD 1, Box 1755, Brooks, ME 04921
Maionchi-L.M.I., Via Di Coselli-Zona Industriale Di Guamo, Lucca, ITALY 55060/011 39-583 94291
Malcolm Enterprises, 1023 E. Prien Lake Rd., Lake Charles, LA 70601
Mandall Shooting Supplies, Inc., 3616 N. Scottsdale Rd., Scottsdale, AZ 85252/602-945-2553; FAX: 602-949-0734
Marble Arms (See CRR, Inc./Marble's Inc.)
Marchmon Bullets, 8191 Woodland Shore Dr., Brighton, MI 48116
Markell, Inc., 422 Larkfield Center 235, Santa Rosa, CA 95403/707-573-0792; FAX: 707-573-9867
Markesbery Muzzle Loaders, Inc., 7785 Foundation Dr., Ste. 6, Florence, KY 41042/800-875-0121; 606-342-2380
MarMik, Inc., 2116 S. Woodland Ave., Michigan City, IN 46360/219-872-7231; FAX: 219-872-7231
Marple & Associates, Dick, 21 Dartmouth St., Hooksett, NH 03106/603-627-1837; FAX: 603-627-1837
Marquart Precision Co., P.O. Box 1740, Prescott, AZ 86302/520-445-5646
Marshall Enterprises, 792 Canyon Rd., Redwood City, CA 94062
Martin Bookseller, J., P.O. Drawer AP, Beckley, WV 25802/304-255-4073; FAX: 304-255-4077
Masen Co., Inc., John, 1305 Jelmak, Grand Prairie, TX 75050/817-430-8732; FAX: 817-430-1715
MAST Technology, 4350 S. Arville, Suite 3, Las Vegas, NV 89103/702-362-5043; FAX: 702-362-9554
Master Lock Co., 2600 N. 32nd St., Milwaukee, WI 53245/414-444-2800
Match Prep—Doyle Gracey, P.O. Box 155, Tehachapi, CA 93581/805-822-5383
Matco, Inc., 1003-2nd St., N. Manchester, IN 46962/219-982-8282
Mathews & Son, Inc., George E., 10224 S. Paramount Blvd., Downey, CA 90241/562-862-6719; FAX: 562-862-6719
Maxi-Mount, P.O. Box 291, Willoughby Hills, OH 44094-0291/216-944-9456; FAX: 216-944-9456
Mayville Engineering Co. (See MEC, Inc.)
McBros Rifle Co., P.O. Box 86549, Phoenix, AZ 85080/602-582-3713; FAX: 602-581-3825
McCament, Jay, 1730-134th St. Ct. S., Tacoma, WA 98444/206-531-8832
McCann's Machine & Gun Shop, P.O. Box 641, Spanaway, WA 98387/206-537-6919; FAX: 206-537-6993
McCann's Muzzle-Gun Works, 14 Walton Dr., New Hope, PA 18938/215-862-2728
McCullough, Ken (See Ken's Rifle Blanks)
McDonald, Dennis, 8359 Brady St., Peosta, IA 52068/319-556-7940
McFarland, Stan, 2221 Idella Ct., Grand Junction, CO 81505/970-243-4704
McGowen Rifle Barrels, 5961 Spruce Lane, St. Anne, IL 60964/815-937-9816; FAX: 815-937-4024
McGuire, Bill, 1600 N. Eastmont Ave., East Wenatchee, WA 98802/509-884-6021
McKee Publications, 121 Eatons Neck Rd., Northport, NY 11768/516-575-8850
McKillen & Heyer, Inc., 35535 Euclid Ave. Suite 11, Willoughby, OH 44094/216-942-2044
McMillan Fiberglass Stocks, Inc., 21421 N. 14th Ave., Suite B, Phoenix, AZ 85027/602-582-9635; FAX: 602-581-3825
McMillan Optical Gunsight Co., 28638 N. 42nd St., Cave Creek, AZ 85331/602-585-7868; FAX: 602-585-7872
McMillan Rifle Barrels, P.O. Box 3427, Bryan, TX 77805/409-690-3456; FAX: 409-690-0156
McMurdo, Lynn (See Specialty Gunsmithing)
MCRW Associates Shooting Supplies, R.R. 1 Box 1425, Sweet Valley, PA 18656/717-864-3967; FAX: 717-864-2669
MCS, Inc., 34 Delmar Dr., Brookfield, CT 06804/203-775-1013; FAX: 203-775-9462
MDS, P.O. Box 1441, Brandon, FL 33509-1441/813-653-1180; FAX: 813-684-5953
Measurement Group, Inc., Box 27777, Raleigh, NC 27611
MEC, Inc., 715 South St., Mayville, WI 53050/414-387-4500; FAX: 414-387-5802
MEC-Gar S.r.l., Via Madonnina 64, Gardone V.T., Brescia, ITALY 25063/39-30-8912687; FAX: 39-30-8910065
MEC-Gar U.S.A., Inc., Box 112, 500B Monroe Turnpike, Monroe, CT 06468/203-635-8662; FAX: 203-635-8662
Meier Works, P.O. Box 423, Tijeras, NM 87059/505-281-3783
Meister Bullets (See Gander Mountain)
Men-Metallwerk Elisenhuette, GmbH, P.O. Box 1263, D-56372 Nassau/Lahn, GERMANY/2604-7819
Meprolight (See Hesco-Meprolight)
Mercer Custom Stocks, R.M., 216 S. Whitewater Ave., Jefferson, WI 53549/414-674-5130
Merit Corp., Box 9044, Schenectady, NY 12309/518-346-1420
Merkuria Ltd., Argentinska 38, 17005 Praha 7, CZECH REPUBLIC/422-875117; FAX: 422-809152
Michael's Antiques, Box 591, Waldoboro, ME 04572
Michaels of Oregon Co., P.O. Box 13010, Portland, OR 97213/503-255-6890; FAX: 503-255-0746
Micro Sight Co., 242 Harbor Blvd., Belmont, CA 94002/415-591-0769; FAX: 415-591-7531
Mid-America Recreation, Inc., 1328 5th Ave., Moline, IL 61265/309-764-5089; FAX: 309-764-2722
Middlebrooks Custom Shop, 7366 Colonial Trail East, Surry, VA 23883/757-357-0881; FAX: 757-365-0442
Midway Arms, Inc., 5875 W. Van Horn Tavern Rd., Columbia, MO 65203/800-243-3220, 314-445-6363; FAX: 314-446-1018
Military Armament Corp., P.O. Box 120, Mt. Zion Rd., Lingleville, TX 76461/817-965-3253
Miller Arms, Inc., P.O. Box 260 Purl St., St. Onge, SD 57779/605-642-5160; FAX: 605-642-5160
Miller Enterprises, Inc., R.P., 1557 E. Main St., P.O. Box 234, Brownsburg, IN 46112/317-852-8187
Miller Single Trigger Mfg. Co., Rt. 209 Box 1275, Millersburg, PA 17061/717-692-3704
Millett Sights, 7275 Murdy Circle, Adm. Office, Huntington Beach, CA 92647/714-842-5575, 800-645-5388; FAX: 714-843-5707
Milstor Corp., 80-975 E. Valley Pkwy. C-7, Indio, CA 92201/619-775-9998; FAX: 619-772-4990
Miniature Machine Co. (See MMC)
Minute Man High Tech Industries, 10611 Canyon Rd. E., Suite 151, Puyallup, WA 98373/800-233-2734
Mirador Optical Corp., P.O. Box 11614, Marina Del Rey, CA 90295-7614/310-821-5587; FAX: 310-305-0386
Mitchell Bullets, R.F., 430 Walnut St., Westernport, MD 21562
Mitchell Optics Inc., 2072 CR 1100 N, Sidney, IL 61877/217-688-2219, 217-621-3018; FAX: 217-688-2505
MI-TE Bullets, R.R. 1 Box 230, Ellsworth, KS 67439/913-472-4575
MJM Mfg., 3283 Rocky Water Ln. Suite B, San Jose, CA 95148/408-270-4207
MMC, 2513 East Loop 820 North, Ft. Worth, TX 76118/817-595-0404; FAX: 817-595-3074
MMP, Rt. 6, Box 384, Harrison, AR 72601/501-741-5019; FAX: 501-741-3104
Mo's Competitor Supplies (See MCS, Inc.)
MoLoc Bullets, P.O. Box 2810, Turlock, CA 95381-2810/209-632-1644
Montana Armory, Inc (See C. Sharps Arms Co. Inc.)
Montana Outfitters, Lewis E. Yearout, 308 Riverview Dr. E., Great Falls, MT 59404/406-761-0859
Montana Precision Swaging, P.O. Box 4746, Butte, MT 59702/406-782-7502
Montana Vintage Arms, 2354 Bear Canyon Rd., Bozeman, MT 59715
Morrison Custom Rifles, J.W., 4015 W. Sharon, Phoenix, AZ 85029/602-978-3754
Mountain Bear Rifle Works, Inc., 100 B Ruritan Rd., Sterling, VA 20164/703-430-0420; FAX: 703-430-7068
Mountain Plains, Inc., 244 Glass Hollow Rd., Alton, VA 22920/800-687-3000
Mountain Rifles Inc., P.O. Box 2789, Palmer, AK 99645/907-373-4194; FAX: 907-373-4195
Mountain South, P.O. Box 381, Barnwell, SC 29812/FAX: 803-259-3227
Mountain View Sports, Inc., Box 188, Troy, NH 03465/603-357-9690; FAX: 603-357-9691
MPI Fiberglass Stocks, 5655 NW St. Helens Rd., Portland, OR 97210/503-226-1215; FAX: 503-226-2661
MSR Targets, P.O. Box 1042, West Covina, CA 91793/818-331-7840
Mt. Baldy Bullet Co., 12981 Old Hill City Rd., Keystone, SD 57751-6623/605-666-4725
MTM Molded Products Co., Inc., 3370 Obco Ct., Dayton, OH 45414/513-890-7461; FAX: 513-890-1747
Mulhern, Rick, Rt. 5, Box 152, Rayville, LA 71269/318-728-2688
Mullins Ammunition, Rt. 2, Box 304K, Clintwood, VA 24228/540-926-6772; FAX: 540-926-6772
Multiplex International, 26 S. Main St., Concord, NH 03301/FAX: 603-796-2223
Multi-Scale Charge Ltd., 3269 Niagara Falls Blvd., N. Tonawanda, NY 14120/905-566-1255; FAX: 905-276-6295
Mundy, Thomas A., 69 Robbins Road, Somerville, NJ 08876/201-722-2199
Murmur Corp., 2823 N. Westmoreland Ave., Dallas, TX 75222/214-630-5400
Muscle Products Corp., 112 Fennell Dr., Butler, PA 16001/800-227-7049, 412-283-0567; FAX: 412-283-8310
Mushroom Express Bullet Co., 601 W. 6th St., Greenfield, IN 46140-1728/317-462-6332
Muzzleload Magnum Products (See MMP)
MWG Co., P.O. Box 971202, Miami, FL 33197/800-428-9394, 305-253-8393; FAX: 305-232-1247

## N

Nagel's Custom Bullets, 100 Scott St., Baytown, TX 77520-2849
National Bullet Co., 1585 E. 361 St., Eastlake, OH 44095/216-951-1854; FAX: 216-951-7761
National Target Co., 4690 Wyaconda Rd., Rockville, MD 20852/800-827-7060, 301-770-7060; FAX: 301-770-7892
Naval Ordnance Works, Rt. 2, Box 919, Sheperdstown, WV 25443/304-876-0998
Navy Arms Co., 689 Bergen Blvd., Ridgefield, NJ 07657/201-945-2500; FAX: 201-945-6859
N.B.B., Inc., 24 Elliot Rd., Sterling, MA 01564/508-422-7538, 800-942-9444
NCP Products, Inc., 3500 12th St. N.W., Canton, OH 44708/330-456-5130: FAX: 330-456-5234
NECO, 1316-67th St., Emeryville, CA 94608/510-450-0420
Necromancer Industries, Inc., 14 Communications Way, West Newton, PA 15089/412-872-8722
NEI Handtools, Inc., 51583 Columbia River Hwy., Scappoose, OR 97056/503-543-6776; FAX: 503-543-6799; E-MAIL: neiht@mcimail.com
Nelson, Stephen, 7365 NW Spring Creek Dr., Corvallis, OR 97330/541-745-5232
Nesci Enterprises, Inc., P.O. Box 119, Summit St., East Hampton, CT 06424/203-267-2588
Nettestad Gun Works, RR 1, Box 160, Pelican Rapids, MN 56572/218-863-4301
New England Ammunition Co., 1771 Post Rd. East, Suite 223, Westport, CT 06880/203-254-8048
New England Arms Co., Box 278, Lawrence Lane, Kittery Point, ME 03905/207-439-0593; FAX: 207-439-6726
New England Custom Gun Service, 438 Willow Brook Rd., RR2, Box 122W, W. Lebanon, NH 03784/603-469-3450; FAX: 603-469-3471
New Win Publishing, Inc., 186 Center St., Clinton, NJ 08809/908-735-9701; FAX: 908-735-9703
Newark Electronics, 4801 N. Ravenswood Ave., Chicago, IL 60640
Newman Gunshop, 119 Miller Rd., Agency, IA 52530/515-937-5775
NgraveR Co., The, 67 Wawecus Hill Rd., Bozrah, CT 06334/860-823-1533
Nickels, Paul R., 4789 Summerhill Rd., Las Vegas, NV 89121/702-435-5318
Nic Max, Inc., 535 Midland Ave., Garfield, NJ 07026/201-546-7191; FAX: 201-546-7419
Niemi Engineering, W.B., Box 126 Center Road, Greensboro, VT 05841/802-533-7180 days, 802-533-7141 evenings
Nightforce (See Lightforce U.S.A. Inc.)
Nikon, Inc., 1300 Walt Whitman Rd., Melville, NY 11747/516-547-8623; FAX: 516-547-0309
Norincoptics (See BEC, Inc.)
Norma Precision AB (See U.S. importers—Dynamit Nobel-RWS Inc.
Norman Custom Gunstocks, Jim, 14281 Cane Rd., Valley Center, CA 92082/619-749-6252
North American Shooting Systems, P.O. Box 306, Osoyoos, B.C. V0H 1V0 CANADA/604-495-3131; FAX: 604-495-2816
North Devon Firearms Services, 3 North St., Braunton, EX33 1AJ ENGLAND/01271 813624; FAX: 01271 813624
North Specialty Products, 2664-B Saturn St., Brea, CA 92621/714-524-1665
Northern Precision Custom Swaged Bullets, 329 S. James St., Carthage, NY 13619/315-493-1711
Northside Gun Shop, 2725 NW 109th, Oklahoma City, OK 73120/405-840-2353
Nosler, Inc., P.O. Box 671, Bend, OR 97709/800-285-3701, 541-382-3921; FAX: 541-388-4667
Novak's, Inc., 1206 1/2 30th St., P.O. Box 4045, Parkersburg, WV 26101/304-485-9295; FAX: 304-428-6722
Now Products, Inc., 1045 South Edward Drive, Tempe, AZ 85281/602-966-6100; FAX: 602-966-0890
Nowlin Mfg. Co., Rt. 1, Box 308, Claremore, OK 74017/918-342-0689; FAX: 918-342-0624
Numrich Arms Corp., 203 Broadway, W. Hurley, NY 12491
Nu-Teck, 30 Industrial Park Rd., Box 37, Centerbrook, CT 06409/203-767-3573; FAX: 203-767-9137
NW Sinker and Tackle, 380 Valley Dr., Myrtle Creek, OR 97457-9717

## O

Oakland Custom Arms, Inc., 4690 W. Walton Blvd., Waterford, MI 48329/810-674-8261
Oakshore Electronic Sights, Inc., P.O. Box 4470, Ocala, FL 32678-4470/904-629-7112; FAX: 904-629-1433
Obermeyer Rifled Barrels, 23122 60th St., Bristol, WI 53104/414-843-3537; FAX: 414-843-2129
October Country, P.O. Box 969, Dept. GD, Hayden, ID 83835/208-772-2068; FAX: 208-772-9230
Oehler Research, Inc., P.O. Box 9135, Austin, TX 78766/512-327-6900, 800-531-5125; FAX: 512-327-6903
Oil Rod and Gun Shop, 69 Oak St., East Douglas, MA 01516/508-476-3687
Oklahoma Ammunition Co., 3701A S. Harvard Ave., No. 367, Tulsa, OK 74135-2265/918-396-3187; FAX: 918-396-4270
OK Weber, Inc., P.O. Box 7485, Eugene, OR 97401/541-747-0458; FAX: 541-747-5927
Old Wagon Bullets, 32 Old Wagon Rd., Wilton, CT 06897
Old West Bullet Moulds, P.O. Box 519, Flora Vista, NM 87415/505-334-6970
Old Western Scrounger, Inc., 12924 Hwy. A-I2, Montague, CA 96064/916-459-5445; FAX: 916-459-3944
Old World Gunsmithing, 2901 SE 122nd St., Portland, OR 97236/503-760-7681
Old World Oil Products, 3827 Queen Ave. N., Minneapolis, MN 55412/612-522-5037
Olympic Optical Co., P.O. Box 752377, Memphis, TN 38175-2377/901-794-3890, 800-238-7120; FAX: 901-794-0676, 800-748-1669
Omark Industries, Div. of Blount, Inc., 2299 Snake River Ave., P.O. Box 856, Lewiston, ID 83501/800-627-3640, 208-746-2351
One Of A Kind, 15610 Purple Sage, San Antonio, TX 78255/512-695-3364
Op-Tec, P.O. Box L632, Langhorn, PA 19047/215-757-5037
Optical Services Co., P.O. Box 1174, Santa Teresa, NM 88008-1174/505-589-3833
Orchard Park Enterprise, P.O. Box 563, Orchard Park, NY 14227/616-656-0356
Ordnance Works, The, 2969 Pidgeon Point Road, Eureka, CA 95501/707-443-3252
Oregon Arms, Inc. (See Rogue Rifle Co., Inc.)
Oregon Trail Bullet Company, P.O. Box 529, Dept. P, Baker City, OR 97814/800-811-0548; FAX: 514-523-1803
Or-Un, Tahtakale Menekse Han 18, Istanbul, TURKEY 34460/90212-522-5912; FAX: 90212-522-7973
Orvis Co., The, Rt. 7, Manchester, VT 05254/802-362-3622 ext. 283; FAX: 802-362-3525
Ottmar, Maurice, Box 657, 113 E. Fir, Coulee City, WA 99115/509-632-5717
Outdoor Connection, Inc., The, 201 Cotton Dr., P.O. Box 7751, Waco, TX 76714-7751/800-533-6076; 817-772-5575; FAX: 817-776-3553
Outdoorsman's Bookstore, The, Llangorse, Brecon, Powys LD3 7UE, U.K./44-1874-658-660; FAX: 44-1874-658-650
Outers Laboratories, Div. of Blount, Inc., Sporting Equipment Div., Route 2,, P.O. Box 39/Onalaska, WI 54650
608-781-5800; FAX: 608-781-0368
Ox-Yoke Originals, Inc., 34 Main St., Milo, ME 04463/800-231-8313, 207-943-7351; FAX: 207-943-2416

## P

P&M Sales and Service, 5724 Gainsborough Pl., Oak Forest, IL 60452/708-687-7149
P&S Gun Service, 2138 Old Shepardsville Rd., Louisville, KY 40218/502-456-9346
Pac-Nor Barreling, 99299 Overlook Rd., P.O. Box 6188, Brookings, OR 97415/503-469-7330; FAX: 503-469-7331
Pachmayr, Ltd., 1875 S. Mountain Ave., Monrovia, CA 91016/818-357-7771, 800-423-9704; FAX: 818-358-7251
Pacific Cartridge, Inc., 2425 Salashan Loop Road, Ferndale, WA 98248/360-366-4444; FAX: 360-366-4445
Pacific Precision, 755 Antelope Rd., P.O. Box 2549, White City, OR 97503/503-826-5808; FAX: 503-826-5304
Pacific Research Laboratories, Inc. (See Rimrock Rifle Stocks)
Paco's (See Small Custom Mould & Bullet Co.)
Rimrock Rifle Stocks, P.O. Box 589, Vashon Island, WA 98070/206-463-5551; FAX: 206-463-2526
P.A.C.T., Inc., P.O. Box 531525, Grand Prairie, TX 75053/214-641-0049
Page Custom Bullets, P.O. Box 25, Port Moresby Papua, NEW GUINEA
Pagel Gun Works, Inc., 1407 4th St. NW, Grand Rapids, MN 55744/218-326-3003
Palmer Manufacturing Co., Inc., C., P.O. Box 220, West Newton, PA 15089/412-872-8200; FAX: 412-872-8302
PanaVise Products, Inc., 7540 Colbert Drive, Sparks, NV 89431/702-850-2900; FAX: 702-850-2929
Paragon Sales & Services, Inc., P.O. Box 2022, Joliet, IL 60434/815-725-9212; FAX: 815-725-8974
Parker Gun Finishes, 9337 Smokey Row Rd., Strawberry Plains, TN 37871/423-933-3286
Parsons Optical Mfg. Co., P.O. Box 192, Ross, OH 45061/513-867-0820; FAX: 513-867-8380
Parts & Surplus, P.O. Box 22074, Memphis, TN 38122/901-683-4007
Pasadena Gun Center, 206 E. Shaw, Pasadena, TX 77506/713-472-0417; FAX: 713-472-1322
Passive Bullet Traps, Inc. (See Savage Range Systems, Inc.)
PAST Sporting Goods, Inc., P.O. Box 1035, Columbia, MO 65205/314-445-9200; FAX: 314-446-6606
Paterson Gunsmithing, 438 Main St., Paterson, NJ 07502/201-345-4100
Patrick Bullets, P.O. Box 172, Warwick QSLD 4370 AUSTRALIA
Pattern Control, 114 N. Third St., P.O. Box 462105, Garland, TX 75046/214-494-3551; FAX: 214-272-8447
Paul Co., The, 27385 Pressonville Rd., Wellsville, KS 66092/913-883-4444; FAX: 913-883-2525
Paulsen Gunstocks, Rt. 71, Box 11, Chinook, MT 59523/406-357-3403
PC Bullet/ADC, Inc., 52700 NE First, Scappoose, OR 97056-3212/503-543-5088; FAX: 503-543-5990
Pease Accuracy, Bob, P.O. Box 310787, New Braunfels, TX 78131/210-625-1342
PECAR Herbert Schwarz, GmbH, Kreuzbergstrasse 6, 10965 Berlin, GERMANY/004930-785-7383; FAX: 004930-785-1934
Pecatonica River Longrifle, 5205 Nottingham Dr., Rockford, IL 61111/815-968-1995; FAX: 815-968-1996
Pedersoli and Co., Davide, Via Artigiani 57, Gardone V.T., Brescia, ITALY 25063/030-8912402; FAX: 030-8911019
Peerless Alloy, Inc., 1445 Osage St., Denver, CO 80204-2439/303-825-6394, 800-253-1278
Pejsa Ballistics, 2120 Kenwood Pkwy., Minneapolis, MN 55405/612-374-3337; FAX: 612-374-3337
Pell, John T. (See KOGOT)
Peltor, Inc. (See Aero Peltor)
PEM's Mfg. Co., 5063 Waterloo Rd., Atwater, OH 44201/216-947-3721
Pence Precision Barrels, 7567 E. 900 S., S. Whitley, IN 46787/219-839-4745
Pend Oreille Sport Shop, 3100 Hwy. 200 East, Sandpoint, ID 83864/208-263-2412
Pendleton Royal, c/o Swingler Buckland Ltd., 4/7 Highgate St., Birmingham, ENGLAND B12 0XS/44 121 440 3060, 44 121 446 5898; FAX: 44 121 446 4165
Penn Bullets, P.O. Box 756, Indianola, PA 15051
Penrod Precision, 312 College Ave., P.O. Box 307, N. Manchester, IN 46962/219-982-8385
Pentax Corp., 35 Inverness Dr. E., Englewood, CO 80112/800-709-2020; FAX: 303-643-0393
Pentheny de Pentheny, 2352 Baggett Ct., Santa Rosa, CA 95401/707-573-1390; FAX: 707-573-1390
Perazone-Gunsmith, Brian, Cold Spring Rd., Roxbury, NY 12474/607-326-4088; FAX: 607-326-3140
Perazzi USA, Inc., 1207 S. Shamrock Ave., Monrovia, CA 91016/818-303-0068; FAX: 818-303-2081
Personal Protection Systems, RD 5, Box 5027-A, Moscow, PA 18444/717-842-1766
Petersen Publishing Co., 6420 Wilshire Blvd., Los Angeles, CA 90048/213-782-2000; FAX: 213-782-2867
Petro-Explo, Inc., 7650 U.S. Hwy. 287, Suite 100, Arlington, TX 76017/817-478-8888
Pettinger Books, Gerald, Rt. 2, Box 125, Russell, IA 50238/515-535-2239
Phil-Chem, Inc. (See George & Roy's)
Phillippi Custom Bullets, Justin, P.O. Box 773, Ligonier, PA 15658/412-238-9671
Phillips, Jerry, P.O. Box L632, Langhorne, PA 19047/215-757-5037
Pinetree Bullets, 133 Skeena St., Kitimat BC, CANADA V8C 1Z1/604-632-3768; FAX: 604-632-3768
Pioneer Arms Co., 355 Lawrence Rd., Broomall, PA 19008/215-356-5203
Pioneer Research, Inc., 216 Haddon Ave., Suite 102, Westmont, NJ 08108/800-257-7742; FAX: 609-858-8695
Plum City Ballistic Range, N2162 80th St., Plum City, WI 54761-8622/715-647-2539
PlumFire Press, Inc., 30-A Grove Ave., Patchogue, NY 11772-4112/800-695-7246; FAX:516-758-4071
PMC/Eldorado Cartridge Corp., P.O. Box 62508, 12801 U.S. Hwy. 95 S., Boulder City, NV 89005/702-294-0025; FAX: 702-294-0121
P.M. Enterprises, Inc., 146 Curtis Hill Rd., Chehalis, WA 98532/360-748-3743; FAX: 360-748-1802
Pohl, Henry A. (See Great American Gun Co.)
Pointing Dog Journal, Village Press Publications, P.O. Box 968, Dept. PGD,
Powley Computer (See Hutton Rifle Ranch)
Professional Hunter Supplies (See Star Custom Bullets)
Traverse City, MI 49685/800-272-3246; FAX: 616-946-3289
Police Bookshelf, P.O. Box 122, Concord, NH 03301/603-224-6814; FAX: 603-226-3554
Polywad, Inc., P.O. Box 7916, Macon, GA 31209/912-477-0669
Pomeroy, Robert, RR1, Box 50, E. Corinth, ME 04427/207-285-7721
Ponsness/Warren, P.O. Box 8, Rathdrum, ID 83858/208-687-2231; FAX: 208-687-2233
Pony Express Reloaders, 608 E. Co. Rd. D, Suite 3, St. Paul, MN 55117/612-483-9406; FAX: 612-483-9884
Portus, Robert, 130 Ferry Rd., Grants Pass, OR 97526/503-476-4919
Powder Horn, Inc., The, P.O. Box 114 Patty Drive, Cusseta, GA 31805/404-989-3257
Powell & Son (Gunmakers) Ltd., William, 35-37 Carrs Lane, Birmingham B4 7SX ENGLAND/121-643-0689; FAX: 121-631-3504
Powell Agency, William, The, 22 Circle Dr., Bellmore, NY 11710/516-679-1158
Prairie River Arms, 1220 N. Sixth St., Princeton, IL 61356/815-875-1616, 800-445-1541; FAX: 815-875-1402
Precise Metalsmithing Enterprises, 146 Curtis Hill Rd., Chehalis, WA 98532/206-748-3743; FAX: 206-748-8102
Precision Cartridge, 176 Eastside Rd., Deer Lodge, MT 59722/800-397-3901, 406-846-3900
Precision Cast Bullets, 101 Mud Creek Lane, Ronan, MT 59864/406-676-5135
Precision Castings & Equipment, Inc., P.O. Box 326, Jasper, IN 47547-0135/812-634-9167
Precision Components, 3177 Sunrise Lake, Milford, PA 18337/717-686-4414
Precision Components and Guns, Rt. 55, P.O. Box 337, Pawling, NY 12564/914-855-3040
Precision Delta Corp., P.O. Box 128, Ruleville, MS 38771/601-756-2810; FAX: 601-756-2590
Precision Munitions, Inc., P.O. Box 326, Jasper, IN 47547
Precision Reloading, Inc., P.O. Box 122, Stafford Springs, CT 06076/860-684-7979; FAX: 860-684-6788
Precision Shooting, Inc., 222 McKee St., Manchester, CT 06040/860-645-8776; FAX: 860-643-8215
Precision Sport Optics, 15571 Producer Lane, Unit G, Huntington Beach, CA 92649/714-891-1309; FAX: 714-892-6920
Premier Reticles, 920 Breckinridge Lane, Winchester, VA 22601-6707/540-722-0601; FAX: 540-722-3522
Prescott Projectile Co., 1808 Meadowbrook Road, Prescott, AZ 86303
Preslik's Gunstocks, 4245 Keith Ln., Chico, CA 95926/916-891-8236
Price Bullets, Patrick W., 16520 Worthley Drive, San Lorenzo, CA 94580/510-278-1547
Prime Reloading, 30 Chiswick End, Meldreth, Royston SG8 6LZ UK/0763-260636
Primos, Inc., P.O. Box 12785, Jackson, MS 39236-2785/601-366-1288; FAX: 601-362-3274

PRL Bullets, c/o Blackburn Enterprises, 114 Stuart Rd., Ste. 110, Cleveland, TN 37312/423-559-0340
Pro Load Ammunition, Inc., 5180 E. Seltice Way, Post Falls, ID 83854/208-773-9444; FAX: 208-773-9441
Pro-Port Ltd., 41302 Executive Dr., Harrison Twp., MI 48045-1306/810-469-7323; FAX: 810-469-0425
Pro-Shot Products, Inc., P.O. Box 763, Taylorville, IL 62568/217-824-9133; FAX: 217-824-8861
Prolix® Lubricants, P.O. Box 1348, Victorville, CA 92393/800-248-LUBE, 619-243-3129; FAX: 619-241-0148
Protector Mfg. Co., Inc., The, 443 Ashwood Place, Boca Raton, FL 33431/407-394-6011
Protektor Model, 1-11 Bridge St., Galeton, PA 16922/814-435-2442
ProWare,Inc., 15847 NE Hancock St., Portland, OR 97230/503-239-0159
PWL Gunleather, P.O. Box 450432, Atlanta, GA 31145/770-822-1640; FAX: 770-822-1704

## Q

Quack Decoy & Sporting Clays, 4 Ann & Hope Way, P.O. Box 98, Cumberland, RI 02864/401-723-8202; FAX: 401-722-5910
Quarton USA, Ltd. Co., 7042 Alamo Downs Pkwy., Suite 370, San Antonio, TX 78238-4518/800-520-8435, 210-520-8430; FAX: 210-520-8433

## R

R&J Gun Shop, 133 W. Main St., John Day, OR 97845/503-575-2130
R&S Industries Corp., 8255 Brentwood Industrial Dr., St. Louis, MO 63144/314-781-5400
Radiator Specialty Co., 1900 Wilkinson Blvd., P.O. Box 34689, Charlotte, NC 28234/800-438-6947; FAX: 800-421-9525
Rainier Ballistics Corp., 4500 15th St. East, Tacoma, WA 98424/800-638-8722, 206-922-7589; FAX: 206-922-7854
Ram-Line Blount, Inc., P.O. Box 39, Onalaska, WI 54650-0039
Rampart International, 2781 W. MacArthur Blvd., B-283, Santa Ana, CA 92704/800-976-7240, 714-557-6405
Ranch Products, P.O. Box 145, Malinta, OH 43535/313-277-3118; FAX: 313-565-8536
Randolph Engineering, Inc., 26 Thomas Patten Dr., Randolph, MA 02368/800-541-1405; FAX: 800-875-4200
Range Brass Products Company, P.O. Box 218, Rockport, TX 78381
Ranger Products, 2623 Grand Blvd., Suite 209, Holiday, FL 34609/813-942-4652, 800-407-7007; FAX: 813-942-6221
Ranging, Inc., Routes 5 & 20, East Bloomfield, NY 14443/716-657-6161; FAX: 716-657-5405
Ransom International Corp., P.O. Box 3845, 1040-A Sandretto Dr., Prescott, AZ 86302/520-778-7899; FAX: 520-778-7993; E-MAIL: ransom@primenet.com; WEB: http://www.primenet.com/˜ransom
Rapine Bullet Mould Mfg. Co., 9503 Landis Lane, East Greenville, PA 18041/215-679-5413; FAX: 215-679-9795
Raptor Arms Co., Inc., 115 S. Union St., Suite 308, Alexandria, VA 22314/703-683-0018; FAX: 703-683-5592
Raytech, Div. of Lyman Products Corp., 475 Smith Street, Middletown, CT 06457-1541/860-632-2020; FAX: 860-632-1699
RCBS, Div. of Blount, Inc., Sporting Equipment Div., 605 Oro Dam Blvd., Oroville, CA 95965/800-533-5000, 916-533-5191; FAX: 916-533-1647
Reagent Chemical & Research, Inc. (See Calico Hardwoods, Inc.)
Reardon Products, P.O. Box 126, Morrison, IL 61270/815-772-3155
Recoilless Technologies, Inc., 3432 W. Wilshire Dr., Suite 11, Phoenix, AZ 85009/602-278-8903; FAX: 602-272-5946
Red Cedar Precision Mfg., W. 485 Spruce Dr., Brodhead, WI 53520/608-897-8416
Red Diamond Dist. Co., 1304 Snowdon Dr., Knoxville, TN 37912
Redding Reloading Equipment, 1089 Starr Rd., Cortland, NY 13045/607-753-3331; FAX: 607-756-8445
Redfield, Inc., 5800 E. Jewell Ave., Denver, CO 80224/303-757-6411; FAX: 303-756-2338
Redman's Rifling & Reboring, 189 Nichols Rd., Omak, WA 98841/509-826-5512
Redwood Bullet Works, 3559 Bay Rd., Redwood City, CA 94063/415-367-6741
R.E.I., P.O. Box 88, Tallevast, FL 34270/813-755-0085
Reiswig, Wallace E. (See Claro Walnut Gunstock Co.)
Rowe Engineering, Inc.; Kapro Mfg. Co., Inc.
Reloaders Equipment Co., 4680 High St., Ecorse, MI 48229
Reloading Specialties, Inc., Box 1130, Pine Island, MN 55463/507-356-8500; FAX: 507-356-8800
Remington Arms Co., Inc., 870 Remington Drive, P.O. Box 700, Madison, NC 27025-0700/800-243-9700; 910-548-8700
Remington Double Shotguns, 7885 Cyd Dr., Denver, CO 80221/303-429-6947
R.E.T. Enterprises, 2608 S. Chestnut, Broken Arrow, OK 74012/918-251-GUNS; FAX: 918-251-0587
R.G.-G., Inc., P.O. Box 1261, Conifer, CO 80433-1261/303-697-4154; FAX: 303-697-4154
Rhino, P.O. Box 787, Locust, NC 28097/704-753-2198
Rice, Keith (See White Rock Tool & Die)
Richards Micro-Fit Stocks, 8331 N. San Fernando Ave., Sun Valley, CA 91352/818-767-6097; FAX: 818-767-7121
Rickard, Pete, Inc., RD 1, Box 292, Cobleskill, NY 12043/800-282-5663; FAX: 518-234-2454
Ridgetop Sporting Goods, P.O. Box 306, 42907 Hilligoss Ln. East, Eatonville, WA 98328/360-832-6422; FAX: 360-832-6422
Riebe Co., W.J., 3434 Tucker Rd., Boise, ID 83703
Rifle Works & Armory, 707 12th St., Cody, WY 82414/307-587-4919
RIG Products, 87 Coney Island Dr., Sparks, NV 89431-6334/702-331-5666; FAX: 702-331-5669
Riling Arms Books Co., Ray, 6844 Gorsten St., P.O. Box 18925, Philadelphia, PA 19119/215-438-2456; FAX: 215-438-5395
R.I.S. Co., Inc., 718 Timberlake Circle, Richardson, TX 75080/214-235-0933
RLCM Enterprises, 110 Hill Crest Drive, Burleson, TX 76028
R.M. Precision, Inc., Attn. Greg F. Smith Marketing, P.O. Box 210, LaVerkin, UT 84745/801-635-4656; FAX: 801-635-4430
RMS Custom Gunsmithing, 4120 N. Bitterwell, Prescott Valley, AZ 86314/520-772-7626
Roberts Products, 25328 SE Iss. Beaver Lk. Rd., Issaquah, WA 98029/206-392-8172
Robinett, R.G., P.O. Box 72, Madrid, IA 50156/515-795-2906
Robinson, Don, Pennsylvania Hse., 36 Fairfax Crescent, Southowram, Halifax, W. Yorkshire HX3 9SQ, ENGLAND/0422-364458
Robinson Firearms Mfg. Ltd., 1699 Blondeaux Crescent, Kelowna, B.C. CANADA V1Y 4J8/604-868-9596
Robinson H.V. Bullets, 3145 Church St., Zachary, LA 70791/504-654-4029
Rochester Lead Works, 76 Anderson Ave., Rochester, NY 14607/716-442-8500; FAX: 716-442-4712
Rockwood Corp., Speedwell Division, 136 Lincoln Blvd., Middlesex, NJ 08846/908-560-7171, 800-243-8274; FAX: 980-560-7475
Rocky Fork Enterprises, P.O. Box 427, 878 Battle Rd., Nolensville, TN 37135/615-941-1307
Rocky Mountain Arms, Inc., 600 S. Sunset, Unit C, Longmont, CO 80501/303-768-8522; FAX: 303-678-8766
Rocky Mountain High Sports Glasses, 8121 N. Central Park Ave., Skokie, IL 60076/847-679-1012, 800-323-1418; FAX: 847-679-0184
Rocky Mountain Rifle Works Ltd., 1707 14th St., Boulder, CO 80302/303-443-9189
Rocky Mountain Target Co., 3 Aloe Way, Leesburg, FL 34788/352-365-9598
Rocky Mountain Wildlife Products, P.O. Box 999, La Porte, CO 80535/970-484-2768; FAX: 970-484-0807
Rod Guide Co., Box 1149, Forsyth, MO 65653/800-952-2774
Rogers Gunsmithing, Bob, P.O. Box 305, 344 S. Walnut St., Franklin Grove, IL 61031/815-456-2685; FAX: 815-288-7142
Rogue Rifle Co., Inc., P.O. Box 20, Prospect, OR 97536/541-560-4040; FAX: 541-560-4041
Rolston, Inc., Fred W., 210 E. Cummins St., Tecumseh, MI 49286/517-423-6002, 800-314-9061 (orders only); FAX: 517-423-6002
Rooster Laboratories, P.O. Box 412514, Kansas City, MO 64141/816-474-1622; FAX: 816-474-1307
Rorschach Precision Products, P.O. Box 151613, Irving, TX 75015/214-790-3487
Rosenthal, Brad and Sallie, 19303 Ossenfort Ct., St. Louis, MO 63038/314-273-5159; FAX: 314-273-5149
Ross, Don, 12813 West 83 Terrace, Lenexa, KS 66215/913-492-6982
Ross & Webb (See Ross, Don)
Roto Carve, 2754 Garden Ave., Janesville, IA 50647
Rowe Engineering, Inc. (See R.E.I.)
Royal Arms Gunstocks, 919 8th Ave. NW, Great Falls, MT 59404/406-453-1149
RPM, 15481 N. Twin Lakes Dr., Tucson, AZ 85739/520-825-1233; FAX: 520-825-3333
Rubright Bullets, 1008 S. Quince Rd., Walnutport, PA 18088/215-767-1339
Rucker Dist. Inc., P.O. Box 479, Terrell, TX 75160/214-563-2094
Rupert's Gun Shop, 2202 Dick Rd., Suite B, Fenwick, MI 48834/517-248-3252
Rusteprufe Laboratories, 1319 Jefferson Ave., Sparta, WI 54656/608-269-4144
Rusty Duck Premium Gun Care Products, 7785 Foundation Dr., Suite 6, Florence, KY 41042/606-342-5553; FAX: 606-342-5556
Rutgers Book Center, 127 Raritan Ave., Highland Park, NJ 08904/908-545-4344; FAX: 908-545-6686
Ryan, Chad L., RR 3, Box 72, Cresco, IA 52136/319-547-4384

## S

S&B Industries, 11238 McKinley Rd., Montrose, MI 48457/810-639-5491
S&K Mfg. Co., P.O. Box 247, Pittsfield, PA 16340/814-563-7808; FAX: 814-563-4067
S&S Firearms, 74-11 Myrtle Ave., Glendale, NY 11385/718-497-1100; FAX: 718-497-1105
Sabatti S.r.l., via Alessandro Volta 90, 25063 Gardone V.T., Brescia, ITALY/030-8912207-831312; FAX: 030-8912059
SAECO (See Redding Reloading Equipment)
Safari Press, Inc., 15621 Chemical Lane B, Huntington Beach, CA 92649/714-894-9080; FAX: 714-894-4949
Samco Global Arms, Inc., 6995 NW 43rd St., Miami, FL 33166/305-593-9782
San Francisco Gun Exchange, 124 Second St., San Francisco, CA 94105/415-982-6097
Sanders Custom Gun Service, 2358 Tyler Lane, Louisville, KY 40205/502-454-3338
Sanders Gun and Machine Shop, 145 Delhi Road, Manchester, IA 52057
Sandia Die & Cartridge Co., 37 Atancacio Rd. NE, Albuquerque, NM 87123/505-298-5729
Saunders Gun & Machine Shop, R.R. 2, Delhi Road, Manchester, IA 52057
Savage Range Systems, Inc., 100 Springdale RD., Westfield, MA 01085/413-568-7001; FAX: 413-562-1152
Saville Iron Co. (See Greenwood Precision)
Savino, Barbara J., P.O. Box 1104, Hardwick, VT 05843-1104
Schaefer Shooting Sports, P.O. Box 1515, Melville, NY 11747-0515/516-379-4900; FAX: 516-379-6701
Scharch Mfg., Inc., 10325 CR 120, Salida, CO 81201/719-539-7242, 800-836-4683; FAX: 719-539-3021
Schiffman, Curt, 3017 Kevin Cr., Idaho Falls, ID 83402/208-524-4684
Schiffman, Mike, 8233 S. Crystal Springs, McCammon, ID 83250/208-254-9114
Schmidtke Group, 17050 W. Salentine Dr., New Berlin, WI 53151-7349
Schmidt & Bender, Inc., Brook Rd., P.O. Box 134, Meriden, NH 03770/603-469-3565, 800-468-3450; FAX: 603-469-3471
Schmidtman Custom Ammunition, 6 Gilbert Court, Cotati, CA 94931
Schneider Bullets, 3655 West 214th St., Fairview Park, OH 44126
Schneider Rifle Barrels, Inc., Gary, 12202 N. 62nd Pl., Scottsdale, AZ 85254/602-948-2525
Schroeder Bullets, 1421 Thermal Ave., San Diego, CA 92154/619-423-3523; FAX: 619-423-8124
Schuetzen Pistol Works, 620-626 Old Pacific Hwy. SE, Olympia, WA 98513/360-459-3471; FAX: 360-491-3447
Schumakers Gun Shop, 512 Prouty Corner Lp. A, Colville, WA 99114/509-684-4848
Schwartz Custom Guns, David W., 2505 Waller St., Eau Claire, WI 54703/715-832-1735
Schwartz Custom Guns, Wayne E., 970 E. Britton Rd., Morrice, MI 48857/517-625-4079
Scope Control, Inc., 5775 Co. Rd. 23 SE, Alexandria, MN 56308/612-762-7295
ScopLevel, 151 Lindbergh Ave., Suite C, Livermore, CA 94550/510-449-5052; FAX: 510-373-0861
Score High Gunsmithing, 9812-A, Cochiti SE, Albuquerque, NM 87123/800-326-5632, 505-292-5532; FAX: 505-292-2592; E-MAIL: scorehi@rt66.com; WEB: http://www.rt66.com/˜score-hi/home.htm
Scot Powder, Rt.1 Box 167, McEwen, TN 37101/800-416-3006; FAX: 615-729-4211
Scot Powder Co. of Ohio, Inc., Box GD96, Only, TN 37140/615-729-4207, 800-416-3006; FAX: 615-729-4217
Scott Fine Guns, Inc., Thad, P.O. Box 412, Indianola, MS 38751/601-887-5929
Scott, Dwight, 23089 Englehardt St., Clair Shores, MI 48080/313-779-4735
Seattle Binocular & Scope Repair Co., P.O. Box 46094, Seattle, WA 98146/206-932-3733
Seebeck Assoc., R.E., P.O. Box 59752, Dallas, TX 75229
Segway Industries, P.O. Box 783, Suffern, NY 10901-0783/914-357-5510
Seligman Shooting Products, Box 133, Seligman, AZ 86337/602-422-3607
Selsi Co., Inc., P.O. Box 10, Midland Park, NJ 07432-0010/201-935-0388; FAX: 201-935-5851
Semmer, Charles (See Remington Double Shotguns)
Sentinel Arms, P.O. Box 57, Detroit, MI 48231/313-331-1951; FAX: 313-331-1456
Service Armament, 689 Bergen Blvd., Ridgefield, NJ 07657
Shappy Bullets, 76 Milldale Ave., Plantsville, CT 06479/203-621-3704
Sharp Shooter Supply, 4970 Lehman Road, Delphos, OH 45833/419-695-3179
C. Sharps Arms Co. Inc., 100 Centennial, Box 885, Big Timber, MT 59011/406-932-4353
Shaw, Inc., E.R. (See Small Arms Mfg. Co.)
Shay's Gunsmithing, 931 Marvin Ave., Lebanon, PA 17042
Shell Shack, 113 E. Main, Laurel, MT 59044/406-628-8986
Shepherd Scope Ltd., Box 189, Waterloo, NE 68069/402-779-2424; FAX: 402-779-4010
Shilen, Inc., 205 Metro Park Blvd., Ennis, TX 75119/972-875-5318; FAX: 972-875-5402
Shiloh Creek, Box 357, Cottleville, MO 63338/314-925-1842; FAX: 314-925-1842
Shiloh Rifle Mfg., 201 Centennial Dr., Big Timber, MT 59011/406-932-4454; FAX: 406-932-5627
Shooter's Choice, 16770 Hilltop Park Place, Chagrin Falls, OH 44023/216-543-8808; FAX: 216-543-8811
Shooter's Edge, Inc., P.O.Box 769, Trinidad, CO 81082
Shooters Supply, 1120 Tieton Dr., Yakima, WA 98902/509-452-1181
Shootin' Accessories, Ltd., P.O. Box 6810, Auburn, CA 95604/916-889-2220
Shooting Chrony, Inc., 3269 Niagara Falls Blvd., N. Tonawanda, NY 14120/905-276-6292; FAX: 416-276-6295
Shooting Components Marketing, P.O. Box 1069, Englewood, CO 80150/303-987-2543; FAX: 303-989-3508
Shoot-N-C Targets (See Birchwood Casey)
Shotgun Shop, The, 14145 Proctor Ave., Suite 3, Industry, CA 91746/818-855-2737; FAX: 818-855-2735
ShurKatch Corporation, 50 Elm St., Richfield Springs, NY 13439/315-858-1470; FAX: 315-858-2969
Siegrist Gun Shop, 8754 Turtle Road, Whittemore, MI 48770

Sierra Bullets, 1400 W. Henry St., Sedalia, MO 65301/816-827-6300; FAX: 816-827-6300; WEB: http://www.sierrabullets.com
Sierra Specialty Prod. Co., 1344 Oakhurst Ave., Los Altos, CA 94024/FAX: 415-965-1536
Sightron, Inc., 1672B Hwy. 96, Franklinton, NC 27525/919-528-8783; FAX: 919-528-0995
Signet Metal Corp., 551 Stewart Ave., Brooklyn, NY 11222/718-384-5400; FAX: 718-388-7488
Sile Distributors, Inc., 7 Centre Market Pl., New York, NY 10013/212-925-4111; FAX: 212-925-3149
Silencio/Safety Direct, 56 Coney Island Dr., Sparks, NV 89431/800-648-1812, 702-354-4451; FAX: 702-359-1074
Silver Eagle Machining, 18007 N. 69th Ave., Glendale, AZ 85308
Silver-Tip Corp., RR2, Box 184, Gloster, MS 39638-9520
Simmons, Jerry, 715 Middlebury St., Goshen, IN 46526/219-533-8546
Simmons Enterprises, Ernie, 709 East Elizabethtown Rd., Manheim, PA 17545/717-664-4040
Simmons Gun Repair, Inc., 700 S. Rogers Rd., Olathe, KS 66062/913-782-3131; FAX: 913-782-4189
Simmons Outdoor Corp., 201 Plantation Oak Parkway, Thomasville, GA 31792/912-227-9053; FAX: 912-227-9054
Sinclair International, Inc., 2330 Wayne Haven St., Fort Wayne, IN 46803/219-493-1858; FAX: 219-493-2530
Siskiyou Gun Works (See Donnelly, C.P.)
Six Enterprises, 320-D Turtle Creek Ct., San Jose, CA 95125/408-999-0201; FAX: 408-999-0216
SKAN A.R., 4 St. Catherines Road, Long Melford, Suffolk, CO10 9JU ENGLAND/011-0787-312942
SKB Shotguns, 4325 S. 120th St., P.O. Box 37669, Omaha, NE 68137/800-752-2767; FAX: 402-330-8029
Skeoch, Brian R., P.O. Box 279, Glenrock, WY 82637/307-436-9655; FAX: 307-436-9034
Skip's Machine, 364 29 Road, Grand Junction, CO 81501/303-245-5417
SKR Industries, POB 1382, San Angelo, TX 76902/915-658-3133
S.L.A.P. Industries, P.O. Box 1121, Parklands 2121, SOUTH AFRICA/27-11-788-0030; FAX: 27-11-788-0030
Slug Group, Inc., P.O. Box 376, New Paris, PA 15554/814-839-4517; FAX: 814-839-2601
Slug Site, Ozark Wilds, Rt. 2, Box 158, Versailles, MO 65084/573-378-6430
Small Arms Mfg. Co., 5312 Thoms Run Rd., Bridgeville, PA 15017/412-221-4343; FAX: 412-221-4303
Small Custom Mould & Bullet Co., Box 17211, Tucson, AZ 85731
Smith, Sharmon, 4545 Speas Rd., Fruitland, ID 83619/208-452-6329
Snider Stocks, Walter S., Rt. 2 P.O. Box 147, Denton, NC 27239
Sno-Seal (See Atsko/Sno-Seal)
Sonora Rifle Barrel Co., 14396 D. Tuolumne Rd., Sonora, CA 95370/209-532-4139
SOS Products Co. (See Buck Stix—SOS Products Co.)
Southern Ammunition Co., Inc., 4232 Meadow St., Loris, SC 29569-3124/803-756-3262; FAX: 803-756-3583
Specialty Gunsmithing, Lynn McMurdo, P.O. Box 404, Afton, WY 83110/307-886-5535
Specialty Shooters Supply, Inc., 3325 Griffin Rd., Suite 9mm, Fort Lauderdale, FL 33317
Speedfeed, Inc., 3820 Industrial Way, Suite N, Benicia, CA 94510/707-746-1221; FAX: 707-746-1888
Speer Products, Div. of Blount, Inc., Sporting Equipment Div., P.O. Box 856, Lewiston, ID 83501/208-746-2351; FAX: 208-746-2915
Speiser, Fred D., 2229 Dearborn, Missoula, MT 59801/406-549-8133
Spence, George W., 115 Locust St., Steele, MO 63877/314-695-4926
Spencer's Custom Guns, Rt. 1, Box 546, Scottsville, VA 24590/804-293-6836
SPG, Inc., P.O. Box 761, Livingston, MT 59047/406-222-8416; FAX: 406-222-8416
Sport Flite Manufacturing Co., P.O. Box 1082, Bloomfield Hills, MI 48303/810-647-3747
Sportsman Supply Co., 714 East Eastwood, P.O. Box 650, Marshall, MO 65340/816-886-9393
Sportsmatch U.K. Ltd., 16 Summer St., Leighton Buzzard, Bedfordshire, LU7 8HT ENGLAND/01525-381638; FAX: 01525-851236
Springfield, Inc., 420 W. Main St., Geneseo, IL 61254/309-944-5631; FAX: 309-944-3676
SSK Industries, 721 Woodvue Lane, Wintersville, OH 43952/614-264-0176; FAX: 614-264-2257
Stackpole Books, 5067 Ritter Rd., Mechanicsburg, PA 17055-6921/717-796-0411; FAX: 717-796-0412
Stalwart Corporation, 76 Imperial, Unit A, Evanston, WY 82930/307-789-7687; FAX: 307-789-7688
Stanley Bullets, 2085 Heatheridge Ln., Reno, NV 89509
Star Ammunition, Inc., 5520 Rock Hampton Ct., Indianapolis, IN 46268/317-872-5840, 800-221-5927; FAX: 317-872-5847
Star Custom Bullets, P.O. Box 608, 468 Main St., Ferndale, CA 95536/707-786-9140; FAX: 707-786-9117
Star Machine Works, 418 10th Ave., San Diego, CA 92101/619-232-3216
Star Master-Match Bullets (See Star Ammunition, Inc.)
Star Reloading Co., Inc. (See Star Ammunition, Inc.)
Starke Bullet Company, P.O. Box 400, 605 6th St. NW, Cooperstown, ND 58425/888-797-3431
Starkey Labs, 6700 Washington Ave. S., Eden Prairie, MN 55344
Starkey's Gun Shop, 9430 McCombs, El Paso, TX 79924/915-751-3030
Stark's Bullet Mfg., 2580 Monroe St., Eugene, OR 97405
Starline, 1300 W. Henry St., Sedalia, MO 65301/816-827-6640; FAX: 816-827-6650
Starr Trading Co., Jedediah, P.O. Box 2007, Farmington Hills, MI 48333/810-683-4343; FAX: 810-683-3282
State Arms Gun Co., 815 S. Division St., Waunakee, WI 53597/608-849-5800
Stegall, James B., 26 Forest Rd., Wallkill, NY 12589
Steiner (See Pioneer Research, Inc.)
Stewart Game Calls, Inc., Johnny, P.O. Box 7954, 5100 Fort Ave., Waco, TX 76714/817-772-3261; FAX: 817-772-3670
Stewart's Gunsmithing, P.O. Box 5854, Pietersburg North 0750, Transvaal, SOUTH AFRICA/01521-89401
Steyr Mannlicher AG & CO KG, Mannlicherstrasse 1, A-4400 Steyr, AUSTRIA/0043-7252-78621; FAX: 0043-7252-68621
STI International, 114 Halmar Cove, Georgetown, TX 78628/800-959-8201; FAX: 512-819-0465
Stiles Custom Guns, RD3, Box 1605, Homer City, PA 15748/412-479-9945, 412-479-8666
Stillwell, Robert, 421 Judith Ann Dr., Schertz, TX 78154
Stoeger Industries, 5 Mansard Ct., Wayne, NJ 07470/201-872-9500, 800-631-0722; FAX: 201-872-2230
Stoeger Publishing Co. (See Stoeger Industries)
Stoney Point Products, Inc., P.O. Box 234, 1815 North Spring Street, New Ulm, MN 56073-0234/507-354-3360; FAX: 507-354-7236
Storey, Dale A. (See DGS, Inc.)
Storm, Gary, P.O. Box 5211, Richardson, TX 75083/214-385-0862
Stott's Creek Armory, Inc., 2526 S. 475W, Morgantown, IN 46160/317-878-5489
Stratco, Inc., P.O. Box 2270, Kalispell, MT 59901/406-755-1221; FAX: 406-755-1226
Strawbridge, Victor W., 6 Pineview Dr., Dover, NH 03820/603-742-0013
Strutz Rifle Barrels, Inc., W.C., P.O. Box 611, Eagle River, WI 54521/715-479-4766
Sturgeon Valley Sporters, K. Ide, P.O. Box 283, Vanderbilt, MI 49795/517-983-4338
"Su-Press-On," Inc., P.O. Box 09161, Detroit, MI 48209/313-842-4222 7:30-11p.m. Mon-Thurs.
Svon Corp., 280 Eliot St., Ashland, MA 01721/508-881-8852
Swann, D.J., 5 Orsova Close, Eltham North, Vic. 3095, AUSTRALIA/03-431-0323
SwaroSports, Inc. (See JagerSport, Ltd.)
Swarovski Optik North America Ltd., One Wholesale Way, Cranston, RI 02920/401-946-2220, 800-426-3089; FAX: 401-946-2587
Swift Bullet Co., P.O. Box 27, 201 Main St., Quinter, KS 67752/913-754-3959; FAX: 913-754-2359
Swift Instruments, Inc., 952 Dorchester Ave., Boston, MA 02125/617-436-2960; FAX: 617-436-3232
Swift River Gunworks, 450 State St., Belchertown, MA 01007/413-323-4052
Swivel Machine Works, Inc., 11 Monitor Hill Rd., Newtown, CT 06470/203-270-6343
Szweda, Robert (See RMS Custom Gunsmithing)

## T

TacStar Industries, Inc., 218 Justin Drive, P.O. Box 70, Cottonwood, AZ 86326/602-639-0072; FAX: 602-634-8781
Talbot QD Mounts, 2210 E. Grand Blanc Rd., Grand Blanc, MI 48439-8113/810-695-2497
Talley, Dave, P.O. Box 821, Glenrock, WY 82637/307-436-8724, 307-436-9315
Talmage, William G., 10208 N. County Rd. 425 W., Brazil, IN 47834/812-442-0804
Talon Mfg. Co., Inc., 621 W. King St., Martinsburg, WV 25401/304-264-9714; FAX: 304-264-9725
Tamarack Products, Inc., P.O. Box 625, Wauconda, IL 60084/708-526-9333; FAX: 708-526-9353
Taracorp Industries, Inc., 1200 Sixteenth St., Granite City, IL 62040/618-451-4400
Tasco Sales, Inc., 7600 NW 26th St., Miami, FL 33122-1494/305-591-3670; FAX: 305-592-5895
Taylor & Robbins, P.O. Box 164, Rixford, PA 16745/814-966-3233
TCCI, P.O. Box 302, Phoenix, AZ 85001/602-237-3823; FAX: 602-237-3858
TCSR, 3998 Hoffman Rd., White Bear Lake, MN 55110-4626/800-328-5323; FAX: 612-429-0526
TDP Industries, Inc., 606 Airport Blvd., Doylestown, PA 18901/215-345-8687; FAX: 215-345-6057
Tecnolegno S.p.A., Via A. Locatelli, 6, 10, 24019 Zogno, ITALY/0345-55111; FAX: 0345-55155
Tele-Optics, 5514 W. Lawrence Ave., Chicago, IL 60630/773-283-7757; FAX: 773-283-7757
Tepeco, P.O. Box 342, Friendswood, TX 77546/713-482-2702
Testing Systems, Inc., 220 Pegasus Ave., Northvale, NJ 07647
Teton Arms, Inc., P.O. Box 411, Wilson, WY 83014/307-733-3395
Tetra Gun Lubricants (See FTI, Inc.)
Texas Platers Supply Co., 2453 W. Five Mile Parkway, Dallas, TX 75233/214-330-7168
T.F.C. S.p.A., Via G. Marconi 118, B, Villa Carcina, Brescia 25069, ITALY/030-881271; FAX: 030-881826
Things Unlimited, 235 N. Kimbau, Casper, WY 82601/307-234-5277
Thomas, Charles C., 2600 S. First St., Springfield, IL 62794/217-789-8980; FAX: 217-789-9130
Thompson Bullet Lube Co., P.O. Box 472343, Garland, TX 75047-2343/972-271-8063; FAX: 972-840-6743
Thompson/Center Arms, P.O. Box 5002, Rochester, NH 03866/603-332-2394; FAX: 603-332-5133
Thompson Precision, 110 Mary St., P.O. Box 251, Warren, IL 61087/815-745-3625
Thompson Target Technology, 618 Roslyn Ave., SW, Canton, OH 44710/216-453-7707; FAX: 216-478-4723
Thompson Tool Mount (See TTM)
3-D Ammunition & Bullets, 112 W. Plum St., P.O. Box J, Doniphan, NE 68832/402-845-2285, 800-255-6712; FAX: 402-845-6546
300 Gunsmith Service, Inc., at Cherry Creek State Park Shooting Center,, 12500 E. Belleview Ave./Englewood, CO 80111
303-690-3300
3-Ten Corp., P.O. Box 269, Feeding Hills, MA 01030/413-789-2086; FAX: 413-789-1549
T.H.U. Enterprises, Inc., P.O. Box 418, Lederach, PA 19450/215-256-1665; FAX: 215-256-9718
Thunderbird Cartridge Co., Inc. (See TCCI)
Tiger-Hunt, Box 379, Beaverdale, PA 15921/814-472-5161
Timber Heirloom Products, 618 Roslyn Ave. SW, Canton, OH 44710/216-453-7707; FAX: 216-478-4723
Time Precision, Inc., 640 Federal Rd., Brookfield, CT 06804/203-775-8343
Timney Mfg., Inc., 3065 W. Fairmont Ave., Phoenix, AZ 85017/602-274-2999; FAX: 602-241-0361
Tioga Engineering Co., Inc., P.O. Box 913, 13 Cone St., Wellsboro, PA 16901/717-724-3533, 717-662-3347
Tirelli, Snc Di Tirelli Primo E.C., Via Matteotti No. 359, Gardone V.T., Brescia, ITALY 25063/030-8912819; FAX: 030-832240
TM Stockworks, 6355 Maplecrest Rd., Fort Wayne, IN 46835/219-485-5389
TMI Products (See Haselbauer Products, Jerry)
Tom's Gun Repair, Thomas G. Ivanoff, 76-6 Rt. Southfork Rd., Cody, WY 82414/307-587-6949
Tombstone Smoke`n'Deals, 3218 East Bell Road, Phoenix, AZ 85032/602-905-7013; Fax: 602-443-1998
Tonoloway Tack Drives, HCR 81, Box 100, Needmore, PA 17238
Totally Dependable Products (See TDP Industries, Inc.)
TR Metals Corp., 1 Pavilion Ave., Riverside, NJ 08075/609-461-9000; FAX: 609-764-6340
Track of the Wolf, Inc., P.O. Box 6, Osseo, MN 55369-0006/612-424-2500; FAX: 612-424-9860
TracStar Industries, Inc., 218 Justin Dr., Cottonwood, AZ 86326/520-639-0072; FAX: 520-634-8781
Traditions, Inc., P.O. Box 776, 1375 Boston Post Rd., Old Saybrook, CT 06475/860-388-4656; FAX: 860-388-4657
Trafalgar Square, P.O. Box 257, N. Pomfret, VT 05053/802-457-1911
Traft Gunshop, P.O. Box 1078, Buena Vista, CO 81211
Trammco, 839 Gold Run Rd., Boulder, CO 80302
Trevallion Gunstocks, 9 Old Mountain Rd., Cape Neddick, ME 03902/207-361-1130
de Treville & Co., Stan, 4129 Normal St., San Diego, CA 92103/619-298-3393
Trico Plastics, 590 S. Vincent Ave., Azusa, CA 91702
Trijicon, Inc., 49385 Shafer Ave., P.O. Box 930059, Wixom, MI 48393-0059/810-960-7700; FAX: 810-960-7725
Trilux Inc., P.O. Box 24608, Winston-Salem, NC 27114/910-659-9438; FAX: 910-768-7720
Trius Products, Inc., P.O. Box 25, 221 S. Miami Ave., Cleves, OH 45002/513-941-5682; FAX: 513-941-7970
Trophy Bonded Bullets, Inc., 900 S. Loop W., Suite 190, Houston, TX 77054/713-645-4499, 888-308-3006; FAX: 713-741-6393
Trotman, Ken, 135 Ditton Walk, Unit 11, Cambridge CB5 8PY, ENGLAND/01223-211030; FAX: 01223-212317
Tru-Square Metal Prods., Inc., 640 First St. SW, P.O. Box 585, Auburn, WA 98071/206-833-2310; FAX: 206-833-2349
True Flight Bullet Co., 5581 Roosevelt St., Whitehall, PA 18052/610-262-7630; FAX: 610-262-7806
TTM, 1550 Solomon Rd., Santa Maria, CA 93455/805-934-1281
Tucker, James C., P.O. Box 575, Raymond, NH 03077
Tucson Mold, Inc., 930 S. Plumer Ave., Tucson, AZ 85719/520-792-1075; FAX: 520-792-1075
Turkish Firearms Corp., 522 W. Maple St., Allentown, PA 18101/610-821-8660; FAX: 610-821-9049
Tuttle, Dale, 4046 Russell Rd., Muskegon, MI 49445/616-766-2250

## U

Ultra Dot Distribution, 2316 N.E. 8th Rd., Ocala, FL 34470
Uncle Bud's, HCR 81, Box 100, Needmore, PA 17238/717-294-6000; FAX: 717-294-6005
Uncle Mike's (See Michaels of Oregon Co.)
Unertl Optical Co., Inc., John, 308 Clay Ave., P.O. Box 818, Mars, PA 16046-0818/412-625-3810

United Binocular Co., 9043 S. Western Ave., Chicago, IL 60620
United States Ammunition Co. (See USAC)
United States Optics Technologies, Inc., 5900 Dale St., Buena Park, CA 90621/714-994-4901; FAX: 714-994-4904
United States Products Co., 518 Melwood Ave., Pittsburgh, PA 15213/412-621-2130
Unmussig Bullets, D.L., 7862 Brentford Drive, Richmond, VA 23225/804-320-1165
USAC, 4500-15th St. East, Tacoma, WA 98424/206-922-7589
USA Sporting Inc., 1330 N. Glassell, Unit M, Orange, CA 92667/714-538-3109, 800-538-3109; FAX: 714-538-1334
Uvalde Machine & Tool, P.O. Box 1604, Uvalde, TX 78802

## V

Valor Corp., 5555 NW 36th Ave., Miami, FL 33142/305-633-0127; FAX: 305-634-4536
Van Gorden & Son, Inc., C.S.~, 1815 Main St., Bloomer, WI 54724/715-568-2612
Van Patten, J.W.~, P.O. Box 145, Foster Hill, Milford, PA 18337/717-296-7069
Vann Custom Bullets, 330 Grandview Ave., Novato, CA 94947
Varner's Service, 102 Shaffer Rd., Antwerp, OH 45813/419-258-8631
Vega Tool Co., c/o T.R. Ross, 4865 Tanglewood Ct., Boulder, CO 80301/303-530-0174
Venco Industries, Inc. (See Shooter's Choice)
Verney-Carron, B.P. 72, 54 Boulevard Thiers, 42002 St. Etienne Cedex 1, FRANCE/33-477791500; FAX: 33-477790702; E-MAIL: Verney-Carron@mail.com
Versa-Pod (See Keng's Firearms Specialty, Inc.
Vest, John, P.O. Box 1552, Susanville, CA 96130/916-257-7228
VibraShine, Inc., P.O. Box 577, Taylorsville, MS 39168/601-785-9854; FAX: 601-785-9874
Vibra-Tek Co., 1844 Arroya Rd., Colorado Springs, CO 80906/719-634-8611; FAX: 719-634-6886
Vic's Gun Refinishing, 6 Pineview Dr., Dover, NH 03820-6422/603-742-0013
Victory USA, P.O. Box 1021, Pine Bush, NY 12566/914-744-2060; FAX: 914-744-5181
Vihtavuori Oy, FIN-41330 Vihtavuori, FINLAND/358-41-3779211; FAX: 358-41-3771643
Vihtavuori Oy/Kaltron-Pettibone, 1241 Ellis St., Bensenville, IL 60106/708-350-1116; FAX: 708-350-1606
Viking Video Productions, P.O. Box 251, Roseburg, OR 97470
Vincent's Shop, 210 Antoinette, Fairbanks, AK 99701
Vintage Industries, Inc., 781 Big Tree Dr., Longwood, FL 32750/407-831-8949; FAX: 407-831-5346/WEB: vintage@sundial.net
Viper Bullet and Brass Works, 11 Brock St., Box 582, Norwich, Ontario, CANADA N0J 1P0
Visible Impact Targets, Rts. 5 & 20, E. Bloomfield, NY 14443/716-657-6161; FAX: 716-657-5405
Vitt/Boos, 2178 Nichols Ave., Stratford, CT 06497/203-375-6859
Voere-KGH m.b.H., P.O. Box 416, A-6333 Kufstein, Tirol, AUSTRIA/0043-5372-62547; FAX: 0043-5372-65752
Volquartsen Custom Ltd., 24276 240th Street, P.O. Box 271, Carroll, IA 51401/712-792-4238; FAX: 712-792-2542
Vom Hoffe (See Old Western Scrounger, Inc., The)
Von Minden Gunsmithing Services, 2403 SW 39 Terrace, Cape Coral, FL 33914/813-542-8946
VSP Publishers (See Heritage/VSP Gun Books)
Vulpes Ventures, Inc., Fox Cartridge Division, P.O. Box 1363, Bolingbrook, IL 60440-7363/708-759-1229

## W

Walker Mfg., Inc., 8296 S. Channel, Harsen's Island, MI 48028
Walnut Factory, The, 235 West Rd. No. 1, Portsmouth, NH 03801/603-436-2225; FAX: 603-433-7003
Walters, John, 500 N. Avery Dr., Moore, OK 73160/405-799-0376
WAMCO—New Mexico, P.O. Box 205, Peralta, NM 87042-0205/505-869-0826
Ward & Van Valkenburg, 114 32nd Ave. N., Fargo, ND 58102/701-232-2351
Warne Manufacturing Co., 9039 SE Jannsen Rd., Clackamas, OR 97015/503-657-5590, 800-683-5590; FAX: 503-657-5695
Warren Muzzleloading Co., Inc., Hwy. 21 North, P.O. Box 100, Ozone, AR 72854/501-292-3268
Wasmundt, Jim, P.O. Box 511, Fossil, OR 97830
WASP Shooting Systems, Rt. 1, Box 147, Lakeview, AR 72642/501-431-5606
Watson Trophy Match Bullets, 2404 Wade Hampton Blvd., Greenville, SC 29615/864-244-7948; 941-635-7948 (Florida)
Watsontown Machine & Tool Co., 309 Dickson Ave., Watsontown, PA 17777/717-538-3533
Wayne Specialty Services, 260 Waterford Drive, Florissant, MO 63033/413-831-7083
WD-40 Co., 1061 Cudahy Pl., San Diego, CA 92110/619-275-1400; FAX: 619-275-5823
Weatherby, Inc., 3100 El Camino Real, Atascadero, CA 93422/805-466-1767, 800-227-2016, 800-334-4423 (Calif.); FAX: 805-466-2527
Weaver Arms Corp. Gun Shop, RR 3, P.O. Box 266, Bloomfield, MO 63825-9528
Weaver Products, P.O. Box 39, Onalaska, WI 54650/800-648-9624, 608-781-5800; FAX: 608-781-0368
Weaver Scope Repair Service, 1121 Larry Mahan Dr., Suite B, El Paso, TX 79925/915-593-1005
Webb, Bill, 6504 North Bellefontaine, Kansas City, MO 64119/816-453-7431
Weber & Markin Custom Gunsmiths, 4-1691 Powick Rd., Kelowna, B.C. CANADA V1X 4L1/250-762-7575; FAX: 250-861-3655
Webster Scale Mfg. Co., P.O. Box 188, Sebring, FL 33870/813-385-6362
Weems, Cecil, P.O. Box 657, Mineral Wells, TX 76067/817-325-1462
Weigand Combat Handguns, Inc., 685 South Main Rd., Mountain Top, PA 18707/717-868-8358; FAX: 717-868-5218
Wells Custom Gunsmith, R.A., 3452 1st Ave., Racine, WI 53402/414-639-5223
Wells, Fred F., Wells Sport Store, 110 N. Summit St., Prescott, AZ 86301/520-445-3655
Welsh, Bud, 80 New Road, E. Amherst, NY 14051/716-688-6344
Wenig Custom Gunstocks, Inc., 103 N. Market St., P.O. Box 249, Lincoln, MO 65338/816-547-3334; FAX: 816-547-2881
Werner, Carl, P.O. Box 492, Littleton, CO 80160
Werth, T.W., 1203 Woodlawn Rd., Lincoln, IL 62656/217-732-1300
Wessinger Custom Guns & Engraving, 268 Limestone Rd., Chapin, SC 29036/803-345-5677
West, Jack L., 1220 W. Fifth, P.O. Box 427, Arlington, OR 97812
West, Robert G., 3973 Pam St., Eugene, OR 97402/541-344-3700
Western Gunstock Mfg. Co., 550 Valencia School Rd., Aptos, CA 95003/408-688-5884
Western Nevada West Coast Bullets, 2307 W. Washington St., Carson City, NV 89703/702-246-3941; FAX: 702-246-0836
Westfield Engineering, 6823 Watcher St., Commerce, CA 90040/FAX: 213-928-8270
Westley Richards & Co., 40 Grange Rd., Birmingham, ENGLAND B29 6AR/010-214722953
White Flyer Targets, 124 River Road, Middlesex, NJ 08846/908-469-0100, 602-972-7528 (Export); FAX: 908-469-9692, 602-530-3360 (Export)
White Laboratory, Inc., H.P., 3114 Scarboro Rd., Street, MD 21154/410-838-6550; FAX: 410-838-2802
White Rock Tool & Die, 6400 N. Brighton Ave., Kansas City, MO 64119/816-454-0478
White Muzzleloading Systems, 25 E. Hwy. 40, Suite 330-12, Roosevelt, UT 84066/801-722-5996; FAX: 801-722-5909
Whitetail Design & Engineering Ltd., 9421 E. Mannsiding Rd., Clare, MI 48617/517-386-3932
Whits Shooting Stuff, Box 1340, Cody, WY 82414
Wichita Arms, Inc., 923 E. Gilbert, P.O. Box 11371, Wichita, KS 67211/316-265-0661; FAX: 316-265-0760
Wick, David E., 1504 Michigan Ave., Columbus, IN 47201/812-376-6960
Widener's Reloading & Shooting Supply, Inc., P.O. Box 3009 CRS, Johnson City, TN 37602/615-282-6786; FAX: 615-282-6651
Wideview Scope Mount Corp., 13535 S. Hwy. 16, Rapid City, SD 57701/605-341-3220; FAX: 605-341-9142
Wiest, M.C., 10737 Dutchtown Rd., Knoxville, TN 37932/423-966-4545
Wilderness Sound Products Ltd., 4015 Main St. A, Springfield, OR 97478/503-741-0263, 800-437-0006; FAX: 503-741-7648
William's Gun Shop, Ben, 1151 S. Cedar Ridge, Duncanville, TX 75137/214-780-1807
Williams Bullet Co., J.R., 2008 Tucker Rd., Perry, GA 31069/912-987-0274
Williams Gun Sight Co., 7389 Lapeer Rd., Box 329, Davison, MI 48423/810-653-2131, 800-530-9028; FAX: 810-658-2140
Williamson Precision Gunsmithing, 117 W. Pipeline, Hurst, TX 76053/817-285-0064
Willow Bend, P.O. Box 203, Chelmsford, MA 01824/508-256-8508; FAX: 508-256-8508
Willson Safety Prods. Div., P.O. Box 622, Reading, PA 19603-0622/610-376-6161; FAX: 610-371-7725
Wilson Arms Co., The, 63 Leetes Island Rd., Branford, CT 06405/203-488-7297; FAX: 203-488-0135
Wilson, Inc., L.E., Box 324, 404 Pioneer Ave., Cashmere, WA 98815/509-782-1328
Wilson Gun Shop, Box 578, Rt. 3, Berryville, AR 72616/870-545-3618; FAX: 870-545-3310
Winchester Div., Olin Corp., 427 N. Shamrock, E. Alton, IL 62024/618-258-3566; FAX: 618-258-3599
Winchester Press (See New Win Publishing, Inc.)
Windish, Jim, 2510 Dawn Dr., Alexandria, VA 22306/703-765-1994
Windjammer Tournament Wads, Inc., 750 W. Hampden Ave. Suite 170, Englewood, CO 80110/303-781-6329

Winkle Bullets, R.R. 1 Box 316, Heyworth, IL 61745
Winter, Robert M., P.O. Box 484, 42975-287th St., Menno, SD 57045/605-387-5322
Wiseman and Co., Bill, P.O. Box 3427, Bryan, TX 77805/409-690-3456; FAX: 409-690-0156
Wolf's Western Traders, 40 E. Works, No. 3F, Sheridan, WY 82801/307-674-5352
Wolfe Publishing Co., 6471 Airpark Dr., Prescott, AZ 86301/520-445-7810, 800-899-7810; FAX: 520-778-5124
Woodleigh (See Huntington Die Specialties)
Working Guns, 250 Country Club Lane, Albany, OR 97321/541-928-4391
World of Targets (See Birchwood Casey)
Worthy Products, Inc., RR 1, P.O. Box 213, Martville, NY 13111/315-324-5298
Wosenitz VHP, Inc., Box 741, Dania, FL 33004/305-923-3748; FAX: 305-925-2217
Wright's Hardwood Gunstock Blanks, 8540 SE Kane Rd., Gresham, OR 97080/503-666-1705
W. Square Enterprises (See Load From A Disk)
Wyant Bullets, Gen. Del., Swan Lake, MT 59911
White Shooting Systems (See White Muzzleloading Systems)
Wyoming Bonded Bullets, Box 91, Sheridan, WY 82801/307-674-8091
Wyoming Custom Bullets, 1626 21st St., Cody, WY 82414

## X

X-Spand Target Systems, 26-10th St. SE, Medicine Hat, AB T1A 1P7 CANADA/403-526-7997; FAX: 403-528-2362

## Y

Yearout, Lewis E. (See Montana Outfitters)
Yee, Mike, 29927 56 Pl. S., Auburn, WA 98001/206-839-3991
Yesteryear Armory & Supply, P.O. Box 408, Carthage, TN 37030
York M-1 Conversions, 803 Mill Creek Run, Plantersville, TX 77363/800-527-2881, 713-477-8442
Young Country Arms, P.O. Box 3615, Simi Valley, CA 93093
Yukon Arms Classic Ammunition, 1916 Brooks, P.O. Box 223, Missoula, MT 59801/406-543-9614

## Z

Z's Metal Targets & Frames, P.O. Box 78, South Newbury, NH 03255/603-938-2826
Zander's Sporting Goods, 7525 Hwy 154 West, Baldwin, IL 62217-9706/800-851-4373 ext. 200; FAX: 618-785-2320
Zanotti Armor, Inc., 123 W. Lone Tree Rd., Cedar Falls, IA 50613/319-232-9650
Z-Coat Industrial Coatings, Inc., 3375 U.S. Hwy. 98 S. No. A, Lakeland, FL 33803-8365/813-665-1734
Zeeryp, Russ, 1601 Foard Dr., Lynn Ross Manor, Morristown, TN 37814/615-586-2357
Zeiss Optical, Carl, 1015 Commerce St., Petersburg, VA 23803/804-861-0033, 800-388-2984; FAX: 804-733-4024
Zero Ammunition Co., Inc., 1601 22nd St. SE, P.O. Box 1188, Cullman, AL 35056-1188/800-545-9376; FAX: 205-739-4683
Zim's Inc., 4370 S. 3rd West, Salt Lake City, UT 84107/801-268-2505
Zonie Bullets, 790 N. Lake Havasu Ave., Suite 26, Lake Havasu City, AZ 86403/520-680-6303; FAX: 520-680-6201
Zriny's Metal Targets (See Z's Metal Targets & Frames)
Zufall, Joseph F., P.O. Box 304, Golden, CO 80402-0304/

# HIGH CALIBER OFFERINGS FOR YOUR GUN LIBRARY

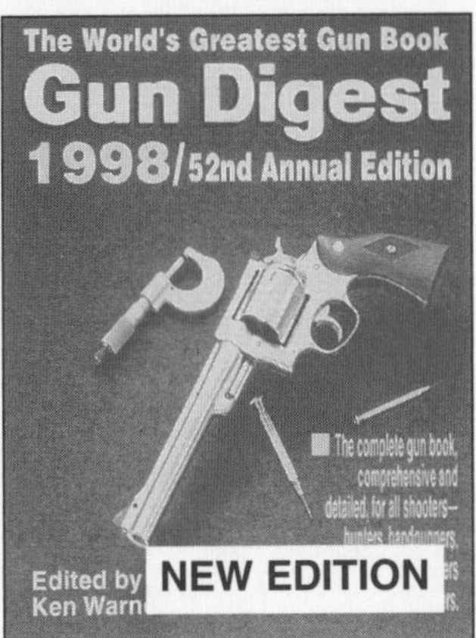


**1998 Gun Digest**, 52nd edition, edited by Ken Warner Explore the comprehensive catalog containing all firearms currently manufactured in or imported to the U.S. Discover full specs and retail prices for more than 3,000 firearms. Plus, learn plenty from the vast array of all-new historical, informational and technical articles in this must-have resource. 8-1/2x11 SC • 544p • 2,000+ photos • **GD98 $24.95 Avail. July 1997**

**Reloading For Shotgunners**
*4th Edition,* by Kurt D. Fackler and M.L. McPherson The one reloading guide every shotgunner should own. Gives the shotshell, slug and buckshot reloader all the basics of the art, plus advanced techniques for loading. The huge data section amasses the most comprehensive and current load data available. 8-1/2x11 SC • 320 pages • 600+ b&w photos • **RFS4 $19.95 Available 10/97**

**Flayderman's Guide to Antique American Firearms and Their Values**, 6th edition, updates you on 3,000 individually priced firearms with full info on assessing values. 4,000 models, variants with marks and specs necessary for quick ID. Never-before listed or illustrated items. 8-1/2x11 SC • 640p • 1,600 photos • **FLA6 $29.95**

**Bolt Action Rifles**, 3rd edition, works out all the details of every major design since the Mauser of 1871. Author Frank de Haas analyzes 124 turn-bolt actions – how they function, takedown/assembly, strengths & weaknesses, dimensional specs. 8-1/2x11 SC • 528p • 615 photos • **BAR3 $24.95**

**The Complete Black Powder Handbook**, 3rd edition, funnels indispensable info into a huge new edition, completely rewritten and refreshed by Sam Fadala. This textbook for black powder shooters is topped off by a catalog of all currently-manufactured black powder firearms. 8-1/2x11 SC • 400p • 600 photos • **BPH3 $21.95**

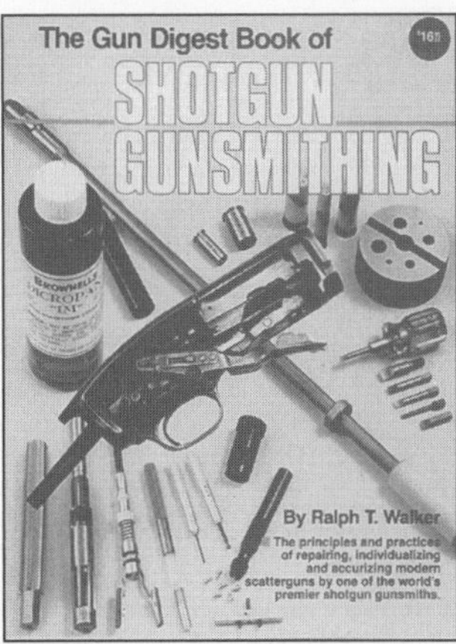


**Shotgun Gunsmithing** is the premier reference in the specialty. Ralph Walker explains the principles and practices of repairing, individualizing and making modern scatterguns more accurate. Never-before covered information. 8-1/2x11 SC • 256p • 410 photos • **SHSM $16.95**

## Great Books Make Great Gifts

## SATISFACTION GUARANTEE

If for any reason you are not completely satisfied with your purchase, simply return it within 14 days and receive a full refund, less shipping.

**To Order Call Toll-free**
**800-258-0929 Dept. DAB2**
Monday-Friday, 7 am. - 8 p.m. • Saturday, 8 a.m. - 2 p.m., CST
Visit our web site: http://www.krause.com